THE QUARTERLY ARMY LIST OF HER MAJESTY'S BRITISH AND INDIAN FORCES ON THE BENGAL ESTABLISHMENT,

EXHIBITING

THE RANK, STANDING AND VARIOUS SERVICES

OF EVERY

OFFICER IN THE ARMY,

DISTINGUISHING THOSE

WHO HAVE RECEIVED MEDALS AND OTHER DISTINCTIONS,

AND

WHO HAVE BEEN WOUNDED, AND IN WHAT ACTIONS;

WITH THEIR PERIODS OF SERVICES AND DATES OF COMMISSIONS.

Corrected to *5th* July 1859

THE QUARTERLY ARMY LIST OF HER MAJESTY'S BRITISH AND INDIAN FORCES ON THE BENGAL ESTABLISHMENT

EXHIBITING

THE RANK, STANDING AND VARIOUS SERVICES

OF EVERY

OFFICER IN THE ARMY

DISTINGUISHING THOSE

WHO HAVE RECEIVED MEDALS AND OTHER DISTINCTIONS,

AND

WHO HAVE BEEN WOUNDED, AND IN WHAT ACTIONS;

WITH THEIR PERIODS OF SERVICES AND DATES OF COMMISSIONS.

Corrected to *5th* July 1859

TO WHICH IS ADDED

A LIST OF CIVIL SERVANTS

IN BENGAL AND THE NORTH - WESTERN PROVINCES,

WITH THE DATES OF THEIR APPOINTMENTS, ETC.

ASIAN EDUCATIONAL SERVICES

NEW DELHI ★ MADRAS ★ 2000

ASIAN EDUCATIONAL SERVICES

* 31, HAUZ KHAS VILLAGE, NEW DELHI - 110016
  Tel : 6560187, 6568594 Fax : 011-6852805, 6855499
  e-mail : asianeds@nda.vsnl.net.in

* 5, SRIPURAM FIRST STREET, MADRAS - 600 014
  Tel : 8265040 Fax : 8211291
  e-mail : asianeds@md3.vsnl.net.in

First Published :Calcutta , 1859
AES Reprints : New Delhi, 1997, 2000
ISBN : 81-206-1279-5

Published by J. Jetley
for ASIAN EDUCATIONAL SERVICES
31, Hauz Khas Village, New Delhi - 110 016
Processed by AES Publications Pvt. Ltd., New Delhi-110 016
Printed at Shubham Offset Press DELHI - 110 032

No. XXXIX.] [PUBLISHED 10TH AUG. 1859.

THE

QUARTERLY ARMY LIST

OF

HER MAJESTY'S BRITISH AND INDIAN FORCES

ON THE

BENGAL ESTABLISHMENT,

EXHIBITING

THE RANK, STANDING, AND VARIOUS SERVICES

OF EVERY

OFFICER IN THE ARMY,

DISTINGUISHING THOSE

WHO HAVE RECEIVED MEDALS AND OTHER DISTINCTIONS,

AND

WHO HAVE BEEN WOUNDED, AND IN WHAT ACTIONS;

WITH THEIR PERIODS OF SERVICES AND DATES OF COMMISSIONS.

Corrected to 5th July 1859.

TO WHICH IS ADDED

A LIST OF CIVIL SERVANTS

IN BENGAL AND THE NORTH-WESTERN PROVINCES,

WITH THE DATES OF THEIR APPOINTMENTS, ETC.

CALCUTTA:

PRINTED BY P. M. CRANENBURGH, MILITARY ORPHAN PRESS,

AND

PUBLISHED AND SOLD BY MESSRS. R. C. LEPAGE AND CO.,

BRITISH LIBRARY.

1859.

CONTENTS OF THE ARMY LIST.

H. M. Troops.

Her Majestys' Indian Forces.

CIVIL LIST.

THE

QUARTERLY ARMY LIST

OF

HER MAJESTY'S BRITISH FORCES

ON THE

BENGAL ESTABLISHMENT.

Corrected to 1*st July* 1859.

The words subscribed to the titles of Regiments, as "Peninsula," "Waterloo," &c. denote the Honorary Distinctions permitted to be borne by such Regiments on their Colours and Appointments, in commemoration of their Services.

EXPLANATION OF ABBREVIATIONS.

K. G. ..	Knight of the Order of the Garter.	
K. T. ..	Knight of the Order of the Thistle.	
K. P. ..	Knight of the Order of St. Patrick.	
G. C. B.	Grand Cross	of the Order of the Bath.
K. C. B.	Knight Commander	
C. B. ..	Companion	
G. C. M. G.	Grand Cross......	of the Order of St. Michael & St. George.
K. C. M. G.	Knight Commander	
C. M. G.	Companion	
G. C. H.	Grand Cross	of the Royal Hanoverian Guelphic Order.
K. C. H.	Knight Commander	
K. H. ..	Knight..........	
K. C.	Knight of the Crescent.	
M	Medal for Waterloo.	
V C or*	The Victoria Cross.	

Head Quarters, Allahabad 13*th August* 1858.

Officers Commanding Her Majesty's Regiments and Troops, of all Arms are directed to introduce, in the column of remarks of the Nominal List of their Officers sent monthly to the Military Secretary and Adjutant General H. M. Forces, the appropriate letters, *in red ink*, indicating the subjects in which Officers, under their Command, have passed, or may pass in future; these letters are:

P. C.	For Passed Interpreter's Test in Calcutta.
P.	Passed Interpreter's Examination in other Stations.
P. H.	Passed in the Hindostanee Language.
H P.	Passed in Hindostanee and Persian Languages.
H. M.	Passed in Hindostanee and Mahratta Languages.
V.	Passed in the Vernacular Hindostanee.
S.	Passed as a Surveyor.
C. E.	Passed in Civil Engineering.
S. D	Passed Senior Department at Sandhurst.

Commanding Officers are to be careful that the Nominal List is despatched not later than the 3rd of the month.

ARMY LIST

OF

HER MAJESTY'S FORCES IN BENGAL.

COMMANDER-IN-CHIEF IN INDIA.

His Excellency General *Baron* CLYDE (OF CLYDESDALE) G.C.B., Colonel of Her Majesty's 93rd Highlanders, Commander-in Chief of Her Majesty's and all other Forces serving in the East Indies, 13th August 1857, and an Extraordinary Member of the Council of India, 31st August 1857, Army Head Quarters Simla.

PERSONAL STAFF OF H. E. THE COMMANDER-IN-CHIEF.

Colonel A. C. Sterling, C. B. unattached, ...	Military Secretary, ..	6 *Mar.* 58
R ~~Maj. Sir David Baird, Bart., H.M. 98th Foot~~,...	Aide-de-Camp.—(*Leave, on M. C. to England,*) ..	13 *Aug.* 57
Captain F. M. Allison, H. M. 19th Foot, ...	Ditto, ...	
Lt. *Hon.* J. C. Dormer, H. M. 13th Lt.Infy. ..	Ditto, ...	*July* 58

CHIEF OF THE STAFF.

Major General *Sir* W. R. Mansfield, K. C. B. ..	*Army Head-Quarters.* ..	
Lieut. R. G. Hope Johnstone, 13th Bombay N.I.	Asst. Adjt. Genl. to ditto, *on Leave.*	
~~Bt. Major H. H. Crealock, 90th Foot~~, ...	*Acting* ditto. ...	7 *Sep.* 58
Lieut. F. R. S. Flood, 53rd Foot, ..	Aide-de-Camp. ..	18 *Feb.* 59

ADJUTANT GENERAL'S DEPARTMENT TO H. M. FORCES.

ADJUTANT GENERAL.

Colonel *the Hon'ble* W. L. Packenham, C .B. unattached, ..	*Army Head-Quarters.* ...	22 *Oct.* 58

DEPUTY ADJUTANT GENERAL

*

Lieut. Col. Kenneth D. Mackenzie, 92nd Foot, ..	(Offg. Depy. Adjutant General,) *In charge of the Presidency Office, Calcutta,* ...	2 *Aug.* 58

ASSISTANT ADJUTANT GENERAL.

Major H. D. Torrens, 23rd Foot, ...	Officiating 1st Assistant, ...	1 *Nov.* 58

QUARTER MASTER GENERAL'S DEPARTMENT OF H. M. FORCES.

QUARTER MASTER GENERAL.

Colonel George Congreve, C. B. H. M. 29th ...	*Army Head Quarters,* ...	1 *July* 57

BRIGADIER'S OFFICE.

Brigadier M. Smith H. M. 81st Regt., ..	Commanding at Fort William.
Major R. Freer, H. M. 29th Regt., ..	Acting, Brigade Major.
Captain R. J. Evans, H. M. 29th Regt., ..	Depy. Adjt. Qr. Mr. Genl.

QUEEN'S MILITARY WIDOW'S FUND.

Lieut. Colonel K. Mackenzie, 92nd Foot. ..	*Honorary Secretary.* ..	25 *Sep.* 58

Officers of H. M. Service, on Staff Duty.

Rank, Names and Corps.	Date of Appointment.	Remarks.
Generals.		
His Excellency Baron Clyde, 93rd Foot,	13 *Aug.* 57	Commander-in-Chief in the East Indies.
Major Generals.		
C. Ash Windham, C. B., - - - -	6 *Oct.* 57	Commanding the Lahore division. (Meean Meer.)
Sir R. Garrett, K.C. B. and K.H., - -	1 *Jan.* 58	Commanding the Sirhind Division. (Umballa.)
Sir S. J. Cotton, K, C. B., - - - -	5 *June* 57	Commanding the Peshawur Division.
Sir William R. Mansfield, K. C. B., (*unattached,*) - - - - - - -	10 *Sep.* 57	Chief of the Staff in the East Indies.
Sir Jas. Hope Grant, K. C. B. -	26 *Feb.* 58	Commanding the Oudh Division.
Sir J. E. W. Inglis, K. C. B., - - -	.. ..	Commanding the Cawnpore Division.
Marcus Beresford, 20th Foot, - - -	.. ..	Commanding Division in Madras.
Brigadier Generals.		
Robert Walpole, C. B. Rifle Brigade, -	29 *June* 58	Comdg. the Rohilcund and Kumaon Divisions
Brigadiers.		
T. Chute, 70th Foot, - - - - - - -	6 *July* 58	Brigadier Comdg. at Lucknow.
Thomas J. Galloway, 70th Foot, ..	.. ..	Brigadier Commanding Peshawur District.
W. G. Brown, 24th Foot, - - - -	28 *July* 58	Brigadier Commanding at Lahore.
G. Hutchinson, 80th Foot, - - - -	27 *Aug.* 58	Brigadier 2nd-Class, Comdg. the Sind Saugor district (Rawul Pindee.)
G. C. W. Milman, 37th Foot, - - -	23 *Aug* 58	Brigadier Commanding at Jullunder.
Maurice George Dennis, C. B., 60th Foot,	.. ..	Brigadier Commanding at Allahabad.
Mathew Smith 81st Foot, C. B., - -	.. ..	Brigadier Commanding at Calcutta.
A. H Horsford, C. B., - - - - -	18 *Feb.* 59	Brigadier Trans Gogra Force.
Colonels.		
C. Stuart, (*unattached,*) - - - -	20 *Jan.* 58	Military Secretary to the Governor General.—On leave.
George Congreve, C. B., 29th Foot, -	1 *July* 57	Quarter Master General to the Queen's Forces serving in the East Indies.—Leave S. C.
The Hon'ble W. L. Pakenham, C. B., (*unattached*) - - - - - -	22 *Oct.* 58	Adjutant Genl. to the Queen's Forces serving in the East Indies.—Army Head Quarters.
A. C. Sterling, C. B., (*unattached,*) -	23 *Dec.* 57	Military Secretary to the Commander-in-Chief in India.
E. H. Greathed, C. B., 8th Foot, - -	.. ...	Deputy Adjutant Genl. at Bombay.
Henry Bates, 98th Foot, - - -	... ...	Military Secretary, Bombay.
H D. Harness, Engineers, - - -	... ..	Comdg. Royal Engineers, Army Head Qrs.
Sir G. R. Barker, K. C. B. - - - - -	.. ..	Commanding Royal Artillery in India.
W. O. G. Haly, 38th Foot, - - - -	.. ..	8th Punjaub Infantry.

OFFICERS OF H. M. SERVICE, ON STAFF DUTY.—*(Continued.)*

Rank, Names and Corps.	*Date of Appointment.*	Remarks.
Lieutenant Colonels.		
C. A. Denison, 52nd Light Infantry, -	23 *Oct.* 55	Depy. Adjt. Genl. to the Queen's Troops Serving in Madras.
Kenneth Mackenzie, 92nd Foot, - -	23 *July* 58	Offg. Dept. Adjutant General to the Queen's Forces.
~~H. H. Crealock, 90th Foot,~~ - - -	13 *Apl.* 58	Acting Dept. Asst. Adjt. Genl. to the Chief of the Staff.
W. C. Mollan, 75th Foot, - - - -	.. ..	Commanding Provisional Battalion Dum-Dum.
J. W. Cox, 13th Lt. Infantry, - - -	.. ..	Commanding Dugshaie Convalescent Depot.
J. Ross, 3rd Batt. Rifle Brigade, - -	.. ..	Commanding Camel Corps.
John C. Guise, - - - - - - - -	.. ..	Commanding Seetapore District.
Sir H. M. Havelock, *Bart*, 18th Foot, -	9 *Sep.* 58	2nd in Comd. of 3rd Hodson's Horse.
R. M. Shipley, 7th Foot, - - - -	.. ..	Comdg. Sind Saugor District.
~~G. Talbot, 43rd Foot,~~ - - - - -	.. ..	Deputy Qr. Mr. Genl. H. M. Forces Madras.
D. D. Muter, 60th Foot, - - - - -	.. ..	Commdg. Convalescent Depot Muree.
R. L. Ross, 93rd Foot, - - - - -	.. ..	Asst. Adjt. General Bombay.
Majors.		
George R. Hopkins, 53rd Foot,- - -	.. ..	Commanding Convalescent Depôt, at Darjeeling.
~~Sir David Baird, Bart 98th Foot~~, -	.. ..	A. D. C. to the Commander-in-Chief,—Leave on M. C. to England.
Joseph Jordan, 34th Foot, - - -	31 *Nov.* 57	Comdg. Depôt of Queen's Troops at Cawnpore.
G. J. Wolseley, 90th Foot, - - -	.. ..	Acting Deputy Assistant Qr. Mr. Genl. Oude Division.
H. D'O. Torrens, 23rd Foot, - - -	1 *Nov.* 58	Assist. Adjt. Genl. H. M. Forces.
Sir E. Fitz-G. Campbell, *Bart.*, 60th Rifles, - - - - - - - - - - -	16 *Sep.* 53	Delhi Prize Agent, at Calcutta, A. D. C. and Mily. Secy. to Governor General.
B. D. W. Ramsay, 75th Foot, - - -	21 *Jan.* 54	Brigade Major, Queen's Troops, Fort William Leave on M. C. to England.
W. F Ring, 87th Foot, - - - - .	.. ..	Commanding 12th Punjaub Infantry.
H. Wilmot, 2nd Batt. Rifle Brigade, -	.. ..	Dep. Judge Adv. Genl. to Oudh Field Force.
W. D. Macdonald, 93rd Foot, -	.. ..	Offg. Deputy Asst. Qr. Mr. Genl. Allahabad.
W. G. A. Middleton 93rd Highrs, -	23 *June* 58	Commanding Nynee Tal Convalescent Depot.
M. Dillon, 2nd Battn. Rifle Brigade, -	.. ..	Brigade Major to Brigadier Horsford.
~~Mark Walker, 3rd Foot~~, - - - -	.. ..	Comdg. Depot Chinsurah.
~~H. H. Crealock, 90th Foot,~~ - - - -	.. ..	Actg. Adjt. Genl. to Chief of the staff.
John Drysdale, 42nd Foot, - - - -	.. ..	Comdt. Nynee Tal Convalescent Depot.
T. H. Cockburn, 43rd Foot, - - -	.. ..	A. D. C to the Governor of Bombay.
A. J. Nixon, 2nd Battn, Rifle Brigade,	.. ..	On duty with Camel Corps.
C. W. Earle, 2nd Battn. Rifle Brigade,	.. ..	Depy. Judge Advocate Genl. to Rohilcund Force.
H. R. Newdigate, 3rd Battn. ditto, - -	.. ..	With Camel Corps.

OFFICERS OF H. M. SERVICE, ON STAFF DUTY.—*(Continued.)*

Rank, Names and Corps.	Date of Appointment.	Remarks.
Captains.		
Valens Tonnochy, 81st Foot,	10 *Apl.* 56	Comdg. 1st Regt. of Jugailchies, Oudh.
F. A. Champion, 52nd Light Infy.,	—— 55	A. D. C. to Major General P. E. Craigie, C. B., Madras.
The Hon'ble John C. Stanley, Gr. Guards,	19 *Jan.* 58	A. D. C. to the Governor General.
R. J. Evans, 27th Foot,	12 *Sep.* 57	Disembarkation and Embarkation Officer, at Calcutta.
E. N. Sandilands, 8th Foot,	15 *Jan.* 56	Dept. of Public Works, Umballa.
Fras. E. Cox, Engineers,	1 *Apl.* 55	Adjutant of the Royal Engineers.—Leave on S. C. to Europe.
~~J. T. N. O'Brien, 20th Foot~~,	.. ..	Dept. of Public Works, at Peshawur Road.
John Hallowes, 87th Foot,	.. ..	Prize Agent at Lucknow.
Wm. H. Cooper, 70th Foot.	.. ..	Deputy Assist Qr. Mr. Genl. Peshawur District.
G. E. Rose, 3rd Batt., Rifle Brigade,	.. ..	A. D. C. to *Sir* Hugh Rose, Bombay.
Stapleton Cotton, 97th Foot,	.. ..	A. D. C. to Major Genl. *Sir* S. Cotton, K. C. B.
J. H. F. Elkington, 6th Foot,	.. ..	A. D. C. to Genl. Mitchel, Bombay.
~~Sydney C. Jackson, 70th Foot~~,	.. ..	Commandant Lahore Light Horse.
O. J. Travers, 70th Foot,	22 *Sep.* 57	2nd in Command Peshawur Light Horse.
C. C. F. Young, Royal Artillery,	18 *Nov.* 58	Deputy Asst. Qr. Mr. General Royal Artillery.
N. D. Robinson, 7th Foot,	13 *Oct.* 58	Dept. of Public Works.
F. M. Allison, 19th Foot,	13 *Aug.* 57	A. D. C. to the Commander-in-Chief in India.
~~A. J. Macpherson, 24th Foot~~,	.. ..	Comdg. 22nd Punjaub Infantry.
J. B. Thelwal. 24th Foot. C. B.,	.. ..	Comdg. 9th Punjab Infantry.
C. F. Brown, 35th Foot,	.. ..	Depy. Judge Adv. Genl. Cawnpore Division.
E. Bowles, 1st Batt. 60th Rifles,	.. ..	Employed in the Military Police.
H. A Chichester, 81st Foot,	.. ..	Assist. Brigade Major at Peshawur.
W. Hanmer, 87th Foot,	.. ..	Commandant of Meerut Levy.
G. D. Cleveland, 98th Foot,	.. ..	Commanding Moradabad Levy.
Edward J. Ellerman, 98th Foot,	.. ..	German Legion, Poona.
R. Gibson, 87th Foot,	.. ..	2nd in Command 3rd Seikh Cavalry.
John Bouchier, 81st Foot,	.. ..	Commandant of Peshawur Fort.
R. H. Gordon, 42nd Foot,	.. ..	Paymaster Benares Depot.
G. A. Macnair, 38th Foot,	.. ..	On Duty at Peshawur.
Stewart Alex. Cleeve, 51st Foot,	.. ..	Brigade Major Queen's Troops Bombay.
Henry E. Warren, 2nd Batt 60 Rifles,	.. ..	Commanding Convalescent Depot, Muree.
~~T. W. Martin, 7th Foot~~,	.. ..	On duty in P. W. D.
Richard Barter, 7th Foot,	.. ..	Commanding Bijnore Military Police.
T. G. Souter, 8th Foot,	.. ..	Commanding Tawana Horse.
A. R. Bayley, 8th Foot,	.. ..	Executive Engineer at Sealkote.
S. Y, Tovey 24th Foot,	.. ..	D. P. W. Peshawur.
R. Freer, 27th Foot,	.. ..	Acting Brigade Major Queen's Troops Calcutta.
E. J. N. Burton, 37th Foot,	.. ..	Brigade Major Lucknow.
W. J. Dorehill, 43rd Foot,	.. ..	Brigade Major 2nd Brigade Saugor Field Division.

OFFICERS OF H. M. SERVICE, ON STAFF DUTY.—(*Continued.*)

Rank, Names and Corps.	Date of Appointment.	Remarks.
Captains.—(Continued.)		
W. Leach, 5th Foot,	.. ..	Commanding Conval. Depot Allahabad.
E. L. Green, 77th Foot,	.. ..	A. D. C. to Commander in Chief Bombay.
G. S. Young, 80th Foot,	.. ..	Actg. Dep. Assist. Adjt. Genl. Cawnpore Divn.
T. Horan, 43rd Foot,	9 *Feb,* 59	Paymaster of Invalids and detachments of H. M. Service at the Presidency.
Edward Gream Daniell, 8th foot,	.. ..	Deputy Judge advocate at Gwalior.
Charles Monsell, 23rd Foot.	.. ..	Commandant Depot Batt. Lucknow.
Hon. J. C. Dormer, 13th Foot,	.. ..	A. D. C. to the Commander-in-Chief.
Lieutenants.		
T. L. Roberts, 87th Fusiliers,	5 *Aug.* 57	2nd in Command of the 3rd Seikh Infantry.
C. E. Goddard, 87th Fusiliers,	6 *Nov.* 57	Adjutant of the 5th Punjaub Infantry.
W. C. Mackinnon, 87th Fusiliers,	19 *Mar.* 56	Dept. of P. Works, Patna Road.
F. E. Beaumont, Engrs,	.. ..	Qr. Master to the Royal Engineers.
R. J. L. Crutchley 24th Foot,	.. ...	Offg. Station Staff Officer at Murree.
H. B. Good, 70th Foot,	.. ...	Pay and Qr. Master Kurrachee Depôt.
W. Musgrave, 81st Foot,	.. ..	Commanding a Rasala of newly raised Irregular Cavalry.
H. J. Fane, 81st Foot,	.. ..	A.D.C. to Commander-in-Chief of Madras.
G. R. Fenwick, 93rd Foot,	.. ..	Acting Paymaster of the Recruit Depôt at Berhampore.
Wm Whitehead, 80th Foot,	.. ..	Adjt. Queen's Troops Cawnpore
T. R. S. Flood, 53rd Foot,	24 *Sep.* 58	A. D. C. to the Chief of the Staff.
R. Harrison, Royal Engineers,	27 *Nov.* 58	Acting Adjutant of Royal Engineers, Army Head Quarters.
Thos. C. J. Ffrench, 53rd Foot,	.. ..	Employed on the Staff of the Oudh Police Lucknow.
C. M. Pym, 75th Foot,	.. ..	Actg. Adjutant of 16th Punjaub Infantry.
G. Sullivan, 80th Foot.	.. ..	2nd in Command of Cawnpore Levy.
C. H. Griffin, 98th Foot,	.. ..	Acting Adjutant to Eurasian Corps.
E. H. Lenon, 67th Foot,	.. ..	Adjt. Recruit Batt Dum-Dum.
C. D. Baillie, 3rd Foot,	.. ..	Acting Qr. Mr. Provisional Batt. Dum-Dum
W. H. I. Lance, 98th Foot,	.. ..	On duty with Moradabad Levy.
Thos. Gardner, 98th Foot,	.. ..	Adjutant of 18th Punjaub Infantry.
R. W. Cox, 94th Foot,	.. ..	On duty with 7th Irregular Cavalry.
M. W. Hyslop, 93rd Foot,	.. ..	Station Staff Officer Kussowlie.
W. P. Mortimer, 80th Foot,	.. ..	Acting Adjutant Cawnpore Levy.
R. Whigham, 70th Foot,	.. ..	Lahore Light Horse.
A. Tibeaudo, 7th Foot,	.. ..	Adjutant, Depôt of Queen's Troops, Kurrachee.
H. Thompson, 19th Foot,	.. ..	Adjt. to Bijnoor Rajpoot Levy.
C. E. Stewart, 27th Foot,	.. ..	Acting Adjt. 5th Punjaub Infantry.
Edward Tedlie, 35th Foot,	.. ..	2nd in Command, Agra Levy.
R. Bunn, 37th Foot,	.. ..	Station Staff Officer, Ghazeepore.
Hon. R. H. Stewart, 42nd Foot,	.. ..	Brigade Major, Ferozepore.
E. H. D. Macpherson, 93rd Foot,	.. ..	A. D. C. to the Lieut. Governor of Bengal.
Ensigns.		
W. Arbuthnot, 3rd Battn. Rifle Brigade,	.. ...	A. D. C. to the Commander-in-Chief at Madras.
H. Manning, 3rd Foot,	.. ..	Acting Paymaster Chinsurah.
Fred. T. Hobson,	.. ..	Pay Master General's Department Calcutta.
A. C. Hennessey, 24th Foot,	.. ..	Adjutant Murray's Jat Horse.
H. W. Fielden, 42nd Foot,	.. ..	Doing duty 1st Gwalior Regt.

HER MAJESTY'S BRITISH FORCES,

IN THE BENGAL AND NORTH-WESTERN PROVINCES.

Corrected to 1st July 1859.

ARTILLERY.

E Battery Horse Artillery, .. *Seetapore.*
F Battery Horse Artillery, .. *Meerut.*

No. 1st Battery.	14th Brigade.	Foot Artillery, ..	*Azimghur, Benares.*
3rd Ditto,	14th Ditto,	ditto, ..	*Oudh.*
4th Ditto,	14th Ditto,	ditto, ...	*Mooltan.*
7th Ditto,	11th Ditto,	ditto, ..	*Peshawur.*
1st Ditto,	11th Ditto,	ditto, ..	*Calcutta.*
8th Ditto,	11th Ditto,	ditto, ..	*Dum-Dum.*
2nd Ditto,	14th Ditto,	ditto, ..	*Benares, Berhampore, Etc.*
5th Ditto,	14th Ditto,	ditto, ..	*Gorruckpore.*
2nd Ditto,	11th Ditto,	ditto, ..	*Lucknow.*
3rd Ditto,	11th Ditto,	ditto, ..	*Luckoow.*
4th Ditto,	11th Ditto,	ditto, ..	*Allahabad.*
5th Ditto,	11th Ditto,	ditto, ..	*Roy Bareilly.*
6th Ditto,	11th Ditto,	ditto, ..	*Futteghur.*

ROYAL ENGINEERS.

4th Company, ... *Fyzcbad* and *Gonda.*
23rd Company, .. *Lucknow.*

CAVALRY.

2nd (Queen's) Regt. of Dragoon Guards, .. *Lucknow.*
6th Regiment of Carabineers, .. *Muttra,* detachment at *Agra.*
7th (Princess Royal's) Regt. of Drag. Guards, *Sealkote.*
7th (Queen's Own) Regt. Hussars, .. *Umballa.*

*

HER MAJESTY'S FORCES.—(*Continued.*)

INFANTRY.

Regiment		Station
3rd (E. Kent) Regt. of Foot (the Buffs,)	..	*Dum-Dum*, detachment at *Fort William Calcutta*
5th Regt. Northumberland Fusiliers	...	*Allahabad.*
6th (1st Warwickshire) Regt. of Foot,	...	*Azimghur*, detachment at *Jaunpore.*
7th Regt. Royal Fusiliers,	..	*Jhelum*, detachment at *Dehra Ismael Khan.*
8th (King's) Regt. of Foot,	..	*Futtyghur*, detacht. at *Mynpoorie.*
13th (Prince Albert's) Regt. of Light Infantry.		*Goruckpore*, Detachments at *Bustee & Lotun.*
19th (Yorkshire) Regt. of Foot,	...	*Dinapore*, Detachment at *Mozufferpore*, and *Dacca.*
20th (East Devonshire) Regt. of Foot,	..	*Camp Gonda, Trans-Gogra.*
23rd Royal Welsh Fusiliers,	..	*Lucknow*,
24th (2nd Warwickshire) Regt. of Foot,	...	*Ferozepore.*
27th (Inniskilling) Regt. of Foot,	..	*Umballa*, detachments at *Kussowlie* and *Kurrachee.*
34th (Cumberland) Reg. of Foot,	..	*Fyzabad.* Right Wing at *Russioul.*
35th (Royal Sussex) Regt. of Foot,	..	*Dinapore*, detachment at *Sewan* and *Bankipore.*
37th (Northampshire) Reg. of Foot,	..	*Ghazeepore.*
38th (1st Staffordshire) Regt. of Foot,	..	*Roy Bareilly.*
42nd Royal Highlanders,	..	*Bareilly.*
43rd (Monmouthshire) Regt. of Light Infantry,		*Saugor, Nagode* and *Banda.*
46th (South Devonshire) Regt. of Foot,	..	*En route to Mooltan.*
48th (Northamptonshire) Regt. of Foot,	..	*Cawnpore.*
51st (2nd Yorkshire) Regt. of Foot,	..	*Meean Meer*, detacht at *Umritsur.*
52nd (Oxfordshire) Regt. of Light Infantry,	..	*Sealkote*, detachment at *Kot Kangra.*
53rd (Shropshire) Regt. of Foot,	...	*Allahabad.*
54th (West Norfolk) Regt. of Foot,	..	*Sultanpore*, and *Fyzabad.*
60th Royal Rifles, 1st Battalion,	..	*Benares.*
60th Ditto 2nd Battalion,	..	*Arrah* and *Benares.*
67th (South Hampshire) Regt. of Foot,	..	*Barrackpore.*
70th (Surrey) Regt. of Foot,	..	*Rawul Pindee.*
71st Regt. of Foot (Highland),	..	*Morar, Gwalior and Goonah.*
73rd Regiment of Foot,	..	*Goruckpore* district (*Camp Bulrumpore.*)
75th Ditto,	..	*Meerut.*
77th (East Middlesex) Regt. of Foot,	...	*Allahabad*, Detachments at *Benares Kunoundeah.*
79th Cameron Highlanders,	..	*Meean Meer.*
80th (Staffordshire Volunteers) Regt. of Foot,.		*Cawnpore.*
81st (Loyal Lincoln Vols.) Regt. of Foot,	..	*Peshawur.*
82nd (Prince of Wales' Vols.) Regt. of Foot,	.	*Shahjehanpore*, a Wing at *Moradabad.*
87th Royal Irish Fusiliers,	..	*Jullunder*, 1 Company at *Phillour.*
88th (Connaught Rangers) Regt. of Foot,	..	*Delhi.*
90th (Perthshire Volunteers) Light Infantry,		*Seetapore.*
93rd Sutherland Highlanders,	..	*Subathoo.*
94th Regiment of Foot,	..	*Peshawur*, Detachts at *Meean Meer.*
97th (Earl of Ulster's) Regt. of Foot,	..	*Banda*, 3 Companies at *Nowgong* 2 Companies at *Kirwee.*
98th Regiment of Foot,	..	*Nowsherra*, detachment at *Attock.*
99th (Lanarkshire) Regt. of Foot,	..	*Fort William, Calcutta*, detacht. at *Berhampore.*
Rifle Brigade, 2nd Battalion,	..	*Lucknow.*
Ditto, 3rd Battalion,	..	*Agra.*

Royal Engineers.

STAFF.

Colonel Henry Drary Harness, C. B., ...	13 *Jan.* 55	*Commanding.*—With Army Head Quarters Simla.
Major Francis Edward Cox, ...	1 *Apl.* 55	*Adjutant.*—Leave on M. C. to Europe.
Capt. Frederick Edward B. Beaumont, ...	1 *Apl.* 59	*Quarter Master.*—Tempory on D. P. W.
Lieut. R. Harrison, ...	31 *July* 55	Acting Ditto, Army Head Qrs.

4TH COMPANY,

Landed in Calcutta, from England, 12th November 1857.

FYZABAD.

Captain and Bt. Lt. Colonel Lothian Nicholson,	2 *Nov.* 55	Leave of Absence on M. C. to England.
Lieut. P. H. Scratchley, ...	20 *June* 54	
Lieut. George Sweetenham, ...	7 *Apl.* 56	Assist. Engineer in Oudh D.P.W
Lieut. Wm. Keith, ...	... ...	
Lieut. J F. H. Barkly. ..	1 *Aug.* 55	

Strength—Total, 134.

23RD COMPANY,

Landed in Calcutta, from England, 13th and 18th September 1857.

Mousa Bagh—LUCKNOW.

Captain Gorald Graham, * ..		
Lieut. Edward Donald Malcolm, ...	16 *Dec.* 54	Tempory on D. P. W.
Lieut. Gordon Douglas Pritchard, ...	31 *July* 55	
Lieut. Richard Harrison, ...	31 *July* 55	Staff Acting Adjutant.
Lieut. J. Hirne, ..	7 *Apr.* 56	
Assist. Surgeon Russel, ..		

Strength Total—132 men.

* Victoria Cross.

H. M. 2nd (or the Queen's Royal) Regiment of Dragoon Guards

The ROYAL CYPHER *within the Garter.*

REGIMENTALS, *Scarlet*—FACINGS, *Buff.*

Landed in Calcutta, from England, 25th and 27th November 1857.

CAMP BYRAM GHAT.

On route to *Lucknow.*

Regimental Depôt, Canterbury.

RANK AND NAMES.	*Regimental Rank.*	*Army Rank.*	REMARKS.
COLONEL.			
Hon'ble Henry F. Compton Cavendish,	2 *June* 53	*l.g* 20 *June* 54	In England.
LIEUTENANT COLONELS.			
William Henry Seymour, C. B.,	7 *July* 58	... ...	Commanding.
C. Pynder B. Walker,	7 *Dec.* 58	9 *Nov.* 55	On Detachment duty.
MAJORS.			
Coote Synge Hutchinson,	7 *July* 58	*l.c.* 26 *Apl.* 59	On Detachment duty.
Henry Miles Stapylton,	17 *Sep.* 57		
CAPTAINS.			
George Bushman,	16 *June* 57	... ...	Absent without leave.
M. James Bradley Dyne,	16 *June* 57	.. ...	Commanding Depôt, England.
Francis Graham Powell,	24 *July* 57	... ..	On Detachment duty.
Henry Holden Steward,	.. ..	11 *July* 56	
Goodrich H. Allfrey,	7 *Mar.* 58	... ..	On Detachment duty.
Pat. Alex. Watson Carnegy,	13 *May* 58	... ...	Leave to England till 31 July 59.
John T. Ling,	5 *Oct.* 58	16 *Oct.* 55	Canterbury Depot.
William W. King,	19 *Nov.* 58	.. ..	Ditto.
Silvester Calvert,	20 *Dec.* 58		
Walter Colquhoun Grant,	29 *Mar.* 59	.. ...	Comdg. Ist Regt. Hodson's Horse.
LIEUTENANTS.			
George Eugene Logan,	16 *June* 57	... ..	On Detachment duty.
Henry Lavington Payne,	24 *July* 57	14 *Sep.* 55	Leave to England to 10 Sep. 60.
Thomas Wm. Sneyd,	24 *July* 57	... ..	Ditto to 22 Oct. 60.
George Fred. Ormsby,	7 *Aug.* 57	... ..	On Detachment duty.
William Thomas Foster,	5 *Mar.* 58		
H. John de Montmorency,	7 *Mar.* 58		
William Jones Thomas,	12 *May* 58	.. ..	Adjutant.
Francis O'Beirne,	7 *July* 58	.. ..	
J. W. Z. Wright,	5 *Oct.* 58	... ...	Canterbury Depot.
Frncis Lamb Philp,	24 *Dec.* 58		
CORNETS.			
Charles J. Alfred Barnes,	15 *Aug.* 57	... ..	On Detachment duty.
Charles Lever,	17 *Aug.* 57	8 *Jan.* 56	
Robert Henry Torrens,	28 *Aug.* 57	.. ..	A. D. C. to *Sir* Hope Grant, K. C. B.
R. N. Betty,	12 *Feb.* 58		
Edward Vandeleur,	23 *July* 58	.. ..	Canterbury Depot.
John Taylor Marshall,	6 *Aug.* 58	.. ..	Ditto.
Frederick Greatorex,	7 *Sep.* 58	26 *Mar.* 58	On Detachment duty.
Howard J. Barton,	20 *Oct.* 58	... ...	Canterbury Depot.
George Batly,	62 *Nov.* 58	.. ...	Ditto.
Westropp McMahon Weir,	11 *Feb.* 59	... ..	Ditto.

H. M. 2ND REGIMENT OF DRAGOON GUARDS.—*Continued.*

RANK AND NAMES.	*Regimental Rank.*	*Army Rank.*	REMARKS.
PAY MASTER.			
Lieut. Fred. Windham Lukin,	10 *Aug.* 55	*lt.* 18 *Nov.* 53	
ADJUTANT.			
Cornet A. Deane,			
QUARTER MASTER.			
William Rae,	9 *Oct.* 55	.. ..	
RIDING MASTER.			
James Russell,	24 *Sep.* 58	25 *Sep.* 55	
SURGEON.			
Hampden Hugh Massy, M. D.,	1 *Mar.* 57	28 *Mar.* 54	
ASSISTANT SURGEONS.			
John Harrison Robotham,	8 *Jan.* 57	23 *Apl.* 55	On Detachment duty.
Robert Fleetwood Andrews,	6 *Apl.* 57	30 *Sep.* 53	
VETERINARY SURGEON.			
Tom Parinder Gudgin,	22 *Feb.* 57	13 *Oct.* 54	
INTERPRETER.			
Capt. R. B. Dundas, 38th N.I.	.. ...	.. ..	

Strength—9 Troops with 48 Sergeants,—32 Corporals,—10 Trumpeters — and 532 Privates.

English Agents,—Messrs. Cox and Co.

Irish Agents,—Messrs. Cane and Co.

Calcutta Agents,—Messrs. Gillanders, Arbuthnot and Co.

WAR SERVICES OF THE OFFICERS H. M. 2ND (QUEEN'S ROYAL) DRAGOON GUARDS.

Lieut-General the Hon. Henry Cavendish served in the Peninsula from July 1808 to January 1809 and was wounded through the wrist at the battle of Corunna, where he served as Aide-de-Camp to Lord William Bentinck, He has received the War Medal with two Clasps for Sahagun and Benevente, and Corunna.

Lt. Col. W. H. Seymour served with the 68th Lt. Infantry during the Crimean campaign of 1854.55 including the battles of Alma, Balaklava, and Inkerman and siege of Sebastopol (Medal and four Clasps). Accompanied the 2nd Dragoon guards to India on the breaking out of the Bengal Mutinies, served with the Regiment at the action of Nusseratpore, and throughout the Lucknow campaign of 1858, including the siege and capture of Lucknow (charger wounded) and subsequent operations and action of Nawabgunge (in command of three squadrons); commanded the Regiment throughout the Oude campaign of 1858-59, including the action of Jamo (wounded) and siege and capture of Birwah.

Lt. Col. C. S. Hutchinson accompanied the 2nd Dragoon guards to India on the breaking out of the Bengal Mutinies, served with the Regiment in the Lucknow campaign of 1858, including the siege and capture of Lucknow and subsequent operations, and action of Barree (in command of a detached squadron).

Major H. M. Stapylton accompanied the 2nd Dragoon guards to India on the breaking out of the Bengal Mutinies, served with the Regiment throughout the Lucknow campaign of 1858, including the action of Nusseratpore, siege and capture of Lucknow (charger wounded) and subsequent operations and actions of Barree and Newabgunge. Served throughout the Oude campaign of 1858-59, including the action of Jamo and siege and capture of Birwah.

Captain F. G. Powell accompanied the 2nd Dragoon guards to India on the breaking out of the Bengal Mutinies; served with the Regiment throughout the Lucknow campaign of 1858, including the action of Nusseratpore and siege and capture of Lucknow, and subsequent operations and action of Koorsee, served also throughout the Oude campaign of 1858-59, including the affair of Selimpore in command of a detached squadron of the Regiment.

Captain H. H. Steward served with the 2nd Dragoon guards at the affair of Dawah.

Captain G. H. Allfrey accompanied the 2nd Dragoon guards to India on the breaking out of the Bengal Mutinies, served with the Regiment throughout the Lucknow campaign of 1858, including the siege and capture of Lucknow, and subsequent operations and action of Koorsee, served in the Oude campaign of 1858-59.

Captain P. A. W. Carnegy accompanied the 2nd Dragoon guards to India on the breaking out of the Bengal Mutinies; served with the Regiment throughout the Lucknow campaign of 1858, including the siege and capture of Lucknow (wounded) and subsequent operations and action of Koorsee, served throughout the Oude campaign of 1858-59, including the action of Jamo, and siege and capture of Birwah, and commanded a detached squadron of the Regiment in the affair of Koorsee.

Captain W. C. Grant (formerly a Captain of the 2nd Dragoons) served with the Eastern army from Novr. 1854, as Captain commandant of the Mounted Staff corps with Local Rank of Major (Medal and Clasp for Sebastopol); served also from Oct. 1855 to the conclusion of the War as Asst. Quarter Master General to the Cavalry division Turkish Contingent with the Local Rank of Lt.-Colonel (4th Class of the Medjidie). Accompanied the 2nd Dragoon guards to India on the breaking out of the Bengal Mutinies; served with the Regiment throughout the Lucknow campaign of 1858, including the action of Nusseratpore and siege and capture of Lucknow and subsequent operations and action of Koorsee.

Captain S. D. Calvert accompanied the 2nd Dragoon guards to India on the breaking out of the Bengal Mutinies; served as Adjutant with the Regiment throughout the Lucknow campaign of 1858, including the siege and capture of Lucknow and subsequent operation and action of Soorsee, served throughout the Oude campaign of 1858-9, including the action of Jamo (charger wounded) and siege and capture of Birwah.

Lieut. G. E. Logan accompanied the 2nd Dragoon guards to India on the breaking out of the Bengal Mutinies; served with the Regiment throughout the Lucknow campaign of 1858, including the siege and capture of Lucknow and subsequent operations and action of Koorsee, served throughout the Oude campaign of 1858-59, including the action of Jamo and siege and capture of Birwah.

Lieut. H. L. Payne served with the 2nd Dragoon guards throughout the Lucknow campaign of 1858, including the siege and capture of Lucknow and subsequent operations, and action of Koorsee and Barree; served also throughout the Oude campaign of 1858-59, and commanded a detached squadron at the crossing of the Gogra at Fyzabad.

*** *For continuation of Services, see page 19b.*

6th Regiment of Dragoon Guards (Carabineers.)

"SEVASTOPOL."

REGIMENTALS, *Blue*—FACINGS, *White*.

Landed in Bengal, from England, on the 22nd November 1856.

MUTTRA.

Right Wing Meerut, *Detachment at* Agra.

Regimental Depôt, Maidstone.

RANK AND NAMES.	*Regimental Rank.*	*Army Rank.*	REMARKS.
COLONEL.			
Alex. K. Clarke Kennedy, C. B., K. C. H., - M	14 *June* 58	*m.g.* 20 *June* 54	In England.
LIEUTENANT COLONELS.			
Henry Richmond Jones, C. B.,	16 *Sep.* 51	*col* 28 *Nov.* 54	Leave of Absence to England on P. A. for 18 months.
William Neville Custance, C. B.,	1 *Aug.* 56		Comdg.
MAJORS.			
Charles Sawyer, S. D. - *V*,	1 *Aug.* 56	*l.c.* 20 *July* 58	
Robert Bickerstaff, - - - -	6 *Nov.* 57	*l.c.* 20 *July* 58	Leave of Absence to England on P. A. for 18 months.
CAPTAINS.			
Alex. George Dickson, - -	7 *Sep.* 55	1 *June* 55	Maidstone Depôt, England.
Charles Potts Rosser, - - -	1 *Aug.* 56	*m* 19 *Jan.* 58	Leave on M. C. to England.
Thomas Bott, - - -	22 *Aug.* 56	*m* 16 *Nov.* 58	
Courtenay Wm. Bruce, - - -	2 *Oct.* 57		
Fras. Nathaniel Astley,- - -	7 *Nov.* 57	.. ..	En route to join.
Wm. Thomas Betty, - - -	15 *Dec.* 57	.. ..	With Right Wing.
Fra. Geo. Savage Curtis, - -	5 *Mar.* 58		
William Oliver Bird, - - -	24 *Aug.* 58	.. ..	Detachment at Agra.
Aurthur Cooper - - - -	11 *Apl.* 59	.. ..	Not joined.
Charles Hill Uniacke, - -	1 *Aug.* 56	23 *Oct.* 55	Leave on M. C. to England.
LIEUTENANTS.			
Jas. John Neil Buchanan, *V*,	1 *Aug.* 56	8 *Sep.* 54	
George Silvester Davies, *V*,	1 *Aug.* 56	26 *June* 55	Convalescent Depot Landour.
Augustus Alfred de Bourbel, -	1 *Aug.* 56	23 *Oct.* 55	Leave on M. C. to England.
John William Doering, - -	22 *Aug.* 56		
Walter Blachford Gifford, *V*,	19 *Dec.* 56	.. ..	With Detachment at Agra.
Fredk. Augustus Weatherley, -	5 *June* 57	26 *June* 55	Adjutant.
Geo. S. LeGrice Stoddart, - -	20 *July* 57	.. ..	Right Wing.
Wm. Wallace Graham, - - -	15 *Nov.* 57	.. ..	Ditto.
R ~~Richard John Grainger~~, -	15 *Nov.* 57	.. ..	Leave, on M. C. to England.
Henry Reginald Forster, -	4 *Dec.* 57	.. ..	Leave on M. C. to England.
William Howley Burder, - -	15 *Dec.* 57	.. ..	Right Wing.
William Greaves Blake, - -	26 *Feb.* 58		

H. M. 6th Regiment of Dragoon Guards (Carabineers.)—*Continued.*

Rank and Names.	*Regimental Rank.*	*Army Rank.*	Remarks.
Cornets.			
John Buchan Hepburn, - -	4 *Dec.* 57		
William Duff Pereira, - - -	5 *Dec.* 57		
Thomas M. Turner, - - -	2 *Feb.* 58		
Geo. Arthur Smith, - - -	19 *Feb.* 58		
William Gair, - - - - -	5 *Mar.* 58	*ens.* 18 *Dec.* 57	
George Selwyn Marryat, - -	16 *Mar.* 58	.. ..	With Right Wing.
Robert S. Blacket, - - - -	4 *Mar.* 59	.. ..	Not joined.
*			
*			
*			
Pay Master.			
Charles Sewell, - - - - -	5 *Jan.* 55	.. ..	On Leave to Landour.
Adjutant.			
Lieut. F. Augustus Weatherley,	5 *Oct.* 58	*lt* 26 *June* 55	
Quarter Master.			
George Fraser, - - - - -	7 *Nov.* 51		
Riding Master.			
William James Hessey, - -	7 *Dec.* 58	.. ..	Not joined.
Surgeon.			
James Prichard Moline, - -	15 *Aug.* 54		
Assistant Surgeons.			
Charles James Davenport, - -	1 *Aug.* 56	15 *Aug.* 54	
Stewart Aaron Lithgow, - -	28 *Jan.* 59	.. ..	With Right Wing.
Veterinary Surgeon.			
Alfred Job Owles, - - - -	19 *Dec.* 51		
Interpreter.			
*			

Strength—9 Troops, with 50 Sergeants—32 Corporals—10 Trumpeters—and 616 Privates.
English Agents, Messrs. Cox & Co.
Calcutta Agents, Messrs. Gillanders, Arbuthnot & Co.

WAR SERVICES OF THE OFFICERS OF 6th (CARABINEERS.) DRAGOON GUARDS.

Major-General Clarke Kennedy served in the Peninsula with the Royal Dragoons from Sept. 1809 to Oct. 1813, including the battle of Busaco, covering the retreat to Torres Vedras, affair at Quinta de Torre, battle of Fuentes d'Onor (horse struck down by a shell), blockade of Almeida, actions at Nave d'Aver, Fuente Guinaldo, and Aldea de Ponte (appointed Brigade-Major to General Slade); covering the Seige of Ciudad Rodrigo, selected to command a party of Cavalry advanced to watch and report the enemy's movements during the siege of Badajoz, for which he was thanked by Lord Lynedoch; engaged with a body of French Infantry under General Clausel, near Salamanca, battle of Vittoria, blockade of Pampeluna, besides various skirmishes and affairs of outposts. Campaign of 1815,—covering the retreat on the 17th June and battle of Waterloo (received two wounds and had two horses killed under him). Whilst leading his squadron in a successful charge against Count D'Erlon's corps at Waterloo, perceiving an Eagle to the left, he charged the direction of his squadron, ran the officer through the body who carried it and captured the Eagle, which belonged to the 105th French Regiment of Infantry, and is now deposited in Chelsea Hospital. Has received the War Medal with two Clasps.

Colonel Jones commanded the Carabineers in the Crimea from 14 Aug. 1855, including the battle of the Tchernaya, siege and fall of Sebastopol (Medal and Clasp, and 5th Class of the Medjidie).

Lieut.-Colonel Custance served in the Crimean campaign from 14 August 1855, including the battle of the Tchernaya, siege and fall of Sebastopol (Medal and Clasp, and Order of the Medjidie, 5th Class); commanded the Carabineers at the outbreak of the Sepoy Mutineers at Meerut on 10th May 1857, as also during the campaign of that year, including the battles of the Hindun, 30th and 31st May (horse killed), battle of Budiekaserai, 8th June (horse wounded), affair of 9th June, and siege of Delhi; and commanded the irregular Cavalry under Brigadier Grant, at the storming of the City 14th September: as also in the subsequent operations under Brigadier Showers.

Major Sawyer and Captain Bott served in the Crimea from 26th May 1855, including the battle of the Tchernaya, siege and fall of Sebastopol (Medal and Clasp.)

Major Rosser served the campaign in the Southern Mahratta Country in 1844. Also at the siege of Sebastopol in 1855, latterly as Aide-de-Camp to General Scarlell and was at the battle of the Tonerpaya (Medal and Clasps.)

Captain Dickson served with the 62nd Regt. at the siege of Sebastopol in 1855, including the attack on the Quarries 8th June, and on the Redan 18th June, (Medal and Clasp).

Lieut. and Adjt. Weatherley served in the Crimea with the 4th Light Dragoons and was present at the battle of the Tchernaya. the siege and fall of Sebastopol and also served in the Expedition to Eupatoria (Medal and Clasps.) campaign in Rohilcund including ambuscade of Kukroulie, battle of Bareilly, attack and relief of Shahjehanpore, action at Mohumdee and Shahabad, Trans Gogra campaign including actions at Buxar Ghaut Majeedias, Churdal and Bankee.

Cornet Gair served with the Field Train of R. Artillery, during the Eastern campaign of 1854-55, including the affairs of Bulganac and McKenzie's Farm, battles of Alma, Balaklava, and Inkerman. siege and fall of Sebastopol (Medal and Clasps).

Qr.-Master Fraser, served at the siege and fall of Sebastopol from 14 Aug. 1855 (Medal and Clasp).

Surgeon Moline served with the 22nd Regt. during the campaign of 1844-45 in the Southern Mahratta country and was present at the taking of the forts of Panulla and Pownghur.

H. M. 7th (The Princess Royal's) Regt. of Dragoon Guards.

REGIMENTALS, *Scarlet*,—FACINGS, *Black*.

Landed at Kurrachie, from England, on 7th January 1858.

SEALKOTE

Regimental Depôt, Canterbury.

RANK AND NAMES.	*Regimental Rank.*	*Army Rank.*	REMARKS.
COLONEL.			
Michael White, C. B - - -	26 *Aug.* 58	m.g 20 *June* 54	In England.
LIEUTENANT COLONELS.			
Arthur Cavendish Bentinck, -	8 *Dec.* 54	*col.* 30 *Jan.* 58	Lv. on M. C. to England, to 30 Sep. 59.
Charles Wm. Thompson, - -	17 *Sept.* 57	.. ..	Commanding.
MAJORS.			
~~William Middleton~~, - -	16 *Sept.* 57	.. ..	Leave on M. C. to England.
Adolphus W. Desart Burton, C.B.	17 *Sept.* 57	12 *Dec.* 54	
CAPTAINS.			
Fitzroy George Smith, - -	30 *July* 52	.. ..	Leave on P, A. to England.
Wm. Wentworth Lamb, - -	8 *Dec.* 54		
Edw. Tho. Dowbiggen, - -	14 *Sep.* 55	.. ..	Canterbury Depôt, England.
A. R. G. Costello, - - - -	16 *June* 57		
Peter Withington, - *V*,	16 *Sept.* 57	... ...	Lv. on P. A. to England to 4 Jan. 61.
Henry Blinkhorn, - -	16 *Sept.* 57		
W. Fombelle Dowdeswell, - -	16 *Sept.* 57		
George E. F. Kauntze, - *V*,	9 *Oct.* 57	14 *Sep* 55	
Newton Chas. Chichester, - -	11 *Dec.* 57	13 *July* 57	Lv. on M. C. to Muree to 14 Nov. 59.
James Vance Cleland, - -	28 *Nov.* 58		
John Richards Welstead, - -	8 *Apl.* 59		
LIEUTENANTS.			
Hume Nicholl, - -	9 *Oct.* 55	... ..	Canterbury Depôt, England.
David Scotland, - -	8 *May* 56	... ...	Adjutant.
Christopher Barton, - -	15 *Sept.* 57		
Wm. Digby Wentworth, - -	15 *Sept.* 57		
D ~~George Ross Caldwell~~, - -	16 *Sep.* 57	5 *Feb.* 55	
Edmund Prideaux Chichester, -	17 *Sept.* 57	3 *Aug.* 55	
Edw. Hy. Ernest Kauntze, *V*,	18 *Sep.* 57	29 *Feb.* 56	
Wm. Bruce Armstrong, - *V*,	18 *Sept.* 57	... ...	At Durmsallah.
William Chaine, - -	9 *Oct.* 57	... ...	Leave on P.A. to England to 4 Jan. 61.
Edmund Molyneux, - -	26 *Nov.* 58		
Robert Stewart Cleland, - -	8 *Apl.* 59		
CORNETS.			
Jas. Jno. Loudon M'Adam, -	18 *Sep.* 57	22 *May* 57	
Wm. Macnaghton Erskine, -	16 *Oct.* 57		
John M'Bryan, -	17 *Oct.* 57	.. ..	On duty with 5th Bengal Light Cavy., Peshawar.
Clavering Redman, - -	6 *Nov.* 57		
Edward Hy. O'Dowd, - -	27 *Nov.* 57		En route to join.
Arthur H. Vincent, - -	29 *Dec.* 57	.. ..	Ditto.
John Alexander Drake, - -	11 *Jan.* 59	.. ...	Canterbury Depôt, England.

7TH (THE PRINCESS ROYAL'S) REGT. OF DRAGOON GUARDS.—*(Continued.)*

RANK AND NAMES.	*Regimental Rank.*	*Army Rank.*	REMARKS.
PAYMASTER.			
Capt. John Smith, - -	17 *Nov.* 57	*c.* 1 *Feb.* 56	
ADJUTANT.			
Lieut. David Scotland, - -	17 *Nov.* 54	*lt.* 8 *May* 56	
QUARTER MASTER.			
George Gillam, - -	17 *Nov.* 54		
RIDING MASTER.			
Henry Pearce Phillips, - -	2 *Oct.* 57		
SURGEON.			
Ed. James Franklyn, M. D., -	6 *Apl.* 59	15 *May* 55	
ASSISTANT SURGEONS.			
Opie Smith, - -	20 *Jan.* 57	4 *Feb.* 53	On Leave to England.
Edward M'Gill, M. D., - -	18 *Sep.* 57	8 *Jan.* 55	
VETERINARY SURGEON.			
William Varley, - -	2 *Oct.* 57	15 *Aug.* 55	
INTERPRETER.			
Lieut. E. H. E. Kauntze, Offg.	26 *May* 59		

Strength—9 Troops with 47 Sergeants,—32 Corporals,—9 Trumpeters, and 486 Privates

English Agents,—Messrs. Cox and Co.
Irish Agents,—*Sir* E. Borough, *Bart.*, Armit & Co.
Calcutta Agents,—Messrs. Colvin, Cowie and Co.

WAR SERVICES OF THE OFFICERS OF THE 7TH REGT. OF DRAGOON GUARDS.

Major-General White was in the field in 1809, on the Banks of the Sutlej; served at the capture of Hatras in 1817, and during the Mahratta campaign of 1817-18; was present at the siege and capture of Bhurtpore in 1825-6 (Medal and one Clasp). Commanded the Cavalry throughout the campaign of 1842 in Affghanistan, and was present at the forcing of the Khyber Pass, storming the heights of Jugdulluck, action of Tezeen and Huft Kotul, and occupation of Cabool (Medal, and nominanted a CB.). Served with the army of the Sutlej in 1845-6; commanded the whole of the cavalry at the battle of Moodkee (charger wounded); a brigade at the battle of Ferozeshah (wounded, charger killed by a round shot); and the 3rd Lt. Drs. at the battle of Sobraon (charger wounded); Medal and two Clasps, and appointed Aide de-Camp to the Queen. Served in the Punjaub campaign of 1848-9, in command of the 1st Brigade of Cavalry; was present in the affair of Ramnuggur, action of Sadoolapore, and battles of Chillianwallah and Goojerat (Medal and two Clasps).

Colonel Bentinck has received a Kaffir Medal for the war of 1847.

Lt.-Colonel Thompson served as a Captain in the British Legion, and was engaged at Hernani 30th Aug. 1835; at Arlaban, 16th, 17th, and 18th Jan,; and the action before San Sebastian, 5th May 1836, when he was severely wounded in the hip and the hand (K. S. F. and Medal), Served the campaign of the Punjaub in the 14th Light Dragoons; was engaged at Ramnuggur (horse wounded), 22nd Nov. 1848, at Chillianwallah, 13th Jan., and at Goojerat. 21st Feb. 1849 (Medal and two Clasps). Present also at the crossing of the Chenab, Jhelum, and Indus; at the surrender of the Seik army at Rawul Pindee, the capture of the Bridge of Boats at Attock, and pursuit of the Affghans to Peshawur.

Major Burton served in the Eastern campaign of 1854-55, and commanded the 5th Dragoon Guards at the battles of Balaklava, Inkerman, Tchernaya, and siege of Sebastopol (Medal and three Clasps. Brevet Major, and *C. B.*)

Capt. Blinkhorn served with the 16th Lancers in the battle of Maharajpore, 29th Dec. 1843 (Medal,) also in the campaign on the Sutlej in 1846, including the battles of Aliwal and Sobraon, for which he has received a Medal and one Clasp.

Capt. Kauntze was present with the 11th Light Dragoons at the siege and capture of Bhurtpore in 1825 (Medal and one Clasp). Served with the 3rd Light Dragoons throughout the campaign of 1842 in Affghanistan (Medal) and was present at the forcing of the Khyber Pass capture of Mamoo Khail storming of the heights of Jugdulluck, actions of Tezeen and Huftkotul and occupation of Cabool. He served also the Sutlej campaign of 1845-46 and was present at the battles of Moodkee (wounded) Ferozeshah (wounded) and Sobraon (severely wounded) Medal and two Clasps. Served in the Punjaub campaign of 1848-49 and was present at the affair of Ramnugger, the passage of the Chenab at Wuzeerabad on the 1st December 1848 with a force under *Sir* Joseph Thackwell, action of Sadoolapore and battles of Chillianwallah and Goojerat (Medal and two Clasps).

Lieut. Armstrong served the Eastern campaign of 1854-55, including the battles of Balaklava and Inkerman, siege and fall of Sebastopol (Medal and Clasps).

Lieut. Chichester served with the 21st Fusiliers during the latter part of 1855 at the siege and fall of Sebastopol and expedition to Kinbourn (Medal and Clasp).

Lieut. Caldwell served at the siege and fall of Sebastopol in 1855, (medal and clasp).

Quarter-master Gillam served with the 7th Dragoon Guards at the Cape of Good Hope, and was with the expedition against the insurgent Boers beyond the Orange River in 1845; and he served throughout the Kaffir war of 1846-7 (Medal).

Surgeon Franklyn served the Eastern campaign of 1854-55, was as Balaklava attending on the wounded during the Cavalry action there; and was placed in charge of Russian wounded after the battle of Inkerman, and served with the 77th Regiment before Sebastopol (Medal and Clasps and 5th class of the Medjidie).

H. M. 7th (The Queen's Own) Regt. of Light. Dragoons (Hussars.)

ROYAL CYPHER, *within the Garter.*

"PENINSULA"—"WATERLOO."

REGIMENTALS, *Blue.*

Landed in Calcutta, from England, 27th November 1857.

UMBALLA.

Regimental Depôt, Canterbury.

RANK AND NAMES.	*Regimental Rank.*	*Army Rank.*	REMARKS.
COLONEL.			
Sir William Tuyll, K.C.H., - -	10 *Mar.* 46	*g* 20 *June* 54	In Europe.
LIEUTENANT COLONELS.			
Sir William Russell, *Bart.*, C.B.	12 *Nov.* 58	*l.c.* 20 *July*. 58	Leave on P. A. England.
William Babington, - -	10 *May* 59	.. ..	Commanding.
MAJORS.			
William Dascon Bushe, - -	1 *Jan.* 59	*l.c.* 26 *July* 59	Leave to 31 July 59.
Charles Craufurd Fraser, - -	10 *May* 59	.. ..	Leave of Absence to England on P. A. to 31 March 60.
CAPTAINS.			
Hon. I. DeV. T. W. Fiennes, -	3 *Mar.* 57	*m.* 20 *July* 58	Leave of Absence to England on P. A. to 31 March 60.
David Philip Brown, - -	14 *Aug.* 57	9 *May* 56	
James Aytoun, - -	14 *Aug.* 57	24 *June* 56	
Thomas H. Stisted, - -	9 *Oct.* 57	*m* 26 *Apl.* 59	Leave in India on P. A. to 25 Oct. 59.
Frank Garforth, - -	5 *Mar.* 58	.. ..	Leave to 31 July 59.
~~Musgrave Dyne Brisco~~, - -	11 *May* 58		
Charles William Paulet, - -	12 *Nov.* 58		
Hon. A. H. A. Anson, - *V. C,*	9 *Oct.* 58	6 *July* 55	Leave of Absence to 28 February 61.
Robert Hale, - -	1 *Jan.* 59	.. ..	Canterbury Depôt, England.
Robt. S. Wms. Bulkeley, - -	10 *May* 59	.. ..	Leave of Absence to England for 6 months.
LIEUTENANTS.			
Richard Topham, - -	14 *Aug.* 57	14 *Mar.* 56	
Henry John Wilkin, - -	14 *Aug.* 57	6 *Feb.* 57	
Richard Newsham Pedder, -	5 *Mar.* 58	.. ..	Leave of Absence to England on P. A. to 31 March 60.
Hon. Caryl Craven Molyneux,	11 *May* 58		
John B. Phillipson, - -	16 *July* 58	.. ..	Leave of Absence on M. C.
Robert D. Stewart, - -	19 *Nov.* 58		
Hon. Walter Harbord, - -	19 *Nov.* 58		
~~Chas. P. *Viscount* Royston~~, - -	11 *Jan.* 59		
John Mould, - -	11 *Mar.* 59		Adjutant.
Charles H. Baillie, - - -	11 *Mar.* 59		
CORNETS.			
Hon. Auberon, W. Edward M. Herbert. - - - - -	7 *May.* 58	.. ..	Regimental Depôt, England.
Arthur Hamilton Scrope, - -	13 *July* 58		
Robert Owen Johnes. - - -	13 *Aug.* 58	26 *Feb.* 56	Leave on M. C. to Kusowlie to 20 Aug. 59.
Edward Metcalfe, - - -	26 *Nov.* 58	.. ..	Regt. Depot.
Edm. H. Rennard, - - -	26 *Nov.* 58	.. ..	Ditto.
Richard Simmons, - - -	*Jan.* 59		
Henry Herbert Wombell, - -	11 *Jan.* 59	.. ..	Ditto.

H. M. 7th Regiment of Light Dragoons (Hussars.)—(*Continued.*)

Rank and Names.	*Regimental Rank.*	*Army Rank.*	Remarks.
Pay Master.			
George Elliott, - -	18 *Sep.* 57		
Adjutant.			
Lieut. John Mould, - -	16 *Mar.* 58	16 *Mar.* 58	
Quarter Master.			
Walter Borthwick, - -	25 *Aug.* 57		
Riding Master.			
William Bray, - - - -	5 *Oct.* 58		
Surgeon.			
Henry J. Kendall, M. D., - -	14 *Aug.* 57	6 *Oct.* 54	
Assistant Surgeons.			
George Moulas Slaughter, - -	14 *Aug.* 57	13 *Dec.* 54	
T, A. Thornhill, M. B. - -	28 *May* 57		
Veterinary Surgeon.			
John Barker, - -	23 *Aug.* 57	27 *July* 55	
Interpreter.			
Lieut. R. Wheeler, 61st N. I. -			

Strength—9 Troops with 49 Sergeants,—32 Corporals—10 Trumpeters, and 551 Privates.

English Agents.—Messrs Cox and Co.

Calcutta Agents.—Messrs. Colvin Cowie and Co.

WAR SERVICES OF THE OFFICERS OF H. M. 7th (HUSSARS).

Sir Wm. Tuyll, K. C. H., served during part of the campaigns of 1793-94 and 95 in the Netherlands; at the Helder in 1799; and in Portugal, Spain and Walcheren in 1808 and 9, as Aide-de-Camp to the Marquis of Anglesey. Sir William has received the War Medal with one Clasp for Sahagun and Benevente.

Colonel Hagart, C. B., served in the Indian campaign from February 1858 to the conclusion of the campaign (Medal) commanded a wing of the 7th Hussars at the repulse of the enemy's attack on the Alumbagh, and the 1st Brigade of Cavalry during the siege and capture of Lucknow (clasp and C. B.) at the attack on the fort of Pinyaghar, and action of Allygunge, the taking of Bareilly, relief of Shahjehanpore and advance to Rohenda, commanded the Cavalry under Sir J. H. Grant at the occupation of Fyzabad, in the affair at the Kandoo Nuddee, at the passage of the Gogra, and during the whole of the Trans Gogra campaign; reverted to the command of his Regiment on the conclusion of the War in Bengal. 9 times mentioned in despatches.

Lieut-Colonel Sir W. Russell, Baronet, served in the Indian campaign from Feby. 1858 to March 59 (Medal) present at the repulse of the enemy's attack on the Alumbagh, the siege and capture of Lucknow (clasp and Bt. Lt. Colonelcy) commanded the 7th Hussars at the affairs of Baree Sirsee, action of Nawabgunge, occupation of Fyzabad, passage of the Goomtee, at Sultanpore, through the Byswarra campaign, including the affairs of Kandoo Nuddee Palee Ghat, Hyderghur and pursuit of Benhi Madho's force to the Goomtee, also the Trans Gogra campaign including the affair near Churda and pursuit, taking the Fort of Mujeedia, attack on Bankee with pursuit to the Raptee, the advance into Nepaul and affair at Silka Ghat. Several times mentioned in despatches, twice honorably.

Lt. Col. W. D. Bushe served in the Indian campaign from Feby 58 to March 59 (Medal) present at the repulse of the enemy's attack on the Alumbagh, the siege and capture of Lucknow (Clasp and brevet Majority) the affairs of Barree, and action of Nawabgunge, occupation of Fyzabad, passage of the Goomtee at Sultanpore, the affair of Shahpore, through the Byswarra campaign including the affairs of Kandoo Nuddee, Palee Ghat, and taking of the Forts of Rehora, and Keowlie, also the Trans Gogra campaign including the affair near Churda and pursuit taking the Fort of Mujeedia, attack on Bankee, with pursuit to the Raptee, advance into Napaul, and affair at Silka Ghat. Honorably mentioned in despatches for Nawabgunge.

Major C. C. Fraser was present as Orderly Officer to Brigr. Campbell at the affair of Munseata near Allahabad, subsequently served in the Indian campaign from Feby. 58 to July 58 and from Decr. 58 to March 59 (Medal) present at the affair of Meangunge the siege and capture of Lucknow (Clasp and brevet Majority) the affairs of Barree, Sirsee and action of Nawabgunge (severely wounded) through the Trans Gogra compaign, including the affair near Churda and pursuit, taking of the Fort of Mujeedia, attack on Bankee with pursuit to the Raptee, the advance into Nepaul and affair at Silka Ghat. Honorably mentioned in despatches for Nawabgunge and Bankee.

Major the Hon'ble J. D. V. Fiennes served in the Indian campaign from Feby. 1858 to March 1859, (Medal) present at the affair of Meangunge, the siege and capture of Lucknow (Clasp and Brevet Majority) the affairs of Barree, Sirsee, and action of Nawabgunge, occupation of Fyzabad, and passage of the Goomtee at Sultanpore,, the affair at the Kandoo-Nuddee, passage of the Gogra, and during the whole of the Trans Gogra campaign as Cavalry Brigade Major to Brigr. Hagart C. B., the advance into Nepaul and affair at Sitka Ghat. Several times mentioned in despatches.

Captain Brown has received the Order of the Medjidie, 4th Class, for service in the Turkish Contingent.

Captain J. Aytoun served in the Indian campaign from Feby. 1858 to March 1859 (Medal) present at the repulse of the enemy's attack on the Alumbagh, the siege and capture of Lucknow (Clasp) the affairs of Barree, Sirsee, and action of Nawabgunge, occupation of Fyzabad, passage of the Goomtee at Sultanpore, through the Byswarra campaign, including the affairs at the Kandoo Nuddee, Hyderghur, and pursuit of Benhi Madho's force to the Goomtee, also the Trans Gogra campaign including the affair near Churda and pursuit, taking the Fort of Mujeedia, attack on Bankee, with pursuit to the Raptee, the advance into Nepaul and affair at Sitka Ghaut.

Captain Stisted served the Sutlej campaign of 1848-9 with the 3rd Light Dragoons and was present at the affair of Ramnuggur, the passage of the Chenab at Wuzeerabad on the 1st Dec. 1848, with the force under Sir Joseph Thackwell, action of Sadoolapore, battles of Chillianwallah (wounded, and charger wounded) and Goojerat (Medal and two Clasps). Served in the Indian campaign from Feby. 1858 to March 1859 (Medal) present at the affair of Meangunge, the siege and capture of Lucknow (Clasp) the affair of Barree, and action of Nawabgunge, occupation of Fyzabad, passage of the Goomtee at Sultanpore, through the Byswarra campaign, including the affairs of Daodpore, Kandoo-Nuddee, Palee-Ghat, Hyderghur, and pursuit of Benhi Madho's force to the Goomtee, also the Trans Gogra campaign including the affair near Churda, and pursuit, taking the Fort of Mujeedia, attack on Bankee, with pursuit to the Raptee, the advance into Nepaul and affair at Sitka Ghat. Twice mentioned in despatches.

Captain F. Garforth served in the Indian Campaign from Feby. 1858 to March 1859 (Medal) present at the affair of Meangunge, the siege and capture of Lucknow (Clasp) the affair of Barree Sirsee and action of Nawabgunge, occupation of Fyzabad, passage of the Goomtee at Sultanpore, through the Byswarra campaign including the affairs of Daodpore, Kandoo-Nuddee, Palee Ghat, Hyderghur, and pursuit of Benhi-Madho's force to the

****For continuation of Services see next page.*

WAR SERVICES OF THE OFFICERS OF H. M. 7TH (HUSSARS.)—*Continued.*

Goomtee, also the Trans Gogra campaign including the affair at Churda and pursuit, taking the Fort of Mujeedia, attack on Bankee, with pursuit to the Raptee, the advance into Nepaul and affair at Sitka Ghat.

Captain M. D. Brisco served in the Indian Campaign from July 1858 to March 1859 (Medal) present at the advance on and occupation of Fyzabad, passage of the Goomtee at Sultanpore, through the Byswarra campaign including the affairs at the Kandoo-Nuddee, and Hyderghur, also the Trans Gogra campaign including the affair near Churda and pursuit, taking the Fort of Mujeedia, attack on Bankee with pursuit to the Raptee, the advance into Nepaul and affair at Sitka Ghat.

Captain Paulet served in the Indian Campaign from Feby. 1858 to March 1859 (Medal) present at the repulse of the enemy's attack on the Alumbagh, the siege and capture of Lucknow, (Clasp) the affairs of Barree, Sirsee, and action of Nawabgunge; occupation of Fyzabad, passage of the Goomtee at Sultanpore, through the Byswarra campaign, including the affairs of Daodpore, at the Kandoo-Nuddee, Hyderghur, and pursuit of Benhi-Madho's force to the Goomtee, also the Trans Gogra campaign including the affair near Churda and pursuit, taking the Fort of Mujeedia, attack on Bankee and pursuit to the Raptee, the advance into Nepaul and affair at Sitka Ghat.

Captain Hon. A. Anson served with the Rifle Brigade at the siege of Sebastopol from Jan. 1855 (Medal and Clasp, and 5th Class of the Medjidie). He was attached to the 9th Lancers at the siege and capture of Delhi (wounded); as Aide-de-Camp to General Grant he accompanied the Commander-in-Chief's column to the second relief of Lucknow (wounded).

Capt. R. S. W. Bulkeley served in the Indian Campaign from Feby. 1858 to Jany. 1859 (Medal) present at the affair of Meangunge, the siege and capture of Lucknow, (Clasp) the affairs of Barree, Sirsee, and action of Nawabgunge, occupation of Fyzabad, passage of the Goomtee at Sultanpore, through the Byswarra campaign, including the affairs at the Kandoo-Nuddee and Palee-Ghat, taking the Fort of Rehora attack on and pursuit from Hyderghur, also the Trans Gogra campaign including the affair near Churda and pursuit, taking the Fort of Mujeedia, and attack on Bankee with pursuit, to the Raptee.

Lieut. R. Tophain served in the Indian campaign from Feby. 1858 to March 1859 (Medal) present at the repulse of the enemy's attack on the Alumbagh, the siege and capture of Lucknow (Clasp) the affairs of Barree, (wounded) Sirsee, and action of Nawabgunge, (slight contusion) occupation of Fyzabad, passage of the Goomtee at Sultanpore, through the Byswarra campaign including the affairs at the Kandoo-Nuddee, Palee Ghat, Hyderghur, and pursuit of Benhi-Madho's force to the Goomtee, also the Trans Gogra campaign including the affair near Churda and pursuit, taking the Fort of Mujeedia, attack on Bankee and pursuit to the Raptee, the advance into Nepaul and affair at Sitka Ghat. Thrice mentioned in despatches.

Lieut, Wilkin served in the 11th Hussars throughout the Eastern campaign of 1854-55, including the affairs of Bulganac and M'Kenzie's Farm, battles of Alma, Balaklava, Inkerman, and Tchernaya, siege and fall of Sebastopol (Medal and four Clasps, and Order of the Medjidie). Served in the Indian campaign Feby. and March 1858 (severely wounded in the operations before Lucknow) and from Dec. 1858 to March 1859 (Medal) present at the affair of Meangunge the siege and capture of Lucknow (Clasp) through the Byswarra campaign including the affair near Churda and pursuit, taking the Fort of Mujeedia attack on Bankee with pursuit to the Raptee, the advance into Nepaul and affair at Sitka Ghat. Honorably mentioned in despatches for Lucknow.

Lieut. R. N. Pedder served in the Indian campaign from Feby. 1858 to March 1859 (Medal) present at the repulse of the enemy's attack on the Alumbagh, the siege and capture of Lucknow (Clasp) the affairs of Barree, Sirsee, and action of Nawabgunge, occupation of Fyzabad, passage of the Goomtee, at Sultanpore, through the Byswarra campaign including the affairs at Kandoo-Nuddee, and Palee Ghat, the taking the Fort of Rehora, and pursuit of Benhi-Madho's force to the Goomtee, also the Trans Gogra Campaign including the affair near Churda and pursuit, taking the Fort of Mujeedia attack on Bankee with pursuit to the Raptee, the advance into Nepaul and affair at Sitka Ghat.

Lieut. the Hon'ble C. C. Molyneux served in the Indian Campaign from Feby. 1858 to March 1859 (Medal) present at the repulse of the enemy's attack on the Alumbagh, the siege and capture of Lucknow (Clasp) the affairs of Barree, Sirsee, and action of Nawabgunge, occupation of Fyzabad, through the Byswarra campaign including the affairs at the Kandoo-Nuddee, Palee Ghat, Hyderghur, and pursuit of Benhi Madho's force to the Goomtee, also the Trans Gogra campaign including the affair near Churda and pursuit, taking the Fort of Mujeedia, attack on Bankee, pursuit to the Raptee, the advance into Nepaul and affair at Sitka Ghat.

Lieut. Phillipson served in the Indian Campaign from Feby. 1858 to Dec. 1858 (Medal) present at the affair of Daodpore 20th October.

Lieut. R.D. Stewart served in the Indian campaign from Feb. 1858 to March 1859 (Medal) including the repulse of the enemy's attack on the Alumbagh, the siege and capture of Lucknow (Clasp) the affair of Barree, and action of Nawabgunge, occupation of Fyzabad, passage of the Goomtee at Sultanpore, and the affair of Shahpore, through the Byswarra campaign including the affairs at the Kandoo-Nuddee, and Palee Ghat, taking the Forts of Rehora and Keowlie, and pursuit of Benhi-Madho's Force to the Goomtee, also the Trans Gogra campaign including the affair near Churda, and pursuit, taking the Fort of Mujeedia, the attack on Bankee with pursuit to the Raptee the advance into Nepaul, and affair at Sitka Ghat.

Lieut. Hon'ble W. Harbord served in the Indian Campaign from April 1858 to March 1859 (Medal) including the affair at Sirsee and action of Nawabgunge, occupation of Fyzabad, passage of the Goomtee at Sultanpore, through the Byswarra campaign including the affairs at the Kandoo Nuddee, Palee Ghat, Hyderghur and pursuit of Benhi Madho's Force to the Goomtee, also the Trans Gogra campaign including the affair near Churda and pursuit, taking the Fort of Mujeedia, attack on Bankee with pursuit to the Raptee, the advance into Nepaul and affair at Sitka Ghat. Mentioned in Despatches for Nawabgunge.

Lieut. Viscount Royston was present at the advance into Nepaul, and attack on the Enemy's position at Sitka Ghat.

Lieut. and Adjutant J. Mould served in the Indian Campaign from Feb. 1858 to March 1859 (Medal) present at the repulse of the Enemy's attack on the Alumbagh, the siege and capture of Lucknow (Clasp) the affairs of Barree, Sirsee and action of Nawabgunge, (wounded) occupation of Fyzabad, passage of the Goomtee, at Sultanpore, through the Byswarra campaign including the affairs at the Kandoo-Nuddee, Palee Ghat, Hyderghur and pursuit of Benhi Madho's Force to the Goomtee, also the Trans Gogra campaign including the affairs near Churda and pursuit, taking the Fort of Mujeedia, attack on Bankee and pursuit to the Raptee, the advance into Nepaul, and affair at Sitka Ghat.

Cornet R. Simmons served in the Indian Campaign from Feb. 1858 to March 1859 (Medal) present at the repulse of the Enemy's attack on the Alumbagh, the siege and capture of Lucknow (Clasp) the affairs of Barree, Sirsee and action of Nawabgunge, occupation of Fyzabad, passage of the Goomtee at Sultanpore, and affair of Shahpore, through the Byswarra campaign including the affairs at the Kandoo-Nuddee, Palee Ghat, Hyderghur, and pursuit of Benhi Madho's Forces to the Goomtee, also the Trans Gogra campaign including the affair near Churda and pursuit, taking the Fort of Mujeedia, attack on Bankee with pursuit to the Raptee, the advance into Nepaul and affair at Sitka Ghat.

Paymaster G. Elliott served in the Indian campaign from Feb. 1858 to March 1859 (Medal) present at the repulse of the Enemy's attack on the Alumbagh, the siege and capture of Lucknow (Clasp) the affair of Barree, occupation of Fyzabad, passage of the Goomtee at Sultanpore, through the Byswarra campaign including the affair at the Kandoo Nuddee and Hyderghur, also the Trans Gogra campaign including the affair near Churda and pursuit, taking the Fort of Mujeedia, attack on Bankee and pursuit to the Raptee, the advance into Nepaul and affair at Sitka Ghat.

Quarter Master W. Borthwick served in the Indian campaign from Feb. 1858 to March 1859 (Medal) present at the repulse of the Enemy's attack on the Alumbagh, the siege and capture of Lucknow (Clasp) the affair

⁎ *For continuation of Services see next page.*

at Barree, occupation of Fyzabad, passage of the Goomtee at Sultanpore, through the Byswarra campaign including the affairs at the Kandoo Nuddee and Hyderghur also the Trans Gogra campaign including the affair near Churda and pursuit, taking the Fort of Mujeedia, attack on Bankee with pursuit to the Raptee, the advance into Nepaul and affair at Sitka Ghat.

Surgeon Kendall served as Asst. Surgeon of 17th Lancers and Surgeon of 4th Light Dragoons in the Eastern campaign of 1854 and 55 including the summer campaign in Bulgaria, the affairs of Bulganak and Mackenzie's farm battles of Alma, Balaklava, Inkerman and Tchernaya, siege and fall of Sebastopol and operations at Eupatoria under General D. Allonville (Medal and 4 clasps,) served as a Volunteer in the French Hospitals on the Bosphorus during the typhus epidemic of the spring of 1856 and received the thanks of the French General Pariset commanding at that station. Served in the Indian campaign from Feb. 1858 to March 1859 (Medal) present at the repulse of the enemy's attack on the Alumbagh, the siege and capture of Lucknow (Clasp) the affairs of Barree Sirsee, and action of Nawabgunge, occupation of Fyzabad, passage of Goomtee at Sultanpore through the Byswarra campaign including the affairs of Doadpore at the Kandoo Nuddee Hyderghur and pursuit of Benhi Madho's force to the Goomtee, also the Trans Gogra campaign including the affair at Churda and pursuit taking the Fort of Mujeedia, attack on Bankee with pursuit to the Raptee, the advance into Nepaul and affair at Sitka ghat.

Assistant Surgeon G. M. Slaughter served in the Indian campaign from Feb. 1858 to March 1859 (Medal) present at the affair of Meangunge, the siege and capture of Lucknow (Clasp) the affairs of Barree, Sirsee and action of Nawabgunge, occupation of Fyzabad, passage of the Goomtee of Sultanpore through the Byswarra campaign, including the affairs at the Kandoo Nuddee, Palee ghat, Hyderghur and pursuit of Benhi Madho's force to the Goomtee, also the Trans Gogra campaign including the affair near Churda and pursuit, taking the fort of Mujeedia, attack on Bankee with pursuit to the Raptee, the advance into Nepaul, and affair at Sitka ghat.

Asst. Surgeon Thornhill served the campaign of 1857-58 against the Mutineers in India, including the action at Kudygunge, siege and fall of Lucknow, attack on the fort of Rooyah, action at Allygunge, and capture of Bareilly—(wounded.)

Veterinary Surgeon Barker served with the 10th Hussars in the Crimean campaign in 1855, including the siege of Sebastopol (Medal and clasp). served in the Indian campaign from Feby. 1858 to March 1859 (Medal) present at the repulse of the enemy's attack on the Alumbagh, siege and capture of Lucknow (Clasp) the affair of Barree, occupation of Fyzabad, passage of the Goomtee at Sultanpore, through the Byswarra campaign including the affairs at Kandoo Nuddee, and Hyderghur, also the Trans Gogra campaign including the affairs near Churda and pursuit, taking the Fort of Mujeedia, attack on Bankee with pursuit to the Raptee, the advance into Nepaul, and affair at Sitka Ghat.

Riding Master W. Bray served in the Indian campaign from March 1858 to March 1859 (Medal) present at the affair of Barree, occupation of Fyzabad, passage of the Goomtee at Sultanpore through the Byswarra campaign including the affairs at the Kandoo Nuddee, Palee ghat, and Hyderghur, also the Trans Gogra campaign including the affair near Churda and pursuit taking the Fort of Mujeedia, attack on Bankee with pursuit to the Raptee the advance into Nepaul and affair at Sitka Ghat.

CONTINUATION OF THE WAR SERVICES OF H. M. 2ND DRAGOON GUARDS.—*From page 13.*

Lieut. T. W. Sneyd accompanied the 2nd Dragoon guards to India on the breaking out of the Bengal Mutinies, served with the Regiment at the action of Nusserutpore, and throughout the Lucknow campaign, including the siege and capture of Lucknow and subsequent operations and actions of Koorsee.

Lieut. G. F. Ormsby accompanied the 2nd Dragoon guards to India on the breaking out of the Bengal Mutinies, was present with the Regiment at the action of Nusserutpore, commanded a Detachment of the Regiment at the relief of Azimghur and served throughout the Oude campaign of 1858 and 59, latterly as Orderly Officer to Brigadier G. R. Barker, C. B. including the action of Jamo and siege and capture of Birwah..

Lieut. W. T. Foster accompanied the 2nd Dragoon guards to India on the breaking out of the Bengal Mutinies, served with the Regiment throughout the Lucknow campaign of 1858, including the siege and capture of Lucknow and subsequent operations and action of Koorsee.

Lieut. W. J. Thomas served with the 2nd Dragoon guards during the Oude campaign of 1858-9, and was present at the siege and capture of Birwah.

Lieut. H. J. DeMontmorency served with the 2nd Dragoon guards during the Oude campaign of 1858-9, and was present at the affair of Koorsee.

Lieut. F. O'Beirne served with the 2nd Dragoon guards during the Oude campaign of 1858-9, and was present at the crossing of the Gogra at Fyzabad.

Cornet C. J. A. Barnes served with the 2nd Dragoon guards during the Oude campaign of 1858-9, and was present at the affair of Dawah.

Paymaster F. W. Lukin served with the 17th foot at the siege of Sebastopol from Dec. 1854 to June 1855, (Medal and Clasps). Accompanied the 2nd Dragoon guards to India on the breaking out of the Bengal Mutinies, served with the Regiment throughout the Lucknow campaign of 1858 including siege and capture of Lucknow.

Surgeon H. H. Massy M. D. served with the 31st Regt. towards the close of the Sutlej campaign in 1846, served the Eastern campaign of 1854-55 with the 17th lancers including the affair of Bulganak, battles of Alma, Balaklava and Inkerman and siege of Sebastopol (Medal and clasp, and 5th class of the Medjidie). Accompanied the 2nd Dragoon guards to India on the breaking out of the Bengal Mutinies, served with the Regiment throughout the Lucknow campaign of 1858, including siege and capture of Lucknow and action of Koorsee.

Asst. Surg. J. H Robotham served with the 2nd Dragoon guards at the action of Nusserutpore and throughout the Lucknow campaign of 1858, including the siege and capture of Lucknow and subsequent operations, and action of Barree, served also through the Oude campaign of 1858 and 59, including the action of Jamo and siege and capture of Birwah.

Asst. Surg. R. F. Andrews served with the 1st Dragoon guards in the Crimea from Aug. 1855 including the battle of Tchernaya and siege of Sebastopol (Medal and clasps). Accompanied the 2nd Dragoon guards to India on the breaking out of the Bengal Mutinies, served with the Regiment throughout the Lucknow campaign of 1855, including the siege and capture of Lucknow and action of Koorsee and Newabgunge.

Vety. Surgeon T. J. Gudgin served the Eastern campaign of 1854-55, including the affair of McKenzie's farm, battles of Balaklava, Inkerman and Tchernaya and siege and fall of Sebastopol (Medal and Clasps) served with the 2nd Dragoon guards throughout the Lucknow campaign of 1858, including the siege and capture of Lucknow also the Oude campaign of 1858-59, including the action of Jamo and siege and capture of Birwah.

Quarter Mr. W. Rae accompanied the 2nd Dragoon guards to India on the breaking out of the Bengal Mutinies, served with the Regiment throughout the Lucknow campaign, including the siege and capture of Lucknow and action of Koorsee.

Royal Artillery

STAFF.

HEAD QUARTERS, CALCUTTA.

Lieut. Col. and Bt. Col. Sir G.R. Barker, K.C.B. Commanding Royal Artillery in Bengal.
Capt. A. M. Calvert. .. Assist. Adjutant General.
Capt. and Bt. Major C. F. Young, .. Deputy Assist. Quarter Master General.

OUDH.

Lieut. R. Biddulph, .. D. A. A. Genl. *Sir* H. Grant's Field Force.

LUCKNOW.

Lieut. Col. & Bt. Col. C. J. B. Riddell, C.B.,.. Commanding Artillery.—*Oudh.*
Lieut. H. M. Fitzmaurice, .. Adjutant to ditto.
Lieut F. G. E. Warren. .. Quarter Master to ditto.

BENARES.

Lieut. Col. H. P. Christie, .. Comdg. Royal Artillery Dinapore and Cawnpore Divisions.
Capt. W. M. Waller, .. Adjt. R. A. Dinapore ann Cawnpore.

Royal Horse Artillery.

Lieut. Col. E. Price C. B., .. Commanding R. H. A. in Bengal.
Lieut. W. Stirling. .. Adj. ditto ditto.
Lieut. H. T. Arbuthnot. .. Q. M. ditto ditto.

E. BATTERY.

Landed in Calcutta, from England, 7th November 1857.

SEETAPORE.

Capt. and Bt. Lt. Col. W. A. Middleton C. B... Leave to England on P. A. for 14 months.
Capt. and Bt. Major S. M. Grylls, ..
Lieut. S. J. M. Maxwell, ..
Lieut. W. D. Milman, ..
Lieut. F. A. Whinyates. ..

ROYAL HORSE ARTILLERY,—*Continued.*

F. BATTERY.

Landed in Calcutta, from England, 7th November 1857.

MEERUT.

Capt. and Bt. Lt. Col. *Hon.* D. M. Fraser, ..
Capt. and Bt. Major W. H. Goodenough, .. Privilege leave to England.
Lieut. A, D. Burnaby. ..
Lieut. A. K. Rideout, ..
Assistant Surgeon T. A. McMunn, M. D. ..
Veterinary Surgeon W. Rollings, ..

Establishment of each Troop,—2 staff Sergeants, 9 Sergeants, 6 Corporals, 9 Bombardiers 90 Gunners and 70 Drivers, 1 Trumpeter, 1 Farrier, 6 Shoeing Smiths, 3 Collar Makers, and 3 Wheelers. Total 200 men and 200 horses.

Royal Foot Artillery.

No. 1 BATTERY 14TH BRIGADE.

Landed in Calcutta, from England, 6th December 1857.

BENARES, AZIMGHUR &C.————.

Captain and Bt. Major J. E. Thring, ..
Lieut. R. C. Smith, ..
Lieut. J. Robertson, ..
Lieut. S. C. Kyle, ...
Assistant Surgeon A. R. Smith, ..

No. 3 BATTERY 14TH BRIGADE.

Landed in Calcutta, from England, 17th January 1858.

FYZABAD,—OUDH.

Capt. and Bt. Major G. C. Henry, ..
Captain R. H Newbolt, ..
Lieut. H. L. Mitchell, ..
Lieut. P. D. L. Trench, ..
Assistant Surgeon E. Bubb, ..
Veterinary Surgeon F. B. Hall, .. Leave on M. C. to Simla to 15 October 59.

No. 4 BATTERY 14TH BRIGADE.

Landed at Kurrachie, from England, 8th March 1858.

MOOLTAN.

Captain and Bt. Major J. Singleton, ..
Captain T. B. Strange. ..
Lieut. M. Tweedie, ..
Lieut. F. A. Anley, ..
Lieut. *Hon.* R. Hare, ..
Assistant Surgeon J. W. Rimmer, ..
Veterinary Surgeon E. Kelly, ..

No. 7 BATTERY 11TH BRIGADE.

Landed at Kurrachie, from England, 31st December 1857

PESHAWUR.

Captain and Bt. Major F. W. Hastings, ...
Captain H. Renny, ..
Lieut. F. J. G. Hill, ..
Lieut. W. R. Llewellyn, ..
Assistant Surgeon F. H. Forshall, ..

ROYAL FOOT ARTILLERY,—*Continued.*

No. 1 BATTERY 11TH BRIGADE.

Landed in Calcutta, from Ceylon, 13th June 1857.

CALCUTTA.

Captain and Bt. Lt.Col. F.C. Maude, C. B.,* ..
Lieut. C. F. Roberts, ..
Lieut. J. N. P. Dadson, .. Leave on M. C. to England
Assistant Surgeon A. T. L. Hepworth, ..

No. 8 BATTERY 11TH BRIGACE.

Landed in Calcutta, from England, 16th January 1858.

DUM-DUM.

Capt. and Bt. Major E. Moubray, ..
Captain *Hon*, L. Addington, ..
Lieut. F. S. Talbot, ..
Lieut. J. E. Cockburn, ..
Lieut. H*on.* A. Stewart, ..
Assistant Surgeon W. Tanner, ..
Veterinary Surgeon J. Cochrane, ..

No. 2 BATTERY 14TH BRIGADE.

Landed in Calcutta, from England, 6th December 1857.

BENARES, BERHAMPORE &c.

Captain E. Maitland, ..
Lieut. E. C. Cuthbert, ..
Lieut. E. D. Tarleton, ..
Lieut. H. A. Tracey, ..
Assistant Surgeon G. Sharp, ..

No. 5 BATTETRY 14TH BRIGADE.

Landed in Calcutta, from England, 28th December 1857.

GORUCKPORE.

Captain and Bt. Major J. R. Gibbon, .. Leave on M. C. to England.
Captain and Bt. Major A. C. Johnson, ..
Lieut. H. L. Geary, ..
Lieut. C. E. Bethune, ..
Assistant Surgeon J. Barker,

No. 2 BATTERY 11TH BRIGADE.

Landed at Calcutta, from England, 11th September 1857.

LUCKNOW.

Captain and Bt. Major C. S. Longden, ... Leave on M. C. to England.
Captain and Bt. Major H. L. Talbot, ...
Lieut. E. S. Burnett, ...
Assit. Surgeon Hearn, ..

No. 3 BATTERY 11TH BRIGADE.

Landed at Calcutta, from England, 23rd September 1857

LUCKNOW.

Captain and Bt. Major F. J. Soady, ...
Captain C. J. Tyler, ...
Lieut. W. Smith, ...
Lieut. C. H. Pickering, ...
Assistant Surgeon A. Y. Jeeves, ..
Veterinary Surgeon H. Withers, ... Leave M. C. England.

* Victoria Cross.

ROYAL FOOT ARTILLERY—*(Continued.)*

No 4, BATTERY, 11TH BRIGADE.

Landed in Calcutta, from England, 24th September 1857.

ALLAHABAD.

Capt. R. P. C. Jones, ..
Capt. and Bt. Lt. Col. W. LeMesurier, C. B.,
Lieut. E. Staveley. .. Convalescent Depot, Kussoulee.
Lieut. J. R. Oliver, ..
Lieut. C. D. Chalmer,
Assistant Surgeon W. Haughton, M. B. ..

No. 5, BATTERY, 11TH BRIGADE,

Landed in Calcutta, from England, 24th October 1857.

ROY BAREILLY.

Captain and Bt. Lt. Colonel, S. E. Gordon,.. Brigade Major England.
Capt. and Bt. Major J. M. Campbell, ..
Lieut. W. Gilmour, ..
Lieut. E. Egan, ..
Lieut. E. R. Cottingham, .. Leave on M. C. to Calcutta.
Assistant Surgeon W. D. Milne, M. D. ...

No. 6, BATTERY, 11TH BRIGADE.

Landed in Calcutta, from England, 24th October 1857.

FUTTEHGUR

Captain & Bt Lt. Col. C. H. Smith, ...
Captain & Bt. Major C. E. Walcott, ...
Lieut. H. Edmeades, ...
Lieut. W, S. Brown, ...
Lieut. J. C. Auchinleck, *V*, ...
Veterinary Surgeon C. Sanderson, ...

Establishment of each Battery.—2 Staff Serjeants, 8 Sergeants, 6 Corporals, 9 Bombardiers, 100 Gunners 70 Drivers, 2 Trumpeters, 1 Farrier, 6 Shoeing Smiths, 3 Collar makers, 2 Wheelers.

Total 209 men and 142 horses.

WAR SERVICES OF THE OFFICERS OF H. M. ROYAL FOOT ARTILLERY.

Colonel Wood commanded the Royal Artillery on the Eastern frontier of the Cape of Good Hope during the insurrection of the Boers and Caffres in 1842-43. Served in the Eastern campaign of 1854-55, and was present at the battles of Balaklava and Inkerman, the siege and fall of Sebastopol, and repulse of the sortie on the 26th Oct. 1854 (Medal and Clasps, C. B. Officer of the Legion of Honor, and 4th Class of the Medjidie.)

Colonel Barker served the Eastern campaign of 1854-55, including the battles of Alma and Balaklava, expedition to Kertch (in command of Royal Artillery) siege of Sebastopol, including the command of the batteries of the left attack at the fall of the fortress (Medal and clasps, C. B. Knight of the Legion of Honor, and 4th Class of the Medjidie).

Lieut. Anley, served in the Eastern campaign in 1855, in the trenches with the siege train before Sebastopol, and at the bombardments of April and June (6th and 17th): Medal and Clasp, and Sardinian Medal.

Major Gibbon served at the siege and fall of Sebastopol in 1855 (Medal and Clasp). Major Clifford has the 5th Class of the Medjidie.

Major Hon. D. M'D. Fraser served in the Eastern campaign of 1854-55, including the battle of Inkerman and siege of Sebastopol (Medal and Clasps, and 5th Class of the Medjidie).

Major C. Strange served at the siege of Sebastopol in 1855, in the trenches with the siege train, and at the bombardments of April and 6th June (Medal and Clasp, and 5th Class of the Medjidie).

Major Charles Smith, served at the siege and fall of Sebastopol, in the trenches with the siege train, and at the bombardments of 6th and 17th June (Medal and Clasp).

Lt. Colonel Gordon served in the Eastern campaign of 1854-55, including the battles of Alma, Balaklava,. and Inkerman, siege and capture of Sebastopol (Medal and Clasps, Sardinian Medal, Brevets of Major and Lt Col., and 5th Class of the Medjidie).

Captain Thring served at the siege and fall of Sebastopol in 1855 (Medal and Clasp).

Major Singleton served the Eastern campaign of 1854-55, including the affairs of Bulganac and M'Kenzie's Farm, the battles of Alma, Balaklava, and Inkerman, the siege and fall of Sebastopol, and repulse of the sortie on the 26th October 1854 (Medal and Clasps, Knight of the Legion of Honor, and 5th Class of the Medjidie).

Major Soady, served in the Eastern campaign of 1854-55, in the trenches with the siege train before Sebastopol, and at the bombardments of April and June (6th and 17th): Medal and Clasp, and 5th Class of the Medjidie.

Major Henry served the Eastern campaign of 1854-55, including the battle of Inkerman, siege and fall of Sebastopol (Medal and Clasp, Brevet Major and Knight of the Legion of Honor). Major Henry has also the Sardinian Medal and the 5th Class of the Medjidie.

Major Yates served the Eastern campaign of 1854, including the affair at M' Kenzie's Farm, battles of Alma and Inkerman, siege of Sebastopol and repulse of the sortie on the 26th October 1854 (Medal and Clasps, Brevet Major, Sardinian Medal, and 5th Class of the Medjidei).

Major N. O. S. Turner served at the siege and fall of Sebastopol in 1855 (Medal and Clasp, and 5th Class of the Medjidie).

****For Continuation of services. see page* 35.

1st Battalion of H. M. 3rd (E. Kent) Regiment of Foot (or the Buffs).

The *Dragon* "Douro"—"Talavera"—"Albuhera"—"Pyrenees"—"Nivelle"—"Nive"—"Peninsula"—"Punniar"—"Sevastopole."

Facings—*Buff.*

Arrived in Calcutta from Corfu on 29th December 1858.
Dum-Dum.
5 Companies on Detachment at *Fort William, Calcutta.*
1 Sergeant and 12 Privates at Cossipore Gun-Foundry.
Regimental Depôt, Limerick.

Rank and Names.	*Regimental Rank.*	*Army Rank.*	Remarks.
Colonel.			
W. Berkeley Drummond, - -	12 *Dec.* 57	*mg.* 11 *Nov.* 51	In Europe.
Lieutenant Colonels.			
George James Ambrose. - -	31 *Dec.* 57		
~~Thomas Henry Somerville~~, -	17 *Sep.* 58	... ...	Leave on P. A. to England.
Majors.			
Henry John King, - - - -	31 *Dec.* 57	.. ..	On Leave to 7 July 59. to Neilgherry [Hills.
Walter Pownall, - - - -	17 *Sep.* 58	.. ..	With Detachment at Calcutta.
Captains.			
Fred. William Gore, - - -	7 *June* 54		
Robt. Sandford Warburton, -	8 *Dec.* 54	.. ..	Regtl. Depôt, Ireland.
Thomas Kains, - - - - -	15 *May* 55	.. ..	Detachment at Calcutta.
Phil. H. Prender. Aplin, - -	15 *May* 55	.. ..	Regtl. Depôt, Ireland.
Penrose John Dunbar, - -	15 *May* 55	.. ..	Leave to England on P. A. to 4 May 60.
Mark Walker,* - - - - -	15 *May* 55	*m.* 5 *June* 56	Commanding Depôt Chinsurah.
E. K. Vaughan Arbuckle, - -	29 *June* 55	.. ..	Lv. on P. A. to Simla, to 18th Nov. 59.
William Ross Turner, - -	22 *May* 57	.. ..	With detachment at Calcutta.
William Stewart, - - - -	16 *Oct.* 57	.. ..	At Behrampore,
George Noble Roe, - - - -	31 *Dec.* 57		
Talbot Ashley Cox, - - - -	17 *Sep.* 58		
Henry Thomas Anley, - - -	10 *Dec.* 58	.. ..	Lv. on M. C. to Fngland.
Lieutenants.			
Harry A. Arth. Breedon - -	15 *May* 55	.. ...	Instructor of Musketry.
Barnes John Caldecott, - -	15 *May* 55	.. ..	Detachment at Calcutta.
Chas. John Roper Tyler, - -	15 *May* 55	.. ...	Ditto at Behrampore.
William Henry, - - - - -	15 *May* 55		
George Grant Suttie, - - -	15 *May* 55	.. ..	On duty at Darjeeling Depot.
Arthur Worthington, . - - -	1 *June* 55	... ...	Regtl. Depôt.
Francis Morley, - - - - -	1 *Sep.* 55		Detachment at Calcutta.
Alfred Benwell Letts, - - -	9 *Nov.* 55	.. ..	Adjutant.
Alfred George Huyshe, - -	11 *Sep.* 57		Detachment at Calcutta.
Walter Aug. Daubeny, - - -	16 *Oct.* 57		Lv. on P. A. to England. to 1st July 60.
George Thomas Gape, - - -	16 *Oct.* 57	... ...	Regimental Depot.
James H. Le Cocq. - - - -	2 *Feb.* 58		
Charles Deyman Baillie, - -	5 *Mar.* 58	.. ..	Acting Qr. Mr. Pro. Batt. Dum-Dum.
~~Bury David Wright~~, - - -	15 *Oct.* 59		
Felix. Thomas Jones, - - -	10 *Dec.* 59	.. ..	With detachment at Calcutta.
Ensigns.			
Theophilus Jones, - - - -	16 *Oct.* 57	.. ..	Detachment at Calcutta.
Fred. Taylor Hobson, - - -	30 *Oct.* 57	.. ...	Staff Employ Calcutta, Pay Mr. Genl. [Dept.
Henry Thos. Halahan, - - -	24 *Nov.* 57	.. ..	Detachment at Calcutta.
Dudley Geo. Cary Elwes, - -	2 *Feb.* 58	.. ..	Ditto.,
Henry Kinahan, - - - -	16 *Mar.* 58	.. ..	Ditto.,
William Fred. Kerr, - -	23 *Mar.* 58		
Ernest Fred. Barnes - - -	24 *Mar.* 58	... ...	Regtl. Depôt.
Henry Harrison, - - -	14 *Apl.* 58	... ...	Ditto.
Joseph Jas. B. Haydock, - -	17 *Apl.* 58	... ...	Ditto.
H. Manning, - - - - -	13 *Oct.* 58	.. ..	Acting Pay Master Chinsurah.
John Raimond, Trevilian, - -	31 *Dec.* 58		

*Victoria Cross.

H. M. 3RD (E. KENT) REGIMENT OF FOOT (OR THE BUFFS).—*(Continued)*.

RANK AND NAMES.	*Regimental Rank.*	*Army Rank.*	REMARKS.
INSTRUCTOR OF MUSKETRY.			
Lieut. H. A. Breedon, - - -	6 *Nov.* 58	15 *May* 55	
PAYMASTERS.			
Fred. Geo. Syms, - - -	25 *June* 47		
ADJUTANTS.			
Lieut. Alfred Benwell Letts, -	15 *Oct.* 58	9 *Nov* 55	
QUARTER-MASTER.			
Thomas Blisset, - - -	19 *June* 55		
SURGEON.			
Joseph Burke, - - -	22 *Dev.* 48		
ASSISTANT SURGEONS.			
Thomas Teevan, - - -	30 *June* 54	.. ...	Detacht at Calcutta.
Theophilus Dolan, - - -	1 *Sept.* 54		At Kiddorpore.
John Henry Beath, M. D., *V* -	15 *Sept.* 57	.. ...	Absent on duty since Appointment.
INTERPRETER.			
Lt. C. Baily 17 N. I. *P. H.* -			

Strength—10 Companies—41 Serjeants—42 Corporals—21 Drummers—and 878 Privates.

English Agents—Messrs. Cox and Co.

Irish Agent.—Sir. E. R. Borough Bt.

Calcutta Agents.—Messrs. Gillanders, Arbuthnot and Co.

WAR SERVICES OF 1ST BATTALION H. M. 3RD REGIMENT OF FOOT.

Major-General Drummond served in the 3rd Guards the campaign of 1814 in Holland, including the storming of Bergen-op-Zoon. Also the campaign of 1855, including the battles of Quatre Bras and Waterloo.

Lieut Colonel Ambrose served at the siege of Sebastopol from April 1855, commanded 200 men of the Buffs, and assisted in holding the Quarries with them on the night of the 7th June—dangerously wounded, mentioned in Dispatches. (Madal and Clasp, Brevet Major, Sardinian Medal, and 5th Class of the Medjidie).

Lieut. Colonel Somerville served with the 68th Regt. during the Kaffir war of 1846-47 (Medal); and with the 5th in the Eastern campaign of 1854-55 including the battles of Alma, Balaklava Inkerman, and siege of Sebastopol (Medal and Clasps, and 5th Class of the Medjidie).

Major Walker served in the Eastern campaign of 1854-1855 as Adjutant of the 30th Regiment, including the battles of the Alma (wounded) and Inkerman, siege of Sebastepol, and sortie on 26th October. On the night of the 21st April he volunteered with a party which took and destroyed a Russian Rifle pit, fer which he was mentioned in the Dispatches, and promoted into the Buffs. On the night of 9th June he was dangerously wounded in the trenches--right arm amputated (Medal and Clasps, Victoria Cross, and 5lh Class of ihe Medjidie.)

Major Pownall, and Lieuts. Breedon and Caldecott, served at the siege of Sebastopol in 1855, and were wounded (Medal and Clasp).

Captain Gore served with the 6th Regt. in the Kaffir wars, of 1846-7, and of 1851-3 (Medal). Served with the Buffs at the siege of Sebastopol (Medal and Clasp) and 4th class of Medjedie.

Captains Warburton, Aplin, Stewart, and Turnen, Lieuts. Anley, Tyler, Henry, Suttie, E. J. Cox, and Worthington Paymaster Syms and Assist.-Surgeon Teavan served at the siege of Sebastopol in 1855 (Medal and Clasp).

Captain Kains was present with the Buffs at the battle of Punniar (Medal). Also at the siege of Sebastopol in 1855 and assault of the Redan on the 8th Sept. (Medal and Clasp).

Captain Dunbar served at the siege of Sebastopol in 1855, and was wounded at the assault of the Redan on the 8th Sept. (Medal and Clasp).

Captain Roe served at the siege of Sebastopol in 1855, and was Acting Adjutant of the Buffs at the assault of the Redan on the 8th Sept.—mentioned in Dispatches (Medal and Clasp, and Knight of the Legion of Honor).

Captain T. A. Cox served at the siege of Sebastopol in 1855, and was wounded at the assault of the Redan on the 8th Sept. (Medal and Clasp, and 5th class of the Medjidie).

Captain Newton served as Aide-de-Camp to Brigadier-General Straubenzee at the siege of Sebastopol in 1855, and at the assault on the Redan on the 8th Sept. (Medal and Clasp).

Lieut. Letts served at the siege of Sebastopol in 1855, and was dangerously wounded at the assault of the Redan on the 8th Sept. (Medal and Clasp,

Ensign Manning served with the Buffs at the Battle of Punniar 29th Dec. 43 (medal) also at the siege of Sebastopol in 1855 and assault of the Redan on the 8th Sept. (medal and clasp.)

Qr.-Master Blisset served with the Buffs at the battle of Punniar, 29th Dec. 1843. (Medal). Also at the siege of Sebastopol in 1855, and assault of the Redan on the 8th Sept. (Medal and Clasp).

Surg. Burke served with the 50th Regt. throughout the campaign on the Sutlej in 1845-6, and was present at the battles of Moodkee, Ferezeshah, Aliwal, and Sobraon. (Medal and three Clasps): in the two latter engagements, and to the end of the war, he was in medical charge of the Regiment. Served with the Buffs at the siege and assault of Sebastopol (Medal and Clasp).

1st Battalion of H. M. 5th Regiment of Foot (Northumberland Fusiliers.)

„ *Quo Fata vocant," surmounting* St. George and the Dragon. *On the corners of the* 2nd *colour the* Rose *and* Crown; *on the caps the* King's Crest; *also* St. George killing the Dragon. "Wilhelmstahl" — "Roleia" — "Vimiera" — "Corunna" "Busaco"—"Ciudad Rodrigo"—"Badajoz"—"Salamanca"— "Vittoria"—"Nivelle"— "Orthes" — "Toulouse"—"Peninsula."

Facings—*Bright Green.*

Arrived in Calcutta, from Mauritius, 4th July and 16th August 1857.

Allahabad.

Depôt, Colchester.

Rank and Names.	Regimental Rank.	Army Rank.	Remarks.
Colonel.			
Wm. Lovelace Walton, - -	20 *Feb.* 56	*l.g.*20 *June* 54	In Europe.
Lieutenant-Colonels.			
P. Melmoth Nelson Guy, C.B., -	28 *Nov.* 54	*col.* 28 *Nov.* 54	Leave on M. C. to England.
William Chester Master, C. B., -	17 *Dec.* 58	.. ..	Leave to the Hills.
Majors.			
George Bryan Milman, - - -	30 *Sep.* 57	*l. c.* 24 *Mar.* 58	Commanding.
John Swaine Hogge, - - -	17 *Dec* 58	.. ..	Leave on M. C. to England to 5 July 59.
Captains.			
George Carden, - - - - -	9 *Nov.* 55	.. ..	Leave on P. A. to England. for 18 months.
Thomas Scovill Bigge, - - -	8 *June* 56	.. ..	Convelescent Depot at Nynee Tal.
Francis Henry Pender, - - -	24 *Oct.* 56	.. ..	Colchester Depôt, England.
William Leach, - - - - -	6 *Oct.* 57	.. ..	Comdg. Convalest Depot Allahabad.
Edw. Reginald Simmons, - -	31 *Oct.* 57		
Geo. Hen. J. M. Chapman, -	26 *Dec.* 57	.. ..	Leave of Absence on P. A. for 18 months.
Fred. James Mylius, - - -	25 *Jan.* 58	.. ..	Leave to Mauritius for 6 months.
Horatio Walpole, - - - -	13 *Mar.* 58		
Philip FitzRoy, - - - - -	13 *Apl.* 58		
Robert Moore, - - - - -	7 *Sep.* 58	.. ..	Leave on M. C. to Calcutta.
John Robson Carlisle, - - -	17 *Dec.* 58	.. ..	
Edward Bolger, - - - - -	11 *May* 59		
Lieutenants.			
John Creagh, - - - V. - -	15 *Jan.* 56	.. ..	Adjutant.
George Eyre Massy, - - -	24 *Oct.* 56	.. ..	Leave on M. C. to Englaud.
Edward Studley Lewis, - - -	24 *Sep.* 57		
Edw. Montgomery Mason, - -	19 *Oct.* 57	.. ..	Leave on M. C. to England.
Frank Astley Cubitt, - - -	20 *Oct.* 57		
Edward James Tyler, - - -	22 *Oct.* 57	.. ..	Instructor of Musketry.
Edward Hoare, - - - - -	31 *Oct.* 57	.. ..	Leave on M. C. to England.
George Alex. Shegog, - - -	26 *Dec.* 57	.. ..	At School of Musketry Hythe.
Henry Bathe, - - - - -	3 *Jan.* 58	.. ..	
Charles L. Dashwood, - - -	16 *Mar.* 58		
Charles John Miles, - - -	13 *Apl.* 58	.. ..	Colchester Depôt, England.
William Enderby, - - - -	23 *Apl.* 58	.. ..	Ditto.
F. R. Brodford, - - - - -	11 *Jan.* 59	.. ..	Mauritius.

H. M. 5th Regiment of Foot (Northumberland Fusiliers.)—*Continued.*

Rank and Names.	Regimental Rank.	Army Rank.	Remarks.
Ensigns.			
T. D. A. Mackinlay - - - -	4 *Jan.* 58		
Adolph Nicols, - - - - -	16 *Mar.* 58	.. ..	
Robert Hull, - - - - -	23 *Mar.* 58	.. ..	
John J. Bradshaw, - - - -	30 *Mar.* 58	.. ..	
Fras. H. D. Brome, - - - -	31 *Mar.* 58	.. ..	
Fred. A. Forsyth, - - - -	1 *April* 58	.. ..	
Herbert Silverthorne Williams.	23 *April* 58	.. ..	
Lucius John Blake, - - -	4 *June* 58	.. ..	Colchester Depot.
William Church Ormand, - -	13 *July* 58	.. ..	Ditto.
Instructor of Musketry.			
Lieut. E. J. Tyler, - - - -	24 *Sep.* 57	*lt.* 22 *Oct.* 57	
Paymaster.			
Capt. Fred. Blanco Forster, -	5 *Dec.* 51	*cap.* 22 *Oct.* 57	
Adjutant.			
Lieut. J. Creagh, - - -	24 *Sep.* 57	*lt.* 15 *Jan.* 56	
Quarter-Master.			
Francis Drake, - - - - -	17 *Nov.* 57	17 *Nov.* 57	
Surgeon.			
W. K. Swettenham, M. D., - -	.. ..	14 *Oct.* 51	Leave on M. C. to the Hills
Assist.-Surgeons.			
Thomas Ravenscroft Whitty, -	25 *Nov.* 53	... ..	
Francis Collins, M. D., - - -	1 *Sep.* 54	.. ..	Leave on M. C. to England.
Interpreter.			
Lt. and *Adjt.* J. Creagh, - -	.. ..	.. ..	Acting.

Strength—10 Companies with 45 Surgeants 38 Corporals 15 Drummers—and 728 Privates.
English Agents—Messrs. Cox and Co.
Calcutta Agents—Messrs. Wm. Spink and Co.

WAR SERVICES OF THE OFFICERS OF H. M. 5th FUSILIERS.

Lieut.-General Walton served with the Coldstream Guards at the siege and capture of Copenhagen in 1807. He embarked for the Peninsula in 1808, and served the campaigns of 1809, 1810, and the first part of 1811; and was present at the passage of the Douro and capture of Oporto, the battles of Talavera and Busaco, the retreat to the Lines of Torres Vedras, and the subsequent advance to the Spanish frontier. He served also in Holland, Belgium, and France, from Nov. 1818; and was present at the bombardment of Antwerp, the attack on Berged-op-Zoom, the battle of Quatre Bras and Waterloo, and the capture of Paris: he was Acting Adjutant of the 2nd Battalion of his Regiment at Waterloo, and was appointed Brigade-Major to the 2nd Brigade of Guards on the march from that place to Paris. He served 40 years in the Coldstream Guards, and commanded the Regiment upwards of six years. He has received the War Medal with Clasps for Talavera and Busaco.

Col. Guy served at Alumbagh and Lucknow from Novr 1857, commanded 3rd Infantry Brigade at siege and capture of Lucknow, C. B.

Lieut. Col. Master served at Lucknow and Alumbagh from Nov. 1857; present at the relief, and commanded 5th fusiliers at the capture (C B.) and subsequently through the Oudh campaign 1858-59.

Lt. Col. Milman served at Lucknow and Alumbagh from Novr. 1857. present at the relief (Bt. Lt. Col.) and capture of Lucknow, and served throughout the Oudh campaign of 1858-1859.

Major J. S. Hogge, served at Lucknow from Novr. 57; Present at the capture.

Capt. Cardin served with the 77th Regt. at siege of Sebastopol from Decr.1854, (medal and clasp), At Lucknow from Novr. 1857, at the relief and capture and in the Oude campaign of 1858-59.

Capt. T. S. Bigge served with 23rd Fusiliers at Sebastopol from Nov. 1854; present at the assaults of the Redan and the Quarries wounded in the trenches, (medal and clasp and 5th Class of the Medjidie,) Before Lucknow from Oct. 1857, at the relief and capture of that city and through campaign of 1858-59, in Oudh.

Maj. W. P. Meara entered the Lucknow Residency with General Hevelock's force in Sept. 1857, commanded 5th Fusiliers when besieged in Lucknow (Bt. Major) served subsequently at Alumbagh and the capture of Lucknow, and throughout the Oudh campaign 1858-59.

Capt. W. Leach served throughout the campaign 1858-59, Oudh.

Capt. E. R. Simmons served against the Rebels at Sasseram in 1858, and throughout the late campaign in Oudh.

Capt. G. H. Chapman, served against the mutineers in Bhaugulpore and adjacent Districts in 1857, and in the Oudh campaign 1858-59.

Capt. Mylius, Asst. Surgeon Whitty, Capt. Walpole and Capt. FitzRoy served at Alumbagh from Nov. 1857, at the relief and the capture of Lucknow and in Lord Clyde's campaign 1858-59, in Oudh.

Capt. Moore served at Alumbagh from Novr. 1857, and at the capture at Lucknow.

Lieut. and Adjutant Creagh, Quarter Master Drake, and Surgeon W. K. Swettenham M. D. entered the Lucknow Residency with General Havelock's Force in September 1857, served subsequently at the Alumbagh and the capture of Lucknow, and throughout the late campaign in Oudh.

Lieut. G. E. Money entered the Lucknow residency with Genl. Havelock's column in Sept. 1857, served subsequently at Alumbagh and at the capture of Lucknow.

Lieut. Lewis served against the Dinapore rebels at Arrah and Jugdespore in 1857, at Alumbagh and Lucknow from Nov. 1857, including the relief.

Lieut. E. M. Mason served against the Dinapore mutineers at Arrah and Jugdespore in 1857, entered the Lucknow Residency with Genl. Havelock's Force, September 1857, and served subsequently at Alumbagh before Lucknow.

Lieut. F. H. Cubitt, served against the Rebels at Kudjwa in 1857, at Alumbagh and Lucknow from Novr. 1857, present at relief and capture, and served in Oudh in the late campaign.

Lieut. E. J. Tyler served at Alumbagh, and at the capture of Lucknow, and in Oudh campaign 1858-59.

Lieut. C. L. Dashwood served against the Gwaliors at Cawnpore in 34th Regt. in Oct. and Nov. 1857 and throughout the late campaign in Oudh, with 5th Fusiliers.

Capt. Forster Pay-master, served at Alumbagh and at the capture of Lucknow.

Asst.-Surgeon Collins, served at Lucknow and Alumbagh from Novr. 1857, present at the relief and at the capture.

1st battalion of H. M. 6th (Royal 1st Warwickshire) Regt. of Foot.

"*The Antelope.*"—On the three corners of the second colour, "*The Rose and Crown.*"—And on the Grenadiers' caps, "*The King's Crest.*"

"Roleia"—"Vimiera"—"Corunna"—"Vittoria"—"Pyrenees"—"Nivelle"—"Orthes'—"Peninsula"—"Niagara."

Facings.—*Blue.*

Landed in Calcutta, from the Cape of Good Hope, 17th January 1858.
Azimghur, Detachments at Jounpore and Buxar.

Depôt of 1*st Battalion,* Colchester.

Rank and Names.	*Regimental Rank.*	*Army Rank.*	Remarks.
Colonel.			
Henry James Riddell, K. H., -	25 *June* 51	*g.* 11 *Nov.* 51	In Europe.
Lieutenant Colonels.			
James Elphinston Robertson, -	5 *Mar.* 58	... ...	Commanding.
William Albert Stratton, - -	6 *May.* 58	... ...	Leave of Absence on M. C.
Majors.			
Edward James Blanckley, - -	5 *Mar.* 58	6 *June* 56	
Charles Parker Catty, - - -	6 *May* 58		
Captains.			
Richard Thompson, - -	1 *July* 53	... ...	Leave on M. C. to England.
Philip Aug. Mosse, - -	6 *June* 54	... ...	With Detacht. at Buxar.
John H. Ford Elkington, - -	2 *Oct.* 54	*l. c.* 7 *Dec.* 58	A.D.C.to Genl. Mitchell, Bombay.
Henry Exley Jones, - -	4 *July* 54	... ...	Comdg. Depôt, Colchester, England.
Robert Unwin, - -	15 *Apl.* 56	.. ..	Regimental Depôt.
Walter Tyler Bartley, - -	30 *Dec.* 57	.. ..	Absent without leave.
John Dawson, - -	5 *Mar.* 58	... ...	With Detacht. at Jounpore.
John L. Otway Mansergh, - -	6 *May* 58		
W. C. F. Burlton Bennett, -	28 *May* 58	... ...	Leave of Absence to England on P. A. for 18 months.
Thomas Eolliott Powell, - -	13 *July* 58		
Henry Parkinson, - -	13 *July* 58	.. ..	Depot England.
R. Bolton, - -	11 *Mar.* 59	.. ...	Doing duty with Convalescent Depôt, [Nynee Tal.
Lieutenants.			
Lewis Blyth Hole, - -	7 *June* 54	... ..	With Detacht at Buxar.
John Edward Tewart, - -	15 *Apl.* 56	.. ..	With Detacht. at Jounpore.
Capt. Henry John Lawrell, - -	.. ...	23 *Nov.* 55	Adjutant.
Richard Sheil, - -	25 *Aug.* 57	... ...	
Aubrey Wm. O. Saunders, - -	29 *Dec.* 57	... ...	Instructor of Musketry and Acting Quarter Master.
Thomas Bowen, - -	29 *Dec.* 57		
John Thomson Bowers, - -	5 *Jan.* 58		
William Wastle, - -	26 *Jan.* 58	... ...	With Detacht at Jounpore.
Dawson Kelly Evans, - -	15 *Feb.* 58	... ...	With Detacht at Jounpore.
James George Cockburn, - -	26 *Feb.* 58		
Charles Whyte, - -	5 *Mar.* 58	... ...	Depôt, England.
Irving Stenning Allfrey, - -	16 *Apl.* 58		
Patrick Browne Simpson, - -	23 *Apl.* 58	... ...	Depôt, England.
George Gandy, - -	23 *July* 58	.. ..	Ditto.
J. Gifford, - -	25 *Mar.* 59	.. ..	Not joined.
Ensigns.			
Chas. Wm. Henry Wilson, -	29 *Dec.* 57		
Patrick Albert Howley, - -	27 *Feb.* 58	.. ..	With Detach at Buxar.
William Smith, - - - - -	5 *Mar.* 58	.. ..	Ditto.
Thos. Greer Saunders, - -	6 *Mar.* 58		
Duncan D. D. Cotter, - -	16 *Mar.* 58		
Jacob Briggs Hopkins, - -	23 *Mar.* 58		
James FitzGerald, - -	23 *Apl.* 58		
Gust W. B. Collis, - -	24 *Apl.* 58	... ..	Depôt, England.
~~Chas. H. Marchant~~, - -	25 *Apl.* 58		
Alex. Courtenay Hall, - -	21 *May* 58	.. ..	Depôt, England.

H. M. 6TH (THE ROYAL 1ST WARWICKSHIRE) REGIMENT OF FOOT.—*Continued.*

RANK AND NAMES.	*Regimental Rank.*	*Army Rank.*	REMARKS.
INSTRUCTOR OF MUSKETRY,			
Lieut. A. W. O. Saunders, -	23 *Sep.* 57	*lt.* 29 *Dec.* 57	
PAY MASTER.			
D. ~~Allan McDonald~~, - - -	26 *Oct.* 58	.. ..	
ADJUTANT.			
Lieut. Henry J. Lawrell, - -	25 *June* 58	*lt.* 23 *Nov.* 55	
QUARTER MASTER.			
James Jameson, - -	28 *Aug.* 57	.. ..	Leave on M.C. to Eng. to 10 Aug. 52.
SURGEON.			
Henry Vereker Bindon, - -	25 *May* 56	... ...	Leave on M. C. to Cape of Good Hope to July 59
ASSIST. SURGEONS.			
Alexander Robert Hudson, M.B.,	26 *May* 54	.. ..	With Detachment at Jounpore.
W. Hillman, - - - - - - -	23 *Mar.* 58	... ...	With Detachment at Buxar.
Hampden Healy Maclean, - -	22 *June* 58	22 *Apl.* 58	

Strength—10 Companies with 47 Sergeants—43 Corporals—16 Drummers—and 699 Privates.

English Agents.—Messrs. Cox and Co.
Calcutta Agents.—Messrs. Gordon, Stuart and Co.

WAR SERVICES OF THE OFFICERS OF H. M. 6TH REGIMENT OF FOOT.

Lieut.-Genl. Riddell served as Deputy-Assist.-Quarter-Master-General at the capture of Copenhagen in 1807; and as Assistant-Quarter-Master-General on the eastern coast of Spain and at Genoa, with the army under Lord William Bentinck.

Lt. Colonel Robertson served with the 6th Regt. in the Kaffir war of 1851-3: commanded the Infantry consisting of three companies of the 6th, and one company of the 73rd Regts. at the engagement of the Boomah Pass in the Amatola Mountains 24th Dec. 1850 (horse shot), and also in the skirmish on the following day between the Keiskamma Hoek and Fort White, when a large body of Kaffirs were defeated with great loss (mentioned in General Orders). Commanded the 6th Regt. on the 6th Feb. when attacked by a large force of Kaffirs between Fort Cox and Fort White, at which time a hundred of the enemy were killed (mentioned in General Orders). Appointed Commandant of Port Elizabeth and the district of Uitenhage in March 1851, and was placed in command of 300 levies and 100 mounted burghers for the purpose of keeping the Zuurberg Mountains clear of the enemy, and also the keeping open the communication between Port Elizabeth and Graham's Town. Was engaged in several minor affairs with the enemy from the above time to the close of the war in March 1853 (Medal).

Major Blanckley served with a detachment of the 6th Regt. sent from Bombay in 1837 against the rebels in Canara. Also in the Kaffir war of 1846-7; and throughout the whole of the Kaffir war and Hottentot rebellion of 1851-2-3, was present with the Regt. on nearly every patrol, and several times engaged with the enemy; commanded the Regt. in a skirmish at the Caboula Hill, 29th June 1851, when it formed the rear-guard to the division then protecting a capture of 1,500 head of Gaika cattle (Medal.)

Major Catty served throughout the Kaffir war of 1850-53 (Medal): acted as Field Adjutant to the Infantry at the commencement of hostilities in the engagement in the Boomah Pass, and on the following day, when incapacitated by wounds, was several times nearly taken prisoner. Present at Fort White when that post was stormed by a large force of the enemy, who were repulsed by the small garrison under Major Mansergh. In May 1851 he was appointed Commandant of an irregular corps of Europeans, designated "Catty's Rifles," and during thirteen months of the most active period of operations this corps did good and gallant service, being engaged in nearly every patrol of the 2nd Division, the same being frequently acknowledged in General Orders, and the various reports of Commanders of Divisions. On the disbandment of "Catty's Rifles," he rejoined his Regt. (the 6th), and proceeded with the expedition against the paramount chief Kreli, and on his return to head-quarters was appointed to the command of Fort Grey, which he held till the cessation of hostilities, during which period, besides rendering the post perfectly defensible, waggons and cattle, which were on three occasions taken by the enemy and driven off, were recaptured by the garrison under Capt. Catty. Was twice severely wounded by musket balls in the Boomah Pass.

Captain Thompson served with the 6th Regt. in the Kaffir war of 1846-7. Also in that of 1851-2-3; was present at the operations in the Waterkloof in Sept. 1851 and in March 1852; and received a complimentary letter from Sir Harry Smith while in command of Fort Grey, for recapturing with a very small party a number of cattle taken by the enemy from the Government train (Medal).

Major Elkington served with the 6th Regt. in the Kaffir wars of 1847 and 1851-52 (Medal),—during which he was present at the operations in the Fish River, Waterkloof, Amatolas, and Trans-Kei Expeditions in command of the Light Company. He served as Assistant Quarter-Master-General to the Ottoman Contingent from its formation in May 1855, to the close of the war, for which he received the Brevet rank of Major.

Captain Dawson served with the 6th Regt. in the Kaffir war of 1846-47; also throughout that of 1850-53 (Medal), including the operations in the Fish River, Amatolas, and both the Trans-Kei Expeditions, on the latter of which as acting Adjutant.

Lieut. Wastle served with the 6th Regt. in the Kaffir war of 1846-47; also throughout that of 1850-53 (Medal), including the operations in the Fish River, Amatolas, and both the Trans-Kei Expeditions.

Surgeon Bindon served in the Kaffir war of 1846-47; and in that of 1851-53 (Medal).

1st battalion of H. M. 7th Regiment of Foot (Royal Fusiliers.)

In the centre of the colours, The "*Rose*" within the "*Garter*" and the "*Crown*" over it
And in the corners of the second Colour, The "*White Horse.*"
"Martinique"—"Talavera"—"Albuhera"—"Badajoz"—"Salamanca"—
"Vittoria"—"Pyrenees"—"Orthes"—"Toulouse"—"Peninsula"
"Alma"—"Inkerman"—"Sevastopol."
Facings—*Blue.*
Landed in India (Kurrachee) on 24th November 1857.
Jhelum.
Right Wing at *Dehra Ismael Khan.*
Depôt of 1st Battalion, Chatham.

Rank and Names.	Regimental Rank.	Army Rank.	Remarks.
Colonel.			
Sir S. Benj. Auchmuty, K.C.B., -	18 *Jan.* 55	*l.g.* 11 *Nov.* 51	In Europe.
Lieutenant Colonels.			
Richard William Aldworth, -	20 *Mar.* 57	.. ..	Leave on P. A. to Cashmere to 31 Oct. [59.
Reginald Yonge Shipley, -	29 *May* 57	27 *May* 56	Commanding Sind Saugor District.
Majors.			
Charles Edward Watson, -	8 *Jan.* 56	2 *Nov.* 55	Commdg. left Wing Rawul Pindee.
Thomas Tryon, - -	20 *Mar.* 57	6 *June* 56	
Captains.			
~~G. W. Wallace Carpenter,~~ -	12 *Jan.* 55	.. ..	Commanding Chatham Depôt, England.
Joshua Harry Cooper, *V.*	23 *Mar.* 55	... ...	Regtl. Depot.
Thomas Wright Martin, *V.*	19 *June* 55	.. ..	On duty in Public Works Department.
Lord Rich. Howe Browne, -	13 *July* 55		
~~James Francis Hickie,~~ -	3 *Aug.* 55	.. ..	Leave of Absence on P. A.
George Henry Waller, *V.*	20 *Mar.* 57	.. ..	With Right Wing.
Napier Douglas Robinson, -	28 *Aug.* 57	.. ..	On duty in Public Work Dept. Dehra [Ishmael Khan.
William Jesser Coope, - -	26 *Feb.* 56	... ...	With left Wing.
A. Bennett, - -	1 *May* 58	.. ..	Instructor of Musketry, ditto.
Richard Barter, - - *V.*	11 *Aug* 58	.. ..	Comdg. Bijnore Military Police.
Thomas G. Dupre Payn, - -	25 *Feb.* 59	24 *Aug.* 58	
H. Stewart Cochrane, - - -	21 *Mar.* 59	.. ..	Leave on M. C. to Australia.
J. K. McAdam			
Lieutenants.			
Heathcote Plummer, - -	13 *April* 55	... ...	Leave of Absence on P. A.
Charles Errol Hope, - -	26 *July* 55	.. ..	Lv. on M. C. to England.
Henry Kerr, - -	27 *July* 55	.. ..	Convalesent Depot, Murree.
Robert Watson Sparks, *V.*	3 *Aug.* 55		
William Pryce Browne, *V.*	19 *Aug.* 55		
James Anthony Gardner, -	9 *Sep.* 55	... ...	With Right Wing.
Henry John Barnard, -	9 *Sep.* 55		
~~Charles Seaver Courtenay,~~ -	3 *Oct.* 55	.. ...	At Rawul Pindee.
Francis Burton Cole, -	16 *Oct.* 55		
Gwynne Orton Lewis, -	1 *May* 57	23 *Oct.* 55	Adjutant.
Henry Alex. Little, -	29 *May* 57		At Rawul Pindee.
Fitzmaurice Beauchamp, *V.*	26 *Jan.* 58	.. ..	Ditto.
Anselm Tibeaudo, -	13 *Apl.* 58	... ...	Adjutant Depôt of Queen's Troops, [Kurrachee.
Edw. W. Cadwall. Lloyd, -	24 *Dec.* 58	.. ..	Leave of Absence on P. A.
J. Herbert R. Stoddart, -	11 *June* 59		
Ensigns.			
~~Carteret Houstoun Kempson,~~ -	4 *Apl.* 56	.. ..	Ditto.
~~J. Douglas Flood,~~ - - -	4 *Apl.* 56	... ..	With Right Wing.
William John Frampton, *V.*	12 *Dec.* 56	... ..	At Rawul Pindee.
Arthur John Harrison, -	10 *Mar.* 57	... ..	Ditto.
Fred. C. Keyser, - -	28 *May* 58	... ...	Regtl. Depot.
Edward Bridges, - -	4 *June* 58	... ...	Ditto.
H. W. L. Paddon, - -	6 *Aug.* 58	.. ..	En route to join.
M. J. Fawcett, - -	31 *Aug.* 58	.. ..	Regtl. Depot.
H. W. Rochfort, - -	25 *Jan.* 59	.. ..	Ditto.

H. M. 7TH REGIMENT OF FOOT (ROYAL FUSILIERS).—(*Continued.*)

RANK AND NAMES.	*Regimental Rank.*	*Army Rank.*	REMARKS.
INSTRUCTOR OF MUSKETRY.			
Capt. A. Bennett, - -	1 *May* 57		
PAYMASTER.			
John Mortimer Scott, - -	18 *Aug.* 56	15 *July* 56	
ADJUTANT.			
Lieut. Gwynne O. Lewis, -	11 *Aug.* 58	*lt.* 3 *Oct.* 55	
QUARTER MASTER.			
Thomas Murphy, - -	4 *Apl.* 56		
SURGEONS.			
Thomas Moorhead, M. D., -	11 *May* 55	3 *Nov.* 54	
ASSISTANT SURGEONS.			
Thomas Egerton Hale, M. D.*	18 *June* 55	14 *Dec.* 54	
Charles Ricketts, - -	29 *June* 55	28 *Apl.* 54	Rawul Pindee.
Thomas Sheehy, M. D., - -	26 *May* 54	26 *May* 54	With Right Wing.
INTERPRETER.			
Lt. R. W. Sparks, - -	3 *Aug.* 55	9 *Apl.* 59	

Strength—10 Companies with 56 Sergeants,—50 Corporals—18 Drummers—and 1097 Privates.

English Agents—Messrs. Cox and Co.

Irish Agents—Sir E. R. Borough Bart Arnut and Co.

Calcutta Agents—Messrs. Wood Oliffe and Co.

WAR SERVICES OF THE OFFICERS OF H. M. 7TH ROYAL FUSILIERS.

Sir Samuel Benj. Auchmuty served several years in the West Indies, and was present at the storming of Morne Fortunée, St. Lucia. In 1809 he accompained the second Battalion Royal Fusiliers to Portugal, and was present at Oporto and Talavera as Major of Brigade to Sir Alex. Campbell; and at the battle of Busaco, the retreat of the army to and subsequent advance from the lines of Torres Vedras, and battle of Fuentes d'Onor as Deputy Assistant Adjutant-General to the Six Divisions. On return to the Peninsula from sick leave he was appointed extra Aide-de-Camp to Sir Lowry Cole, and was in action with the Fourth Division at Vittoria and the Pyrenees,—at the latter was promoted to the Brevet rank of Major. Succeeding soon afterwards to the Regimental Majority, he commanded the light companies of Major-General Ross's Brigade, and served with them at Orthes and Toulouse,—at the latter was promoted Brevet Lieut.-Colonel. He has received the Gold Medal and one Clasp for the battles of Orthes and Toulouse; and the Silver War Medal with five Clasps for the other battles

Lt.-Col. Aldworth served the Eastern campaign of 1854 up to 8th November, including the battles of Alma and Inkerman, siege of Sebastopol, and sortie of 26th October (Medal and Clasps).

Lt.-Col. Shipley served the Eastern campaign of 1854, including the battles of Alma and Inkerman (severely wounded), siege of Sebastopol, and sortie on 26th Oct., (Medal and Clasps Brevet Major, and Sardinian-Medal).

Major Watson served in the Eastern campaign of 1854, and was severely wounded at the battle of Alma (Medal and Clasp).

Major Tryon served in the Eastern campaign of 1854, including the battle of Inkerman, siege of Sebastopol and sortie on 26th Oct. (Medal and Clasps).

Captain Carpenter served it the Eastern campaign of 1854, and was wounded at the battle of Alma (Meda and Clasp).

Captain Cooper served in the Crimea in Sept. and. Oct. 45 (Medal and Chasp, and 5th Claas of the Medjidie.)

Captain Marten served with the Royal Fusiliers at the siege of Sebastopol, from 17th June 1855, including the assaults of the Redan on the 18th June and 8th Sept., on which last occasion he succeeded to the command of the Regiment, led it across the ditch of that work, and subsequently brought it out of action—mentioned in dispatches (Medal and Clasp).

Lord Richard Browne served at the siege of Sebastopol from 20th March 1855, including sorties on 22nd March and 9th May, defence of the Quarries 7th June, and assault on the Redan on the 18th June (severely wounded); also slightly wounded by the bursting of a shell in Sebastopol, 1st Dec. 1855 (Medal and Clasp).

Captain Hickie served at the siege of Sebastopol from 17th June 1855, including assaults on the Redan on 18th June and 8th Sept, (severely wounded): Medal and Clasp.

Captain Waller served at the siege of Sebastopol from 21st Nov. 1854, including sortie on 9th May, attack and capture of the Quarries 7th June (wounded), assault on the Redan 18th June (wounded), and was in the trenches on the 18th Sept. (Medal and Clasp, and Knight of the Legion of Honor).

Captain Robinson served at the siege of Sebastopol from 17th Feb. 1855, including the assaults on the Redan on the 18th June (wounded): Medal and Clasp.

Captain Cooper served in the Crimea in Sept. and Oct. 1854 (Medal and Clasp, and 5th Class of the Medjidie).

Capt. Barter served in the campaign of 1857-58 as adjutant H. M. 75th Regiment and was present at the battle of Badreaka Serai, 8th June 1857 (severely wounded) siege, storming, and final capture of Delhi, including the six days street fighting, with the moveable column under Col. Greathed in persuit; was present at the action of Bulundshuhur in 28th September 1857, affair at Allyghur, and battle of Agra in the 10th October 57. the advance under Major General Sir Hopegrant, K. C. B. Cawnpore, including the skirmishes en route, with the force which accompanied His Excellency the Comander-in-Cheief Sir Colin Campbell into Oude including affairs of Maragunge and Alumbagh, and the occupation after the relief of the Lucknow garrision of the fortified position and camp with the force under Lt. General Sir James Outram, G. C. B., and repulse of the enemys attacks, commmaded two Ressallahs of irregular cavalry in the advance into Rohilcund and re-occupation of Bijnore, medal and 2 clasps for Delhi and the relief of Lucknow.

Lieut. Plummer served at the siege of Sebastopol from 12th July 1855 (Medal and Clasp).

Lieuts. C. E. Hope, and Gardner served at the siege of Sebastopol from 7th July, 1855 (Medal and Clasp).

Paymaster Scott served the Eastern campaign of 1854-55, including the battles of Alma and Inkerman, and siege of Sebastopol (Medal and Clasps).

Assist.-Surgeon Hale served in the Crimea from Jan. 1855, and was in the trenches during the bombardments of April and 7th June, and in the assault of 8th Sept. (Medal and Clasp, and Victoria Cross).

Assist.-Surgeon Ricketts served the Eastern campaign of 1854-55 including the battles of Balaklava and Inkerman, siege of Sebastopol, sortie of 26th October, and capture of Kertch and Yenikale (Medal and Clasps).

* Victoria Cross.

1ST BATTALION OF H. M. 8th (the King's) Regiment of Foot.

The " WHITE HORSE*" on a red ground within the " Garter," and the " Crown" over it.*
In the three corners of the second Colour, the " ROYAL CYPHER *and* CROWN.*"*
" Nec Aspera Terrent."
" EGYPT*" with the Sphinx,—"* MARTINIQUE*"—"* NIAGARA.*"*

FACINGS—*Blue.*

Arrived in India 1st August 1846.
Transferred from the Bombay to the Bengal Establishment, from the 26th December, 1853.
FUTTYGHUR.
Detachment at *Mynpooree.*
Regimental Depot,—Chatham.

RANK AND NAMES.	*Regimental Rank.*	*Army Rank.*	REMARKS.
COLONEL.			
Roderick Macneil, - - - -	18 *Mar.* 55	*l.g.* 20 *June* 54	In Europe.
LIEUTENANT COLONELS.			
John Longfield, C. B., - - -	3 *Apl.* 46	*col.* 20 *June* 54	Leave of Absence on M. C.
Edward Harris Greathed, C.B., -	26 *June* 58	*col.* 19 *Jan.* 58	Deputy Adjutant General at Bombay.—Leave on M. C. to England.
MAJORS.			
James Croft Brooke, - - -	2 *Oct.* 45	*l.c.* 14 *Apl.* 57	Lv. on M. C. to England, to, 7th July 59.
Alex. Cunningham Robertson, *P H*, - - - - - -(*a*)	24 *Aug.* 58	*l.c.* 20 *July* 58	Commanding.
CAPTAINS.			
Edwin Gream Daniell, - (*b*)†	29 *Apl.* 46	*m.* 19 *Jan.* 58	Dety. Judge Advocate Genl. at Gwalior.
William Bayly, - - - - -	29 *May* 48	.. ...	Leave on M. C. to England.
George Edward Baynes, - -(*c*)	17 *Oct.* 48	*m.* 19 *Jan.* 58	Regimental Depot.
Robert Stuart Baynes, - - *P*	15 *Mar.* 53	*m.* 26 *Dec.* 56	Ditto.
Astell Thomas Welsh, - -(*V*)	22 *July* 56	17 *Oct.* 52	Leave on M. C. to England. [Oct. 59.
Richard Raphael Meade, -	16 *Jan.* 57	31 *Aug.* 55	Leave on M. C. to Nynee Tall to 27
John Whiteside, - - - -	3 *Mar.* 57	14 *Mar.* 56	Comdg. Detachment, Mynpooree.
Thomas Geo. Souter, - - *P*.	21 *Oct.* 57	.. ..	Commanding Tawana Horse.—Leave of Absence on M. C. to 1 Nov. 59.
Erskine N. Sandilands, *PH*(*d*)	21 *Oct.* 57	.. ..	Executive Engineer at Umballa.
Alex. Ross Bayly, - - - (*e*)	14 *May* 58	.. ..	Ditto at Sealkote.
Fred. Bradford McCrea, - -*V*	26 *June* 58		
Forster Longfield, - - - -	24 *Sep.* 58		
LIEUTENANTS.			
~~William Fredk. Metge~~, - -	7 *Sep.* 55	.. ..	Leave on M. C. to England
Fred. Anderson Stebbings, -	12 *Apl.* 56	.. ..	Leave to Simla on P. A, to 15th Oct. 59.
Alfred Dowrie Corfield, - - *V*	15 *May* 57		
Æneas Gordon Blair, - - -	5 *Sep.* 57		
Andrew Moynihan,* - - -	10 *Sep.* 57	.. ..	Instructor of musketry.
Charles Norris Fry, - - - -	.. ..	24 *Feb.* 57	Regimental Depôt, England.
William Edward Whelan, - -	18 *Sep.* 57	.. ..	Adjutant.
Richard Thos. B. Brown, - -	15 *Nov.* 57	.. ...	With Detachment at Mynpooree.
Robert Yallop Stokes, - -	23 *Mar.* 58		
Reginald Whitting, - - - -	23 *Mar.* 58	.. ..	Leave on M. C.
Walter John Tarte, - - - -	23 *July* 58		
Ashle George Westbey, - -	20 *Sep.* 58	.. ..	With Detacht. at Mynpooree.
J. W. Hughes, - - - - -	1 *Oct.* 58	.. ..	En route to join.
J. M. Lovekin. - - - - -	1 *Oct.* 58	.. ..	Ditto.
Philip H. Page, - - r - -	11 *June* 59		
R. Leeson, - - - - -	1 *Oct.* 58	... ..	With Detacht. at Mynpooree.

(*a*) Has passed the examination in Surveying and Civil Engrg. prescribed by G. O. 2nd March 54.
(*b*) Has passed an examination in Surveying. (*c*) Has passed an examination in Surveying
(*d*) Has passed the examination in Surveying and Civil Engineering prescribed by G. O. 2nd March 1854.
(*e*) Has passed the examinations in Hindustani, Marathee, Scindee, Guzeratee, Persian and received the donation of Rs. 1,000 for general proficiency, also passed in Surveying.

* Victoria Cross.

H. M. 8TH (THE KING'S) REGIMENT OF FOOT—(*Continued.*)

RANK AND NAMES.	*Regimental Rank.*	*Army Rank.*	REMARKS.
ENSIGNS.			
Richard Chute, - -	17 *Nov.* 57	.. ..	At Mynpooree.
William J. Watson, - -	21 *Nov.* 57	.. ..	Instructor of Musketry.
Arundel Hill Cotter, - -	11 *Dec.* 57		
John George Brown, - -	13 *Dec.* 57		
A. Cook, - - - *V,*	16 *Mar.* 58		
W. J. Cooper, - -	23 *Mar.* 58		
Chas. B. Crease, - -	24 *Mar.* 58	.. ..	En-route to join.
Jeremy Peyton Jones, - -	3 *July* 58	.. ..	Regimental Depôt.
INSTRUCTOR OF MUSKETRY.			
Ens. William J. Watson, - -	21 *Nov,* 57	17 *Feb.* 59	
PAY MASTER.			
Lieut. G. Egerton Huddleston, -	23 *Mar.* 55	*lt.* 27 *June* 54	Leave on M. C.
ADJUTANT.			
Lieut. Wm. Edw. Whelan, -	30 *Apl.* 58	*lt.* 18 *Sep.* 57	
QUARTER MASTER.			
Joseph Hamilton, - -	16 *Apl.* 58		
SURGEONS.			
Francis Charles Annesley, - -	15 *July* 51	15 *Aug.* 48	
ASSISTANT SURGEONS.			
William Henry Yates, - - -	26 *Feb.* 56	24 *Nov.* 54	
Thomas James Biddle, - - -	12 *Sep.* 56	15 *Aug.* 54	At Mynpooree.
Richard Westrop Saunders, M.D.	11 *Feb.* 59		
INTERPRETER.			
Lt. A. D. Corfield, - - - -	17 *Mar.* 59		

Strength—10 Companies, with 54 Sergeants—49 Corporals—21 Drummers—**180 Privates.**

English Agents,—Sir Chas. McGrigor, *bart,* and W. McGrigor.
Irish Agents,—Sir E. R. Borough, *bart,* Armit and Co.
Calcutta Agents,————————

SERVICES OF THE 8TH, THE KING'S REGIMENT.

Siege of Delhi—Sorties of the 9th, 14th, 18th, and 23rd July—12th August a party of the Regiment furnished part of a Force under Brigadier Showers which captured 4 Guns—14th September, assault of the city of Delhi.—14th to 20th in city—24th September, the Regiment marched with a moveable column commanded by Lieut. Colonel Greathed—28th September, action of Bolundshur—5th October, affair of Allygurh—10th, Battle of Agra—14th November, the advance on Lucknow by the Dilkoosha—the affair of the 2nd, and action of the 6th December 1857, at Cawnpore—2nd January 1858, action of Khudagunj.

WAR SERVICES OF THE OFFICERS OF H. M. 8TH REGIMENT OF FOOT.

Lieut.-General Macneil served in Sir John Moore's retreat and subsequently at Malcheren in 1809; in Swedish Pomerania in 1813; in Holland in 1814, including the attack on Bergen-op-Zoom; and the campaign of 1815, including the battle of Waterloo.

Colonel J. Longfield, commanded the 2nd Infantry Brigade of the Field Force at the siege of Delhi in 1857. The Reserve during the assault on the 14th September and served in the city during the six days fighting that ensued.

Lieut. Colonel E. H. Greathed, C. B., served with the 8th, "The King's" Regt. at the siege of Delhi in1857; and commanded that Regiment from the 30th June to the end of the siege, present at the repuulse of the Sorties on the 9th, 14th, and 18th July, and commanded the 3rd Infantry Brigade during the repulse of the enemy's attack on the 23rd July. Selected as Field Officer of the trenches by Major General Wilson to command the column sent to occupy the Khoodsia Bagh and Ludlow Castle, 7th September, by this operation the Batteries were advanced to within 180 yards from the walls of Delhi. Led the Regiment to the assault on the 14th September and served with it in the city till the 19th of the month. Seleted for command of the moveable column which left Delhi September the 24th, and in that capacity was present at the action of Bolundshuhur September the 28th; Allyghur October 5th; and Battle of Agra, October the 10th. Commanded the 3rd Infantry Brigade of the Army under Sir Colin Campbell from the 10th November 1857 to the 9th January 1858, served with his Brigade at the action of Dil-koosha November 14th in Lucknow during the operation, resulting in the relief of Sir James Outram's garrison from the 5th to 22nd November, commanded advanced picquets from 30th November to 7th December 1857. At the affair of the 2nd, and action of the 6th December 1857 at Cawnpore, and the action of Khudagunge and occupation of Futtygurh on the 2nd January 1858.

Lieut.-Colonel Brooke served with the 31st Regt. throughout the campaign of 1842 in Affghanistan (Medal) under General Pollock, and was present in the actions of Mazeena, Tezeen, and Jugdulluck (wounded), the occupation of Cabool, and the different engagements leading to it. He commanded a Company during the campaign, and received his wound whilst protecting some guns attached to the rear-guard. Lieut. Colonel J. C. Brook served with the 8th, "the King's" Regt. at the seige of Delhi 1857, present during the repulse of the Sortie on the 9th, 14th, and commanded the Regiment during the repulse of the enemy's attack on the 22nd of that month; present with the Regiment at the assault of the city on the 14th September (severely wounded) was one of the Four field Officers commanding in the trenches during the siege.

*** *For continuation of services, see next page.*

WAR SERVICES OF THE OFFICERS OF H. M. 8TH REGIMENT OF FOOT.—*Continued.*

Major Robertson served in the Anglo-Spanish Legion from July 1835 to June 1837. Received a Medal for the action of 5th May 1837; the cross of the 1st class of San Fernando, for the actions of the 15th and 16th March 1837; and another Medal for the storming of Irun, 27th May following: severely wounded in the face by a splinter in the general action on the heights of Ametza, 1st Oct. 1836. Major A. C. Robertson served with the 8th the King's Regiment at the siege of Delhi 1857, present during the repulse of the enemy's sorties of the 9th, 14th, 18th (in command of the Regiment) and 23rd July, present in command of detachments of 8th and 61st Regiments on the 12th August during the capture of four of the enemy's Guns in front of the advanced picquet, acted as Deupty Assistant Quarter Master General to a Column under Brigadier Seaton C. B. in December 1857, and was present with it in the affairs of Gungeree 14th, Puttiala 18th and Mynpooree 26th of that month; present during operations from 2nd to 22nd March resulting in occupation of Lucknow, in the capacity of Deputy Judge Advocate General to the army in the field.

Bt. Major Daniel served with the 55th in China (Medal), and was present at Amoy, Chusan, and Chinhæ including the repulse of the night-attack. Captain B. G. Daniell served with the 8th the King's Regiment, at the siege of Delhi in 1857, present with his Company the Grenadiers during the repulse of the enemy's sorties, &c. on the 9th July (severely wounded.)

Bt. Major W. Bayly was present at the battle of Plattsburg in 1814. Captain Bayly served with the 8th, the King's Regiment, at the siege of Delhi, from 28th June to 3rd September 1857; present during the repulse of the enemy's sorties on the 9th, 14th, 18th and 23rd July; commanded the two flank companies the greater part of the day of the repulse of the 18th.

Bt. Major G. E. Baynes served with the 8th, the King's Ragiment at the siege of Delhi in 1857, present during the repulse of the enemy's sorties on the 9th, 14th, 18th and 23rd July, commanded the storming party of the 2nd Column of attack at the assault of the city on the 14th September 1857.

Bt. Major R. S. Baynes served with the 8th the King's Regiment at the siege of Delhi 1857, present at the assault of the city on the 14th September (severely wounded.)

Captain Welsh served with the 80th Regt. in the Burmese war of 1852-53 (Medal); including the bombardment of Rangoon and subsequent operations of the 12th, 13th, and 14th April, and capture of the great Dragon Pagoda (with the storming party); bombardment and capture of Prome (specially thanked by the Governor-General of India in Council), night-attack of the enemy on the camp on the heights of Prome, and expedition into the Poungdey district in Feb. and March 1853.

Captain R. R. Meade was present as a Volunteer with the Artillery in the action at Agra on the 5th July, served with the 8th "the King's" Regiment at the affair; relief of the Garrison of Lucknow under Sir Colin Campbell of the 2nd, and action of the 6th December 1857 at Cawnpore, and in the action at Khudagunge on the 2nd January 1858.

Captain Whiteside served throughout the campaign under General Pollock n Affghanistan in 1842 (Medal) and that on the Sutlej in 1845-46 (Medal and Clasps), including the battles of Moodkee, Ferozeshah, and Sobraon.

Captain T. G. Souter was present with the Buffs in the action of Punniar, and has received the Bronze Star. Captain Souter served with the 8th "the King's" Regiment at the siege of Delhi in 1857, present during the repulse of the enemy's sorties on the 14th, 18th and 23rd July 1857.

Captain E. N. Sandilands served with the 8th "the King's" Regiment at the siege of Delhi in 1857, present during the repluse of the enemy's sorties on the 14th, 18th and 23rd July. When on picquet on the morning of the 10th August, wounded by a splinter of a shell, commanded the Light Company of his Regiment at the assault of the city on the 14th September (wounded); present in the action of Dilkoosha on the 14th November; relief of the Garrison of Lucknow under Sir Colin Campbell, the affair of the 2nd and action of the 6th December 1857 at Cawnpore and at Khudagunge in the action of the 2nd January 1858.

Captain F. Longfield served with the 8th "the King's" Regiment at the siege of Delhi in 1857; present during the repulse of the enemy's sorties on the 9th, 14th, 18th and 23rd July; present on the 12th August during the capture of four of the enemy's guns on the left advance picquet, present in the action of Dil-koosha 14th November, relief of the Garrison of Lucknow under Sir Colin Campbell, and in the affair of the 2nd and action of the 6th December 1857 at Cawnpore, and in the action at Khudagunge 2nd January 1858.

Captain A. R. Bayly served with the 8th "the King's" Regt. at the siege of Delhi in 1857; present during the repulse of the enemy's sorties on the 9th, 14th and 18th July; present at the assault of the city on the 14th September and during the six days' fighting in the city which ensued; present at the action of Bolundshur 28th September, affair at Allygurh 5th battle of Agra 10th October, action of Dil-Koosha on the 14th November, relief of the Garrison of Lucknow under Sir Colin Campbell; affair of the 2nd and action of the 6th December 1857 at Cawnpore, and at the action of the 2nd January 1858 at Khudagunge.

Lieut. W. F. Metge served with the 8th "the King's" Regiment at the siege of Delhi in 1857; present during the repulse of the enemy's sorties on the 9th, 14th and 18th July; was present with the storming party of the left attack at the assault of the city on the 14th September 1857, (wounded).

Lieut. F. A. Stebbing served with the 8th "the King's" Regiment at the siege of Delhi in 1857; present at the assault of the city on the 14th September and during the six days' fighting which ensued; present with Colonel Seaton's Column at the action of Gungaree 14th, attack on the enemy's position at Puttiala 18th and the affair of Mynpoore 26th December 1857.

Lieut. R. L. G. McGrigor served with the 8th "the King's" Regiment at the siege of Delhi (slightly wounded) in 1857; present at the assault of the city 14th September and during the six days' fighting which ensued; present at the action of Bolundshuhur 28th September, affair at Allyghur 5th, battle of Agra 10th October, action of Dil-koosha 14th November, relief of the Garrison of Lucknow under Sir Colin Campbell, affair of the 2nd and action of the 6th December 1857 at Cawnpore, and action of Khudagunge on the 2nd January 1858.

Pay Master G. E. Huddleston served with the 8th "the King's" Regiment at the siege and capture of Delhi in 1857; present at the action of Bolundshuhur 28th September, affair of Allygurh 5th, battle of Agra 10th Oct.; affair of the 2nd and action of the 6th December 1857 at Cawnpore, and action of Khudagunge on the 2nd January 1858.

Surgeon F. C. Annesley served with the 8th "the King's" Regiment at the siege and capture of Delhi in 1857.

Assistant Surgeon W. H. Yates served with the 8th "the King's" Regiment at the siege and capture of Delhi 1857, accompanied Colonel Greathed's moveable Column in medical charge of the Regiment and was present in the action of Bolundshuhr 28th September, affair at Allygurh on the 5th, battle of Agra 10th October, action of Dil-koosha on 14th November, relief of the Garrison of Lucknow under Sir Colin Campbell, affair of the 2nd and action of the 6th December 1857 at Cawnpore, and action of Khudagunge on the 2nd January 1858.

Assist.-Surgeon Biddle served in the Crimea during the winter of 1854 (Medal and Clasp for Sebastopol), he served with the 8th "the King's" Regiment at the siege and capture of Delhi 1857.

CONTINUATION OF SERVICES OF THE OFFICECS OF H. M. ROYAL FOOT ARTY.—*From page* 23.

Major Walcott, served at the siege of Sebastopol in 1855 (Medal and Clasp). Major Walcott has the 5th Class of the Medjidie. Captain Twiss served at Canton with the force under Rear Admiral Seymour in 1856-57.

Lt.Colonel F. C. Maude commanded the Royal Artillery throughout the operations with General Havelock's moveable column in 1857 including the defeat of the Rebels at Futtehpore, actions of Aoung, Pandoo Nuddee, Cawnpore, Oonao, Buseerut, Gunge, relief and defence of the Residency of Lucknow (repeatedly mentioned in Dispatches, Brevets of Major and Lt.Col., C. B. Victoria Cross, Medal and Clasp).

Major Grylls served the Eastern campaign of 1854-55, including the affairs of Bulganac and M'Kenzie's Farm, the battles of Alma, Balaklava, and Inkerman. capture of Balaklava, and siege of Sebastopol (Medal and Clasps).

Captain A. C. Johnson, and Tyler (wounded), served at the siege and fall of Sebastopol in 1855 (Medal and Clasp).

Lieuts. Vaughan, and Cuthbert served in 1855 at the siege and fall of Sebastopol, in the trenches with the siege train, and bombardments of 6th and 17th June (Medal and Clasp). Lieut. Vaughan is a Knight of the Legion of Honour. Lieuts. Doyne and Cuthbert have the 5th Class of the Medjidie.

Lieut. Lyon served in the Eastern campaign of 1854-55, including the siege of Sebastopal, and in the trenches with the siege train at the bombardments of April, and 6th and 17th June (Medal and Clasp). Lt. Griffiths has the 5th Class of the Mejidie.

Lieut. Tweedie served at the siege and fall of Sebastopol, and battle of Tchernaya (Medal and Clasp).

Lieuts. Burnaby, Majendie F. A. Whinyates, and served at the siege and fall of Sebastopol (medal and Clasp). Lieut. Ward has also the Sardinian Medal, and the 5th Class of the Medjidie).

Lieut. Arbuthnot served the Eastern campaign of 1854-55, including the affair at M' Kenzie's Farm, battles of Alma and Inkerman, siege and fall of Sebastopol, and repulse of the sortie on the 26th Oct. 1854 (Medal and Clasps, and Knight of the Legion of Honor).

Lieut. Biddulph served the Eastern campaign of 1854-55, including the battles of Alma and Balaklava, siege and fall of Sebastopol, and expedition to Kertch (Medal and Clasps, and 5th Class of the Medjidie).

Lieut Maxwell served the Eastern campaign of 1854-55, including the affairs of Bulganac and M'Kenzie's Farm, the battles of Alma, Balaklava, and Inkerman, the siege and fall of Sebastopol, and repulse of the sortie on the 26th October 1854(medal and Clasps, and Knights of the Legion of Honor).

Lieut. Rideout served in the Eastern campaign of 1854-55, including the battle of Inkerman. siege and fall of Sebastopol, in the trenches with the siege train, and bombardments of October, April, 6th and 17th June, and August (Medal and Clasps, and Knight of the Legion of Honor).

Lieut Hall, served in the campaign of 1854-55, including the siege and fall of Sebastopol, in the trenches with the siege train, and bombardments of April and 6th and 17th June (Medal and Clasp, and Knight of the Legion of Honor).

Lieut. Trench served at the siege and fall of Sebastopol and expedition to Kertch in 1855 (medal and Clasp).

Lieut. Geary, served in 1855 in the trenches, with the siege train at teh siege and fall of Sebastopol, and bombardments of 6th and 17th June and August. Lieut. Roberts was Subsequently very severely wounded by the explosion of the French powder magazine in camp on the 15th Nov. 1855 (Medal and Clasp). Lieuts. Browne, Maule, and Roberts have also the Sardinian Medal, Captain Taylor, Lieuts Scott and Geary have the 5th Class of the Medjidie.

Veterinary Surgeons Withers and Harpley served the Eastern campaign of 1854-55, including the affairs of Bulganac and M' Kenzie's Farm, battles of Alma Balaklava, and Inkerman, siege of Sebastopol and repulse of the sortie on the 26th Oct, 1854 (Medal and Clasps).

Veterinaty Surgeons Cochrane and Sanderson served at the siege and fall of Sebastopol in 1855 (Medal and Clasp).

1st Battalion of 13th (or Prince Albert's) Regiment of Light Infantry.

The "*Sphinx*," with the words "Egypt"
"Martinique"—"Ava"—"Affghanistan"—"Ghuznee"—
A Mural Crown, superscribed,—"Jellalabad"—"Cabool, 1842"—"Sevastopol"
Facings—*Blue*
Landed in India on 3rd October 1857.
Goruckpore
4 Companies at *Bustee* and 1st at *Lotun.*
Depôt of 1*st Battalion*—Fermoy.

Rank and Names.	Regimental Rank.	Army Rank.	Remarks.
Colonel.			
Sir Wm. Maynard Gomm, K.C.B.,	10 *Mar.* 46	*g* 20 *June* 54	In England.
Lieutenant Colonel.			
Lord Mark Kerr, B. C., - -	30 *Dec.* 53	*col.* 28 *Nov.* 54	Commanding.
George King, - -	17 *Nov.* 57	26 *Dec.* 56	Comdg. Left Wing, Bustee.
Majors.			
John William Cox, C. B., - *V*,	25 *Jan.* 56	*l. c.* 20 *July* 58	Comdg. Dugshaie Convalescent Depot,
George Henry Tyler, - -	17 *Nov.* 58	*l.c.* 26 *Apl.* 59	Leave of Absence to England on P. A. for 18 months, from 27 Mar. 59.
Captains.			
Robert Peel, - -	25 *Nov.* 53	.. ..	With Left Wing.
Fred. Van Straubenzee, - -	6 *June* 54	*m* 26 *Apl.* 59	Leave on M. C. to England to 11 Nov. 59.
Robert B. Montgomery, - -	4 *Aug.* 54	... ...	Comdg. Depôt at Fermoy.
Gerald FitzGerald King, - -	26 *June* 55	... ...	With Left Wing.
Melville Browne, - -	26 *June* 55		
Edward Boyd, - -	26 *June* 55	... ...	Lv., to England on P.A. for 18 months
Arthur Bainbrigge, - -	26 *June* 55		
Charles Poore Long, - -	17 *Aug.* 55	.. ..	Leave on M. C. to England.
G. S. Twynam, - - - -	11 *Jan.* 58	11 *Jan.* 58	With detachment at Lotun.
John Angerstein Rowley, - -	14 *Mar.* 58		
Cornwallis Henry Chichester, -	7 *Apl.* 58		Fermoy Depôt, England.
O'Neil Stewart Segrave, - -	11 *Feb.* 59	.. ..	Leave on M. C, to England,
Hon. James Charlemagne Dormer, - *V*,	11 *Mar.* 59	.. ..	A. D. C, to the Commander-in-Chief.
Lieutenants.			
Henry Lewis FitzGerald, - -	2 *Feb.* 55	.. ..	With Left Wing.
John Frederick Everett, - -	13 *Feb.* 55	.. ..	Ditto.
Philip Edw. Victor Gilbert, -	26 *June* 55	.. ..	Ditto.
Henry Gillett, - -	26 *June* 55	.. ..	With detachment at Lotun.
William Williams, - -	26 *June* 55		
H. Alex. C. Wroughton, - *V*,	3 *Aug.* 55		
Allan Shafto Adair,. - -	31 *Aug.* 65		
William Knox Leet, - -	1 *Feb.* 56	.. ..	Adjutant, leave on M. C. to Calcutta.
John Fencott James, - -	7 *Mar.* 56	.. ..	Acting Adjutant.
Thomas McNeille Gill, - -	30 *June* 57	19 *Feb.* 57	
William Cox, - -	8 *Jan.* 58	... ...	Depot Fermoy.
Gresham Herrick, - -	7 *Sept.* 58		
Francis Drewe Edwards, - -	1 *Oct.* 58	1 *July* 55	On leave to England.
Charles Fraser, - -	11 *May* 59		
Ensigns.			
R. FitzGerald King, - -	30 *Mar.* 58	.. ..	Instructor of Musketry. With Left Wing.
Alexander M. Rowan, - -	31 *Mar.* 58		
Pierce W. Hughes, - -	28 *May* 58	... ...	En route to join.
Dudley, T. Persse, - -	29 *May* 58	... ...	
Matthew John Bell, - -	24 *Aug.* 58	.. ..	Depot Fermoy.
William Lea Smith, - -	5 *Oct.* 58	.. ..	Ditto.
Instructor of Musketry.			
Ensign R. Fitgerald King, -	16 *May* 59	30 *Mar.* 58	

13TH (OR PRINCE ALBERT'S) REGIMENT OF LIGHT INFANTRY—(*Continued.*)

RANK AND NAMES.	*Regimental Rank.*	*Army Rank.*	REMARKS.
PAY MASTER.			
Duncan Cameron M'Naughten,	25 *May* 55	.. ..	At Bustee.
ADJUTANTS.			
Lieut. Wm. Knox Leet, - -	2 *Aug.* 58	*lt.* 1 *Feb.* 56	Leave on M C.
Liut. J. F. James - - - -	7 *Mar.* 56	.. ..	Acting.
QUARTER MASTER.			
Ensign Thomas Hoban, - *V,*	12 *Jan.* 55	*ens.* 12 *Jan.* 55	
SURGEON.			
James Jackson, - - - -	19 *Nov.* 58	.. ..	On Staff employ.
ASSISTANT SURGEONS.			
Peter Nevil Jackson, - -	28 *Apl.* 54	.. ..	With Left wing.
Arthur Edwin T. Longhurst, -	4 *Dec.* 57	27 *Oct.* 54	
Charles John Kirwan, - - -	20 *Mar.* 55	.. ..	With Detacht. at Bustee.
INTERPRETER.			
Capt. H. R. Corfield, 9th N. I.			

Strength—10 Companies with 55 Sergeants—49 Corporals—19 Drummers—and 932 Privates.

English Agents—Messrs. Cox and Co.

Irish Agents—*Sir* E. R. Borough, *bart;* Armit and Co.

Calcutta Agents—Messrs. Gillanders Arbuthnot and Co.

WAR SERVICES OF THE OFFICERS OF THE 13TH REGT. OF LIGHT INFANTRY.

Sir William Gomm served in the expedition to the Helder, in 1799, including the action of the 19th Sept. at Bergen. Expedition on the coast of France and Spain, under Sir James Pulteney, in 1800. Expedition to Hanover in 1805; and that to Stralsund and Copenhagen in 1807. Campaign of 1808-9, including the battles of Roleia, Vimiera, and Corunna. Expedition to Walcheren, and siege of Flushing in 1809. Proceeded again to the Peninsula in 1810, where he served during the remainder of the war, the principal part of the time as an Assistant-Quarter-Master-General, including the battles of Busaco and Fuentes d'Onor, assault and capture of Badajoz, battle of Salamanca; action at Villa Muriel, battle of Vittoria, siege of San Sebastian, and battle of the Nive. Served also the campaign of 1815, including the battle of Waterloo. Sir William has received the Gold Cross and one Clasp for Badajoz, Salamanca, Vittoria, St. Sebastian, and Nive; and the Silver War Medal with six Clasps for Roleia, Vimiera, Corunna, Busaco, Fuentes d'Onor, and Nivelle.

Lord Mark Kerr commanded the 13th Light Infantry in the Crimea from the 30th June 1855, and was at the battle of the Tchernaya, siege and fall of Sebastopol (Medal and Clasps). Commanded the 13th Light Infantry from the 2nd Oct. 1857, in the suppression of the mutiny in India. Commanded the Column at the relief of Azimghur on the 6th April 1858, and the Regt. in the escort of a large convoy of stores and ammunition into the garrison on the 9th April and in the subsequent pursuit on the retreat of the principal portion of Koer Sing's army on the 14th April. Commanded the Column despatched for the dispersion of rebels and in the attack on and retreat from the Fort of Jugdeespore, 26th October (Wounded) near the Oude Frontier. Commanded the Regt. in the Trans Gogra Campaign including the action at Toolseepore.

Lt.-Colonel King served throughout the campaigns in Affghanistan from 1838 to 1842 inclusive, including the storm and capture of Guznee (Medal), storming the Khoord Cabool Pass, affair of Tezeen, forcing the Jugdulluck Pass, reduction of the fort of Mamoo Khail, defence of Jellalabad, and sorties on the 14th Nov. and 1st Dec. 1841, 11th March, 24th March and 1st April 1842, general action and defeat of Akbar Khan before Jellalabad (Medal), storming the heights of Jugdulluck, general action of Tezeen, and recapture of Cabool (Medal). Served in the Crimea, from 30th June 1855, and was at the siege and fall of Sebastopol (Medal and Clasp, and Knight of the Legion of Honor). Commanded the left wing of the 13th in the operations under Col. Kelly in Tirhoot and the Terai, including actions at Bootwal, March 25th and 28th, &c.

Lt. Col. Cox served in the 13th Light Infantry the campaigns of 1840, 41, and 42, in Affghanistan, and was present at the assault and capture of the town and fort of Tootumdurrah, storm of Jhoolghur, night-attack of Baboo Koosh Ghur, attack on Khardurrah, storming the Khoord Cabool Pass, affair of Tezeen, forcing the Jugdulluck Pass, reduction of the Fort of Mamoo Khail, heroic defence of Jellalabad and sorties on the 14th Nov. and 1st Dec. 1841, and 11th March, 24th March, and 1st April 1842; the general action with and defeat of the besieging force under Akbar Khan before Jellalabad on the 7th April; the storming of the Jugdulluck heights, general action at Tezeen, and recapture of Cabool, for which he has a Medal, as also another for Jellalabad. Served in the Crimea from 30th June 1855, and was at the battle of the Tchernaya, siege and fall of Sebastopol (Medal and Clasp). Commanded the left wing in Brigadier Rowcroft's Force from the 29th March 1858, including actions on the 17th and 25th April, in Command of force at the capture of the Fort of Nuggur, and an attack on the rebels at Debureah. Served as D. A. Q. M. Gen. to the Goruckpore Field Force from the 10th Oct. including actions at Dumouriergunge, 27th Nov. and 3rd Dec. and Toolseepore in the Trans Gogra Campaign (mentioned in Brig. Rowcroft's despatches Bt. Lieut. Colonel.

Major Tyler landed with the Regt. in the Crimea on the 30th June 1855, and was present at the battle of the Tchernaya, siege and fall of Sebastopol (Medal and Clasp, and Knight of the Legion of Honor). Commanded the rear guard at the relief of Azimghur on the 6th April 58, and the left wing at the action at Dumouriergunge and was present at Toolseepore in the Trans Gogra Campaign.

Major Jones landed with the Regiment in the Crimea on the 30th June 55, and was at the battle of the Tchernaya, and seige of Sebastopol. (Medal and Clasp).

Captains Montgomery, King, Boyd, Bainbrigge, Long, Rowley, Chichester, and Lieut. Segrave landed with the Regt. in the Crimea on the 30th June 1855, and were at the battle of the Tchernaya, siege and fall of Sebastopol (Medal and Clasp.) Capts. Montgomery, and Long have the 5th Order of the Medjidie. Captain Rowley served with the left wing under Brigadier Rowcroft including actions on the 17th and 25th April and at Nuggur at Hurreah, (as Orderly Officer to Col. Byng, 18th June) at Debureah, Amorah, Jugdeespore, Dumouriergunge and Toolseepore.

Captain Boyd was present at the relief of Azimghur and the subsequent operations in that district and at Bhanpore, Dumouriergunge and Toolseepore.

Capt. Browne commanded detachment of troops in an attack and defeat of Rebels at Bhanpore; was present at the actions at Demouriergunge, Toolseepore, &c.

Captain Twynam served with the 61st Regiment at the siege of Delhi, and with the 13th at Demouriergunge, Toolseepore, and Bootwal.

****For continuation of Services, see page* 41*b.*

1st Battalion of H. M. 19th (The 1st Yorkshire North Riding) Regiment of Foot.

"Alma"—"Inkerman"—"Sevastopol."

Facings—*Green.*

Landed in India on 16th November and 18th December, 1857.

Dinapore.

Detacht at Mozufferpore 3 Companies at *Dacca.*

Depôt of 1st Battalion, Chatham.

Rank and Names.	*Regimental Rank.*	*Army Rank.*	Remarks.
Colonel.			
Sir William Rowan, K.C.B.,	15 *June* 54	*l.g.* 20 *June* 54	In England.
Lieutenant Colonels.			
George Valentine Edward Mundy, C. B., -	19 *Sep.* 55	12 *Dec.* 54	Commanding.
Robert Onesiphorus Bright, -	28 *Nov.* 57	26 *Dec.* 56	
Majors.			
George Bingham Jennings, -	30 *Sep.* 56	... ...	On Sick Leave, (India.)
Edward Chippindall, -	28 *Nov.* 57	2 *Nov.* 56	Leave on M. C. to England to 11 July 59.
Captains.			
Hugh Francis Massy, - -	3 *Feb.* 54	.. ..	Leave to England on P. A. to 4 Oct. 1860.
Richard Doyle Barrett, -	29 *Dec.* 54		
George Clay, -	29 *Dec.* 54	.. ...	Regt. Depôt.
Charles Henry Lambert, -	14 *Sep.* 55		
Edw. Robert Ward Bayley, -	14 *Sep.* 55	.. ..	At Meerut in charge of Volunteers from 10th Foot.
Edward St. John Griffiths, -	24 *July* 57		
Ames Goren, -	29 *Nov.* 57	... ..	Detach at Mozufferpore.
Edwin Fletcher Foster, - -	9 *Mar.* 58	.. ..	En-route to join..
Frederick M. Alison, -	13 *Apl.* 58	*m* 28 *Apl.* 59	A. D. C. to Commander-in-Chief.
3 George Forbes, - -	... ...		With detachment at Dacca.
Thos. Conway Lloyd, -	13 *July* 58	24 *Apl.* 55	Regtl Depôt, England.
2 Francis Davis, -	24 *Dec.* 58	.. ...	Ditto.
R. C. Martin			
Lieutenants.			
Godfrey Baldwin, -	8 *Dec.* 54	.. ..	Instructor of Musketry.
Edward William Evans, -	8 *Dec.* 54		
Thomas Thompson, -	12 *Jan.* 55	.. ..	Adjutant.
Henry John Browne, -	17 *Feb.* 55	.. ..	Regt. Depôt.
Richard Molesworth, -	9 *Mar.* 55		
James Robert Dalton, -	9 *Mar.* 55		
Chas. Vincent Hiffernan, -	15 *Sep.* 55	.. ..	Detach at Mozafferpore
William Henry Moffatt, -	12 *Dec.* 56	.. ..	Ditto at Dacca.
Alexander Brooke Morgan, *V,*	28 *Nov.* 57	.. ..	Acting Quarter Master at Mozufferpore
Henry Thompson, *P.H.,*	26 *Mar.* 58	.. ..	Adjt. to the Bijnour Rajpoot Levy.
Fred. George Frith, -	4 *Nov.* 58	.. ..	With detachment at Dacca.
George F. Vesey, -	24 *Dec.* 58		
R. Briscoe			
Ensigns.			
William Bennett, -	26 *Mar.* 58		
John C. Taylor Humphrey, -	27 *Mar.* 58		
Horace Arthur Wells, -	24 *Apl.* 58		
Augustus M. Handley, - - -	2 *July* 58	... ..	En route to Join.
Jas. Francis Feaser, - -	3 *July* 58	.. ..	Ditto.
Fransis Herbert Evans, -	4 *July* 58	.. ...	Regt. Depot.
Robert Gayer Traill, -	16 *July* 58	... ...	Ditto.
Cortlandt Skinner, -	6 *Aug.* 58	... ...	Ditto.
C. Charles Barrow Tribe, -	19 *Nov.* 58	.. ..	Ditto.

1st Battn. of H. M. 19th (the 1st Yorkshire North Riding) Regt. of Foot.—*(Continued.)*

Rank and Names.	*Regimental Rank.*	*Army Rank.*	Remarks.
Instructer Musketry.			
Lieut. Godfrey Baldwin, - -	8 *Dec.* 54		
Pay Master.			
Thomas Palmer, - -	7 *Dec.* 55		
Adjutant.			
Lieut. Thomas Thompson, -	21 *Sep.* 55	*lt.* 12 *Jan.* 55	
Quarter Master.			
Lieut. A. B. Margan, - -	17 *June* 58	.. ..	Acting.
Surgeon.			
Henry Fowle Smith, M. D. - -	31 *Dec.* 58		
Assistant Surgeons.			
William Marshall Webb, - -	28 *Mar.* 54	.. ..	With detachment at Dacca.
Exham Long Hiffernan, - -	16 *June* 54		
James Castor Smith, - -	1 *Sep.* 54		
Interpreter.			
Lieut. H. C. Smith, 9th N. I.,	13 *Jan.* 59		

Strength—10 Companies with 56 Sergeants,—50 Corporals;—21 Drummers—and 963 Privates.

English Agents—Messrs. Cox and Co.

Calcutta Agents—Messrs. Wm. Spink and Co.

WAR SERVICES OF THE OFFICERS OF H. M. 19th REGT. OF FOOT.

Sir William Rowan served with the 52nd Regt. in Sicily in 1806-7; on the expedition to Sweden in 1808; in Portugal and Spain under Sir John Moore, from August 1808 to the embarkation of the Army at Corunna, at the bombardment and capture of Flushing in 1809; in Portugal in 1811, including the action at Sabugal; in the Peninsula and South of France, from January 1813 to the end of the war including the battles of Vittoria and the Pyrenees; attack of the entrenched camp at Vera during the passage of the Bidassoa River; attack of the fortified positions of La Rhune and Sarre during the passage of the river Nivelle; battle on passing the river Nive, and attack by the French of the heights of Arcanguez; battles of Orthes and Toulouse, and intermediate affairs. Served also the campaign of 1815, and was present at the battle of Waterloo and capture of Paris, when he was appointed Commandant of the first arrondissement of that city. Promoted to Brevet-Major for the battle of Orthes, and Brev. Lieut.-Col. for services in the field. He has received the War Medal with six Clasps.

Lieut.-Colonel Mundy served in the Coldstream Guards during the Canadian Rebellion in 1838-39. Served in the 33rd Regt. throughout the Eastern campaign of 1854-55, including the battles of Alma (horse shot) and Inkerman (commanded the Regt.), siege and fall of Sebastopol (severely wounded in the trenches), attack on the Rifle Pits 19th April, and that of the Redan on the 18th June—wounded (Medal with three Clasps, C. B., Brevet Lt.-Colonel, Knight of the Legion of Honor, Sardinian Medal, and order of the Medjidie).

Lt.-Col. Bright served the Eastern campaign of 1854-55, including the battles of Alma and Inkerman, siege of Sebastopol, and storming of the Redan on the 8th Sept. (Medal and Clasps, and Knight of the Legion of Honor).

Major Jennings served the Eastern campaign of 1854 (Medal and Clasp).

Major Chippindall served with the 32nd Regt. during the latter part of the siege operations before Mooltan, and was present at the surrender of that Fortress; also at the surrender of the Fort and Garrison of Cheniote, and at the battle of Goojerat (Medal and Clasps). Served the Eastern campaign of 1854-55, with the 19th Regt., including the affair of Bulgunak, battles of Alma and Inkerman, in the trenches during the whole of the siege operations before Sebastopol, assaults of the Redan on the 18th June and 8th Sept.,—wounded. Appointed Major of Brigade 2nd Brigade Light Division, 1st April 56: (Medal and clasps, Brevet Major, and Knight of the Legion of Honor. Order of Medjidie).

Capt. Massy served in the Eastern campaign (Medal and Clasp for Sebastopol).

Captains Barrett and Clay served the Eastern campaign of 1854 and part of 1855, including the battles of Alma and Inkerman, and siege of Sebastopol (Medal and Clasps).

Captain Bayley served the Eastern campaign of 1854-55, including the battle of Alma, siege of Sebastopol (wounded,) and storming of the Redan: wounded (Medal and Clasps, Sardinian Medal. Order of the Medjidie).

Capt. Goren served in 1854-55, at the battle of Inkerman, siege of Sebastopol (wounded), and storming of the Redan on the 8th Sept.: dangerously wounded (Medal and Clasps, Order of the Medjidie).

Captain Forbes and Lieut. Browne served at the latter part of the siege of Sebastopol, and at the assault on the Redan on the 8th Sept. (Medal and Clasp).

Lieut. Evans served in 1855 at the siege of Sebastopol (severely wounded), and at the storming of the Redan on the 8th Sept. (Medal and Clasp).

Lieut. Thompson served the Eastern campaign of 1854 and part of 1855 including the battles of Alma (carried the colours) and Inkerman and siege of Sebastopol (Medal and Clasps and Sardinian Medal).

Lieut. Molesworth served in the Crimea from May 1855, and was engaged in the attack on the Quarries 7th June, and in the attacks of the Redan on 18th June and 8th Sept. (severely wounded): Medal and Clasp.

Paymaster Palmer and Assist.-Surg. Webb served the Eastern campaign of 1854-55, including the battles of Alma and Inkerman, siege and fall of Sebastopol (Medal and Clasps).

Assist.-Surgeon Hiffernan served the Eastern campaign of 1854-55, including the battles of Alma and Inkerman and siege of Sebastopol (Medal and Clasps).

Assist.-Surgeon J. C. Smith served with the 21st Regt. during 1855 at the siege and fall of Sebastopol, and expedition to Kinbourn (Medal and Clasp.)

1st Battalion of H. M. 20th (the East Devonshire) Regiment of Foot.

"Minden"—"Egmont-op-Zee"—The *Sphinx*, with the words "Egypt"—"Maida"—"Vimiera"—"Corunna"—"Vittoria"—"Pyrenees"—"Orthes"—"Toulouse"—"Peninsula"—"Alma"—"Inkerman"—"Sevastopol."

Facings—*Yellow.*

Landed in India from England, 19th November 1859.

Camp Gonda Oude.

Regimental Depôt, Chatham.

Rank and Names.	*Regimental Rank.*	*Army Rank.*	Remarks.
Colonel.			
Marcus Beresford, - -	22 *Sep.* 58	*m.g.* 20 *June* 54	Commanding a Division in Madras.
Lieutenant Colonels.			
Fred. Chas. Evelegh, C. B., - -	11 *May* 55	*col.* 12 *May* 58	Leave to England to 31st Dec, 60.
John Cormick, - -	12 *Feb.* 59	.. ...	Commanding.
Majors.			
Charles Richard Butler, - -	3 *Oct.* 56	*l.c.* 26 *Apl.* 59	Leave of Absence on M. C. to 8 May [60
Edward Allan Holditch, C. B., -	26 *Mar.* 58	*col.* 28 *Nov.* 54	
Captains.			
Aug. Riversdale Warren, - -	1 *May* 55	.. ..	Leave of Absence to England on P. A. to 25 Sep. 60.
Thomas Casey Lyons, - V	27 *July* 55	*m.* 26 *Apl.* 59	Leave to Mussoorie on P. A. to 15. Oct. 59.
George Edward Francis, - -	31 *July* 57	.. ..	Leave on M. C. to England.
Fred. Lockwood Edridge, - -	7 *Aug.* 57		
J. T. Nicolls O'Brien, *PH*,(*a*) -	12 *Feb.* 58	*m.* 26 *Apl.* 59	Assistant Engineer at Peshawur.
B. Davies, - -	.. ..	.. ..	Regimental Depôt.
Hector Barlow Vaughan, - -	26 *Mar.* 58		
John James S. O'Neill, *V.* - -	3 *June* 58	.. ..	Instructor of Musketry.
H. E Quin, *V.* (*a*) - - -	24 *Dec.* 58	.. ..	En-route to join.
W. Fraser Forbes Gordon, - -	24 *Dec.* 58		
William David Nunn, - -	21 *May* 59		
Lieutenants.			
Edward Aug. Patrickson, - -	11 *May* 55	.. ..	Convalescent Depot, Nynee Tal.
Francis George Holmes, - -	15 *June* 55		
Hon. Adolp. E. P. Vereker, - -	16 *Oct.* 55	.. ..	Leave to England on P. A. for 18 [months.
George Blair Duffin, - -	16 *Oct.* 55		
George Gethin, - -	16 *Oct.* 55		
J. C. Cox, - - - - - -	.. ..	.. ..	Regimental Depôt.
Owen Tudor Burne, - *H,*	10 *Apl.* 58	.. ..	Adjutant.
Conroy Fahie, - -	10 *Apl.* 58		
R. Blonn, - -	.. ..	.. ..	En-route to Depôt.
Fred. Gowland Horn, - -	15 *June* 58	.. ..	
N. R. Gwynne, - -	... ...	.. ..	Regimental Depôt.
Frederick Mansel, - -	10 *Sep.* 68		
William Unwin, - -			
Ensigns.			
G. E. Bolger, - -	1 *Mar.* 58		
George R. Gibbs, - -	25 *June* 58	.. ..	En-route to join.
James Smith, - -	2 *July* 58	.. ..	Chatham Depôt, England.
Cliff. Gabourel Gibaut, - -	3 *July* 58	.. ..	Ditto,
Ed, Alex. Hawtrey Parks, - .	6 *Aug.* 58	.. .	Ditto.
George F. Harris, - -	31 *Dec.* 58	.. ..	Ditto.
George Dancan Wahab, - -	28 *Jan.* 59	.. ..	Ditto.
C. S. Elliot, - -	.. ..	.. ..	Ditto,
C. E. Massey, - -	.. ..	.. ..	Ditto,

(*a*) Has passed the examination in Civil Engineering and Surveying.

H. M. 20TH (THE EAST DEVONSHIRE) REGIMENT OF FOOT.—(*Continued.*)

RANK AND NAMES.	*Regimental Rank*	*Army Rank.*	REMARKS.
INSTRUCTOR OF MUSKETRY.			
Capt. John J. S. O'Neill, - -	4 *Dec.* 57		
PAYMASTER.			
Capt. John Matthew Gibbs, -	4 *Dec.* 57	c. 19 *Oct.* 49	
ADJUTANT.			
Lieut. Owen Tudor Burne, -	17 *Nov.* 58	lt. 10 *Apl.* 58	
QUARTER MASTER.			
William Smith, - -	23 *Mar.* 59		
SURGEON.			
Edward Howard, - -	24 *Feb.* 54	.. ..	Absent without leave.
J. C. Haverty, - - - - -	24 *Apr.* 58	.. ..	Doing Duty.
ASSISTANT SURGEONS.			
Henry Kelsall, - *V.*	8 *Sep.* 55		
John Munday, - -	4 *Feb.* 56		
W. A. Mackinnon, - -	.. ..	.. ..	Calcutta.
INTERPRETER.			
Lieut. H. D. Metcalfe 25 N. J.	26 *Mar.* 58		

Strength—10 Companies with 53 Sergeants,—46 Corporals—20 Drummers—and 885 Privates.

English Agents.—Messrs. Cox and Co.

Calcutta Agents.—Messrs. Wood, Oliffe and Co.

WAR SERVICES OF THE OFFICERS OF THE 1ST BATTN. H. M. 20TH REGIMENT OF FOOT.

Col. Evelegh C. B., served in the Eastern campaign of 1854-55 with the 20th Regt., including the battles of Alma, Balaklava, and Inkerman (brought the Regt. out of action), siege and capture of Sebastopol; commanded the Regt. at the capture of Kinbourn (Medal and Clasps, Brevet Lt.-Col. Knight of the Legion of Honor. and 4th class of the order of the Medjidie,) Served in the Oudh campaign of 1857-58. Appointed as Brigadier, 2nd class to the Jaunpore field Force and was present at the Battles of "Churda, Ameerapore" and Sultanpore" siege and capture of Lucknow, (Medal and Clasp) Subsequently appointed to field force at Nawabgunge, Cawnpore Road, and commanded at the Battles of Mohun Hussengunge, Meangunge, Morar Mow capture of Simree. Actions of Beerah and Buxar-Ghat; afterwards commanded a special field Force as Brigadier of the 2nd class and was engaged at the capture of Oomreah—(Repeatedly thanked in General Orders.)

Lieut. Col. Cormick was present with the 40th Regt. in the actions of Marajpore, 20th Decr. 1843, under Genl. Lord Gough, (Medal;) served with the 18th Royal Irish in the Burmah Campaign of 1852-53, including the capture of Martaban Rangoon and Prome (under General Goodwin) Medal; also the siege of Sebastopol from December 1854, (under General Lord Raglin) and was wounded 18th June 1855, (Medal and Clasp and Bt. Major,) also commanded a field Force in the operation in Oudh against the Rebels in the beginning of 1859, (thanked in General Orders.)

Major Butler served in the Eastern campaign of 1854-55, including the battles of Alma, Balaklava, and Inkerman, (severely wounded), siege and capture of Sebastopol, sortie of 23rd March, and affair of 18th June (Medal and Clasps, Brevet Major, Knight of the Legion of Honor and 5th class of the order of the Medjidie) also in the Oudh campaign of 1857-58 and was present at the Battles of Chanda, Ameerpore and Sultanpore; siege and capture of Lucknow (Medal and clasp) affairs of Churdah and capture of Fort Musjeedia under General Lord Clyde, (Appointed Bt. Lt. Col.)

Colonel Holditch C. B. served as Aide-de-Camp to Sir Harry Smith throughout the campaign on the Sutlej (Medal and Clasps), was present at the battles of Moodkee, Ferozeshah (wounded), Buddiwal, Aliwal, and Sobraon (severely wounded). He served also as Aide-de-Camp to Sir Harry in the actions with and defeat of the Rebel Boers at Boem Plaats (South Africa) 29 Aug. 1848; and in the Kaffir campaign of 1850 to 1852 (Medal). He served with the 80th Regiment in the Burmese war of 1853 (Medal), and was with the expedition under Sir John Cheape against the Rebel chief Myattoon, and succeeded to the command of the right wing at the assault and capture of his stronghold on the 19th March, (appointed a C. B.)

Captain Warren served at the siege of Sebastopol (Medal and Clasp); also was present at the capture of Kinbourn (5th Class of the order of the Medijdie) also in the Oudh Campaign of 1857-58, including the Battles of Chanda, Ameerapore, and Sultanpore; siege and capture of Lucknow (wounded) Medal and Clasp, and the affairs of Mohun and Meangunge, Churdah and capture of Fort Musjeedia and Bankee under General Lord Clyde.

Captain Lyons, served in the Oudh Campaign of 1857-58, commanded the Marksmen of the Regiment at the Battles of Chanda, Ameerapore and Sultanpore; attack of Fort Dhouraha when he assisted in bringing off two guns, siege and capture of Lucknow (Medal and Clasp) affairs of Mohun; commanded 4 companies of the Regiment at Morar Mow Brigade Major in the Trans Gogra campaign of 1858, including the capture of "Oomreah" under Brigadier Evelegh C. B. (mentioned in Despatches.)

Captain Francis, served in the Oudh campaign of 1857-58, including the Battles of Chanda, Ameerapore and Sultanpore siege and capture of Lucknow, (Medal and Clasp.)

Captain Edridge served in the operations in the Northern frontier of Oudh during the latter part of 1858-1859, (Mentioned in Despatches).

Captain O'Brien served in the Oudh campaign of 1858, as Deputy Assistant Quarter Master General under Brigadier Wetherall C. B.

Captain Vaughan served in the Eastern campaign of 1854-55, including the battles of the Alma, Balaklava, and Inkerman, siege and capture of Sebastopol and the affair of the 18th June; also present at the capture of Kinbourn, (Medal and clasps and Sardinian War Medal, and 5th Class of the order of the Medjidie,) served in the Oudh campaign of 1857-58-59, including the battles of Chanda, Ameerapore and Sultanpore, siege and capture of Lucknow, (Medal and Clasp) and also at the affairs of Churdah, capture of Fort Musjeedia and Bankee under General Lord Clyde, and subsequent operations against the Rebels in the northern frontier of Oudh (Thanked in General Orders.)

*** *For continuation of Services see next page.*

WAR SERVICES OF THE OFFICERS OF H. M. 20TH REGT. OF FOOT,—(*Continued.*)

Capt. O'Neil served at the siege of Sebastopol including the affair of the 18th June (wounded); also present at the capture of Kinbourn (Medal and Clasp) also served in the Oudh campaign of 1857-58-59, including the Battles of Chanda, Ameerpore and Sultanpore, siege and capture of Lucknow (Medal and Clasp) and the affairs of Meangunge; served as Brigade Major to Brigadier Evelegh C. B. at the affairs of Beerah and Buxar Ghat, was also present at the affairs of Churdah and capture of fort Musjeedia under Genl. Lord Clyde, and subsequent operations in the Northern frontier of Oudh.

Captain Gordon served in the Oude campaign of 1857-1858-1859, including the Battles of Chanda Ameerapore, Sultanpore and attack of fort Dowraha; siege and capture of Lucknow (Medal and Clasp, thanked in despatches) was present at the affairs of Meangunge and also at Churdah and capture of fort Musjeedia under Genl Lord Clyde, and subsequent operations in the Northern frontier of Oude.

Capt. Nunn served at the siege of Sebastopol, and also the capture of Kinbourn (Medal and Clasp) also served in the Oude campaign of 1857-58-59, including the battles of Chanda, Ameerapore and Sultanpore, siege and capture of Lucknow (Medal and Clasp) also at Mohun Hussingunge and Meangunge (as Orderly officer to Brigr. Evelegh, C. B.) was present at the affairs of Churdah and capture of fort Musjeedia and Bankee (under Genl. Lord Clyde) and subsequent operations in the Northern frontier of Oude.

Lieutenant Patrickson served in the Oude campaign of 1857-58, including the battles of Chanda, Ameerapore and Sultanpore, siege and capture of Lucknow (Medal and Clasp) affairs of Simree Beerah and Buxar-Ghat, and of Churdah, capture of Musjeedia and Bankee under Genl. Lord Clyde.

Lieut. Holmes served at the siege of Sebastopol (Medal and Clasp), including the affair of the 18th June (wounded) also present at the capture of Kinbourn, served in the Oudh campaign of 1857-58-59, including the Battles of Chanda. Ameerapore and Sultanpore, siege and capture of Lucknow (Medal and Clasp) affairs of Mohun, Meangunge, Morar-mow (as Orderly Officer to Bridgr. Evelegh, C. B.) was present also at the affair of Simree, Beerah and Buxar-Ghat, Churdah and capture of Fort Simree, and Bankee under General Lord Clyde, and subsequent operations in the Northern frontier of Oude.

Lieut *Hon.* Vereker served at the siege of Sebastopol, (Medal and Clasp), present at the capture of Kinburn, also served in the Oude campaign of 1857-58-9, including the battles of Chanda, Ameerapore, Sultanpore and attack of Fort Dowraha, siege and capture of Lucknow, (Medal and Clasp), affairs of Churdah, capture of Fort Musjeedia and Bankee under General Lord Clyde, and subsequent operations in the Northern Frontier of Oude.

Lieut. Duffin served in the Oude campaign of 1857-58, including the battles of Chanda, Ameerapore. and Sultanpore, siege and capture of Lucknow, (Medal and Clasp), affairs of Simree, Beerah and Buxar Ghat, Churdah, capture of fort Musjeedia and Bankee under Genl. Lord Clyde.

Lieut. Gethin served in the Oude campaign of 1857-58-59, including the battles of Chanda, Ameerapore and Sultanpore, siege and capture of Lucknow, (Medal and Clasp), affairs of Meangunge Churdah and capture of Musjeedia under Genl. Lord Clyde, and subsequent operations in the Northern fron ier of Oude.

Lieut. Fahie served in the Oude campaign of 1857-58-59, including the battles of Chanda, Ameerapore and Sultanpore, siege and capture of Lucknow, (Medal and Clasp), affairs of Churdah and capture of fort Musjeedia under Genl. Lord Clyde. and subsequent operations in the Northern frontier of Oude.

Lieut. Horn served in the Oude campaign of 1858-59. including the affairs of Churdah and capture of Fort Musjeedia under Genl. Lord Clyde and subsequent operations in the Northern Frontier of Oude.

Lieut. Mansel served in the Oude campaign of 1858-59, including the affairs of Mohun and Meangunge, Churdah and capture of Fort of Musjeedia under Genl. Lord Clyde, and subsequent operations in the Northern frontier of Oude.

Lieut. Unwin served in the Eastern campaign of 1854-55, including the battles of Alma, Balaklava and Inkerman, siege and capture of Sebastopol (Medal and Clasps), and was present at the capture of Kinburn, also served in the Oude campaign of 1857-58, including the battles of Chanda. Ameerapore, and Sultanpore, siege and capture of Lucknow (Medal and Clasp) affairs of Churdah and capture of Fort Musjeedia under Genl. Lord Clyde.

Pay Master Gibbs served in the Oude campaign of 1858, and was present at the capture of Lucknow, (Medal and Clasp) affairs of Churdah and capture of fort Musjeedia, under Genl. Lord Clyde.

Lieut. and Adjutant Burne served in the Oude campaign of 1857-58-59, as Brigade Quarter Master and Brigade Major to Brigadier Evelegh C. B. and was present at the battles of Chanda, Ameerapore and Sultanpore, siege and capture of Lucknow (Medal and Clasp) affairs of Mohun, Hussengunge, Meangunge, Morar-Mow and capture of fort Simree, was present also as Adjutant of the Regiment at Churdah and capture of fort Musjeedia under Genl. Lord Clyde, and subsequent operations in the Northern frontier of Oude (several times mentioned in despatches.)

Qr. Mr. Smith served with the 29th Regt. in the Sutlej campaign in 1845, and was severely wounded at the battle of Ferozshah, (Medal) served also in the Punjaub campaign of 1848-49, including the passage of the Chenab and battles of Chillinwallah and Goojerat, (Medal and 2 clasps).

Surgeon Howard served in the Eastern campaign of 1854-55, including the battles of Alma and Inkerman, siege and capture of Sebastopol, and assault of the 8th Sept. (Medal and Clasps) 5th class of the order of the Medjidie, also served in the Oude campaign of 1857-58, including the battles of Chanda, Ameerapore and Sultanpore siege and capture of Lucknow, (Medal and Clasps).

Asst. Surgn. Kelsall served in the Oude campaign of 1857-58-59, including the battles of Chanda, Ameerapore and Sultanpore, siege and capture of Lucknow, (Medal and Clasp) affairs of Meangunge, Morar-mow Simree Beerah and Buxar-Ghat, Churdah, capture of fort Musjeedia and Bankee under Gen. Lord Clyde, and subsequent operations in the Northern frontier of Oude.

Asst. Surgn. Munday served in the Oude campaign of 1857-58-59, including the battles of Chandah, Ameerapore and Sultanpore, siege and capture of Lucknow, (Medal and Clasp) affairs of Hussengunge and Meangunge, Churdah and capture of Fort Musjeediah under Genl. Lord Clyde and subsequent operations in the Northern frontier of Oude.

CONTINUATION OF SERVICES OF THE OFFICERS OF 13TH REGT. OF LIGHT INFY.—*From page* 37.

Captains Peel, and Hon. J. C. Dormer, landed with the Regt. in the Crimea on the 30th June 1855, and were at the battle of the Tchernaya, and siege of Sebastopol (Medal and Clasp). Captain Peel commanded the rear guard in the retreat from Jugdeespore; was present at Toolseepore and in the actions at Bootwal, March 25th and 28th.

Captain Dormer was present at the relief of Azimghur (Staff Officer) and the subsequent operations in that District as A. D. C. to the Commander-in-Chief in the Oude Campaign in 1858.

Captain Straubenzee served the campaigns of 1840, 41, and 42, in Affghanistan with the 13th Light Infantry, including the assault and capture of the town and forts of Tootumdurrah, storm of Jhoolghur, night-attack at Baboo Koosh Ghur, destruction of Khardurrah, assault of Perwandurrah, storming the Khoord Cabool Pass, affair of Tezeen, forcing the Jugdulluck Pass, reduction of the fort of Mamoo Khail, heroic defence of Jellalabad, and sorties on the 14th Nov. and 1st December, 1841, 11th March, 24th March and 1st April 1842. General action and defeat of Akbar Khan before Jellalabad (Medal), storming the heights of Jugdulluck; general action of Tezeen, and recapture of Cabool (Medal). Landed with the Regt. in the Crimea on the 30th June 1855, and was at the battle of the Tchernaya, siege and fall of Sebastopol (Medal and Clasp) and 5th Order of the Medjidie, was present with the left wing under Brig. Rowcroft and commanded the Infantry in an action at Hurreah, 18th June 58.

Lieuts. FitzGerald served at the siege and fall of Sebastopol from 3rd Sep. 1855 (Medal and Clasp) served as Orderly Officer to Col. Kelly at the action at Bootwal, &c.

Lieuts. Everett, and Gilbert, landed with the Regt. in the Crimea on the 30th June 1855, and were at the battle of Tchernaya, siege and fall of Sebastopol (Medal and Clasp).

Lieut. Everett was present at the relief of Azimghur and at Hurreah and Debureah, Dumouriergunge, Toolseepore, Bootwal.

Lieut. Gilbert was present at the relief of Azimghur, &c. at Amorah and Jugdeespore, Dumouriergunge, Toolsepore, Bootwal.

Lieut. Gillett served at the siege and fall of Sebastopol from 2nd Sept. 1855 (Medal and Clasp). Was present at Amorah, Jugdeespore, Toolseepore.

Lieut. Williams served at the siege and fall of Sebastopol from 7th Sept. 1855 (Medal and Clasp). Served at Jugdeespore (Orderly Officer) and Toolsepore.

Lieut Adair was present at the relief of Azimghur.

Lieut James was present at the relief of Azimghur, &c., at Dumouriergunge and Toolseepore.

Lieut Cox served at Amorah and Nuggur.

Lieut. Wroughton served at the relief of Azimghur (did duty with the R. A. Guns) at Hurreah, Bhanpore (Staff Officer) Dumouriergunge and Toolseepore.

Paymaster M'Naughten served with the Regt. in the Crimea on the 30th June 1855, and was at the siege and fall of Sebastopol (Medal and Clasp).

Qr.-Master Hoban served with the 13th Lt. Infantry throughout the campaigns in Affghanistan from 1838 to 1842 inclusive, and was present at the storm and capture of Ghuznee (Medal), assault and capture of the town and fort of Tootumdurrah, storm of Jhoolghur, night-attack of Baboo Koosh Ghur, destruction of Khandurrah, assault of Perwandurrah, storming of the Khoord Cabool Pass, affair of Tezeen, forcing the Jugdulluck Pass, recapture of the fort of Mamoo Khail, heroic defence of Jellalabad and sorties of 14th Nov. and 1st Dec. 1841, 24th March and 1st April 1842; general action and defeat of Akbar Khan before Jellalabad, 7th April (Medal), storming the heights of Jugdulluck, general action of Tezeen, and recapture of Cabool (Medal). Served in the Crimea from 30th June 1855, including the battle of the Tchernaya, siege and fall of Sebastopol (Medal and Clasp). Present at the relief of Azimghur, &c., at Jugdeespore and Toolseepore.

Dr. James Jackson served with the Force under Genl. Outram at the Alumbagh from the 16th January to fall of Lucknow in charge of Military Train (Medal and Clasp) also with Sir E. Lugard's Force at the 2nd relief of Azimghur, April 15, capture of Jugdeespore, several skirmishes in the jungles with rebels with the Shahabad Field Force under Brigadier Douglas, and Cavalry pursuit under Sir H. Havelock's by whom the Rebels were driven into the Khymoor Hills.

Assist. Surgeon Jackson served in the Eastern campaign of 1854-55, including the battles of Balaklava and Inkerman, and siege of Sebastopol (Medal and three Clasps). Served in charge of Left Wing at Bootwal, &c.

Assist. Surgeon Longhurst was present at Jugdeespore (in charge) and Toolseepore.

Assist.-Surgeon Kirwan served at the siege of Sebastopol from the 14th to the 30th June 1855, including the assault of the 18th June (Medal and Clasp). Present with Left Wing at Amorah and Nuggur (India).

1st Battalion of H. M. 23rd (Royal Welsh Fusiliers) Regiment of Foot.

The *Prince of Wales's Plume*, "*Ich Dien*;" the *Rising Sun*, the *Red Dragon*, the *White Horse*, "*Nec aspera terrent.*"
"Minden," the *Sphinx*, "Egypt"—"Corunna"—"Martinique"—"Albuhera"—"Badajoz"—"Salamanca"—"Vittoria"—"Pyrenees"—"Nivelle"—"Orthes"—"Toulouse"—"Peninsula"—"Waterloo"—"Alma"—"Inkerman"—"Sevastopol."
Facings—*Blue.*

Landed in India 18*th September and* 16*th November* 1857.
Lucknow.
Depôt of 1*st Battalion*, Chatham.

Rank and Names.	Regimental Rank.	Army Rank.	Remarks.
Colonel.			
Henry Rainey, C. B., K. H.,	22 *May* 55	*l.g.* 20 *June* 54	In Europe.
Lieutenant Colonels.			
Samuel Wells, C. B.,	16 *Jan.* 57	9 *May* 56	Leave on M. C. to England, to 15 July 59.
Robert Pratt, C. B.,	27 *Mar.* 57	9 *Sep.* 55	Commanding.
Majors.			
Edwd. Gascoigne Bulwer, C. B.,	26 *Jan.* 58	*l.c.* 26 *Apl.* 59	Leave to England to 30 Sept. 60.
Henry D'Oyley Torrens,	18 *Oct.* 58	*l.c.* 26 *Apl.* 59	Assist. Adjt. Genl.
Captains.			
Jervoise Clarke Jervoise,	21 *Sep.* 54	*m* 20 *July* 58	
Hon. Savage Mostyn,	8 *June* 55		
Geo. Henry John Heigham,	6 *July* 55	*m* 26 *Apl.* 59	
Chas. G. Campbell, Norton,	7 *Sep.* 55	.. ...	Leave of absence to England on P. A. for 18 months.
~~Herbert Delmé Radcliffe~~,	1 *May* 57		
Charles Monsell,	26 *Mar.* 58	8 *Dec.* 54	Commandant Depot Bat. Lucknow.
Tho. Bernard Hackett, *	26 *Jan.* 58		
Wm. Munning Lees,	26 *Mar.* 58	18 *Aug.* 48	Comdg. Regimental Depôt, England.
Donald Maclean Fraser,	2 *July* 58	26 *Mar.* 58	Leave of absence to Australia for 18 months.
Luke O'Connor,*	24 *Aug.* 58		
Hon. Nathiniel Fiennes,	18 *Oct.* 55	.. ..	Chatham Depôt, England.
R. P. Armstrong,	7 *Sep.* 58	.. ..	En route to join.
James Williamson,	.. ..	.. ..	Instructor of Musketry.
Lieutenants.			
John Lawrence,	9 *Mar.* 55	.. ..	Convalescent Depot, Kussowlie.
Chas. Fred. Gregorie,	30 *June* 55	... ..	Adjutant. Leave of absence to England on P. A. for 18 months.
Philip Henry Knight,	9 *Sep.* 55	.. ..	Acting Adjt.
John Tilly,	9 *Sep.* 55		
Edwin Utterton,	10 *Sep.* 55	.. ...	Leave of absence to England on P. A. for 18 months.
W. Dowdeswell Bloxsome,	30 *Sep.* 55		
Geo. Fred. Russell Colt,	13 *Oct.* 58		
Arch. R. Winstanley,	13 *Oct.* 58		
Fred. Gerrard,	18 *Oct.* 58	.. ..	Regimental Depôt.
Lorenzo G. Lysons,	26 *Oct.* 58	.. ..	Ditto.
J. Twyford,	12 *Feb.* 59		
Henry Edmund Stanley,	18 *Jan.* 59	.. ..	Chatham Depot.
Ensigns.			
Henry John Tulloch,	30 *Apl.* 58	.. ...	Leave on M. C. to Hills North of Deyrah to 12 October 59.
Nicholas Gosselin,	4 *June* 58		
Fras. Palmer Jones,	4 *June* 58		
Thomas James Bowyer,	6 *June* 58	.. ..	Chatham Depôt, England.
Henry Fred. Seagram,	7 *June* 58	.. ...	En route to join.
Rob. Albert Evans Haye,	8 *June* 58	.. ...	Regimental Depôt.
Robert Cæsar Bacon,	13 *July* 58		
James Clayton,	30 *July* 58		
Francis Edward Dowler	29 *Oct.* 58		
Henry F. Hutton,	1 *Apl.* 59		

* Victori Cross.

1st Battalion of H. M. 23rd (Royal Welsh Fusiliers) Regiment of Foot.—*(Continued)*

Rank and Names.	*Regimental Rank.*	*Army Rank.*	Remarks.
Instructor of Musketry.			
Capt. James Williamson, - -	1 *Nov.* 56		
Pay Master.			
Thomas Newton Young, - -	7 *Dec.* 58		
Adjutant.			
Lieut. Charles Fred. Gregorie, -	22 *May* 57	*lt.* 30 *June* 55	Leave to England.
Phillip Hervoy Knight. - -	... ..	.. ..	Acting
Quarter Master.			
Michael O'Donnell, - -	26 *Jan.* 59		
Surgeon.			
Patrick Sinclair Laing, - -	29 *Dec.* 57	6 *Jan.* 54	
Assist. Surgeons.			
Hy. Thos. Sylvester, M. D.,* -	22 *Sep.* 54	3 *Mar.* 54	
Charles Fred. Morris, - -	2 *Feb.* 55	.. ..	
John Noble Shipton, - -	20 *Mar.* 57	23 *Mar.* 55	
Interpreter.			
Ens. H. U. Smith 46th N I., -			

* Victoria Cross.

Strength—10 Companies with 56 Sergeants,—50 Corporals,—21 Drummers—and 1040 Privates.

English Agents.—Messrs. Cox and Co.
Calcutta Agents.—Messrs. Grindlay and Co.

WAR SERVICES OF H. M. 23rd REGIMENT OF FOOT.

Lieut.-General Rainey served with the 82nd at the siege and capture of Copenhagen in 1807: with Sir Brent Spencer's expedition off the coast of Spain, and at Cadiz on surrender of the French fleet: from thence joined Sir Arthur Wellesley's army at Mondego Bay, and was afterwards present at the battles of Roleia, Vimiera, and Corunna, also the retreat under Sir John Moore. Accompanied the Regiment to Walcheren in 1809, and was present at the surrender of Middleburgh, siege and capture of Flushing. Joined the army in the Peninsula in May 1812, and served as Aide-de-Camp to Sir Thomas Bradford during the siege of the Forts of Salamanca, battle of Salamanca, capture of Madrid, siege of Burgos, and retreat therefrom. Served afterwards in the Portuguese service in advance through the Trasos-Montes in 1813, at the battle of Vittoria, actions of Villa Franca and Toloso, storm of the fortified convent in front of San Sebastian, at both the sieges and storm of San Sebastian, passage of the Bi lassoa, battle of the Nivelle, battles of the Nive on the 9th and 10th Dec.—severely wounded: wounded also at the siege of San Sebastian. Served in France with the army of Occupation from the capitulation of Paris in 1815 to the end of 1818. He has received the war Medal with eight Clasps.

Lt.-Colonel Pratt served with the 41st throughout the campaign of 1842 in Affghanistan (Medal), and was present in the engagements with the enemy on the 28th April in the Pisheen Valley; in those of the 29th May near Candahar, 30th Aug. at Goine, 5th Sept. before Ghuznee; at the occupation and destruction of that Fortress and of Cabool, the expedition into Kohistan, storm, capture, and destruction of Istaliff, and the various minor affairs in and between the Bolan and the Khyber Passes. Served at the siege of Sebastopol, was present at the attacks of the Redan on the 18th June and 8th Sept.—wounded (Medal and Clasp, and Brevet of Lieut.-Col. dated 2 Nov. 1855, and Sardinian Medal).

Lt.-Colonel Bulwer served in the Eastern campaign of 1854-55, including the battles of Alma and Inkerman, and siege of Sebastopol (Medal and three Clasps).

Lt.-Colonel Torrens served in the Eastern campaign as Aide-de-Camp to Brig.-General Torrens, including the battle of Inkerman (wounded) and siege of Sebastopol; was appointed D. A. Q. M. Gen. at Head Quarters in Feb. 1855, and served in that capacity until the end of the war, having been present at both attacks on the Redan (Medal and Clasps, Brevet Major, and Knight of the Legion of Honor),

Captain *Hon.* S. Mostyn served at the siege of Sebastopol in 1855, including the attack of the Redan on the 18th June (Medal and Clasp).

Capt. Radcliffe served at the siege of Sebastopol from Feb. 1855, including the attacks of the Redan on the 18th June and 8th Sept.—wounded (Medal and Clasp).

Capt. Monsell served the Eastern campaign of 1854-55, including the battle of Alma and Balaklava, siege and fall of Sebastopol, and both attacks on the Redan (Medal and Clasps).

Capt. Hackett served at the siege of Sebastopol from June 1855, including the assault of the Redan on the 18th June (Medal and Clasp).

Capt. O'Connor served the Eastern campaign of 1854-55 including the battle of Alma (severely wounded) and Inkerman, siege and fall of Sebastopol, attack on the Quarries and assaults of the 18th June and 8th Sept.—dangerously wounded (Medal and Clasps, Victoria Cross and Sardinian Medal).

Capt. *Hon.* N. Fiennes served at the siege and fall of Sebastopol from 17th June 1855, including assaults of the Redan on the 18th June and 8th Sept.—(Medal and Clasp).

Capt. Williamson, served at the siege and fall of Sebastopol in 1855, including the assault of the Redan on 8th Sept.—severely wounded (Medal and Clasp).

Lieuts. Lawrence, and Utterton served at the siege and fall of Sebastopol in 1855, including the assault on the Redan on 8th Sept. (Medal and Clasp).

Assist-Surg. Sylvester served at the siege of Sebastopol (Medal and Clasp, Victoria cross and Knight of the Legion of Honor.)

Assist--Surgeon Morris served at the siege of Sebastopol in 1855 (Medal and Clasp).

* Victoria Cross.

1st Battalion of H. M. 24th (or the 2nd Warwickshire) Regt. of Foot.

The Sphinx *with* "Egypt,"—"Cape of Good Hope"—"Talavera" "Fuentes d'Onor"—"Salamanca"—"Vittoria"—"Pyrenees"—"Nivelle" "Orthes"—"Peninsula"—"Punjaub"—"Chillianwalla"—"Goojerat."

Facings—*Green.*

Landed in Bengal, from England, on the 27th August 1846.

Ferozepore.

Regimental Depôt, Chatham.

Rank and Names.	*Regimental Rank.*	*Army Rank.*	Remarks.
Colonel.			
Hon'ble John Finch, c. b. *P,*	19 *June* 56	*l.g.* 20 *Feb.* 55	In Europe.
Lieutenant Colonels.			
William Gustavus Brown, - -	21 *Dec.* 49	*col.* 28 *Nov.* 54	Brigadier Commdg. at Lahore.
Augustus George Blachford, -	30 *Mar.* 58	*col.* 28 *Nov.* 54	Commanding.
Majors.			
Edmund Wodehouse, - - -	8 *Aug.* 51	*l. c.* 12 *Dec.* 57	Leave on P A. to Simla, six months,
John Henry Lutman, - - -	17 *Apl.* 58	.. ..	Lv. on M. C. to Simla, to 3rd Aug. 59.
Captains.			
Francis Charles Skurray, - -	14 *Jan.* 49	.. ..	Leave on P. A. to England.
Andrew John Macpherson, -	14 *Jan.* 49	*m* 19 *Jan.* 59	Comdg. 22nd Punjab Infy.—Leave on M. C. to England.
George Frederick Berry, *P. H,* -	20 *Oct.* 49	.. ..	Leave on M. C. to England.
J. Bulkeley Thelwall, c.b. *PH, (a)*	21 *Dec.* 49	*m* 26 *Apl.* 58	Comdg. 9th Punjaub Infantry.
Henry Macdonald Burns, - -	20 *July* 56		
William Winniett, - - - -	12 *May* 57	21 *Dec.* 55	
Robert G. A. de Montmorency,	9 *July* 57		
Robert Halahan, - - - -	21 *July* 57	.. ..	
Richard Henry Travers, - -	7 *Aug.* 57	.. ..	Leave on M. C. to England.
James Stewart, - - - - -	16 *Apl.* 58		Chatham Depôt, Instructor of Musketry.
Richard Henry Holland, - -	16 *Apl.* 58		
William Vesey Munnings, - -	17 *Apl.* 58	.. ..	On duty with Indus party of Invalids.
J. Y. Tovey, *P. & C. E.,* - -	3 *Jan.* 59	10 *Sep.* 58	D. P. W. Pashawur.
H. B. Church, - - - - -	15 *Jan.* 59		
Lieutenants.			
Robt. Joseph L. Crutchley, *PH,*	26 *June* 52	.. ..	Offg. Station Staff Officer, Murree.
Samuel John J. Burns, *PCH,*	26 *Nov.* 52	.. ..	Acting Interpreter.
Alfred William Adcock,	4 *May* 55		
Walter Bernardino Logan, - -	20 *July* 56	.. ..	Lv. on M. C. to Murree to 15 Oct. 59.
John Cordeiro Warne, - - -	30 *Sep.* 56	26 *Feb.* 56	
Alex. John Colvin Birch, - -	3 *Nov.* 56	.. ..	Acting Quarter-Master.
G. Scott, - - - - - - -	8 *July* 57	.. ..	Leave on M. C. to England.
~~John Johnstone~~, - - - - -	21 *July* 57		
Robert Paterson Fox, - - -	27 *Nov.* 57	.. ..	Adjutant.
John Moore Gurnell Tongue, -	5 *Dec.* 57		
Jonathan Christian Thomas, -	16 *Apl.* 58	.. ..	En-route to join.
Henry Charles Marsack, -	13 *July* 58	.. ..	Chatham Depôt, England.
Arthur William FitzMaurice, -	7 *Sep.* 58		
George Clarkson Ross, - - -	10 *Sep.* 58	.. ..	En-route to join.
H. B. Church, - - - -	24 *Sep.* 58		
T. P. Butler, - - - - -	7 *Dec.* 58	.. ..	Instructor of Musketry.
Ensigns.			
E. M. Pearson, - - - - -	25 *Apl.* 58	... ...	En route to join.
Charles Henry Fellowes, - -	26 *Apl.* 58	... ...	Regimental Depôt.
Edw. Fred. Aug. MacCarthy, -	21 *May* 58		
W. Magill, - - - -	3 *Apl.* 58		
Alex. Carden. Hennessey, - -	4 *June* 58	... ..	Adjutant, Murray's Jat Horse.
John Fletcher Caldwell, - -	28 *May* 58	.. ..	Chatham Depôt, England.
William Maxwell Brander, - -	13 *Jan.* 59	.. ..	Ditto.
Henry Francis Brouncker, - -	28 *Jan.* 59	.. ..	Not joined.

(a) Have passed an examination in Civil Engineering prescribed by G. O., 2nd March 1854.

H. M. 24th Regiment of Foot—(*Continued.*)

Rank and Names.	Regimental Rank.	Army Rank.	Remarks.
Instructor of Musketry.			
Ensign W. Magill, - -	1 *Mar.* 59	3 *Apl.* 58	
Pay Master.			
Lieut. Francis Freeman White,	11 *July* 56	*lt* 5 *May* 54	
Lieut. A. J. C. Birch, - -	3 *Nov.* 56	.. ..	Acting.
Adjutant.			
Lieut. Robert Peterson Fox, -	16 *July* 58	*lt.* 27 *Nov.* 57	
Quarter Master.			
Lieut. Thomas Airey, - *V.*	28 *May* 52	*lt* 15 *Jan.* 49	Leave on M. C. to England.
Lieut. A. J. C. Birch, - -	3 *Nov.* 56	.. ..	Acting.
Surgeon.			
Richard Gamble, M. D.,- - -	6 *May* 53	12 *Mar.* 52	
Assistant Surgeons.			
Richard Wolseley, - - - -	6 *Jan.* 57	28 *July* 54	Leave on M. C. to England
Charles Carroll Dempster, - *V.*	16 *Jan.* 57	5 *May* 54	
Robert Sutherland, - - -	22 *June* 58		
Interpreter.			
Lieut. S. J. J. Burns, - - -	2 *Jan.* 57	*lt* 26 *Nov.* 52	Officiating.

Strength—10 Companies, with 58 Sergeants—50 Corporals—21 Drummers—1010 Privates.

English Agents—Messrs. Cox and Co.

Irish Agents, Sir E. Borough—*Bart.*, Armits and Co.

Calcutta Agents—Messrs. Gillanders, Arbuthnot and Co.

WAR SERVICES OF THE OFFICERS OF H. M. 24th REGIMENT OF FOO .

Lieut.-Gen. Hon. John Finch served in the 15th Light Dragoons the Peninsular campaigns of 1813 and 1814 and was present at the battle of Vittoria (sabre wound), blockade of Pampeluna, affair of Turbes, and battles of Orthes and Toulouse, besides outpost affairs. Served as aide-de-camp to Viscount Combermere with the army of occupation in France; accompanied his lordship, as Military Secretary, to the West Indies in 1817; to Ireland in 1822 (receiving for his services the brevet rank of Lieut.-Col. in 1823), and to India in 1825; present at the siege and capture of Bhurtpore, for which he was nominated a C. B., and has received Medals for Vittoria, Orthes, Toulouse, and Bhurtpore,

Colonel Brown served throughout the Punjaub campaign, and was present with the 24th at the passage of the Chenab and battles of Sadoolapore and Chillianwalah (wounded), and as Major of the 29th Regt. at the battle of Goojerat (Medal and Clasps).

Colonel Blachford served with the 24th in the Punjaub campaign of 1848-9 (Medal), including the passage of the Chenab and battles of Sadoolapore and Chillianwallah (succeeded to the command of the Regt.) and Goojerat (Medal and Clasps).

Major Lutman served in the Punjaub campaign of 1848-9, including the passage of the Chenab and battles of Sadoolapore, Chillianwallah, and Goojerat (Medal and Clasps).

Capt. Macpherson served in the Punjaub campaign of 1848-9, and was present at the passage of the Chenab and battles of Sadoolapore and Chillianwallah (severely wounded) : Medal and Clasps. Served in action against the Mutineers of 14th N. I. at Jhelum, 7th July 1857.

Capt. Berry seaved in the Punjaub campaign of 1848-9, including the passage of the Chenab, and battles of Sadoolapore, Chillianwallah (slightly wounded), and Goojerat (Medal and Clasps).

Captain Thelwall served in the Punjaub campaign of 1848-9, and was present at the passage of the Chenab, and battles of Sadoolapore, Chillianwallah (severely wounded), and Goojerat (Medal and Clasps).

Capt. Winniett served with the 4th Regt. at the siege of Sebastopol from April 1855 (Medal and Clasp).

Capt. R. G. A. de Montmorency served with a detachment of the 24th Regt. at the defeat of the Jhelum mutineers on 7th July 1857.

Capt. Travers served the Punjaub campaign of 1848-9, and was present with the 10th Regiment during the whole of the siege operations before Mooltan, action of Soorjkoond, and surrender of the fortress of Mooltan: afterwards present at the battle of Goojerat (Medal and Clasps).

Capt. Stewart served in the Punjaub campaign of 1848-9, and was present at the battle of Goojerat (Medal).

Lieut. R. P. Fox served with 34th Regt. on the 26th 27th and 28th Nov. 1857 at Cawnpore; seige of Cawnpore under Major Genl. Windham C. B.,; Siege of Lucknow, in March 1858 under Genl. Sir Colin Campbell, K. C. B.; engaged in the capture of the Fort of Meer Gunge on 24th Feb. 1858 under Major Genl. Hope Grant C. B.

Lieut. Burns served with a detachment of the 24th Regt. at the defeat of the Jhelum mutineers on the 7th July 1857.

Lieut. Butler as a Lieut. 56th Regt. served at the siege and fall of Sebastopol from 25th Aug. 1855 (Medal and Clasp.

Qr -Master Airey served with the 13th Regt. throughout the campaigns in Affghanistan from 1838 to 1842 inclusive, and was present at the storm and capture of Ghuznee (Medal), assault and capture of the twn and forts of Tootumdurrah, storm of Jhoolghur, night-attack at Baboo Koosh Ghur, destruction of Khardurrah, assault of Perwandurrah, storming of the Khoord Cabool Pass, affair of Tezeen, forcing the Jugdulluck Pass, reduction of the fort of Mamoo Khail, defence of Jellalabad (Medal) and sorties on the 14th Nov. and 1st Dec. 1841, 11th Mar., 24th Mar., and 1st April 1842; general action and defeat of Akbar Khan before Jellalabad, storming the heights of Jugdulluck, general action of Tezeen, and recapture of Cabool (Medal).

Assist.-Surgeon Wolseley served the Eastern campaign of 1854-55, with the 20th Regt., including the battles of Alma, Balaklava, and Inkerman (wounded), siege and fall of Sebastopol, and assaults of the 18th June and 8th Sept. (Medal and Clasps).

Assist.-Surgeon Dempster served with the 46th Regt. in the Crimea from 8th Nov. 1854, including the siege and fall of Sebastopol, and attack of the 18th June (Medal and Clasp).

H. M. 27th (or Inniskilling) Regt. of Foot.

The Castle of Inniskilling, with St. George's Colours.—THE WHITE HORSE. "*Nec asper terrent.*" "ST. LUCIA."—The *Sphinx* with the words "EGYPT"—"MAIDA"—"BADAJOZ"—"SALAMANCA"—"VITTORIA"—"PYRENEES"—"NIVELLE"—"ORTHES"—"TOULOUSE"—"PENINSULA"—"WATERLOO."

FACINGS—*Buff.*

Landed in Bengal, from England, on the 12*th October* 1854.
UMBALLA.
Detachments at *Kussowlie* and *Kurrachee.*
Regimental Depôt, at Buttevant, Ireland.

RANK AND NAMES.	Regimental Rank.	Army Rank.	REMARKS.
COLONEL.			
Edward Fleming, C. B., ..	19 *Sep.* 53	*l.g.* 20 *June* 54	In England.
LIEUT. COLONELS.			
Usher Williamson, ..	26 *May* 54	*col.* 24 *Nov.* 54	Leave on M. C. to England to 31 Dec. [59.
Oliver G. Langley, ..	11 *Jan.* 59	.. ..	Absent on M. C. to England.
MAJORS.			
Herman Stapylton, ..	9 *Oct.* 56	.. ..	Commanding.
Barclay Thomas, ..	25 *Jan.* 59		
CAPTAINS.			
John Vize O'Donnell, ..	8 *Nov.* 50	15 *June* 49	
Edw. Nassau Molesworth, ..	2 *Dec.* 51	.. ..	Proceeding to England with invalids.
James Henry Creagh, ..	6 *May* 53	.. ..	Comdg. Regtl. Depôt, Ireland.
John Samuel Manly, ..	26 *May* 54	.. ..	At Regtl. Depot.
Charles Warren, ..	26 *May* 54		
Richard Freer, *PH,*	4 *Apl,* 56	*m* 19 *Jan.* 58	On duty in Qr. Mr. Dept. at Calcutta.
John Ball Campbell, ..	12 *May* 56	27 *Jan.* 55	
William Croker, *V,*	17 *Feb.* 57	12 *May* 54	
Henry Mitford, *V,*	13 *Mar.* 57	8 *Aug.* 56	
Henry Bethune Patton, *V,*	26 *Oct.* 58		
Richard John Evans, *P.C.H.*	12 *Nov.* 58	13 *Aug.* 57	Deputy Asst. Qr. Mr. Genl. Calcutta.
Francis Eastwood Murphy, ..	25 *Jan.* 59	.. ..	Leave on P. A. to England.
LIEUTENANTS.			
Arthur Sisson Cooper, ..	11 *Mar.* 53	.. ..	On duty at Kussowlie.
Walter Hamilton Twemlow, *V,*	6 *Jan.* 54	9 *July* 52	Adjutant.
William Henry Gresson, ..	26 *May* 54	.. ..	Proceeding to England with Invalids.
William Henry Davis, ..	26 *May* 54		
Walter Macpherson, *PH,*	26 *May* 54	15 *July* 53	Regtl. Depot.
Wm. S. Church Pinwill, ..	28 *May* 54	.. ..	Instructor of Musketry.
Geo. Stewart White, ..	29 *Jan.* 55		
Chas. Ed. Stewart, ..	1 *May* 55	.. ..	Acting Adjt. of 5th Punjaub Infantry.
Andrew David Geddes, ..	7 *Sep.* 55	.. ..	Interpreter.
Robert Lloyd, ..	9 *Oct.* 56		
Henry Scott Simeon, *V,*	19 *Dec.* 56		
William Magenis Stafford, ..	3 *Apl.* 57	.. ..	Leave on M. C. to England.
Frederic Richard Attwood, ..	1 *May* 57	.. ..	Regtl. Depot.
William James Surman, ..	12 *May* 57	4 *Aug.* 54	
Henry Monteath Caine, ..	19 *June* 57		
Laurence William Desborough,	12 *Oct.* 57		
Aiskew Clay, ..	26 *Oct.* 58		
F. Alexr. Campbell, ..	25 *Jan.* 59		

H. M. 27th Regiment of Foot—(*Continued.*)

Rank and Names.	Regimental Rank.	Army Rank.	Remarks.
Ensigns.			
Albert Dixon, ..	3 *Apl.* 57	26 *Feb.* 56	
Richard Hamilton, ..	18 *Sep.* 57	.. ..	At Regtl. Depôt.
George Power Cobbe, ..	15 *Jan.* 58	.. ..	
Frederick Tottenham, ..	29 *Oct.* 58	.. ..	Regtl. Depôt, Ireland.
Francis Coffey, ..	9 *Nov.* 58		Ditto.
Ormsby Cox, ..	16 *Nov.* 58	.. ..	Ditto.
James Mortimer Vernon Cotton,	18 *Mar.* 59		
Instructor of Musketry.			
Lieut. W. S. C. Pinwill, ..	16 *Dec.* 58	28 *May* 54	
Pay Masters.			
Capt. John Urquhart, ..	25 *Jan.* 59		
Adjutant.			
Lieut. Walter H. Twemlow, *V.*	23 *Nov* 54	*lt.* 9 *July* 52	
Quarter Master.			
John Trenor, ..	28 *Apl.* 54		
Surgeon.			
Mark Stanley Todd, ..	12 *May* 57	28 *Mar.* 54	
Assistant Surgeons.			
John M'L. Cameron, M. B., ..	26 *May* 54		
Leonard Kidd, M. B.,† *V.*	26 *May* 54	.. ..	Proceeding to England with Invalids.
Alex. Stevenson Russell, M. D.,	30 *July* 58	.. ..	
Interpreter.			
Lieut. A. D. Geddes, ..	1 *Sep.* 58	.. ..	Acting.

Strength.—10 Companies, with 56 Sergeants—50 Corporals—20 Drummers—945 Privates.
English Agents—Messrs. Cox and Co.
Calcutta Agents—Messrs. Saml. Smith and Sons., Clive Street.

WAR SERVICES OF H. M. 27th (OR INNISKILLING) REGT. OF FOOT.

Lieut.-General Fleming served with the 31st Regt. in Sicily, and part of the Grenadier Battalion in Calabria in 1806 under Sir John Stuart. In Egypt in 1807 under General Mackenzie Fraser, at the taking of Alexandria and storming of Rosetta, when he obtained his Company in action. Joined the expedition under Sir David Baird to Corunna, and served the Peninsular campaigns of 1808-9-10, and 11, including the passage of the Alberhe with the advanced Brigade, the pursuit of Massena from Santaren, battles of Talavera, Busaco, and Albuhea (very severely wounded in the head); and commanded the Light Company of his Regiment, forming part of the advance, at the spirited affair with and retreat of the enemy from Camdo Mayor to Badajoz on the 25th March 1811. Served in the West Indies from 1813 to 1819, including the expedition up the river St. Mary's in Georgia, United States of America; in the East Indies from 1820 to 1823 inclusive, and in Canada from 1829, to 1833. He has received the Silver War Medal with three Clasps.

Colonel Williamson served in the Kaffir war of 1834-35.

Captain Molesworth served as Adjutant to the Force which proceeded overland to Natal in 1841, under Captain T. C. Smith, 27th Regt., was present at the attacks by the Insurgent Bœrs in May and June 1842, and twice wounded by spent balls in the shoulder and hand. Served with the troops proceeding from Graham's Town to Colesbery, in Dec. 1842, and in the Kaffir war of 1846-47 (Medal). Part of the time as Field Adjutant to the 1st Division.

Capt. Warren was senior officer of the troops on board the *Charlotte*, when that ship went to pieces during a gale of wind in Algoa Bay, in Sept. 1854; 63 soldiers 11 women, and all the children were drowned. Captain Warren remained to the last with the Captain of the ship, encouraging and cheering his men and was specially mentioned in General Orders by General Jackson for his gallantry and good conduct on this trying occasion.

Capt. Manly was present at the capture of Port Natal, 26th June 1842; and served throughout the Kaffir war of 1846-47 (Medal).

Capt. Freer served as a volunteer with H. M. 75th Regt. at the action of Budle-ke-Serai on 8th June 1857, and in all the subsequent affairs in which the 75th Regt. was engaged during the siege of the city of Delhi. Commanded the Stables, Picquet at the capture of 4 field pieces at "Ludlow castle" on the 12th August, was severely wounded near the "Burn" Bastion on the afternoon of the assault of Delhi (Medal.) For the two last named services he was mentioned in the Reports of the officers in command.

Captain Campbell served with the 49th Regt. in China, from May 1842 to the end of the war.

Captain Mitford served with the 19th Regt. the Eastern campaign of 1854, including the battles of Inkerman and siege of Sebastopol (Medal and Clasps.)

Lieut. Simeon served as a Volunteer with the 61st Regt. at the siege, assault and capture of Delhi in 1857, including repulse of sorties on the 4th, 9th and 18th July, and the action of Nudjufghur.

Lieut. Surman served with the 48th Regt. at the siege and fall of Sebastopol from 12th Aug. 1855; Medal and Clasps.

Qr.-Master Trenor served throughout the Kaffir war of 1846-47 (Medal).

H. M. 34th (The Cumberland) Regt. of Foot.

"ALBUHERA"—"ARROYO DOS MOLINOS"—"VITTORIA"—PYRENEES"—"NIVELLE"—"NIVE"—"ORTHES"—"PENINSULA"—"SEVASTOPOL."

FACINGS—*Yellow*

Landed in India, from England, 15*th October* 1857.

CAMP FYZZABAD.

Right wing detached at *Russioul.*

Regimental Depôt, Colchester.

RANK AND NAMES.	*Regimental Rank.*	*Army Rank.*	REMARKS.
COLONEL.			
~~*Sir*~~ Thomas Makdougall Brisbane, ~~*Bart.* G. C. B., G. C. H.~~	16 *Dec.* 26	*g* 23 *Nov.* 41	In Europe.
LIEUTENANT COLONELS.			
Richard Dennis Kelly, C. B. -	9 *March* 55	*col.* 30 *Jan.* 58	
John Simpson, C. B., - -	28 *July* 57	15 *July* 55	
MAJORS.			
John Gwilt, - -	26 *Oct.* 55	*l. c.* 6 *June* 56	Leave of absence on A. P. to Simla [to 1st Nov. 59.
James Maxwell, - -	28 *July* 57	2 *Nov.* 55	
CAPTAINS.			
~~Mawdistly Gausson Best~~, - -	7 *Mar.* 51	*m.* 20 *July* 68	Regimental Depôt.
Joseph Jordan, - -	29 *Oct.* 52	*m.* 2 *Nov.* 55	Comdg. Depôt of Queen's Troops at Cawnpore,
Francis P. Cassidy, - -	10 *Nov.* 48	*m.* 20 *July* 58	Leave on M. C. to England.
David Steuart, - -	29 *Dec.* 54	... ...	Leave on P. A. to England.
Granville William Puget, - -	29 *Dec.* 54		
Arthur George Shawe, - -	... ..	7 *Feb.* 51	Colchester Depôt, England.
Edward Herman Marsh, - -	19 *June* 55	.. ..	Leave on M. C. to England.
Arth. Trevor L. Chapman, -	26 *Oct.* 55	.. ..	Instructor of Musketry, Depot England
Abel Woodroffe Boyce, - -	25 *Aug.* 57		
John Leslie Moore, - -	4 *June* 58		
Charles Nedham, - -(*a*)	17 *Sep.* 58	8 *Jan.* 58	
Thomas Harry Saunders, - -	26 *Aug.* 58	... ...	Acting Paymaster.
LIEUTENANTS.			
Edmund P. L. Mathew, - -	6 *June* 54	11 *Mar.* 53	Leave on M. C. to England.
Capt. Francis Peel, - -	29 *Dec.* 54	... ..	Leave on M. C. to England.
John Francis Wyse, - -	29 *Dec.* 54	... ...	Regtl. Depot.
Rupert Inglis Cochrane, - -	9 *Feb.* 55	.. ..	
Wm. Mathew Dunbar, - -	23 *Mar.* 55		
Tysseen Sowley Holroyd, - -	8 *June* 55		
Henry Lampen, - -	19 *June* 55		
Alexander Watson, - -	19 *June* 55		
Spencer Ley Greaves, - -	19 *June* 55	.. ..	Colchester Depôt, England.
Julius Dyson Laurie, - -	13 *July* 55	.. ..	Instructor of Musketry.
Rich. John P. Leeson, - -	27 *July* 55	... ...	Adjutant.
John Brown Rutlege, - -	25 *Sept.* 55		
George Malcolm, - -	29 *Nov.* 57	.. ..	Leave on M. C.
Richard Newton, - -	17 *Dec.* 58	.. ..	On Leave on exchange.
H. T. Sheppard, - -	10 *Sep.* 58	.. ..	Doing duty with H. M. 48th Regt.
*			
ENSIGNS.			
Thos. H. M'D. Murray, -	4 *Dec.* 57	.. ..	
Lutley Jordan, - -	24 *Nov.* 57	.. ...	
Chas. Edmund Leeson, - -	16 *Mar.* 58	.. ..	
Andrew George Walker, - -	17 *Mar.* 58	.. ..	
Charles Michael Fox, - -	13 *Apl.* 58	... ..	Regt Depot.
Charles H Webb, - - - -	13 *July* 58	.. ..	Leave on M. C.
John MacCarthy O'Leary, -	17 *Sep.* 58	.. ..	Regt. Depot.
Montage Hornsby Jones, -	12 *Nov.* 58	.. ..	Ditto.
James L. N. Willis, - - -	12 *Nov.* 58	... ..	Ditto.
* G. Brenan.			
*			

(*a*) Has passed an examination in surveying.

H. M. 34TH (THE CUMBERLAND REGT. OF FOOT.—*(Continued.)*

RANK AND NAMES.	*Regimental Rank.*	*Army Rank.*	REMARKS.
INSTRUCTOR OF MUSKETRY.			
Lieut. J. D. Laurie, - -	21 *April* 57	*lt.* 13 *July* 55	
PAYMASTER.			
Capt. Thos. H. Saunders, - -	.. ..	.. ..	Acting.
ADJUTANT.			
Lt. Richd. John Philip Leeson,	19 *Sept.* 56	*lt.* 17 *July* 55	
QUARTER MASTER.			
Terence Rowan, - -	28 *April* 54		
SURGEON.			
Michael Fenton Manifold, - -	31 *Dec.* 58		
ASSISTANT SURGEONS.			
Richard Jukes Worthington, -	26 *May* 54	... ...	Absent without Leave.
Wallace Haward, - -	7 *June* 54		
William Thos. Paliologus, - -	24 *July* 57	1 *Sept.* 54	Leave on M. C. to England.

Strength—10 Companies with 50 Sergeants,—48 Corporals,—15 Drummers and 1031 Privates.

English Agents.—Messrs. Cox and Co.

Calcutta Agents.—Messrs. Samuel Smith aud Sons, 75, Clive Street.

WAR SERVICES OF THE OFFICERS OF H. M. 34TH, REGT. OF FOOT.

Sir Thomas Brisbane joined the Duke of York's army in the beginning of the war, and was present in every action except that of the 22nd May 93, when he was confined from a wound received in the action of the 18th of the same month. He was subsequently present at the taking of various islands, forts, &c. in the West Indies, under Sir Ralph Abercromby, Sir Thomas has received the Gold Cross and one Clasp for Vittoria, Pyrenees, Nivelle, Orthes, and Toulouse (were he was wounded); and the Silver War Medal with one Clasp for the Nive.

Colonel Kelly served at the siege of Sebastopol in 1855; commanded the Guards in the trenches on the 22nd March, when he was wounded and taken prisoner in a sortie of the Russians (Medal and Clasp, Brev. Lt.-Col. and Knight of the Legion of Honor).

Lt.-Col. Simpson served at the siege of Sebastopol in 1854-55; commanded a party in the assault (wounded) and capture of the Quarries; also present at the assault of the Redan on the 8th Sept. (Medal and Clasp, Brevet Lt.-Col., Knight of the Legion of Honor, and Sardinian Medal).

Lieut.-Col. Gwilt served at the siege of Sebastopol in 1854-55; was present at the capture of the Rifle Pits on the 19th April, and commanded the 34th Regt. at the assault of the Redan on the 18th June—severely wounded (Medal and Clasp, Brevet of Major and Lt.-Col., and Knight of the Legion of Honor).

Major Maxwell served at the siege of Sebastopol in 1854-55, and was severely wounded by the bursting of a shell in the trenches, 25th May (Medal and Clasp, and Brevet Major).

Major Best served at the siege of Sebastopal in 1855, and assault of the Redan on the 8th Sept. (Medal and Clasp).

Maj. Jordan served at the siege of Sebastopol in 1855 sortie of the 22nd March, capture of the Rifle Pits 19th April, sortie of 9th May, and assault of the Redan on the 18th June—severely wounded (Medal and Clasps, Brevet Major, and Sardinian Medal).

Captains Puget, Marsh, and Chapman, and Lt. Cochrane, served at the siege of Sebastopol in 1854-55 (Medal and Clasp).

Captain Boyce served at the siege of Sebastopol in 1855, and assaults on the Redan on the 18th June and 8th Sept. (Medal and Clasp, and Sardinian Medal).

Capt. Nedham served the Punjaub campaign of 1848-9 with the 10th, including the whole of the siege operations before Mooltan, affair of 9th Sept., storming the enemy's strongly-entrenched position, capture of the Dowlat Gate, action of Soorjkoond, and surrender of the fortress: afterwards present at the battle of Goojerat (Medal and Clasps).

Capt. Moore, Lieuts. Dunbar, Holroyd, Lampen, Watson, Greaves, and Leeson, served at the siege of Sebastopol in 1855 (Medal and Clasp.)

Capt. Saunders served at the siege of Sabastopol in 1855, and was severely wounded at the capture of the Quarries on the 7th June (Medal and Clasp).

Lieut. Peel served at the siege of Sebastopol in 1855, and was wounded at the assault of the Redan on the 18th June (Medal and Clasp, and Sardinian Medal).

Lieut. Wyse served at the siege of Sebastopol in 1854-55, and at the assault of the Redan on the 18th June (Medal and Clasp)

Lieut. Laurie served at the sige of Sebastopol in 1855 and was severely wounded at the assault of the Redan on the 8th Sept. was also wounded on a former occasion (Medal and Clasp).

Qr.-Master Rowan, and Assist-Surgeon Haward, served at the siege of Sebastopol in 1854-55 (Medal and Clasp).

Assist-Surgeon Worthington served at the siege of Sebastopol in 1855 (Medal and Clasp).

35th (Royal Sussex) Regiment of Foot.

"MAIDA."

FACINGS—*Blue.*

Landed in Bengal from England on the 14*th November* 1854.

DINAPORE.

Detachment at *Bankipore* and *Sewan.*

Regimental Depôt, Chatham.

RANK AND NAMES.	*Regimental Rank.*	*Army Rank.*	REMARKS.
COLONEL.			
John Leslie, K. H. ..	26 *Sep.* 57	*l.g.*26 *Oct.* 58	In Europe.
LIEUT. COLONELS.			
~~Edward Hely Hutchinson~~, ..	20 *June* 54	*col* 20 *June* 57	Leave on M. C. to Europe.
John M'Neill Walter, C. B., ..	9 *Jan.* 57	17 *Oct.* 56	Commanding.
MAJORS.			
Charles Beamish, ..	20 *June* 54	*l.c.*12 *Nov.* 58	Comdg. detachment at Sewan.
Patrick Wm. Sydenham Ross, ..	13 *Jan.* 57	17 *Oct.* 56	Comdg. Depôt. of European Troops, at Benares.
CAPTAINS.			
Thomas Teulon, ..	31 *Dec.* 47	*m.* 12 *Nov* 58	Commanding Depôt, at Chatham.
Robert Henry Price, ..	23 *June* 48	.. ..	Chatham Depôt, England.
Archibald Tisdall, ..	11 *May* 49		
William Ranby Goate, ..	14 *Dec.* 49		
M. Villiers Sankey Morton, ..	20 *June* 54		
Charles Fred. Browne, *P. H.*	7 *July* 51	22 *Apl.* 53	Depy. Judge Advocate Genl of Cawnpore Divison.
Samuel Fritche Blythe, ..	16 *May* 56		
Robert Crosse Stewart, *V*	16 *Oct.* 56	*m* 20 *July* 58	Leave on M. C. to England.
Charles John Patterson, ..	5 *May* 57	10 *Feb.* 54	Leave on M. C. to England.
William Henry Ballingall, ..	30 *May* 57	.. ..	Instructor of Musketry, on detachment at Sewan.
Randulph Charles Lee, ..	30 *Aug.* 58	.. ..	Leave on P. A. in Innia.
John Ormsby Vandeleur, ..	20 *Feb.* 59		
LIEUTENANTS.			
John Davis, ..	20 *June* 54	.. ..	With detachment at Bankipore.
Alfred John Ford, ..	20 *June* 54	18 *July* 51	
Edward Tedlie, *P,*	23 *June* 54	.. ..	2nd in Command of Agra Levy.
Robert J. Gordon Grant, ..	23 *July* 54	10 *Dec.* 52	Absent without leave.
Cortland G. Macregor Skinner, ..	23 *Aug.* 54	7 *June* 54	Leave on M. C. to England.
Thomas Lloyd, ..	24 *Nov.* 54	.. ..	At School of Musketry, Hythe.
Albert John Revell, ..	26 *Jan.* 55	.. ..	Leave to England on P. A. to 14 October 60.
Mars Mourier Pohle, ..	3 *Aug.* 55		
Woodford W. Sherlock, *P. H.*	9 *May* 56		Convalescent Depot, Darjeeling.
Richard Trimen, ..	16 *May* 56	.. ..	With detachment at Bankipore.
Richard Ross, ..	9 *May* 56		
Robert Henry W. Troup, *V,*	30 *Jan.* 57	.. ..	Interpreter.—Leave of absence on M. C. to Landour to 30 Nov. 59.
Richard Parsons, ..	15 *May* 57		
William Henry Bayly Payn, ..	24 *Apl.* 58		
Robert Hill Ross, ..	7 *Sep.* 58	.. ..	Adjutant.
Thomas Broun, ..	24 *Apl.* 58		
Henry Edmund Fryer, ..	30 *Aug.* 58	.. ..	With detachment at Sewan.

35TH (ROYAL SUSSEX) REGIMENT OF FOOT.—*(Continued.)*

RANK AND NAMES.	Regimental Rank.	Army Rank.	REMARKS.
ENSIGNS.			
Timothy John Dillon, ..	15 *May* 57	.. ..	With detachment at Sewan.
Edward Laws, ..	13 *July* 58	.. ..	Not joined.
Fred. Bowdler Gipps, ..	24 *Aug.* 58	.. ..	
William Poste, ..	24 *Aug.* 58	.. ..	Regimental Depot.
William Trocke, ..	7 *Sep.* 58	.. ..	Ditto.
Charles John Stone, ..	29 *Oct.* 58	.. ..	Not joined
Arthur Chichester Crookshank,..	11 *Jan.* 59	.. ..	Ditto.
INSTRUCTOR OF MUSKETRY.			
Lieut. Thomas Lloyd, ..	11 *Dec* 58	.. ..	En-route to join.
PAY MASTER.			
Lieut. John Mills Hewson, ..	28 *Sep.* 47	*lt.* 29 *Dec.* 43	
ADJUTANT.			
Lieut. Robert Hill Ross, ..	5 *Apl.* 57	*lt.* 24 *Ap.* 58	
QUARTER MASTER.			
Michael McLaughlin, ..	13 *Jan.* 54		
SURGEON.			
James Walker Chambers, M. D.,..	6 *Aug.* 47		
ASSISTANT SURGEONS.			
Edward Thiselton, ..	20 *June* 54		
Richard T. G. Cotton, ..	25 *June* 58	7 *May* 58	
John Mahon, ..	11 *May* 59		
INTERPRETER.			
Lieut. R. H. W. Troup, ..	9 *Oct.* 58		

Strength—10 Companies, with 48 Sergeants—41 Corporals—19 Drummers—865 Privates.

English Agents—*Sir* John Kirkland.

Calcutta Agents—Messrs. Gillanders, Arbuthnot and Co.

WAR SERVICES OF THE OFFICERS OF H. M. 35TH REGT. OF FOOT.

Major-General John Leslie was at the taking of Travancore in 1808 and at the capture of Bourbon and the Isle of France in 1810; after which he served in Java and was present in the engagements of the 10th, 22nd, and 26th August 1811. He served also in the Pindaree war in 1817, and with the Army of Occupation in France. He has received the War Medal with one Clasp for Java.

Lt.-Colonel Walter served throughout the Kaffir campaign of 1846-7 as Adjutant of the 90th Regt., and Field Adjutant of the 1st Division (Medal). Served with the 53rd Regt. in the Punjaub campaign in 1849, and was present at the battle of Goojerat (Medal and Clasp).

Major Stewart served as D. A. A. Gen. to the 2nd Division at the capture of Lucknow in March 1858 and was severely wounded (Brevet Major).

Lt. Grant was present at the storm and destruction of the fortified native Mandingo town of Sobajee, on the Gambia, on the 1st June 1853.

Lieutenant Pohle served with the Field Force against the rebel Karens in Burmah in Jan. 1857, and was severely wounded.

H. M. 37th (The North Hampshire) Regt. of Foot.

"MINDEN"—"TOURNAY"—"PENINSULA."

FACINGS—*Yellow*.

Landed at Calcutta, from Ceylon, on 12th June 1857.

GHAZEEPORE.

Regimental Depôt, Colchester.

RANK AND NAMES.	*Regimental Rank.*	*Army Rank.*	REMARKS.
COLONEL.			
John Fraser, - -	11 *Jan.* 58	*m.g.* 20 *June* 54	Ceylon.
LIEUTENANT COLONELS.			
Egerton Chas. W. M. Milman,-	30 *Nov.* 49	*col.* 28 *Nov.* 54	Brigadier, 2nd class, Jullunder.
Edward D. Atkinson, - -	20 *Aug.* 58	.. ..	Lv. on P. A. to England, to 9 Dec. 60.
MAJORS.			
Henry McManus Sall, - -	24 *Oct.* 58		
Robert Prescott Harrison, -	26 *Nov.* 58		
CAPTAINS.			
Raymond Richard Pelly, - -	7 *June* 50	.. ..	Leave on M. C. to England.
Joseph Jones, - -	16 *June* 53	.. .	With detachment Dargeling.
John William Boissier, -	13 *Dec.* 53	30 *Jan.* 52	[to 30 Sep. 59.
Wm. Joseph Bazalgette, - -	6 *June* 54	... ...	Lv. of absence on M. C. to Mussoorie
John Richard Heaton, - -	24 *Feb.* 43	*m* 20 *June* 54	Regtl. Depôt, England. [18 months 59.
Charles Luxmoore, - -	26 *Oct.* 55	.. ..	Leave of absence to England on P. A. for
Edward Joseph N. Burton,-	20 *Mar.* 56		Brigade Major Lucknow.
John Brown, - -	15 *June* 57		
John Deering Collum, - -	15 *June* 58		
George William Savage, - -	26 *Oct.* 58		
Fred. John Nash Ind, - -	7 *Dce.* 58	.. ..	Leave of absence on P. A. to Ceylon
Saml. Lavalliere Curgenven, -	.. ..		[to 30 September 59.
LIEUTENANTS.			
William Henry Henzell, - -	6 *Jan.* 54		
Chas. Edw. Ascough Evered -	11 *Aug.* 54	.. ...	Leave on M. C. to England.
Edw. Robt. Bigsby Barnes, -	10 *Aug.* 55	.. ..	At School of Musketry, Hythe.
Richard Bunn,- - - -	26 *Oct.* 55	.. ...	Adjutant.
Bezsin Reece, -	26 *Oct.* 55		
James Frederick Reyne, -	20 *Mar.* 56		[to 30 September 59.
Henry Edward Glass, -	29 *Apl.* 56	7 *Sept.* 55	Leave of absence on P. A. to Madras,
James Drummond Græme,-	31 *July* 57		
Geo. Goodridge Fraser, -	31 *July* 57		
Tho. Sheridan Gore Jones,-	28 *Mar.* 58		
Samuel Hawkes, -	21 *May* 58	.. ..	Instructor of Musketry.
George John Usil Mason, -	15 *June* 58	.. ...	Leave on M. C. to England. to 27 Apl. 59.
Michl. Andrews Borthwick, -	12 *Oct.* 58		
Francis Charteris Forbes, -	26 *Oct.* 58	... ...	Leave of absence to Mussoorie, on P. A. to to 30 Sep. 59.
ENSIGNS.			
Albert Jones, - - - - -	30 *Oct.* 57	... ..	Leave to Dargeling to 30 Sep. 59.
William Hodgkinson, - -	6 *Nov.* 57		
William Belcher, - - -	17 *Nov.* 57		
John Ennis, - - - -	15 *Jan.* 58	.. ..	Leave on M. C. to England.
Francis Openshaw Sargeant, -	28 *May* 58	.. ..	Colchester Depôt, England.
John Reilly, - - - - -	4 *June* 58	.. ..	
Henry Bullen, - - - -	30 *July* 58	.. ..	
Charles Edward King, - -	24 *Sept.* 58	... ...	Depôt England.
John Everard Whitting, - -	19 *Nov.* 58		
Thomas Noble Holton, - -	18 *Jan.* 59	.. ..	Depôt England.

H. M. 37TH (THE NORTH HAMPSHIRE) REGT. OF FOOT.—(*Continued.*)

RANK AND NAMES.	*Regimental Rank.*	*Army Rank.*	REMARKS.
INSTRUCTOR OF MUSKETRY.			
Lieut. Samuel Hawkes, - -	4 *June* 57	*lt.* 21 *May* 58	
PAYMASTER.			
Lieut. Raynsford Taylor. - -	15 *Feb.* 56	*lt.* 5 *May* 53	
ADJUTANT.			
Lieut. Richard Bunn, - -	26 *Oct.* 55	*lt.* 13 *Sep.* 53	Station Staff Officer.
QUARTER-MASTER.			
William Crutchley, - -	13 *Sept.* 53		
SURGEON.			
J. C. Fleming, - -	... ...	.. ..	En route to join.
ASSISTANT-SURGEONS.			
William Ramsay, M. D., - -	15 *Dec.* 54		
Wm. Samuel Chapman, - -	6 *Nov.* 57	15 *Sep.* 57	
J. Hoysted, - - -	16 *May* 58		
INTERPRETER.			
*			

Strength—10 Companies with 49 Sergeants—43 Corporals,—20 Drummers, and 730 Privates.

English Agents,—Messrs. Price and Bousted.
Calcutta Agents,—Wm. Spink and Co.

WAR SERVICES OF THE OFFICERS OF H. M. 37TH REGT. OF FOOT.

Colonel Fraser served in the Peninsula with the 24th, from June 1809 to June 1813, including the action at Foz d'Arouce, battle of Busaco, battle of Fuentes d'Onor, on 3rd and 5th May, siege of Ciudad Rodrigo, covering the siege of Badajoz, battle of Salamanca, capture of Madrid, and siege of Burgos where he was at the taking of the Horn Work, 19th Sept.; and he led the storming party to the breach formed by the mine on the 4th Oct. Employed in the field throughout the whole of the Kandian rebellion in Ceylon in 1817 and 18, as Aide-de-camp to the Commander of the Forces. He has received the War Medal with four Clasps.

Captain Sall served with the 10th Foot in the Punjaub campaign of 1848-9, including the whole of the siege operations before Mooltan, repulse of the enemy and night-attack upon the British camp at Muttee Thol 17th Aug. 1848; action of Soorjkoond and capture of the enemy's guns Nov. 7th; carrying the heights and suburbs before Mooltan Dec. 27th; and surrender of the fortress 22nd Jan. 1849; after which joined with the Mooltan force the army under Lord Gough, and was present at the battle of Goojerat (Medal and two Clasps).

Captain Boissier served with the 32nd Regt. at the second siege operations before Mooltan, including the attack on the suburbs on 27th Dec. 1848, and surrender of the fortress. Also present at the surrender of the fort and garrison of Cheniote, and at the battle of Goojerat (Medal and Clasps).

Lieut. Barnes volunteered on the outbreak of the Kaffir war in 1850, and was appointed a Lieut. in a native corps, and served under Sir Harry Smith and Sir George Cathcart from January 1851, until March 1853. He accompanied the first patrol that left King William's Town on the 30th Jan. 1851, and was present at the engagements of the 17th February, 6th March, 16th April, of 1851, and at the passage of the Kei on the 4th December of the same year; besides many other minor encounters with the enemy during the war (Medal.)

Assist.-Surgeon Ramsay served in Turkey from Jan. to May 1855, in the Crimean campaign from May 1855 to July 1856 (Medal and Clasp).

H. M. 38th (The 1st Staffordshire) Regt. of Foot.

"Montevideo"—"Roleia"—"Vimiera"—"Corunna"—"Busaco"—"Badajoz"—"Salamanca"—"Vittoria"—"St. Sebastian"—"Nive"—"Peninsula"—"Ava"—"Alma"—"Inkerman"—"Sevastopol."

Facings—*Yellow.*

Landed in Calcutta, from England, 15*th October and November* 1857.

Roy Bareilly.

Regimental Depot, Colchesteter.

Rank and Names.	*Regimental Rank.*	*Army Rank.*	Remarks.
Colonel.			
Hon. Hugh Arbuthnott, c. b., -	4 *Apl.* 43	*g* 20 *June* 54	In Europe.
Lieutenant Colonels.			
James Pattoun Sparks, c. b., -	9 *Mar.* 55	*col.*28 *Nov.* 54	
W. O. Grady. Haly, c. b., - -	4 *Feb.* 59	*col.* 24 *Nov.* 54	Not joined, 8th Punjaub Infantry.
Majors.			
James S. Hawker Farrer, - -	29 *June* 55	12 *Dec.* 54	Leave to England on P. A. for 18 months.
William James Loftus, - -	29 *July* 55	*l.c.* 2 *Nov.* 55	
Captains.			
Edward Thomas Gloster, - -	30 *July* 52	*lt.col.*20*July* 58	Leave on M. C. to England.
~~Ludford Harvey Daniel~~, - -	18 *Oct.* 53	*m* 2 *Nov.* 55	Convalescent Depot, Kussowlie.
Horatio Page Vance, - -	4 *Aug.* 54	*m* 20 *July* 58	Lv. to England on P.A. for 18 months.
James Thomas Craster, - -	22 *Dec.* 54	.. ..	Depot England.
Hon. Chas. J. Addington, - -	29 *Dec.* 54	*m* 20 *July* 58	
Const. Wm. Sept. Gaynor, - -	14 *Aug.* 57		
Henry Charles Evans, - -	25 *June* 58		
William Kidston Elles, - -	13 *July* 58	.. ..	Instructor of Musketry
George Augustus McNair, - -	30 *July* 58	10 *Mar.* 58	Doing duty at Peshawur.
David W. Martin, - -	23 *Mar.* 59	30 *Sep.* 58	On Sick leave to Kussowlie, Acting Interpreter,
Wm. de W. R. Thaekwell, -	.. ..	26 *Feb.* 58	Not joined,
B. Walton. - -	.. ..	*m* 24 *Mar* 58	Ditto.
Lieutenants.			
Jno. Fred. Clinton Boyle - -	8 *Dec.* 54		
George Wm. Fred. Snell, - -	2 *Feb.* 55		
Philip Homan Eyre, - -	2 *Feb.* 55	.. ..	Adjutant.
Arthur Johnson Allix Ewen, *V*,	2 *Feb.* 55		
Walter Hume, -	9 *Mar.* 55		
Rob. Johnston Stansfeld, - -	17 *June* 55		
Arthur Alexander Wilkie, -	29 *June* 55		
Alexander Walker, - -	29 *July* 55	.. ..	Colchester Depôt, England.
John Alex. Caldecott, - *V*.	16 *Aug.* 55		
John Thomas Carroll, - -	29 *Feb.* 56		
Artupr William Barron, - -	25 *Oct.* 56		
John Mayo, - -	7 *July.* 57	.. ..	Leave on M. C. to Calcutta.
James Hughes Pope, - -	14 *Aug.* 57		
Wm. Henry Russel Skey, - -	24 *Aug.* 58		
Andrew Macdonold Grote, - -	31 *Dec.* 58	.. ..	Depôt, England.
Edward Condint Bicknell, - -	31 *Dec.* 58	.. ..	Ditto.
Alfred Stokes, - - - -	28 *Jan.* 59	.. ..	Ditto.
Arthur Bailey, - -	22 *Apl.* 59		
Ensigns.			
Thos. Throphimus Hodges, -	6 *Sept.* 55		
Dyas R. Lofthouse, -	13 *July* 58	.. ..	Regtl. Depôt, England.
Norman Wm. D. Pringle, - -	10 *Sep.* 58	.. ..	Ditto.
William Uvedale Miller, - -	12 *Nov.* 58	.. ..	Ditto.
John Barrett Brody, - -	29 *Nov.* 58	.. ..	
Benjamin Parnell Bromhead, -	18 *Jan.* 59	.. ..	Ditto.
John Smyth Nelson, - -	28 *Jan.* 59	.. ..	Ditto.

H. M. 38TH (THE 1ST STAFFORDSHIRE) REGT. OF FOOT.—*(Continued)*

RANK AND NAMES.	*Regimental Rank.*	*Army Rank.*	REMARKS.
INSTRUCTOR OF MUSKETRY.			
Capt. W. T. Elles,	13 *July* 58		
PAYMASTER.			
James Twibill,	23 *June* 54		
ADJUTANT.			
Lieut P. H. Eyre,	.. ..		
QUARTER-MASTER.			
Robert Smith,	7 *Dec.* 55		
SURGEON.			
Thomas Fred. Wall,	12 *Jan.* 55		
ASSISTANT-SURGEONS.			
Digby William Lawlor,	10 *June* 53		
James Henry Lewis,	24 *Mar.* 54		
Thomas Wright,	21 *Apl.* 54		
INTERPRETER.			
Capt. D. W. Martin,	6 *May* 59		

Strength—10 Companies with 55 Sergeants,—47 Corporals,—21 Drummers, and 932 Privates

English Agents.—Messrs. Cox and Co.
Irish Agents.—Messrs. Cane and Co.
Calcutta Agents.—Messrs. Wm. Spink and Co.

WAR SERVICES OF THE OFFICERS OF H. M. 38TH REGT. OF FOOT.

General the *Hon.* Hugh Arbuthnott served with the 49th Regt. at the Helder in 1799; also on the expedition to the Baltic, and battle of Copenhagen in 1801. In July 1807 embarked with the expedition to Zealand, and was present at the siege and capture of Copenhagen. Accompanied the expedition to Sweden, and afterwards to Portugal and Spain under Sir John Moore, and was present at the battle of Corunna. Served also in the Peninsula under the Duke of Wellington, and commanded the 52nd Regt. at the battle of Busaco, for which he has received the Gold Medal: he has also received the Silver War Medal with two Clasps for Corunna and Fuentes d'Onor; and the Naval War Medal for Copenhagen.

Colonel Sparks served on the N. E. frontier of the Cape of Good Hope against the Kaffirs in 1817; on the expedition into Kaffraria under Col. Brereton in 1818; in the action at Graham's Town 22nd April 1819, and the campaign of the same year in Kaffraria under Col. Wiltshire; on the N. E. frontier when the Kaffirs invaded it in Dec. 1834, and during the war which ensued he commanded a local corps—the Graham's Town Volunteers—with the colonial Commission of Lt.-Colonel. In 1848 he was sent from Jamaica to the Mosquito Coast, in consequence of the death of H. M.'s Agent and Consul-General, to attend to British interests there, and received the thanks of H.M.'s Government. Served throughout the Eastern campaign of 1854-55, except from the middle of Feb. to the end of May 1855 (sent to England on duty); succeeded to the command of the 38th Regt. on the morning of the 18th June when Lt.-Col. Louth was wounded, was the senior unwounded officer of the 2nd Brigade 3rd Division at the close of the action, and commanded it for ten days. Has the Kaffir Medal, the Crimean Medal with three Clasps for Alma, Inkerman, and Sebastopol, and the Sardinian Medal, and the 4th class of Medjidie, is a CB. and an Officer of the Legion of honor. Served in the Indian Campaign from November 1857; Commanded 3rd Infantry Brigade at the assault and capture of "Meangunge," during the siege and capture of Lucknow (Medal and Clasp).

Colonel Haly served in the Eastern campaign of 1854-55 including the battles of Alma (charger killed) and Inkerman (received four bayonet wounds), capture of Balaklava, siege and fall of Sebastopol, and sortie on 26th Oct. (Medal and Clasps, *CB.*, Officer of the Legion of Honer, and 3rd Class of the Medjidie).

Major Farrer served in the Eastern campaign of 1854-55, including the battles of Alma and Inkerman, and siege of Sebastopol (Medal and Clasps, 5th class of Medjedie, and Brevet Major). Served in the Indian campaign from November 1857; was present at the assault and capture of "Meangunge," during the siege and capture of Lucknow, (Medal and Clasp); also at the affairs of Barree and "Nugger" under Sir James Hope Grant.

Lt.-Colonel Loftus served throughout the Eastern campaign of 1854-55, including the battles of Alma and Inkerman, and siege and fall of Sebastopol, attack and occupation of the Cemetery on the 18th June (Medal with three Clasps, Brevet Lt.-Colonel, 5th class of the Medjedie and Sardinian Medal). Served in the Indian campaign from November 1857; was present at the assault and capture of "Meangunge," during the siege and capture of Lucknow [Medal and Clasps]; also at the affairs of Barree and Nugger under Sir James Hope Grant, severely wounded in the assault of Lucknow.

Lieut. Colonel Gloster served in the Eastern campaign of 1854-55, including the battles of Alma and Inkerman siege and fall of Sebastopol (Medal with three Clasps, and Brevet Major). Served in the Indian campaign from November 1857; was present at the assault and capture of "Meangunge," during the siege and capture of Lucknow [Medal and Clasp]; also at the affairs of "Barree and" "Nugger" under Sir James Hope Grant. Dangerously wounded in the assault on Lucknow.

Major L. H. Danial served at the siege and fall of Sebastopol in 1855 and at the attack and occupation of the Cemetery on the 18th June severely wounded (Medal and Clasps, 5th class of Medjedie and Brevet Major Served in the Indian campaign from November 1857; was present at the battle of Cawnpore on 6th December 1857; at the assault and capture of Meangunge; the siege and capture of Lucknow [Medal and Clasp]; also at the affairs of "Barree" and "Nugger"

Major Walton. and Capt. Dalzell, served in the Punjaub campaign in 1849, and were present at the battle of Goojerat (Medal and Clasp.).

*** *For continuation of services, see next page.*

WAR SERVICES OF THE OFFICERS OF H. M. 38TH REGT. OF FOOT.—(*Continued.*)

Major Vance served at the siege of Sebastopol from Jan. to 15th April 1855 [Medal and Clasp]. Served in the Indian campaign from November 1857; was present at the assault and capture of "Meangunge," during the siege and capture of Lucknow [Medal and Clasp]; also at the affairs of Barree and Nugger under Sir Jas. Hope Grant.

Captain Craster served in the Eastern campaign of 1854, including the battles of Alma and Inkerman, and siege of Sebastopol [Medal and three Clasps]. Served in the Indian campaign from November 1857; was present at the battle of Cawnpore and at the assault and capture of "Meangunge," [Medal and Clasp].

Major Hon. C. J. Addington served the Eastern campaign of 1854 and up to 26th June 1855, including the battles of Alma and Inkerman, siege of Sebastopol, attack and occupation of the Cemetery on the 18th June —severely wounded [Medal and three Clasps and 5th class of Medjedie]. Served in the Indian campaign from November 1857; was present at the assault and capture of "Meangunge," during the siege and capture of Lucknow [Medal and Clasp]; also at the affairs of Barree and "Nugger" under Sir Jas. Hope Grant.

Captain Gaynor served the Eastern campaign of 1854 and until 25th Feb. 1855, including the battles of Alma and Inkerman, and siege of Sebastopol, and was shot through the leg in the trenches on 21 Feb. [Medal and three Clasps, and Sardinian Medal]. Served in the Indian campaign from November 1857, was present at the battle Cawnpore on 6th December 1857; at the assault and capture of Meangunge, the siege and capture of Lucknow [Medal Clasp]; also at the affairs of the Barree and Nugger.

Captain Evans, served in the Indian campaign from November 1857; was present at the assault and capture of Meangunge during the siege and capture of Lucknow [Medal and Clasp]; also at the affairs of Barree and Nugger under Sir Jas. Hope Grant.

Capt. Elles served at the siege and fall of Sebastopol in 1854-55, including the attack and occupation of the Cemetery on the 18th June [Medal and Clasp, and Knight of the Legion of Honor]. Served in the Indian campaign from November 1857, was present at the battle "Cawnpore" on 6th December 1857; at the assault and capture of Meangunge; the siege and capture of Lucknow [Medal and Clasp]; also at the affairs of the Baree and Nugger.

Captain Thackwell served at the siege and fall of Sebastopol in 1855, and at the attack on the 18th June, and 18th September. (Medal and Clasps. 5th class of the Medjedie).

Lieut. Boyle served with the 38th Regt. throughout the Eastern campaign of 1854-55, including the battles of Alma and Balaklava [carried the colours], siege and fall of Sebastopol, attack and occupation of the Cemetery on the 18th June [Medal and three Clasps]. Served in the Indian campaign from November 1857; was present at the capture of "Meangunge," during the siege and capture of Lucknow [Medal and Clasp]; also at the affairs of Barree and Nugger under Sir Jas. Hope Grant.

Lieuts. Snell and Stansfeld served at the siege and fall of Sebastopol from 1st June 1855, including the attack and occupation of the Cemetery on the 18th June [Medal and Clasp]. Served in the Indian campaign from November 1857; was present at the capture of Meangunge, during the siege and capture of Lucknow [Medal and Clasp]; also at the affairs of Barree and Nugger under Sir Jas. Hope Grant.

Lieut. Eyre served in the Eastern campaign from 10th Nov. 1854 to 10th May 1855 (including the siege of Sebastopol [Medal and Clasp]. Served in the Indian campaign from November 1857; was present at the assault and capture of "Meangunge," during the siege and capture of Lucknow [Medal and Clasp]; also at the affair of Nugger under Sir Jas. Hope Grant.

Lieut. Ewen served at the siege and fall of Sebastopol from 13th Jan. 1855, including the attack and occupation of the Cemetery on the 18th June (Medal and Clasp, and Sardinian Medal). Served in the Indian campaign from November 1857, was present at the battle "Cawnpore" on 6th December 1857; at the assault and capture of Meangunge, the siege and capture of Lucknow [Medal and Clasp].

Lieut. Mayo served at the siege and fall of Sebastopol from 29th Aug. 1855 (Medal and Clasp). Served in the Indian campaign from November 1867, was present at the battle Cawnpore on 6th December 1857; at the capture of Meangunge; the siege and capture of Lucknow [Medal and Clasp]; also at the affairs of the "Barree" and "Nugger."

Lieut. Hume served at the siege and fall of Sebastopol from 1st July 1855 (Medal and Clasp). Served in the Indian compaign from November 1857; was present at the capture of "Meangunge," during the siege and capture of Lucknow [Medal and Clasp]; also at the affairs of "Barree" and "Nugger" under Sir Jas. Hope Grant.

Lieut. Wilkie served at the siege and fall of Sebastopol from 23rd July 1855 (Medal and Clasp). Served in the Indian campaign from November 1857; was present at the battle of Cawnpore and at the capture of Meangunge," during the seige and capture of Lucknow [Medal and Clasp]; also at the affairs of "Barree" and "Nugger" under Sir Jas. Hope Grant.

Lieut. Caldecott served in the Crimea from 7th Sept. 1855, and was at the fall of Sebastopol [Medal and Clasp]. Served in the Indian campaign from November 1857; was present at the capture of "Meangunge" during the siege and capture of Lucknow [Medal and Clasp].

Lieut. Pope & Carroll, served in the Indian Campaign from November 1857; was present at the battle "Cawnpore" in 6th December 1857; at the capture of "Meangunge," the siege and capture of Lucknow [Medal and Clasp]; also at the affairs of the "Barree" and "Nugger."

Lieut. Barron served in the Indian campaign from November 1857; was present at the capture of "Meangunge" during the siege and capture of Lucknow [Medal and Clasp]; also at the affairs of "Barree" and "Nugger" under Sir Jas. Hope Grant.

Lieut. Grote served with the 95th Regiment in the campaign in central India, including the assault and capture of Awah, Rajpootana, the siege and capture of Kotah the recapture of Chendaree, the battle of Kotah-ka-Sarai, the capture of the City and fortress of Gwalior under Major General Sir Hugh Rose, siege and capture of Powrie and the surprise and defeat of Maun Sing near Kaoudrye, (Medal.)

*** *For continuation of services, see next page.*

WAR SERVICES OF THE OFFICFRS OF H. M. 38TH REGT. OF FOOT.—(*Continued.*)

Licut. Skey served in the Indian campaign from November 1857; was present at the capture of Meangunge; during the siege and capture of Lucknow, [Medal and Clasp]; also at the affairs of "Barree" and "Nugger" under Sir Jas. Hope Grant.

Ensign Bailey served in the Indian campaign from November 1857; was present at the Battle of Cawnpore, capture of Meangunge; during the seige and capture of Lucknow [Medal and Clasp]; also at the affairs of "Baree" and "Nugger" under Sir Jas. Hope Grant.

Ensign Hodges served in the Indian campaign from November 1857; was present at the capture of Meangunge; during the siege and capture of Lucknow [Medal and Clasp]; also at the affairs of "Barree" and "Nugger" under Sir Jas. Hope Grant.

Qr.-Master Smith served at the siege and fall of Sebastopol, including the attack and occupation of the Cemetery (Medal and Clasp). Served in the Indian oampaign from November 1857; was present at the capture of "Meangunge," during the siege and capture of Lucknow [Medal and Clasp]; also at the affairs of "Barree" and "Nugger" under Sir Jas. Hope Grant.

Surgeon Wall served at the siege and fall of Sebastopol from 19th Dec. 1854, and at the attack of the 18th June 1855 (Medal and Clasp). Served in the Indian campaign from November 1857; was present at the capture of "Meangunge," during the siege and capture of Lucknow [Medal and Clasp]; also at the affairs of "Barree" and "Nugger" under Sir Jas. Hope Grant.

Assist.-Surgeon Lawlor served throughout the Eastern campaign of 1854-55, including the battles of Alma and Inkerman, siege and fall of Sebastopol, and attack of the 18th June (Medal and three Clasps, order of Medjidie of 5th Class. Served in the Indian campaign from November 1857; was present at the assault and capture of "Meangunge," during the siege and capture of Lucknow [Medal and Clasp]; also at the affairs of "Barree" and "Nugger" under Sir Jas. Hope Grant.

Assist.-Surgeon Lewis served throughout the Eastern campaign of 1854-55, ncluding the battles of Alma and Inkerman, siege and fall of Sebastopol, attack and occupation of the Cemetery (Medal and three Clasps). Served in the Indian campaign from November 1857, was present at the battle "Cawnpore" on 6th December 1857; at the capture of "Meangunge," the siege and capture of Lucknow [Medal and Clasp]; also at the affairs of the "Barree" and "Nugger."

Assist.-Surgeon Wright served with the 20th Regt. the Eastern campaign of 1854-55, including the battles of Alma and Inkerman, and siege of Sebastopol (Medal and Clasps). Servedin the Indian campaign from November 1857; was present at thecapture of "Meangunge," during the siege and capture of Lucknow [Medal and Clasp].

Paymaster Twibill served throughout the Eastern campaign of 1854-55, including the battles of Alma and Inkerman, siege and fall of Sebastopol, and attack of the 18th June [Medal and three Clasps]. Served in the Indian campaign from November 1857; during the siege and capture of Lucknow [Medal and Clasp]; also at the affairs of "Barree" and "Nugger" under Sir Jas. Hope Grant.

H. M. 42nd (The Royal Highland) Regt. of Foot.

St. Andrew, "*Nemo me impune lacessit.*"—*The Sphinx.*—"EGYPT"—"CORUNNA"—"FUENTES D'ONOR"—PYRENEES"—"NIVELLE"—"NIVE"—"ORTHES"—"TOULOUSE" —PENINSULA"—"WATERLOO"—"ALMA"—SEVASTOPOL." .

FACINGS—*Blue*.

Landed in Calcutta, from England, on 1st November 1857.

BAREILLY.

Regimental Depôt, Stirling.

RANK AND NAMES.	*Regimental Rank.*	*Army Rank.*	REMARKS.
COLONEL.			
Sir James Douglas, K. C. B., -	10 *Apl.* 50	g 20 *June* 54	In Europe.
LIEUTENANT COLONELS.			
Frederick Green Wilkinson,- -	16 *Mar.* 58	.. ..	Commanding.
Edward Ramsden Priestley, -	10 *Aug.* 58	.. ..	
MAJORS.			
John Chetham M'Leod, - -	16 *Mar.* 58		
John Drysdale, - -V.	10 *Aug.* 58	20 *July* 58	Comdt. Nynee Tal Convalescent Depôt
CAPTAINS.			
George Fraser, - -	6 *Apr.* 55	.. ..	
William Crofton Ward, - -	24 *Apr.* 55	.. ..	
Duncan Macpherson, - - V.	24 *Apr.* 55	.. ..	[60.
Joseph Chas. Ross Grove, -	17 *July* 55	.. ..	Leave on P. A. to England to 30 Nov.
William G. Everard Webber, -	10 *Aug.* 55	.. ..	Regtl. Depôt, Scotland.
Rowland Hill Gordon, - -	23 *Feb.* 55	.. ..	Pay Master, Benares Depôt.
Fra. Cunningham Scott, - -	6 *Sept.* 55	... ...	Leave on P. A. in India.
Herbert Henry Moseley, - -	9 *Oct.* 55	.. ..	Regimental Depot.
Adam Ferguson, - - -	1 *May* 57	.. ..	Regtl. Depôt, Scotland.
William Baird, - -	22 *May* 57	... ..	
John Wilson, - -	16 *Mar.* 58	.. ..	[Tal.
D ~~William Lawson,~~ - -	10 *Aug.* 58	.. ..	Instructor of Musketry Sick at Nynee
LIEUTENANTS.			
Capt. William Green, - -	13 *Apr.* 55		
~~Fras. Ed. H. Farquharson,~~ -	24 *Apr.* 55	.. ..	Absent without leave.
William Wood, - -	25 *May* 55	.. ..	Adjutant.
Murdoch Macleod, - -	1 *June* 55		
George Wm. Cockburn, - V.	17 *July* 55	.. ..	
Hon. Rand. Hy. Stewart, - V,	10 *Aug.* 55	.. ..	Brigade Major, Ferozepore.
Richard Kerr Bayly, - -	2 *Oct.* 55		
George Armand Furse, - V,	9 *Oct.* 55	.. ..	
Charles Shuttleworth, -	23 *Oct,* 55	.. ...	Leave on M. C. in India.
Thos. Mansfield James, -	23 *Nov.* 55	.. ..	
Jonathan W. Haynes, - -	23 *Nov.* 55		
William Underwood, - -	23 *Nov.* 55	.. ..	
William Thomas Fraser, - -	14 *Dec.* 55	.. ..	Regtl. Depôt.
James Wm. Mitchell, - -	.. ..	28 *Aug.* 57	Ditto.
William James, - -	16 *Apl.* 58	.. ..	
Arthur James Ceely, - -	7 *Oct.* 58		
ENSIGNS.			
James Edmund Christie, - V,	17 *Aug.* 55		
William Henry Spooner, - -	9 *Oct.* 55	.. ..	
Samuel Gordon McDakin, - -	23 *Oct.* 55	.. ..	Acting Quarter Master. [Depot
Francis Geo. Coleridge, - V,	11 *Jan.* 56	.. ..	Station Staff Nynee Tal Convalescent
William Sanders Walter, - V,	25 *Jan.* 56	.. ..	
Henry Wemyss Feilden, - V,	1 *Feb.* 56	.. ..	Doing duty 1st Gwalior Regiment.
Geo. Thos. Carus Moore, -	12 *Dec.* 56	.. ..	
Edward Whitehead, - -	22 *May* 57	.. ..	Regtl. Depôt, Scotland.
~~*Hon.* Henry Thomas Fraser,~~ -	10 *Sep.* 58	.. ..	Ditto.
Alexander Ferrier Kidston, -	9 *Nov.* 58	.. ..	Ditto.

H. M. 42ND (THE ROYAL HIGHLAND) REGT. OF FOOT.—(*Continued*).

RANK AND NAMES.	*Regimental Rank.*	*Army Rank.*	REMARKS.
INSTRUCTOR OF MUSKETRY.			
Capt. Wm. Lawson, - - -	10 *Aug.* 58		
PAYMASTER.			
James Arnold Bazalgette, - -	24 *Apr.* 55		
ADJUTANT.			
Lieut. William Wood, - -	16 *Feb.* 55	*lt.* 25 *May* 55	
QUARTER MASTERS.			
Alexander Macgregor, - -	25 *May* 55	.. ..	Leave on M. C.
Ensign S. G. McDakin, - -	.. ..	.. ..	Acting.
SURGEON.			
John Sheldon Furlong, M. D., -	9 *Feb.* 55		
ASSISTANT-SURGEONS.			
Alexander Maclean, - -	7 *Apr.* 54	.. ..	Medical Charge of Convalescent Depôt, [Darjeeling.
Alfred Hooper, - -	16 *June* 54	.. ...	Leave on M. C. to England.
W A. Mackinnon, - -	26 *Mar.* 59	18 *Feb.* 53	On the staff of the Commander-in-Chief.
INTERPRETER.			
Capt. T. P. Clarkson, 44th N. I.	.. ..	.. ..	

English Agents—Messrs. Cox and Co.
Calcutta Agent—J. H, Fergusson, Esq.

Strength—10 Companies with 55 Sergeants,—50 Corporals,—25 Drummers and 866 Privates.

WAR SERVICES OF THE OFFICERS OF H. M. 42ND REGT. OF FOOT.

Sir James Douglas accompanied the Expedition to South America under Gen. Craufurd on the Quarter-Master-General's Staff, and was engaged in the attack on Buenos Ayres. Subsequently in the same capacity he proceeded to Portugal with the Expedition under Sir Arthur Wellesley: was senior officer of the Quarter-Master-General's Department on the landing of the army; and was present at the battles of Roleia, Vemiera, and Corunna. Joined the Protuguese army with the command of a Regiment in 1809: was present at the passage of the Douro and battles of Busaco, Fuentes d'Onor, Salamanca, and the Pyrenees (wounded); after which he obtained command of the 7th Portuguese Brigade, and commanded it in the battles of the Nivelle, Nive, Orthes, and Toulouse Bwice wounded, occasioning the loss of a leg). Sir James has received the Gold Cross and three Clasps forl (tusaco, Salamanca, Phyrenees, Nivelle, Nive, Orthes. and Toulouse.

Lt.Col. Wilkinson served the Eastern Campaign of 1854-55, including the battle of Alma and siege of Sebastopo (Medal and Clasps).

Major M'Leod, and Lieut. Wood, served the Eastern campaign of 1854-55 including the battles of Alma and Balaklava, expedition to Kertch, siege and fall of Sebastopol, and assault on the outworks on 18th June (Medal and Clasps). Captain M'Leod and Lieut. Wood are Knights of the Legion of Honor.

Major Drysdale served the Eastern campaign of 1854-55, including the battles of Alma and Balaklava (as Adjutant at both battles), expedition to Kertch, siege and fall of Sebastopol, and assault on the outworks on the 18th June (Medal and Clasps, and Knight of the Legion of Honor).

Captain Ward served the Eastern campaign of 1854-55, including the battles of Alma and Balaklava, expedition to Kertch, siege and fall of Sebastopol (received a slight contusion from the fragment of a shell in the trenches), and assault on the outworks 18th June (Medal and Clasps).

Captains Grove and Scott served throughout the Eastern campaign of 1854-55, including the battles of Alma and Balaklava, expidition to Kertch. siege and fall of Sebastopol, and assault on the outworks on the 18th June (Medal and Clasps, and 5th Class of the Medjidie).

Captains Webber and Lawson served the Estern campaign of 1854-55, including the battles of Alma and Balaklava, expedition to Kertch, siege and fall of Sebastopol, and assault on the outworks on 18th June (Medal and Clasps).

Captain Gordon served with the 38th Regt. throughout the Eastern campaign, including the battles of Alma and Inkerman, siege of Sebastopol, and commanded the party of 38th which was engaged in repulsing the sortie on the 20th Dec. for which he was honourably mentioned by Lord Raglan and promoted into the Coldstream Guards (Medal and Clasps).

Capt. Wilson served the Eastern campaign of 1854-55, including the battle of Balaklava, expedition to Kertch, siege and fall of Sebastopol and assault upon the outworks on 18th June (Medal and Clasps).

Capts. Ferguson and Baird, Lts. Green, Farquharson. and Hon. R. H. Stewart, served at the siege and fall of Sebastopol from July 55 (Medal & Clasp).

Paymaster Bazalgette served at the siege of Sebastopol from June 1855 (Medal and Clasp).

Quartermaster M'Gregor served the Eastern campaign of 1854-55, including the battle of Alma, expedition to Kertch, siege and fall of Sebastopol, and assault on the outworks 18th June (Medal and Clasps).

Surgeon Furlong served the Eastern campaign of 1854-55, including the affair of Bulganak, battles of Alma, Ballaklava, and Inkerman, expedition to Kertch, siege of Sebastopol, and assault on the outworks 18th June (Medal and Clasps).

Assist.-Surgeon Maclean served the Eastern campaign of 1854-55, including the battle of Balaklava, expedition to Kertch, siege of Sebastopol, and assault on the outworks 18th June (Medal and Clasps).

Assist.-Surgeon A. Hooper served in the Eastern campaign of 1854-55, was present at siege of Sebastopol (Medal and Clasp).

H. M. 43rd (Monmouthshire) Regiment of Foot.

(LIGHT INFANTRY.)

"VOMIERA"—"CORUNNA"—"BUSACO"—"FEUNTES D' ONOR"—CUIDAD RODRIGO" —"BADAJOZ"—"SALAMANCA"—"VITTORIA"—"NIVELLE"—NIVE"— "TOULOUSE"—"PENINSULA,"

SAUGOR.

3 Companies at *Nagcde,* 5 Companies on *Field Service,*

SAUGOR DISTRICT.

Depôt Chatham.

RANK AND NAMES.	*Regimental Rank.*	*Army Rank.*	REMARKS.
COLONEL.			
Sir James Fergusson, K.C.B.,..	26 *Mar.* 50	11 *Nov.* 51	In Europe.
LIEUTENANT COLONELS.			
George Talbot, ..	7 *Nov.* 56	.. ..	Dpy. Qr. Master Genl. H. M. Forces Madras.
James M. Primrose, ..	20 *Mar.* 57	.. ..	Commanding.
MAJORS.			
H. J. P. Booth, ..	3 *Apl.* 57	.. ..	On Detachment, Nagode.
F. H Synge, ...	24 *July* 57	.. ..	
CAPTAINS.			
T. H. Cockburn, ..	28 *Nov.* 51	*m*	A. D. C. to the Right Hon'ble the Governor of Bombay,
W. J. Dorehill, ..	29 *July* 53	11 *Jan.* 50	Brigade Major 2d Brigade Saugor Field Division.
I. G. C. Disbrowe, ..	20 *Jan.* 54	31 *Mar.* 48	
T. E. Holmes. ..	26 *Dec.* 54	15 *Aug.* 52	Commanding Depot Chatham.
H. B. H. Rocke, ..	1 *May.* 55	17 *Aug.* 25	Lv. Cape of G. H. on M. C. for 6 months from 5th Sept. 1858 not rejoined.
F. M. Colvile, ..	9 *Oct.* 55	.. ..	On 18 months leave from 5 Apl. 59 Eu.
R. C. Glover, ..	30 *Jan.* 57	.. ..	
Thomas Horan, ..	16 *Mar.* 57	24 *Apl.* 55	Pay Master of Invalids H. M. Forces Calcutta.
H. T. Trafford, ..	3 *Apl.* 57	.. ..	On Detachment, Nagode.
C. R Mure, ..	10 *Apl.* 57	8 *Jan.* 56	
W. S. Richardson, ..	24 *Aug.* 58	.. ..	
John Hudson, ..	11 *Jan.* 59	.. ..	Exchanged from 15th Foot, 11th Jan. 59, it is not known where he is.
LIEUTENANTS.			
S. T. Sargent, ..	29 *July.* 53	9 *July* 52	Instructor of Musketry,—Leave India medical certificate, Calcutta.
F. E. Medhurst, ..	29 *July.* 53	24 *Jan.* 53	Lv. on P.A. to England for 18 Months.
A. G. E. Morley, ..	29 *July.* 53	25 *Aprl* 53	Ditto.
Hon. A. E. Harris, ..	23 *Mar.* 55	.. ..	Leave to Neilgherries.
H. J. Berners, ..	13 *Apl.* 55		
H. A. Brett, ..	1 *May.* 55	.. ..	
T. C. Maguire, ..	10 *Aug.* 55	.. ..	Detachment, Nagodc.
F. G. E. Glover, ..	29 *Aug.* 55	.. ..	Leave on M. C. to England.
A. R. Close, ..	9 *Oct.* 55		
Harry Gorton, ..	14 *Dec.* 55	.. ..	Leave to Europe on medicalce rtificate.
Stanley Crozier, ..	8 *Jan.* 56	.. ..	
C. H. Hatchel, ...	5 *Sep.* 56	.. ..	
Vere Benett, ..	26 *Sep.* 56	.. ..	At Depot Chatham,
William Livesay, ..	3 *Apl.* 57	.. ..	
H. O. Bateman, ..	24 *July.* 57	.. ..	At Depot Chatham.
D. U. W. F. Blyth, ..	24 *May.* 58	.. ..	
H. C. Talbot, ..	24 *Aug.* 58	.. ..	

H. M. 43rd Regiment of Foot—(*Continued.*)

Rank and Names.	Regimental Rank.	Army Rank.	Remarks.
Ensigns.			
Thoms McGoun, ..	26 *Sep.* 56	8 *July.* 56	
J. E. K. Morley, ..	24 *Feb.* 57	14 *Mar.* 56	At Depot Chatham.
G. H. B. Young, ..	3 *Apl.* 57		
Ernest Villers, ..	24 *July.* 57	.. ..	At Depot Chatham.
Joseph Hogarth, ..	31 *Aug.* 58	.. ..	Ditto.
R. M. Tod, ..	7 *Sep.* 58	.. ..	Ditto.
John McNeill, ..	17 *Sep.* 58	.. ..	Ditto,
Instructor of Musketry.			
Lieut. S. T. Sargent, ..	13 *Oct.* 58		
Pay Master.			
Horatio Morgan, ..	17 *Sep.* 58	.. ..	
Adjutant.			
George Garland, ..	6 *Feb.* 57	.. ..	
Quarter Master.			
Arthur Williams, ..	29 *Oct.* 58	.. ..	
Surgeon.			
Alexander Barclay, ..	13 *Apl.* 52	.. ..	
Assistant Surgeons.			
C D. Madden, M. D ..	31 *Aug.* 55	31 *Dec.* 54	
John J. Henry, ..	28 *Aug.* 57	18 *Jan.* 56	Nagode.
James Good, ..	3 *Nov.* 57	3 *Oct.* 57	
Interpreter.			
*			

Strength—10 Companies, 54 Sergeants—50 Corporals—24 Drummers—851 Privates.

Calcutta Agents—Messrs. Gillanders, Arbuthnot & Co. | *Madras Ditto.*—Messrs. Arbuthnot & Co.

Irish Agents—*Sir* Edward Borough and Co. | *English Agents*—Messrs. Cox and Co.

WAR SERVICES OF THE OFFICERS OF THE 43rd REGT. OF FOOT.

Sir James Fergusson served on the campaign of 1808-9, including the battles of Vimiera and Corunna, Expedition to Walcheren in 1809. Peninsular campaigns from March 1810 to the end of that war in 1814. including the passage of the Coa, near Almeida, battle of Busaco, actions at Pombal, Redinha, Miranda de Corvo, Foz d'Arouce, and Sabugal; battle of Fuentes d'Onor, sieges and assaults of Ciudad Rodrigo and Badajoz, battle of Salamanca, action of San Munos, passage of the Bidassoa, battle of the Nivelle, battles of the Nive on the 9th, 10th, 11th, 12th, and 13th Dec. 1813; and investment of Bayonne. Major-General Fergusson has received five wounds, viz. at Vimiera, slightly; at the storming of Ciudad Rodrigo, severely in the body and slightly in the foot; at Badajoz, slightly in the side by a splinter of a shell in the trenches, and in the head at the assault. He has received the Gold Medal for Badajoz, as senior surviving Officer of the Light Division Storming Party; and he also served in the Storming Party at Ciudad Rodrigo and at the taking of the outworks of that place Fort Reynard. He has also received the Silver War Medal with eight Clasps.

Lt Colonel Primrose served with the 43rd in the Kaffir war of 1851-53 (Medal) Engaged in the operations of General Whitlock's division in Bundlekund. Medal.

Major Booth, and Lient. Garland served with the 43rd in the Kaffir war of 1851-53 (Medal), Engaged in the operations of General Whitlock's division in Bundlekund. Medal.

Captan Glover and Lieut. Sargent served with the 51st Regt. throughout the Burmese War of 1852 (Medal); on board the E. I. C. steam frigate *Feroze* during the naval action and destruction of the enemy's stockades on the Rangoon River; during the succeeding three days'. operations in the vicinity, and at the storm and capture of Rangoon. Engaged in the operations of General Whitlock's division in Bundlekund. Medal.

Captain Dorehill served with the Buffs in the battle of Punniar (Medal), and was severely wounded on the right side of his breast. Engaged in the operations of General Whitlock's division in Bwndlekund Medal.

Captain Horan served with the 54th Regt. during the whole of the campaign of 1842 in Affghanistan (Medal). and was present in the engagements with the enemy on 28th March and 28th April in the Pisheen Valley; in that of the 29th May near Candahar, 30th Aug. at Goaine. 5th Sept. before, Guznee, occupation and destruction of that fortress and of Cabool, expedition into Kohistan, storm, capture, and destruction of Istaliff, and in the various minor affairs in and between the Bolan and Khyber Passes. Engaged in the operations of General Whitlock's division in Bundlekund Medal.

Capt, Trafford served with the 51st Regt, in Burmah from Sept, 1852 to the end of the war, and was present with Capt. Irby's detachment of four Companies with Brigadier-General Cheape's force during the whole of the successful operations in the Donabew district, ending in the assault and capture, on the 19th March 1853, of the stronghold of the Burmese chief Myat-toon (Medal). Engaged in the operations of General Whitlock's division in Bwndlekund Medal.

Captain Mure served with the 43rd Light Infantry in the Kaffir war of 1851-53 (Medal). Served also in the Crimea from 29th July to 29th Sept. 1855, as Aide-de-Camp to Major Gen. Markham (Medal and Clasp for Sebastopol, and 5th Class of the Medjidie).

Lieut. Medhurst served with the 51st Regt. throughout the Burmese war of 1852 (Medal); on board the E. I. C. steam sloop *Sesostris* during the naval action and destruction of the enemy's stockades on the Rangoon River; served during the succeeding three days' operations in the vicinity (including the storming of the White House Redoubt) and at the storm and capture of Rangoon; also at the assault and capture of Bassein 19th May. Engaged in the operations of General Whitlock's division in Bundlekund. Medal.

Lt. Morley served with the 51st Regt. throughout the Burmese war of 1852 (Medal); on board the E. I. C, steam frigate *Ferooz* during the naval action and destruction of the enemy's stockades on the Rangoon River; served during the succeeding three days' operations in the vicinity (including the storming of the White House Redoubt), and at the storm and capture of Rangoon. Engaged in the operations of General Whitlock's division in Bundlekund Medal.

Major Cockburn, served as A. D. C. to Sir H. Rose in the operations in Central India, present at the action of Koond Calpee and the taking of Gwalior.

Major Synge. Captains Disbrowe, Colville and Richardson. Lieuts. Berners, Brett, Maguire, Close, Crozier, Hatchell, Livesay, Blyth and Talbot, Ensigns Macgown and Young. Qr. Mr. Williams, Asst. Sergeons Madden, Henry and Good were engaged in the operations of General Whitlock's division in Bundlekund. Medal.

Doctor Barclay served in the Kaffir war of 1846-7, and in that of 1851-2-3 (Medal).

H. M, 46th (South Devonshire) Regiment of Foot.

"DOMINICA" "SEVASTOPOL."

FACINGS—*Yellow.*

Landed at Bombay————

En route to MOOLTAN.

Depot, Templemore.

RANK AND NAMES.	*Regimental Rank.*	*Army Rank.*	REMARKS.
COLONEL.			
Sir John L. Pennefather, K.C.B.	.. ..	*m.g.* 19 *Nov.* 54	Europe.
LIEUTENANT COLONELS.			
Alexander Maxwell, C. B., ..	12 *Dec.* 55	*c.* 12 *Dec.* 57	
Arthur George Vesey, ..	31 *Aug.* 58	.. ..	Leave of absence to Simla to 18th Augt. 1859.
MAJORS.			
Colin Fred. Campbell, ..	.. ..	*l.c.* 11 *May* 55	
Algernon Robt. Garrett, ..	31 *Aug.* 58	2 *Nov.* 55	
CAPTAINS.			
James George Clarke, ..	20 *Jan.* 54		
Albert Nicholas, ..	28 *Apl.* 54		
Henry Fuller Sandwith, ...	6 *June* 54		
George Fred. Dallas, ...	.. ..	*m.* 6 *June* 56	
Charles S. M'Alester, ..	29 *Dec.* 54	.. ..	Regimental Depot.
Alfred Henry Waldy. ..	29 *Dec.* 54		
Thomas Douglas Forde, ..	5 *June* 55		Ditto.
George Henry Knapp, ..	29 *May* 57	.. ..	
William Thomas Waldy, ..	17 *July* 57		
Richard Coote, ..	24 *Aug.* 58	.. ..	Leave on P. A. to Cashmere to 31st Oct. 1859.
Edw. Hawker Helyar, ..	1 *June* 59	.. ..	Leave on P.A. to Simla to 19th Sep. 59
Edward Townshend, ..	1 *June* 59		
LIEUTENANTS			
Hen. Carr Wm. Hamond, ..	8 *Dec.* 54		
Thos, Geo. B. Atkinson, ..	9 *Feb.* 55		
Percy Malcolm Jones, ..	9 *Feb.* 55	.. ..	Leave on M. C. to Bombay.
Richard Edw. Brookes, ..	9 *Mar.* 55	.. ..	Leave on P. A. to Meerut to 30th Sept. 1859.
Andrew Whitten, ..	9 *Mar.* 55	.. ..	Instructor of Musketry.
John Spencer Churchill, ..	9 *Mar.* 55	.. ..	Leave of absence on M. C. to Mussoorie to 30th Nov. 1?59.
Charles John Burgess, ..	4 *May.* 55		
Frank Grieve, ..	6 *July* 55	.. ..	Regimental Depot.
Frederick Coucher, ..	22 *June* 58		
Peter A. John Ducrow, ..	2 *July* 58		
Vesey Daly, ..	31 *Aug.* 58		
Allan Joshua Kentish, ..	31 *Aug.* 58	.. ..	Ditto.
Charles Benj. Col. Speke, ..	1 *June* 59		
Geo. T. Delme Radcliffe, ..	1 *June* 59		
ENSIGNS.			
Stewart James Carlow, ..	2 *Oct.* 55		
Robert Bole Morrow, ..	26 *Feb.* 56		
John Dwyer, ..	25 *Mar.* 56	..	Adjutant.
Rd. F. Armytage Howorth ..	14 *July* 57		
Wm. G. M'Crae, ..	13 *July* 58	.. ..	Regimental Depot.
Fra. L. Priestley, ..	16 *July* 58	.. ..	Ditto.
Henry B. Scott, ..	7 *Sep.* 58	.. ..	Ditto.
Lawrence W. Herchmer, ..	12 *Nov.* 58	.. ..	Ditto.
Wm. F. Spencer, ..	31 *Dec.* 58		

H. M. 46th Regiment of Foot—(*Continued.*)

Rank and Names.	Regimental Rank.	Army Rank.	Remarks.
Instructor of Musketry.			
Lieut. Andrew Whitten, ..	15 *Jan.* 57	*lt.* 9 *Mar.* 58	Leave on P. A. to Bombay to 31 July [59.
Pay Master.			
Lieut. Henry Wm. Sibley, ..	27 *Oct.* 54	*lt.* 9 *Feb.* 48	
Adjutant.			
Ens. John Dwyer, ..	25 *Mar.* 56	*ens.* 25 *Mar.* 56	
Quarter Master.			
George Sanderson, ..	28 *Apl.* 54		
Surgeon.			
Vere Webb. ..	28 *Mar.* 54		
Assistant Surgeons.			
John Meane, ..	24 *Dec.* 52		
John George Faught, ..	5 *Jan.* 55		
Geo. R. Woodhouse, ..	7 *May* 58		
Interpreter.			
*			

Strength.—10 Companies, with 55 Sergeants—47 Corporals—19 Drummers—792. Privates.

English Agents—Messrs. Cox and Co.
Irish Agents—Messrs. *Sir* E. Borough, *Bt.* and Co.
Calcutta Agents ———

WAR SERVICES OF THE OFFICERS OF THE 46th REGT. OF FOOT.

Sir John Pennefather served in Sir Charles Napier's campaign in Scinde, and commanded the Infantry Brigade at the battle of Meeanee (Medal), and was shot through the body; he was also at the destruction of the Fort of theFort of Imaumghur. Served throughout the Eastern campaign of 1854, in command of a brigade in the 2nd division at the battle of the Alma (horse twice wounded) and siege of Sebastopol (inclnding the repuls. of the powerful sortie on the 29th October), and in command of the division at and after the battle of Inkerman (horse killed under him), (Medal and Clasp, KCB. Grand Officer of the Legion of Honor, Commander 1st Class of St. Maurice and St. Lazarus, and 2nd Class of the Medjidie.)

Colonel Maxwell served at the siege of Sebastopol in in 1854-55, (Medal and Clasp, Companion of the Bath Knight of the Legion of Honor, and 5th Class of the Medjidie).

Lieut.-Colonel Vesey served at the siege of Sebastopol in 1854-55, (Medal and Clasp, and 5th Class of the Medjidie.

Lieut. Col. Campbell served at the siege of Sebastopol in 1854-55, and was wounded in the trenches (Medal and Clasp. Brevet Lt.-Colonel, Knight of the Legion of Honor, Sardinian Medal, and 5th Class of the Medjidie).

Major Garrett served at the siege of Sebastopol in 1854-55, Medal and Clasp, Brevet Major, Sardinian Medal, and 5th Class of the Medjidie).

Captains Piper, Nicholas, and M'Alester, served at the siege of Sebastopol in 1854-55, (Medal and Clasp, and 5th Class of the Medjidie).

Captains Clark, Waldy, and Sandwith, served at the siege of Sebastopol in 1854-55, (Medal and Clasp).

Captain Forde served at the siege and fall of Sebastopol from 8th Nov. 1854, as Aide-de-Camp to Maj.-Gen. Garrett from 1st Dec. 1854, (Medal and Clasp, and 5th Class of the Medjidie).

Captain Knapp, Lieuts. Helvar (wounded at Inkerman) and Townshend, served the Eastern campaign of 1854-55, including the battles of the Alma, Balaklava, and Inkerman, and siege of Sebastopol (Medal and Clasps). Captain Knapp has also the Sardinian Medal and 5th Class of the Medjidie. Lieut. Townshend has the 5th Class of the Medjidie).

Major Dallas served in the Eastern campaign of 1854, including the siege of Sebastopol and battle of Inkerman, where he succeeded to the command of the two campanies 46th Reg. (Medal and Clasps, Brevet Major, Knight of the Legion of Honor, and 5th Class of the Medjidie).

Lieutenant Jones served in the Eastern campaign of 1855, during a considerable portion of which he acted as an Assistant Engineer, (Medal and Clasp, and 5th Class of the Medjidie).

Captain Waldy, Connell, Coote, Lieuts. Hamond, Atkinson, Brooks, Whitten, Churehill, Burgess, and Grieve, and Ens. Dwyer served at the siege of Sebastopol in 1854-55, (Medal and Clasp).

Paymaster Sibley and Quarter-Master Sanderson served at the siege of Sebastopol in 1854-55, (Medal and Clasp).

Surgeon Webb served with the 10th Reg. throughout the Punjaub campaign of 1848-9, including the whole of the siege operations before, and surrender of, Mooltan, and battle of Goojerat (Medal and two Clasps) Served with the 46th Reg. at the siege of Sebastopol in 1854-55, (Medal and Clasp).

Assist.-Surgeon Meane served with the 31st Regt. in the Crimea from 22nd May 1855, including the siege and fall of Sebastopol, and attacks of the 18th June and 8th Sept., and received a contused wound on the knee from a shell in the trenches on 7th June (Medal and Clasp).

H. M. 48th (the Northamptonshire) Regiment of Foot.

"DOURO"—"TALAVERA"—"ALABUHERA"—"BADAJOZ"—"SALAMANCA"—"VITTORIA"—
"PYRENEES"—"NIVELLE"—"ORTHES"—"TOULOUSE"—
"PENINSULA"—"SEVASTOPOLE."
FACINGS—*Buff.*

Arrived in Calcutta from Giblraltar on the 20th October 1858.
CAWNPORE.

Regimental Depôt, Cork, Ireland.

RANK AND NAMES.	*Regimental Rank.*	*Army Rank.*	REMARKS.
COLONEL.			
Sir J. H. Reynett, K. C. H. -	13 *Dec.* 50	*l.g.* 11 *Nov.* 51	England.
LIEUT.-COLONELS.			
Benjamin Riky, - - - - -	13 *Dec.* 53	*col.*28 *Nov.* 54	Commanding.
Alfred Augustus Chapman, -	17 *Sep.* 58	.. ..	On Leave in England on M, C.
MAJORS.			
John Guise Rogers Aplin, - -	20 *Apl.* 58	17 *July* 55	
Robert Blakeney, - - - -	24 *Sep.* 58	6 *June* 56	
CAPTAINS.			
Oliver Matthew Latham, - -	20 *Feb* 52	.. ..	Regtl. Depôt, Cork, Ireland.
Jams Mancor, - - - - -	27 *Dec.* 52	.. ..	Ditto.
William Henry Cairnes, - -	13 *Dec.* 53	.. ..	Ditto.
William Roberts Williamson, -	6 *June* 54		
John Richard Lovett, - - -	15 *May* 55		
Henry William Knight, - -	15 *May* 55		
Hy. Glynne Earle Welby, -	27 *July* 55	.. ..	Leave on S. C. to England.
Francis Constantine Trent, -	21 *Dec.* 55		
John Bedingfeld, - - - -	31 *Dec.* 57		
George Percival Drought, - -	.. ..	16 *Oct.* 55	
Frederick John Castle, - -	16 *Mar.* 58		
Henry Francis Brooke, - - -	24 *Sep.* 58		
LIEUTENANTS.			
Edward Feneran, - - - -	6 *June* 54	... ..	Instructor of Musketry.
Edmund Garland Horne, - -	6 *June* 54	.. ...	Adjutant.
Arthur George Wyse, - - -	11 *Aug.* 54		
Richard Eyre, - - - - -	15 *Mag* 55	.. ...	Depôt, Cork.
James Farquhar, - - - -	15 *May* 55		
William Cumming, - - - -	15 *May* 55	... ..	Depôt, Cork.
George Thomas Miller, - - -	.. ..	15 *Feb.* 53	Leave on M. C. to Mussoorie to 30 Nov. 59.
Edward Benbow, - - - -	27 *July* 55	.. ..	Leave on M. C. to England.
John Rawlins, - - - - - -	.. ..	16 *Oct.* 55	
~~Geo. G. Graham Foster Pigott,~~	16 *Oct.* 55		
Henry J. William Wilkinson -	16 *Oct.* 55		
Colin Campbell, - - - - -	16 *Oct.* 55		
Cornwallis Wade Browne, - -	12 *Dec* 56		
Geo. Nugent R. Goddard. - -	24 *Sep.* 58		

H. M. 48TH (THE NORTHAMPTONSHIRE) REGIMENT OF FOOT.—(*Continued.*)

RANK AND NAMES.	*Regimental Rank.*	*Army Rank.*	REMARKS.
ENSIGNS.			
Pembroke O'M. H. Marshall,	15 *June* 55		
Charles Henry Chauncy,	15 *Oct.* 55		
Thomas Hall,	28 *Dec.* 55		
Edward Cecil Brown,	16 *Mar.* 58		
Pulteney Edwd. Bowlby,	30 *Mar.* 58		
John Walter Keyworth,	13 *Apl.* 58		
William Rapp Tudor,	28 *May* 58	.. ...	Regtl. Depôt Cork. Ireland.
Reginald Pennell,	13 *July* 58	.. ...	Ditto.
William Farley,	12 *Nov.* 58	.. ..	Ditto,
Charles Wheler Hume,	19 *Nov.* 58		
INSTRUCTOR OF MUSKETRY.			
Lieut. Edward Feneran,	14 *Aug.* 58	*lt.* 6 *June* 54	
PAYMASTER.			
Alexander William McKeuzie,	6 *Feb.* 37	1 *Jan.* 55	
ADJUTANT.			
Lieut. Edmund Garland Horne,	6 *June* 54	*lt.* 14 *July* 54	
QUARTER-MASTER.			
John Maitland,	3 *Aug.* 55		
SURGEON.			
Geo. Aug. Fred, Shelton, M. B.	5 *May* 54		
ASSISTANT-SURGEONS.			
Jean Valleton de Boissiere, M.D.	31 *Aug.* 58	6 *Jan.* 57	
John Gordon Grant,	10 *Sep.* 58	7 *May* 55	
William Henry Leslie, M. B.	31 *Dec.* 58		
INTERPRETER.			
Capt. M. F. Evatt, 36th N. I.	.. ..	.. ..	Offg.

Strenght—10 Companies with 49 Sergeants—44 Corporals—20 Drummers—and 798 Privates.

English Agents—Sir John Kirkland and Co.

Irish Agents—Messrs. Cane and Sons.

Calcutta Agents—Messrs. Wood, Olliffe and Co.

WAR SERVICES OF THE OFFICERS OF H. M. 48TH REGT. OF FOOT.

Sir Jas. Reynett served with the 52nd Regt. on the expedition against Ferrol in 1800, and was present at the action before that place. Appointed to the Quarter-Master-General's staff upon the army entering Spain in Nov. 1808; present at Lugo, the affairs upon the retreat to Corunna, and also at the battle of Corunna. Re-appointed to the quarter-Master-General's staff in Portugal, in April 1809; present at the affairs previous to and at the passage of the Douro, and capture of Oporto; affair of Salamonde, battles of Talavera and Busaco, affairs upon the retreat to the lines before Lisbon, and subsequently in 1811 at those upon the advance from thence, at Pombal, Redinha, Sabugal, and Foz d'Arouce; also at the battle of Fuentes d'Onor. He has received the War Medal with four Clasps.

Colonel Riky commanded the 48th Regt. in the Crimea from 21st April 1855, at the siege and fall of Sebastopol (Medal and Clasp, Knight of the Legion of Honor, and 5th Class of the Medjidie).

Major Aplin served the Eastern campaign of 1844-55, including the battles of Alma and Inkerman, siege and fall of Sebastopol, and affair in the Cemetery. Wounded while in command of the sharpshooters of the 28th Regt. (Medal and three Clasps, Brevet Major, Knight of the Legion of Honor, and 5th Class of the Medjidie).

Captains Latham and Bedingfeld, Lieuts. Rawlins, Pigott, and Wilkinson, served at the siege and fall of Sebastopol from 3rd Sept. 1855, (Medal and Clasp). Lieut. Wilkinson served also on detached duty in the Dock-yard from 14th January to 14th March 1856.

Major Blakeney served in the Crimea from 2nd June 1855, at the siege and fall of Sebastopol, and on detached duty in the Dockyard from 14th January to 14th March 1856 (Medal and Clasp, and Brevet Major).

Captains Cairnes, Knight, Castle, and Brooke, Lieut. Feneran, and Surgeon Shelton, landed with the Regt. in the Crimea on the 21st April 1855. and served at the siege and fall of Sebastopol (Medal and Clasp). Captain Cairnes has also the Sardinian Medal. Capt. Knight has the 5th Class of the Medjidie.

Captain Williamson served in the Crimea at the siege of Sebastopol from 21st April to 28th July 1855 (Medal and Clasp).

Captain Lovett, and Lieuts. Eyre and Farquhar, landed with the 48th Regt. in the Crimea, served at the siege and fall of Sebastopol, and on detached duty in the Dockyard from 14th January to 14th March 1856, (Medal and Clasp). Capt. Lovett has the 5th Class of the Medjidie.

Captain Trent served in the Crimea from 21st April 1855, including the siege and fall of Sebastopol—wounded on 4th June (Medal and Clasp, and 5th Class of the Medjidie).

Captain Drought served with the 62nd Regt. the Sutlej campaign in 1846, including the affair of Buddiwal, and actions of Aliwal and Sobraon (Medal and Claps). Also the Eastern campaign of 1854-55, including the siege of Sebastopol from 13th Nov. 1854 (Medal and Clasp).

Lieut. Horne served as Adjutant of the 48th Regt. in the Crimea from 27th April 1855, and at the siege and fall of Sebastopol—wounded 18th Aug. (Medal and Clasp, and 5th Class of the Medjidie).

Lieut. Wyse served in the Crimea from 14th May to 7th Sept. 1855, and at the siege of Sebastopol (Medal and Clasp).

Lieut. Cumming served in the Crimea at the siege of Sebastopol from 21st April to 7th August 1855 (Medal and Clasp).

Qr.-Master Maitland was present at the attack and capture of Coorg, in the East Indies, in April 1834; served also in the Crimea from 21st April 1855, at the siege and fall of Sepastopol (Medal and Clasp).

Assist.-Surgeon M'Dermott served the Eastern campaign of 1854-55, including the battles of Alma and Balaklava, siege and fall of Sebastopol (Medal and Clasps).

H. M. 51st (The 2nd Yorkshire, West Riding,) or The Kings own Light Infantry.

"MINDEN"—"CORUNNA"—"SALAMANCA"—"VITTORIA"—"PYRENEES"—
"NIVELLE"—"ORTHES"—"PENINSULA"—"WATERLOO"—"PEGU"

Facings—BLUE.

Landed at Bombay.

MEEAN MEEAR,

Detachment at UMRITSUR.

Regimental Depot, Chichester.

RANK AND NAMES.	*Regimental Rank.*	*Army Rank.*	REMARKS.
COLONEL.			
Sir Thos. Willshire, *Bt.* K.C.B.,	.. ..	*l.g.* 26 *June* 49	Europe.
LIEUTENANT COLONELS.			
Arnold Chas. Errington, ..	.. ..	*c.* 13 *Feb.* 55	Commanding.
Augustus Henry Irby, ..	18 *Sep.* 57		
MAJORS.			
John Henry Dickson, ..	18 *Sep.* 57		
William Agg, ..	17 *Sep.* 58	.. ..	Comdg. detachment at Umritsur.
CAPTAINS.			
Saml. Alexander Madden, ..	6 *June* 54	... ..	Lv. on P. A. to Europe, for 18 months.
Stewart Alex. Cleeve, ..	1 *June* 55	... ..	Brigade Major Queens Troops Bombay.
George Warde, ..	10 *Avg.* 55	17 *Dec.* 52	Lv. on P. A. to Europe for 18 months.
Charles Acton, ..	8 *Jan.* 56	.. ..	Regimental Depot.
Hen. R. De Anyers Willis, ..	4 *Apl.* 56	.. ..	With Detachment at Umritsur.
Geo. Hen. Hibbert Ware, ..	21 *Dec.* 55		
R. G. Sanders Mason, ..	18 *Sep.* 57		
Fra. Jas. Buchanan Reed, ..	17 *Nov.* 57	.. ..	With Detachment at Umritsur.
~~William Henry Herrick,~~ ..	20 *Feb.* 59	.. ..	Regimental Depot.
Malcolm Chas. Farrington, ..	23 *June* 58	.. ..	With Detacht. at Umritsur.
Augustus Brigstocke, ..	17 *Sep.* 58		
Charles James Hughes, ..	1 *Apl.* 59		
LIEUTENANTS.			
Percy Chaplin, ..	1 *June* 55	.. ..	Lv. on P. A. to Europe, for 18 months.
Martin Bud Lewin, ..	4 *Apl.* 56	.. ..	With Detachment at Umritsur.
Eust Beaumont Burnaby ..	5 *Sep.* 56		
Wm. Charles Edw. Scott, ..	19 *Sep.* 56	.. ..	Instructor of Musketry, en route to [join.
Riland W. Oldham, ..	16 *Jan.* 57	.. ..	Regimental Depot.
Chas. L. Baillie Hamilton, ..	18 *Sep.* 57		
Arthur W. Crewe Read, ..	17 *Nov.* 57		
Edmund Moresby Crowe, ..	23 *Mar.* 58	.. ..	With Detachment at Umritsur.
William Clements, ..	23 *Mar.* 58	.. ..	Adjutant.
Smeeton Walker, ..	23 *Mar.* 58	.. ..	With Detachment at Umritsur.
William Henry Saunders, ..	9 *May* 58	.. ..	Ditto.
Henry Chambers, ..	20 *May* 58		
Edward Dudley Oliver, ..	23 *June* 58		
Henry Steuart Tompson, ..	24 *Sep.* 58		
Robert Norton Cobb, ..	1 *Apl.* 59		
ENSIGNS.			
Fred. Thomas Humfrey, ..	26 *Sep.* 56		
W. Price Llewellyn Lewes, ..	17 *Nov.* 57		
Empson Edw. Middleton, ..	30 *Mar.* 58		
Dudley Villiers Stuart, ..	31 *Mar.* 58		
Robert Stratford, ..	25 *June* 58		En route to join.
Geo. S. Robertson, ..	26 *June* 58	.. ..	Ditto.
Arf. Shaen Carter, ..	24 *Sep.* 58	.. ..	Regimental Depot,
John V. Nugent, ..	9 *Nov.* 58	.. ..	Ditto.
~~Francis Barnstone,~~ ..	11 *Mar* 59		

H. M. 51st Regiment of Light Infantry—*(Continued.)*

Rank and Names.	Regimental Rank.	Army Rank.	Remarks.
Instructor of Musketry.			
Lieut. W. C. E. Scott, ..	16 *Dec.* 58		
Pay Master.			
Geo. H. Shutlleworth, ..	17 *Sep.* 58	8 *June* 58	
Adjutant.			
Lieut. William Clements, ..	18 *May* 55		
Quarter Master.			
Thomas Lawrence, ..	29 *June* 55		
Surgeon.			
Henry Marsh Webb, M. D., ..	8 *Dec.* 54		
Assistant Surgeons.			
George Thomas Bourke, ..	8 *Apl.* 55	.. ..	With detachment at Umritsur.
John Folliott, ..	7 *May* 55		
George Samuel Burnside, ..	1 *Aug.* 57		
Interpreter.			
*			

Strength.—10 Companies with 57 Sergeants—50 Corporals—20 Buglers and 1082 Privates.

English Agent—A. Lawrie, Esq.
Irish Agents—Messrs. Cane and Co.
Calcutta Agents————

WAR SERVICES OF THE OFFICERS OF THE 51st REGT. OF LIGHT INFANTRY.

Sir Thomas Willshire served with the 38th Regt. in the West Indies from August 1797 to August 1800, the campaign of 1808-9, including the battles of Rolaia and Vimiera, retreat to and battle of, Corunna. Accompanied the expedition to Walcheren in 1809. Served afterwards in the Peninsula from June 1812 to the end of that war in 1814; commanded the Light Company at the battle of Salamanca (twice wounded), on the retreat from Burgos and Action at Villa Muriel, the action of Osma, battle of Vittoria, first assault of San Sebastian, also second assault and capture, when he received the brevet rank of Major. Commanded a Brigade of Light Companies at the passage of Bidassoa, battle of Nivelle, and battles of the Nive on the 9th, 10th, and 11th Dec. 1813, for which services he was in 1815 appointed Brevet Lieut.-Colonel. Repulsed with three hundred men in the attack of ten thousand Kaffirs upon the open village of Graham's Town, on the frontier of the Cape of Good Hope, on the 22nd April 1819, and commanded during the subsequent operations against the Kaffirs in the same year. Served afterwards in the East Indies from May 1822 to 1840. Commanded a wing of the 46th Regt. at the capture of Kitoor in the Dooab, in Dec. 1824. Served also throughout the whole of the campaign in Affghanistan under Lord Keane; present at the capture of the fortress of Ghuznee, 23rd July 1839, upon which occasion he was appointed K. C. B.; and while in command of the Bombay column of the army of the Indus he captured the fortress of Khelat, on the 13th Nov. following, for which service he was created a Baronet. Has received the Silver War Medal with seven Clasps.

Colonel Errington served with the 51st during the war in Burmah from April to Dec. 1852; was on board the E. I. C steam sloop *Sesostris* during the naval action and destruction of the enemy's stockades on the Rangoon River; served during the succeeding three days' operations in the vicinity, and commanded the Regiment at the storm and capture of Rangoon: he also commanded the troops engaged at the assault and capture of Bassein, 19th May (wounded), and received the special approbation of the Governor-General in Council for his services upon this occasion (medal and clasp, and Brevet Lt. Colonel.

Lt Col. Irby served with the 51st throughout the Burmese war of 1852-53, on board the E. I. C. steam frigate *Sesostris* during the naval action and destruction of the enemy's stockades on the Rangoon River; served during the succeeding three days' operations in the vicinity, and at the storm and capture of Rangoon; also at the assault and capture of Bassein 19th May. Commanded a Detachment consisting of four Companies of the 51st with Brigadier-General Cheape's force during the whole of the successful operations in the Donobew District, ending in the assault and capture, on the 19th March 1853, of the stronghold of the Burmese chief Myat-toon (Medal and Clasp).

Major Dickson served with the 51st in Burmah from Feb. 1853 to the end of the war, and was present with Captain Irby's Detachment of four Companies with Brigadier-General Cheape's force untill shortly before the capture of Myat-toon's stronghold, when he was left in command of a Detachment to protect the sick and wounded of the force (Medal and Clasp).

Captain Madden served with the 51st throughout the Burmese war of 1852-53, on board the E. I. C. steam sloop *Sesostris* during the naval action and destruction of the enemy's stockades on the Rangoon River; served during the succeeding three days' operations in the vicinity (including the storming of the White House Redoubt), and at the storm and capture of Rangoon; also at the assault and capture of Bassein, 19th May, (Medal and Clasp.)

Major Agg served with the 51st throughout the Burmese war of 1852-53, on board the E. I. C. steam frigate *Feroze* during the navel action and destruction of the enemy's stockades on the Rangoon River served during the succeeding three days' operations in the vicinity (including the storming of the White House Redoubt), and at the storm and capture of Rangoon; also at the assault and capture of Bsseiu, 19th May, (Medal and Clasp).

Captains Cleeve (as Adjutant) and Mitford served with the 51st throughout the Burmese war of 1852-53 on board the E. I. C. steam frigate *Ferooz* during the naval action and destruction of the enemy's stockade, on the Rangoon River; served during the succeeding three days operations in the vicinity (including the storms ing of the White House Redoubt), and the storm and capture of Rangoon (Medal and Clasp).

Captain Acton served with the 51st in Burmah from Feb. 1853 to the end of the war, and was present with Capt. Irby's Detachment of four Companies with Brigadier-General Cheape's force during the whole of the successful operations in the Donabew district, ending in the assault and capture, on the 19th March 1853, of the stronghold of the Burmese chief Myat-toon (Medal and Clasp.)

Captain Hibbert Ware served with the 97th Regt. at the siege and fall of Sebastopol from 20th Nov. 1854 and was severely wounded on the night of the 20th Aug in a sortie made by the Russians on our trenches (Medal, Clasp, and Sardinian Medal).

Captain Warde has received the 4th Class of Medjidie for service, as Major, with the Turkish Contingent.

H. M. 52nd (Oxfordshire) Regiment of Foot.

(LIGHT INFANTRY.)
"HINDOOSTAN"—"VIMIERA"—"CORUNNA"—"BUSACO"—"FUENTES D'ONOR"—
"CIUDAD RODRIGO"—"BADAJOZ"—"SALAMANCA"—"VITTORIA"—"NIVELLE"—
"NIVE"—"ORTHES"—"TOULOUSE"—"PENINSULA"—"WATERLOO."
FACINGS—*Buff.*

Landed in Bengal from England, on the 5th October, 1853.
SEALKOTE.
Detachment at *Kote Kanyra.*
Regimental Depôt, Chatham.

RANK AND NAMES.	Regimental Rank.	Army Rank.	REMARKS.
COLONEL.			
Sir Archibald Maclaine, K. C. B.,	8 *Feb.* 47	*l. g* 5 *June* 55	In Europe.
LIEUT. COLONELS.			
D ~~George Campbell, C. B.,~~ ..	27 *May* 53	*col.* 28 Nov. 54	Leave on M. C. to England. [Hope.
John Leslie Dennis, ..	24 *Oct.* 56	*col.* 28 *Nov.* 54	Leave on M. C. to Cape of Good
MAJORS.			
Charles Albert Denison, .	11 *July* 56	*l.c.* 23 *Oct.* 55	Depy. Adjutant Genl. Queen's Troops, Madras.
William Corbett, ...	15 *Oct.* 58	... ...	Commanding.
CAPTAINS.			
Arthur Lennox Peel, ...	22 *Aug.* 51		
James Johnes Bourchier, ..	15 *Oct.* 52	.. ..	Comdg. Regtl. Depôt. Chatham.
Hon. Ernest George Curzon, ..	12 *Nov.* 52	.. ..	En route to join.
George Charles Synge, *PH,*	27 *May* 53	*m* 19 *Jan.* 58	Commanding detachment at Kanyra,
D ~~James Abercromby Dick~~, ..	26 *Oct.* 54	28 *Feb.* 51	
Hon. D. John Monson, ...	20 *July* 55	.. ..	Leave on M. C. to England.
Charles Kenrick Crosse, ..	15 *Apl.* 56	*m* 19 *Jan.* 58	
Frederick A. Champion, ..	11 *July* 56	.. ..	A. D. C. to Maj. Genl. Craigie at Madras.
Seymour John Blane, ..	19 *Sep.* 56	*m* 19 *Jan.* 58	Acting Brigade Major of Queen's Troops, Calcutta.
Walter James Stopford, ...	15 *Oct.* 58	.. ..	With Invalids en route to England.
Arthur Henley, ...	30 *Mar.* 59	.. ..	Leave on M. C. to Simla.
LIEUTENANTS.			
Alexander Hope Graves, *V,*	27 *May* 53	12 *Dec.* 52	Acting Interpreter.
Hon. Geo. H. Windsor-Clive, *V,*	20 *Jan.* 54	.. ..	Leave on M. C. to England with Invalids.
~~Hon. F. LePoer Trench~~, ..	25 *May* 55	.. ...	Leave on M. C. to England.
Thomas Archer Julian, ..	6 *July* 55	.. ..	Adjutant & Instrtr. of Musketry.—Leave on M. C. to Dhurmsala
Robert Westropp Ellis, ..	31 *Aug.* 55	29 *Dec.* 54	Leave on M. C. to England.
George Cruden Fraser, ...	18 *Apl.* 56		
Stephen Murphy, ...	16 *May* 56		
Richard Davies Burroughs, ..	11 *July* 56	.. ..	Leave on M. C. to England.
Henry Richard Beattie, ..	7 *Sep.* 57	.. ..	Leave on M. C. to England.
Thomas Simpson, ..	15 *Sept.* 57	.. ..	Leave on M. C. to England.
William Owen, ...	27 *Nov.* 57		
F. Herbert Suckling, ...	23 *Apl.* 58	29 *June* 55	Leave on M. C. to England.
Charles Keyworth, ...	13 *July* 58	13 *Apl.* 58	Regtl. Depôt, England,
Richard Wingfield, ...	31 *Dec.* 58	.. ..	With detachment at Kanyra
Reginald G. Wilberforce, ..	30 *Mar.* 59		

H. M. 52ND (OXFORDSHIRE) REGIMENT OF FOOT.—(*Continued.*)

RANK AND NAMES.	Regimental Rank.	Army Rank.	REMARKS.
ENSIGNS.			
Sydenham Lott Pidsley, ..	7 *Nov.* 56		
Charles Middeton Prendergast, ..	18 *Dec.* 57		
Thos. Brett Cowburn, ..	19 *Dec.* 57	.. ..	Acting Adjt.
Henry Atkinson Adair, ..	16 *Mar.* 58		
Edmund Pakenham, ..	23 *Mar.* 58	.. ..	Regtl. Depôt, England.
Willoughby B P. Burrall, ...	7 *May* 58	.. ..	Ditto.
John Philip Mickleburgh, ...	9 *Oct.* 58		
John Charles Wm. Lever, ...	8 *Nov.* 58		
Henry Crawley Norris, ..	18 *Jan.* 59		
INSTRUCTOR OF MUSKETRY.			
Lieut. T. A. Julian, ..	20 *May* 57	*lt* 6 *July* 55	Leave on M. C. to Dhurmsala.
PAY MASTER.			
Lieut. Francis W. Fellows, ..	3 *June* 53	*lt* 29 *Oct.* 47	
ADJUTANT.			
Lieut. Thomas Archer Julian, ..	8 *Apl.* 58	*lt* 6 *July* 55	Leave ou M. C. to Dhurmsala.
Ensiyn. T. B. Cowburn, ..	16 *Dec.* 57	.. ..	Acting.
QUARTER MASTER.			
William Knott, ...	25 *Feb.* 45		
SURGEON.			
John Coghlan Haverty, ...	18 *Jan.* 59		
ASSISTANT SURGEONS.			
Charles Alexander Innes, M. D. ..	14 *Mar.* 55		
Henry Alexander Gogarty, .. V.	29 *Aug.* 55		
Alex. Thorburn McGown, M. D...	24 *Aug.* 58	15 *Sept.* 57	
INTERPRETER.			
Lieut. A. H. Graves, ...	.. ..	... ...	Acting.

Strength—10 Companies, with 57 Sergeants—50 Corporals—21 Drummers—1071 Privates.

English Agents.—Messrs. Sir Chas. R. and W. McGrigor.

Calcutta Agents.—Messrs. Gillanders, Arbuthnot and Co.

WAR SERVICES OF THE OFFICERS OF H. M. 52ND REGT. OF FOOT.

Sir Archibald Maclaine's services:—Mysore campaign of 1799 against Tippoo Sultan, including the battle of Mallavely, siege and storming of Seringapatam, where he received three wounds, from the effects of which he was confined in hospital for upwards of a year. Capture of the Danish settlement of Tranquebar, and the Polyga war in 1801, including the battle of Ardingy, and affair of Serungapore, where he was wounded. Mahratta war of 1802, 3, and 4, against Scindia, Holkar, and the Bera Rajah. including the storming of Julnaghur, siege and storming of Gawilghur, siege of Asseerghur (wounded), and battle of Argaum. Ordered home in 1804, in consequence of severe wounds received in the different actions from 1799 to 1804. Peninsular campaigns of 1810, 11. and 12 including the defence of Cadiz, the defence of Matagorda (an outwork of Cadiz, and a ruined redoubt when taken possession of from the enemy), from 22nd February to 22nd April 1810, during which long period Sir Archibald, then a Captain in the old 94th Regiment, with a very small force under his command, most gallantly kept at bay 8,000 of the enemy under Marshal Soult, who conducted the siege, and did not evacuate until ordered to do so by Lieut.-General Sir Thomas Graham, his men being nearly all either killed or wounded. Served also at the battle of Barrosa (dangerously wounded, and his horse killed) and capture of Seville. Sir Archibald has received the War Medal and one Clasp for Barrosa.

Colonel Campbell commanded the 52nd Light Infantry at the defeat of the Sealkote mutineers on the 12th, and 16th July 1857, and commanded the third column at the assault of Delhi.

Colonel Dennis served with the 49th Regt. in China (Medal), and was present at Chusan (both operations) Canton and Amoy; after which he was employed as a military magistrate at Chusan. In August 1849, a determined and desperate band of insurgent fanatics having defeated a native force which had been marched against them, killing a European officer and several Sepoys, Major Dennis, with a force consisting of the Grenadier Company of the 94th and 100 Sepoys of the Madras Native Infantry, encountered them at a Pagoda near Teermanam Coonettos, in Malabar. On the approach of our troops these madmen, armed with matchlocks, spears, swords, and war knives, rushed out upon the detachment, and a sanguinary conflict ensued, terminating in the destruction of the entire Mopla band, 64 in number, three of whom were killed by Major Dennis, who received a contusion on the chest and a few slight wounds, at the defeat of the Sealkote mutineers and the siege of Delhi.

Captain Dick served with the 43rd Regt, in the Kaffir war from Dec. 1851 to June 1852 (Medal).

Major Blane served the Eastern campaign of 1854-55, including the battles of Balaklava and Inkerman (wounded), siege of Sebastopol, and sortie on the 26th Oct. (Medal and Clasps, Sardinian Medal, and 5th Class of the Medjidie), Brigadier Major Nicholson's Moveable Column at the defeat of the Sealkote mutineers on the 12th and 16th July 1857, and to the 4th Infantry Brigade at the assault of Delhi.

Major Synge, and Lieut. Wingfield, were at the siege of Delhi. Major Synge was Brigade Major, to 3rd Column of attack under Major Crosse.

Major Cross commanded supports of storming party in the assault.

Captains Monson, and Stopford, Lieuts. Windsor, Clive, Trench, Simpson and Wilberforce, and Quarter Master Knott and Asst. Surgeon Gogarty were at the action with the Sealkote Mutineers and the siege of Delhi,

Lieut. Ellis and Bourroughs were at the action with the Sealkote Mutineers.

Lieut. Graves served with the 18th Royal Irish in the Burmese war of 1852-53 (Medal).

Assistant Surgeon Innes served in the Eastern Campaign and at the siege of Delhi.

H. M. 53rd (or the Shorpshire) Regt. of Foot.

NIEUPORT"—"TOURNAY"—"ST. LUCIA"—"TALAVERA"—"SALAMANCA"—"VITTORIA"—"PYRENEES"—"NIVELLE"—"TOULOUSE"—"PENINSULA"—"ALLIWAL"—"SUBRAON"—"PUNJAUB"—GOOJERAT."

FACINGS—*Red.*

Landed in Bengal, from England, on the 30*th December* 1844.

ALLAHABAD.

Regimental Depôt, Chatham.

RANK AND NAMES.	Regimental Rank.	Army Rank.	REMARKS.
COLONEL.			
William Sutherland, C. B., - -	25 *May* 55	*l.g.* 20 *June* 54	In Europe.
LIEUTENANT COLONEL.			
Fred. English, C. B., - - - -	2 *Nov.* 57	.. ..	Commanding.
William Payn, C, B., - - -	13 *July* 58	24 *Mar.* 58	Leave on P. A. in India.
MAJORS.			
Annesley Paul Gore,- - - -	19 *Nov.* 57	.. ..	Leave on M. C. to England.
Thomas Moubray, - - - -	6 *Aug.* 58	.. ..	Leave on P. A. to England.
CAPTAINS.			
John H. Lothian, - - - -	17 *June* 53	15 *Feb.* 53	Chatham Depôt, England.
Wm. F. Adams Colman, *PC,*	15 *July* 53	*m.* 15 *Mar.* 53	Ditto.
George Robert Hopkins, - -	7 *Nov.* 53	*m.* 24 *Mar.* 58	Comdg. convalescent Depôt, at Darjeeling.
Joseph Maycock, - - -*PH,*	7 *July* 54	*m.* 24 *Mar.* 58	Leave on M. C. in India.
Fred. Arthur Walter, - - -	1 *Sep.* 54	26 *Nov.* 52	
George Newton Fendall, - -	7 *Nov.* 56	*m.* 24 *Mar.* 58	Leave on M. C.
Henry Buck, - - - - -	29 *Sep.* 57	*m* 20 *July* 58	
George Herbert Cox, *PH,(a)* -	17 *Nov.* 58	.. ..	
James Winsmore Corfield, - -	18 *Nov.* 57	.. ..	Leave ou M. C. to Englad.
John Alexander Dalzell, - *V,*	19 *Nov.* 57	.. ..	Acting Interpreter.
Graham Taylor, - - - - -	6 *Aug.* 58	.. ..	Leave on P. A to England to 10th Oct. 59.
Sidney G. Quicke, - - - -	8 *Apl.* 59		
LIEUTENANTS.			
Fredk. Richd. Solly Flood, *V,*	8 *Aug.* 51	.. ..	A. D. C. to the Chief of the Staff.
Henry Helsham,- - - - -	12 *Oct.* 52	.. ..	Leave to England.
Thomas Acton, - - *C.P,(b)*	6 *May* 53	.. ..	Civil Employ.
Wale Rymer Byrne, - - - -	20 *Oct.* 53		
William Henry J. Clarke, - -	2 *Dec.* 53	.. ..	
Thomas Chas. Ffrench, - - -	9 *Oct.* 55	.. ..	Employed on the Staff of the Oude Police, Lucknow.
Alfred Kirke Ffrench,* - - -	21 *Oct.* 55		
John Maxwell Macneill, - -	27 *Feb.* 56	.. ..	Leave on M. C. England.
Richard Annesley Eyre. - -	3 *Sep.* 56	.. ..	Instructoı of Musketry.
Robert Fannin Stoney, - - -	7 *Nov.* 56		
Charles Bagnall, - - - - -	9 *Jan.* 57		
Joseph C. Smythe, - - - -	26 *Mar.* 57		
Robert Holt Truell, - - - -	29 *Sep.* 57		
Robert Prince, - - - - -	19 *Nov.* 57		
William Lamb Barr, - - - -	11 *May* 58		
John Charles Bell, - - - -	3 *Sep.* 58		
*			
ENSIGNS.			
Wm. Lowry Auchinleck, - -	29 *Dec.* 57	.. ..	Leave of Absence on M. C. in India to 15th Nov. 1859.
Samuel James Nicholls, - -	8 *Jan.* 58	.. ..	Regtl. Depôt, Chathan.
Francis Tuach Rolls, - -	15 *Jan.* 58		
Robert Brown, - -	30 *Mar.* 58	.. ..	Regtl. Depôt, England.
Charles Pye,* - -	2 *July* 58	.. ..	Adjutant.
Charles Salmon, - - - - -	29 *Oct.* 58	.. ...	Regl. Depot, Chatham.
Henry John Beckwith , - -	30 *Dec.* 58		
George Peresford Deare, - -	31 *Dec.* 58		
C. H. Bonney. - - -	.. ..	.. ...	Not joined.

(*a*) Has passed the examination in Civil Engineering.

(*b*) Has passed an examination in Hindee, prescribed by G. O. 9th March 1852.

* Victoria Cross.

H. M. 53rd Regiment of Foot—(*Continued*).

Rank and Names.	Regimental Rank.	Army Rank.	Remarks.
Instructor of Musketry.			
Lieut. R. A. Eyre, - - - -	6 *Feb.* 59		
Pay Master.			
Robert Thompson, - - -	19 *Aug.* 56	1 *Nov.* 55	
Adjutants.			
Ensign C. Pye, - - - - -	30 *May* 59		
Quarter Master.			
Thomas Marshall, - - -	30 *July* 52		
Surgeon.			
James Simpetson Grant, M. D.,	25 *June* 58	28 *Aug.* 57	
Assistant Surgeons.			
Richard Hungerford, - - -	26 *May* 54		
Robert Henry Beale, - -	27 *Mar.* 57		
William Ashton, M. B., - -	5 *Oct.* 58		
Interpreter.			
Capt. J. A. Dabzell, - - V,	19 *Nov.* 57	.. ..	Acting.

Strength—10 Companies, with 55 Sergeants—50 Corporals—19 Drummers—885 Privates.

English Agent.—Mess. Col. and Co.

Calcutta Agents.—Messrs. Wood, Olliffe and Co.

WAR SERVICES OF THE OFFICERS OF H. M. 53rd REGIMENT OF FOOT.

Lt.-General Sutherland commanded the few troops on the Gold Coast in the successful operations and actions against the Ashantees, (whom he defeated and dispersed about 20,000 strong) in June and July 1824.

Colonel English C. B. served during the Indian campaign of 1857-58-59, and while in command of the Left Wing 53rd Regt. (consisting of 180 men) with 100 Seikhs attacked and completely routed at the village of Chutra a force of 1,000 mutineers composed chiefly of the Ramghur Battalion taking all their guns, treasure and camp equipage. Received the thanks of the Commander-in-Chief, and nominated a C. B. for his services. Received the thanks of Governor General for having cleared the Behar district of the mutinous Sepoys of the 32d N. I., whom he encountered and defeated at Gopalgunge. Commanded the 53d Regt. at the action of Khodagunge and entry into Futtyghur the affair of Shumshabad. Commanded the right Column of attack at the storm and capture of Meangunge; commanded, the 53d Regt. throughout the siege and capture of Lucknow, the affair of Koorsie, passage of the Gogra at Fyzabad on the 25th Novr. 1858, action of Toolsepore (Horse wounded) and minor affairs (medal and clasp.)

Colonel Payn, served in the campaign of 1851-52 against the Hill Tribes on the Peshawur frontier, served in the Indian campaign of 1857-58-59, and was present in the actions of the 26th, 27th, and 28th, Novr. at Cawnpore under General Wyndham; present with the 53rd. Regt. at the battle of Cawnpore on the 6th Decr. and pursuit of the Gwalior Contingent to Serai-Ghaut the action of Khodagunge and entry into Futtehghur the affair of Shumshabad; commanded the left Column of attack at the storm and capture of Meangunge; served during the siege and capture of Lucknow, and the affair of Koorsie. Commanded the 53rd during the hot weather campaign, including the passage of the Goomtee at Sultanpore and the occupation of Cantonments; present with the 53rd, at the passage of the Gogra at Fyzabad on the 25th Novr. 1858, the action of Toolsepore and minor affairs, (medal and clasp,) and mentioned 5 times in dispatches.

Major Gore served with the 53d during the Indian campaign of 1857-58, present at the action of Khujwah, the relief of the Lucknow garrison, (under the personal command of Sir Colin Campbell G. C. B.) the battle of Cawnpore 6th Decr, and pursuit of the Gwalior Contingent to Serai-Ghaut; the action of Khodagunge and entry into Futtehghur, the affair of Shumshabad, storm and capture of Meangunge, siege and capture of Lucknow, and the affair of Koorsie, (medal and clasps.)

Major Mowbray, served in the Indian campaign of 1857-58, and was present at the action of Khujwah (wounded), the relief of the Lucknow garrison (under the personal Command of Sir C. Campbell, G. C. B.) battle of Cawnpore on the 6th Decr. and pursuit of the Gwalior Contingent to Serai-Ghaut, the action of Khodagunge and entry into Futtehghur, and also the affair of Shumshabad, (medal and clasp).

Capt. Hopkins served against the Hill tribes on the Peshawar frontier in 1851-52; served during the Indian campaign of 1857-58, present at the action of Khujwah the relief of the Lucknow garrison (under the personal Command of Sir C. Campbell G. C. B.) battle of Cawnpore on the 6th Decr. and pursuit of the Gwalior Contingent to Seraighaut, action of Khodhagunge and entry in Futtehghur, the affair of Shumshabad, storm and capture of Meangunge, siege and capture of Lucknow, (wounded,) medal and clasps, Bt. Major, and mentioned in dispatches.

Capt. Walter served during the Indian campaign of 1858-1859; was present at the passage of the Gogra at Fyzabad on the 25th Novr. 1858; action of Toolsepore and minor affairs (medal.)

Capt. Walton served against the Hill Tribes on the Peshawur frontier in 1851-52. Served in the Indian Rebellion of 1857 and was present at the relief of the Lucknow garrison, under the personal command of Sir C. Campbell, G. C. B. (severely wounded), mentioned in dispatches, Bt. Major (medal and clasp.)

Capt. Fendall, served against the Hill Tribes in 1851-52, on the Peshawur Frontier, served during the Indian campaign of 1857-58-59, present at the actions of Chutra and Gopalgunge; the action of Khodagunge and entry into Futtehghur and the affair of Shumshabad, served as Brigade Major to the 3rd Brigade 2nd Infantry Division at the storm and capture of Meangunge and also at the siege and capture of Lucknow, after which he officiated as Dy. Asst. Qr. Master General at Lucknow until the close of the rebellion in Oude (medal and clasp,) mentioned in dispatches and has received the Bt. of Major.

For continuation see next page.

WAR SERVICES OF THE OFFICERS OF H. M. 53RD REGT. OF FOOT.—(*Continued.*)

Captain Buck, served against the Hill Tribes on the Peshawur frontier in 1851-52, served in the campaign of 1857-58-59, present at the action of Khodagunge and entry into Futtehghur, storm and capture of Meangunge, siege and capture of Lucknow, the affair of Koorsie, passage of the Goomtee at Sultanpore, and occupation of Cantonments, passage of the Gogra at Fyzabad on the 25th Novr., the action of Toolsepore and minor affairs, (medal and clasp) and Bt. Major.

Captain Cox served in the campaign of 1851-52, against the Hill Tribes on the Peshawur frontier; served in the Indian campaign of, 1857-58, was 2d. in Command of the 4th Seikhs in the pursuit of the mutineers from the Jullunder force, also served in the Trans Gogra campaign of 1859 (medal.)

Captain Corfield served in the Punjab campaign of 1848-49, (medal) served in 1851-52 against the Hill Tribes on the Peshawur frontier, served during the Rebellion of 1857, present at the action of Khujwah, (severely wounded,) medal.

Captain Dalzell, served in 1851-52, against the Hill Tribes on the Peshawur frontier; served during the Indian campaign of 1857-58-59, present at the action of Khodagunge, and entry into Futtehghur passage of the Gogra at Fyzabad on the 25th Novr. also the action of Toolsepore and minor affairs—(medal.)

Captain Taylor, served in the campaign of 1851-52, against the Hill Tribes on the Peshawur frontier; served in the Indian campaign of 1857-58, of present at the action of Chutra, Gopalgunge, Khodagunge and entry into Futtehghur, the affair of Shumshabad, storm and capture of Meangunge, and the siege and capture of Lucknow, (medal and clasps,) mentioned in dispatches.

Lieut. Flood, served in the campaign of 1851-52, against the Hill tribes, served during the Indian campagin of 1857-58-59,— including the relief of Cawnpore on the 29th. Novr. 1857, action of the 6th. Decr. and pursuit of the Gwalior Contingent to Seraighaut. The action of Khodagunge and entry into Futtehghur, affair of Shumshabad, the storm and capture of Meangunge; served as extra A. D. C. to General Mansfield at the siege of Lucknow, (severely wounded,) present with the 53rd. during the hot weather campaign in Oude, including the passage of the Goomtee at Sultanpore and occupation of cantonments, served as A. D. C. to Sir William Mansfield, during the Baiswara and Trans Gogra-campaign— (medal and clasp) and mentioned in dispatches.

Lieut. Helsham, served in the Indian campaign, of 1857-58, present at the action of Chutra, Gopulgunge action of Khodagunge and entry into Futtehghur, affair of Shumshabad storm and capture of Meangunge, and the siege and capture of Lucknow, (wounded), medal and clasp, mentioned in dispatches.

Lieut. Acton, served in the Indian campaign of 1857-58-59, was present at the action of Khujwah (severely wounded), rejoined the Regiment at Futtehghur, 20th January 1858: present at the affair of Shumshabad, storm and capture of Meangunge, siege and capture of Lucknow and the affair of Korsie—present at the passage of the Goomtee at Sultanpore and occupation of Cantonments, served as Major of Brigade to Brigadier Witherall's columns and was present at the storm and capture of Rampore Cassia, also as Major of Brigade to Brigadier Taylor, was present at the passage of the Gogra at Fyzabad on the 25th Novr. and minor affairs. Mentioned in dispatches, (medal and clasp.)

Lieut Byrne, served in the campaign of 1851-52, against the Hill Tribes on the Peshawur frontier; served during the Indian Rebellion of 1857-58-59, present at the relief of the garrison of Lucknow, under the personal command of Sir C. Campbell, G. C. B. battle of Cawnpore, on the 6th. Dec. and pursuit of the Gwalior Contingent to Serai-ghaut, the action of Khodagunge and entry into Futtehghur, storm and capture of Meangunge, siege and capture of Lucknow; affair of Koorsie, passage of the Goomtee at Sultanpore and occupation of Cantonments, the passage of the Gogra at Fyzabad on the 25th Novr. 1858, the action of Toolsepore, and minor affairs, (medal and clasps.)

Lieut. Clarke, served in the Indian campaign of 1857-58-59, present at the actions of Chuttra Gopalgunge, Khodagunge and entry into Futtehghur, storm and capture of Meangunge, siege and capture of Lucknow, the affair of Koorsie, passage of the Gogra at Fyzabad on the 25th Novr. 1858, the action of Toolsepore, and minor affairs, (medal and clasp.) Mentioned in dispatches.

Lieut. T. French, served in the Indian campaign of 1857-58 and was present at the relief of Lucknow under the personal Command of Sir C. Campbell, G. C. B. the battle of Cawnpore on the 6th Dec. and pursuit of the Gwalior Contingent to Seraighat, the action of Khodagunge and entry into Futtehghur, storm and capture of Meangunge and the siege and capture of Lucknow, served subsequently with the Oude Military Police and when in Command of 500 of them defeated a body of rebels posted in the Village of Rahamabad, was also present at the attack of the Fort of Biswah—(medal and clasps.)

Lieut. A.K. Ffrench, served in the Indian campaign of 1857-58-59, present at the relief of the Lucknow garrison, under the personal command of Sir. C. Campbell, G. C. B. the battle of Cawnpore on the 6th Decr. 1857, and pursuit of the Gwalior Contingent to Serai-ghaut; the action of Khodagunge and entry into Futtehghur, storm and capture of Meangunge, siege and capture of Lucknow, the affair of Koorsie, passage of the Goomtee at Sultanpore and occupation of Cantonments, passage of the Gogra at Fyzabad on the 25th Novr. 1858, action of Toolsepore and minor affairs—Medal and clasp. Victoria Cross.

Lieut. Macneill, served in the Indian campaign of 1857-58, present at the action of Khujwah, the relief of the Lucknow Garrison under the personal command of Sir. C. Campbell G. C. B., the battle of Cawnpore on the 6th, Decr. (severely wounded), the action of Khodagunge, and entry into Futtehghur, affair of Shumshabad, storm and capture of Meangunge, siege and capture of Lucknow, and the affair of Koorsie (Medal and clasp).

Lieut. Stoney, served in the Indian campaign of 1857-58-59, present at the action of Khodagunge and entry into Futtehghur, the affair of Shumshabad, storm and capture of Meangunge, siege and capture of Lucknow, the affair of Koorsie, passage of the Gogra at Fyzabad on the 25th. Novr. the action of Toolsepore and minor affairs (Medal and clasp).

Lieut. Bagnall, served in the Indian campaign of 1857-58-59, present at the action of Khodagunge, and entry into Futt . ghur, storm and capture of Meangunge, siege and capture of Lucknow, the affair of Koorsie and the passage of the Gogra at Fyzabad on the 26th. Novr., (Medal and clasp).

Lieut. Smythe, served in the campaign of 1857-58-59, present at the action of Chatra, storm and capture of Meangunge, siege and capture of Lucknow, affair of Koorsie, passage of the Goomtee at Sultanpore and occupation of Cantonments, passage of the Gogra at Fyzabad on the 26th. Novr. and action of Toolsepore, and minor affairs, (Medal and clasp) mentioned in despatches.

Lieut. Truell, served in the Indian campaign of 1857-58-59, present at the action of Khujwah relief of the garrison of Lucknow under the personal command of Sir. C. Campbell G. C. B., the defeat of Gwalior Contingent at Cawnpore on the 6th Decr. and pursuit to Seraighaut, the action of Khodagunge and entry into Futtehghur, affair of Shumshabad, storm and capture of Meangunge, siege and capture of Lucknow. present with the Oude Field Force under Sir. H. Grant, including the affair of Koorsie, passage of the Goomtee at Sultanpore, and occupation of Cantonments, the passage of the Gogra at Fyzabad on the 25th Novr. present at the action of Toolsepore and minor affairs (Medal and clasps) mentioned in dispatches.

Lieut. Prince, served in the Indian campaign of 1857-58-59, present at the action of Khujwah, the relief of the garrison of Lucknow under the personal command of Sir, C. Campbell, G. C. B., the defeat of the Gwalior Contingent at Cawnpore on the 6th, Decr. and pursuit to Seraighaut, the action of Khodagunge and entry into Futtehghur, the affair of Shumshabad, the storm and capture of Meangunge, siege and capture of Lucknow, the affair of Koorsie, passage of the Gogra at Fyzabad on the 25th Novr. the action of Toolsepore. and minor affairs (Medal and clasps.)

WAR SERVICES OF THE OFFICERS OF H. M. 53RD REGT. OF FOOT.—(Continued.)

Lieut. Barr, served with the Oude Field Force in 1858-59, present at the passage of the Goomtee at Sultanpore and occupation of Cantonments the passage of the Gogra at Fyzabad on the 25th Novr. action of Toolsepore and mimor affairs—(Medal.)

Lieut. Bell and Ensigns Auchinleck and Rolls, served with the Oude field force in 1858-59, present at the action of Toolsepore, and minor affairs, (Medals.)

Ensign Pye, served with the 40th. Regt. at the battle of Moharajpore (Bronze star) with the 31st Regt. during the Sutlej campaign of 1845-46, present at the battles of Moodkee, Ferozeshah, Aliwal and Sobraon, (Medal and clasps) served with the 53d. Regt. during the Punjaub campagin of 1848-49, (medal) served against the Hill Tribes on the Peshawur Frontier in 1852, served in the Indian campaign of 1857-58-59. present at the action of Khujwah the relief of the garrison of Lucknow, under the personal command of Sir. C. Campbell G. C B. (severely wounded) the battle of Cawnpore on the 6th Decr. and pursuit of the Gwalior Contingent to Seraighaut, the action of Khodagunge and entry into Futtehghur, the affair of Shumshabad, storm and capture of Meangunge siege and fall of Lucknow, affair of "Koorsie" and passage of the Goomtee at Sultanpore and occupation of Cantonments, (Medal and clasps and Victoria Cross.)

Pay Master Thompson, served in the Indian, campaign of 1857-58-59, present at the battle of Cawnpore on the 6th Decr. and pursuit of the Gwalior Contingent to Seraighaut. action of Khodagunge and entry into Futtehghur, siege and capture of Lucknow and the passage of the Gogra at Fyzabad on the 25th. Novr., (Medal and clasp.)

Quarter Master Marshall, served with the 53d. in the Sutlej campaign of 1845-46, present at the affair of Buddiwal, the actions of Aliwal and Sobraon (Medal and clasp) served in the Punjaub campaign of 1848-49 present at the battle of Goojerat (Medal and clasp) served against the Hill Tribes on the Peshawur Frontier in 1851-52, served in the Indian campaign, of 1857-58-59. present at the battle of Khujwah, relief of the Lucknow Garrison, under the personal command of Sir C. Campbell G. C. B. The battle of Cawnpore on the 6th. Dec. and pursuit of the Gwalior Contingent to Seraighaut, the action of Khodagunge and entry into Futtehghur, the affair of Shumshabad, storm and capture of Meangunge, siege and capture of Lucknow, the affairs of Koorsie, passage of the Gogra at Fyzabad on the 26th. Novr. the action of Toolsepore, and minor affairs, (Medal and clasps.)

Surgeon Grant served in the Kaffir War of 1847 (Medal) served with the 53d. in 1851-52 against the Hill Tribes on the Peshawur Frontiers; served during the Indian campaign of 1857-58-59, and was present at the action of Khujwah the relief the Lucknow garrison under the personal command of Sir. C. Campbell G. C. B. The defeat of the Gwalior Contingent at Cawnpore on the 6th. Decr. 1857, and pursuit to Seraighaut, the action of Khodagunge and entry inte Futtehghur, the affair of Shumshabad, storm and capture of Meangunge siege and capture of Lucknow, the affair of Koorsie, the passage of the river Goomtee at Sultanpore, and occupation of Cantonments, passage of the Gogra at Fyzabad on the 25th. Nov. the action of Toolsepore, (Horse killed) and minor affairs, (Medal and clasps) mentioned in despatches.

Asst. Surgn. Hungerford served with the 53d Regt. in the Indian compaign of 1857-58, present at the action of Khodagunge, and entry into Futtehghur, storm and capture of Meangunge, siege and capture of Lucknow and the affair of Koorsie, (Medal and clasps).

Asst. Surgn. Beale, served with the 31st Regt. in the Crimea, including the siege of Sebastopol, and attacks of the 18th June and 8th Sept. (Medal and clasp) served with the 53d Regt. in the Indian campaign of 1858-59, present at the storm and capture of Meangunge siege and capture of Lucknow, affair of Koorsie, passage of the Goomtee at Sultanpore and occupation of Cantonments, passage of the Gogra at Fyzabad in the 26th Novr. and minor affairs, (Medal and clasp.)

Asst. Surgn. Ashton, served in the Indian campaign of 1858-59, and was present with the 79th. Regt. at the storm and capture of Rampore-kussia, the passage of the Gogra at Fyzabad, on the 25th Novr. served with the 53d Regt. at the action of Toolsepore and minor affairs, (Medal.)

H. M. 54th (The West Norfolk) Regt. of Foot.

The *Sphinx*, with the words — "EGYPT"
"MARABOUT" —"AVA."
FACINGS—*Green*.
Landed in Calcutta, from England, on the 2nd January 1858.
SULTANPORE OUDH.
Left Wing at *Fyzabad*.
Regimental Depôt, Colchester.

RANK AND NAMES.	*Regimental Rank.*	*Army Rank.*	REMARKS.
COLONEL.			
Sir Wm. J. Codrington, K.C.B.	11 *Aug.* 56	*l.g.* 6 *June* 54	Governor of Gibralter.
LIEUTENANT COLONELS.			
Charles Edward Michel, - -	26 *Feb.* 56	24 *Nov.* 54	Lv. on P. A. to England for 18 months.
Charles Herbert, C. B. - -	7 *Dec.* 28	*Col.* ..	Commanding at Fyzabad.
MAJORS.			
John Charles Hill Jones, - -	5 *Sept.* 56	.. ..	Lv. on M. C. to England.
William Freeland Brett, - -	14 *Aug.* 57	*l.c.* 11 *Nov.* 57	At Fyzabad.
CAPTAINS.			
James Sinclair Thomson, - -	9 *July* 52	.. ..	Convalescent Depôt Landour.
John S. Ferguson Fowke, - -	4 *Mar.* 53	.. ..	Colchester Depôt, England.
Pridaux William Gillum, - -	4 *Aug.* 54	*m* 11 *Nov.* 57	Leave of absence on P. A. to England for 18 months.
W. Ed. Freeman O'Brien - -	1 *Dec.* 54		
Wm. Hill Dawe Clarke, - -	2 *Feb.* 55	.. ..	Leave to Mussoorie on P. A. to 31 Aug. [59.
Edward Thomas Shiffner, - -	15 *Feb.* 56		
Francis Geo. C. Probart, - -	19 *Aug.* 56	29 *Feb.* 56	
J. Sackville Swann, - -	5 *Sept.* 56	.. ..	Regtl. Depot.
Charles Alex. Thomson, - -	26 *Sept.* 56	.. ...	At Fyzabad.
Charles FitzRoy Barnett, - -	5 *June* 57	.. ..	Leave to Mussoorie on P. A. to 31 August 59.
Robert Baret Stokes, - -	14 *Aug.* 57	.. ..	Staff College England.
And. Robert Guy Evered, - -	19 *Nov.* 58	.. ..	At Fyzybad.
LIEUTENANTS.			
Edward Cliffe, - -	6 *June* 54	.. ...	At Fyzabad.
Wm. Arthur Galbraith, - -	2 *Feb.* 55		
Francis Geo. S. Parker, - -	2 *Feb.* 55	... ...	Instructor of Musketry, at Thomasson [College, Roorkee.
John Stevenson, - -	1 *Feb.* 56	.. ..	At Fyzabad, Acting Adjt. Left Wing.
Vere Temple Bayly, - -	29 *Feb.* 56		
Henry Ridout Floyd, - -	22 *Sept.* 56	1 *Dec.* 54	Colchester Depôt, England.
~~Thomas Parr~~, - -	22 *July* 56	.. ..	Lv. to Nynee Tall on M. C. to 31 Oct. [59.
Joseph William Hughes, - -	26 *Sept.* 56	.. ..	Adjutant.
George Cronyn, - -	5 *June* 57	.. ..	Offg. Instructor of Musketry.
~~William Ker Gray~~, - -	17 *July* 57	.. ..	Colchester Depôt, England.
John Ayton Wood, - -	14 *Aug.* 57	.. ..	Leave on P. A. to England.
Joshua Gladwyn Jebb, - -	13 *Feb.* 58		
~~Lancelot Kerby Edwards~~, - -	30 *Mar.* 58		
Matthew Wm. Edw. Gosset, -	31 *Aug.* 58		
ENSIGNS.			
Sir Chas. W. Burdett, *Bt.* - -	16 *Mar.* 56	18 *Jan.* 56	At Fyzabad.
Dudley B. Coppinger, - -	24 *Feb.* 57	.. ..	Ditto, Barrack Master.
James Chute, - -	5 *June* 57	.. ..	Ditto.
Warren Edward Evans, - -	24 *July* 57	.. ..	Ditto.
Charles Gooden Loveridge, -	14 *Aug.* 57	.. ..	Ditto.
Robert Magill, - -	16 *Mar.* 58	.. ..	Ditto.
James Hearn Tarleton, - -	14 *May* 58		
Henry Lambard, - -	13 *July* 58	... ...	Regt. Depôt.
Charles Samuel Chapman, -	31 *Aug.* 58	.. ..	Ditto.
William Patrick Hodnett, - -	9 *Nov.* 58	.. ..	Ditto.

H. M. 54TH (THE WEST NORFOLK) REGT. OF FOOT.—(*Continued*).

RANK AND NAMES.	*Regimental Rank.*	*ArmyRank.*	REMARKS.
INSTRUCTOR OF MUSKETRY.			
Lieut. Fras. Geo. S. Parker, -	8 *May.* 57	*lt.* 2 *Feb.* 55	At Thomason College, Roorkee.
Lieut. C. Cronyn, - - - -	5 *June* 57	.. ..	Acting.
PAYMASTER.			
William Marriott, - - - -	1 *Oct.* 58		
ADJUTANT.			
Lieut. Joseph Wiliiam Hughes,	21 *June* 58	*lt.* 26 *Sep.* 56	
QUARTER-MASTER.			
Ensign Thomas Hipkin, - -	6 *July.* 52	*ens.* 1 *Aug.* 56	
SURGEON.			
James McGrigor Grant, M. D. -	12 *Aug.* 53	29 *Nov.* 50	
ASSISTANT SURGEONS.			
George Youell, - -	26 *May* 54	... ..	At Fyzabad.
Alexander Reid, - - -	13 *July* 58		
Charles Bartholomew Matthew,	10 *Dec.* 58	.. ..	At Fyzabad.
INTERPRETER.			
Lieut. Gordon Cavanagh, 39th N. I. -	10 *June* 49		

Strength—10 Companies with 53 Sergeants,—47 Corporals,—21 Drummers, and 979 Privates.

English Agents—Messrs. Cox and Co.
Calcutta Agents—Messrs. Wm. Spink and Co.

WAR SERVICES OF THE OFFICERS OF H. M. 54TH REGIMENT OF FOOT.

Sir William Codrington commanded a Brigade of the Light Division, and afterwards a Division throughout the Eastern campaign of 1854-55, including the battles of Alma and Inkerman, siege and fall of Sebastopol (Medal and Clasps, K.C.B., Commander of the Legion of Honor, and Grand Cross of the Military Order of Savoy). From October 1855, and until the evacuation of the Crimea, he was Commander-in-Chief of the Eastern Army.

Colonel Herbert C. B. served during the East Indian campaign of 1857-58, from 12th May 1857 the commencement of the Outbreak, commanded H. M. 75th Regt. in advance under His Excellency the Commander-in-Chief General Anson on Delhie and after his death at Kurnal, under Major Genl. Sir H. Barnard K. C. B., was present at the battle of Badree-ke-Serai, siege, storming and capture of Delhie; appointed C.B. slightly wounded at Delhie 14th Septr. 1857.

Bt. Major Gillum, Capt. Shiffner Lieutenants Galbraith, and Cronyn were present at the attack on Tyzhaul fort on 21st March 58 and taking of Tyzhaul and Dehein forts Oudh in July 1858.

Captain Probart served with the 95th Regt. at the siege and fall of Sebastopol from 24th Nov. 1854 (Medal and Clasp).

Lieut. Bayly was engaged at the taking of Tyzhaul and Dehein forts Oudh in July 1858.

Assist. Surgeon Reid served with the Royals at the siege and fall of Sebastopol from 15th July 1855 [Medal and Clasp.]

1st BATTALION OF H. M. 60th (The King's Royal) Rifle Corps.

(Celer et Audax.)

"Roleia"—"Vimiera"—"Martinique"—"Talavera"—"Fuentes D'Onor"—"Albuhera"—"Cuidad Rodrigo"—"Badajoz"—"Salamanca"—"Vittoria"—"Pyrenees"—"Nivelle"—"Nive"—"Orthes"—"Toulouse"—"Peninsula"—*1st Battalion* "Punjaub."—"Mooltan"—"Goojerat."

Regimentals, *Green*—Facings, *Scarlet.*

Arrived from England on the 15th October 1845,—Transferred from the Bombay to the Bengal Establishment, from the 1st November 1849.

Benares,

Regimental Depôt, Winchester.

Rank and Names.	Regimental Rank.	Army Rank.	Remarks.
Colonel-in-Chief.			
Genl. Hugh *Viscount* Gough, K. P.; G. C. B.,	.. ..	*g* 21 *Jan.* 54	In Europe.
Colonel Commandant.			
Joseph Paterson, - - - -	14 *Apl.* 57	*l.g.* 11 *Aug.* 58	In Europe.
Lieutenant Colonels.			
Maurice Griffin Dennis, C. B., -	19 *Oct.* 51	*col* 28 *Nov.* 54	Brigadier Commanding at Allahabad.
Sir John Jones, K. C. B., - -	20 *June* 54	*col* 19 *Jan.* 58	Leave on P. A. to England to 28th February 61.
Majors.			
Charles Napier North, *P.C.H.,*	19 *June* 57	*l. c.* 20 *July* 58	Commanding.
Sir Edward Fitzgerald Campbell, *Bart.,* - - - *PCH,*	9 *Sep* 58	*m* 19 *Jan.* 58	On duty in Calcutta as Prize Agent, A. D. C and Offg. Military Socy, to the Governor General.
Captains.			
Thomas Biggs, - - - - -	8 *Apl.* 53	.. ..	Winchester Depôt, England.
Henry Francis Williams, -	3 *Mar.* 54	*m* 19 *Jan.* 58	Leave on M. C. to England.
John Maguire, - - - - -	20 *June* 54	*m* 16 *Nov.* 58	Leave on M. C. to England.
John Robert Wilton, - -	14 *July* 54	*m* 19 *Jan.* 58	Depot Winchester.
Edward Bowles, - *-PCH,*	23 *Mar.* 55	.. ..	Employed in the Mily. Police, Bareilly.
Charles D. C. Ellis, - - - -	14 *Dec.* 55		
William Tedlie, - - - *H V,*	25 *Jan.* 56	*m* 20 *July* 58	Lv. to England on P, A. 6th Oct. 60.
Conyngham Jones, - -	6 *May* 56		
George Bliss MacQueen, - -	19 *June* 57		
John Durham Dundas, - - -	22 *June* 58		
Herbert George Deedes, - *H,*	2 *July* 58		
James Hare, - - - - - -	9 *Sep.* 58		
Lieutenants.			
Anthony Carlisle, - - - - -	24 *Dec.* 56	22 *Sep.* 54	On duty at Gooruckpore.
D ~~John Steel,~~ - - - - -	29 *June* 55	27 *June* 54	Lv. in India, on P. A. for six months.
Francis V. Northey, - - - -	27 *July* 55	.. ..	Depot Winchester.
Philip Julian Curtis, - - - -	3 *Aug.* 55	.. ..	
William F. Carleton, - - -	17 *Aug,* 55		Lv. in India, on P. A.
Cromer Ashburnham, - - -	26 *Oct.* 55	.. ..	Convalescent Depot, Nynee Tal.
Augustus Morgan, - - - -	25 *Jan.* 56	.. ..	Lv. in India, on P. A.
Fred. Austin, - - - - -	9 *May* 56	.. ..	Adjutant.
George Charles Kelly, - - -	16 *Nov.* 56	.. ..	
Jenies Preston, - - - - -	19 *June* 57		
John Owen Young, - - - *H,*			Acting Paymaster.
Richard Fra. Jennings, - -	15 *Jan.* 58	.. ..	Depot Winchester.
William Greer Turle, - - -	23 *Mar.* 58	.. ..	
Cary H. Borrer, - - - - -	23 *Apl.* 58		Lv. in India, on P. A.
Stanley Mortimer, - - - -	21 *May* 58	.. ..	
Ashley Henry Woodgate, - -	15 *June* 58		
J. W. King, - - - - -	22 *June* 58		

1st Battn. 60th (The King's Royal) Rifle Corps—(*Continued.*)

Rank and Names.	Regimental Rank.	Army Rank.	Remarks.
Ensigns.			
Eaton Stannard Steward,	26 *Aug.* 57	.. ..	England.—Leave on M. C.
Henry Richard Treeve,	27 *Aug.* 57		
Charles Henry Cox,	11 *Sep.* 57	26 *Dec.* 56	
H. Barker,	2 *Oct.* 57	.. .	Lv. P. A. to Nynee Tal to 25 Sep. 59.
H. Broderick,	27 *Nov.* 57	.. ..	Lv. of absence on M.C. to Nynee Tal, to 8 Sep. 59.
J. Tottentram,	5 *Feb.* 58		
J. W. Marshall,	27 *Mar.* 58	.. ..	Depot Winchester.
Charles Gosling,	14 *May* 58	.. ..	Ditto.
Marcus W. O'Rorke,	25 *Apl.* 58		
Courtenay Forbes Terny,	8 *Apl.* 59	.. ..	Ditto.
Instructor of Musketry.			
Lieut. Fras. Northey,	27 *July.* 55		
Pay Master.			
Capt. John Henry Chads,	29 *May* 57	*cap.* 15 *Jan.* 56	Leave of absence to Cape of Good Hope for 6 months.
Lieut. R. F. Sennings,	15 *Jan.* 56	.. ..	Acting.
Adjutant.			
Lieut. George Charles Kelly,	1 *May* 55	*lt.* 16 *Nov.* 56	
Quarter Master.			
William Hunter,	13 *July* 55		
Surgeon.			
Edward Willsam Young, M. D.,	31 *Dec.* 58	8 *Dec.* 54	
Assistant Surgeons.			
E. John Hatchell,	15 *Jan.* 56		
J. A. Wade,	3 *Nov.* 57		
William Silver Oliver,	6 *Nov.* 57	.. ..	Leave on M. C. to England.
Interpreter.			
Capt. C. S. T. Terrot, 29th N.I.			

Strength—10 Companies, with 52 Sergeants—45 Corporals—19 Drummers—787 Privates.

English Agents.—Messrs. *Sir* C. R. McGrigor, *Bt.* and W. McGrigor.

Irish Agents,—Messrs. R. Cane and Sons.

Calcutta Agents.—Messrs. Wood, Olliffe and Co.

WAR SERVICES OF THE OFFICERS OF 1st BATTALION H. M. 60th RIFLES.

Lieut.-General Paterson served with a corps of Cavalry as a volunteer in the Rebellion in Ireland in 1798. He served the Egyptian campaign of 1801 in the 28th Regt., and was present in the actions of the 8th, 13th, and 21st March, as also at the capture of Grand Cairo and Alexandria. In 1805 he accompanied Lord Cathcart's expedition to the Continent. He served in the 77th in the Peninsula and South of France during the campaigns of 1811, 12, 13, and 14, including the affair at El Bodon, siege and capture of Cuidad Rodrigo and of Badajoz, investment of Bayonne and repulse of the sortie, besides various skirmishes. When the rebellion broke out in Canada in 1837 he volunteered his services, which were accepted. Served five years in the West Indies. He has received the Gold Medal from the Grand Seignior for the Egyptian campaign, and the Silver War Medal with three Clasps for Egypt, Cuidad Rodrigo, and Badajoz.

Colonel Dennis served with the 1st Battalion 60th Rifles during the second siege operations at Mooltan, and commanded the Battalion 27th Dec. 1848, when the enemy's outposts and suburbs of Mooltan were captured (wounded); was afterwards present at the battle of Goojerat, pursuit of the fugitive Sikh army until its final surrender at Rawul Pindee, and expulsion of the Affghan force beyond the Khyber Pass (Medal and two Clasps). Served in the campaign in Oudh in 1858, and commanded the 1st Battalion. 60th Rifles in the action at Biswah on the 1st December 1858, commanded a column in the Khyreghur district from 24th Dec. 1858, thanked by His Lordship the Commander-in-Chief in India, recommended to the favorable consideration of the Viceroy, the Right Honorable the Governor General for the energy he displayed in driving the rebels out of the district.

Colonel Sir. J. Jones, K.C.B., served in the campaign of 1857-58 against the Mutineers in India; commanded the 1st Batn. 60th Rifles at the actions on the Hindun on the 30th and 31st May; battle of Bualee-ke-serai and forcing the heights before Delhi on 8th June, throughout the siege operations before Delhi, action of the 19th June, attack on the Subzeemundi on the 18th July, commanded column of attack and covering the assaulting columns at the storming of the City on the 14th September; commanded the left attacking column within the City from 15th to 20th September, forced through the City, blew open the gates and took possession of the Palace on 20th September 1857. Commanded as Brigadier General, the Roorkee field force throughout the operations in Rohilcund from 17th April to 21st May 1858, including the actions of Bagowalla and Nugeena, relief of Mooradabad, action on the Dojura, assault and capture of Bareilly, attack and bombardment of Shahjehanpore, defeat of the rebels, relief of the garison, capture of the Fort of Bunnai—pursuit of the enemy to the left bank of the Goomtee and destruction of the Fort of Mahumdee (C. B. and Colonel for distinguished service in the field. Good service pension and K. C. B.) Served in the campaign in Oude in 1858, including the action at Pusgaon on the 19th October 1858.

Lt.-Col. North, served the Punjaub campaign of 1849 (Medal and two Clasps) and was present during the second siege operations at Mooltan (including the siege and storm of the town and capture of the citadel); battle of Goojerat pursuit of the Sikh army until its final surrender at Rawal Pindee, occupation of Attock and Peshawur, and expulsion of the Affghan force beyond the Kyber Pass. Served with Havelock's Column in 1857, attached to 78th Highlanders and on the Staff in the actions of Futtehpore, Aoung, Pandoo Nuddee, Cawnpore, Oonas, Buseerutgung (29th July) Bithoor, Alumbagh, and relief of Lucknow, slightly wounded; (thanked by Governor General in Council and in General Outram's despatch for "valuable services").

Major Sir Edward Campbell served the Punjaub campaign of 1849 (Medal and two Clasps), and was present during the second siege operations at Mooltan (including the siege and storm of the town and capture of the citadel) battle of Goojerat, persuit of the Sikh army until its surrender at Rawul Pindee, occupation of Attock and Peshawur, and expulsion of the Affghan force beyond the Khyber Pass. Served with the expedition against the Affreedies in the Kohat Pass in 1850 as Aide-de-Camp to Sir Charles Napier. Served from 3rd July during the siege operations before Delhi, assault and capture of the City with the final attack on and occupation of the Palace on the 20th September 1858 (Bt. Major). [*⁎* *For continuation of Services, see next page.*

WAR SERVICES OF THE OFFICERS OF H. M. 60TH RIFLES.—*(Continued.)*

Major Williams, served with the 1st Battalion 60th Rifles during the second siege operations at Mooltan, including the siege and storm of the town and capture of the citadel. Afterwards at the battle of Goojerat, the persuit of the Sikh army, and the expulsion of the Affghans beyond the Khyber Pass. Also present during the operations in the Euzofzye country, and capture of the insurgent villages on the 11th and 14th Dec. 49.(Medal and two Clasps). Served in the campaign of 1857 against the Mutineers in India. including the actions on the Hindun on the 30th and 31st May, battle of Bualee-ke-serai and taking of the heights before Delhi on the 8th June, subsequent siege operations to 16th August. Severely wounded on the 19th June, (Brevet Major.)

Major Maguire served with the 55th Regt. in China (Medal), at Amoy, Chusan and Chinhæ ; and with the 60th throughout the Punjaub campaign of 1848-9 including the siege and storm of the town and capture of the citadel of Mooltan, battle of Goojerat, and subsequent opperations (Medal and two Clasps). Served throughout the Campaign in Rohilcund in 58 including the actions of Bagawalla and Nugeena, relief of Moradabad, action on the Dojura, assault and capture of Bareilly, attack and bombardment of Shahjehanpore, defeat of the rebels and relief of the garrison, capture of the Fort of Bunnie; pursuit of the enemy to the left bank of the Goomtee, and destruction of the Fort of Mahumdee, commanded a wing of the 1st Battn. 60th rifles at the attack and destruction of Shahabad, commanded the Battalion at the action at Bung-ka-Gong on the 8th October 1858. (Bt. Major.)

Major Tedlie and Captain Bowles served in the campaign in Rohilcund in 1858, including the actions of Bagawalla and Nugeena, relief of Moradabad, action on the Dojura, assault and capture of Bareilly, attack and bombardment of Shahjehanpore, defeat of the rebels and relief of the garrison, capture of the Fort of Bunnai, pursuit of the enemy to the left bank of the Goomtee, and destruction of the Fort of Mahumdee. Major Tedlie served as D. A. Qr. M. General to the Roorkee Field force. Present at the action of Bung-ka-Gong on the 8th October 1858, as Brigade Major. (Brevet Major.)

Major Wilton served in the 55th Regiment during the Chinese expedition (Medal), and was present at the operations before Nankin. Served in the 1st Battblion 60th Rifles in the campaign of 1857 against the Mutineers in India, including the actions on the Hindun, battle of Bualee-Ke-Serai and taking of the heights before Delhi on the 8th June, and subsequent siege operations to 1st September 1857. (Brevet Major).

Captain Ellis served in the Kaffir War of 1851-53, Medal, served in the Crimea from Decr. 1855 to June 1856 as D. A. Q. Mr. General in the Turkish Contingent. Served in the campaign in Oude in 1858-9, commanded a detachment of the 1st Battn. 60th Rifles at the action at Mehndee on the 18th Novr. 1858, when 9 Guns were operations in captured, present at the action at Biswah; on the 1st Decr. 1858, commanded the 1st Battn. 60th Rifles during the the Khyreeghur District.

Captain C. Jones served in the campaign against the mutineers in India from 3rd June 1857, including the battle of Bualee-ke-serai and taking of the heights before Delhi—the subsequent siege operations until severely wounded on 23rd June. Served in the campaign in Rohilcund in 1858, including the actions at Bagawalla and Nugeena and relief of Moradabad, action on the Dojura, assault and capture of Bareilly, attack and bombardment of Shahjehanpore, defeat of the rebels and relief of the garrison, capture of the Fort of Bunnai, pursuit of the enemy to the left bank of the Goomtee, and destruction of the Fort of Mohumdee, attack and capture of Shahabad; present at the action of Bung-ka-gong, 8th October 1858, served in the campaign in Oudh, in 1858-59, including the action at pusgaon, 19th October, commanded the 1st Battalion 60th Rifles at the battle of Russoolpore on the 25th October. The attack and capture of Fort Mittowlie on the 8th November 1858. Sever contusion from round shot.

Captain MacQueen was engaged with the mutineers near Cawnpore on the 26th and 27th November and commanded a company of the 34th Regt. at the defence of Cawnpore from 28th November to 24th December 1857. Served with the 1st Bt. 60 Rifles, the campaign in Rohilcund in 1858, including the actions of Bagawalla and Nugeena, relief of Moradabad, action on the Dojura, assault and capture of Bareilly, attack and bombardment of Shahjehanpore, defeat of the rebels and relief of the garrison, capture of the Fort of Bunnai, pursuit, of the enemy to the left bank of the Goomtee and destruction of the Fort of Mahumdee, attack and capture of Shahabad. Present at the action of Bung-ka-gong, 8th Octr. 1858. Served in the campaign in Oude in 1858, including the action at Pusgaon on the 19th Octr., battle of Russoolpore on the 25th Octr. and attack and capture of Fort Mittowlie on the 8th, in which he command the Battalion on Capt. Jones being wounded, was present at the action at Biswah on the 1st December 1858.

Captain Dundas served in the campaign in 1857 against the mutineers in India from 7th June, including the battle of Bualee-ke-Serai and taking the heights before Delhi, the subsequent siege operations to 6th August (wounded on the 19th June. Served in the campaign of 1858 in Rohilcund, including the actions of Bagawalla and Nugeena, relief of Moradabad, action on the Dojura assault and capture of Bareilly, attack and bombardment of Shahjehanpore, defeat of the rebels and relief of the garrison, capture of the Fort of Bunnai, pursuit, of the enemy in the left bank of the Goomtee, and destruction of the Fort of Mahumdee; served in the campaign in Oude in 1858, including the action at Pusgaon on the 19th October 1858, attack and capture of the fort of Mittowlie on the 8th Novr. 1858 and the action at Biswah 1st December 1858.

Captain Hare served in the campaign of 1857, against the mutineers in India from 7th June, including the battle of Bualee-ke-Serai, and taking of the heights before Delhi. The subsequent siege operations, assault and capture of the city with the final attack on, and occupation of the Palace, served in the campaign of Oudh in 1858, including the action at Pusgaon on the 19th Oct. 1858, the battle of Russoolpore on the 25th, and the attack and capture of Fort Mittowlie on the 8th November 1858. The action at Biswah on the 1st December 1858.

Captain Deedes served with the 1st Battalion 60 Rifles, the campaign of 1857, against the mutineers in India, including the actions on the Hindun, battle of Bualee-ke-Serai and taking of the heights before Delhi the subsequent siege operations (wounded on 12th June) assault and capture of the city with the final attack on and occupation of the Palace, served as Aide-de-Camp to Brigadier General Jones during the campaign in Rohilcund including the actions on Bagawalla and Nugeena, relief of Mooradabad, action on the Dojura, assault and capture of Bareilly attack and bombardment of Shahjehanpore, defeat of the rebels and relief of the garrison, capture of the Fort of Bunnai pursuit of the enemy to the left bank of the Goomtee and destruction of the Fort of Mahumdee, served as Extra Aide-de-Camp to Sir A. Wilson at the siege and capture of Lucknow, served in the campaign in Oudh in 1858, as Aide-de-Camp to Brigadier Barker, C. B.

Capt. Chads served in the campaign in Rohilcund in 1858 including the actions of Bagawalla and Nugeena and relief of Mooradabad, the action on the Dojura, assault and capture of Bareilly, attack and bombardment of Shahjehanpore, defeat of the rebels and relief of the garrison, capture of the Fort of Bunnai, and destruction of the Fort of Mahumdee; served in the campaign in Oude in 1858 including the action at Pusgaon on the 19th, and the battle of Russoolpore on the 25th October 1858.

Lieut. Carlisle served from 12th November 1857, against the mutineers in India, including the operations at Cawnpore on 26th, 27th and 28th November and its defence till the defeat of the Gwalior mutineers on the 6th December, and action of Kallee-Nuddee, campaign in Rohilcund, including the actions of Bagawalla and Nugeena, relief of Mooradabad, action on the Dojura, assault and capture of Bareilly, attack and bombardment of Shahjehanpore, defeat of the rebels and relief of the garrison, capture of the Fort of Bunnai, pursuit of the enemy to the left bank of the Goomtee, and destruction of the Fort of Mahumdee, attack on and destruction of Shahabad, present at the action of Bung-ka-gong on 8th October 1858. Served in the campaign of Oude in 1858, including the action at Pusgaon on the 19th, and battle of Rissoolpore, 25th October 1858—The attack and capture of Fort Mittowlie on the 8th Novr. and the action at Biswah on the 1st December 1858.

Lieut. Northey served in the campaign in Oudh in 1858, including the attack and capture of fort Mittowlie on the 8th Novr., and at the action at Biswah on the 1st December 1858.

Lieut. Curtis served in the campaign of 1857, against the mutineers in India, including the actions on the Hindun, battle of Bualee-ke-Serai and taking the heights before Delhi, subsequent siege operations, assault and capture of the city with the final attack on and occupation of the Palace. Was wounded on the 12th June and again at the assault on the 14th September.

WAR SERVICES OF TEH OFFICERS OF H. M. 60TH RIFLES.—*(Continued.)*

Lieut. Ashburnham served in the campaign of 1857, against the mutinous sepoys in India, including the actions on the Hindun, battle of Bualee-ke-Serai and taking the heights before Delhi, subsequent siege operations, assault and capture of the city with the final attack on and occupation of the Palace, campaign in Rohilcund, including the actions of Bagawalla and Nugeena, relief of Mooradabad, action on the Dojura, assault and capture of Bareilly, attack and bombardment of Shahjehanpore, defeat of the rebels and relief of the garrison, capture of the Fort of Bunnai, pursuit of the enemy to the left bank of the Goomtee, and destruction of the Fort of Mahumdee, attack and destruction of Shahabad.

Lieut. Morgan served in the campaign of 1857-1858 against the mutineers in India, including the battles of Bualee-ke-Serai and taking the heights before Delhi, subsequent siege operations, assault and capture of the city with the final attack on and occupation of the Palace ; campaign in Rohilcund, including the actions of Bagawalla and Nugeena, relief of Mooradabad, action on the Dojura, assault and capture of Bareilly, attack and bombardment of Shahjehanpore, defeat of the rebels and relief of the garrison ; capture of the Fort of Bunnai, pursuit of the enemy to the left bank of the Goomtee and destruction of the Fort of Mahumdee ; attack and destruction of Shahabad, present at the action of Bung-ka-Gong on the 8th October 1858 ; served in the campaign in Oude in 1858, including the action at Pusgaon on the 19th, the battle of Russoolpore on the 25th October, attack and capture of Fort Mittowlie on the 8th November and the action at Biswah on the 1st December 1858.

Lieut. Austin was engaged in active service in India in 1857, in dispersing Insurgent villagers. Served in the campaign in Rohilcund in 1858, including the actions of Bagawalla and Nugeena relief of Moradabad, action on the Dojura, assault and capture of Bareilly, attack and bombardment of Shahjehanpore, defeat of the rebels and relief of the garrison, capture of the Fort of Bunnai, pursuit of the enemy to the left bank of the Goomtee and destruction of the Fort of Mahumdee, attack and destruction of Shahabad. Present at the action of Bung-ka-Gong, 8th October 1858. Served in the campaign in Oude in 1858, including the action at Pusgaon on the 19th. The battle of Russoolpore on the 25th October, attack and capture of Fort Mittowlie on the 8th Novr., and the action at Biswah on the 1st December 1858.

Lieut. Kelly served in the campaign in 1857, against the mutineers in India, including the actions on the Hindun, battle of Bualee-ke-Serai and taking the heights before Delhi, subsequent siege operations, assault and capture of the city with the final attack on and occupation of the Palace, campaign in Rohilcund, including the actions of Bagawalla and Nugeena, relief of Mooradabad, action on the Dojura, assault and capture of Bareilly attack and bombardment of Shahjehanpore, defeat of the rebels and relief of the garrison, capture of the Fort of Bunnai pursuit of the enemy to the left bank of the Goomtee and destruction of the Fort of Mahumdee, attack and destruction of Shahabad, present at the action of Bung-ka-Gong, 8th October 1858. Served in the campaign in Oude in 1858.

Lieut. Preston served in the campaign in Rohilcund, including the actions of Bagawalla and Nugeena, relief of Moradabad, action on the Dojura, assault and capture of Bareilly, attack and bombardment of Shahjehanpore, defeat of the rebels and relief of the garrison ; served in the campaign in Oude in 1858, including the capture of the Fort of Mittowlie on the 8th November, and the action at Biswah on the 1st December 1858.

Lieut. Young was engaged in active service in India in 1857, in dispersing insurgent villagers, present at the action of Bung-ka-Gong, 8th October 1858 ; served in the campaign in Oude in 1858, including the actions at Pusgaon on the 19th battle of Russoolpore on the 25th October, attack and capture of Fort Mittowlie 8th Nov. and the action at Biswah on the 1st December 1858.

Lieut. Jennings served in the campaign in 1857, against the mutineers in India, including the action on the Hindun, battle of Bualee-ke-Serai and taking the heights before Delhi, subsequent siege operations, assault and capture of the city with the final attack on and occupation of the Palace ; campaign in Rohilcund including, the actions of Bagawalla and Nugeena, relief of Mooradabad, action on the Dojura, assault and capture of Bareilly, attack and bombardment of Shahjehanpore, defeat of the rebels and relief of the garrison ; capture of the Fort of Bunnai, pursuit of the enemy to the left bank of the Goomtee and destruction of the Fort of Mahumdee, attack and destruction of Shahabad, present at the action of Bung-ka-Gong, 8th Octr, 1858. Served in the campaign in Oude in 1858, including the action at Pusgaon on the 19th October, battle of Russoolpore on the 25th, attack and capture of Fort Mittowlie on the 8th Novr and the action at Biswah 1st December 1858.

Lieut. Turle served in the campaign of 1857, against the mutineers in India, including the action on the Hindun, battle of Bualee-ke-Serai and taking the heights before Delhi, the subsequent siege operations until dangerously wounded on the 10th August.

Lieut. Mortimer served in the campaign in 1857, against the mutineers in India, including dispersion of insurgent villagers, siege of Delhi from 7th September, assault and capture of the city with the final attack on and occupation of the Palace campaign in Rohilcund, including the action of Bagawalla and Nugeena, relief of Mooradabad, action on the Dojura, assault and capture of Bareilly, attack and bombardment of Shahjehanpore, defeat of the rebels and relief of the garrison, capture of the Fort of Bunnai ; pursuit of the enemy to the left bank of the Goomtee and destruction of the Fort of Mahumdee ; attack on and destruction of Shahabad, present at the action of Bung-ka-Gong, 8th October 1858 ; served in the campaign in Oude in 1858, including the action at Pusgaon on the 19th, battle of Russoolpore on the 25th October, attack and capture of Fort Mittowlie on the 8th November, and the action at Biswah 1st December 1858.

Ensign Treeve served in the campaign in Oude in 1858, including the actions at Pusgaon on the 19th, battle, of Russoolpore 25th October, attack and capture of Fort Mittowlie on the 8th November and the action at Biswah 1st December 1858.

Ensign Cox was present at the action at Bung-ka-Gong on the 8th October 1858, served in the campaign in Oude in 1858, including the actions at Pusgaon on the 19th, battle of Russoolpore 25th October, attack and capture of Fort Mittowlie on the 8th November, and the action at Biswah 1st December 1858. Present at the action of Mehndee on the 18th November 1858.

Ensign Barker served in the campaign in Oude in 1858.

Ensign Ororke served in the campaign in Oude in 1858 including the action at Biswah 1st December.

Qr. Mr. Hunter served in the campaign of 1848-9, including the siege and capture of Mooltan from 28th December 1848 to 22nd January 1849, battle of Goojerat, pursuit and surrender of Shere Sing, occupation of Attock and Peshawur (Medal and two Clasps). Served the campaign of 1857-58 against the mutineers in India including the actions on the Hindun on the 30th and 31st May, battle of Bualee-ke-Serai and attack of the heights before Delhi, subsequent siege operations, assault and capture of the city with the final attack on and occupation of the Palace ; campaign in Rohilcund, including actions of Bagawalla and Nugeena, relief of Mooradabad, action on the Dojura, assault and capture of Bareilly, attack and bombardment of Shahjehanpore, defeat of the Rebels and relief of the garrison, capture of the Fort of Bunnai, pursuit of the enemy to the left bank of the Goomtee, and destruction of the Fort of Mahumdee, attack and destruction of Shahabad. Present at the action of Bung-ka-gong, 8th October 1858, served in the campaign in Oude in 1858, including the action at Pusgaon on the 19th, battle of Russoolpore on the 25th October, attack and capture of Fort Mittowlie on the 8th Novr. and the action at Biswah 1st December 1858.

Asst. Surgt. Oliver served in the campaign in Rohilcund in 1858, including the actions at Bagawalla and Nugeena and relief of Mooradabad, the action on the Dojura, assault and capture of Bareilly, attack and bombardment of Shahjehanpore, defeat of the rebels of the garrison, capture and relief of the Fort of Bunnai, pursuit of the enemy to the left bank of the Goomtee and destruction of the Fort of Mahumdee ; attack and destruction of Shahabad, present at the action of Bung.ka-Gong, 8th October 1858, served in the campaign in Oude in 1858, including the action at Pusgaon on the 19th, and the battle of Russoolpore, 25th October 1858, the attack and capture of Fort Mittowlie on the 8th November 1858, present at the action at Mehndee, 18th November 1858, and the action at Biswah on the 1st December 1858.

Surgeon Young served in the eastern campaign of 1854 and 1855, including the battles of Alma, Balaclava, Inkerman, and siege of Sebastopol, and expedition to Kertch ; served in the Indian campaign of 1858-9 as Surgeon in charge of Her. M's. 13 Lt. In ; present at the actions at Dumoorigunge on the 26th November and 3rd December, and of Toolseepore on the 23rd December 1858.

2nd Battalion of H. M. 60th Regiment of (King's Royal) Rifles.

Landed in Calcutta, from Cape of Good Hope, on 14th May 1858.

BENARES AND ARRAH.

Regimental Depôt, Winchester.

RANK AND NAMES.	*Regimental Rank.*	*Army Rank.*	REMARKS.
COLONEL.			
Sir W. G. Moore K. C. B., -	26 *Jan,* 56	.. ..	In England.
LIEUTENANT COLONEL.			
Francis Roger Palmer, C. B. -	22 *June* 58	... ...	Commanding.
Webbe Butler, - - -	9 *Sep.* 58		
MAJOR.			
George Waldegrave Bligh, -	24 *April* 58	.. ..	Leave on P. A. to Nainee Tal to 15 Oct. [59.
Gibbes Rigaud, - - -	22 *June* 58		
CAPTAIN.			
Peter Burton Roe, - -	17 *June* 51	.. ..	Leave of absence to England on P. A. for 18 months.
James Fraser, - - -	7 *Jan.* 53	.. ..	Leave of absence on M. C.
Dunbar Douglas Muter, -	31 *May* 54	*l.c.* 16 *Nov.* 58	Commdg. Convalescent Depôt, Muree.
Henry E. Warren, -	4 *Aug.* 54		
Robt. Wilmot Brooke, -	23 *Mar.* 55	.. ..	Winchester Depôt, England.
F. C. Feilden, -	23 *Mar.* 55		
R. J. E. Robertson, -	23 *Mar.* 55		
Hugh P. Montgomery, -	17 *Aug.* 55	.. ..	Winchester Depôt, England.
Hon. Athol C. J. Liddell, -	21 *Dec.* 55		
W. Douglas Phelips, -	7 *Apl.* 56	.. ..	Winchester Depot.
Francis Dundas Farquharson, -	24 *Apl.* 58	.. ..	England.
J. W. Medhurst, - - - -	16 *Feb.* 59		
LIEUTENANTS.			
Llewellyn E. Traherne, -	23 *Mar.* 55	.. ..	Leave to England. on M. C.
D. G. N. Watts-Russell, -	23 *Mar.* 55		
Arthur W. Knox-Gore, -	11 *May* 55	.. ...	Leave of absence to England on P. A. [for 18 months.
James Arthur Morrah, -	11 *May* 55	.. ..	Leave to England on P. A.
Hon. R. P. Vereker, -	11 *May* 55		
Geo. Kennedy Shaw, -	26 *Oct.* 55		
Kenneth G. Henderson, -	6 *May* 56		
James S. H. Algar, -	9 *May* 56		
Matthew Tilford, - -	17 *Mar.* 57	.. ..	Adjutant.
Frank Sadlier Brereton, -	13 *Feb.* 58	.. ..	Instructor of Musketry.
Nurton Jones Pauli, -	4 *June* 58	.. ..	Winchester Depôt, England.
William Henry Moseley, -	15 *June* 58	.. ..	Ditto.
James Walker King, -	1 *Aug.* 58	... ...	Ditto.
Alfred Spencer Heathcote, -	22 *June* 58		
Fred. Augustus Campbell, -	9 *Sep.* 58		
ENSIGNS.			
Richard R. Gubbins, -	19 *June* 57		
F. deBarry Barry, -	30 *Oct.* 57		
Pierce O'B. Butler, -	2 *Feb.* 58		
Richard Meade, -	28 *Mar.* 58		
Charles Prust, -	29 *Mar.* 58		
Arthur Morris, - -	21 *May* 58	.. ..	
Redvers Henry Buller, -	23 *May* 58	.. ..	
Chas. Pierson Cramer, - - -	24 *Aug.* 58		England.
H. M. Pryor, - - - -	25 *June* 58	.. ...	Ditto.
J. A. Hudson, - - - - -	13 *July* 58	... ...	Ditto.

2ND BATTALION OF H. M. 60TH REGIMENT OF ROYAL RIFLES—*(Continued.)*

RANK AND NAMES.	*Regimental Rank.*	*Army Rank.*	REMARKS.
INSTRUCTOR OF MUSKETRY.			
Lieut. Frank S. Brereton, -	13 *Feb.* 58		
PAY MASTER.			
Francis Fitzpatrick, - -	2 *Mar.* 55		
ADJUTANT.			
Lieut. Matthew Tilford, -	17 *Mar.* 57		
QUARTER MASTER.			
Luke FitzGibbon, - - -			
SURGEON.			
H. J. Schooles M. D., - -	1 *Oct.* 47		
ASSISTANT SURGEONS.			
Grahame Young, - - -	5 *May* 54		
R. O. Hayden, - - -	15 *Sep.* 57		
James Doran, M. D. - -	13 *Aug.* 58	9 *Nov.* 57	Winchester Depôt, England.
INTERPRETER.			
*			

Strength,—8 Companies with 39 Sergeants,—31 Corporals,—19 Drummers,—and 593 Privates.

English Agents—Messrs C. R. and W. McGregor.
Irish Agents—Messrs. R. Canes and Sons.
Calcutta Agents—Messrs. Wood, Olliffe and Co.

WAR SERVICES OF THE OFFICERS OF 2ND BATTN. H. M. 60TH RIFLES.

Sir William George Moore served in the Peninsula with the 52nd, and was present at the sieges of Ciudad Rodrigo, Badajoz, and St. Sebastian; and at the battles of Salamanca, Vittoria, Nivelle, and Nive, for which he has received the War Medal with seven Clasps. He was also at the repulse of the sortie from Baynane as Aide-de-Camp to Sir John Hope, and was severely wounded and taken prisoner with that General. He served also the Waterloo campaign on the staff of the Quarter-Master-General.

Colonel Butler, Capt. Liddell, Lieuts. Knox-Gore, Shaw, Henderson, Algar, and Tilford, Surgeon Schooles and Assistant Surgeon Hayden, served in 1858, in the supppression of the rebellion in the Shahabad district.

Lt. Col. Muter, served with 1st Batt. of the 60th Rifles in the Punjaub campaign of 1849 (Medal and two Clasps) and was present during the second siege operations at Mooltan (including the siege and storm of the town and capture of the citadel), battle of Goojerat, pursuit of the Sikh army until its final surrender at Rawul Pindee, occupation of Attock and Peshawur, and expulsion of the Affghan force beyond the Khyber Pass.

Major Rigaud served in the Kaffir war of 1851-53, [Medal].

Captain Warren, served in the Kaffir war of 1851-53 (Medal); served in 1859 in the suppression of the rebellion in the Shahabad district.

Assist-Surgeon Young served with the 2nd Batt. Rifle Brigade in the Crimea, and was present throughout the siege of Sebastopol (Medal and Clasps).

H. M. 67th (the South Hampshire) Regiment of Foot.

"Barrosa"—"Peninsula"—The *Royal Tiger*, superscribed, "India."
Facings—*Yellow.*
Arrived in Calcutta from England on the—December 1858.
Barrackpore.
Detachment at Ishapore.
Regimental Depôt. Athlone.

Rank and Names.	*Regimental Rank.*	*Army Rank.*	Remarks.
Colonel.			
Francis John Davies, - - P,	15 *Jan.* 58	*m.g.* 20 *June* 54	Europe.
Lieutenant Colonels.			
Thomas Edmond Knox, - -	17 *Sept.* 58	.. ..	Commanding.
John Wellesley Thomas, - -	31 *Dec.* 58		
Majors.			
John Porter, - - - - - -	17 *Sept.* 58		
Charles Barnard Hague, - -	31 *Dec.* 58	20 *June* 54	
Captains.			
Henry Collette, - - - -	23 *Feb.* 44	*m.* 6 *Jan.* 55	Leave on M. C.
Robert Hudson Wood, - - -	28 *Aug.* 49	.. ...	Depot Athlone.
Dugald Stewart Miller, - - -	31 *Jan* 51		
Henry Crofton, - - - -	17 *Jan.* 51		
Daniel Thomson, - - - -	30 *Nov.* 55	.. ..	District Inspector of Musketry Cork.
Henry C. Worthington,- - -	9 *May* 56	.. ..	Depot Athlone.
Frederick William Jebb, - -	30 *Sep.* 56	8 *July* 56	Staff College, England.
Edward Daubeny, - - - -	15 *Jan.* 58		
~~William Serjeant Arnold~~, - -	13 *Apl.* 58	9 *Mar.* 58	
Arthur Henry Coney, - - -	15 *June* 58		
George T. Horton Atchison, V,	17 *Sept.* 58		
Thomas Stack, - - - - -	28 *June* 59	29 *Apl.* 56	Not joined.
Lieutenants.			
Malachy Nugent, - - - -	21 *Sep.* 55		
Arthur Forbes Robertson, - -	30 *Nov.* 55		
John Richard Crane, - - -	15 *Jan.* 56	.. ..	Depot Athlone.
Edward Coxen, - - - - -	1 *June* 56	.. ..	Instructor of Musketry.
Edmund Henry Lenon, - - -	14 *Nov.* 56	.. ..	Adjutant Recruit Battn. Dum-Dum.
Thomas Dawson, - - - -	17 *July* 57	.. ..	Recruit Battn. Dum-Dum.
Wm. Henry Bell Kingsley, -	30 *Oct.* 57		
Charles Edward Morgan, - -	30 *Oct.* 57		
George Thomson, - - - -	23 *Mar.* 58		
William Digby Lloyd, - - -	23 *Mar.* 58		
George Masters Cardew, - -	15 *June* 58		
Nathaniel Burslem, - - - -	13 *July* 58	12 *Feb.* 58	
Charles William Creyke - -	24 *Sep.* 58		
John Trevor Hall Gardiner, -	31 *Dec.* 56		
Ensigns.			
Charles Henry B. Turner, -	25 *Sep.* 57		
James Hardie Fraser, - - -	30 *Oct.* 57		
George Baker, - - - - -	18 *Dec.* 57		
Alfred Adams Price, - - -	5 *Mar.* 58		
Lorenzo Nickson Mosse, - -	26 *Mvr.* 58		
Miles Charles Seaton, - - -	30 *Mar.* 58		
John Worthy Chaplin, - - -	13 *Apl.* 58		
Wm. Southby Middleton, - -	13 *July* 58	.. .	Depot Athlone.
Cha. Preice Killeen, - - -	17 *Sep.* 58		
Arthur J. Porle,- - - - -	11 *Jan.* 59	.. ..	Depot Athlone.
George C. Colmes, - - - -	18 *Feb.* 89	.. ..	Ditto.

H. M. 67TH (THE SOUTH HAMPSHIRE REGIMENT OF FOOT.—*(Continued.)*

RANK AND NAMES.	*Regimental Rank.*	*Army Rank.*	NAMES.
INSTRUCTOR OF MUSKETRY.			
Lieut. Edward Coxen, - - -	*lt.* 1 *June* 56	26 *Jan.* 58	
PAYMASTER.			
Capt. John Andrew Pope, - -	*c.* 17 *Sep.* 58	24 *Mar.* 54	
ADJUTANT.			
Ens. Charles Preice Killeen, -	17 *Sep.* 58	17 *Sep.* 58	
QUARTER-MASTER.			
John Staniforth, - - - - -	24 *Feb.* 57	24 *Feb,* 57	
SURGEON.			
Thomas Parr, - - - - - -	28 *Jan.* 58	21 *Oct* 53	
ASSISTANT-SURGEON.			
Alex. Clark Ross, M. D. - -	30 *Nov.* 58	1 *July* 53	
Robert Heard, M. D. - - -	3 *Nov.* 57	15 *Sep.* 57	
J. as George Stewart Mathison,	10 *Sep.* 58	5 *Aug.* 58	
INTERPETER.			
R. T. H. Barber Capsain, 63rd N. I. - - - - -	*Jan.* 59		

Strength—10 Companies with 55 Sergeants,—50 Corporals,—21 Drummers and 742 Privates.
English Agents—Messrs. Cox and Co.
Irish Agents—*Sir* E. R. Borough, *Bt.* Armit and Co.
Calcutta Agents—Messrs. Colvin, Cowie and Co.

WAR SERVICES OF THE OFFICERS OF H. M. 67TH REGT. OF FOOT.

Major-General Davies served in the Peninsula with the 52nd, and was present at the battles of Fuentes d'Onor, Salamanca, Vitoria and the Pyrenees, and at the siege of Badajoz (wounded), for which he has received the war Medal with five Clasps.

Lt. Col. Thomas served with the 40th Regt. throughout the operations in Candahar and Affganistan in 1841-42. (Medal); also in the action of Maharajpore 29th December 1843—wounded (Medal). commanded detachments of the 12th and 40th Regiments at the capture of a stockade occupied by insurgents at the Ballarat Gold Fields in Australia, on 3rd December 1854, for which he received the rank of Major.

Captain Worthington served with the 28th Regt. the Eastern campaign of 1855, including the siege of Sebastopol (Medal and Clasp).

Captain Jebb. served with the 23rd Fusiliers at the siege and fall of Sebastopol from 14th November 1854 [Medal and Clasp].

Capt. Stack served throughout the operations in Scinde [Medal] including the destruction of Imaumghur and the battles of Meeanee and Hydrabad [severely wounded] was afterwards present at Punulla, Pownghur' Mannahur, and Mansuntosh.

Paymaster Pope served with the 47th Regt. in the Eastern campaign of 1854-55, including the battles of Alma, and Inkerman, siege and fall of Sebastopol, and sortie of 26th October [Medal and clasps].

H. M. 70th (or the Surrey) Regt. of Foot.

FACINGS—*Black.*

Landed in Bengal on the 17th May 1849.

RAWUL PINDEE.

Regimental Depôt, Chatham.

RANK AND NAMES.	*Regimental Rank.*	*Army Rank.*	REMARKS.
COLONEL.			
George Wm. Paty, C. B., K. H.,..	8 *May* 54	*l. g.* 20 *June* 54	In Europe.
LIEUTENANT COLONELS.			
Thomas James Galloway, ..	22 *Dec*, 48	*col.* 28 *Nov.* 54	Brigadier, Comdg. Peshawur District.
Trevor Chute, ...	14 *Dec.* 49	*col.* 28 *Nov.* 54	Brigadier Comdg. at Lucknow.
MAJORS.			
~~George Durnford,~~	26 *May* 50	*l.c.* 29 *Aug.* 57	Lv, on M. C. to Muree to 30 Sep. 59.
Thomas Edmonds Mulock, ..	7 *Feb.* 59	.. ..	Commanding.
CAPTAINS.			
~~Edward L'Estrange,~~	8 *Jan.* 47	*col* 12 *Nov.* 58	Leave to Landour on P. A.
George A. Ryan, ..	15 *Nov.* 50	.. ..	
Sydney Cosby Jackson, *H,*	8 *Nov.* 50	.. ..	Commandant Lahore Light Horse.
Oswald Pilling, ..	9 *Apl.* 52		
Archibald John O. Rutherfurd,	15 *Mar.* 53	.. ..	Instructor Musketry, Chatham.
Henry Fredk. Saunders, ..	.. ..	*m* 24 *Mar.* 58	Regimental Depôt, England.
William H. Cooper, *SPC,*	26 *Jan.* 55	.. ..	Deputy Assistant Qr. Mr. General Peshawur.
~~Charles Alfred Poyntz~~ James,..	15 *Sep.* 57	.. ..	At the Kurrachie Depôt.
Paul F. de Quincy, *P,*	16 *July* 58	9 *June* 58	Interpreter.
Oates Joseph Travers, ..	18 *July* 58	.. ..	2nd in Comd. Peshawur Light Horse.
Arthur Saltmarshe, ...	7 *Feb.* 59	27 *Feb.* 50	
LIEUTENANTS.			
~~Robert Whigham,~~ .. *V,*	17 *Jan.* 51	.. ..	With Lahore Light Horse.
George Richards Greaves, *V,*	16 *Jan.* 52	7 *Feb.* 51	Adjutant.
Alexr. C. Hughes Tovey, *PH,* (*a*)	26 *Jan.* 55	.. ..	Regimental Depot.
James Green, ...	5 *June* 55	.. ..	Leave of Absence on P. A.
Charles William Quin, ..	9 *May* 55	.. ..	Leave on M. C. to England.
Henry Berkeley Good, ..	30 *July* 56	13 *May* 55	Pay and Quarter Master Recruit Depôt, Kurrachie.
Eustace Cay, ..	30 *June* 57		
Thomas Deering Backhouse, ..	15 *Sep.* 57		
Chas. G. Stuart Monteath, ..	18 *May* 58		
~~George Aislabie Hilton,~~ ..	18 *July* 58	.. ..	Regimental Depot.
William Henry Ralston, ..	23 *July* 58		
Henry Leak, ..	30 *July* 58	.. ..	Instructor of Musketry.
John Beldham, ...	24 *Sep.* 58	.. ..	Acting Quarter Master.
Arthur William Crozier, ..	7 *Feb.* 59	11 *Sep.* 57	
Alexander Boyd Wright, ..	25 *Mar.* 59	.. ..	Regimental Depôt, England.
ENSIGNS.			
Arthur S. Gilbert, ..	.. ..	22 *Aug.* 56	At Hythe.
Christopher Garcia, ...	23 *Mar.* 58	.. ..	Regimental Depôt England.
Charles C. Richardson, ..	26 *Mar.* 58		
Herbert J. Hill, ..	23 *July* 58	.. ..	Regimental Depôt,
Norman Huskisson, ..	24 *Sep.* 58	.. ..	Not joined.
Charles Roger, ..	20 *Nov.* 58		
J. Frederick Augustus Grierson,	31 *Dec.* 58		
R. S. Riddell, ..	8 *Apl,* 59		

(*a*) Has passed an examination in Civil Engineering.

H. M. 70TH REGIMENT OF FOOT—(*Continued.*)

RANK AND NAMES.	*Regimental Rank.*	*Army Rank.*	REMARKS.
PAY MASTER.			
M. Thompson, ..	10 *Nov.* 54		
ADJUTANT.			
Lieut. George Richd. Greaves,	8 *May* 58	*lt* 16 *Jan.* 52	
QUARTER MASTER.			
William Nevell, ..	1 *June* 55	.. ..	En route to Kurrachee with invalids.
Lieut. J. Beldham, ..	24 *Sep.* 58	.. ..	Acting.
SURGEON.			
Richard Robert Dowse, - -	18 *Jan.* 59	12 *Feb.* 47	
ASSISTANT SURGEONS.			
Henry James Rogers, *H*,	16 *June* 54	.. ..	Leave on M. C.
James Francis Deakin, M. D.,..	28 *July* 55	.. ..	Medical charge of the Convalescent Depôt, Murree.
Joseph Watts, .. *V*,	5 *Apl.* 50		
INTERPRETER.			
Capt. P. F. de Quincey, ..	17 *Mar.* 59		

Strength—10 Companies, with 56 Sergeants—50 Corporals—19 Drummers—845 Privates.

English Agents—Messrs. Cox and Co.
Calcutta Agents—Messrs. Gillanders, Arbuthnot and Co.

WAR SERVICES OF THE OFFICERS OF H. M. 70TH REGIMENT OF FOOT.

Lieut.-General Paty served on the expedition to Copenhagen in 1807. Served afterwards in the Peninsula from June 1811 to the end of that War in 1814, including the siege and capture of Badajoz, battle of Salamanca retreat from Madrid to Burgos, battles of Vittoria, the Pyrenees and Nivelle, battles of the Nive on the 9th 10th, 11th, 12th, and 13th Dec. 1813, besides various minor affairs. He has received the War Medal with six Clasps and is Commander of St. Bento d'Avis and Knight of the Tower and Sword of Portugal.

Lt.-Col. L'Estrange served in the campaign of 1808-9 in Spain with the 14th, and was present at the battle of Corunna. Capture of the Isle of France in 1810. Capture of Java in 1811, and engaged with a Dutch brigade at St. Nicholas. At the storming of a strong Dutch Fort on the coast of Bantam. On board H. M. S. *Roscius* at the boarding and capture of eleven French gun-boats. Present at the siege and storm of Cornelis, and storm and capture of the heights of Serandole. At the capture of the town and fortress of Sambas, Isle of Born eo, in March 1813. Nepaul war in 1815; siege and capture of Hattras in March 1817: Mahratta campaign in 1817 and 18: siege and storm of Bhurtpore under Lord Combermere. He has received the War Medal and two Clasps for Corunna and Java.

Major Saunders served on the western coast of Africa with the Royal African Crops from1836 to 1842, and was present with the expeditionary force in the Interior in 1837. Was employed on a mission to convey Dispatches to the French at Senegal in 1838; commanded the troops at a riot up the Gambia in 1838, and whilst at night patrolling captured a gun. Attached to the 64th Regt. at Cawnpore in Nov. 1857; commanded the outlying piquets which protected General Windham's camp after the action of the 26th; commanded the right wing of the 64th in action on the 27th Nov.; led the Regt. into action and succeeded to its command on the fall of Colonel Wilson and Major Stirling on the 28th Nov.—mentioned in the Dispatches as having distinguished himself, and for mostdevoted and gallant conduct (Brevet Major).

Captain Cooper served with the 18th Royal Irish throughout the campaign of 1852-53 in Burmah (Medal).

Capt. James served with the 50th Regt. in the campaign on the Sutlej, and was present in the battles of Aliwal and Sobraon (Medal and Clasps).

Captain de Quincey was present with the 8th Regt. at the battle of Sobraon (Medal.)

Paymaster Thompson served with the 2nd Batt. Royal Regt. throughout the Mahratta war, with the army in the Deccan, under Sir John Doveton, in the years 1817, 18, and 19. Also, during the Burmese war, from Jan. 1825 until its conclusion in 1826 (Madal).

H. M. 71st (Highland) Regiment of Foot (L. I.)

"HINDOOSTAN" "CAPE OF GOOD HOPE" "ROLEIA" "VIMIERA" "CORUNNA"
"FUENTES D'ONOR" "ALMARAZ" "VITTORIA" "PYRENEES" "NIVE"
"ORTHES" "PENINSULA" "WATERLOO" "SEVASTOPOL."

FACINGS—*Buff.*

Landed at Bombay, from Corfu———

MORAR.

3 Companies at *Gwalior*, 3 Companies at *Goonah.*

Depôt—Stirling.

RANK AND NAMES.	*Regimental Rank.*	*Army Rank.*	REMARKS.
COLONEL.			
Thomas Erskine Napier, C. B.,	.. ..	*col.* 16 *May* 57	Europe.
LIEUTENANT COLONELS.			
Robt. Dennistoun Campbell, C. B..	2 *Oct.* 57		
William Hope, C. B., ..	26 *Dec.* 57	.. ..	At Goonah.
MAJORS.			
George Whitworth Talbot Rich,	2 *Oct.* 57	*l. c.* 20 *July* 58	Regimental Depot.
James Arthur Gore, ..	4 *Mar.* 59	.. ..	
CAPTAINS.			
Henry Loftus, ..	22 *Dec.* 48	*m.* 26 *Dec.* 56	Leave.
Arthur Charles Parker, ..	26 *Dec.* 51	*m.* 7 *Dec.* 58	Gwalior.
John Ignatus Macdonell, ..	29 *Dec.* 54	.. ..	Lv. of absence Europe to 22nd June 60.
Charles Francis Smith, ..	29 *Dec.* 54	.. ..	Leave on M. C. to Landour to 10th Dec. 59.
Wm. Francis Segrave, ..	29 *Dec.* 54	.. ..	Ditto to 5th December 59.
Francis Bonham, ..	17 *Apr.* 57	.. ..	At Goonah.
Fred. William Lambton, ..	23 *Oct.* 57	.. ..	Regtl. Depot.
George Campbell, ..	30 *Oct.* 57	.. ..	
James Dalgleish, ..	26 *Dec.* 57	.. ..	Ditto.
Edward P. Wade Browne, ..	12 *Nov.* 58	.. ..	At Goonah.
Charles James Mounsey. ..	4 *Mar.* 59	.. ..	Regtl. Depot.
John C. H. Poyer Callen, ..	1 *Apl.* 59	.. ..	
LIEUTENANTS.			
Courtenay H. Salt. Scott, ..	8 *Dec.* 54	.. ..	
William O' Malley, ..	9 *Feb.* 55	.. ..	Leave on M. C. to Landour to 24th Sept. 59.
Robt. Barttelot Aldridge, ..	9 *Feb.* 55	.. ..	
C. J H. Howard, ..	9 *Mar.* 55	.. ..	
Arthur Kindersley Blair, ..	1 *June* 55	.. ..	Leave of absence on P. A. to Europe till 30th November 60.
Robert Lewis, ..	31 *Oct.* 55	.. ..	Gwalior.
Stratton Boulnois, ..	30 *Jan.* 57	.. ..	Ditto.
Robert Heron, ..	17 *Nov.* 57	.. ..	
Le Marchant James Carey, ..	26 *Dec.* 57	.. ..	
Wm. Fred. Vernon Harris, ..	15 *April* 58	.. ..	Ditto.
Robert James Isacke, ..	17 *June* 58	.. ..	
James Hay Campbell, ..	26 *Nov.* 58	.. ..	Adjutant.
Francis Fawkes, ..	11 *Jan.* 59	.. ..	Acting Adjutant.
John Boulderson, ..	11 *Mar.* 59	.. ..	On Leave in India.
John Henry Leslie, ..	1 *Apl.* 59	.. ..	At Goonah.
ENSIGNS.			
Richard Kane.	11 *Sept.* 57	.. ..	Leave on M. C. at Landour to 15th Sept, 59,
Rich. Courtenay Musgrave, ..	17 *Nov.* 57	.. ..	At Goonah.
John Younger Allan, ..	18 *Nov.* 57	.. ..	At Bombay.
Arthur Edward Morgan, ..	8 *Jan.* 58	.. ..	Regtl. Depot.
Henry Brooke Wilson, ..	24 *Aug.* 58	.. ..	Ditto.
Henry Craster, ..	18 *Jan.* 59	.. ..	Ditto.
Henry Renebald Clinton, ..	19 *Jan.* 59	.. ..	Ditto.
Edward Francis Brownlow, ...	11 *Feb.* 59	.. ..	Ditto.
Charles Balfour Murray, ..	18 *Mar.* 59	.. ..	Ditto.

H. M. 71st (Highland) Regt. of Foot (L. I.)—(Continued).

Rank and Names.	Regimental Rank.	Army Rank.	Remarks.
Instructor of Musketry.			
Lieut. Le M. James Carey, ..	26 *Dec.* 59		
Paymaster.			
Joseph Cartmail, ..	25 *Aug* 54	*ens.* 7 *Dec.* 38	Leave on P. A. 9 Apl. 60.
Adjutant.			
Lieut. James Hay Campbell, .	26 *Nov.* 58		
Quarter Master.			
Robert Anderson, ..	29 *April* 56		
Surgeon.			
Willim Simpson, M. B., ..	8 *Dec.* 54		
Assist-Surgeons.			
Walter Leach, ..	24 *Nov.* 54	.. ..	At Goonah.
Edwin Wilson, ..	19 *May* 55		
John Warren, ..	9 *Nov.* 57		
Interpreter.			
*			

English Agents—Messrs. Cox and Co.
Calcutta Agents—Messers. Wood, Olliffe and Co.

WAR SERVICES OF THE OFFICERS OF H. M. 71st REGT. OF FOOT.

Lt.-General Napier served with the 52nd Regt. at the siege of Copenhagen and battle of Kioge in 1807 Aide-de-Camp to Sir John Hope in the expedition to Sweden in 1808; and subsequently in Sir John Moore's campaign in Spain, including the retreat to, and Battle of Corunna. In Sicily with the Regiment until the autumn of 1810. served afterwards in the Peninsula on the staff, including the defence of Cadiz, battle of Fuentes d'Onor, second siege of Badajoz, battles of Salamanca, Vittoria, Nivelle, and the Nive—including the various engagements near the Mayor's house—slightly wounded on the 10th Dec., and severely on the 11th—lost left arm. He has received the War Medal with seven Clasps.

Lt.- Colonel Campbell served with the 4th Light Dragoons during the campaign in Affghanistan under Lord Keane, and was present at the siege and capture of Ghuznee (Medal.) Landed in the Crimea in 1855 and served with the 71st Regt. in the trenches at the siege of Sebastopol and was present at its fall (Medal and Clasp, and 5th Class of the Medjidie.)

Lieut. Col. Rich landed in the Crimea in 1855, served in the trenches at the siege of Sebastopol, and was present at its fall (Medal and Clasp, and Brevet Major).

Lt.-Colonel Hope landed in the Crimea in 1854, and served in the trenches and at the siege of Sebastopol, and on the expedition to Kertch (Medal and Clasp, Knight of the Legion of Honor, and 5th Class of the Medjidie).

Major Loftus served in the Crimea in 1855, including the siege and fall of Sebastopol, expedition to Kertch, affairs at and destruction of Taman (Medal aud Clasp, and 5th Class of the Medjidie).

Captain Lambton and Lieut. Aldridge landed in the Crimea in 1855, served in the trenches at the siege of Sebastopol, and were present at its fall (Medal and Clasp).

Captains Macdonell and Browne, Lieuts. Scott and Callen landed in the Crimea in 1855, and served in the trenches at the siege of Sebastopol, and on the expedition to Kertch [Medal and Clasp]. Captain Scott served at the destruction of and affairs at Taman in Sept. 1855.

Captains Bonham, G. Campbell, and Mounsey anded in the Crimea in 1854, and served in the trenches at the siege of Sebastopol and expedition to Kertch [Medal and Clasp]. Captains Campbell and Mounsey served at the destruction of and affairs at Taman in Sept. 1855. Captains Bonham and Campbell have the 5th Class of the Medjidie.

Major Parker served in the Crimea from Dec. 1854-57, including the siege and fall of Sebastopol, expedition to Kertch, affairs at and destruction of Taman [Medal and Clasp, and 5th Class of the Medjidie].

Captain Smith landed and served in the Crimea in 1855 [Medal and Clasp].

Captain Dalgleish and Lieut. O'Malley, and Qr.-Master Anderson landed in the Crimea in 1855, and served at the siege of Sebastopol and expedition to Kertch [Medal and Clasp]. Lieut. O'Malley served at the destruction of and affairs at Taman in Sept. 1855.

Paymaster Cartmail landed in the Crimea in 1855 [Medal and Clasp].

Surgeon Simpson landed in the Crimea in 1854, and served at the siege of Sebastopol [Medal and Clasp.

H. M's. 73rd Regiment of Foot.

Landed in Calcutta from Cape of Good Hope 29th Apl. 1858.

GORUCKPORE *District* (Camp Bulrampore.)

Regimental Depôt, Jersey.

☞ Since removed to Lucknow.

RANK AND NAMES.	*Regimental Rank.*	*Army Rank.*	REMARKS.
COLONEL.			
C. G. Falconar, K. H., -	11 *Feb.* 57	*l.g.* 20 *July* 58	In Europe.
LIEUTENANT COLONELS.			
F. G. A. Pinckney, C. B.,	14 *Apl.* 54	*col.* 24 *Nov.* 54	
G. Hankey Smith, -	21 *May* 58	*col.* 24 *Nov.* 51	
MAJORS.			
Thomas Ross, - - -	9 *June* 54	*l.c.* 12 *Nov.* 58	
William L. Peto, - - -	8 *May* 58	.. ..	Leave of Absence to England.
CAPTAINS.			
Wyndham E. Bewes, - -	3 *Aug.* 49	*l.c.* 12 *Nov.* 58	Instructor of Musketry, Ireland.
George Renny, - - -	25 *Oct.* 50	28 *Dec.* 49	Depôt, Jersey.
Godfrey James Burne, -	18 *Apl.* 51	.. ..	Ditto.
Wm. Creagh O'Brien, -	21 *Dec.* 52	.. ..	Leave of Absence to England.
William Henry Barry, -	15 *July* 53	18 *Feb.* 53	
John Cox Gawler, - -	14 *Apl.* 54	*l.c.* 18 *Feb.* 59	
Frederick Reeve, - -	6 *June* 54	.. ..	Leave of Absence to England.
James Whittaker Barnes,	22 *Sept.* 54		
Alex. Allan Aitchison, -	17 *Feb.* 57	.. ..	Leave on M. C. to England.
Spencer Vassall F. Henslowe, -	27 *Nov.* 57		
Richard James Hereford,	16 *May* 58		
Albert Henry Godfrey, -	21 *May* 58		
Philip Gibaut, - -	11 *May* 59		
LIEUTENANTS.			
Poole Francis Shuldham,	14 *Apl.* 54		
Fred. Tichfield Greatrex,	11 *Aug.* 54	.. ..	Leave on S. C. to England.
Mathew Smith Blyth, -	31 *Aug.* 55		
Wm. John Lane Milligan,	17 *Apl.* 57		
William Mitford, - - -	28 *Aug.* 57		
Hugh Fraser, - - -	27 *Nov.* 57	.. ..	Convalescent Depot, Nynee Tal.
William Gordon, - -	23 *Mar.* 58	.. ..	Adjutant.
William Bayley, - - -	14 *May* 58	.. ..	Regtl. Depot.
Thomas Wm. Shore Miles, V,	21 *May* 58	.. ..	Acting Interpreter.
Wm. Henry Samuel Pigott,	9 *July* 58		
Archibald Henry Sharp, -	12 *July* 58		
Hastings D'Oyly Farrington, -	16 *July* 58		
William Clarke, - -	2 *Nov.* 58		
Thomas Monsell Warren,	2 *Nov.* 58	.. ..	Depôt Jersey.
James Kirk, - - - - -	11 *May* 59		
ENSIGNS.			
Arthur Hare Palmer, - -	29 *Dec.* 57	.. ..	En-route to join.
James T. Turner, - - -	13 *Apl.* 58	.. ..	Regtl. Depot, Instructor of Musketry.
Archd. C. F. Armstrong, -	22 *June* 58	.. ..	Ditto.
Hugh F. H. Gibson, - - -	13 *July* 58	.. ..	Regtl. Depôt.
James Fraser, - - - - -	23 *July* 58	28 *May* 58	Ditto.
St. John Dupond Galwey -	30 *July* 58	.. ..	Ditto.
Bolton Jas. Alfred Monsell. -	7 *Sep.* 58	.. ..	Ditto.
Thos. Nepean Edward Kenny, -	31 *Dec.* 58	.. ..	En-route to join.

H. M. 73RD REGT. OF FOOT.—(*Continued.*)

RANK AND NAMES.	*Regimental Rank.*	*Army Rank.*	REMARKS.
INSTUCTOR OF MUSKETRY.			
Ens. James Trench Turner, ..	13 *Apl.* 58	26 *Feb.* 59	
PAY MASTER.			
Capt. Loftus Cassidy, - -	30 *June* 54	c. 6 *June* 54	
ADJUTANT.			
Lieut. W. M. Gordon, - -	23 *Mar.* 58		
QUARTER MASTER.			
Jonathan Gortly Scott, - -	24 *Feb.* 57		
SURGEON.			
Edward Booth, - - -	13 *Feb.* 52		
ASSISTANT SURGEON.			
Robert Thomas Scott, - -	8 *Dec.* 57		
John Anderson, M. B., - -	7 *May* 58	10 *Mar.* 58	
John McKinnell, M D, - -	4 *June* 58	.. ..	
INTERPRETER.			
Lieut. T. W. S. Miles. - - -	21 *May* 58	.. ..	Acting.

Strength.—8 Companies—53 Serjeants—49 Corporals—21 Drummers—620 Privates.

English Agents—Messrs. Cox and Co.
Calcutta Agents—Messrs. Wm. Spink and Co.

WAR SERVICES OF THE OFFICERS OF H. M. 73RD REGT. OF FOOT.

Major-General Falconar joined the 61st Regt. at the Cape in February 1801, and accompanied it to Egypt joining General Baird's army at Cosier—crossed the Dessert with it, and remained with the Army of Egypt until 1803. In 1804 and 1805 he served in the campaign in Italy under Sir James Craig. Served with the 78th Highlanders the Campaign of 1806 in Italy under Sir John Stuart—at the battle of Maida, siege of Scylla, capture of Catrone, &c. In 1807, the campagin in Egypt including the attack on the fortified heights and forts of Alexandria, 1st affair at Lake Elcho and Elhamet, investment and siege of Rosetta, actions at Rosetta and Elhamet 21st April. Served the campagin of 1814 and 1815 in Holland and Flanders—commanded Light Infantry 78th at both attacks on Merxem, attack of French at Brescat, and bombardment of Antwerp. Has received the Egyptian Gold Medal; also the Silver War Medal with two Clasps for Egypt and Maida, at which last battle he had a horse shot under him when acting as Aide-de-Camp to General Acland.

Colonel Pinckney served in the Kaffir war of 1846–7, and was honourably mentioned in Sir George Berkeley's General Order of the 17th Dec. 1847, as the commanding officer of the 73rd Regiment, in the active operations in the field under that General's Command (Medal).

Lieut.-Colonel Smith served in the Kaffir war of 1846-7, and was severely wounded. In Sir George Berkeley's General Order of 17th Dec. 1847 he was mentioned in the following handsome terms:—"The Lieut. General begs to thank Major Smith, 73rd Regt., who has commanded the Head Quarter Camp during the whole of the active operations, for the zeal and ability which he has shown" (Medal).

Major Peto served in the Kaffir war of 1846-7 (Medal).

Major Bewes served the Kaffir campagin of 1846-47 (Medal) with the 45th Regt.

Major Gawler served with the 73rd Regt. throughout the Kaffir war of 1850–53 (Medal and Bt.-Major); commanded the Light Company in nearly all the principal actions in Kaffirland and in the Colony, as also at the battle of Berea; served at different periods during the operations as Field Adjutant and as D. A. Qr.-Master General to the Divisions under Colonel Eyre, and was honorably mentioned eight times in official Reports: was appointed District Adjutant of Natal at the close of the war.

Captains Renny and Burne served in the Kaffir war of 1851-53 (Medal), including the operations in the Amatolas, Fish River, Waterkloof, and Trans-Kei expeditions.

Captain O'Brien served in the 40th Regt. in the action of Maharajpore (wounded), and has received the Bronze Star.

Captain Barnes served as Lieut. and Adjutant in Major Hogg's Battalion of Native Infantry in the Kaffir war of 1846-7; was present in several engagements; accompanied the expedition into the Tambookie country in August, and that over the Kei in Dec. 1846. Served with the 73rd Regt. in the Kaffir war in 1851 (Medal).

H. M. 75th Regiment of Foot.

"SERINGAPATAM"—*The* ROYAL TIGER *superscribed* "INDIA.
FACINGS—*Yellow.*

Landed in Bengal, from England, on the 10*th August* 1849.
MEERUT.

Regimental Depôt, Chatham.

RANK AND NAMES.	*Regimental Rank.*	*Army Rank.*	REMARKS.
COLONEL.			
St. John Aug. Clerke, K. H.. ..	22 *Mar* 45	*m.g.*20 *June* 54	In England.
LIEUTENANT COLONELS.			
~~Alexander Jardine,~~ ..	1 *June* 49	*col* 28 *Nov.* 54	Leave to England.
William Radcliff, ..	7 *Dec.* 58	.. ..	Commanding.
MAJORS.			
Legendre Charles Bourchier, ..	12 *Dec.* 51	*l.c.* 9 *Aug.* 58	
Edward Knollys, ..	2 *June* 57	.. ..	
CAPTAINS.			
Wm. Campbell Mollan, C.B. *V*,	13 *Oct.* 43	*l.c.* 20 *July* 58	Commandant of Depot H. M. Troops [at Dum-Dum.
Charles E. P. Gordon, *PH*, (*a*)	25 *Apl.* 45	*l.c.* 19 *Jan.* 58	Lv. of absence to England for 18 months.
~~Balcarras D. W. Ramsay,~~ ..	25 *June* 47	*m* 12 *Nov.* 58	Leave on M. C. to England.
William Brookes, ..	28 *Jan.* 48	*m* 19 *Jan.* 58	
John Hamilton Cox, *V*,	31 *Mar.* 48	*m* 19 *Jan.* 58	Comdg. Murree Convalescent Depot.
Thomas Clement Dunbar, ..	25 *Apl.* 51	*m* 19 *Jan.* 58	Leave of absence on M. C. to England.
Richard Dawson, ..	22 *Dec.* 54	*m* 19 *Jan.* 58	Leave on M. C. to England.
Thomas Milles, *V*,	15 *May* 57		
George William Muriel, *V*,	2 *June* 57		
Browning Drew, ..	13 *June* 57		
William John James Smith, ..	5 *Oct.* 57	... ..	Leave on M. C. to England.
Charles H. Malan, ..	10 *Dec.* 58		
LIEUTENANTS.			
Ernest Le Pelley, *V*,	27 *Aug.* 52	.. ..	Leave on M. C. to England.
William Henry Urquhart, ..	.. ..	10 *Apl.* 40	Leave on M. C. to England.
Thomas Carlisle, ..	.. ..	23 *June* 54	
William Clive Justice, *V*,	20 *July* 55		
Reginald Brocas, *V*,	..	9 *Oct.* 55	
Charles Melville Pym, *V*,	9 *June* 57	.. ..	Actg. Adjt. of 16th Punjab Infantry.
Henry Hurford, ..	13 *June* 57	.. ..	Chatham Depôt, England.
George Home Row, ..	19 *July* 57	.. ..	Leave on M. C. to Calcutta.
Montague C. Morris, ..	15 *Sep.* 57		
Richard Wadeson,* ..	19 *Sep*, 57	.. ..	Adjutant.
Frederick Cornwall ..	16 *July* 58	21 *May* 58	Chatham Depôt, England.
James Streets, ..	1 *Nov.* 57	.. ..	Lv. on M. C. to Kussowlie till Oct. 59.
Bentinck L. Cumberland, ..	7 *Sep.* 58	.. ..	En route to join.
John Thomas H. Butt, ..	1 *Oct.* 58	.. ..	Regtl. Depôt, England.
~~Augustus L'Estrange,~~ ..	1 *Oct.* 58	..	Leave on M. C. to England.
ENSIGNS.			
Henry O'Brien,	11 *Dec.* 57	16 *Oct.* 55	
Wilmsdorf G. Mansergh, ..	.. ..	8 *Feb.* 56	
Hugh Barton Gledstanes, ..	.. ..	26 *Feb.* 56	
George Benjamin Singer, *V*,	15 *Jan.* 58		
Denzil Hammill, ..	16 *Jan.* 58		
Charles Finnerty, ..	17 *Jan.* 58		
F. Buller Morris, ..	23 *July* 58	.. ..	Chatham Depôt. England.
Frederick Francis Daniel, ..	7 *Sep.* 58	.. ..	Not joined.
J. Tarby, ..	8 *Oct.* 58		
Harry Philip Dawson, ..	9 *Nov.* 58	.. ..	Ditto.

(*a*) Passed an examination in Surveying and Civil Engineering.
* Victoria Cross.

H. M. 75th Regiment of Foot—(*Continued*).

Rank and Names.	Regimental Rank.	Army Rank.	Remarks.
Pay Master.			
Lieut. David Francis Chambers,	26 *Jan.* 49	*lt.* 6 *May* 42	
Adjutant.			
Lieut. R. Wadeson, - - -	11 *Mar.* 59	19 *Sep.* 59	
Quarter Master.			
Ensign John Dunlop, - - -	9 *Feb.* 49	*ens.* 1 *May* 46	
Surgeon.			
Richard Domenichetti, M. D., -	4 *Sep.* 57		
Assistant Surgeons.			
Watkin Sandom Whylock, M.D.,	20 *Apl.* 56	26 *Nov.* 52	
Harry Reid, M. D., - - - V	13 *July* 58		[10 Aug. 59.
Charles W. Semple, - - -	28 *Jan.* 59	.. ..	Leave of absence to Deyrah Dhoon to
Interpreter.			
*			

Strength—10 Companies, with 57 Sergeants—50 Corporals—21 Drummers—681 Privates.

English Agents—Messrs. Barron and Smith.
Calcutta Agents—Messrs. B. Smyth and Co.

WAR SERVICES OF THE OFFICERS OF H. M. 75th REGIMENT OF FOOT.

Major-General Sir John Clerke served with the old 94th at Cadiz during the siege, in the Lines of Torres Vedras, during the retreat from Santarem; having been present in the actions of Pombal, Rediuha, Condeixa, Foz d'Arouce Sabugal, and Fuentes d'Onor. He joined the 77th Regt. (also in the Peninsula) on promotion, and served with it in the actions of El Bodon and Aldea de Ponte, at the siege and assault of Cuidad Rodrigo, siege of Badajoz, assault and capture of Fort Picurina, and storming of the castle of Badajoz (severely wounded in the right knee): he has received the War Medal with three Clasps.

Lt. Col. W. C. Mollan commanded the 75th Regiment with the force under Major General Sir James Outram G. C. B., at Alum Bagh from 30th Decr. 1857 to the 10th Feby. 81 8 including the most important of the enemy's attacks on the 12th and 16th January. Served as Major of Brigade at the siege and capture of Lucknow in March 1858 and at the following actions in Oude, under Major General Sir H. Grant K. C. B. viz. Koorsee 23rd March, Baree 13th April, Simree 12th May, Nawabgunge 13th June (Horse killed under him) and at the advance on Fyzabad 13th July; served with Brigadier Horsford's force in the action at Sultanpore 13th Aug. and during the subsequent operations under Sir Hope Grant; action of Doad 20th Oct. served during the campaign of the ensuing season under Sir H. Grant and Lord Clyde including the surrender of the Forts of Ameethee, Shunkerpoor and the advance of the Army upon Barraitch.—Brevet Lieut. Colonel for services in the Field and C. B.

Lieut.-Colonel Gordon served in the campaigns against the Kaffir Tribes of south Africa in 1834-35 (Medal). Also as Assistant Engineer during 1837 and 1838, on the eastern frontier of the Cape Colony; and employed under Colonel Lewis, commanding Royal Engineers, to execute a confidential survey (trigonometrical and statistical) on that frontier. Present at the operations before Delhi from the 15th Septr. to the 20th Septr. the final capture of that City and with the moveable column under Colonel Greathead, the actions of Bolunashuhur, the affairs of Allyghur and Ackrabad. Battle of Agra and subsequent advance on Cawnpore under Brigadier Hope Grant including the affairs of Aliagunge and Alumbagh. Garrison of the fortified outposts and camp with the force under Major General Outram, G. C. B.

Lt.-Col. Bourchier served with the 17th throughout the campaign in Affghanistan and Beloochistan under Lord Keane, and was present at the storm and capture of Ghuznee (Medal) and of Khelat, at which last he was twice wounded.

*** *For continuation of services, see next page.*

WAR SERVICES OF THE OFFICERS OF H. M. 75TH REGT. OF FOOT—*(Continued.)*

Major Brookes served the Kaffir campaigns of 1834-35 as a Field Adjutant (Medal). He received the special thanks of Sir George Napier for service in the field on the 5th July 1839. Present at the siege operations before Delhi on the 23rd June 1857, also from the 15th to the 20th Sep. the final capture of that City and with the moveable column under Colonel Greathead, the action of Bolundshuhur, the affairs of Allyghur and Ackrabad. Battle of Agra, and subsequent advance on Cawnpore under Brigadier Hope Grant including the affairs of Alaiagunge and Alumbagh. Garrison of the fortified outposts and camp with the force under Major General Outram, G. C. B.

Major. Dunbar served with the flank companies 98th Reg. in the force under Sir Colin Campbell at the forcing of the Kohat Pass in Feb. 1850. Served during the Indian campaign of 1857, including the advance under Genl. Anson on Delhi, subsequently under Major Genl. Sir H. Bernard, K. C. B., the battle of Budleeka Serai, 8th June, subsequent siege operations before Delhi until the final capture of that City, 20th Sep. 1857.

Major Dawson was attached to the 22nd Regt. at the battle of Hyderabad (Medal), and he was present with the 40th Regt. in the action of Maharajpore, at which he was wounded (Medal). Served during the Indian campaign of 1857, including the advance under Genl. Anson on Delhi, subsequently under Major Genl. Sir H. Bunard, K. C. B., the battle of Budleeka Serai, 8th June, subsequent siege operations before Delhi until the final capture of that City, 20th Sep. 1857.

Captain Drew served with the 75th Regt. throughout the campaign before Delhi in 1857, including the battle of Bulee ke Serai; commanded the Grenadier Company at the assault of Delhi and ultimately the Regt.; accompanied Colonel Greathead's pursuing column and was present at the affairs of Allyghur and Akbarabad, and battles of Bolundshuhur and Agra; served in the advance in Oude under Sir Colin Campbell, and on the relief of the Garrison of Lucknow remained with General Outram's force at Alumbagh, and took part in the several repulses of the enemy.

Captain Smith served the campaign in Oude and relief of the Garrison of Lucknow, afterwards at the Alum Bagh, and took part in the several repulses of the enemy.

Capt. C. H. Malan, present during the siege operations before Sebastopol from 12th June 1855, to 11th June 1856 at the attack on the Redan 18th June 1855, (wounded severely) medal for the Crimea.

Lieut. Pelley served during the Indian Campaign of 1857-58 at the battle of Budleeka Serai 8th June 1857 and subsequent siege operations against Delhi until the final capture of that city up the 20th Sep. 1857, and with the moveable column under Colonel Greathead, the action of Bolundshuhur, the affairs of Allyghur and Ackrabad. Battle of Agra, and subsequent advance on Cawnpore under Brigadier Hope Grant including the affairs of Alaiagunge and Alumbagh. Garrison of the fortified outposts and camp with the force under Major General Outram G. C. B.

Lieut. W. C. Justice served in the campaign of 1857. Present at the siege and final capture of Delhi 20th Sept. 1857.

Lieuts. Brocas and Morris served during the campaign of 1857-8 with the Oude field force in position at Alumbagh under command of Major General Sir James Outram G. C. B.

Lieuts. Pym, Row, Wadeson, Paymaster Chambers and Quarter Master Dunlop served during the Indian Campaign of 1857, including the advance under Genl. Anson on Delhi, subsequently under Major General Sir H. Bernard K. C. B. the battle of Budlee ka Serai 8th June, subsequent siege operations before Delhi until the final capture of that city 20th Septr. 1857.

Lieut. James Streets, served in the Indian campaign of 1857. Present at the capture of Delhi 20th Sep severely wounded.

Lieut. Hurford served in Burmah (Medal).

Ensign J. Tarby, served as a volunteer with the field force at the relief of Arrah, action of Kiander and Puttee and capture of Jugdispore, siege and capture of Lucknow, occupation of Alum Bagh under Sir J. Outram, G. C. B.

Dr. Domenichetti served on the staff of the late Maj. Genl. Sir H. Havelock, K. C. B., during his advance to Cawnpore and Lucknow in July 1857, and was present at the battles of Futtehpore, Aoung, Pandoo Nuddee and re-capture of Cawnpore, also throughout the operations in Oude; battle of Bithoor, and in the second advance on Lucknow for the relief of that garrison, when he was Medical Store Keeper of the Force, including several actions with the Rebels. Mentioned in despatches for his services at Alum Bagh. Also served with H. M. 75th before Lucknow under Maj. Genl. Sir J. Outram G. C. B. and was present in the attacks on his position on the 12th and 16th January 1858.

Asst. Surgeon, W. S. Whylock, present at the battle of Budleeka Serai 8th June 1857.

CONTINUATION WAR SERVICES OF THE OFFICERS OF H. M. 80TH REGT. OF FOOT.—*From page* 93.

Captain Woods served with the Buffs in the action of Punnier, 29th Dec. 1843 (Medal).

Captain Hon. J. H. M. Browne, Lieutenants G. Sullivan, H. H. St. Legar, W. Whitehead, and W. P. Mortimer, served during the suppression of the mutiny in India in 1858-59, present at the capture of Calpee. Lieut. Sullivan served with the 80th Regt. in the Burmese war of 1852-53 (Medal), including the bombardment and capture of Prome and subsequent operations.

Captain J. L. W. Nunn, Lieutenants R. Maxwell, and S. G. Huskisson served in India during the mutiny of 1558-89, served in the campaign in Oudh in 1858-59, present at the capture of Simree Fort, 9th Nov. Berar, 7th and Doondeakeira, 24th Nov. Brigadier Evelegh commanding. Captain Nunn (wounded), served with the 80th Regt. in the Burmese war of 1852, and was present at the capture of Martaban, operations before Rangoon on the 12th, 13, and 14th April, and capture of the Great Dagon Pagoda (with the storming party), and capture of Prome (Medal).

Captain J. J. Dudgeon served in India during the suppression of the mutiny in 1858-59, and in the campaign in Oudh.

Captains B. J. Hume, and C. F. Amiel, Lieutenants W. G. Trevor, H. B. B. L. Gower, F. Goddard, Ensign D. Beaumont V. O'Connor, W. Howard, and Asst. Surg. P. Frank served during the suppression of the mutiny in India 1858-59, Captain Hume served with the 80th Regt. in the Burmese war of 1852-53 (Medal,) including the bombardment and capture of Prome and subsequent operations.

Captain Amiel, served with the 80th Regt. in the Burmese war of 1852 and was present at the capture of Martaban, operations before Rangoon on the 12th. 13th and 14th April, and capture of the great Dagon Pagoda (with the storming party), and capture of Prome (Medal).

Capt. Borrowes served in the Burmese war of 1853 as Adjutant of the 80th Regt. (Medal) served during the suppression of the mutiny in India in 1858-59, served in the campaign in Oudh in 1858-59, present at the action at Morarmow, 8th Novr. with the 1st Seik Cavalry and at the capture of Simree Fort, 9th, as Adjt. of the Regiment and Orderly Officer to Major Miller Commanding the Infantry, Brig. Evelegh Commanding on each occasion, also at the affair at Bussingpore 23rd December as Detachment staff Officer to Colonel Christie Commanding.

Lieutenant W. B. B. Christie served in India during the mutiny of 1858-59, present at the capture of Calpee on the 22nd and 23rd May 1858, served in the campaign in Oude in 1858-59, present at the capture of Simree Fort, 9th November Berar, 17th Novr. and Doondeakeira, 24th November, also present at the affair of Bussingpore, 23rd December 1858, as Orderly Officer to Colonel Christie commanding.

Lieutenant F. B. N. Craufurd served with the 80th Regiment in Burmah in 1853,—(Medal) Served during the suppression of the mutiny in India in 1858-59 in the campaign in Oudh in 1858-59, Present at the capture of Simree Fort 9th and at the defence of Poorwan 19th Novr. 1858.

Pay Master W. Browne served in India during the mutiny in 1858-59, and in the campaign in Oudh.

Qr. Master Maloney served in the Sutlej campaign of 1845-46, including the battles of Moodkee, Ferozeshah and Sobraon, (Medal and two Clasps) served also in the Burmese war of 1852-53, including the capture of Martaban, operation before Rangoon, and capture of Porme (Medal and Clasp) served in India during the suppression of the mutiny in 1858-59, was present at the affair at Hurria under Major General Sir J. Inglis K. C. B. on the 5th April, at Simree, Berar, 9th and 17th Novr. under Brig. Evelegh at Doondeakiera on the 24th Novr. 1858, under command of His Excellency, the Commander-in-Chief and at the affair of Bussingpore under Colonel Christie on 23rd Decr. 1858.

Surgeon Irwin was in medical charge of the 27th Regiment from the 1st July 1846, and during the Kaffir war of 1846-47-48, (Medal). and in medical charge of the 1st Division in the field, in the operations under Major-General Hare, from July until November 1846.

CONTINUATION OF THE WAR SERVICES OF H. M. 88TH REGT. OF FOOT.—*From page* 101.

Captain Radcliffe served in the Eastern campaign of 1854-55, including the battle of Alma and siege of Sebastopol (Medal and Clasps).

Captain Pearson served at the battle of Inkerman, siege of Sebastopol, attack on the Quarries, and attacks on the Redan on the 18th June and 8th Sept. (Medal and Clasps) order of the Medjiddie 5th Class.

Captain Jones served in the 7th Fusiliers the Eastern compaign from 20th Oct. 1854, and was persent at the battle of Inkerman (wounded) and siege of Sebastopol, including sorties on the 26th Oct., 5th April (wounded), and 9th May, attack and capture of the Quarries on 7th June (wounded), and assault of the Redan on 18th June (severely wounded in three places); he was also wounded in the trenches on 27th March (Medal and Clasps).

Capt. Lambert and Lieut. Perceval served at the siege of Sebastopol, including the attack on the Quarries, and attack on the Redan on the 18th June and 8th Sept.—severely wounded (Medal and Clasp) order of the Medjiddie 5th Class.

Capt. Hall, Lieuts. Blythe, Waring, Birch, and Burke, served at the siege of Sebastopol, and attack on the Redan on the 8th Sept. (Medal and Clasp).

Lieut. Evans served at the siege of Sebastopol, attack on the Quarries 7th June, on the Redan 18th June, and was wounded in the trenches 8th Aug. (Medal and Clasp).

Lieut. Priestley served at the siege of Sebastopol, and assaults on the Redan on the 18th June and 8th Sept., in which last he commanded the Grenadier Company (Medal and Clasp, and Sardinian Medal).

Lieut. Vernor served at the siege of Sebastopol, attack on the Quarries, and attack on the Redan on the 18th June and 8th Sept. (Medal and Clasp) order of the Medjiddie 5th Class.

Lieut. Hopton served at the siege of Sebastopol, attack on the Redan 13th June and 8th Sept. (severely wounded): Medal and Clasp.

Lieuts. Scott and Watson, and Ensign Walker, served at the siege of Sebastopol, and were severely wounded at the attack on the Redan on the 8th Sept. (Medal and Clasp).

Ensign Dwyer served the Eastern campaign of 1854-55, including the battles of Alma and Inkerman, siege of Sebastopol, and attack on the Quarries—severely wounded (Medal and Clasps).

Paymaster Cunningham served with the 18th Royal Irish in the Crimea from June 1856, and was present at the siege of Sebastopol (Medal and Clasp).

Doctor Dunlop served with the 32nd Regt. during the Punjaub campaign of 1848-49, and was present at the first and second siege operations before Mooltan, including the capture of the city and surrender of the fortress; also present at the surrender of the fort and garrison of Cheniote, and battle of Goojerat (Medal and Clasps). Served the Eastern campaign of 1854-55, including the battles of Alma and Inkerman, siege of Sebastopol, and attack on the Redan on the 18th June and 8th Sept. (Medal and Clasps).

Assist.-Surgeon Williams served the Eastern campaign of 1854-55, including the battle of Alma and Inkerman, and siege of Sebastopol (Medal and Clasps).

Assist.-Surgeon Meade served with the 88th Regt. at the siege of Sebastopol (Medal and Clasp).

H. M. 77th Regiment of Infantry.

The *Plume of the Prince of Wales.*—"SERINGAPATAM" "CIUDAD RODRIGO" "BADAJOZ" "PENINSULA" "ALMA" "INKERMAN" "SEVASTOPOL."

Landed in Calcutta, from Australia 16th June 1858.

ALLAHABAD.

Left Wing at BENARES.

2 Companies at KUNOUNDEAH.

Regimental Depôt, Parkhurst, Isle of Wight.

RANK AND NAMES.	*Regimental Rank.*	*Army Rank.*	REMARKS.
COLONEL.			
Geo. Leigh Goldie, C. B., - -	22 *Dec.* 54	*l.g.* 20 *June* 54	In Europe.
LIEUTENANT COLONEL.			
The Hon'ble A.G.C. Chichester,	16 *June* 58	.. ..	Leave on P. A. to Calcutta.
Thomas Josephus Deverell, -	24 *Aug.* 58	*col.* 26 *Oct.* 58	Commanding Left Wing at Benares.
MAJORS.			
Henry Robert Carden, - - -	16 *June* 58	*lc.* 26 *Dec* 56	
Henry Kent, - -	24 *Aug.* 58		
CAPTAINS.			
Henry A. Macdonald, - -	26 *Jan.* 55	... ...	Left Wing at Benares.
William Joseph Carden, - -	2 *Mar.* 55	... ..	Instructor of Musketry in England.
Richard B. Willington, - -	20 *Apl.* 55	.. ..	With detachment at Kunoundeah.
Frederick J. Butts, - -	20 *Apl.* 55	.. ..	Lv. of absence to England on P. A. for 18 months
William N. M. Orpen, - -	5 *June* 55		
Matthew W. Dickson, - -	24 *July* 55	.. ...	With detachment at Kunoundeah.
H. M. L. Colquhoun, - -	17 *July* 57	.. ..	Instructor of Musketry.
George Edward Leggett, - -	30 *Apl.* 58		
James M. Daly, - *V,*	4 *June* 58	.. ..	With Left Wing at Benares.
William T. E. Fosbery, - -	16 *June* 58	.. ..	Leave on M. C. to England.
Thomas P. Harvey, - -	24 *Aug.* 58		
Edward Lister Green, - - -	28 *Jan.* 59	.. ...	A.D.C. to Commander-in-Chief, Bombay.
LIEUTENANTS.			
Marcus A. Waters, - -	23 *Feb.* 55	.. ..	
William Minister, - -	9 *Mar.* 55	.. ..	
H. F. L. Browne, - -	9 *Mar.* 55	.. ..	
John George Skene, - -	9 *Mar.* 55	.. ..	Adjutant.
Wm. D. Alderson, - -	20 *Apl.* 55	.. ..	Depôt.
Charles B. Knowles, - *V,*	20 *Apl.* 55	.. ..	With detachment at Kunoundeah.
Aubrey Thomas Butts, - -	25 *May* 55	.. ...	Depôt.
Philip S. Dauncey, - -	5 *June* 55	.. ..	Leave to Australia for 18 months.
Charles B. Saunders, - -	4 *Sept.* 55	... ..	Lv. on P. A. to England for 18 months from 1 July 1859.
H. M. Bengough, - -	3 *Oct.* 55	.. ..	Lv. on P. A. to Simla the 31 Oct 1859
~~Rowland B. Hill,~~ - -	9 *Oct.* 55	.. ..	On leave till 1st Feb. 1860.
~~Nathaniel Peach,~~ - -	1 *Feb.* 56	.. ..	With Left Wing at Benares.
John Jordan, - -	30 *Apl.* 58		
Henry S. Weigall, - -	16 *June* 58		
John Wordsworth, - -	4 *Mar.* 59		
ENSIGNS.			
Cecil P. Stone, - -	6 *Nov.* 55	.. ..	On duty at Dum Dum.
Henry R. Bate, - -	9 *Nov.* 55	.. ..	On Sick leave Calcutta.
Reginald Hoskins, - -	7 *Dec.* 55	.. ..	Left Wing Benares
Percy Kirk - -	1 *Feb.* 56		
Randle Jackson, - -	12 *Dec.* 56		
~~John H. Bridger,~~ - -	30 *Jan.* 57	.. ..	Depôt.
John L. Davids, - -	31 *Aug.* 55	.. ..	Left Wing Benares.
Oscar Henry Blunt, - -	28 *May* 58	.. ..	Depôt.
George Augustus White, - -	19 *Nov.* 58	.. ..	Depot.

H. M. 77th Regt. of Infantry.—(*Continued.*)

Rank and Names.	Regimental Rank.	Army Rank.	Remarks.
Instructor of Musketry.			
Capt. H. M. L. Colquhoun. -	.. ..	*c.* 17 *July* 57	
Paymaster.			
Lieut. William Fortescue Scott,	13 *Jan.* 54	*lt.* 18 *Feb.* 48	
Adjutant.			
Lieut. John George Skene, -	24 *Mar.* 58	*lt.* 9 *Mar.* 55	
Quarter Master.			
Henry Blissett, -	3 *Nov.* 54		
Surgeon.			
Duncan D. McCay McDonald, -	31 *Dec.* 58		
Assistant Surgeon.			
Alexander Humfrey, - -	7 *Apl.* 54		
George C. Hyde, - -	17 *Jan.* 55	.. ..	On leave on M. C. to England.
Thomas Norton Hoysted, - -	24 *Aug.* 58		
Interpreter.			
Capt. R. J. H. Barber, - -			

Strength.—9 Companies—49 Serjeants—39 Corporals—16 Drummers—493 Privates.

English Agents—Messrs. Ridgway and Sons.
Irish Agents—*Sir* C. Borough, Armit &c. Co.
Calcutta Agents—Messrs. Colvin, Cowie &c. Co.

WAR SERVICES OF THE OFFICERS OF H. M. 77th REGIMENT OF FOOT.

Lieut. Genl. Goldie served in the Peninsula from March 1809 to Nov. 1813, including the passage of the Douro, battles of Talavera, Busaco, and Albuhera, covering siege of Badajoz, affairs of Arroyo de Molino, and Campo Mayor, battles of Vittoria and the Pyrenees, besides minor actions and skirmishes. Severely wounded in the Pyrenees on the 30th July 1813 by a musket-ball, which is still lodged in the lungs—this wound was long considered mortal. He has received the Gold Medal for Albuhera, and the Silver War Medal with four Clasps for Talavera, Busaco, Vittoria, and Pyrenees. He held an important command in the disputed territory in Canada in 1838-39.

Lieut.-Colonel Carden served the Eastern campaign of 1854-55, including the battles of Alma and Inkerman, and siege of Sebastopol (Medal and Clasps, Brevet Major, Knight of the Legion of Honor, and 5th Class of the Medjidie),

Capt. William Carden served the Eastern campaign of 1854-55, including the siege of Sebastopol (Medal nad Clasp).

Major Kent served the Eastern campaign of 1854-55, including the battles of Alma and Inkerman, and siege of Sebastopol (Medal and Clasps, and 5th Class of the Medjidie).

Capt. Willington served the Eastern campaign of 1854-55, including the battles of Alma and Inkerman, and siege of Sebastopol (Medal and Clasps, Sardinian Medal, and 5th Class of the Medjidie).

Capt. Butts served the Eastern campaign of 1854-55, including the battles of Alma and Inkerman, siege of Sebastopol, and attack on the Redan on the 8th Sept.—severely wounded (Medal and Clasps, and 5th Class of the Medjidie).

Captain Orpen served at the siege of Sebastopol in 1855 (Medal and Clasp).

Captain Dickson served in the Eastern campaign of 1854-55, including the battles of Alma and Inkerman, and siege of Sebastopol, until severely wounded 8th June (Medal and Clasps).

Capt. Daly served at the siege of Sebastopol in 1855 (Medal and Clasp).

Capt. Leggett served at the siege of Sebastopol from December 1854, and was wounded at the attack on the Redan on the 8th Sept. (Medal and Clasp).

Capt. Fosbery served at the siege of Sebastopol from July 1855, and was dangerously wounded—left leg amputated (Medal and Clasp).

Capt Harvey served at the siege and fall of Sebastopol from the 7th June 1855, and at the assault of the Redan on the 8th Sept.; he was selected to cross the open space, under a heavy fire, to stop the fire of our own eight gun battery (Medal and Clasp).

Capt. Green served in the Kaffir wars 1847-50-53 (Medal) was severely wounded in the former war when commanding the rear-guard and in the latter war served as A. D. C. to Major Genl. Somerset and D. A. Qr. Mr. Genl. with the Head Quarter of Sir G. Cathcart.

Lieut. Waters served with the 53rd Regt. against the Hill Tribes on the western frontiers of India in 1851-52. Served with the 77th Regt. at the siege of Sebastopol in 1855, and was present at the assault on the 18th June, and engaged at the storming of the Redan on the 8th Sept.—severely contused (Medal and Clasp).

Lieut. Minister served in the Eastern campaign of 1854-55, including the battles of Alma and Inkerman, and siege of Sebastopol (Medal and Clasps).

Lieut. Knowles served at the siege of Sebastopol in 1855, and was severely contused at the assault on the Redan on the 8th Sept. (Medal and Clasp).

Paymaster Scott, Qr.-Master Blissett, and Assist.-Surgeon Humfrey. served the Eastern campaign of 1854-55, including the battles of Alma and Inkerman, and siege of Sebastopol (Medal and Clasps). Assist.-Surgeon Humfrey has also the Sardinian Medal. Paymaster Scott has the 5th Class of the Medjidie.

Surgeon Franklyn served the Eastern campaign of 1854-55, was at Balaklava attending on the wounded during the cavalry action there; and was placed in charge of the Russian wounded after the battle of Inkerman; and served with the 77th Regt. before Sebastopol (Medal and Clasps, and 5th Class of the Medjidie.)

H. M. 79th Regt. of Foot (Cameron Highlanders).

"EGMONT-OP-ZEE,"—*The Sphinx* with the words—"EGYPT".

"FUENTES D'ONOR"—"SALAMANCA"—"PYRENEES"—"NIVELLE"—"NIVE' —"TOULOUSE." —"PENINSULA"—"WATERLOO"—"ALMA"—"SEVASTOPOL"

FACINGS.—*Green.*

Landed in Calcutta, from England, 21ts *November* 1857.

MEEAN MEER.

Regimental Depôt, Stirling.

RANK AND NAMES.	*Regimental Rank.*	*Army Rank.*	REMARKS.
COLONEL.			
William Henry Sewell, C B.,	24 *Mar.* 54	*l.g* 20 *June* 54	In Europe.
LIEUTENANT COLONELS			
John Douglas, K. C. B. ...	13 *Aug.* 54	*col* 1 *Aug.* 57	Leave on P. A. to England to 30th [Sep. 60.
R. Chambre Hays Taylor C. B.	17 *July* 57	*col.*21 *May* 58	Leave to England.
MAJORS.			
Thomas Bromhead Butt, ...	17 *July* 57	.. ...	Commanding.
Wm. Chauval Hodgson, ...	7 *Aug.* 57	2 *Nov.* 55	Leave to Simla to 31st July 1859.
CAPTAINS.			
Keith Ramsay Maitland, ...	24 *Dec.* 52	*m* 20 *July* 58	
Alex. Cockburn M'Barnet, ...	10 *Mar.* 54	*m* 20 *July* 58	
~~George Murray Miller,~~ ...	4 *Aug.* 54		
Edward William Cuming, ...	8 *Oct.* 54	... ...	Commanding Depôt.
Henry Holford Stevenson, ...	29 *Dec.* 54	*m* 20 *July* 58	Leave of absence to Fngland for 18 [months from 1st May 59.
Phillip Percival, ...	27 *Mar.* 55		
Francis Gore Currie, ...	17 *Feb.* 57		
John Macdonald Leith, ...	15 *May* 57		
George Thomas Scovell, ...	16 *June* 57	... ...	Regtl. Depot.
Donald M'Donald, ...	17 *July* 57		
George Alex. Harrison, ...	7 *Aug.* 57	13 *July* 55	Regtl. Depôt
~~Somon George Newport,~~ ...	4 *Feb.* 59		
LIEUTENANTS.			
William Henry Mackesy, ...	8 *Dec.* 54	... ..	Convalescent Depot, Muree.
John Edward Allen, ...	19 *Jan.* 55	.. ...	Permitted to retire.
John Miller M'Nair, ...	9 *Feb.* 55		
Wm. John M. Crawfurd, ...	9 *Feb.* 55		
Havilland J. De Carteret, ...	9 *Feb.* 55		Convalescent Depot, Muree.
James Young, ..	9 *Feb.* 55		Regimental Depot.
Wm. Barclay G. Cleather, ...	9 *Feb.* 55	.. ..	
Francis Pembrtn. Campbell, *V*,	9 *Mar.* 55		Lv. on P. A. to England for 12 months
Chas. Edward M'Murdo, ...	9 *Mar.* 55	.. ..	Leave on M. C. to Fngland.
Rich. B. Roland Bedford, ...	7 *Sept.* 55	.. ..	Regtl. Depôt.
Edward Everett, ...	14 *Sept.* 55	... ...	Leave on M. C. to Muree to Aug. 59.
Neil Campbell, ...	21 *Sept.* 55		
Douglas Alleyne, ...	2 *Nov.* 55		
Theophilus Rt. Howkins, ...	4 *Apl.* 56		Regtl. Depôt.
Arthur Walker, ...	16 *June* 57		Leave on M. C to England.
Douglas Wimberley, ...	15 *July* 57	5 *Jan.* 56	Leave on M. C. to England.
Wm. Buxton Robertson, ...	28 *Aug.* 57	1...	Adjutant Benares depot.
~~Armorie Russell McGwire,~~ ...	11 *Auy.* 58	..	
Robert Stewart, *V*,	16 *Feb.* 59	.. ..	Adjutant.
Albert Newby Clay, ...	11 *May* 59	.. ..	Instructor of Musketry.
ENSIGNS.			
R. P. O. P. *Lord* Louth, ...	3 *Aug.* 55	.. ...	Leave on M. C. to England.
Thomas Ballard Dougal, ...	14 *Sep.* 55	.. ..	Enroute to join.
Garden Duff, ...	28 *Dec.* 55	.. ..	Regimental Depot.
G. W. Coventry, ..	31 *Aug.* 58	1 *Feb.* 58	Ditto.
W. H. McCausland, ..	24 *Feb.* 57	.. ..	Leave on M. C. to England.
A. Bruce Murray, ...	18 *Mar.* 59	.. ..	Regimental Depot.
A. C. Wood, ..	19 *Mar.* 59	.. ..	Ditto.
A. P. B. Baillie, ...	1 *July* 59	... ...	Ditto.

H. M. 79TH HIGHLANDERS.—(*Continued*).

RANK AND NAMES.	*Regimental Rank.*	*Army Rank.*	REMARKS.
INSTRUCTOR OF MUSKETRY.			
Lieut. Albert, N. Clay, ..	7 *Apl.* 58	7 *Sep.* 55	
PAYMASTER.			
Lieut. David Cant, ...	24 *June* 56	*lt.* 8 *Dec.* 54	
ADJUTANT.			
Lieut. R. Stewart, ..	21 *May* 59		
QUARTER MASTER.			
Lieut. William McGill, ...	14 *Nov.* 56	*lt.* 9 *Mar.* 55	
SURGEON.			
Thomas Goldie Scot, M. D., ...	28 *May* 54	18 *Feb.* 53	
ASSISTANT SURGEONS.			
Andrew Knox Drysdale, ...	10 *Jan.* 55	24 *Mar.* 54	
Edmund Humphery Roberts,	15 *July* 57	23 *June* 54	Leave on M. C. to England.
Patrick Kilgour, ...	15 *July* 57	17 *Jan.* 55	Leave on M. C. to England.

Strength,—10 Companies with 54 Serjeants,—49 Corporals—22 Drummers, and 858 Privates.

English Agents, Messrs. Cox and Co.
Calcutta Agents,—Messrs. Wood, Olliffe and Co.

WAR SERVICES OF THE OFFICERS OF H. M. 79TH REGT. OF FOOT.

Lieut.-Gen. Sewell was appointed Aide-de-Camp to General Beresford, and proceeded with the expedition that left England in 1807. Joined the Duke of Wellington's army in Portugal in 1808. Was present with Sir John Moore's army in its advance and in its retreat to Corunna Was with the Duke's Head Quarters through the Peninsular war as Aide-de-Camp to Lord Beresford, and was present at the battles of Corunna, Talavera (actions on the Goa and Agueda, with the Light Division), Busaco the sieges of Ciudad Rodrigo, Badajoz, St Sebastian battles of the Nivelle, Nive, before Bayonne (10th, 11th, and 13th Dec.) Orthes, and Toulouse, besides Cavalry affairs and skirmishes. Had six horses killed and wounded under him in general actions. Has received the War Medal with ten Clasps, Served twenty-eight years in India.

Colonel Douglas served the Eastern campaign of 1854-55 in command of the 79th Highlanders, including the battles of Alma and Balaklava, siege of Sebastopol, assault of the 18th June, and expedition to Kertch and Yenikale (Medal and three Clasps, *C. B.*, and Sardinian Medal and 4th Class of the Medjidie). Served in the Indian campaign 1858-59.

Colonel Taylor served the Eastern campaign of 1854-55, including the battles of Alma and Balaklava and siege of Sebastopol (Medal and Clasps and 5th Class of the Medjidie). Served in the Indian campaign 1858-59.

Major Hodgson served the Eastern campaign of 1854-55, including the battles of Alma and Balaklava, expedition to Kertch and Yenikale, siege and fall of Sebastopol, and assaults of the 18th June and 8th Sept. (Medal and three Clasps, Brevet of Major, and Knight of the Legion of Honor and 5th Class of the Medjidie. Served in the Indian campaign 1858-59.

Major Maitland and Captain Miller served the Eastern campaign of 1854, and early part of 1855, including the battles of Alma and Balaklava, and siege of Sebastopol (Medal and three Clasps). Served in the Indian campaign 1858-59.

Major McBarnett served the Eastern campaign of 1854-55, including the battles of Alma and Balaklava, siege and fall of Sebastopol, and assaults of the 18th June and 8th Sept., expedition to Kertch and Yenikale (Medal and three Clasps). Served in the Indian campaign 1858-59.

Major Stevenson served throughout the Eastern campaign of 1854-55, including the battles of Alma and Balaklva, siege and fall of Sebastopol, assults of the 18th June and 8th September. expedition to Kerteh and Yenikale (Medal and three Clasps, Sardinian Medal, and 5th Class of tbe Medjidie). Served in the Indian campaign 1858-59.

Major Butt, Capt. Newport, Lieut. Everett, McGwire, Stewart and Clay served in the Indian campaign 1858-59.

Capt. Percival served the Eastern campaign of 1854-55, including the battles of Alma and Balaklava, siege of Sebastopol, assault of the 18th June, expedition to Kertch and Yenikale (Medal and three Clasps). Served in the Indian campaign 1858-59.

Captains Cuming and Currie and Quarter-Master McGill served throughout the Eastern campaign of 1854-55 including the battles of Alma and Balaklava, siege and fall of Sebastopol, assults of the 18th June and September, expedition to Kertch and Yenikale (Medal and three Clasps, and 5th Class of the Medjidie). Capts. Cuming and Quarter Master McGill served in the Indian campaign 1858-95.

Capt. Leith served the Eastern compaign of 1854-55, including the battle of Balaklava, siege and fall of Sebastopol, assaults of 18th June and 8th Sept, and expedition to Kertch and Yenikale, (Medal and two Clasps). Served in the Indian campaign 1858-59.

Captain M'Donald, Lieuts. Mackesy, Allen. M' Nair, Cleather, F. P. Campbell, McMurdo, and Alleyne served at the siege and fall of Sebastopol from July 1855, and assault of 8th Sept. (Medal and Clasp). Served in the Indian eampaign 1858-59.

Capt. Scovell. Lieuts. Walker and Winberly served in the Indian campaign of 1858.

Lieut. Young served throughout the Eastern campaign of 1854-55, including the battles of Alma and Balaklava, siege and fall of Sehastopol, assults of the 18th June and 8th September, expedition to Kertch and Yenikal (Medal and three Clasps. and Knight of the Legion of Honor), Served in the Indian campaign for 1858.

Lieut. Crawfurd, Neil Campbell, and Howkins, served at the siege of Sebastopol from July 1855 (Medal and Clasp.) Lieut. Crawfurd and Campell served in the Indian campaign of 1858-59.

Lieut. D. Carteret served at the siege and fall of Sebastopol from June 1855, including the assaults of 18th June and 8th Sep. (Medal and Clasp). Served in the Indian campaign 1858-59.

Paymaster Cant served the Eastern campaign of 1854-55, including the battles of Alma and Balaklava, siege of Sebastopol, and assault of 18th June (Medal and three Clasps).

Surgeon Scot served the Eastern campaign of 1854-54, including the battle of Alma and siege of Sebastopol (Medal and two Clasps). Served in the Indian campaign 1858-59.

Assist.-Surgeon Drysdale served the Eastern campaign of 1854-55, including the battles of Alma and Balaklava, and siege of Sebastopol (Medal and three Clasps). Served in the Indian campaign 1858-59.

Assist.-Surgeon Roberts served with the 72nd Highlanders in the Eastern campaign from 13th June 1855, including the expedition of Kertch, siege and fall of Sebastopol, and attack of the 18th June (Medal and Clasp.) Served in the Indian campaign 1858-59.

H. M. 80th Regiment of Foot. (Staffordshire Volunteers),

The *Sphinx*, with the words—"Egypt"
"Moodkee"—"Ferozeshah"—"Sobraon"—Pegu."
Facings—*Yellow*.
Landed in Calcutta, from Cape of Good Hope, on 18th January 1858.
Cawnpore.

Regimental Depôt, Buttevant.

Rank and Names.	*Regimental Rank.*	*Army Rank.*	Remarks.
Colonel.			
Thomas Robbins, - - - -	12 *Mar.* 55	*l.g.* 20 *June* 54	In England.
Lieutenant Colonel.			
Samuel Tolfrey Christie, C. B. -	5 *Mar.* 58	*col.* 28 *Nov.* 54	
Majors.			
Anthony Ormsby, - -	28 *July* 54	.. ..	Leave of absence previous to retiring.
Robert Hawkes, - -	5 *Mar.* 59	16 *Dec.* 56	
Captains.			
Edward Hardinge, - -	22 *Dec.* 48	.. ..	Leave on M. C. to England to Apl. 59.
George Dean Pitt. - -	4 *May* 49	.. ..	Musketry Instructor, Australia.
Chas. FitzGerald Studdert, -	4 *May* 49	.. ..	Regtl. Depôt, England.
George Samuel Young, *V*,	31 *Oct.* 52	.. ..	Acting Depy. Asst. Adjt. Genl. Cawnpore Division.
Hamilton Charles Smith, - -	1 *May* 53	.. ..	
Hon. John Howe M. Browne, -	6 *June* 54	.. ..	Lv. on M. C. to England.
Bliss John Hume, *V*,	4 *Aug.* 54	.. ..	Acting Interpreter.
Frederick Miller, - -	1 *Dec.* 54	*m* 6 *June* 56	Lv. to England on P. A. for 18 months.
Richard William Woods, -	12 *Apr.* 56	.. ..	Regtl. Depôt, England.
Jas. L. Winniett Nunn, -	27 *Nov.* 57	.. ..	Lv. to Nynee Tal, Simla, on P. A. to 15 Oct. 59.
Charles Frederick Amiel, -	5 *Mar* 58	.. ..	
John James Dudgeon, - -	30 *Mar* 58	.. ..	
Erasmus Borrowes, - -	8 *Mar.* 59	.. ..	
Lieutenants.			
George Sullivan, *P. C.*,	31 *Oct.* 51	.. ..	2nd in Command of Cawnpore Levy.
William Whitehead, - -	17 *Aug.* 52	.. ..	Adjutant of the Queen's Troops Depôt, Cawnpore.
Fred Brown Numa Craufurd *V*.	6 *June* 54	.. ..	Adjutant.
Horatio Pettus Batchelor, -	6 *June* 54	... ..	Leave on M. C. to England.
William Picton Mortimer, *V*,	11 *Aug.* 54	.. ..	Acting adjutant Cawnpore Levy.
Hen. Hungerford St. Leger, -	1 *Dec.* 54	.. ..	Leave on M. C. to England.
Robert James Maxwell, *V*,	1 *Apl.* 56	.. ..	Doing duty at Depot Kussowlie.
William Gordon Trevor, -	27 *Nov.* 57	.. ..	
Hugh B. B. Leaveson Gower, -	12 *Feb.* 58	.. ..	
Fred. FitzClarence Goddard, -	5 *Mar.* 58	.. ..	
Wm. Beaver B. Christie, -	30 *Mar.* 58	.. ..	
Samuel George Huskisson, -	1 *Jan.* 59	.. ..	
~~George Weir Cosens~~, - -	8 *Mar.* 59	.. ..	Leave on England to 24 May 59.
Alexander Ewing, - -	1 *Apl.* 59	.. ..	
Ensigns.			
Dudley Beaumont, - -	8 *July* 56	.. ..	
Valentine O'Connor, - -	17 *Feb.* 57	.. ..	
Henry James Brown, - -	12 *Feb* 58	.. ..	
Walter Howard, - -	16 *Mar.* 58	.. ..	
Joseph B. Ridout, - -	13 *Apl.* 58	.. ..	Regtl. Depôt, England.
Sam. P. Muirhead, - -	26 *Nov.* 58	... ..	Ditto.
Thomas Barnard Michell, - -	10 *Dec.* 58	24 *Nov.* 58	Ditto.
~~Thomas Lee~~, - -	18 *Jan.* 59	24 *Nov.* 58	Ditto,

H. M. 80TH REGT. OF FOOT.—(*Continued*).

RANK AND NAMES.	Regimental Rank.	Army Rank.	REMARKS.
INSTRUCTOR OF MUSKETRY.			
Capt. James L. W. Nunn, -	.. ..	*lt.* 27 *Nov.* 57	
PAY MASTER.			
Wellington Browne, - -	1 *July* 55		
ADJUTANT.			
Lieut. F. B. Cranford, - -	6 *June* 54		
QUARTER MASTER.			
William Maloney, - -	23 *Oct.* 55		
SURGEON.			
William Nelson Irwin, - -	3 *Mar.* 54	.. ..	Leave on M. C. to England.
ASSISTANT SURGEONS.			
Philip Franks, M. D., *V*,	14 *Dec.* 54		
William Jackson, - -	31 *Dec.* 58	.. ..	Leave on M. C. to England.
James Intson, M. D. - -	12 *Mar.* 59		
INTERPRETER.			
Captain B. J. Hume, - -	23 *Mar.* 58	.. ..	Acting.

Strength—10 Companies with 56 Sergeants,—50 Corporals,—15 Drummers, and 722 Privates.

English Agents,—Messrs. Cox & Co.
Calcutta Agents,—Gillanders, Arbuthnot and Co.

WAR SERVICES OF THE OFFICERS OF H. M. 80TH REGT. OF FOOT.

Lt. General Robbins served in Sicily in 1806-7 with the 1st Brigade of Guards under Sir John Moore. Subsequently with the 7th Hussars in the Peninsula and France in the campaigns of 1813 and 14, including the investment and surrender of Pampeluna, the battles of Orthes and Toulouse, with several intermediate affairs of outposts. Served also in Flanders in 1815 with the 7th Hussars; was present at Quatre Bras, Commanded a squadron of the Rear Guard in the affair at Genappe, also at the battle of Waterloo, where he was severely wounded. He has received the War Medal with two Clasps for Orthes and Toulouse

Col. Christie served with the 80th Regt. throughout the Burmese war of 1852-53; present at the capture of Martaban (where he commanded the storming party) at the operations before Rangoon on the 12th, 13th, and 14th April—on the 14th commanded the skirmishers in front of the light guns during the advance on Rangoon, and was with the storming party at the capture of the great Dagon Pagoda; also present at the capture of Prome, and received the especial thanks of the Governor-General of India in Council for his services on that occasion; and commanded the flank companies of his Regt. at the affair of the stockades on the heights opposite Prome, 12 Nov. 1852, and also at the repulse of the night-attack (Medal and Brevet of Lieut.-Colonel) served in India during the suppression of the mutiny in 1858-59, commanded a moveable Column in the Futtehpore District during the siege of Lucknow, engaged with the enemy on the banks of the Jumna on the 5th March 1858, also commanded a Field Force detached from the Commander-in-Chief's camp during the latter part of the campaign in Oudh, wounded on the 23rd Decr. 1858, and had a horse shot under him.

Major Ormsby served with the 80th Regiment during the Sutlej campaign of 1846, and was present at the affair of Biddiwal, and in the battles of Aliwal and Sobraon (Medal and one Clasp). Served during the Burmese war of 1852-53, and was present at the assault and capture of Pegu on 4th June 1852, where he commanded the storming party commanded at the Pagoda Hill stockade at Martaban on the night of the 18th July 1852, when attacked by the enemy; and was also at the capture of Prome (Medal).

Major Hawkes served in the Burmese war of 1852-53 as Brigade Major to the second Bengal Brigade, and was present at the relief of the garrison of Pegu, and in the subsequent operations against the enemy in that vicinity (Medal). Served in India during the suppression of the mutiny in 1858-59.

Major Miller served in the last Burmese war, and was engaged in the principal action (Medal) served during the mutiny of 1858-59, present at the engagement on the banks of the Jumna, Futtehpore District, 5th March 1858, served in the campaign in Oudh 1858-59, present at the capture of the Fort of Simree, 9th Novr. Berar, 17th and action at Doondeakeira 24th Novr. in command of the Infantry.

Capt. Hardinge was present with the 39th Regt. in the action of Maharajpore on the 29th Dec. 1843 (Medal) Served with the 80th Regt. the Sutlej campaign of 1845-6, including the battles of Moodkee and Sobraon (Medal and one Clasp). Also in the Burmese war of 1852-53, and was present at the capture of Prome and subsequent, night-attack of the the enemy on the heights. Commanded a detachment at the defence of the post of Toomboot, 22nd Dec. 1852, and at several operations in its vicinity in Jan. and Feb. 1853. Present at the capture of the intrenched position of Tomah and at the destruction of the force of Moung Shoe-Moug (Medal).

Capt. Studdert served in the 9th Lancers during the campaign in 1843-44, against Gwalior, including the battle of Punniar (Medal), and the investment and surrender of Gwalior.

Capt. Young served the campaign on the Sutlej with the 80th, including the battles Moodkee, of Ferozeshah, and Sobraon (wounded): Medal and two Clasps. Served in the Indian mutiny in 1858-59, Commanded the Head Quarter wing of the Regiment with a Column in Oudh. At the capture of the Fort of Simree, 9th November, Berar, 17th Novr. and Doondeakeira, 24th Nov. under the Command of the Commander-in-Chie Lord Clyde.

Captain Smith served with the 80th Regt. in the Burmese war of 1852 and was present at the capture of Martaban, operations before Rangoon on the 12th, 13th and 14th April, and capture of the great Dagon Pagoda (with the storming party), and capture of Prome [Medal] served in India during the mutiny of 1858-59 present at the capture of Calpee 22nd, and 23rd May 1858, and served in the campaign in Oudh 1858-59.

*** *For continuation of services, see page 87b.*

H M 81st Regt. of Foot (Loyal Lincoln Volunteers.)

"MAIDA"—"CORUNNA"—"PENINSULA."

FACINGS—*Buff.*

Landed in Bengal, from England, on the 7th October 1853.

PESHAWUR.

Regimental Depôt Chatham.

RANK AND NAMES.	*Regimental Rank.*	*Army Rank*	REMARKS.
COLONEL.			
Thomas Evans, C. B.,	12 *July* 47	*g.* 18 *May* 55	In Europe.
LIEUT. COLONELS.			
Henry Renny,	27 *May* 53	*col.* 24 *Nov.* 54	Commanding.
Matthew Smith,	5 *June* 55	*col.* 24 *Nov.* 54	Brigadier Commanding at Calcutta.
MAJORS.			
Andrew Timbrell Allan,	3 *June* 53	*l.c.* 12 *Nov.* 58	On leave to England.
J. Arthur Gildea,	9 *Apl.* 56	.. ..	
CAPTAINS.			
John B. Flanagan,	11 *Nov.* 45	*m* 13 *Mar.* 58	
Robert B. Chichester, *V.*	7 *Oct.* 51	.. ..	Leave to England on P. A. for 18 Ms.
John Bourchier,	27 *May* 53	.. ..	Commandant of Peshawur Fort.
James Woods, *V,*	27 *May* 53		
Charles James Skerry,	27 *May* 53		Regtl. Depot, England,
William B. Browne,	25 *Jan.* 54	.. ..	Leave to England on P. A. for 18 Ms.
George Betts,	15 *June* 55		
Alfred Wright,	16 *June* 55		Regimental Depôt, and Instructor of Musketry in England.
Valens Tonnochy, *P,(a)*	7 *Aug.* 55	20 *June* 54	Comdg. 1st Regt. of Jugailchees.
William Egerton Todd,	9 *Apl.* 56	.. ..	
Hugh A. Chichester, *H,*	18 *Apl.* 56	.. ..	Offg. Brigade Major at Peshawur.
~~Malachi Henley,~~	9 *Sep.* 57	.. ..	Chatham Depôt, England.
LIEUTENANTS.			
Richard G. Charlton,	27 *May* 53	.. ..	Regtl. Depot, England.
Stanley John Lowe,	27 *May* 53	.. ..	Ditto.
Geo. Wm. Moyse Harmer,	27 *May* 53	.. ..	Leave to England on P. A. for 18 Ms.
John Wilkinson,	27 *May* 53	13 *July* 52	Chatham Depôt, England.
Richard Swift,	27 *May* 53	31 *Oct.* 52	Instructor of Musketry.
William Minchin Harnett,	17 *June* 53	25 *Mar.* 53	
James Alexander Deans,	13 *Oct.* 54	..	
Walter Musgrave, *V,*	19 *Jan.* 55	.. ..	Comdg. a Rasala of newly raised Irregular Cavalry. [for 6 months.
William Dare Sladen, *V,*	1 *June* 55	9 *Feb.* 55	On leave to Murree from 20 Apl. 59,
Henry John Faircloth,	3 *Aug.* 55	13 *Apl.* 55	
Tristram Chas. Sawyer Speedy, *V,*	23 *Oct.* 55	.. ..	On duty with 10th Punjab Infantry.
Daniel Weir,	9 *Apl.* 56	.. ..	Regimental Depôt.
~~Henry Harrison Briscoe,~~	22 *July* 56	.. ..	[Madras.
Henry John Fane,	10 *Mar.* 57	1 *Dec.* 54	A. D. C. to Commander-in-Chief of
George Frederick Jellicoe, *V,*	9 *Sep.* 57	.. ..	
Fred. Keppel FitzRoy,	5 *Dec.* 56		
William Henry Munton Jackson.	16 *May* 59		
ENSIGNS.			
Sydney William Bell,	6 *Jan.* 57		
Michael Curry,	2 *Feb.* 58	.. ..	Adjutant.
Thomas George Kerans,	16 *Mar.* 58		
William Henry Warren	23 *Mar.* 58		
Cowper Rochfort,	30 *Mar.* 58	.. ..	En-route to join.
Henry Maturin.	16 *Apl.* 58		
Thomas Rogers,	26 *Oct.* 58	.. ..	Chatham Depôt, England.

(*a*) Has passed an examination in Civil Engineering, prescribed by G. O. 2nd March 1854.

H. M. 81st Loyal Lincoln Volunteers.—(*Continued.*)

Rank and Names.	Regimental Rank.	Army Rank.	Remarks.
Instructor of Musketry.			
Lieut. Richard Swift, - - - - -	27 *Sep.* 58	*lt.* 31 *Oct.* 52	
Pay Master.			
Wm. Fred. Nixon, - - - - -	8 *Jan.* 41	*lt.* 22 *Jan.* 36	
Adjutant.			
Ensign Michael Curry, - - -	24 *Sep.* 58	*ens.* 2 *Feb.* 58	
Quarter Master.			
Charles Correll, - - - - - - -	28 *June* 44		
Surgeon.			
Grahame Auchinleck, M. D. - *V*,	25 *Mar.* 58	2 *Oct.* 57	
Assistant Surgeons.			
S. Herman Bicknell, - - - *V*.	16 *May* 55	.. ..	
William Henry Corbett, M. D., - *V*.	4 *Feb.* 56	15 *Dec.* 54	In charge of 8th Punjab Infy.
William James Mullan, - - - -	15 *Sep.* 57		

Strength—10 Companies, with 56 Sergeants—50 Corporals—21 Drummers—950 Privates.
English Agents—Messrs. Cox and Co.
Calcutta Agents—Messrs. Gillanders, Arbuthnot and Co.

WAR SERVICES OF THE OFFICERS OF H. M. 81st REGT. OF FOOT.

General Evans's services:—Entered the army in 1793 as a volunteer, and enlisted 150 men for the service Operations in the West Indies and Ireland in 1794 and 95; capture of Demerara and Berbice in 1796. Captured returning from South America, and kept a close prisoner in France in 1797. Operations at Minorca and Guernsey in 1798 and 99; ditto on the coast of Spain, Malta, and Marmorice, in 1800. Egyptian campaign of 1801 (Medal), including the actions of the 8th, 13th, and 21st of March: battle of Rahmanie on the Nile, and reduction of that fortress, sieges and surrender of Cairo and Alexandria (as Lieut. and Adjutant of the 8th). Operations at Gibraltar in 1802 and 3; ditto in the West Indies (as Captain in the 8th and Aide-de-Camp to Sir Gordon Drummond) in 1804, 5, and 6. Operations in Nova Scotia in 1807 and 8; ditto in the Canadas (as Aide-de-Camp and Military Secretary to Sir G. Drummond) in 1809, 10, and 11. Campaigns of 1812, 13, and 14, in Upper Canada (as Brigade-Major, discharging duties of Deputy-Adjutant-General, and in command of the 8th), including the preparation of the force against Detroit and Michilimackinac, the defence of Fort George, and destruction of the enemy's attacking batteries, and directing the reinforcements on Queenston, which enabled Major-General Sheaffe to defeat and capture the American army, after General Brock's fall in a gallant attempt on the enemy with inadequate means. Assault on Sackett's Harbour, expulsion of the enemy's army from Forty Mile Creek, and capture of his army *materiel*, with many prisoners; battle of Chippewa, covering the army's retirement on Fort George, and retrograde on Twenty Mile Creek, until resuming the offensive. Night-attack on the enemy's investing forces of Fort George, on which the American commander, General Swift, was slain. Battle of Lundy's Lane, two repulses of the enemy's sorties, with severe loss, on the 5th and 12th Aug. 1814, before Fort Erie, by the pickets under his command; assault of Fort Erie, and the series of affairs on the Niagara frontier. For these services, and conducting the 2nd Battalion of the King's Regiment from New Brunswick to Canada, through the Wilderness, General Evans has had honorable mention made of his name in the London Gazettes, and in General Orders on ten several occasions; and so unremitted have been this officer's services in all quarters, that out of forty-five years of practical work, two only were in England. Wounded in three places at Sackett's Harbour; sword struck from his grasp and shivered at Lundy's Lane; contused and had his horse shot at Fort Erie.

Colonel. H. Renny commanded the 1st Infantry Brigade of the force in the Euzoofzai expedition of 1858, under Major General Sir Sydney Cotton, K. C. B.

Colonel Smith served as Major of Brigade with the army under General Pollock during the campaign of 1842 in Affghanistan (Medal), and was present (as D. A. Adj.-Gen. of the Inf. Div.) at the forcing of the Khyber Pass, action at Mamoo Khail, forcing the Tezeen and Huft Kotul Passes, attack and capture of Istalifl (received the Brevet rank of Major). He served with the 29th in the Punjab compaign in 1848-9, including the passage of the Chenab and battle of Chillianwallah (wounded); and he commanded the 24th Regt. at the battle of Goojerat (Medal and Clasps).

Lt.-Col. Allan served with a detachment 57th Regt. against the Rebels in Canara in 1837. Commanded 2nd Infantry Brigade of the force in the Euzoofzai expedition of 1858 under Major General Cotton.

Capt. Browne commanded the 81st Regt. on the Euzoofzai expedition of 1858 under Major General Cotton.

Captain Tonnochy served with the 29th Regt. in the Sutlej campaign in 1846, including the battle of Sobraon (Medal). Served also in the Punjab campaign of 1848-49, including the passage of the Chenab, and battles of Chillianwallah and Goojerat (Medal and Clasps). Present in the Fort of Agra, and in the action at Agra with the Mutineers on the 10th Oct. 57 as Capt. under Col. E. H. Greathead, officiated as Major of Brigade to the 1st Infantry Brigade in the Euzoofzai expedition of 1858 under General Cotton.

Captains H. A. Chechester, H. J. Faircloth, T. C. Speedy, H. H. Briscol, W. H. M. Jackson, and Qr. Mr. C. Corell, served with the Regt. in the Eusoofzai campaign of 1858, under Major General Sir Sydney Cotton, K. C. B.

Captain J. Woods, Lieut. J. A. Deans, and Asst. Surg. H. Bicknell, served against the Rebels in the Googaria district in 1857.

Lieut. Wilkinson served with the 80th in the Burmese war of 1852-53, and was present at the capture of Martaban, operations before Rangoon on the 12th, 13th, and 14th April, and capture of the Great Dagon Pagoda with the storming party; and he was severely wounded when in command of the detachment 80th Regt., at the assault and capture of Myattoon's stronghold, on the 19th March 1853 (Medal).

Lieut. Musgrave commanded a body of Irregular Troops during the Kaffir Campaign of 1851 and 1852 and was present at all the engagements of any importance which took place during that time. He subsequently joined the Cape Mounted Rifles and served with them during the remainder of the War in 1853 (Medal); served in the Eusoofzai campaign of 1858.

Lieut. Swift served with the Army in Burmah, Commanded Depot of the 80th Regt. at Rangoon in 1853 (Medal for Pegu.)

Surg. Auchinleck served in the Burmese War of 1852-53 (Medal); served in the Eusoofzai campaign of 1858.

Assist.-Surgeon Corbett served in the Crimean campaign of 1854-55, including the siege of Sebastopol (Medal and Clasp); served in the Eusoofzai campaign of 1858.

H. M. 82nd Regt. of Foot (The Prince of Wales's Volunteers).

The *Prince of Wales's Plume.*

"Roleia"—Vimiera—"Vittoria"—"Pyrenees"—"Nivelle"—"Orthes"—"Peninsula"—Niagara"—"Sevastopol."

Facings—*Yellow.*

Landed in Calcutta, from England, 22nd Sept. and 12th Oct. 1857.

Shahjehanpore.

Right Wing at *Moradabad.*

Regimental Depôt, Canterbury.

Rank and Names.	Regimental Rank	Army Rank.	Remarks.
Colonel.			
Nicholas Hamilton, K. H. - -	10 *Dec.* 56	*l.g.* 11 *Nov.* 51	In England.
Lieutenant Colonels.			
Edward Blagden Hale, C. B., -	7 *Sep.* 55	.. ..	Commanding.
Hon. P. Egerton Herbert, C. B.,	19 *Feb.* 58	*col.* 18 *Nov.* 54	Leave of absence on P.A. to 12 Mar. 60.
Majors.			
David Watson, - -	1 *Sept.* 54	*l.c.* 26 *Dec.* 56	Commanding Right Wing.
C. T. Vesey Bunbury Isaac, -	13 *Mar.* 57	.. ..	Lv. on M. C. to England to 30 Sep. 59.
Captains.			
Henry Chris. Marriott, - -	2 *Feb.* 49	.. ..	With Right Wing.
George Edmund Halliday, -	10 *Aug.* 49	.. ..	Convalescent Depot Nynee Tal.
Samuel Peters Jarvis, - -	21 *Sep.* 52	.. ..	
Wm. Roberts Farmar, - -	13 *May* 53	.. ..	Leave on M. C. to England.
William Alex. Bailie, - -	4 *Aug.* 44	.. ..	Canterbury Depôt, England.
Stanley Slater, - -	31 *Jan.* 55		
~~Thomas Edward Green,~~ - -	7 *Sep.* 55	.. ..	Leave on M. C. to England.
Robert Maule, - -	7 *Sep.* 55		
Henry Chandler Wilkinson, -	1 *May* 57	.. ..	With Right Wing.
John Frederick Pilkington, -	9 *Jan.* 58		
Patrick Hunter, - - - -	18 *Feb.* 59	... ...	Regimental Depot.
H. T. Macpherson, - - - -M	26 *Feb.* 59	... ...	Doing duty with 1st Gwalior Regt. of [Infantry.
E. M. Palliser			
Lieutenants.			
John Sidney Hand, V,	18 *Aug.* 54	.. ..	Adjutant of 18th Irregular Cavalry.
R. F. H. Macgregor Skinner, V,	18 *Aug.* 54	.. ..	Acting Adjutant, With Right Wing.
C. Edw. Gore Browne, - -	1 *Sep.* 54	.. ..	Lv. to England on P.A. for 18 months.
~~Cecil James East,~~ - -	5 *June* 55	.. ..	Regimental Depot.
Henry Dyke Marsh, V,	20 *July* 55	.. ..	With Right Wing.
Edward Hugo Budgen, - -	6 *Sep.* 55	.. ..	Station Staff.
Charles Spencer, - -	7 *Sep.* 55	.. ..	Adjutant.
Daniel Sullivan, - -	7 *Sep.* 55		
James Athol Brock, - V,	7 *Sep.* 55		
William Carden Seton, - -	7 *Sep.* 55		
Louis Walter Fisher, - -	9 *Feb.* 55		
Charles Studdert Maunsell, -	21 *Sep.* 55	.. ..	With Right Wing.
Graham Mylne, - - V,	22 *Sep.* 55	.. ..	Leave to England for 18 months.
~~Wm. Henry Craven Allen,~~ -	27 *Oct.* 55		
George Porter, - -	26 *Feb.* 56		
William Boyd O'Malley, - -	23 *Oct.* 55	.. ..	Lv. to England on P.A. for 18 months.
Bertram C. Henderson, - -	10 *Mar.* 57	.. ..	Regtl. Depot, England.
Thomas Ryan, - V,	30 *Nov.* 57	.. ..	On duty with 22nd Punjaub Infantry.
Edward Seppings Lock, - -	20 *Jan.* 58	... ..	Lv. to England on P.A. for 15 months.
Ensigns.			
Edward Snow Mason, - V,	9 *Oct.* 55		
Henry Mount Parkerson, - -	23 *Nov.* 55		With Right Wing, Instructor of Mus- [ketry.
~~Frederick Helyar,~~ - -	8 *Jan.* 56		Ditto.
James Johnston, - -	25 *Jan.* 56		Ditto.
Charles Paget Miller, - -	26 *Feb.* 56	.. ...	Regimental Depot.
Nicholas Maurant Brock, - -	... ...	21 *Dec.* 55	Leave on M. C. to England.
Charles Neville, - -	20 *Mar.* 57		
John Butler Mackenna, - -	30 *Mar.* 58	.. ..	Regtl. Depôt England.
William Reeves Bunbury, - -	31 *Mar.* 58	... ..	Ditto.
Charles Worthy, - - - -	7 *Dec.* 58	.. ..	Regimental Depot.

H. M. 82ND REGT. OF FOOT (THE PRINCE OF WALES'S VOLUNTEERS.—(*Continued.*)

RANK AND NAMES.	*Regimental Rank.*	*Army Rank.*	REMARKS.
INSTRUCTOR OF MUKSETRY.			
Ensign, H. M. Parkinson, - -	23 *Nov.* 55		
PAYMASTER.			
Wm. Hughes, - -	29 *May* 57	1 *Apl.* 56	
ADJUTANT.			
Lieut. Charles Spencer, - - -	26 *Jan.* 59	*lt.* 7 *Sep.* 55	
QUARTER-MASTER.			
John Connor, - -	10 *Mar.* 57	1 *Apl.* 56	Leave of absence to England.
SURGEON.			
Henry Day Fowler, - -	20 *July* 55		
ASSISTANT-SURGEONS.			
Rowland Winburn Carter, *V,*	6 *Feb.* 57	28 *July* 54	
William Henry Muschamp, *V,*	7 *Feb.* 57	23 *Jan.* 55	With Right Wing.
Robert Spence, - - - - -	31 *Dec.* 58		

Strength—10 Companies with 55 Sergeants,—52 Corporals—18 Drummers—and 995 Privates.

English Agents, Messrs. Cox and Co.
Calcutta Agents, Messrs. Grindlay and Co.

WAR SERVICES OF THE OFFICERS OF H. M. 82ND REGT. OF FOOT.

Major-General Hamilton served with the 5th Regt. the campaign of 1799 in Holland, including the actions of the 19th Sept. 2nd and 6th Oct. In 1805 he embarked for the expedition on the Weser, but was wrecked off the coast of Holland and made prisoner of war. In 1806 he sailed with his Regt. on the secret expedition which eventually proceeded to Buenos Ayres, and was engaged in the attack on that city in July 1807, as also in all the skirmishes which took place before and after that battle. After the unsuccessful result of this campaign he became one of the hostages given up to the Spanish authorities. In Jan. 1808 he returned from South America; and in July following embarked with the 5th at Cork with Sir Arthur Wellesley's expedition to the Peninsula, and was present at the battles of Roleia and Vimiera, as also on the retreat to and battle of Corunna. In 1809 he accompanied his regiment to Walcheren, and was present at the successful attack on the French outposts at Flushing, driving them within the fortress, on the 7th August he commanded the line of out-picquets in front of Flushing when the French made their most desperate sortie, against which he held his ground against a very superior force; on this occasion he lost a leg. He has received the Silver War Medal with three Clasps for Roleia, Vimiera, and Corunna.

Colonel Hon. Percy Herbert served with the 43rd Light Infantry in the Kaffir War of 1851-53 (Medal); also in the Expedition into the Orange River Sovereignty, including the battle of Berea. Served as Asist. Qr.-Master General to the 2nd Division of the Eastern Army from its formation to Nov. 1855, and subsequently as Quarter-Master General to the Army of the East until June 1856; was present at the battle of Alma (wounded), affair of 26th October, battle of Inkerman, siege and fall of Sebastopol (wounded), (Medal and Clasps), Aide-de-Camp to the Queen, (*CB.,* Knight of the Legion of Honor, Commander of 2nd Class of St. Maurice and St. Lazarus, and 3rd Class of the Medjidie) was wounded in action at Shahjahanpore in 8th May 1858.

Lieut. Colonel E. B. Hale, C. B., served in the N. W. Provinces and Oude in suppressing the Mutiny in 1857-58, and 59; commanded 3 Companies of the 82nd Regiment at the relief of Lucknow, under Sir Colin Campbell, G. C. B. in November 1857, and succeeded to the command of the 5th Brigade on Brigadier Russell being severely wounded, and Colonel Biddulph killed, (wounded, Horse killed under him by a round shot) Commanded the 82nd Regiment during the latter part of the defence, and at the Battle of Cawnpore Dec. 6th, and the 5th Brigade at the action of Khodagunge, and subsequent occupation of Futtehghur. Served throughout the Rohilcund campaign and was left in command of the post of Shajehanpore on the advance of the Army under Lord Clyde to Bareilly (wounded); commanded the 82nd Regiment at the actions of Khankur and Bun-ka-gaon, under Sir Thomas Seaton, was appointed to the command of a Brigade for Field Service in Oude in October 1858, which he held until the end of the campaign (Frequently mentioned in despatches, C. B.)

Major Isaac. served at the siege of Sebastopol from 2nd September 1855 (Medal and Clasp); was wounded in action before Cawnpore 28th Nov. 1857.

Major D. Watson (Bt. Lt. Col.) served at the siege of Sebastopol from 2nd September 1855 (Medal and Clasp) Served in the N. W. Provinces in suppressing the Mutiny in 1857 and 1858, including the operations at Cawnpore under General Wyndham and defeat of the Gwalior Mutineers, the actions of Kala-Nuddee, and Khankur, siege of the Jail and subsequent operations at Shahjehanpore, the affairs of Mohomdee, Shahabad, and Bun-ka-gaon.

Captain Bailie, and Lieuts. Hand, and East served at the siege and fall of Sebastopol from 2nd Sept. 1855 (Medal and Clasp). Lieut. East was wounded in action near Cawnpore in 26th Nov. 1857.

Captain Farmar served with the 50th Regt. in the campaign on the Sutlej, and was present at Buddiwal and Aliwal (Medal), at which last action he was severely wounded in the right thigh by a grape-shot while carrying the Queen's colour.

WAR SERVICES OF THE OFFICERS OF H. M. 82ND REGT. OF FOOT.—(*Continued.*)

Captain H. C. Marriott served at the siege of Sebastopol from 2nd Sepr. 1855 (Medal and Clasp). Served in the N. W. Provinces in suppressing the Mutiny in 1857, and 1858, and was present at the operations and defence of Cawnpore under General Wyndham, and defeat of the Gwalior Mutineers, the actions of Kala-Nuddee and Khankur, siege of the Jail and subsequent operations at Shahjehanpore.

Captain G. E. Halliday served at the siege of Sebastopol from 2 Sept. 1855, (Medal and Clasp). Served in the N. W. Provinces in suppressing the Mutiny in 1858, was present at the action of Khankur, siege of the Jail and subsequent operations at Shahjehanpore.

Captain S. Slater served in Bengal and N. W. Provinces, during the suppression of the Mutiny in 1857-58, and 59, including the operations and defence of Cawnpore under General Wyndham, defeat of the Gwalior Mutineers on the 6th Decr. 1857, under Lord Clyde, also the advance on, and occupation of Furruckabad, including the destruction of Tetteha and action of Khodagunge, was present at the action of Khankur under Sir T. Seaton, C. B.; advance on, and capture of Bareilly by Lord Clyde, served at the Bombardment and relief of Shahjehanpore, and the subsequent affairs of the 15th and 18th of May 1858. Capture of the fort of Bunnai and destruction of Mahomdee, under Sir J. Jones, K. C. B., also at the attack and destruction of the Fort of Shahabad, and was present at the action of Bun-ka-gaon under Sir T. Seaton, K. C. B.

Captain R. Maule served at the siege of Sebastopol from 2 Sepr. 1855, (Medal and Clasp) Served during the suppression of the Indian Mutiny in 1857-58 and 59. In Oudh and Rohilcund, comprising the action of Khankur, defence of the Jail of Shajehanpore, and affairs subsequent to its relief under Sir John Jones, K. C. B. capture of the Fort of Bunnai, attack on, and destruction of the Forts of Mahomdee and Shahabad, and action of Bun-ka-gaon under Sir T. Seaton, K. C. B.

Captain H. C. Wilkinson served at the siege of Sebastopol from 2 Sepr. 1855, (Medal and Clasp) served in the N. W. Provinces in suppressing the Mutiny in 1857-58, at the 2nd relief of Lucknow, the defeat of the Gwalior Contingent at Cawnpore, the actions of Kala-Nuddee and Bun-ka-gaon, the siege of the Jail and subsequent operations at Shajehanpore, the affairs of Mahomdee, Shahabad, and Bun-ka-gaon.

Captain J. F. Pilkington served at the siege of Sebastopol from 2 Sepr. 1855, (Medal and Clasp) Served in India during the suppression of the Mutiny in 1857-58 and 59, and was present at the action of Khankur under Sir T. Seaton, K. C. B.; served also during the campaign in Rohilcund, including the defence of the Jail of Shahjehanpore under Colonel Hale, C. B.; and attack and occupation of Shahabad, also affair at Bun-ka-gaon under Sir T. Seaton K. C. B.

Lieut. R. F. H. M. Skinner. served at the siege of Sebastopol from 2nd Sep. 1855, (Medal and Clasp) Served in the N. W. Provinces in suppressing the mutiny in 1857 and 1858, was present at the second relief of Lucknow, the defeat of the Gwalior mutineers at Cawnpore, the action at Kala-Nuddee and Khankur, the siege of the Jail and subsequent operations at Shahjehanpore, in the affairs of Mahomdee, and Bun-ka-gaon.

Lieut. C. E. G. Browne served at the siege of Sebastopol from 2nd September 1855, (Medal and Clasp) Served in Bengal and N. W. Provinces in suppressing the mutiny in 1857-58, and 1859, (as adjutant) including the operations at Cawnpore under General Wyndham, defence of Cawnpore and defeat of the Gwalior mutineers on the 6th December under Lord Clyde; was present at the action of Khankur under Sir T. Seaton, C. B.; defence of the Jail at Shahjehanpore and also the affairs subsequent to its relief under Sir John Jones, K. C. B.

Lieut. H. D. Marsh served at the siege of Sebastopol from 2nd September 1855, (Medal and Clasp) Served in the N. W. Provinces in suppressing the mutiny in 1857 and 1858, was present in the operations at Cawnpore under General Wyndham, the defence of Cawnpore and defeat of the Gwalior mutineers, the actions of Kala Nuddee, Khankur and Bun-ka-Gaon, capture of Bareilly, relief of Shahjehanpore, and the affairs of Mahomdee and Shahabad.

Lieut Budgen served in the Crimea from 23rd Nov. 1854 (Medal and Clasp for Sebastopol).

Lieut. Sullivan served in the Eastern campaign of 1854-55, and was present with the 30th Regt. at the battles of Alma and Inkerman, siege of Sebastopol to May 1855, and sortie of 26th Oct. 1854, (wounded) for which last he was mentioned in the Dispatches. Served afterwards with the 82nd Regt. at the siege and fall of Sebasto pol from 2nd Sept. 1855, (Medal and Clasps). Served in Bengal and N. W. Provinces in suppressing the mutiny of 1857, 1858 and 1859, including the operations at Cawnpore under General Wyndham, also defeat of the Gwalior mutineers under Lord Clyde, destruction of the Fort Tetteha, and action of Khodagunge, was present at the action of Khankur under Sir T. Seaton C. B., defence of the Jail of Shahjehanpore under Colonel Hale C. B, and affairs subsequent to its relief under Sir John Jones, K. C. B. Capture of the Fort of Bunnai, attack and destruction of the Forts of Mahomdee and Shahabad.

Lieut. J. A. Brock served in the suppression of the mutiny in Bengal during the campaign of 1857, and 1858, including an expedition against rebel villages near Allahabad, capture of Bareilly under Lord Clyde, relief of the garrison of Shahjehanpore, destruction of the Fort of Bunnai, the attack and destruction of Mahomdee and Shahabad, subsequent operations before Shahjehanpore and the action of Bun-ka-Gaon.

Lieut. W. C. Seton was present at the defeat of the Gwalior Contingent rebels at Cawnpore under Lord Clyde on the 6th Decr. 1857, served the Rohilcund campaign, including the capture of Bareilly, the attack and bombardment of Shahjehanpore, defeat of the rebels, and relief of the Garrison, and subsequent operations under General Jones, was present at the affairs of Khankur, and Bun-ka-gaon, under Sir T. Seaton, also the attack on, and capture of Shahabad under Colonel Taylor, C. B.

Lieut. C. S. Maunsell served in the N. W. Provinces in suppressing the Mutiny in 1857 and 1858, was present at the operations of Cawnpore, under General Wyndham, the defence of Cwanpore and defeat of the Gwalior Mutineers, the actions of Kala-Nuddee, and Khankur, capture of Bareilly, and relief of Shahjehanpore.

Lieut. G. Mylne served in Bengal and the N. W. Provinces in suppressing the Mutiny of 1857-58 and 1859, acted as adjutant to part of the Regiment at the relief of Lucknow in November 1857, was present at the battle of Cawnpore December the 6th, also at the action of Khodagunge and subsequent occupation of Futtehghur, served in the Rohilcund campaign, (orderly officer to Brigadier Stisted C. B.) including the capture of Bareilly, under Lord Clyde, relief of the Garrison of Shahjehanpore and affairs subsequent to its relief under Sir J. Jones, K. C. B. attack and destruction of the Fort of Shahabad. Present at the actions of Khankur and Bun-ka-gong under Sir T. Seaton, K. C. B., was orderly officer to Brigadier, E. B. Hale, C. B., when commanding a Field Force in Oudh from October 1858 until the end of the campaign.

Lieut. G, Porter served in Bengal in the suppression of the Mutiny in the N. W. Provinces in 1857-58 including the operations and defence of Cawnpore, and the defeat of the Gwalior Mutineers on the 6th December 1857, under Lord Clyde, served at the destruction of Tetteha, and the action of Goorsagunge, at the action of Khankur under Sir T. Seaton C. B. engaged in the defence of the Jail at Shahjehanpore, attack on, and capture of the Fort of Bunnai, and the destruction of Mahomdee, and subsequent operations of the 15th and 18th of May 1858, under Sir John Jones, K. C. B., at the capture and destruction of Shahabad and also at the action of Bun-ka- gaon.

Lieut E. S. Lock served in the N. W. Provinces in suppressing the Mutiny in 1858, was present at the action of Khankur, the siege of the Jail and subsequent operations at Shahjehanpore, in the affairs of Shahabad, Mohamdee and Bun-ka-gaon.

WAR SERVICES OF THE OFFICERS OF H. M. 82ND REGT. OF FOOT.—(Continued.)

Ensign E. S. Mason was present at Cawnpore under General Wyndham in November 1857, and defeat of the Gwalior Mutineers under Lord Clyde on the 6th December 1857, at the action of Khankur, taking of Bareilly, subsequent operations under Sir J. Jones in Rohilcund and defence of Powagne.

Ensign H. M. Parkerson served in the N. W. Provinces in suppressing the Mutiny in 1857-58, was present in the second relief of Lucknow, and defeat of the Gwalior Mutineers at Cawnpore, the actions of Kala-Nuddee, the siege of the Jail and subsequent operations at Shahjehanpore.

Ensign F. Helyar served in the N. W. Provinces in suppressing the Mutiny in 1858, was present in the action of Khankur, the siege of the Jail, (wounded) and subsequent operations at Shahjehanpore.

Ensign J. Johnston served in the N. W. Provinces in suppressing the Mutiny in 1857 and 58, was present at the operations at Cawnpore under General Wyndham, and defeat of the Gwalior Mutineers, the actions of Kala-Nuddee and Khankur, the siege of the Jail and subsequent operations at Shahjehanpore.

Ensign C. Neville served in India during the suppression of the Mutiny in the years 1857-58 and 59, was present during the advance on, and occupation of Furruckabad, and the capture of Bareilly by Lord Clyde, was present under Sir J. Jones, C. B. at the relief of Shahjehanpore, the pursuit of the Enemy to the Goomtee and occupation of Mahomdee ; was present at the affair of Shahabad. Was present under Sir T. Seaton, K. C. B. at the action of Khankur on the 7th of April 1858, and at the action of Bun-ka-gaon, on the 8th Octr. 1858.

Paymaster W. Hughes served throughout the operations in Scinde (Medal), including the destruction of Imaumghur, and at the battles of Meeanee and Hyderabad. He was also present at Panulla and Pownghur. Served in the N. W. Provinces in suppressing the Mutiny of 1857 and 58 ; was present at the operations at Cawnpore under General Wyndham, defence of Cawnpore, and defeat of the Gwalior Mutineers ; the actions of Kala-Nuddee, advance on and occupation of Furruckabad, the siege of the Jail and subsequent operations at Shahjehanpore.

Adjutant C. Spencer (Lieut.) served in the N. W. Provinces in suppressing the Mutiny in 1858, was present at the siege of the Jail at Shahjehanpore from 3rd to 11th of May under Lieut. Colonel E. B. Hale, C. B. and subsequent operations at Shahjehanpore.

Surgeon H. D. Fowler served in the Crimea from 12th Octr. 1855 to the end of the war. Served in India during 1858 and 59, present at the attack on the Gwalior Mutineers by General Wyndham's force, and subsequent operations at Cawnpore, advance on Futtehghur and campaign in Rohilcund and defence of Shahjehanpore &c.

Assist. Surgeon R. W. Carter served with the 20th Regt. the Eastern campaign of 1854, including the battle of Alma and siege of Sebastopol and at the Capture of Kinbourn (Medal and Clasps) with the 20th Regiment; at the suppression of the Indian Mutiny including the actions of Khankur and Bun-ka-gaon, with H. M. 82nd Regiment.

Asst. Surg. W. H. Muschamp served in the Crimea during the latter part of 1855, including the action of the 8th of September (Medal and Clasp) Served in the N. W. Provinces in suppressing the Mutiny of 1857-58, was present at the operations at Cawnpore under General Wyndham, and defeat of the Gwalior Mutineers, the actions of Kala-Nuddee and Khankur, capture of Bareilly, relief of Shahjehanpore, and the affairs of Mahomdee, and Shahabad and Bun-ka-gaon.

Quarter master Connor served the campaign of 1842-43 in Scind under Sir Charles Napier, including the battles of Meeanee and Hyderabad (Medal). Served also the campaign of 1844-45 in the Southern Maharatta country including the taking of the forts of Panulla and Pownghur.

H. M. 87th Regt. of Foot (Royal Irish Fusiliers.)

"MONTE VIDEO"—"TALAVERA"—*An* Eagle, *with a* Wreath of Laurel *above the* Harp, *in addition to the* Arms of the Prince of Wales, *in commemoration of their distinguished Services on various occasions, and particularly at the Battle of* "BARROSA"—"TARIFA"—"VITTORIA"—"NIVELLE"—"ORTHES"—"TOULOUSE"—"PENINSULA"—"AVA"

FACINGS—*Blue.*

Landed in Calcutta, from England, 14*th August* 1849.

JULLUNDER.

1 Company *at Phillour.*

Regimental Depôt, Buttevant.

RANK AND NAMES.	*Regimental Rank.*	*Army Rank.*	REMARKS.
COLONEL.			
Sir James Simpson, G. C. B.,	29 *June* 55	*g.* 8 *Sept.* 55	In Europe.
LIEUTENANT COLONELS.			
Alexander Murray	2 *Nov.* 55	.. ...	Commanding.
Bartholomew O'Brien,	9 *Nov.* 55	12 *Dec.* 54	Leave on M. C. to England.
MAJORS.			
Alexander Hugh Cobbe,	2 *Nov.* 55		
Charles F. Campbell,	29 *Mar.* 59		
CAPTAINS.			
Louis Herries Hamilton.	22 *July* 47	*m.* 22 *July* 55	Leave to England P. A. for 18 Ms.
James Bailie, PH,	22 *Feb.* 50	.. ..	Leave on M. C. to England.
~~William Francis Ring~~,	15 *Mar.* 50	*m.* 26 *Dec.* 56	Comdg. 12th Punjab Infantry.
William Hanmer, P,	26 *Mar.* 51	12 *Oct.* 49	Commandant of Meerut Levy.
John Theophilus Ussher,	9 *June* 54	1 *Jan.* 54	On duty with Invalids.
William Wiltshire,	6 *July* 55	.. ..	Regimental Depot, England.
Hon. D'Arcy G. Osborne,	30 *Nov.* 55	.. ..	Regimental Depôt, England.
Jas. Arch. Ruddell Todd,	12 *Dec.* 56	13 *July* 55	
John Hallowes,	17 *July* 57	.. ...	Prize Agent at Lucknow.
~~Ormond Fitzgerald~~, P,	9 *Nov.* 58	1 *Apl.* 47	
Robert Gibson,	18 *Feb.* 59	.. ..	
John Rawson Simpson,	29 *Mar.* 59	... ..	
~~Robert Gibson~~,	.. ..	.. ..	2nd in Command 3rd Seikh Cavalry.
LIEUTENANTS.			
Edw. Hen. John Meredyth,	8 *Apl.* 53	.. ...	Regimental Depôt, England.
Anthony Butler, PH,	30 *Sept.* 53		
Joseph Noble Beasley,	11 *Nov.* 53	24 *June* 53	Doing duty with 5th Punjaub Cavalry.
Thomas Law Roberts, PH,	25 *Nov.* 53	27 *Dec.* 50	2nd in Comd. 3rd Seikh Infantry.
Charles Edmund Goddard, PH,	30 *Dec.* 53	.. ..	2nd in Command 5th Punjaub Cavalry.
Edward Dampier Cockell,	4 *Apl.* 54	11 *Nov.* 53	Leave on M. C. to Dhurmsalla to 15th Nov. 59.
Colmer Lynch,	6 *July* 55	.. ..	Adjutant.
Robert Lampen,	30 *Nov.* 55		
~~Sackvile Geo. Lane Fox~~,	22 *July* 56	13 *Apl.* 55	Leave on M. C. to England.
Walter Carr Mackinnon, PH,	17 *July* 57	.. ..	Staff employ on the Patna Road.
Benj. D'Urban Musgrave,	15 *Mar.* 58	.. ..	Leave on M. C. to England.
George William Marsden,	17 *Sep.* 56	... ...	Instructor of Musketry.
John Graham Leadbitter,			
Richard Throckmorton,	29 *Mar.* 59		
Fred. Flood Devereux,			
ENSIGNS.			
Arthur Anderson,	5 *Mar.* 58		
Rentone Geo. T. Poynter,	26 *Mar.* 58		
George Robert Storey,	30 *Mar.* 58	.. ..	Regimental Depôt, England.
Adrian Aug. Von. Beverhoudt,	31 *Mar.* 58		
John Hooker Vowell,	17 *Sep.* 58	.. ..	Regimental Depôt, England.
John Leigh Hollest,	17 *Sep.* 58	.. ..	Ditto.
Edward Wellonghby Pardoe,	31 *Dec.* 58		
Alfred H. H. Smith,	25 *Mar.* 59		

H. M. 87TH REGT. OF FOOT (ROYAL IRISH FUSILIERS).—*(Continued.)*

RANK AND NAMES.	*Regimental Rank.*	*Army Rank.*	REMARKS.
INSTRUCTOR OF MUSKETRY			
Lieut. Geo. Wm. Marsden,- -	15 *May* 58	*lt.* 17 *Sep.* 58	
PAY MASTER.			
Lieut. Charles James Perry, -	3 *May* 50	*lt.* 30 *Nov.* 49	
ADJUTANT.			
Lieut. Colmer Lynch, - -	6 *Jan.* 57	*lt.* 6 *July* 55	
QUARTER MASTER.			
Lieut. Henry Thomas, - - -	20 *Apl.* 49	*lt* 19 *Dec* 45	
SURGEON.			
Richard George Davys Banon,-	24 *Apl.* 54	1 *July* 53	Leave on M. C. to England.
ASSISTANT SURGEONS.			
David Chambers, Mc Fall - -	6 *Nov.* 57	15 *Sep.* 57	
Philip Brooke Smith, M. D., -	2 *Feb.* 52		
John Collins, - -	1 *Dec.* 58		
INTERPRETER.			
Capt O. FitzGerald, - - -			

Strength,—10 Companies with 56 Serjeants—50 Corporals—21 Drummers—950 Privates.

English Agents,—Messrs. Cox and Co.

Calcutta Agents.—Messrs Gillanders, Arbuthnot and Co.

WAR SERVICES OF THE OFFICERS OF H. M. 87TH REGIMENT OF FOOT.

Sir James Simpson served in the Peninsula from May 1812 to May 1813, including the latter part of the defence of Cadiz, and the attack on Seville. Served also the campaign of 1815, and was severely wounded at Quatre Bras. He served as second in command to Sir Charles Napier during the campaign against the Mountain and Desert Tribes situated on the right bank of the Indus, early in 1845. Served in the Eastern campaign in 1855, first as Chief of the Staff and afterwards as Commander-in-Chief, including the siege and fall of Sebastopol (Medal and Clasp, *GCB.*, Grand Cross of the Legion of Honor, and Grand Cross of the Military Order of Savoy).

Lt. Col. Murray served in the 18th on the China expedition (Medal), and was present at Canton, Amoy. Chusan, Chinhae, Ningpo, Segoan, Chapoo (wounded), Shanghai, Woosung, and Chin Kiang Foo.

Lieut. Col. B. O'Brien, served the Eastern campaigns of 1854-55 with the 77th Regt. including the battles of Alma, Inkerman, and siege of Sebastopol. (Brevet Majority, medal and clasps, and the order of Medjidee.)

Major Hamilton served as Assist.-Adjutant-General in the Burmah war (Medal); name twice honorably mentioned in General Godwin's Dispatches, and in Orders of the Governor-General.

Major King served in 1855-56 with the Anglo-Turkish Army as Deputy Quarter-Master General, and has received the 4th class of the Medjidie.

Capt. Ussher served the campaign of 1844-5 in the Southern Mahratta country, with the 22nd, and was present at the investment and capture of the Forts of Panulla and Pownghur.

Captain Todd served with the 1st Batt. Royals in the Eastern campaign of 1854-55, including the battles of Alma and Inkerman, siege and fall of Sebastopol (Medal and Clasps, and Knight of the Legion of Honor).

Lieut. Fox served with the 21st Fusiliers during 1855, at the siege and fall of Sebastopol, and attack on the Redan on 18th June; also the expedition to Kinbourn (Medal and Clasp).

Qr.-Mr. Thomas served the campaign on the Sutlej in 1845-6 with the 9th Regt., including the battles of Moodkee, Ferozeshah, and Sobraon (Medal and Clasps).

Surgeon Banon served with the army on the Sutlej, and was taken prisoner by the Sikhs at the affair of Buddiwal; after a captivity of twenty-five days, twelve of which in irons, he was released, on the advance of British forces on Lahore.

H. M. 88th Regt. of Foot (Connaught Rangers).

The *Harp and Crown*, "*Quis separabit?*" The *Sphinx, with the words.*
"EGYPT"—"TALAVERA"—"BUSACO"—"FUENTES"—"D'ONOR"—"CIUDAD RODRIGO"—
"BADAJOZ"—"SALAMANCA"—"VITTORIA"—"NIVELLE"—"ORTHES"—"TOULOUSE"—
"PENINSULA"—"ALMA"—"INKERMAN"—"SEVASTOPOL."
FACINGS—*Yellow.*
Landed in Calcutta, from England on 2nd November 1857.
DELHI.
Regimental Depôt, Colchester.

RANK AND NAMES.	*Regimental Rank.*	*Army Rank.*	REMARKS.
COLONEL.			
Har. G. Broke, - -	24 *Dec* 58	*m.g.* ..	Europe.
LIEUTENANT COLONELS.			
George Vaughan Maxwell, C.B.,	23 *Mar.* 55	*col* 23 *Mar.* 58	Commanding.
Edward Herbert Maxwell. -	16 *June* 57		
MAJORS.			
Hon. John Jocelyn Bourke, -	27 *May* 56	... ...	Leave to England on P. A. for 15 Ms. to 4 July 60.
Edmund Gilling Maynard, -	16 *June* 57	2 *Nov.* 55	
CAPTAINS.			
Ben. Banbury Mauleverer, -	28 *July* 54	*m.* 6 *June* 56	
Joshua Grant Crosse, - *V*,	30 *Aug.* 54	*m.* 26 *Dec.* 56	
Thomas Gore, - -	29 *Dec.* 54	*m.* 6 *June* 56	Comdg. Regtl. Depôt, England.
H. J. Le Marchant Baynes, -	29 *Dec.* 54	.. ..	Regtl Depot, England.
John Edward Riley, - -	26 *Jan.* 55	... ...	Leave to England
Shurlock Henning, - -	23 *Mar.* 55		
George Richard Browne, - -	24 *Apl.* 55	*m* 4 *June* 58	Convalescent Depôt Landour.
Emil. C. Delmé Radcliffe, - -	8 *June* 55		
William Charles Pearson, - -	8 *June* 55		
Lewis John Fillis Jones, - -	17 *July* 57	27 *May* 56	Leave on M. C. to Simla to 1st Oct. 59.
William Lambert, - -	27 *Dec.* 57	.. ..	Ditto ditto to Mussoorie to 4 Sep. 59.
Frederick Hall, - *V*,	23 *Mar.* 58		
LIEUTENANTS.			
George Priestley, - -	29 *Dec.* 54		
Robert Vernor, - -	9 *Feb.* 55		
Ernest Aug. Perceval, - -	9 *Feb.* 55		[59.
John Evans, - -	9 *Feb.* 55	.. ..	Leave on M. C. to England to 4 Aug.
Edward Hopton, - -	9 *Feb.* 55		
Caleb Robertson, - -	15 *Apl.* 55		
Lucas Clements Scott, - -	21 *May* 55		
Holt Waring, - -	8 *June* 55		
George Stretton Watson, - -	8 *June* 55		
Edgar Edward Austin, - -	8 *June* 55	... ..	Adjutant
Theobald Burke, - -	17 *Aug.* 55		
Fred. Napleton Dew, - -	21 *Sept.* 55	.. ..	Leave on M. C. to England.
John D. Garner Dodgin, - -	16 *Oct.* 55		
Edward Charles Mallet, - -	16 *Oct.* 55	... ..	Leave on M. C. to England
Mortimer Neville Woodard, *V*,	16 *Oct.* 55		
John Irwin, - -	26 *Oct.* 55		
H. Garrett Moore, - -	26 *Oct.* 55		
Rowley Miller, - -	14 *Dec.* 55		
W. J. Saul			
ENSIGNS.			
Patrick Dwyer, - -	16 *Aug.* 55	.. ...	Instructor of Musketry.
R ~~Edmund de Blaquiere,~~ - -	16 *Oct.* 55		
Lt. James Buchanan Whitla, - -	26 *Oct.* 55		
William Hatfield, - *V*,	28 *Dec.* 55		
Lewis Mans. Buchanan, - -	29 *Feb.* 56		
Thos. H. Cuthbertson, - - -	16 *Mar.* 58	... ...	Regtl. Depôt, England.

H. M. 88th Regt. of Foot (Connaught Rangers).—(*Continued.*)

Rank and Names.	*Regimental Rank.*	*Army Rank.*	Remarks.
Instructor of Musketry.			
Ensign, P. Dwyer, -	17 *Mar.* 59	16 *Aug.* 55	
Paymaster.			
Michael Joseph Cunningham, -	24 *Oct.* 56		
Adjutant.			
Lieut Edgar E. Austin, - -	20 *June* 58	*lt.* 8 *June.* 55	
Quarter-Master.			
Mathew Evans, - -	28 *Dec.* 55		
Surgeon.			
John Dunlop, M. D., - -	8 *Dec.* 54	... ...	
Assistant Surgeons.			
Thomas Robert Williams, M. D.,	24 *Mar.* 54		
Richard William Meade, - -	1 *Sept.* 54		
John Copeland Knipe, - -	14 *Mar.* 55		
Interpreter.			
Lieut. A. Merewether, 61 N. I.	.. ..	*lt.* 18 *May* 53	

Strengh,—10 Companies with—55 Serjeants,—50 Corporals,—23 Drummers and 792 Privates.

English Agents,—Messrs. Cox and Co.
Calcutta Agents,—Messrs. Grindlay and Co.

WAR SERVICES OF THE OFFICERS OF H. M. 88th REGT. OF FOOT.

Major General Broke accompanied the 52nd on the expedition to Copenhagen in 1807; and the following year on that to Portugal, and was present at the battle of Vimiera, the advance into Spain and retreat under Sir John Moore. In 1809 he served on the Walcheren expedition. In 1811 he joined the Light Division on the retreat of Massena from the lines of Lisbon, and served in Spain till the end of the war. In 1812 he joined Sir Henry Clinton as Aide-de-Camp, at the siege of Burgos, and was shot through the lungs while serving with him at the battle of Orthes. He served with the Army of occupation in Francé from 1815 to 1818 as Aide-de-Camp to Sir Henry Clinton. Has the War Medal with four Clasps for Vimiera, Salamanca, Nive, and Orthes.

Lieut.-Colonel G. V. Maxwell served the Eastern campaign of 1854-55, including the battles of Alma and Inkerman, siege of Sebastopol, attack on the Quarries 7th June; commanded the 88th Regt. at the attacks on the Redan on the 18th June and 8th Sept.—severely wounded (Medal and Clasps, and *CB.*, Brevet Lt.-Col., Knight of the Legion of Honor, and Sardinian Medal order of the Medjiddie 4th Class).

Colonel E. H. Maxwell served the Eastern campaign of 1854-55, including the battles of Alma and Balaklava, siege of Sebastopol, attack on the Quarries 7th June, and on the Redan 18th June and 8th Sept. (Medal and Clasps; Brevet Lt.-Col., and Knight of the Legion of Honor order of the Medjiddie 5th Class).

Major Hon. J. J. Bourke served the Eastern campaign of 1854-55, including the battles of Alma and Inkerman, and siege of Sebastopol (Medal and Clasps).

Major Maynard served at the siege of Sebastopol, the attack on the Quarries 7th June (severely wounded), and attacks on the Redan on the 18th June and 8th Sept. (Medal and Clasp, Brevet Major, and Sardinian Medal order of the Medjiddie 5th Class.

Major Mauleverer served at the siege of Sebastopol, and was severely wounded at the attack on the Redan on the 8th Sept. (Medal and Clasp, and Brevet Major).

Major Crosse and Captain Baynes served the Eastern campaign of 1854, including the battles of Alma and Inkerman (severely wounded), and siege of Sebastopol (Medal and Clasps, and Brevet Major).

Major Gore served the Eastern campaign in 1854-55, including the battles of Alma and Inkerman, siege of Sebastopol, attack on the Quarries 7th June, and on the Redan 18th June and 8th Sept. (Medal and Clasps, Brevet Major, and Sardinian Medal).

Captain Riley served the Eastern campaign of 1854-55, including the battles of Alma and Inkerman and siege of Sebastopol (Medal and Clasps, and Sardinian Medal).

Captain Henning served in the Eastern campaign of 1854-55, including the battle of the Alma, siege of Sebastopol, and attack on the Redan 8th Sept. (Medal and Clasps).

Major Browne served the Eastern campaign of 1854-55, including the battles of Alma and Inkerman, siege of Sebastopol, and attack on the Redan on the 18th June—dangerously wounded, right arm amputated (Medal and Clasps, and Knight of the Legion of Honor).

_ *For continuation of services see page 87b.*

H. M. 90th Regt. of (Perthshire Volunteers). Light Infantry.

MANDORA." –The *Sphinx*, "EGYPT"—"MARTINIQUE"—"GUADALOUPE"—"SEVASTOPOL."

FACINGS.—*Buff*.

Landed in Calcutta, from ——— *on 19th July* 1857.

SEETAFORE,

Regimental Depôt, Canterbury.

RANK AND NAMES.	*Regimental Rank.*	*Army Rank.*	REMARKS.
COLONEL.			
Alex. Fisher Macintosh, K. H.,-	4 *Mar.* 57	*l.g.* 2 *Aug* 58	In England.
LIEUT.-COLONELS.			
William P. Purnell, C. B., - -	9 *Oct.* 55	*col.* 24 *Mar.* 58	Leave of absence to England to 1st [Mar. 60.
Thomas Smith, C. B., - -	13 *Nov.* 57	6 *June* 56	Leave of absence England for 18 months
MAJORS.			
John Christopher Guise,* -	13 *Nov.* 57	*l.c.* 24 *Mar.* 58	Commanding Setapore District.
William Pattison Tinling, -	24 *Dec.* 57	.. ...	Commanding.
CAPTAINS.			
Henry Hope Crealock, - V.	29 *Dec.* 54	*l.c.* 20 *July* 58	Acting Dep. Assist. Adjut. Genl. to the [Chief of the Staff.
Garnet Joseph Wolseley, - -	26 *Jan.* 55	*m* 24 *Mar.* 58	Acting Dep. Assist. Qr. Mr. Genl. to Oude Division.
James Herne Wade, - -	2 *Feb.* 55	*m* 20 *July* 58	Leave to England to 30th Sept. 60.
Richard Henry Magenis, - -	25 *Feb.* 55	*m* 20 *July* 58	Leave to England to 1st Sept. 60.
James Clerk Rattray, - -	9 *Sep.* 55	.. ..	Leave of absence to England on P. A for 18 months.
Lawrence N. D. Hammond, -	8 *July* 56	.. ..	Regtl. Depôt, England.
Leonard H. Lloyd Irby, - -	24 *Feb.* 57	.. ..	Leave on P A. to Nynee Tal.
Percy Julius Deverill, - -	1 *Oct.* 57		
Oswald William Every, - -	30 *Oct* 57	.. ..	Leave on M. C. to England.
H. Holyoake Goodricke, - -	24 *Dec.* 57		
Frederick Edward Sorell, - -	5 *Mar* 58	17 *Sep.* 50	Commanding Regtl. Depot.
William Thomas McGrigor, -	2 *July* 58		
LIEUTENANTS.			
Charles B. Wynne, - -	25 *Feb.* 55		Leave of absence to England on P. A.
Ivan S. Andrew Herford, - -	29 *Apl.* 55		Ditto.
Henry Bingham, - -	9 *Sep.* 55	.. ..	
William Knight, - -	23 *Oct.* 55	.. ..	Leave on M. C. to England.
Charles Dawson Barwell - -	30 *Nov.* 55	.. ..	Instructer of Muskety.
Willam Rennie, * - -	30 *Nov.* 55	... ..	Adjutant.
George Robert Miller, - -	7 *Dec.* 55	.. .	Leave on M. C. to Simla to 28 Sept. 59.
Henry Carver Treacher, - -	7 *Dec.* 55	.. ..	Canterbury Depôt, England.
Apsley Cherry, - -	18 *Jan.* 56	.. ..	Convalescent Depot Nynee Tal.
Edward Cooper Wynne, - -	18 *Jan.* 56	.. ..	Leave on M. C. to England.
Edward Carter, - -	8 *Feb.* 56		
George Edward Perryn, - -	24 *Feb.* 57		
Henry B. Savory, - -	24 *Sep.* 57		
Louis Worthington Wilmer, -	25 *Sep.* 57		
Gerald Andrew Agnew, - -	28 *Sep.* 57	.. ..	Lv. on M. C. to Nynee Tal to 1st Oct. 59.
Annesley Eyre, - -	13 *Nov.* 57	... ..	Leave on M. C. to England.
George Gregg, -	20 *Apl.* 58		
ENSIGNS.			
Henry James Edgell, - -	15 *Feb.* 56		
James Felix Haig, - -	1 *Apl.* 56	.. ...	Leave on M. C. to England to 10 May 59
Samuel Roden Handy, - -	16 *Oct.* 55		
John Williamson, - -	24 *Feb.* 57	.. ..	Leave to England on P. A, for 18 moths.
David Patterson Murray,- -	25 *June* 58	.. ..	Regtl. Depôt, England.
Francis Russell, - -	2 *July* 58	.. ..	Ditto.
Oscar William de Thoren, - -	13 *Aug.* 58	.. ..	Ditto.
Frederick Home Carleton, - -	16 *Nov.* 58		

* Victoria Cross.

H. M. 90th Regt. of Foot (Perthshire Volunteers).—(*Continued*).

Rank and Names.	*Regimental Rank.*	*Army Rank.*	Remarks.
Instructor of Musketry.			
Lieut. C. D. Barwell, - -	2 *Mar.* 59		
Paymaster			
Thomas Cassidy, - -	8 *Apl.* 59		
Adjutant.			
Lieut. William Rennie, V. C.	30 *Nov.* 55	*lt.* 30 *Nov.* 55	
Quarter-Master.			
Ens. David Jackson, - -	15 *Dec.* 54	*ens.* 10 *Aug.* 54	
Surgeon.			
Patrick Joseph Clarke, - -	.. ..	11 *May* 55	
Assistant Surgeons.			
Edmond Joseph Crane, - -	3 *Nov.* 57		
George Bell Popplewell,- - -	4 *June* 58	9 *June* 54	
Charles George Lumsden, - -	8 *Oct.* 58	28 *May* 57	Leave on M. C. to Muree.
Interpreter.			
Capt. W. T. McGrigor, - -	10 *Mar.* 58	.. ..	Acting.

Strength—10 Companies with 51 Sergeants,—45 Corporals—19 Buglers—and 734 Privates.

English Agents—Andrew Lawrie, Esq.
Calcutta Agents,—Messrs. Wood, Oliffe and Co.

WAR SERVICES OF THE OFFICERS OF H. M. 90th REGT. OF FOOT.

Major-General Macintosh served in the Peninsula with the 3rd Dragoon Guards from Aug. 1812 to the end of that war in 1814, including the retreat from Madrid to Salamanca, and action at Alba de Tormes, retreat of Ciudad Rodrigo and action at San Munos, passage of the Tormes above Salamanca, and attack on the French rear-guard under General Villate, action at Hormasa before Burgos, battle of Vittoria, investment of Pampeluna, action at Tarbes, attack on the French cavalry rear-guard at St. Gaudens, and battle of Toulouse. He has received the War Medal with two Clasps for Vittoria and Toulouse.

Colonel Purnell served at the siege of Sebastopol (Medal and Clasp and 5th class of the Medjidie).

Lt.-Colonel Smith served at the siege and fall of Sebastopol from 5th Dec. 1854 (Medal and Clasp. Brevets of Major and Lt.-Col., Knight of the Legion of Honor, and Sardinian Medal).

Lt.-Colonel Guise served in the Crimea from 5th to 24th Dec. 1854 (Medal with Clasp for Sebastopol).

Major Tinling served in the Crimea at the siege and fall of Sebastopol from 10th Aug. 1855, and was severely wounded at the assault of the Redan on the 8th Sept. (Medal and Clasp, and Brevet Major).

Lt.-Colonel Crealock served in the Crimea from 5th Dec. 1854 to 10th Feb. 1855, and again from 28th March 1855, including the siege and fall of Sebastopol (Medal and Clasp, and Brevet Major and 5th class of the Medjidie).

Major Wolseley served with the 80th Regt. in the Burmese war of 1852-53 (Medal); was with the expedition under Sir John Cheape against the robber chief Myattoon, and severely wounded when leading the storming party against that chief's stronghold on the 19th March (mentioned in Dispatches). Landed in the Crimea with the 90th Light Infantry on 5th Dec. 1854, and employed in the trenches as Acting Engineer until Sebastopol was taken; was engaged in the assault and defence of the Quarries on 7th June, and on duty in the trenches at the attack of the 18th June: severely wounded in a sortie 30th Aug. when in charge of the advanced sap—several times mentioned in Dispatches (Medal and Clasp, Knight of the Legion of Honor and 5th class of the Medjidie).

Captains Wade and Rattray served at the siege and fall of Sebastopol from 5th Dec. 1854, and were severely wounded at the assault of the Redan on the 8th Sept. (Medal and Clasp). Captain Wade has also the Sardinian Medal and 5th class of the Medjidie.

Captain Magenis served with the 90th Light Infantry at the siege and fall of Sebastopol; commanded a party of the regt. at the taking of the Rifle Pits on the 19th April 1855, and was of the storming at the assault of the Redan on the 8th Sept.—mentioned in Dispatches (Medal and Clasp and 5th class of the Medjidie).

Capt. Deverill served at the siege and fall of Sebestopol from 5th Dec. 1854, and was severely wounded at the assault of the Redan on the 8th Sept. (Medal and Clasp).

Capt. Every served at the siege and fall of Sebastopol from 10th Aug. 1855 (Medal and Clasp).

Capt. Goodricke served at the siege and fall of Sebastopol from 31st Aug. 1855, and was severely wounded at the assault of the Redan on 8th Sept. (Medal and Clasp),

Lieut. Wynne served at the siege and fall of Sebastopol from 12th July 1855, and was of the storming party at the assault of the Redan on the 8th Sept. (Medal and Clasp).

Lieut. Herford served at the siege and fall of Sebastopol from 7th Sept. 1855, and assault of the Redan on the 8th Sept. (Medal and Clasp).

Paymaster Williams served throughout the Kaffir war of 1846-47 (Medal). Served also in the Crimea during the siege and fall of Sebastopol from 5th Dec. 1854 (Medal and Clasp).

Quarter-Master Jackson served throughout the Kaffir war of 1846-47 (Medal). Served also in the Crimea during the siege and fall of Sebastopol from 5th Dec. 1854 (Medal and Clasp).

Assist.-Surgeon Poppelwell served on the Staff in the Eastern campaign of 1854-55, and was present with the 31st Regt. at the siege of Sebastopol, and attack of the Redan on the 18th June (Medal and Clasps). Served with General Havelock's field force in the actions of 21st and 23rd Sept. 1857, the relief of Lucknow, and storming the Hirn Khannah.

H. M. 93rd (Sutherland Highlanders) Regt. of Foot,

"CAPE OF GOOD HOPE"—"ALMA"—"BALAKLAVA"—"SEVASTOPOL,"
FACINGS—*Yellow.*
Landed in Calcutta, from England, on 22nd September 1857.
SUBATHOO.
Regimental Depôt, Aberdeen.

RANK AND NAMES.	*Regimental Rank.*	*Army Rank.*	REMARKS.
COLONEL.			
Rt. Hon. Lord Clyde, G. C. B.,	15 *Jan.* 58	*g.* 14 *May* 58	Commander-in-Chief in India.
LIEUT. COLONELS.			
Alex. Sebastian Leith Hay, C.B.,	9 *Mar.* 55	*col.* 16 *Apl.* 54	Commanding.
John Alexander Ewart, C. B., -	19 *Apl.* 58	2 *Nov.* 55	Leave on M. C. to England, to 31st Oct. 59.
MAJORS.			
Robert Lockhart Ross, - -	8 *Jan.* 58	*l.c.* 26 *Dec.* 56	Assist. Adjutant General, Bombay.
George Cornwall, - -	16 *Apl.* 58		
CAPTAINS.			
Wm. G. Alex. Middleton, - -	6 *June* 54	*m* 20 *July* 58	Commandant Nynee Tal. Convalescent Depot,
Wm. Donald Macdonald, - -	10 *Oct.* 54	*m.* 26 *Dec.* 56	Dep. Ass. Qr. Mr. Genl. at Allahabad
Fred. William Burroughs,- -	10 Nov. 54	*m* 20 *July* 58	Leave on M. C. to England.
~~W. G. Drummond Stewart~~,* -	29 *Dec.* 54	.. ..	
E. S. Fra. Geo. Dawson, - -	do	*m* 24 *Mar.* 58	Leave of absence to England on P. A. for 18 months
James Montagu Brown, - -	12 *Jan.* 55	*m* 12 *Nov.* 58	Aberdeen Depôt.
Reginald Stewart Williams, -	15 *Aug.* 55		
Edward Welch, -	12 *Mar.* 58	.. ..	Leave on M. C. to England.
William M'Bean,* - -	16 *Apl.* 58		
9 William Wallingford Knollys, -	28 *May* 58	6 *Nov.* 54	
~~Rolland V. S. Grimston~~, - -	10 *Dec.* 58		
10 Charles H. Levenge, - -	2 *Feb.* 59		
12 W. J. Bell LIEUTENANTS.			
Archibald Butter, - -	8 *Dec.* 54		
Capt. Ewen H. D. Macpherson, - -	9 *Feb.* 55	.. ..	A. D. C. to the Lieut. Governor of Bengal.
Arthur C. Nightingale, - -	9 *Mar.* 55	.. ..	Regtl. Depot, Aberdeen.
Maxwell Wither Hyslop, V	9 *Mar.* 55	.. ..	Station Staff Officer Kussowlie.
George Roe Fenwick, - -	28 *Nov.* 54	.. ..	Acting Paymaster of recruit Depôt, at Berhampore.
Wm. Gordon Alexander, - V,	1 *May* 55	.. ..	Doing Duty with Rohilcund Horse.
Anthony Olivier Tabuteau, -	1 *May* 55	.. ..	
Edward Septimus Wood, - -	10 *June* 55		
Samuel Edward Wood, - -	14 *June* 55	.. ..	Studying at Thomason C. E. College Roorkee.
Charles Warner Losack, - -	27 *July* 55	.. ..	Leave on M. C. to England.
Roderick dhu G. H. Burgoyne,	15 *Aug.* 55		
George Cecil Gooch, - -	23 *Oct.* 55		
FitzRoy M'Pherson, - -	2 *Nov.* 55	.. ..	Adjutant.
Edward Court Haynes, - -	2 *Nov.* 55	.. ..	On Privilege leave to the Hills.
George Greig, - -	8 *Jan.* 56	.. ..	Ditto.
Waller Scott Mackenzie, - -	17 *Nov.* 57		
George Forbes Robertson,- -	13 *Dec.* 57	.. ..	Ditto.
Geo. John Malcolm Taylor, -	12 *Mar.* 58		
Rt. K. A. Dick Cunyngham, -	16 *Apl.* 58		
R ~~John E. Deans Campbell~~, -	16 *Dec.* 58		
ENSIGNS.			
Charles Hastie, - -	2 *Nov.* 55	.. ..	Leave on M. C. to England.
Lt. Fra. Rawdon Macnamara, - -	28 *Dec.* 55		
Wm. Fullarton Fullarton, - -	8 *Jan.* 56		
Charles Dennis Potts, - -	18 *Jan.* 56		
Dunlop Hay, - -	14 *Mar.* 56		
Robt. W. T. Gordon, - -	28 *Feb.* 58	... ...	Aberdeen Depôt.
Henry T. Butter, - - - -	25 *June* 58	.. ..	Ditto.
William Forbes, -	10 *Dec.* 58		
Charles Edward Condell, - -	18 *Jan.* 59	.. ..	Regimental Depôt.
INSTRUCTOR OF MUSKETRY.			
Lieut A. O. Tabuteau, - -	11 *Dec.* 58		
PAYMASTER.			
Lieut. Stephen Blake, - -	26 *Jan.* 49	*lt.* 21 *July* 46	

* Victoria Cross.

H. M. 93rd Regt. (Southerland Highlanders) of Foot.—(Continued)

Rank and Names.	Regimental Rank.	Army Rank.	Remarks.
Adjutant.			
Lieut. FitzRoy McPherson,	16 *Apl.* 58	*lt.* 2 *Nov.* 55	
Quarter-Master.			
John Joiner,	6 *July* 55		
Surgeon.			
Wm. Munro, M. D.,	5 *May* 54		
Assistant Surgeons.			
William Sinclair,	2 *Sep.* 53		
Robert Menzies,	24 *Feb.* 54		
James Nicholas Bell, M. D.,	20 *May* 57	1 *Apl.* 53	In M. C. at Kussowlie.
Interpreters.			
Capt. F.G. Thellusson 29th N.I.			

Strength—10 Companies with 56 Serjeants,—49 Corporals,—27 Drummers and 776 Privates.

English Agents,—Messrs. Cox and Co.

Calcutta Agents.,—Messrs. Wm. Spink and Co.

WAR SERVICES OF THE OFFICERS OF H. M. 93rd REGT. OF FOOT.

General *Baron* Clyde of Clydesdale G. C B., (Sir Colin Campbell) served with the 9th Regt. in the Peninsula and at Walcheren, and was present at the battle of Vimiera, in the advance and retreat of the army under Sir John Moore, and battle of Corunna; at the battle of Barossa and the defence of Tarifa. He was attached to the army of Ballesteros at the latter end of 1812, and was present at several affairs; also in an expedition to relieve Taragona; was at the affair ofOsma, battle of Vittoria, siege of St. Sebastian, where he received two severn wounds, and passageof the Biddassoa, where he was again severely wounded. Served in America in 1814-15 in the 60th Rifles. Was Brigade Major of the troops engaged in quelling the insurrection in Demerara in 1823. Commanded the 98th Regt. in the expedition to China in 1842, including the capture of Chinkiangfoo and subsequent operations near to Nankin. Commanded the 3rd Division of the army of the Punjaub throughout the Punjaub campaign of 1848-49, including the affair of Ramnuggur, passage of the Chenab, affair of Sadoolapore, battles of Chillianwallah (wonaded)undGoojerat, and the final operations. He was constantly employed in 1851 and 1852, when Brigadier-General commanding the Peshawur districts, in operations against the Hill Tribes surrounding the valley, including theforcing of the Kohat Pass under Sir Charles Napier, and repeated affairs with the Momunds, who finally made terms after their defeat at Punj Pao by a small detachment of cavalry and horse artillery under Sir Colin's immediate command, the com bined tribes numbering upwards of 8,000 men. In 1852 he commanded an expedition against the Ootmankbail and Ranazai Tribes, whom he attacked in their valleys, and destroyed thestrongly- defended village of Nowadund, the fortified village of Pranghur, and he finally routed them with great saughter at Iskakote, where they mustered 8,000 men, while the force under Sir Colin was under 3,000 men Commanded the Highland Brigade and Highland Division throughout the Eastern campaign of 1854-55, including the battles of the Alma and Balaklava, and the seige of Sebastopol (Medal and Clasps, *GCB.*, Grand Officer of the Legion of Honor, Grand Cross of St. Maurice and St. Lazarusand 1st Class of the Medjidie); SirColin has also received the War Medal with five Clasps, the Chinese Medal, the Punjaub Medal with two Clasps, and was nominated KCB. after the Punjaub campaign. Wounded at the second relief of Lucknow 16th Nov. 57.

Colonel Leith Hay served in Canada during the Rebellion, and was in the affair at Prescot. Served, the Eastern campaign of 1854 up to 8th Feb. 1855, and again from 13th Aug. 1855, including the battles of Alma and Balaklava, siege and fall of Sebastopol, and commanded the 93rd Highlanders at the assault on the 8th Sept. (Medal aad Clasps, and Knight of the Legion of Honor aud 5th class of the Medjidie.)

Lt.-Colonel Ewart served throughout the Eastern campaign of 1854-55; present with the 93rd at the battle of Alma, and until after the occupation of Balaklava; appointed a D.A.Q M.G. 26th Sept. 1854, and as such was presen at the battles of Balaklava and Inkerman, and throughout the siege operations before Sebastopol up to 13th Feb. 1855, when he rejoined the 93rd on promotion; accompanied the expedition to the Sea of Azoff, and was at the capture of Kertch and Yenikale; afterwards present at the siege and fall of Sebastopol, and assaults on the 18th June and 8th Sept. (Medal and four Clasps, Brevet of Major and Lt.-Col., Knight of the Legion of Honor, and Sardinian Medal and 5th class of the Medjidie)

Lt.-Colonel Ross served the Eastern campaign of 1854-55 with the 93rd Highlanders, including the battles of Alma and Balaklava, and siege of Sebastopol (Medal and Clasps, Brevet Major and Sardinian Medal, and 5th class of the Medjidie.)

Major Cornwall served the Eastern campaign of 1854-55 with the 93rd Highlanders, including the battles of Alma and Balaklava, capture of Balaklava, expedition to the Sea of Azoff and capture of Kertch and Yenikale; afterwards present at the siege and fall of Sebastopol, and assaults of the 18th June and 8th Sept.—wounded in the trenches on the 3rd Aug. 1855 (Medal and three Clasps, and Knight of the Legion of Honor).

Major Macdonald served the Eastern campaign of 1854, and up to 8th January 1855, as provost Marshal, including the battle of the Alma and siege of Sebastopol (Medal and Clasps and 5th class of the Medjidie.)

Major Burroughs served throughout the Eastern compaign of 1854-55, including the battles of Alma and Balaklava, siege and fall of Sebastopol (Medal and three Clasps and 5th class of the Medjidie.)

Captain Steward served in the Eastern campaign of 1854-55, including the battles of Alma and Balaklava, siege and fall of Sebastopol (Medal and Clasps Capt. Stewart has the 5th class of the Medjidie.)

Major Dawson served in the 45th the Kaffir campaign of 1846-7, and that of 1851-2 (Medal). Served the Eastern campaign of 1854, and up to 8th Feb. 1855, with the 93rd Regt., including the battles of Alma and Balaklava, and siege of Sebastopol (Medal and Clasps).

Captain Welch, Lieuts. Macpherson, Nightingale, Hyslop, and Alexander served at the siege and fall of Sebastopol from 14th July 1855 (Medal and Clasp).

Capt. M'Bean served at the siege and fall of Sebastopol from 10th Dec. 1854 (Medal and Clasp and 5th class of the Medjidie.)

Captain Knollys served with the Scotch Fusilier Guards in the Eastern campaign up to Sept. 1854 including the siege of Sebastopol. (Medal and Clasp).

Lieut. Fenwick served with the 1st Battalion of the Royals the Eastern campaign of 1854, and up to 19th May 1855, including the battles of Alma and Inkerman, and siege of Sebastopol (Medal and three Clasps).

Paymaster Blake served at the siege of Sebastopol from 13th Oct. 1854 (Medal and Clasp).

Qr.-Master Joiner served at the siege and fall of Sebastopol from 6th July 1855 (Medal and Clasp).

Doctor Munro served as Assistant Surgeon of the 91st Regt. throughout the Kaffir war of 1846-7 (Medal) and as Surgeon of the 93rd Highlanders during the campaign in the Crimea, including the battles of Alma and Balaklava, and siege and fall of Sebastopol (Medal and three Clasps and 5th class of the Medjidie.)

Doctor Bell served with the 79th Highlanders the Eastern campaign of 1854-55, including the battle of Balaklava siege and fall of Sebastopol, and assaults of the 18th June and 8th Sept. (Medal and two Clasps).

Asst.-Surgn. Sinclair served at the siege of Sebastopol from 13th Oct. 54 to 21st March 1855 (Medal and Clasp.

H. M. 94th Regiment of Foot.

FACINGS—*Green*

Landed at Kurrachie, from England, on 14th January 1858.

~~PESHAWUR.~~

Detachment at *Meean Meer, Lahore*,

Regimental Depôt, Chatham.

RANK AND NAMES.	*Regimental Rank.*	*Army Rank.*	REMARKS.
COLONEL.			
George Powell Higginson, ..	29 *Jan.* 55	*l.g.* 20 *June* 54	In Europe.
LIEUT. COLONELS.			
Charles James Conway Mills,	24 *Oct.* 56	11 *July* 56	Commanding.
Henry George Buller, ..	18 *Sep.* 57		
MAJORS.			
William Humphrey Kirby, *H.*	29 *Dec.* 54	.. ..	Leave in India to 31st Oct. 59.
Septimus Lyster, ...	18 *Sep.* 57	... ...	Leave to Cashmere 16th Aug. 59.
CAPTAINS.			
Edward Smyth Mercer, *H. P.*	23 *Mar.* 49	.. ..	Interpreter.
Haydon Lloyd Cafe, ..	16 *May* 51	28 *Dec.* 49	Regtl. Depot.
Wm. West James Bruce, ..	22 *July* 54	29 *July* 53	Ditto.
Henry Hamilton Pratt, ..	29 *Dec.* 54	.. ..	Leave to England for 18 months.
Francis Barry Drew, ..	26 *Jan.* 55	21 *Nov.* 51	Ditto.
Thomas George Gardiner, ..	1 *May* 55	5 *Nov.* 52	Murree Depot.
Charles William St. John, ..	17 *Aug.* 55		
Osmond De Lancey Priaulx, ..	31 *July* 57		
Robert A. Boothby Tod, ..	14 *Aug.* 57		
John Murray, ..	19 *Nov.* 59	.. ...	Instructor of Musketry.—Leave on P. A. to Murree for 2 months.
George Lake Hedley, ..	18 *Jan.* 59	29 *Dec.* 54	
~~Wm. Plumer Gaskell~~, ..	1 *Apl.* 59		
LIEUTENANTS.			
Sydenham Malthus, ..	11 *Aug.* 54	.. ..	Adjutant.—Leave on P. A. to Cashmere to 15th Aug. 59.
Arthur Charles Elliot, ..	26 *Jan.* 55		
Josiah Robert Rolls, ..	17 *Aug.* 55		
Francis Hamilton Elliot, ..	14 *Sep.* 55		
Poltimore Ridgway, ..	19 *Aug.* 56	30 *Nov.* 55	
William Collum, ..	17 *July* 57		
~~John Marriot Aytoun~~, ..	31 *July* 57		
Arthur Chute, ..	14 *Aug.* 57	.. ..	Leave on M. C. to England.
~~Charles Thomas Paley~~, ..	18 *Sep.* 57		
Arthur Brinckman, ..	15 *Jan.* 58		
Robert Wingfield Cox, ..	23 *Mar* 58	.. ..	On duty with 7th Irregular Cavalry.
George James Teevan, ...	15 *Apl.* 59	... ..	Regimental Depôt.
ENSIGNS.			
William Fermer Godfrey, ...	8 *July* 56		
Charles Butler, ...	19 *Aug.* 56		
Henry Samuel Hall, ...	31 *July* 57		
Caulfield French, ..	6 *Nov.* 57		
Ramsay Stewart, ..	5 *Feb.* 58		
John Ingle, ...	13 *Apl.* 58	.. ..	Regimental Depot.
Edward Logan Stehelin, ..	10 *Sep.* 58	6 *Aug.* 58	Ditto.
Henry Farrer, ..	16 *Nov.* 58	.. ..	Ditto.
Percival Richards., ...	16 *Nov.* 58	.. ..	Ditto.
R. Anstruther, ..	31 *Dec.* 58	.. ..	Ditto.
J. R. Pilkington, ..	18 *Jan.* 59	... ...	

H. M. 94TH REGIMENT OF FOOT.—*(Continued)*.

RANK AND NAMES.		*Regimental Rank.*	*Army Rank.*	REMARKS.
INSTRUCTOR OF MUSKETRY.				
Capt. John Murray,	..	20 *Mar.* 57	*cap.* 19 *No.* 58	
PAYMASTER.				
Capt. Henry John Wahab,	..	8 *Dec.* 54	*c.* 21 *July* 45	
ADJUTANT.				
Lieut. Sydenham Malthus,	..	21 *May* 59		
QUARTER MASTER.				
Thomas Harper,	..	21 *No.* 56		
SURGEON.				
*				
ASSISTANT SURGEONS.				
Edward M'Grath,	..	11 *Sep.* 57	1 *Aug.* 57	
James Greig Leask, M. B.,	..	18 *Sep.* 57	28 *Aug.* 55	
John Wallace,	..	25 *Sep.* 57	2 *June* 57	
INTERPRETER.				
Capt. E. S. Mercer,	*HP,*			

Strength—10 Companies with 56 Sergeants—5(Corporals—19 Drummers—and 979 Privates.

English Agents—Messrs. Cox and Co.

Calcutta Agents.—Messrs. Gillanders, Arbuthnot and Co.

WAR SERVICES OF THE OFFICERS OF H. M. 94TH REGT. OF FOOT

Lt.-General Higginson served with the Grenadier Guards in Sicily in 1807, in the campaign in the north of Spain with Sir John Moore in 1808-9, and was present at the battle of Corunna. Went with the expedition to Welcheren in 1809. Joined his Regiment in Portugal in 1812, and advanced with the army into Spain in 1813; cammanded a detachment of the Grenadier Guards at the storming and capture of San Sebastian, 31st August in the same year, entered France by the Pyrenees was present at the passages of the Nive, the Nivelle, and the Adour, also during the investment of Bayonne. Embarked with his Regiment at Bordeaux when the army left France in 1814. Went with reinforcement to the Netherlands in June 1815, arrived at Paris shortly after its capture, and remained in France during the three years of its occupation by the Allied Army. In 1830 he was appointed Aide-de-Camp to Lord Hill, then Commander-in-chief, and continued on his staff upwards of twelve years, until his Lordship's resignation of office from ill health. He has received the War Medal with four Clasps.

Major Lyster served in the War of Succession in Spain as Lieut. of Infantry, and was present in the operations before San Sebastian, and was severely wounded through the body in the attack upon the fortified heights of Arambura near Hernani.

Captain Mercer served in the Turkish Contingent at Varna, and in the entrenched camp at Kertch, commanding successively the 3rd (Albanians), 6th, and 8th Regiments. 4th class of the Medjidie.

Capt. Bruce served with the 74th Highlanders throughout the Kaffir war of 1851-53 (Medal), and was wounded on the 26th June 1851

H. M. 97th (The Earl of Ulster's) Regt. of Foot.

"Quò fas et gloria ducunt."—"SEVASTOPOL."

FACINGS—*Sky Blue.*

Landed in Calcutta, from England, 20th November 1857.

BANDA.

Detachment at Nowgong and Kirwee.

Regimental Depôt, Colchester.

RANK AND NAMES.	*Regimental Rank.*	*Army Rank.*	REMARKS.
COLONEL.			
~~Henry Adolphus Proctor, C. B.,~~ -	29 *Nov.* 52	*m.g.* 20 *June* 54	In England.
LIEUTENANT COLONELS.			
Fowler Burton, -	15 *Mar.* 58	26 *Dec.* 56	Leave to England.
MAJORS.			
Wm. West Turner, C. B., - -	9 *Nov.* 55	*l.c.* 2 *Nov.* 55	Commanding.
Chas. Raleigh Chichester, - -	15 *Mar.* 56	6 *June* 56	Leave on P. A. to England.
CAPTAINS.			
Septimus Moore Hawkins, -	23 *Dec.* 53	*m* 20 *July* 58	Ditto.
Archibald Richard Harenc, -	6 *June* 54	*m* 20 *July* 58	Ditto.
Thomas Venables, - -	18 *Aug.* 54	.. ..	On command at Nowgong
Edward D. Harvest, - -	29 *Dec.* 54	.. ..	Colchester Depôt, England.
Edward Kent Jones, - -	29 *Dec.* 54		
Wm. Richard Annesley, - -	29 *Dec.* 54	.. ..	Instructor of Musketry.
Osborne Barwell Cannon, - -	23 *Mar* 55	.. ..	Colchester Depôt, England.
Charles Henry Browne, - -	15 *May* 57		
Roger Swire, - -	11 *Sep.* 57	23 *Nov.* 55	On leave on M. C. to England. [K. C. B.
Stapleton Cotton, - -	30 *July* 58	16 *Mar* 58	A. D. C. to Major Genl. Sir S. Cotton,
Henry Broome, - -	28 *Dec.* 58	4 *June* 58	Acting paymaster 84th Regt.
G. A. Ferris, - -	18 *Mar.* 58	4 *June* 58	
LIEUTENANTS.			
Isaac Harmond, - -	9 *Mar.* 55	.. ...	Acting Pay Master.
Jonathan Morgan, - -	6 *Apl.* 58	.. ..	On command at Kirwee.
Rob. Tho. Fra. Hamilton, V,	13 *Apl.* 55	.. ...	Interpreter.
Andrew George Onslow, - -	24 *Apl.* 55	8 *Sep.* 54	Leave on M. C. to England.
Maurice G. B. Fitzgerald, -	25 *May.* 55	.. ..	Ditto.
John Edwin Dickser Hill, -	19 *Aug.* 55	.. ..	Leave on M. C. to England.
Arthur Robert N. Gould, - -	31 *Aug.* 55		
John Wright Shaw, -	9 *Sep.* 55		With Detacht. at Nowgong.
David Jn, Dickson Safford, -	9 *Sep.* 55		Ditto.
James Clophane Minto, - -	9 *Sep.* 55	.. ..	Colchester Depôt, England.
Robert George Macdonald, -	4 *Apl.* 56	21 *Sep.* 55	
Frederick Wyer Parker, -	11 *Dec.* 58		
Robert Wheatley Barbor, - -	4 *Mar.* 58		
Robert Smith, - -	6 *Aug.* 58	.. ..	Adjutant.
Rich. B. Hamilton Lowe, - -	14 *Feb.* 59		
ENSIGNS.			
John Cooper, - -	2 *Nov.* 55	.. ...	Leave on M. C. to England.
Robert Thompson, - -	8 *Nov.* 55	.. ..	Leave on M. C. to England.
Robert Lefroy, - -	7 *Dec.* 55	.. ..	With Detachment at Kirwee.
Henry Grantham Fulford, - -	21 *Dec.* 55		
Thomas Evans Stuart, - -	1 *Apl.* 56	.. ..	Colchester Depôt, England.
Robert Gray, - -	10 *Apl* 57	.. ..	With Detachment at Kirwee.
Henry C. Crespin, - -	11 *Dec.* 57	... ..	Colchester Depôt, England. [now.
Peter Lawless. - - -	10 *Sep.* 58	.. ..	Acting Adjt.—Amenabad Depôt, Luck-
Thomas Candler Wharton. -	11 *Sep.* 58	... ..	

H. M. 97TH (THE EARL OF ULSTER'S) REGT. OF FOOT.—(*Continued.*)

RANK AND NAMES.	Regimental Rank.	Army Rank.	REMARKS.
INSTRUCTOR OF MUSKETRY.			
Capt. W. R. Annesley, - -	16 *Oct.* 56	.. ..	At Kirwee.
Lieut. I. Hammond, - - -	.. ..	.. ..	Acting.
PAYMASTER.			
Lieut. Thomas Smith, - -	28 *July* 54	*lt.* 2 *Aug.* 50	Leave on M. C. to England.
ADJUTANT.			
Lieut. Robert Smith, - -	.. ..	*lt.* 6 *Aug.* 58	
QUARTER-MASTER.			
William John Woodruffe, - -	2 *Nov.* 55		
SURGEON.			
Alexander Macrae, M. D., - -	6 *Apl.* 58		
ASSISTANT-SURGEONS.			
Joshua Henry Porter, - -	24 *Mar.* 54	17 *June* 53	
Edward Malcolm Sinclair, M.D.	28 *Mar.* 54	.. ..	With Detachment at Nowgong.
Thomas Starkey, - -	23 *July* 58	1 *Aug.* 57	Ditto, Kirwee.
INTERPRETER.			
Lieut. R. T. F. Hamilton, - -			

Strength—10 Companies with 56 Sergeants—50 Corporal,—21 Drummers, and 949 Privates.

English Agents,—Andrew Lawrie, Esq.

Calcutta Agents.—Messrs. Wm. Spink and Co.

WAR SERVICES OF THE OFFICERS OF H. M. 97TH REGT. OF FOOT.

Lieut.-General Proctor served with the 82nd on the expedition to Walcheren, in 1809, and was present at the siege of Flushing. Served also at Gibraltar, Tarifa, and in the Peninsula, from 1810 to Dec. 1812, and subsequently in the Peninsula and south of France, from April to July 1814, including the affair of Posts near Malaga, battle of Barrosa (contusion on the body) and retreat from Madrid. Embarked from Bordeaux for Canada in July 1814, and commanded the 82nd before Fort Erie from 2nd Sept., and throughout the successive operations of the campaign on the Niagara frontier. Received the Brevet promotion of Lieut.-Colonel for his conduct in the repelling of the attack made by the Americans on our batteries and position before Fort Erie on the 17th Sept. 1814. He has received the War Medal with one Clasp for Barrosa.

Lt.-Col. Burton served at the siege of Sebastopol from 20th Nov. 1854 to 5th July 1855; commanded the Light Company, 97th Regt., in the sortie on the night of the 20th Dec. 1854, and succeeded in driving the Russians out of the most forward parallel, from which the Guard had been compelled to withdraw, and retained its possession (Medal and Clasp, Bt. Lt.-Colonel, and Sardinian Medal, and 5th Class of the Medjidie). Served in Bengal in suppressing the Mutiny in 1857-58,—with the Jounpore field force in the actions of Nusrutpore Chanda, Ummeerpore, and Sultanpore, afterwards at the siege and capture of Lucknow.

Lt.-Colonel Turner served with the 26th Cameronians in China and was present at the defence of Ningpo, action of Tscke, storm and capture of Chapoo, Woosung, Shanghai, and Chinkiangfoo, and demonstration before Nankin (Medal). Served with the 15th Regt. in Ceylon and during the Kandian rebellion of 1848. Served with the 7th Fusiliers in the Eastern campaign during the siege of Sebastopol in 1855, including the sorties of 5th April and 9th May, assault and capture of the Quarries on 7th June (in command of the storming party of his Regt. and slightly wounded), assault of the Redan on 18th June (brought the Regt. out of action), assault of the Redan on 8th Sept. (in command of the Regt. and wounded), and was commandant of the Karabelnaia at Sebastopol from 3rd Dec. 1855 to the end of June 1856 (Medal and Clasp, Brevets of Major and Lieut.-Col., *CB.*, and Knight of the Legion of Honor and 5th Class of the Medjidie). Served in Bengal in suppressing the Mutiny in 1857-58, with the Jounpore field force in the actions of Chanda, Ummeerpore and Sultanpore, afterwards at the siege and capture of Lucknow.

Major Chichester served at the siege of Sebastopol from 20th Nov. 1854 (Medal and Clasp, and Brevet Major). Served in Bengal in suppressing the Mutiny in 1857-58. with the Jounpore field force in the actions of Nusrutpore. Chanda, Ummeerpore, and Sultanpore, afterwards at the siege and capture of Lucknow.

Major Hawkins served at the siege and fall of Sebastopol from 12th July 1855 (Medal and Clasp). Served in Bengal in suppressing the Mutiny in 1857-58, with the Jounpore field force in the actions of Nusrutpore, Chanda, Ummeerpore, and Sultanpore, afterwards at the siege and capture of Lucknow.

Maj. Harenc, Capt. Venables, Lieuts. Hamilton, Onslow, Gould, Shaw, Ensigns Macdonald, Lowe, and Fulford. and Gray served in Bengal in suppressing the Mutiny in 1857-58,—with the Jounpore field force in the actions Nusrutpore, Chanda, Ummeerpore, and Sultanpore, afterwards at the siege and capture of Lucknow.

Captain Jones served at the siege and fall of Sebastopol from 4th Sept. 1855 (Medal and Clasp). Served in Bengal in suppressing the Mutiny in 1857-58, with the Jounpore field force in the actions of Nusrutpore, Chanda. Ummeerpore, and Sultanpore. afterwards at the siege and capture of Lucknow.

Captain Cannon served at the siege of Sebastopol from 20th Nov. 1854 to 14th June 1855, (Medal and Clasp).

Captain Browne served at the seige of Sebastopol from 4th May 1855, and was on the storming party at the assault of the Redan on the 8th Sept.—Wounded (Medal and Clasp, and Sardinian Medal, and 5th Class of the Medjidie). Served in Bengal in suppressing the Mutiny in 1857-58, with the Jounpore field force in the actions of Nusrutpore, Chanda, Ummeerpore, and Sultanpore, afterwards at the siege and capture of Lucknow.

Captain Henry Broome served in Bengal and was present in the action of Onas 29th July 1857 under General Havelock, [severely woudned] occupation of the camp at Alumbagh under Sir J. Outram G. C. B., siege and capture of Lucknow under General Lord Clyde. With the Azimghur field force in all the minor actions under Sir E. Lugard, served in Shahabad until the final suppression of the Rebellion in that district under Brigadier Douglas, C. B.

Captain Wilkie served at the siege of Sebastopol from 16th June 1855 (Medal and Clasp). Served in Bengal in suppressing the Mutiny in 1857-58, with the Jounpore field force in the actions of Chanda, Ummeerpore, and Sultanpore, afterwards at the siege and capture of Lucknow.

*** *For continuation of services, see page* 113.

H. M. 98th Regiment of Foot.

"The Dragon"—"CHINA"—"PUNJAUB."
FACINGS—*White.*
Landed at Kurrachie, from England, on 2nd January 1858.
NOWSHERA.
Detachment at *Attock.*
Regimental Depôt, Canterbury.

RANK AND NAMES.	*Regimental Rank.*	*Army Rank.*	REMARKS.
COLONEL.			
William Lindsay Darling, ..	17 *Apl.* 54	*l.g.* 24 *June* 54	In England.
LIEUTENANT COLONELS.			
Daniel Rainier, ..	1 *Apl.* 53	*col.* 28 *Nov.* 54	Commanding.
Henry Bates, ..	18 *Sep.* 57	*col.* 28 *Nov.* 54	Military Secretary, Bombay.
MAJORS.			
Francis Peyton, ..	12 *May* 54	*l.c.* 12 *Nov.* 58	
Granville G. C. Stapylton, ..	18 *Sep.* 57	.. ..	Leave to Murree to 15th Sep. 59.
CAPTAINS.			
Francis Haden Crawford, ..	27 *Dec.* 50	1 *Oct.* 50	Ditto.
Edward John Ellerman, ..	6 *June* 51	9 *July* 50	Major British German Legion, Poona.
Edward Grantham, ..	28 *May* 52	.. ..	Comdg. Regtl, Depôt, Canterbury.
S. Hen. Hutchins Edwards, ..	28 *May* 52	.. ..	
G. D. Dickson Cleveland, ..	11 *Oct.* 53	.. ..	Comdg. Moradabad Levy.
Molyneux Batt, ..	22 *Nov.* 54	.. ..	Commanding detachment at Attock.
Frederick Rhodes, ..	17 *Feb.* 57	14 *Apl.* 54	Leave on M. C. to England.
Sir David Baird, Bart, ..	17 *Feb.* 57	*m* 24 *Mar.* 58	Leave on M. C. to England.
Robert Reid, ..	10 *Apl.* 57		
Henry Wallace Stroud, ..	18 *Sep.* 57	.. ..	Interpreter.
Attilio Scheberras, ..	16 *July* 58	9 *May* 58	Barrack Master at Peshawur.
William Blackett, ..	17 *Dec.* 58		
LIEUTENANTS.			
Thomas Gardiner, ..	3 *Sep.* 50	.. ..	Adjt. of 18th Punjab Infantry.
Wm. Hy Joseph Lance, *P, C, H,*	7 *Feb.* 51	.. ..	On duty with Moradabad Levy.
Samuel Cooper Walker, ..	7 *Sep.* 55	.. ..	Duty at the Depot, Murree.
William Langmead Lewes, ..	8 *July* 56	2 *Oct.* 55	
David J. Copeland Jones, ..	19 *Aug.* 56	.. ..	Leave on M. C. to England.
Sidney Henry Heywood, ..	30 *Sep.* 56	9 *Nov.* 55	Acting Instructor of Musketry.
Thomas Francis Lloyd, ..	15 *May* 57	.. ..	With detachment at Attock.
Kingston Brett, ..	18 *Sep* 57		
Edward Frank Gregory, ..	30 *Oct.* 57	... ...	Adjutant.
Charles Henry Griffin, ..	30 *Oct.* 57	.. ..	Acting Adjutant of the Eurasian Corps,
Geo. Washington Smith, ..	23 *Apl.* 58		
George Thomas West, ..	15 *Oct.* 58		
Thomas R. Bingham, ..	24 *Dec.* 58		
George B. Wolseley, ..	24 *Aug.* 57		
Chas. Edward Woodward, ..	11 *Mar.* 59		
ENSIGNS.			
Charles Graham Heathcote, ..	15 *May* 57		
Thos. Thomson Simpson, ..	30 *June* 57		
Percival Herbert Dobbs, ..	25 *Sep.* 57		
Thomas T. Swinford, ..	23 *Oct.* 57		
Robert Thorp, ..	2 *Feb.* 58		
William O'Toole, ..	5 *Mar.* 58		
Richard Townley, ..	21 *May* 58	... ..	Canterbury Depôt, England.
James George Ballantyne, ...	28 *May* 58	.. ..	Ditto.
William H. Simmonds, ..	31 *Dec.* 58	.. ..	Ditto.

H. M. 98th Regiment of Foot.—(*Continued.*)

Rank and Names.	Regimental Rank.	Army Rank.	Remarks.
Instructor of Musketry.			
Lieut. Sidney H. Heywood, ..	.. ..	.. ..	Acting.
Pay Master.			
Lieut. Henry Leigh, ..	8 *Sep.* 54	*lt.* 23 *Jan.* 52	
Adjutant.			
Lieut. E. F. Gregory, ..	8 *May* 58	*lt.* 30 *Oct.* 57	
Quarter Master.			
William Walsh, ..	29 *June* 55		
Surgeon.			
Neil Henry Stewart, M. D., ..	22 *June* 55		
Assistant Surgeons.			
John Sparrow, ..	30 *June* 54		
James McNeill Beatty, ..	26 *Sep.* 56	14 *Dec.* 54	
William Collis, ..	23 *Sep.* 57	14 *Sep.* 55	Leave on M. C. to England.
Interpretor.			
Capt Henry W. Stroud, ..			

10 Companies with 57 Serjeants—50 Corporals—21 Drummers—and 950 Privates.

English Agents.—Messrs Downes and Son.
Bombay Agents.—Mavuchjee Cowasjee.
Calcutta Agents.—Messrs Charles Cantor and Co.

WAR SERVICES OF THE OFFICERS OF H. M. 98th FOOT.

Lieut.-General Darling served at the reduction of Guadaloupe in 1810, and was severely wounded in the left knee by a musket-shot in storming the heights of Matauba. Proceeded to the Peninsula, and joined the 51st Light Infantry at Castello Branco in May 1812; engaged on the heights of San Christoval, the battle of Salamanca and surrender of the Retiro at Madrid; employed with his regiment before Burgos: and after retreat from thence he was attacked by typhu sfever, and sent to England for recovery in May 1813. Rejoined the army on the heights of Echallar in September following, and was present at the battle of Nivelle, and the subsequent attack of the heights of St. Pé. Appointed Major of Brigade in Dec. 1813, and attached to Major-General Hay's brigade in the 5th Division, and was employed throughout the blockade and operations before Bayonne. Appointed Assistant-Adjutant-General to the 5th Division in April 1814, and remainded in charge of that department until the embarkation of the division in Aug. 1814. On the renewal of the war in 1815 he was re-appointed to the staff as Assistant-Adjutant-General, and attached to the 4th division, under Sir Charles Colville; employed with his division in the operations connected with the battle of Waterloo, the storming of Cambray, and capitulation of Paris. He has received the War Medal with three clasps for Guadaloupe, Salamanca, and Nivelle.

Colonel Rainier and Captain Grantham served in the 98th with the expedition to the north of China in 1842, (Medal), and were present at the attack and capture of Chinkiangfoo, and at the landing before Nankin.

Colonel Bates served as Aide-de-Camp to Sir Robert Dick (who was killed) in the battle of Sobraon (Medal); and was appointed after that action Aide-de-Camp to the Commander-in-Chief in India, in which capacity he served the Punjaub campaign of 1848-9, and was present at the affair of Ramnuggur and battles of Chillianwallah and Goojerat (Medal and two Clasps).

Lieut. Colonel Peyton served in the 98th with the Expedition to the north of China in 1842 (Medal), and was present at the attack and capture of Chinkiangfoo, and at the landing before Nankin. He also served with the Flank Companies at the forcing of the Kohat Pass, in the force under Sir Colin Campbell in Feb. 1850. Served also in the Punjaub campaign of 1848-49 (Medal.)

Major Stapylton served in the 13th Light Infantry the campaigns of 1841 and 1842 in Affghanistan, and was present at the storming of the Khoord Cabool Pass, affair of Tezeen, forcing the Jugdulluck Pass, reduction of the Fort of Mamoo Khail, heroic defence of Jelalabad, and sorties on the 14th Nov. and 1st Dec. 1841, 11th March 24th March and 1st April 1842; the general action, with defeat of the besieging force under Akbar Khan before Jellalabad on the 7th April; the storming of the Jugdulluck heights, general action, at Tezeen, and recapture of Cabul, for which he has a Medal, as also for Jellalabad.

Captains Edwards, Richmond, and Reid, served in the Punjaub campaign of 1848-49 (Medal); served also with the Flank Companies 98th Regt. in the force under Sir Colin Campbell, at the forcing of the Kohat Pass in Feb. 1850.

Captains Cleveland and Stroud, served in the Punjaub campaign of 1848-49 (Medal).

Sir David Baird served with the 74th Highlanders throughout the Kaffir war in 1851-53 (Medal).

Paymaster Leigh was present at the storm and destruction of the fortified native Mandingo town of Sabajee on the Gambia, on the 1st June 1853.

Qr. Master Walsh served with the 9th Regt. throughout the campaign of 1842, in Affghanistan under Sir George Pollock, including the storming of the Khyber Pass, action of Mamoo Khal, storming the heights of Jugdul-uck, forcing the Tezeen Pass, clearing the heights of Huft Kotul, recapture of Cabul, assault of the Istaliff (Medal.) Served in the Sutlej campaign of 1845-46 including the battles of Moodkee and Ferozeshah—severely wounded Medal and Clasp) also in the Punjaub campaign of 1848-49 (Medal).

H. M. 99th (The Lanarkshire) Regiment of Foot.

FACINGS.—*Yellow.*
Landed in Calcutta from England—December 1858.
CALCUTTA.

Detachment of Berhampore.
Regimental Depot, Fermoy.

RANK AND NAMES.	*Regimental Rank.*	*Army Runks.*	REMARKS.
COLONEL.			
Sir John Hanbury, K. C. H., -	6 *Oct.* 51	*g.* 20 *June* 54	Europe.
LIEUT.-COLONELS.			
George Marmaduke Reeves, -	17 *Sep.* 58	*col.*28 *Nov.* 54	
Philip Smyly, - - - - -	26 *Oct.* 58	*col.*16 *Jan.* 59	
MAJORS.			
Henry James Day, - - - -	17 *Sep.* 58	*l. c.* 13 *Feb.* 59	
~~Rupert Barber Deering~~, - - H M Dowbiggin	36 *Oct.* 58	.. .	With detachment at Berhampore.
CAPTAINS.			
2 P. Johnston			
1 Charles Blamire, - - - -	22 *Feb.* 50		
3 Lempster R Elliot, - - -	6 *June.* 54	.. ..	With detachment at Berhampore.
Fred. Wm. Despard, - - -	13 *May.* 55		
Loftus John Nunn, - - - -	25 *Sep.* 55	.. ..	Regtl. Depot, England.
John Hart Dunne, - - - -	27 *July.* 55	... ..	Wfth detachment at Berhampore.
Wm. H. D. Reeves Welman, -	30 *Oct* 57	.. ..	Ditto.
Henry Fred. W. Ely, - - -	17 *Nov.* 57	.. ..	Ditto.
Francis Seymour Gaynor, - -	17 *Sep.* 58		
W. S. Dickinson, - - - -	26 *Oct.* 58		
T. Holling. Clarkson, - - -	29 *Mar.* 59	.. ..	Loave on M. C. to England.
Charles Burton, - - - - -	16 *May* 59	.. ..	With detachment at Berhampore.
LIEUTENANTS.			
Capt. Malcolm Brown Purcell, - -	21 *Sep.* 55	.. ..	Regtl. Depot, England.
Geo. Robt. Stewart Black, - -	29 *Aug.* 56	.. ..	Adjutant.
William John Kempson, - -	16 *June.* 57	.. ..	Regt. Depot, England.
Thomas Lowrie Grenville, - -	30 *Jan.* 57		
Henry James Day, - - - -	30 *Oct.* 57		
Eustace Wilberforce Jacob,- -	24 *Nov.* 57		
George Richards Harvey, - -	24 *Nov.* 57		
George Clayton, - - - - -	11 *Dec.* 57		
R ~~Edward Colpoys Johnson~~, - -	7 *Sep.* 58		
Aug. Wm. Hy. Atkinson, - -	17 *Sep.* 58		
Edward Beevor Batcheler, - -	26 *Oct* 58	.. ..	With detachment at Berhampore.
Martin Joseph Browne, - - -	26 *Oct.* 58		
Alexander Gray, - - - - -	29 *Mar.* 59	... ...	Ditto.
Henry Richmond Sayce, - -	6 *May* 59		
Horace Townsend, - - - -	16 *May* 59	.. ..	Ditto.
ENSIGNS.			
Lt. Charles Coates, - - - - -	24 *Nov.* 57		
Albert Lancelot Walker, - -	1 *Dec.* 57	.. ..	Regtl. Depot, England.
Phillip Homan ffolliott, - - -	7 *Sep.* 58	.. ..	Ditto.
Charles B. H. Somerset, - -	17 *Sep.* 58	.. ..	Ditto
Edward Egan, - - - - -	19 *Nov.* 58	.. ..	Ditto.
Joseph Ward, - - - - -	25 *Jan.* 59	.. ..	Ditto.

H. M. 99TH (THE LANARKSHIRE) REGIMENT OF FOOT.—(*Continued.*)

RANK AND NAMES.	Regimental Rank.	Rank Army.	REMARKS.
INSTRUCTOR OF MUSKETRY.			
*			
PAYMASTER.			
Charles Schomberg Thomas,	17 *Sep.* 58	29 *Dec.* 57	
ADJUTANT.			
Lieut, G. R. S. Black,	6 *May* 59		
QUARTER-MASTER.			
John Johnston,	24 *Sep.* 58		
SURGEON.			
Richard Cooper Todd,	3 *Nov.* 57		
ASSISTANT SURGEONS.			
George Whitla.	15 *Sep.* 57	.. ..	With detachment at Berhampore.
James Whinyates George Allen,	12 *Nov.* 57		
Samuel Halliday Macartney,	5 *Aug.* 58	5 *Aug.* 54	
INTERPRETER.			
Capt. G. F. F. Vincent,			

Strength—10 Companies with 47 Serjeants—39 Corporals—21 Drummers and 674 Privates.
English Agents—Messrs. Cox and Co.
Irish Agents—*Sir* E. R. Borough, *Bt.* Armit and Co.
Calcutta Agents—Messrs. Grindlay and Co.

WAR SERVICES OF THE OFFICERS OF H. M. 99TH REGT. OF FOOT.

Sir John Hanbury served the Egyptian campaign of 1801 as a Lieutenant in the 58th, including the actions of the 8th, 13th, and 21st March; and has received the Gold Medal from the Grand Seignior He was Aide-de-camp to Major General Warde in the campaign of 1808-9, and was present on Sir John Moore's retreat, and at the battle of Corunna. He served with the 1st Guards at Walcheren in 1809, and subsequently in the Peninsular campaign, including the retreat from Burgos, passage of the Bidassoa and Adour, battles of Nivelle and Nive, investment of Bayonne and repulse of the sortie. He has received the War Medal with four Clasps for Egypt, Corunna, Nivelle, and Nive.

Captain Elliot volunteered with the 58th on that Regt. proceeding to New Zealand, and served throughout the northern and southern campaigns of 1845 and 1846; was present at Okaihau, Ohaeawai, Ruapekapeka, and Horokiwi, and in several skirmishes in the north.

Captain Dunne served the Eastern campaign of 1854 and early part of 1855, including the battles of Alma, Balaklava, and Inkerman, siege of Sebastopol, and attack on the Redan on the 18th June (Medal and four Clasps, and 5th Class of the Medjidie).

Lieut. Johnston served in the Eastern campaign of 1854 in the Commissariat department, and was present at the battle of Alma (Medal and one Clasp).

Surgeon Todd served with the 71st Regt. in the Crimea in 1855, the greater part of the time in medical charge of the Regt.—including the siege of Sebastopol and expedition to Kertch (Medal and Clasp).

Continuation of the War Services of the 97th Regt. of Foot from page 109.

Capt. Swire served at the siege of Sebastopol from Dec. 54, latterly as Aide-de-Camp to Brigdr. Genl. Wyndham, and led the assaulting party at the attack on the Redan on the 8th Sept. and was dangerously wounded was also at the assault of the Redan on 18th June (Medal and Clasp, Sardinian Medal, and 5th Class of the Medjidie).

Lieut. Harmond served at the siege of Sebastopol from 20th Nov. 1854 to 2nd May 1855 (Medal and Clasp). Served in Bengal in suppressing the Mutiny in 1857-58. with the Jounpore field force in the actions of Nusrutpore. Chanda, Ummeerpore, and Sultanpore. afterwards at the siege and capture of Lucknow.

Lieut. Morgan served at the siege and fall of Sebastopol from 31st July 1855 (Medal and Clasp). Served In Bengal in suppressing the Mutiny in 1857-58, with the Jounpore field force in the actions of Nusrutpore, Chanda, Ummeerpore. and Sultanpore, afterwards at the siege and capture of Lucknow

Lieuts. Fitzgerald and Hill served at the siege of Sebastopol from 31st July 1855, and were on the ladder party at the assault on the Redan on the 8th Sept. (Medal and Clasp). Lieut. Fitzgerald served in Bengal in suppressing the Mutiny in 1857-58, with the Jounpore field force in the actions of Nusrutpore, Chanda, Ummeerpore, and Sultanpore, afterwards at the siege and capture of Lucknow.

Lieuts. Safford served in Bengal in suppressing the Mutiny in 1857-58,—with the Jounpore field force in the actions of Chanda, Ummeerpore, and Sultanpore. afterwards at the siege and capture of Lucknow.

Lieut. Smith served at the siege and fall of Sebastopol from 20th Nov. 1854, and sortie of the 20th Dec. (Medal and Clasp). Served in Bengal in suppressing the Mutiny in 1857-58, with the Jounpore field force in the actions of Nusrutpore, Chanda, Ummeerpore, and Sultanpore. afterwards at the siege and capture of Lucknow.

Paymaster Smith, served at the siege of Sebastopol from 20th Nov. 1854, (Medal and Clasp).

Qr. Mr. Woodroffe served at the siege of Sebastopol from 20th Nov. 1854 [Medal and Clasp.]

Assist.-Surgeon Porter served st the siege of Sebastopol from 20th Nov. 1854 (Medal and Clasp, and 5th Class of the Medjidie). Served in Bengal in suppressing the Mutiny in 1857-58,—with the Jounpore field force in the actions of Nusrutpore, Chanda. Ummeerpore, and Sultanpore, afterwards at the siege and capture of Lucknow.

Doctor Sinclair served at the siege of Sebastopol from 20th Nov. 1854 (Medal and Clasp). Served in Bengal in suppressing the Mutiny in 1857-58.—with the Jounpore field force in the actions of Chanda, Ummeerpore, and Sultanpore, afterwards at the siege and capture of Lucknow.

Asst. Surgeon Starkey served in Bengal in suppressing the Mutiny of 1857-58 with the Azimgurh field force under Sir E. Lugard.

H. M. 2nd Battalion Rifle Brigade.

REGIMENTALS, *Green*—FACINGS, *Black*.

Landed in India, from England, in November **1857.**

LUCKNOW,—OUDE.

Regimental Depôt, Winchester.

RANK AND NAMES.	*Regimental Rank.*	*Army Rank.*	REMARKS.
LIEUT. COLONELS.			
Percy Hill, C. B., - -	22 *June* 55	*col* 29 *Dec.* 57	Commanding.
Sir Robert Walpole, K. C. B., - -	31 *July* 57	*col.* 28 *Nov.* 54	Bridgr. General Comdg. Rohilcund and Kumaon Divisions.
MAJORS.			
William Aug. Fyers, C B., - -	16 *June* 57	*l.c.* 26 *Dec.* 56	Leave to England.
Hercules Walker - -	29 *Nov.* 57	6 *June* 56	Leave on M. C. to England.
CAPTAINS.			
Arthur James Nixon, - -	29 *Dec.* 54	*m.* 20 *July* 58	On duty with Camel Corps.
Arthur Fred. Warren, - -	29 *Dec.* 54	*m.* 2 *Nov.* 55	Leave to England.
Henry Wilmot, * - -	1 *May* 55	*m* 20 *July* 58	Depy. Judge Adv. Genl. to Oude Field [Force.
Riversdale Richard Glyn, - -	10 *Aug.* 55		
Hon. Lewis Watson Milles, -	10 *Apl.* 55	.. ..	Regimental Depôt.
Martin Dillon, - -	2 *Nov.* 55	*m.* 20 *July* 58	Brigade Major Trans-Gogra.
Charles William Earle, -V,	23 *Mar.* 55	... ...	Dep. Judge Adv. Genl. to Rohilcund [force.
John Brett, -	24 *Nov.* 57	.. ..	Regimental Depôt, England.
FitzRoy W. Fremantle, -	24 *Nov.* 57		
George Robert Saunders, - -	29 *Nov* 57	.. ..	Regimental Depôt, England.
James Singer, -	30 *Apl.* 58		
A. L. Tottenham, - - - -	7 *Dec.* 58	.. ..	Ditto.
J. B. Coulson, - - - -	25 *Mar.* 59	.. ..	Ditto.
LIEUTENANTS.			
~~Grenville Chas. Lane,~~ - -	11 *May* 55		
Fredk. Carle Playne, - -	11 *May* 55	.. ...	Duty at the Depot, Nynee Tal.
Christopher Rice H. Nicholl, -	11 *May* 55		
Frederick Edward Sotheby, -	11 *May* 55		
William Hall Eccles, - -	19 *June* 55	.. ..	Leave to England.
R ~~David A. Gordon,~~ - -	31 *Aug.* 55	.. ..	Adjutant.
Henry Martin Moorsom, - -	11 *Nov.* 55	.. ..	Instructor of Musketry. Regimental Depôt.
Henry Chas. G. Dugdale, - -	1 *Sep.* 57	.. ..	
Hugh Lawton, - -	27 *Nov.* 57		
William C. Purdon, - -	27 *Nov.* 57	... ..	Winchester Depot, England.
Edward J. Fryer, - -	12 *Feb.* 58	.. ..	
Frederick Ames, - -	26 *Mar.* 58		
Frederick W. Ramsbottom, -	10 *May* 58	.. ..	On duty with Camel Corps.
Alex Angus A. Kinloch, - -	24 *Sep.* 58	.. ..	Regtl. Depot, England.
C. D. Broadhurst, - - - -	19 *Nov.* 58		
Jas. Hook			
W. Arbuthnot			
ENSIGNS.			
William J. K. Myers, - -	25 *Jan.* 56		
Charles W. Robinson, - -	27 *Nov.* 57		
FitzRoy Wilson, - -	21 *Feb.* 58	.. ..	En route to join.
Lucius F. B. Carey, - -	22 *Feb.* 58	.. ..	Ditto.
George S Byng, - -	27 *Feb.* 58	.. ..	Acting Interpreter.
Charler F Blackett, - -	30 *Mar.* 58	... ...	Leave on M. C. to Moosoorie to 31 [Oct. 59
~~Christopher H. Turner,~~ - -	3 *June* 58	.. ..	Regtl. Depot England.
Robert Hamilton L. Austruther,	25 *June* 58		
Hugh William Reid, - -	30 *July* 56	.. ..	Regimental Depôt.
Hon. A. Hood, - - - -	31 *Dec.* 58	.. ..	Ditto.

* Victoria Cross.

H. M. 2ND BATTALION RIFLE BRIGADE.—(*Continued.*)

Rank and Names.	Regimental Rank.	Army Rank.	Remarks.
INSTRUCTOR OF MUSKETRY.			
Lieut. Henry M. Moorsom, -	27 *Aug.* 56	*lt.* 11 *Nov.* 55	Depot, England.
PAY MASTER.			
Lieut. Mich. W. Lade Coast, -	1 *Dec.* 54	*lt.* 21 *July* 54	At Lucknow.
ADJUTANT.			
Lieut. David A. Gordon,, - -	25 *June* 57	*lt.* 31 *Aug.* 55	
QUARTER MASTER.			
George Rogers, - -	.. ..	14 *Sep.* 55	
SURGEON.			
J. C. Dempster, - - -	31 *Dec.* 58	5 *Nov.* 50	Sick at Calcutta.
ASSISTANT SURGEONS.			
John By. Cole Reade, - -	.. ..	24 *Mar.* 54	
Alexander C. Robertson, - -	.. ..	1 *June* 55	Leave on M.C. to Calcutta.
A. F. Bradshaw, - -	27 *May* 57		
INTERPRETER.			
Ensign G. S. Byng, - - - -			

Strength—10 Companies with 58 Sergeants—50 Corporals—20 Buglers—and 928 Privates.

English Agents—Sir John Kirkland.

Calcutta Agents—Messrs. Wood, Olliffe and Co.

WAR SERVICES OF THE OFFICERS OF H. M. 2ND BATTALION RIFLE BRIGADE.

Colonel Hill, Captains, Glyn, Freemantle and Singer, Lieuts. Lane Ames, Fryer, and Sotheby, Adjutant Gordon was present at the siege and capture of Lucknow, campaign in Oude, up to Novr. 1858, and served in the Trans Gogra camapign Decr. 1858.

Colonel Walpole, Captain Earle, Lieut. Eccles, and Asst. Surgeon Bradshaw, were present at the engagements at Cawnpore 26ht Novr. to 6th Decr. 1857, siege and capture of Lucknow and served in the campaign in Rohilcund, fort of Roya and Allegunge.

Lt.-Col. Fyers served in the 40th throughout the operations in Candahar and Affghanistan in 1841 and 1842 (Medal), and was present in the actions at Kale Shukh, Kunje Kuk, Pangwaie, Tiloo Khan, and Baba Wallie; also at the relief of Khelat-i-Ghilzee; subsequently at Killa Aziem, Goaine, Ghuznee, and occupation of Cabool; and in all the affairs in which the Candahar Division of the Army of Affghanistan, under General Nott, was engaged in its progress through the Khoord Cabool, Tezeen, Jugdulluck, and Khyber Passes. Served the Eastern campaign of 1854-55 with the 2nd Batt. Rifle Brigade, including the Battle of Alma, siege and fall of Sebastopol, and attack on the Redan on 8th Sept. In October 1854 he commanded a party of Rifles and 23rd Fusiliers from Pickets of the light Division, and repulsed an attack made by the enemie's riflemen on our pickets, and he commanded the covering party of 200 men on the attack of the Redan (Medal and Clasps, Brevets of Major and Lieut. Col., Knight of the Legion of Honor, and 5th Class of the Medjidie). Was present at the engagements at Cawnpore 26th Nov. to 6th Dec. 1857, siege and capture of Lucknow, and served in the campaign in Oude up to May 1858.

Major Walker served at the siege of Sebastopol from Jan. 1855 (Medal and Clasps, Brevet Major, and 5th Class of the Medjidie); also the Trans Gogra campaign, Dec. 1858.

Ensigns Myers, Robinson and Byng served in the campaign Trans Gogra Decr. 1858.

Major Nixon served in the Eastern campaign of 1854, including the battle of Alma (Medal and Clasps and 5th Class of the Medjidie.) Was present at the engagements at Cawnpore 26th Nov. and 6th Dec. 1857, and at the capture of Calpee.

Major Warren served in the Eastern campaign of 1854-55, including the battle of Alma and siege of Sebastopol (Medal and Clasps, Brevet Major, and 5th Class of the Medjidie).

Major Dillon served with the 98th Regt. in the Punjaub campaign of 1848-49 (Medal), also with the Flank Companies in the force under Sir Colin Campbell at the forcing of the Kohat Pass in Feb. 1850, (severely wounded) Lieuts. Playne, Nickolls, Dugdale, Lawson [wounded] and Ramsbottom were present at the engagements at Cawnpore Nov. 1857, siege and capture of Lucknow, served in the Oude campaign and in the Trans Gogra campaign Dec. 1858.

Capt. Riversdale Glyn served the Eastern campaign of 1854-55 with the 8th Hussars, including the expedition into the Dobrudscha, battles of Alma, Balaklava, and Inkerman, and siege of Sebastopol; promoted to a Company in the 1st Batt. Rifle Brigade in Aug. 1855, and served with the reserve at the storming of the Redan on the 8th September (Medal and Clasps).

Capt. Hon. L. W. Milles served with the 43rd Light Infantry in the Kaffir war in 1851-52 (Medal) was present at the engagements at Cawnpore 27th Novr, 1857, (severely wounded.)

*** *For continuation of serviees see page* 118.

H. M. 3rd Battalion of Rifle Brigade.

Regimentals, *Green*—**Facings**, *Black*.

Landed in Calcutta, from England, on 6*th November* 1857.

Agra.

Regimental Depôt, Winchester.

Rank and Names.	Regimental Rank.	Army Rank.	Remarks.
Lieut. Colonels.			
Alfred H. Horsford, c. b., - -	2 *Feb.* 55	*col.* 28 *Nov.* 54	Brigadier Tarns Gogra Force.
Alexander Macdonell, c. b., -	16 *June* 57	*col.* 20 *July* 58	Leave to England.
Majors.			
Julius Richard Glyn, c. b. - -	5 *June* 57	*l.c.* 6 *June* 56	Commanding.
Charles Vernon Oxenden, - -	1 *Sep.* 57	6 *June* 56	
Captains.			
John Ross, - -	29 *Dec.* 54	*l. c.* 20 *July* 58	Comdg. Camel Corps.
James Rowles, - -	do		Comdg. Regimental Depôt, England.
R ~~Henry Gore Lindsey~~, - -	do		Regimental Depôt, England,
Claud T. Bourchier, V. C. - -	do	*m.* 17 *July* 55	On leave to England.
Horace Fred. Hill, -	23 *Mar.* 55		Leave on M. C. to England.
Henry R. L. Newdigate, - -	do	*m* 20 *July* 58	With Camel Corps.
Adolphus Haggerstone Stephen,	do		
George S. Windham, - -	do		
William Deedes, - -	do		Permitted to sell out.
Boyd F. Alexander, - -	do		
George E. Rose, - -	2 *May* 56		A. D. C. to Sir Hugh Rose, Bombay.
Stewart Smyth Windham, - -	7 *Sep.* 58		Instructor of Musketry.
James Frederick Henley, - -	5 *Oct.* 58		Regimental Depot.
G. C. Lane.			
Lieutenants.			
E. Fortescue.			
~~Palmer Whalley~~, - -	23 *Mar.* 55		
Walter R. Lascelles, - -	6 *July* 55		Leave to England.
Cecil Webb Cragg, - -	2 *Aug.* 55		With Oudh Military Police.
Geoffrey L. Austin, - -	do		With Camel Corps.
Charles E. Buckley, - -	9 *Sep.* 55		Ditto.
Andrew Green, - -	10 *Sep.* 55		Leave to England.
Lewis Percival, - -	23 *Oct.* 55		
FitzRoy Stephen, - -	do		Adjutant.
George M. L. Egerton, - -	23 *Dec.* 55		Regimental Depôt England.
Henry L. Wickham, - -	3 *Mar.* 57		Ditto.
Emanuel Jeames, - -	27 *Nov.* 57		With Camel Corps.
James E. Vaughan, - -	7 *Sep.* 58		
Arthur B. G. S. Hill, - -	7 *Sep.* 58		
Arthur R. Keene, - -	9 *Nov.* 55		
Albert Divett Rickman, - -	24 *Oct.* 55		Joined.
~~James Hook~~, - -	26 *Oct.* 58		
Ensigns.			
Lt Edward H. Chamberlin, - -	8 *Jan.* 56		
Hon'ble C. E. Edwardes, - -	15 *Feb.* 56		
William Arbuthnot, *H*,	25 *Mar.* 56		A.D.C. to Commander-in-Chief of Madras.
James Dunlap, - -	26 *Oct.* 58		Ditto.
Viscount Glenworth, - -	30 *Oct.* 58		Regimental Depôt.
S. S. Hardy, - -	30 *Dec.* 58		Ditto.
Hon. E. Lawless, - -	11 Jan. 59		Ditto,

H. M. 3RD BATTALION OF RIFLE BRIGADE—(Continued.)

RANK AND NAMES.	Regimental Rank.	Army Rank.	REMARS.
INSTRUCTOR OF MUSKETRY.			
Capt. Stewart S. Windham, -	7 *Sep.* 58	*lt.* 9 *Mar.* 55	
PAY MASTER.			
Thomas Gough, - -	14 *Sep.* 55		
ADJUTANT.			
Lieut. FitzRoy Stephen, - -	10 *Feb.* 58	*lt.* 23 *Oct.* 55	
QUARTER MASTER.			
Henry Harvey, - -	24 *Apl.* 55		
SURGEON.			
D. LaPresle, - - -	24 *Apl.* 55		
ASSIST. SURGEONS.			
AlexanderGuthrie, M. D., - -	28 *Apl.* 54		
David Cullen, M. D., - -	1 *Sep.* 54		
John Storey, - -	7 *Dec.* 55		

Strength—9 Companies with 58 Sergeants—50 Corporals—21 Buglers—and 824 Privates.
1 Company with Camel Corps 4 Corporals—2 Buglers—and 98 Privates.

English Agents—Sir John Kirkland and Co.
Calcutta Agents—Messrs. Colvin, Cowie and Co.

WAR SERVICES OF THE OFFICERS OF H. M. 3RD BATTALION OF RIFLE BRIGADE.

Brigadier Horsford served with the Rifle Brigade in the Kaffir war of 1846-47, and commanded the 1st Battalion in that of 1852-53 Medal and Brevet Lt. Colonel]. Also commanded the 1st Battalion in the Eastern campaign of 1854, including the battles of the Alma, Balaklava, and Inkerman, and siege of Sebastopol [Medal and Clasps, *CB.*, Sardinian Medal, and 5th Class of the Medjidie].

Colonel Macdonell served in the Kaffir war of 1846-47 [Medal]. Also the Eastern campaign of 1854 as Aide-de-Camp to Sir George Brown, including the battles in the Crimea, and siege of Sebastopol [Medal and Clasps, Brevets of Major and Lt.-Col., *CB.*, Knight of the Legion of Honor, Sardinian Medal, and 5th Class of the Medjidie.

Lt.-Col. Glyn served as Field Adjutant to the force under Sir Harry Smith in the action with and defeat of the rebel Boers at Boem Plaats [horse killed]. Served in the Kaffir war of 1852-53 [Medal]. Also the Eastern campaign as a Brigade-Major in the Light Division. including the battles of the Alma and Inkerman, and siege of Sebastopol [Medal and Clasps, Brevets of Major and Lieut.-Col., Knight of the Legion of Honor, and 5th Class of the Medjidie].

Major Oxenden served on the Eastern Frontier of the Cape of Good Hope against the Kaffir Tribes in 1846-7-8 [Medal], and was engaged in the successful operations in the Amatola Mountains against Sandilli. Served at the siege and fall of Sebastopol from June 1855 [Medal and Clasp, and Brevet Major].

Lt. Col. Ross served in the Eastern campaign. including the battles of Alma and Inkerman, and siege of Sebastopol until Feb. 1855 [Medal and Clasps, Brevet Major, and 5th Class of the Medjidie].

Captain Rowles served in the Eastern campaign, including the battles of Alma and Inkerman, and siege of Sebastopol until Feb. 1855 (Medal and three Clasps).

Captain Lindsay served in the Kaffir war of 1852-53 [Medal]; and was also present at the battle of Berea. Served the Eastern campaign of 1854-55 [Medal and Clasps], including the battle of Alma and siege of Sebastopol.

Major H. R. L.Newdigate served in the Eastern Campaign of 1854, including the battle of Alma [Medal and Clasps].

Major Bourchier served in the Kaffir war of 1852-53 (Medal). Also in the Eastern campaign of 1854 including jthe battles of Alma, Balaklava, and Inkerman, [as Aide-de-Camp to General Torrens], siege of Sebastopol, night attack and capture of the Ovens, where he succeeded to the command of the detachment of Riflemen on the death of Lieut. Tryon, for which he was mentioned in the Dispatches, and promoted, Brevet Major [Medal and Clasps, Victoria Cross, Knight of the Legion of Honor, and 5th Class of the Medjidie].

Captain Stephen served at the siege of Sebastopol from Jan. to April 1855 [Medal and Clasps].

Captain Windham served in the Eastern campaign, including the battles of Alma and Balaklava, and siege of Sebastopol until April 1855 [Medal and three Clasps].

Capt. Deedes served the Eastern campaign of 1854, including the Battles ef Alma and Inkerman, and siege of Sebastopol [Medal and Clasps].

Lieut. Cragg served in the Eastern campaign of 1855, including the siege and fall of Sebastopol [Medal and Clasp].

Quarter-Master Harvey served in the Eastern Campaign. including the battles of Alma and Inkerman, and siege of Sebastopol until June 1855 [Medal and three Clasps, also the Medal for distinguished conduct in the Field].

Doctor Cullen was attached to the 68th and 48th Regts. for nine months during the siege of Sebastopol; and was with the 4th Light Dragoons on the cavalry expedition to Eupatoria [Medal and Clasp].

WAR SERVICES OF THE OFFICERS OF H. M. 2ND BATTN. RIFLE BRIGADE.—*Continued.*

Captain Earle served on the staff of Sir George Cathcart in the Kaffir war of 1851-53 (Medal).

Captain Fremantle served in the Eastern campaign from Nov. 1854 to June 1855, and was severely wounded in the attack of the Redan on the 18th June (Medal and Clasp, and Sardinian Medal).

Captain Singer served the Eastern campaign of 1854-55, including the Battles of Alma and Inkerman, and siege of Sebastopol [Medal and Clasps, and 5th Class of the Medjidie].

Captain Saunders served at the siege of Sebastopol from Jan. 1855, and was with the covering party leading the attack on the Redan on the 18th June (Medal and Clasp, Sardinian Medal. and 5th Class of the Medjidie).

Lieut. Lane served in the Eastern campaign of 1855. including the siege and fall of Sebastopol [Medal and Clasp].

Lieut. Playne served at the siege of Sebastopol in 1855, and was wounded at the attack on the Redan on the 8th Sep. [Medal and Clasp].

Lieut. Sotheby served at the siege and fall of Sebastopol in 1855, and storming of the Redan of 8th Sep. [Medal and Clasp].

Lieut. Eccles served at the siege of Sebastopol in 1855, and was wounded at the attack on the Redan on the 8th Sep. [Medal and Clasp].

Lieut. Moorsom was present at the siege and capture of Lucknow March 1858.

Assist.-Surgeon Reade served the Eastern campaign of 1854-55, including the battles of Alma and Inkerman siege of Sebastopol, and sortie of 26th Oct. [Medal and Clasp.] Was present at the engagements at Cawnpore 26th Novr. to 6th Decr. 1857, siege and capture of Lucknow, served in the Oude campaign up to Sepr. 1858.

Asst. Surgeon Robertson was present at the engagements at Cawnpore 26th Novr. to 6th Decr. 1857 served in the Oude campaign up to Sept 1858.

Royal Medical Officers in Bengal.

NAMES.	*Date of last Commission.*	REMARKS.

INSPECTOR GENERAL OF H. M.'s HOSPITALS.

NAMES.	*Date of last Commission.*	REMARKS.
William Linton, M. D., C. B., ...	1 *Oct.* 57	In charge of the Medical Department of H. M. Forces in India.

DEPUTY INSPECTORS GENERAL OF H. M.'s HOSPITALS.

NAMES.	*Date of last Commission.*	REMARKS.
Thos. David Hume, M. D., ...	29 *June* 55	P. M. O. Kurrachie.
Samuel M. Hadaway, ..	25 *Jan.* 56	P. M. O. Umballa.
Arthur Anderson, M. D, ..	31 *Dec.* 58	Superintending Surgeon and President of Invaliding Committee, Calcutta.
J. C. Tice, M. D. C. B., ..	31 *Dec.* 58	Superintending Surgeon, Bareilly.
R. Gammie, ..	31 *Dec.* 58	Meerut.
Archd. Stewart, ...	31 *Dec.* 58	Central India Field Force.
F. W. Innes, M. D., C. B., ..	31 *Dec.* 58	Cawnpore.
John Fraser, M. D., C. B., ..	31 *Dec.* 58	Lahore.
J. H. K. Innes, C. B., ..	31 *Dec.* 58	Lucknow.
Thos. Longmore, ..	31 *Dec.* 58	Member of Invaliding Committee and Sanitary Officer, Calcutta.

STAFF SURGEONS.

NAMES.	*Date of last Commission.*	REMARKS.
G. Z. Bone M. D., ...	21 *Oct.* 53	Depot Hospital, Dum-Dum.
W. M. Dowding, ..	19 *May* 54	Secretary to Inspector General of H. M. Hospitals, Calcutta.
Alexander Smith, M. D., ..	12 *Jan.* 55	Azimghur (6th Rl. Regt.)
W. Poole, ..	9 *Feb.* 55	With 19th Regiment Dinapore.
T. Rhys, ...	20 *July* 55	Depot Hospital, Benares.
John Alex. Wm. Thompson, M. D.,	26 *Feb.* 56	With 2nd Battn. Rifle Brigade, Baraitch.
Thomas Ligertwood, M. D., ...	20 *Oct.* 56	In charge of Officers' Hospital and General Staff, Calcutta.
A. P. Cahill, M. D., ...	28 *Aug.* 57	(80th Regt.) Cawnpore.
John James Clifford, M. D., ...	28 *Aug.* 57	Landour.
James Wm. Fleming, ...	2 *Oct.* 57	Surgeon, 37th Rgt. Ghazepore.
G. K. Hardie, M. D., ...	2 *Oct.* 57	In charge of Lower Orphan School Hospital, Calcutta.
Henry M. Fraser, M. D., ...	2 *Oct.* 57	With the 20th Regt. Gonda.
J. Lamprey, M. D., ...	3 *Nov.* 57	In charge of Hindoo College Hospital, Calcutta.
John Gibbons, ...	3 *Nov.* 57	Depot, Chinsurah.
A. H. Fraser, ...	26 *Jan.* 58	Jullundur.
T. R. Ried, ..	5 *Oct.* 58	
L. C. Stewart, ..	1 *June* 52	With 70th Regt. Rawul Pindee.
P. McDermott, ...	31 *Dec.* 58	Depot Hospital, Cawnpore.
J. L. Jameson, ...	31 *Dec.* 58	
D. S. Smith, ...	28 *Jan.* 59	With 5th Fusiliers, Allahabad.
T. E. Moffat		

Royal Medical Officers in Bengal.—(*Continued.*)

Names.	Date of last Commission.	Remarks.
	ASSISTANT SURGEONS.	
J. R. Tobin, 36th Foot, ...	21 *Oct.* 53	Shajehanpore.
W. H. Pollard, 22nd do. ...	7 *Apl.* 54	In charge of Camel Corps.
F. S. B. DeChaumont, Rifle Brigade, ...	28 *Apl.* 54	Attached to Royal Artillery.
W. T. Rendall, 55th Foot, ...	26 *May* 54	In charge of 23rd Company Royal Engineers.
C. Beaufoy, ..	23 *Dec.* 54	Futtygurh.
R. Woods, ..	7 *Apl.* 54	Delhi.
R. B. Scott, ..	28 *July* 54	Muttra.
Wm. Alexander, ..	28 *Sep.* 55	Doomrie.
T. Callaway, ..	17 *Nov.* 55	Baraitch.
E. B. Kearney, ..	10 *Apl.* 58	Kurrachee.
E. Masterson, ..	22 *Jan.* 58	Kurrachee.
E. Hopkins, ..	*Ditto,*	Cawnpore.
A. Croker, ..	7 *May* 58	Allahabad.
Wm. A. Hope, M. B., ..	*Ditto,*	Cawnpore.
G. S Cameron, ..	*Ditto,*	Chowparun.
T. Gardiner, ..	*Ditto,*	Dehree.
J. Wiles, ..	4 *June* 58	Shergotty.
A. W. Pinkerton, ..	22 *June* 58	Nynee Tal.
J. Mahon, ..	*Ditto,*	Dinapore.
T. M. OBrien, ..	*Ditto,*	Calcutta.
W. P. Mackesey, ..	1 *July* 58	Allahabad.
S. Archer, ..	5 *Aug.* 58	Fitcoorie.
F. A. Turton, ..	13 *Oct.* 58	Sasseram.
J. S. Killery, ..	22 *Sep.* 58	Calcutta.
G. F. Adams, ..	13 *Oct.* 58	Calcutta.
G. S. Davie, ..	1 *Nov.* 58	Banda.
F. E. McFarland, ..	*Ditto.*	Lucknow.
T. Ramsay, ..	*Ditto.*	Benares.
W. K. Stewart, M. D., ..	*Ditto.*	Allahabad.
J. Martin, ...	*Ditto.*	Dum-Dum.
J. W. Longheed, ...	*Ditto.*	Bareilly.
G. Smith, ...	*Ditto.*	Allahabad.
T. Hession, ..	*Ditto.*	Seetapore.
E. Wilkes, ..	*Ditto.*	Delhi.
G. Park, ..	14 *Dec.* 58	Cawnpore.
G. E. Gascoyen, ..	1 *Dec.* 58	Lucknow.
J. S. Duncan, ..	14 *Dec.* 58	Cawnpore.
R. Harry, ...	14 *Dec.* 58	With 34th Foot, Fyzabad.
R. M. Gilchrist, ..	14 *Dec.* 58	Cawnpore.
W. Armstrong, ..	12 *Jan.* 59	Umballa.
W. Venour, ...	22 *Aug.* 58	Cawnpore.
H. Walker, ..	12 *Jan.* 59	Bareilly.
C. S. Wikeley, ..	12 *Jan.* 59	Delhi.
D. R. Pearson, M. D., ..	12 *Jan.* 59	Allahabad.
G. A. Moorhead, ..	22 *July* 59	Calcutta.

INDEX

TO

HER MAJESTY'S FORCES ON THE BENGAL ESTABLISHMENT.

A.

B.

S

C.

THE
QUARTERLY ARMY LIST
OF
HER MAJESTY'S INDIAN FORCES
ON THE
BENGAL ESTABLISHMENT.

Corrected to 5th July 1859.

LIST OF CORPS THAT HAVE MUTINIED OR BEEN DISARMED.

Corps.	*Mutinied or Disarmed.*	*Station.*
5th light field battery, ...	Mutinied,	Delhi.
6th ,, ...	Ditto,	Nusseerabad.
13th ,, ...	Ditto,	Fyzabad, Oude.
15th ,, ...	Ditto,	Bareilly.
18th ,, ...	Ditto,	Nowgong.
4th T. 1st B. H. A., ...	Ditto,	Neemuch.
2nd co. 7th battn. arty.,	Ditto,	Nusseerabad.
3rd ,, 7th ,, ...	Ditto,	Delhi.
5th ,, 7th ,, ...	Ditto,	Fyzabad, Oude.
6th ,, 7th ,, ...	Ditto,	Cawnpore.
1st ,, 8th ,, ...	Ditto,	Cawnpore.
2nd ,, 8th ,, ...	Ditto,	Lucknow.
3rd ,, 8th ,, ...	Disbanded,	Almorah.
6th ,, 8th ,, ...	Mutinied,	Bareilly.
4th ,, 9th ,, ...	Ditto,	Nowgong.
2nd ,, 9th ,, ...	Ditto,	Dacca.
6th ,, 9th ,, ...	Ditto,	Azimgurh, Allahabad.
Sappers and Miners, ...	Ditto,	Roorkee.
G. G. Body-guard, ...	Disarmed,	Calcutta.
1st Light Cavalry, ...	Mutinied,	Mhow, Neemuch
2nd ,, ...	Ditto,	Cawnpore.
3rd ,, ...	Ditto,	Meerut.
4th ,, ...	Disarmed,	Umballah.
5th ,, ...	Ditto,	Peshawur.
6th ,, ...	Mutinied,	Jullundur.
7th ,, ...	Ditto,	Lucknow.
8th ,, ...	Disarmed,	Lahore.
9th ,, ...	Mutinied,	Sealkote.
10th ,, ...	Ditto,	Ferozepore.
1st Native Infantry, ...	Ditto,	Cawnpore.
2nd ,, ...	Disarmed,	Barrackpore.
3rd ,, ...	Mutinied,	Phillour, Loodianah.
4th ,, ...	Disarmed,	Kangra, Noorpore.
5th ,, ...	Mutinied,	Umballah.
6th ,, ...	Ditto,	Allahabad, Futtehpore.
7th ,, ...	Ditto,	Dinapore.
8th ,, ...	Ditto,	Dinapore.
9th ,, ...	Ditto,	Allygurh, Boolundshuhur, Etawah, Mynpoorie.
10th ,, ...	Ditto,	Futtehgurh.
11th ,, ...	Ditto,	Meerut.
12th ,, ...	Ditto,	Nowgong, Jhansi.
13th ,, ...	Ditto,	Lucknow.
14th ,, ...	Ditto,	Jhelum.
15th ,, ...	Ditto,	Nusseerabad.
16th ,, ...	Disarmed,	Lahore, Goojerat.
17th ,, ...	Mutinied,	Azimghur.
18th ,, ...	Ditto,	Bareilly.
19th ,, ...	Disbanded,	Barrackpore.
20th ,, ...	Mutinied,	Meerut.
22nd ,, ...	Mutinied,	Fyzabad, Oude.
23rd ,, ...	Ditto,	Mhow.
24th ,, ...	Disarmed,	Peshawur.
25th ,, Wing, ...	Ditto,	Benares.
26th ,, ...	Mutinied,	Lahore.
27th ,, ...	Disarmed,	Peshawur.
28th ,, ...	Mutinied,	Shahjehanpore.
29th ,, ...	Ditto,	Moradabad.
30th ,, ...	Ditto,	Nusseerabad, Ajmere, Jeypore.
32nd ,, Dets. ...	Ditto,	Deogurh, Rampore Haut.
33rd ,, ...	Disarmed,	Hosheyarpore.
34th ,, ...	7 Companies Disbanded,	Barrackpore.
35th ,, ...	Disarmed,	Sealkote, Shahpore, Goojranwallah, Goojerat.
36th ,, ...	Mutinied,	Jullundur.
37th ,, ...	Ditto,	Benares.
38th ,, ...	Ditto,	Delhi.
39th ,, ...	Disarmed,	Dera Ishmael Khan.
40th ,, ...	Mutinied,	Dinapore.
41st ,, ...	Ditto,	Seetapore, Mulaon.
42nd ,, ...	Ditto,	Saugor.
43rd ,, ...	Disarmed,	Barrackpore.
44th ,,	Disarmed & dispersed,	Agra, Muttra.
45th ,, ...	Mutinied,	Ferozepore.
46th ,, ...	Ditto,	Sealkote.
47th ,, ...	Disarmed,	Mirzapore.
48th Native Infantry, ...	Mutinied,	Lucknow.
49th ,, ...	Disarmed,	Lahore.
50th ,, ...	Mutinied,	Nagode.
51st ,, ...	Ditto,	Peshawur.
52nd ,, ...	Ditto,	Jubbulpore.
53rd ,, ...	Ditto,	Cawnpore, Oorie
54th ,, ...	Ditto,	Delhi.
55th ,, ...	Ditto,	Nowshera.
56th ,, ...	Ditto,	Cawnpore, Banda
57th ,, ...	Ditto,	Ferozepore.
58th ,, ...	Disarmed,	Rawul Pindee.
59th ,, ...	Ditto,	Umritsir.
60th ,, ...	Mutinied,	Rohtuck.
61st ,, ...	Ditto,	Jullundur.
62nd ,, ...	Ditto,	Mooltan.
63rd ,, ...	Disarmed,	Berhampore.
64th ,, ...	Ditto,	Peshawur, Forts Mackeson, Barrah.
65th ,, ...	Ditto,	Ghazeepore.
67th ,,	Disarmed & dispersed,	Agra, Muttra.
68th ,, ...	Mutinied,	Bareilly.
69th ,, ...	Disarmed,	Mooltan.
70th ,, ...	Ditto,	Barrackpore.
71st ,, ...	Mutinied,	Lucknow.
72nd ,, ...	Ditto,	Neemuch.
73rd ,, 2 Cos. ...	Ditto,	Dacca.
74th ,, ...	Ditto,	Delhi.
Regiment of Loodianah,	Mutinied, in part,..	Juanpore.
Calcutta Militia, ...	Disarmed,	Allypore.
Ramgurh Battalion, ...	Mutinied,	Chota Nagpore.
Hurrianah Light Infy., ...	Ditto,	Hansi, Sirsa, Hissar.
3rd Irregular Cavalry, ...	Ditto,	Saugor.
4th ,, ...	Ditto,	Hansi, Hissar, Sirsa.
5th ,, ...	Ditto,	Bhaugulpore.
8th ,, ...	Mutinied,	Bareilly.
9th ,, ...	Ditto,	Procdg. to Bunnoo.
10th ,, ...	Disbanded,	Nowshera.
11th ,, ...	Disarmed,	Berhampore.
12th ,, ...	Mutinied,	Segowlee.
13th ,, ...	Ditto,	Benares.
14th ,, ...	Ditto,	Jhansi, Nowgong
15th ,, ...	Ditto,	Sultanpore, Seetapore, Fyzabad.
Oude Irregular Force:		
No. 1 Battery, ...	Ditto,	Secrora.
2 ,, ...	Ditto,	Lucknow.
3 ,, ...	Ditto,	Ditto.
4 ,, ...	Ditto,	Ditto.
1st Cavalry, ...	Ditto,	Secrora.
2nd ,, ...	Ditto,	Lucknow.
3rd ,, ...	Ditto,	Pertaubgurh, Secrora.
1st Infantry, ...	Ditto,	Persadeepore.
2nd ,, ...	Ditto,	Secrora, Baraitch.
3rd ,, ...	Ditto,	Gonda.
4th ,, ...	Ditto,	Lucknow.
5th ,, ...	Ditto,	Durriabad.
6th ,, ...	Ditto,	Fyzabad.
7th ,, ...	Ditto,	Lucknow.
8th ,, ...	Ditto,	Sultanpore.
9th ,, ...	Ditto,	Seetapore.
10th ,, ...	Ditto,	Mullaon.
Gwalior Contingent:		
1st Company Artillery, ...	Ditto,	Seepree.
2nd ,, ...	Ditto,	Gwalior.
3rd ,, ...	Ditto,	Augur.
4th ,, ...	Ditto,	Gwalior.
1st Cavalry Regiment, ...	Ditto,	Gwalior, Goonah.
2nd ,, ...	Ditto,	Augur.
1st Infantry Regiment, ...	Ditto,	Gwalior.
2nd ,, ...	Ditto,	Ditto.
3rd ,, ...	Ditto,	Seepree.
4th ,, ...	Ditto,	Gwalior.
5th ,, ...	Ditto,	Augur.
6th ,, ...	Ditto,	Jubbulpore.
7th ,, ...	Ditto,	Neemuch.
Malwah Contingent, ...	Ditto,	Mehidpore.
Kotah ,, ...	Ditto,	Agra.
Bhopal ,, ...	Ditto,	Sehore.
Joudpore Legion, ...	Ditto,	Erinpoorah.

EXPLANATIONS.

K. T. Knight of the Order of the Thistle.
G. C. B. Grand Cross of the Order of the Bath.
K. C. B. Knight Commander of the Order of the Bath.
C. B. Companion of the Order of the Bath.
G. C. H. Grand Cross of the Royal Hanoverian Guelphic Order.
K. C. H. Knight Commander of ditto ditto.
K. H. Knight of the Royal Hanoverian Guelphic Order.
G. G. Governor General.
C. C. Commander-in-Chief.
L. G. B. Lieutenant Governor, Bengal.
L. G. N. W. P. Lieutenant Governor, North Western Provinces.
L. G. Lieutenant General.
M. G. Major General.
M. S. Military Secretary.
P. S. Private Secretary.
A. D. C. Aide-de-Camp.
H. A. D. C. Hony. Aide-de-Camp.
F. R. C. S. Fellow of Royal College of Surgeons.
P. A. Private Affairs.
S. C. Sick Certificate.
D. P. W. Department of Public Works.
N. W. P. North Western Provinces.
S. W. P. South Western Provinces.
C. P. Central Provinces.
L. P. Lower Provinces.
I. C. Irregular Cavalry.
L. C. Light Cavalry.
L. I. Light Infantry.
N. I. Native Infantry.
B. F. Bengal Fusiliers.
M. N. I. Madras Native Infantry.
H. M. Her Majesty's.
H. C. Honorable Company's.
P. Passed district examination in the Persian and Hindoostanee languages.
P. C. Passed College examination in the Persian and Hindoostanee languages.
P. C. H. Ditto in the Hindoostanee ditto.
P. H. Passed District examination in the Hindoostanee language.
V. C. Victoria Cross.
† After their names, have attained colloquial knowledge of the Hindoostanee language

* The words subscribed to the titles of Regiments, as "BHURTPORE," "DELHI," &c., denote the Honorary Distinctions permitted to be borne by such Regiments on their Colors and Appointments in commemoration of their Services.

MEMO.

The following occurred while printing, *viz*:—

PROMOTIONS.

Fort William, 1st July 1859.

His Excellency the Governor General in Council is pleased to direct the following promotions in the Subordinate Medical Department, to fill existing vacancies, and to complete the Establishment required for the additions made to the European Branch of Her Majesty's Indian Forces:—

Hospital Steward William Moore Martin to be Apothecary Hospital Steward Robert William Beale to be Apothecary Hospital Steward Joseph Vyall to be Apothecary Hospital Steward William Buckley to be Apothecary	From the 11th May 1858, for the Augmentation.
Assistant Apothecary Thomas Green to be Hospital Steward Assistant Apothecary Christopher Doyle, (deceased,) to be Hospital Steward Assistant Apothecary Thomas Briscoe to be Hospital Steward Assistant Apothecary Henry David Cooper to be Hospital Steward	From the 11th May 1858, *vice* Martin, Beale, Vyall and Buckley, promoted.
Assistant Apothecary Frederick Volkers to be Hospital Steward Assistant Apothecary Edward Vyall to be Hospital Steward Assistant Apothecary William Charles Giddons to be Hospital Steward Assistant Apothecary Thomas Cullen to be Hospital Steward	From the 11th May 1858, for the Augmentation.
Hospital Apprentice Joseph Henry Lockwood to be Assistant Apothecary Hospital Apprentice James Stephens to be Assistant Apothecary Hospital Apprentice John Alexander Kidd to be Assistant Apothecary Hospital Apprentice John Donald Berkeley to be Assistant Apothecary Hospital Apprentice Henry Francis McDonald to be Assistant Apothecary Hospital Apprentice Daniel John Tresham to be Assistant Apothecary Hospital Apprentice James Cullen to be Assistant Apothecary Hospital Apprentice Robert George Philpott to be Assistant Apothecary	From the 11th May 1858, *vice* Green, Doyle, Briscoe, Cooper, Volkers, Vyall, Giddons and Cullen, promoted.
Hospital Apprentice Robert Barker to be Assistant Apothecary Hospital Apprentice Richard Pereira to be Assistant Apothecary Hospital Apprentice Jeremiah Francis Mills to be Assistant Apothecary Hospital Apprentice John P. Lamb to be Assistant Apothecary	From the 11th May 1858, for the Augmentation.
Hospital Steward William Cox to be Apothecary Assistant Apothecary Thomas Davis to be Hospital Steward Hospital Apprentice Charles Briscoe to be Assistant Apothecary	From the 25th May 1858, *vice* Apothecary J. Ogden, transferred to the Pension Establishment.
Assistant Apothecary James Fenn to be Hospital Steward Hospital Apprentice James Matthew Courtney to be Assistant Apothecary	From the 8th June, 1858, *vice* Steward D. G. Kelly, dismissed.

PROMOTIONS.—*Continued.*

Promotion	Date and reason
Hospital Steward Francis J. Grose to be Apothecary Assistant Apothecary Lewis Augustus Sakes to be Hospital Steward Hospital Apprentice David Cunningham to be Assistant Apothecary	From the 30th June 1858, *vice* Apothecary J. Green, deceased.
Assistant Apothecary John Edwin Tanks to be Hospital Steward Hospital Apprentice Benjamin Prince to be Assistant Apothecary.	From the 12th July 1858, *vice* Steward Boezalt, deceased.
Assistant Apothecary Frederick H. A. Leach to be Hospital Steward. Hospital Apprentice Simon DeCruize to be Assistant Apothecary	From the 3rd August 1858, *vice* Steward J. Collins, deceased

Hospital Apprentice Samuel Bond to be Assistant Apothecary, from the 11th August 1858, *vice* Assistant Apothecary S. Hayes, dismissed.

Hospital Apprentice Jacob Aaron Ward to be Assistant Apothecary, from the 17th August 1858, *vice* Assistant Apothecary Osburne, deceased.

Promotion	Date and reason
Assistant Apothecary William Price to be Hospital Steward Hospital Apprentice Alexander Lyons to be Assistant Apothecary	From the 23rd August 1858, *vice* Steward C. Doyle, deceased.
Hospital Steward John Tresham to be Apothecary Hospital Steward Robert D. Logg to be Apothecary Hospital Steward James Edward Harrison to be Apothecary	From the 3rd September 1858, for the Augmentation.
Assistant Apothecary Charles Levlin Fox to be Hospital Steward Assistant Apothecary John Hemming to be Hospital Steward Assistant Apothecary James Greene to be Hospital Steward	From the 3rd September 1858, *vice* Tresham, Logg and Harrison, promoted.
Assistant Apothecary Richard Edward Wrafter to be Hospital Steward Assistant Apothecary James Hughes to be Hospital Steward Assistant Apothecary Michael John Carney to be Hospital Steward	From the 3rd September 1858 for the Augmentation.
Hospital Apprentice Thomas Price to be Assistant Apothecary Hospital Apprentice Stephen Brooke to be Assistant Apothecary Hospital Apprentice John Harrison to be Assistant Apothecary	From the 3rd September 1858, *vice* Fox, Hemming and Greene, promoted.
Hospital Apprentice Thomas Alexander Earle to be Assistant Apothecary Hospital Apprentice Timothy Keefe to be Assistant Apothecary Hospital Apprentice John Maher to be Assistant Apothecary	From the 3rd September 1858, *vice* Wrafter, Hughes and Carney, promoted.
Hospital Apprentice Frederick E. G. Mathews to be Assistant Apothecary Hospital Apprentice Francis Sanders to be Assistant Apothecary Hospital Apprentice Peter John Doyle to be Assistant Apothecary	From the 3rd September 1858, for the Augmentation.

Hospital Apprentice John Robert Newlan to be Assistant Apothecary, from the 23rd September 1858, *vice* Assistant Apothecary H. H. Niven, dismissed.

Promotion	Date and reason
Hospital Steward James Joseph O'Brien to be Apothecary Assistant Apothecary William Sinclair to be Hospital Steward Hospital Apprentice George Davies to be Assistant Apothecary	From the 25th September 1858, *vice* Apothecary T. Hefferan, deceased.
Hospital Steward Robert Davis to be Apothecary Assistant Apothecary Richard William Harrison to be Hospital Steward Hospital Apprentice Hugh Russell to be Assistant Apothecary	From the 26th September 1858, *vice* Apothecary G. H. Lyons, deceased.
Hospital Steward Thomas Sharpe to be Apothecary	From the 23rd October 1858, for the Augmentation.
Assistant Apothecary Robert Freeland to be Hospital Steward	From the 23rd October 1858, for the Augmentation.
Assistant Apothecary Richard James Quinnell to be Hospital Steward	From the 23rd October 1858, for the Augmentation.

PROMOTIONS.—*Continued.*

Hospital Apprentice George Herbert Jackson to be Assistant Apothecary
Hospital Apprentice Robert Kennelly to be Assistant Apothecary
} From the 23rd October 1858, *vice* Freeland and Quinnell, promoted.

Hospital Apprentice William Joseph Higgins to be Assistant Apothecary } From the 23rd October 1858, for the Augmentation.

Hospital Apprentice Michael Morley to be Assistant Apothecary, from the 16th November 1858 vice Assistant Apothecary McEvoy, deceased.

Hospital Steward John Richmond to be Apothecary
Assistant Apothecary James Connor to be Hospital Steward
Hospital Apprentice George Blackburn to be Assistant Apothecary.
} From the 18th November 1858, *vice* Apothecary C. Simons, transferred to the Pension Establishment.

Hospital Apprentice Robert Henry Hamer to be Assistaut Apothecary, from the 28th November 1858, *vice* Assistant Apothecary S Jones, dismissed.

Hospital Apprentice Thomas Lynch to be Assistant Apothecary, from the 29th November 1858, *vice* Assistant Apothecary W. Gaffney, dismissed.

Hospital Apprentice William Reid Gray to be Assistant Apothecary, from the 6th December 1858, *vice* Farrell, deceased.

Hospital Apprentice Thomas Michael Sullivan, to be Assistant Apothecary, from the 15th December 1858, *vice* S. Grose, dismissed.

Hospital Apprentice Daniel Edwin Young to be Assistant Apothecary, from the 18th December 1858, *vice* Lamb, dismissed.

Hospital Steward James Johnstone to be Apothecary
Assistant Apothecary William Arnold Kidd to be Hospital Steward.
Hospital Apprentice William Francis Browne to be Assistant Apothecary.
} From the 24th February 1859, *vice* Apothecary M. R. Crawford, transferred to the Pension Establisment.

Hospital Steward Thomas Briscoe to be Apothecary
Assistant Apothecary John Rehill to be Hospital Steward
Hospital Apprentice Robert Crossley
} From the 24th February 1859, *vice* Apothecary J. Hefferan, transferred to the Pension Establishment.

Hospital Steward Henry David Cooper to be Apothecary } From the 4th March 1859, for the Augmentation.

Assistant Apothecary Edwin Pearsall to be Hospital Steward } From the 4th March 1859, *vice* Cooper, promoted.

Assistant Apothecary James Ellis to be Hospital Steward } From the 4th March 1859, for the Augmentation.

Hospital Apprentice James Grey Numantly to be Assistant Apothecary
Hospital Apprentice Henry Pearson Smith to be Assistant Apothecary
} From the 4th March 1859, *vice* Pearsall and Ellis, promoted.

Hospital Apprentice James Hogan to be Assistant Apothecary } From the 4th March 1859, for the Augmentation.

Assistant Apothecary Samuel Wale to be Hospital Steward
Hospital Apprentice John Robert Charles Hall to be Assistant Apothecary
} From the 15th March 1859, *vice* Steward Hennessey, transferred to Pension.

Hospital Steward Frederick Volkers to be Apothecary
Assistant Apothecary Richard McCurley to be Hospital Steward
} From he 20th May 1859, *vice* Apothecary E. Reilly, resigned.

Hospital Steward William Charles Giddons to be Apothecary
Assistant Apothecary John Hart to be Hospital Steward
} From the 26th May 1859, *vice* Apothecary J. Hurst, Pensioned.

The promotions of some of the Warrant Officers above named, announced in Government Genera Order, No. 169 of 1859, are cancelled.

PROMOTIONS.

Corps.	*Rank and Names.*	*To what rank promoted.*	*From what date*		*In whose room.*
42nd L. I., ..	Lt. W. N. Lees, L. L. D. ..	Capt., ..	11 Sep.	58	Capt. C. W. Ford, retired.
	Ensign R. H. Eades, ..	Lieut., ..	1 Mar.	59	
16th N. I., (Grs.) ..	Lt. T. Lamb. ..	Capt., ..	25 Nov.	58	Capt. and Bt. Maj. T. J. Gardiner, promoted.
	Ensign, C. T. Lane, ..	Lieut., ..	29 Mar.	59	
38th N. I., ..	Lt. R. B. Dundas, ..	Capt., ..	23 Oct.	58	Captain A. B. Hawes, retired.
	Ensign, G. B. Stevens, .	Lieut., ..	29 Mar.	59	
5th Eu. Regt. ..	Capt. and Bt. Major J. Gordon, ..	Major, ..	1 Apl.	59	Major G. O.'B. Ottley, retired.
	Lt. and Bt. Capt. H. J. Templer, ..	Capt., ..			
	Ensign, J. S. Bagshaw, ..	Lieut., ..			
66th N. I., ..	Capt. W. S. Sherwill, ..	Major, ..	2 Apl.	59	Maj. J. Macdonald, retired.
	Lieut. J. A. Tytler, ..	Capt., ..			
	Ensign P. Story, ..	Lieut, ..			

Alteration of Rank.

Corps.	Rank and Names.	To Rank from	In whose room.
16th N. I. (Grs.)	Capt. J. J. O'Bryen,* ..	24th July 58	Capt. R. T. Stannus, retired.
	Lieut. R. P. Davis, ..	24th July 58	
39th N. I.	Lieut. W. F. Bartleman, ..	18th May 58	Lieut. F. Wetherell, (deceased) struck off.

* This Cancels his Rank as Captain by Brevet, announced in G. G. O. No. 1669.

Corps.	Rank and Names.	To what Rank promoted.	From what date.	In whose room.
4th En. L. C.	Lieut. J. Boyd Saunders,	Capt. by Bt. under the operation of G.G.O. No.217of1840.	8th April 1859.	Capt. and Bt. Major F. J. Harriott, deceased.
68th N. I.,..	Capt. P. A. Roberton, ..	Major, ..	4th June 1859.	*
Infantry, ..	Unattached, Lieut. Col. (Major Genl.) T. Polwhele, ..	Colonel, ..	26th May 1859,	Lieut. Genl. W.H.Kemm, deceased.
Regt. of Arty.	1st Lieut. Clement John Mead. ..	2nd Captain, ..	27th Aug. 1858.	For the Augmentation.
	2nd Lieut. Edward Draper Elliot, ..	1st Lieut. ..	18th Aug. 1858.	1st Lieut. E.W.E. Walker, promoted.
39th N. I. ..	Ensign W. G. Maitland,	Lieut. ..	4th June 1859.	Lieut. and Bt. Capt. G. H. Gordon, promoted.

N. B.—The promotion of Ensign F Wetherell, published in Government G. O. No. 1268, of 3rd Sept. 1858, is cancelled.

Alteration of Rank.

Corps.	Rank and Names.	To Rank from	In whose room.
Regiment of Arty.	1st Lieut. A. H. Davidson, ..	15th Feb. 1858	1st Lieut. C A. Gaskoin, deceased.
	,, E. Fraser, ..	27th Mar. 1858	1st Lieut. H. M. Boddam, promoted.
	,, F. E. Lewes, ..	14th April 1858	1st Lieut. J. Oldfield, retired.
	,, H. Smithett, ..	21st ,,	1st Lieut. F. E. Gammell, retired.
	,, A. Douie, ..	27th ,,	For the Augmentation.
	,, R. T. Hare, ..	,,	,,
	,, C. E Nairne, ..	,,	,,
	,, H. Munro, ..	,,	,,
	,, W. Gully, ..	,,	,,
	,, Sir R. de La T. St. George, Bart, ..	,,	,,
	H. Chichester, ..	,,	,,
	,, D. S. Pemberton, ..	,,	,,
	W. R. Craster, ..	,,	,,
	E T. Hume, ..	,,	,,
	,, T. Ryan, ..	,,	,,
	,, W. O'Brien, ..	,,	,,
	,, A. Walker, ..	,,	,,
	,, H. Girardot, ..	,,	,,
	W. J. Stewart, ..	,,	,,
	,, A. Dixon, ..	,,	,,
	,, F. Coddington, ..	,,	,,
	,, E. H. Dyke ..	,,	,,
	,, J. R. Macleay, ..	,,	,,
	,, R. S. Robinson, ..	,,	,,
	,, A Swinton, ..	,,	,,
	,, H. de G. Warter, ..	,,	,,
	,, E. H. Ryan, ..	,,	,,
	,, C. A. Baylay, ..	,,	,,
	,, P. B. Raikes, ..	21st May 1858	1st Lieut. H. V. Timbrell, promoted.
	,, C. E. Armstrong, ..	4th July 1858	1st Lieut. J. C. Griffith, promoted.
	,, K. W. S. M. Cameron,	27th ,,	1st Lieut. J. McK. Fraser, deceased.

PROMOTIONS.—*Continued.*

MEMO.—The promotion of 1st Lieutenant Clarke Avery Gaskoin to the rank of 2nd Captain, published in Government General Order, No. 1262 of 1858, is cancelled.

24th Regiment of Native Infantry.

Ensign G. B. P. Alcock, to be Lieut. from the 13th June 1859, *vice* Lieut. A. Shaw, deceased.

Sergeant B. Brady, attached to the Department of the Adjutant General of the Army, is promoted to the rank of Conductor, G. O. 12th July 1859.

To be Conductors, of Ordnance.

Sub-Conductor J. Goulder from the 22nd Oct. 58, *vice* Shea pensioned.

Ditto. T. Heathcote, from the 14th Feb. 59. *vice* White.

Acting Conductor J. Warburton, promoted in G. G. O. No. 1352, of the 28th September 1858, is remanded until further orders to the grade of Sub-Conductor.

58th, N. I	Capt. R. Duffin, Major, ..	8th July 59'	Major A. Meyer, deceased.
	Lieut. J. M. Mackenzie, Captain,..	8th July 59'	
	Ensign F. M. Newbery, Lieut. ..	15th,July 59*	

* The date in which he was posted to the Regiment.

APPOINTMENTS.

Lieut. E. K. O. Gilbert of the 27th N. I. and Offg. Major of Brigade, Dinapore, is appointed a Brigade Major on the Establishment, G. C. 1st July 1859.

Her Majesty has been pleased to appoint the undermentioned Gentlemen to be Cadets for the Infantry and Cavalry in Her Majesty's Indian Military forces at the Presidency of Bengal. They are accordingly admitted into the service and promoted to the rank of Ensign, leaving the dates of their commissions for future adjustment.

	Date of arrival at Fort William.
INFANTRY.	
Mr. H. F. Bunbury, ..	24th June 1859.
,, J. Hay, ..	15th July 1859.
CAVALRY.	
Mr. H. Coghlan, ..	15th July 1859.

The services of Captain W. F. Stephens, of the 5th European Light Cavalry, Director of Public Instruction in Mysore are placed at the disposal of the Right Hon'ble the C. C.—G. O. 5th July 1859.

Captain J. D. Campbell 1st class Executive Engineer is appointed to officiate as Superintending Engineer, 2nd circle North Western Provinces, during the absence on leave of Lieut. Col. N. C. McLeod, G. O. 9th July 1859.

His Excellency the Governor General in Council is pleased to appoint Lieut. T. N. Baker second in command of the 2nd Sikh Police Corps, to be a District Commandant in the Oude Military Police, G. O. 13th July 1859.

The transfer of Captain Charles Mc C. Cotton, from the 10th to the 2nd Regt. L. C. made in Government G. O. No. 713, dated the 7th of May 1858, with effect from the 30th April of that year, is to be considered as having effect from the 16th of July 1857; and his Regimental Rank in the 2nd European Cavalry, to which he now belongs, will accordingly date from the 16th of July 1857.

The 7th July 1859.

The following arrangements in the Public Works Department, sanctioned by the Lieut. Governor of the Punjaub, are confirmed in supersession of those notified in No. 162, dated the 10th Ultimo

Captain F. Davies to continue in charge of the Hazara Division, in lieu of being transferred to the Goozerat Division of the Lahore and Peshawur Road.

Mr. T. Wilson Assistant Engineer, 1st class, to take charge of the Goozerat Division of the Lahore and Peshawur Road.

Captain F. W. Marten, probationary Assistant Engineer, Department Public Works, Punjaub is posted to the Lahore and Peshawur Road.

Lieutenant. O. B. C. St. John, of Engineers, is appointed a probationary Assistant Engineer in the Public Works Department, and posted to Oude, G. O. 8th July 1859.

The undermentioned unposted Cornets are posted to the Corps specified.

Cornet A. W. Roberts, 1st En. L. C.
,, C. E. Benthall, 4th En. L. C.
,, F. E. Farquharson, 5th En. L. C.
,, H. C. Creak, 4th En. L. C.

This cancels G. G. O. No. 948 of the 28th June 1859.

G. O. 12th July 1859.

The following promotions are made to fill existing vacancies.

Cornet Arthur William Roberts of the 1st European Light Cavalry to be Lieutenant.

Cornet C. E. Benthall of the 4th En. L. C., to be Lieutenant.

PAY DEPARTMENT.

Captain A. H. Bogle of the Regiment of Artillery to officiate as Deputy Pay Master at Benares, on the responsibility of Major Edgell during that Officers absence on sick leave or until further orders.

G. O 13th July 59.

The under-mentioned unposted Ensigns are posted to the corps specified.

Ensign, J. M. Sym, 58th N. I.
,, C. H. Bridges, 15th N. I.,
,, H. G. Oldham, 9th N. I.,
,, S. C. Mac Tier, 24th N. I.,
,, I. M. Urquhart, 18th N. I.

Ensign, Thos. J. Quin, 16th N. I.
,, F. J. Wheeler, 14th N. I.
,, H. W. J. Senior, 39th N. I.
,, J. L. Ferris, 22nd N. I.,
,, A. B. Chalmers, 21st N. I.

APPOINTMNETS,—*Continued.*

Ensign, A. W. Graham, 25th N. I.
,, E. M Bethune, 70th N. I.,
,, H. W. Williams. 44th N. I.
,, A. Harrison, 59th N. I.
,, J. May, 72nd N. I.
,, W. H. Beckett, 42nd N. I.
,, J. W. Watson, 38th N. I.
,, F. M. Newbery, 58th N. I.
,, Chas Mercer, 15th N. I.

Ensign, C. Middlemass, 6th En. R.,
,, N. F. Parker, 11th N. I..
,, C. W. Riggs. 37th N. I.,
,, C. N. Hodgson 9th N. I.
,, T. F. Bruce, 24th N. I.
,, A. B. Douglas, 52nd N. I ,
,, W. R. Hamilton, 71st N. I.,
,, A. C. Anderson, 36th, N. I.,

The undermentioned promotions are made to fill existing vacancies.

Ensign J. M. Sym, of the 58th N.I. to be Lieutenant, G. O. 15th July 1859.

Ensign C. H. Bridges, of the 15th N. I. to be Lieutenant, G. O. 15th July 1859.

Captain C. W. Hutchinson, Executive Engineer 1st Class, is appointed permanently Superintending Engineer of the 2nd circle, Punjaub *vice* Lieutenant Colonel J. Laughton. G. O. 15th July 1859.

His Excellency the Governor General in Council is pleased to appoint Assistant Surgeon W. S, Playfair M. D. to the medical charge of the Meenah Regiment, *vice* Dr. Mathias, G. O. 15th July 1859

The appointment of Lieutenant W. F. Edwards, of the 45th N. J. to officiate as 2nd in Command of Malwah Bheel Corps notified in G. O. dated 10th May last No. 2556 is cancelled at the request of that officer and his services replaced at the disposal of the Military Department G. O. 15th July 1859.

Lieut W. C. Mackinnon H. M. 87th Foot Assistant Engineer 2nd Class, is transferred from the N. W. P. to Nagpore with the grade of special Assistant Engineer from the Date of joining, G. O. 9th July 1859.

Lieut W. B. Holmes, of Engineers, is appointed a Probationary Assistant Engineer in the Public works Department, and posted to Punjaub

Lieut H. Macdonald Adjutant Dehrah Dhoon to be District Comdt, at Moradabad vice Major Roberton subject to the condition of passing an examination in the Hindoostanee language within the period prescribed by G. O. G. G. in the Military Department No. 734, dated the 20th May.

His Excellency the Viceroy and Governor of Fort william has been pleased to appoint Captain. (unattached) H. Bingham, Offg. Intr and Quarter Mr. of the Sappers and Miners, to be Garrison Qr. Mr. of Fort William. G. O. 22nd July 1859.

LEAVE OF ABSENCE.

The undermentioned Officers are permitted to proceed to Europe, on leave of absence on sick Certificate:—

Lieut. H. R. Wintle of the 28th N. I. for 18 Months under the new Regulations, G. O. 12th July 1859.

Lieut. W. G. Davies, of the 71st N. I. Deputy Commr. of Jhung, for 15 Months, under the new Regulations, G. O. 12th July 59.

Lieut N. W. Elphinistone, of the 4th N. I., Deputy Commissioner of Googaira, for 15 Months under the new Regulations. G. O. 12th July 1859.

Captain and Bt. major R. J. Edgell, of the 53th N. I. Deputy Pay Master. Benares circle for 15 Months, under the new Regulations G. O. 14th July 1859.

Captain J. H. Dyas, of the Corps of Engineers, Director of Canals in the Punjaub for 15 Months, under the new Regulations G. O. 14th July 1859.

Lieut. S. Grant Warde, of the 11th N. I. for two years, under the old Regulations, G. O. 15 July 59.

2nd Captain A. W. Garnett, of the Corps of Engineers, Dept Public Works, 1st circle, Punjaub for 15 Months, under the new Regulations, G. O. 19th July 1859.

Lieut. T. Quin, of the 22 N. I. 2nd in Command 6th Punjaub Infantry, for 15 Months, under the new Regulations, G. O. 19th July 59.

The undermentioned Officers are permitted to proceed to Europe, on Furlough, on Private Affairs.

Captain W. M. Gowan, of the Regt. of Artillery for two years, under the new Regulations, G. O. 12th July 1859.

Major R. J. Hawthorne, of the 2nd En. L. C. for two years and a half under the old Regulations. G. O. 15th July 1859

Captain J. A. Angus, of the 9th N. J. Offg. Sub. Asst. Commy. Genl, is permitted to proceed to Europe, on private affairs under the old Regulations, for the residue of the Furlough on the same account granted to him in G. G. O. No. 1320 of the 24th October 1856.

Lieut. C. V. Arbuckle, of Artillery, Deputy Commissary of Ordnance, is allowed leave of absence from the 4th June to the 1st November 1859, to remain at Simla, on Medical Certificate, G. O. 1st July 1859.

Lieut. O. R. Newmarch of the 44th N. I., Offg. Deputy Assistant Commy. Genl. is allowed leave of absence for 6 months from the 10th June to the 10th Dec. 1859, to visit Moosoorie, on Medical Certificate, under the New Regulations, G O. 5th July 1859.

RESIGNATIONS.

2nd Captain F. C. Simons of the Regiment of Artillery, is permitted to resign the service from the 18th July 1859.

Lieut. J. B. Tudor, of the 5th European Regiment, Adjt. 1st Regt. Beatson's Horse, is permitted to resign the service G. O. 22nd July 1859.

RETURNED FROM FURLOUGH.

	Date of arrival at Fort William.
Captain John Eliot, of Artillery, Dept. Public Works, 1st circle Bengal, on leave for 15 months, from the 11th April, 1858.	15th July 1859.

MEMBERS

OF THE

MOST HONORABLE ORDER OF THE BATH.

KNIGHTS GRAND CROSS.

Lieutenant General.

Sir George Pollock, Artillery.

KNIGHTS COMMANDERS.

Generals.

Sir Robert Houstoun, Cavalry.
Sir William Richards, Infantry.

Lieutenant General.

Sir George Petre Wymer, Infantry.

Major Generals.

Sir John Cheape, Engineers.
Sir Patrick Grant, Infantry.
Sir John Bennett Hearsey, Cavalry.
Sir Archdale Wilson, *Bart.*, Artillery.

Colonel.

Sir Justin Sheil, Infantry, (*Civil.*)
Sir Robert Napier, Engineers.

COMPANIONS.

General.

~~Sir Robert Henry Cunliffe, Bt.~~, Infantry.

Lieutenant Generals.

Alexander Lindsay, Artillery.
~~James Kennedy,~~ Cavalry.
Edmund Frederick Waters, Infantry.
Thomas Monteath Douglas, Infantry.
William Pattle, Cavalry.
Henry Hall, Infantry.

Major Generals.

Abraham Roberts, Infantry.
John Tulloch, Infantry.
George Edward Gowan, Artillery.
~~James Stuart~~, Infantry.
George William Aylmer Lloyd, Infantry.
Charles Montabin Carmichael, Cavalry.
Christopher Godby, Infantry.
James Parsons, Infantry.
Henry Fisher Salter, Cavalry.
Archibald Fullerton Richmond, Infantry.
James Eckford, Infantry.
Andrew Hervey, Infantry.
Christopher Dixon Wilkinson, Infantry.
Francis Spencer Hawkins, Infantry.
Alexander Carnegy, Infantry.
Charles Richard William Lane, Infantry.
William John Gairdner, Infantry.
George Brooke, Artillery.
John Hoggan, Infantry.
George Huyshe, Infantry.
Charles Hamilton, Infantry.
John Hoggan, Infantry.
Philip Francis Story, Cavalry.
George Hicks, Infantry.
Joseph Nash, Infantry.

Major Generals.

James Alexander, Artillery.
John Theophilus Lane, Artillery.
Edward Huthwaite, Artillery.
Richard James Holwell Birch, Infantry.
John Fowler Bradford, Cavalry.
Charles Grant, Artillery.
Stuart Corbett, Infantry.

Colonels.

Augustus Abbott, Artillery.
~~James Steel~~, Infantry.
Henry Forster, Shekhawattee Battalion.
Neville Bowles Chamberlain, Infantry.
Arthur Mitford Becher, Infy.
St. George Daniel Showers, Infy.
John Welchman, Infy.
J. M. B. F. Tytler, Infy.
Vincent Eyre, Artillery.
John Craigie Halkett, Infantry.
Auchmuty Tucker, Cavalry.
Frank-Turner, Artillery.
Henry Tombs, Artillery.
Francis Rowcroft, Infantry.
Henry Marion Durand, Engineers.
John Coke, Infantry.
J. D. Macpherson, Infantry.
C. Hogge, Artillery.
J. K. McCausland, Infantry.

Lieutenant Colonels.

Charles Devaynes Blair, Invalid Establishment.
Herbert Benjamin Edwardes, Infantry.
Frederick Gaitskell, Artillery.
Charles Reid, Infy.
Richard Baird Smith, Engineers.
Robert Augustus Master, Cavy.
Jeremiah Brasyer, Infantry.
W. B. Thomson, Infantry.
R. Drought, Infantry.
H. F. Dunsford, Infantry.
K. Young, Infantry.
F. F. Remmington, Artillery.
G. Bourchier, Artillery.
C. H. Blunt, Artillery.
James Brind, Artillery.
H. A. Carleton, Artillery.
E. B. Johnson, Artillery.
W. Olpherts, Artillery.
G. W. G. Green, Infantry.
A. Taylor, Engineers.
~~T. J. W. Hungerford~~, Artillery.

Majors.

D. M. Probyn, Cavalry.
W. A. Crommelin, Engineers.
C. H. Barchard, Infantry.
G. Moir, Artillery.
W. A. Mackinnon, Artillery.
J. F. Richardson, Infantry.
T. F. Wilson, Infantry.

Medical.

John Campbell Brown.
William Brydon.
John Campbell.

OFFICERS WHO HAVE RECEIVED FOREIGN ORDERS.

SPANISH—*San Fernando.*

Lt. Col. W. F. Beatson, Infantry.

AFFGHAN.	*Dooranee.*	AFFGHAN.	*Dooranee.*
Maj. Genl. A. Roberts, C. B., Infy.,	2nd Class.	Col. F. Wheler, Cavalry, ..	3rd Class.
Maj. Genl. J. Parsons, C. B., Infy.,	ditto.	Col. G. St. P. Lawrence, Cavy...	ditto.
Lt. Genl. T. M. Douglas, Infy., ..	ditto.	Col. *Sir* R. C. Shakespear, Arty...	ditto.
Maj. Genl. C. M. Carmichael, C. B. Cavy.	3rd ditto.	Col. A. G. F. J. Younghusband, I.	ditto.
Maj. General G. Warren, Infantry,	ditto.	Lt. Col. J. H. Craigie, C. B., Infy.,	ditto.
Maj. Genl. H. F. Salter, C. B., Cavy.,	ditto.	Colonel C. Troup, Infantry, ..	ditto.
Colonel D. Birrell, Infantry, ..	ditto.	Col. B. Bygrave, Infantry, ..	ditto.
Colonel A. Abbott, C. B., Artillery,..	ditto.	Col. J. Abbott, Artillery, ..	ditto.
Col. G. C. Ponsonby, Cavalry, ..	ditto.	Supg. Surg. J. Forsyth, Medl. Dept.	ditto.
Col. J. Christie, Cavalry, ...	ditto.		

Honorary Distinctions have been granted to the undermentioned Regiments, in commemoration of their Services, in the following Campaigns, Battles, Actions, &c.

Artillery Regiment—*Ubique.*

Plassey, battle of, ... 23rd June 1757.

G. G. O., 23rd Feb. 1829,
- 1st European Bengal Fusiliers.
- 1st Native Infantry.

Buxar, battle of, ... 23rd October 1764.

G. G. O., 23rd Feb. 1829,
- 1st European Bn. Fusiliers.
- 2nd Native Infantry, (Grs.)
- 3rd ditto
- 5th ditto
- 8th ditto
- 9th ditto
- 10th ditto

Korah, battle of, ... 10th June 1776.

G. G. O., 23rd Feb. 1829,
- 1st Native Infantry.
- 10th ditto .. 2 Honorary colors.

Guzerat, campaign in, from 1778 to 1784 inclusive.

G. G. O., 23rd Feb. 1829,
- 1st European Bn. Fusiliers.
- 2nd Native Infantry, (Grs.)
- 3rd ditto
- 5th ditto
- 7th ditto
- 11th ditto
- 13th ditto

Carnatic, campaign in the, from 1781 to 1784 inclusive.

G. G. O., 23rd Feb. 1829,
- 4th Native Infantry.
- 5th ditto
- 12th ditto
- 22nd ditto

Mysore, campaign in the, from 1790 to 1793 inclusive.

G. G. O., *3rd Feb. 1829,
- 4th Native Infantry.
- 6th ditto
- 13th ditto
- 16th ditto (Grs.)

Seringapatam, assault and capture of, 4th May 1799.

G. G. O., 23rd Feb. 1829,
- 14th Native Infantry.
- 16th ditto (Grs.)
- 36th ditto
- 37th ditto
- 38th ditto (L. I.)
- 39th ditto

Allygurh, action near, and assault and capture of, 29th Aug. and 4th Sept. 1803.

G. G. O., 23rd Feb. 1829,
- 7th N. I.
- 23rd ditto
- 35th do (L. I.)

Honorary colors, and extra Jemadars.

Delhi, battle of, ... 11th Sep. 1803.

G. G. O., 23rd Feb. 1829,
- 2d Lt. Cavy. †
- 3rd ditto †
- 1st N. I.
- 5th ditto
- 22nd ditto
- 23rd ditto
- 28th ditto

Honorary standards, colors, and extra Jemadars.

G. O. C. C., 15th Aug. 1839, 29th Native Infantry.

G. G. O., 23rd Feb. and 25th Apl. 1829,
- 30th ditto
- 31st ditto
- 35th do (L. I.)

Honorary colors and extra Jemadars.

Laswarrie, battle of, ... 1st Nov. 1803.

G. G. O., 23rd Feb. 1829,
- 1st Light Cavalry.
- 2nd ditto†
- 3rd ditto
- 4th ditto (Lancers.
- 6th ditto
- 1st Native Infantry.
- 12th ditto
- 21st ditto
- 24th ditto
- 30th ditto
- 31st ditto
- 33rd ditto

Deig, battle of, ... 13th Nov. 1804.

G. G. O., 23rd Feb. 1829,
- 2nd Light Cavalry.
- 3rd ditto†
- 1st European Bn. Fusiliers.
- 5th Native Infantry.
- 7th ditto
- 9th ditto
- 30th ditto
- 31st ditto
- 44th ditto

Java, campaign in, ... Aug. and Sept. 1811.

G. G. O., 23rd Feb. 1829,
- Governor Genl.'s Body Guard.
- 25th Native Infantry.
- 40th ditto

Seetabuldie, Cavalry charge, .. 27th Nov. 1817

6th Light Cavalry.

---

† Vide G. G. O. No. 553 of the 24th October 1851.

***Bhurtpore*, assault and capture of, 18th Jan. 1826.**

G. G. O., 30th May 1826,
- 3rd Light Cavalry.
- 4th ditto (Lancers.)
- 6th ditto
- 8th ditto
- 9th ditto
- 10th ditto
- 1st European Bn. Fusiliers.
- 6th Native Infantry.
- 11th ditto
- 15th ditto
- 18th ditto
- 21st ditto
- 23rd ditto
- 31st ditto
- 32nd ditto
- 33rd ditto
- 35th ditto (L. I.)
- 36th ditto
- 37th ditto
- 41st ditto
- 58th ditto
- 60th ditto
- 63rd ditto
- 1st Irregular Cavalry.

***Arracan*, campaign in, from 1824 to 1826 inclusive.**

G. G. O., 22nd Apl. 1826,
- 26th Native Infantry, (L. I.)
- 40th ditto
- 42nd ditto (L. I.)
- 49th ditto
- 62nd ditto
- 2nd Irregular Cavalry.

***Assam*, campaign in, from 1824 to 1826 inclusive.**

G. G. O., 22nd Apl. 1826,
- 46th Native Infantry.
- 57th ditto

***Ava*, campaign in, from 1824 to 1826 inclusive.**

G. G. O., 22nd Apl. 1826,
- Governor Genl.'s Body Guard.
- 40th Native Infantry.

***Affghanistan*, campaign in, ... 1838-39.**

G. O. G. G., 19th Nov. 1839,
- 2nd Light Cavalry.†
- 3rd ditto†
- 1st European Bn. Fusiliers.
- 16th Native Infantry, (Grs.)
- 31st ditto
- 35th ditto (L. I.)
- 37th ditto
- 42nd ditto (L. I.)
- 43rd ditto (L. I.)
- 48th ditto
- 4th Irregular Cavalry.

***Ghuznee*, assault and capture of, 23rd July 1839**

G. O. G. G., 19th Nov. 1839,
- 2nd Light Cavalry. †
- 3rd ditto†
- 1st European Bn. Fusiliers.
- 16th Native Infantry, (Grs.)
- 35th ditto (L. I.)
- 48th ditto
- 4th Irregular Cavalry.

***Kelat*, assault and capture of, 13th November 1839.**

G. O. G. G., 15th Feb. 1840,
- 31st Native Infantry.

***Kelat-i-Ghilzie*, defence of,........... 1842.**

G. O. G. G., 4th Oct. 1842,
- Kelat-i-Ghilzie Regiment.

***Candahar*, actions, &c., in the vicinity of, 1842.**

G. O. G. G., 4th Oct. and 13th Dec. 1842,
- 2nd Native Infy. (Grs.)
- 16th ditto (Grs.)
- 38th ditto (L. I.)
- 42nd ditto (L. I.)
- 43rd ditto (L. I.)
- Kelat-i-Ghilzie Regiment.
- 1st Irregular Cavalry.

***Ghuznie*, recapture of, ... 6th Sept. 1842.**

G. O. G. G., 4th Oct. 1842,
- 2nd Native Infy. (Grs.)
- 16th ditto (Grs.)
- 38th ditto (L. I.)
- 42nd ditto (L. I.)
- 43rd ditto (L. I.)
- Kelat-i-Ghilzie Regiment.

***Caubul*, capture of, ... 17th Sept. 1842.**

G. O. G. G., 4th Oct. and 8th Nov. 1842,
- 1st Light Cavalry.
- 5th ditto
- 10th ditto
- 2nd Native Infantry, (Grs.)
- 6th ditto
- 16th ditto (Grs.)
- 26th ditto (L. I.)
- 30th ditto
- 33rd ditto
- 35th ditto (L. I.)
- 38th ditto (L. I.)
- 42nd ditto (L. I.)
- 43rd ditto (L. I.)
- 53rd ditto
- 60th ditto
- 64th ditto
- Kelat-i-Ghilzie Regiment.
- 3rd Irregular Cavalry.

***Jellalabad*, defence and battle of, 7th April 1842**

G. O. G. G., 30th Apl. 1842,
- 5th Light Cavalry.
- 35th Native Infantry, (L. I.)

† Vide G. O. No. 553 of the 24th October 1851.

Meeanee, battle of, ... 17th Feb. 1843.

G. O. G. G., 5th Mar. and 11th Apl. 1843, — 9th Light Cavalry.

Hyderabad, battle of, ... 24th Mar. 1843.

G. O. G. G., 11th Apl. 1843, — 9th Light Cavalry.

Maharajpore, battle of, ... 29th Dec. 1843.

G. O. G. G., 4th Jan. 1844,
- Governor Genl.'s Body Guard.
- 1st Light Cavalry.
- 4th ditto (Lancers.)
- 5th ditto } Detachments.
- 8th ditto } Detachments.
- 10th ditto
- 2nd Native Infy. (Grs.)
- 14th ditto
- 16th ditto (Grs.)
- 31st ditto
- 39th ditto (6th Company.)
- 43rd ditto (Lt. Infantry.)
- 56th ditto
- Kelat-i-Ghilzie Regiment. (flank Companies.)
- 4th Irregular Cavalry.

Punniar, battle of, ... 29th Dec. 1843.

G. O. G. G., 4th Jan. 1844,
- 2nd Lt. Cavy. (2 Squadrons.)
- 5th ditto (2 Squadrons.)
- 8th ditto
- 39th Native Infantry.
- 50th ditto
- 51st ditto
- 58th ditto
- 8th Irregular Cavalry.

Moodkee, battle of, ... 18th Dec. 1845.

G. O. G. G., 12th Aug. 1846,
- Govr. Genl.'s Body Guard.
- 4th Lt. Cavalry, (Lancers.)
- 5th ditto
- 2nd N. I. } (Grenadiers.)
- 16th ditto } (Grenadiers.)
- 24th ditto
- 26th Light Infantry.
- 42nd ditto
- 45th Native Infantry.
- 47th ditto
- 48th ditto
- 73rd ditto
- 4th Irr. Cavy. } Detachts.
- 8th ditto } Detachts.
- 9th ditto

Ferozeshuhur, battle of, 21st and 22nd Dec. 1845.

G. O. G. G., 12th Aug. 1846,
- Governor Genl.'s Body Guard.
- 4th Light Cavalry (Lancers.)
- 5th ditto
- 8th ditto

G. O. G G., 12th Aug. 1846,
- 1st European Bengal Fusiliers.
- 2nd Native Infy. (Grenadiers.)
- 12th ditto
- 14th ditto
- 16th ditto (Grenadiers.)
- 24th ditto
- 26th ditto (Light Infy.)
- 33rd ditto
- 42nd ditto (ditto.)
- 44th ditto
- 45th ditto
- 47th ditto
- 48th ditto
- 54th ditto
- 73rd ditto
- 3rd Irregular Cavalry.
- 4th ditto } Detachments.
- 8th ditto } Detachments.
- 9th ditto } Detachments.

Alliwal, battle of, ... 28th Jan. 1846.

G. O. G. G., 12th Aug. 1846,
- Governor Genl.'s Body Guard.
- 1st Light Cavalry.
- 3rd ditto
- 5th ditto
- 24th Native Infantry.
- 30th ditto
- 36th ditto
- 47th ditto
- 48th ditto
- 66th or Goorka Regt.
- 4th Irregular Cavalry.
- Nusseree Battalion.
- Sirmoor Battalion.
- Shekhawattee Brigade (now Battalion.)

Sobraon, battle of, ... 10th Feb. 1846.

G. O. G. G., 12th Aug. 1846,
- Governor Genl.'s Body Guard.
- 3rd Light Cavalry.
- 4th ditto (Lancers.)
- 5th ditto
- 1st European Bengal Fusiliers.
- Det. 1st Co. 7th Native Infy)
- 16th Native Infy. (Grenadiers.
- 26th ditto (Lt. Infy.)
- 33rd ditto
- 41st ditto
- 42nd ditto (Lt. Infy.)
- 43rd ditto (ditto.)
- 47th ditto
- 59th ditto
- 63rd ditto
- 66th or Goorka Regt.
- 68th Native Infantry.
- The Head-quarters and Right Wing 2nd Irregular Cavalry
- 8th Irregular Cavalry.
- 9th ditto
- Nusseree Battalion.
- Sirmoor Battalion.

Punjaub, campaign in,...... 1848 and 1849.

G. G. O., 7th Oct. 1853.

1st Light Cavalry.
5th ditto
6th ditto
7th ditto
8th ditto
11th ditto (now 2nd.)
2nd Eur. Bengal Fusiliers.
1st Native Infantry.
3rd ditto
4th ditto
8th ditto
13th ditto
15th ditto
18th ditto
20th ditto
22nd ditto
25th ditto
29th ditto
30th ditto
31st ditto
36th ditto
37th ditto
45th ditto
46th ditto
49th ditto
50th ditto
51st ditto
52nd ditto
53rd ditto
56th ditto
69th ditto
70th ditto
71st ditto
72nd ditto
73rd ditto
2nd Irregular Cavalry.
3rd ditto
7th ditto
9th ditto
11th ditto
12th ditto
13th ditto
14th ditto
15th ditto
16th (the Head-quarters and Detachments.)
17th ditto Left Wing.
1st Seikh Local Infantry.
2nd ditto
Corps of Guides (Detachment.)

Mooltan, siege of,........... 22nd Jan. 1849.

G. G. O., 7th Oct. 1853.

11th (now 2d) Light Cavalry.
8th Regt. Native Infantry.
49th ditto
51st ditto

G. G. O., 7th Oct. 1853.

52nd Regiment Native Infantry.
72nd ditto
7th Regiment Irregular Cavalry.
11th ditto
14th Irregular Cavalry (Dett.)
Corps of Guides (Detachment.)

Chillianwalla, battle of,...... 13th Jan. 1849

G. G. O., 7th Oct. 1853.

1st Light Cavalry.
5th ditto
6th ditto
8th ditto
2nd European Bengal Fusiliers.
15th Regiment Native Infantry.
20th ditto
25th ditto
30th ditto
31st ditto
36th ditto
45th ditto
46th ditto
56th ditto
69th ditto
70th ditto
3rd Regiment Irregular Cavalry.
9th ditto

Goojerat, battle of,....... 21st Feb. 1849.

G. G. O., 7th Oct. 1853.

1st Light Cavalry.
5th ditto
6th ditto
8th ditto
2nd European Bengal Fusiliers.
8th Regiment Native Infantry.
13th ditto
15th ditto
20th ditto
25th ditto
30h ditto
31t ditto
36th ditto
45th ditto
46th ditto
51st ditto
52nd ditto
56th ditto
69th ditto
70th ditto
72nd ditto
3rd Regiment Irregular Cavalry.
9th ditto
11th ditto
12th ditto
13th ditto
14th Irregular Cavalry (Detachment.)
Corps of Guides (Detachment.)

Pegu, campaign in,

G. O. P. C., 18th May 55.

1st European Bengal Fusiliers.
2nd European Bengal Fusiliers. Head Qrs. and 4 Companies.
10th Native Infantry.
40th ditto
67th ditto
68th ditto
4th Seikh Local Infantry.
Arracan Local Battalion.
Ramgurh Irregular Cavalry.

N. B.—Original dates of raising the several Corps were published in G. O. G. G., 20th May 1824—Revised ditto first inserted in the Adjutant General's Quarterly Army List for October 1844.

THE

NEW QUARTERLY ARMY LIST.

VICEROY AND GOVERNOR GENERAL AND PRESIDENT OF THE SUPREME COUNCIL OF INDIA.

The Right Hon'ble CHARLES JOHN VISCOUNT CANNING, ..	*Presidency,* ..	29 *Feb.* 56

COMMANDER-IN-CHIEF IN INDIA.

His Excellency General the Right Hon'ble LORD CLYDE, G. C. B., ..	*N. W. Provinces,* ..	13 *Aug.* 57

LIEUTENANT GOVERNOR, BENGAL.

The Hon'ble J. P. Grant, ..	*Presidency,* ..	1 *May* 59

LIEUTENANT GOVERNOR, PUNJAUB.

The Hon'ble R. Montgomery,	.. ..	1 *May* 59

LIEUTENANT GOVERNOR, NORTH-WESTERN PROVINCES.

The Hon'ble G. F. Edmonstone, ..	*N. W. Provinces,* ..	20 *Jan.* 59

PERSONAL STAFF OF THE RIGHT HONORABLE THE GOVERNOR GENERAL OF INDIA.

Mr. L. B. Bowring, *Civil Service,* ..	Private Secretary, ..	1 *Apl.* 58
Maj. *Sir* E. F. Campbell, *Bart,* H.M. 60th Foot,	Military Secretary and 1st Aide-de-Camp, .	6 *July* 59
Capt. R. Baring, 1st E. L. C., ..	Aides-de-Camp, ..	1 *July* 56
Capt. *Hon'ble* J. C. Stanley, H. M. Gr. Guards,	Aides-de-Camp, ..	19 *Jan.* 58
Major H. M. Jones, H. M. 13th L. I., ..	Aides-de-Camp, ..	24 *Dec.* 58
Surgeon A. Beale, ..	Surgeon, ..	24 *Feb.* 59

PERSONAL STAFF OF THE GOVERNOR GENERAL OF INDIA—*Continued.*

Name	Appointment	Date
Colonel A. Abbott, C. B., Artillery, .. Lt.Col.A.J. Hadfield, Madras 2nd (or Asnee) Native Veteran Battalion, .. Lt. Col. R. Henderson, C. B., Mad. Engrs., Lt. Col. S. A. Abbott, 51st N.I. .. Colonel A. M. Becher, C. B., 61st N. I., .. Colonel G. St. P. Lawrence, 2nd E. L. C., Col. N. B. Chamberlain, C. B., 16th Grendrs., Major Fred. Wm. Lambert, 56th N.I. ...	Honorary Aides-de-Camp,	.. 1 *Mar.* 56
Captain J. W. W. Osborne, 24th M. N. I.,	..	.. 12 *Feb.* 58
Major W. H. R. Green, 19th Bombay N. I.,	..	.. 8 *June* 59
The Subadar for the time being, in command of the guard of Infantry at the Government House, for the month during which such Subadar shall be employed on that duty,	Aide-de-Camp.	

PERSONAL STAFF OF HIS EXCELLENCY THE COMMANDER-IN-CHIEF IN INDIA.

Name	Appointment	Date
Col. A. C. Stirling, C. B., H. M. Service, ..	Military Secretary,	.. 6 *Mar.* 58
R ~~Captain Sir David Baird, Bart.~~, H. M. 98th Foot, ..	Aide-de-Camp, (Leave to Europe,)..	13 *Aug.* 57
Capt. F. M. Alison, H. M. 19th Foot, ..	Aide-de-Camp,	.. do.
Lieut. *Hon'ble* J. C. Dormer, H. M. 13th Foot, ..	Aide-de-Camp,	.. 6 *July* 58
Assist. Surgn. W. A. Mackinnon, H. M. Service,	Surgeon,	.. 24 *Apl.* 58

PERSONAL STAFF OF THE LIEUTENANT GOVERNOR OF BENGAL.

Name	Appointment	Date
Captain A. C. Plowden, 50th N. I., ..	Private Secretary and Aide-de-Camp,	.. 1 *May* 59
Lieut. E. H. D. Macpherson, H. M. 93rd Highlanders, ..	Aide-de-Camp,	.. 4 *June* 59

PERSONAL STAFF OF THE LIEUTENANT GOVERNOR OF PUNJAUB.

Name	Appointment	Date
Col. J. D. McPherson, 22nd N. I., ..	Military Secretary,	.. 1 *Feb.* 59
Captain W. Wyld, 3rd En. L. Cavy., ..	Offg. Assistant Military Secretary,	.. 1 *Feb.* 59

PERSONAL STAFF OF THE LIEUTENANT GOVERNOR NORTH-WESTERN PROVINCES.

Name	Appointment	Date
Lieut. Col. G. W. Williams, 29th N. I. ..	Military Secretary,	.. 29 *Jan.* 59
Lieut. H. A. Prinsep, 3rd En. Regt., ..	Private Secretary and Aide-de-Camp,..	2 *Mar.* 59
* ..	Aide-de-Camp,	..

SECRETARIAT OF THE GOVT. OF INDIA MILITARY DEPT.

Name	Appointment	Date
Major Genl. R. J. H. Birch, C. B., 2nd En. B. F. ..	Secy. to the Govt. of India,	.. 4 *Aug.* 54
Major F. D. Atkinson, 2nd En. B. F. ..	Depy. Secy. to the Govt. of India, ..	11 *Feb.* 56
Capt. H. K. Burne, 2nd N. I., (Grends.,) ..	1st Asst. Secy. to the Govt. of India,..	15 *Jan.* 58
Major H. M. Wilson, 6th En. Regt. ..	2nd Asst. Secy. to the Govt. of India,	15 *Jan.* 58

CHIEF OF THE STAFF.

Name	Appointment	Date
Major Genl. *Sir* W. R. Mansfield, K. C. B., H. M.'s Service, ..	Chief of the Staff,	.. 10 *Sep.* 57
Lt. R. G. H. Johnstone, 13th B. N.I. ..	Depy. Asst. Adjt. Genl.—Fur.S.C. 4 Sep.58	7 *Oct.* 57
Major H. H. Crealock, H. M. 90th Foot, ..	Offg. Deputy Asst. Adjt. Genl.	.. 17 *May* 58
Lieut. F. R. S. Flood, H. M. 53rd Foot. ..	Aide-de-Camp.	.. 9 *Sep.* 58

ADJUTANT GENERAL'S DEPARTMENT

Lt. Col. W. A. J. Mayhew, 6th En. Regt.	Adjutant General of the Army,—Fur. S. C. 29 Mar. 59. ..	15 *Dec.* 57
*Major H. W. Norman, 31st N. I.	Deputy Adjt. Genl. of the Army, ..	15 *Dec.* 57
	Offg. Adjt. Genl. of the Army,	8 *Apl.* 59
Captain S. H. Becher, 61st N.I.	1st Asst. Adjt. General of the Army,	1 *May* 56
	Offg. Depy. Adjt. Genl. of the Army,	8 *Apl.* 59
*Lieut. Col. D. M. Stewart, 9th N. I.,	2nd Asst. Adjutant Genl. of the Army,	30 *Dec.* 57
	Offg 1st Asst. Adjt. Genl. of the Army,	8 *Apl.* 59
Lieut. G. L. Fraser, 23rd N. I., ..	Offg. 2nd Asst. Adjt. Genl. of the Army,	8 *Apl.* 59

QUARTER MASTER GENERAL'S DEPARTMENT.

Quarter Master General of the Army.

Colonel A. M. Becher, C. B. 61st N. I. ..		.. 11 *June* 52

Deputy Quarter Master General of the Army.

Col. J. S. Paton, 14th N. I.	.. Presidency Office,	.. 15 *Apl.* 58

Assistants Quarter Master General of the Army.

Major H. R. Garden, 2nd Gredrs.,	Oude,—Fur. S. C. 19 Jan. 58,	23 *Apl.* and 21 *Oct.* 53
Lieut. P. S. Lumsden, 60th N. I.	.. Peshawur Divn. Fur. P.A. 28 Apl.59,..	15 *Apl.* 58

Deputy Assistants Quarter Master General of the Army.

1st Class,	*Lieut. G. Allgood, 49th N.I. ..		.. 10 *Aug.* 55
	Major D. C. Shute, 19th N.I. ..	Umballah, (Offg. Asst. Qr. Mr. Genl. of the Army,)	.. 15 *Apl.* 58
	Capt. B. E. Bacon, 50th N. I., ..	Offg. Presidency,	.. 24 *June* 59
2nd Class,	*Capt. C. C. Johnson, 33rd N I. ..	Meerut,	.. 10 *Aug.* 55
	Lieut. F. S. Roberts, Arty., ..	Eur. S. C. 29 Apl. 58,	.. 15 *Apl.* 58
	Lieut. F. B. Norman, 14th N I.,	Offg. Lahore,	.. 15 *Apl.* 58
	Capt. J. T. N. O'Brien, H. M., 20th Foot, ..	Offg. Soraon,	.. 22 *Oct.* 58
	Capt. A. B. Fenwick, 5th En. Regt.	Offg. Umballah,	.. 25 *Oct.* 58
	Major W. D. Macdonald, H. M., 93rd Foot, ..	Offg. Allahabad,	.. 28 *Jan.* 59
	Lieut. E. T. Sadler, 19th N. I.,..	Offg.	.. 24 *June* 59

JUDGE ADVOCATE GENERAL'S DEPARTMENT.

Judge Advocate General of the Army.

*Lieut. Col. K. Young, C.B. 50th N.I. ..		.. 4 *Aug.* 54

Deputy Judge Advocates General.

Major G. C. Hatch, 57th N. I.	.. Presidency Division (Barrackpore,)	.. 14 *Apl.* 48
Captain A. Turner, 4th En. Regt.	.. Dinapore, (with his Regt-,)	.. 7 *Jan.* 53
Capt. J. N. Young, 3rd En. Regt.,	.. Lahore,	.. 11 *Mar.* 56
Major F. C. Maisey, 67th N. I.,	.. Sirhind Division (Umballah,)	.. 5 *Sep.* 56
Capt. L. B. Jones, 56th N. I.,	.. Peshawur,—(Comdg. 1st Sikh Irr. Cavy)	27 *Apl.* 57
Capt. C. F. Browne, H. M. 35th Foot,	.. Cawnpore Division,	.. 25 *Nov.* 58
Capt. C. P. Trower, 23rd N. I.,	.. Offg. Saugor,	.. 4 *Mar.* 58
Major H. D'O. Torrens, H. M. 23rd Fusiliers,	Offg. Lucknow Field Force,	.. 3 *July* 58
Capt. H. B. A. Poulton, 64th N. I.	.. Offg. Dinapore,	.. 17 *Nov.* 58
Major E. G. Daniell, H. M. 8th Foot,	.. Offg. Gwalior Division,	.. 17 *Nov.* 58
~~Capt. R. Blackall, H. M. 75th Foot~~,	.. Offg. Meerut,	.. 6 *Dec.* 58

AUDIT DEPARTMENT.

Lt. Col. E.G. J. Champneys, 5th En, Regt...	Military Auditor General,	.. 8 *Sep.* 57
Lt. Col. J. C. Hannyngton, 34th N. I.	.. Depy. Mily. Auditor General,	.. 23 *Feb.* 59
Major W. S. Ferris, 12th N.I.	.. 1st Asst. Mily. Auditor General,	.. 17 *Sep.* 57
Captain G. B. Malleson, 33rd N.I.	.. 2nd Asst. Mily. Auditor General,	.. 17 *Sep.* 57
Capt. F. D. Urquhart, Artillery,	.. 3rd Asst. Military Auditor General,	.. 6 *Feb.* 56

PAY DEPARTMENT.

Major G. M. Hill, 17th N. I. ..	Pay Master Presidency, and to the Queen's Troops, ..	13 *Sep.* 58

The Presidency Circle, consists of Allipore, Arracan, Akyab, Barrackpore, Ballygunge, Berhampore, Bhaugulpore, Balasore, Cachar, Chittagong, Cossipore, Dacca, Dum-Dum, Fort William, Gowhatty, Hazareebaugh, Darjeeling, Ishapore, Jumaulpore, Kyouk Phyoo, Luckimpore, (Upper Assam) Mymensing, Midnapore, Pooree, Presidency, Monghyr, Dorunda, Sandoway, Ramree, and Sylhet.

* Army Head Quarters.

Deputy Pay Masters.

Name	Stations	Date	Year
Lt. Col. H. J. Stannus, 5th En. Lt. Cavy.—Meerut Circle, ..	Ajmere, Allygurh, Almorah, Bareilly, Beaur, Delhi, Erinpoorah, Meerut, Moradabad, Landour, Hansi, Muttra, Mussoorie, Kherwarrah, and Murad-i-Munzil, Agra, ..	21 *Sep.*	53
Major T. G. St. George, 17th N.I.—Jullundur Circle. ..	Boodee Pind, Goordaspore, Hajeepore, Hoosheyarpore, Jullundur, Kurturpore, Mokerian, Nakodah, Noorpore, Phillour, Sealkote, and Wuzeerabad, ..	23 *Sep.*	58
Major H. S. Grimes, 46th N. I., Cawnpore Circle, (Offg.) ..	Cawnpore, Etawah, Futtehgurh, Jhansi, Lucknow, Mynpoorie, Nowgong, Nagode, Seetapore, (Oude) Shahjehanpore, Mhow and Nagode,	18 *Mar.*	59
Captain F. C. Tombs, 18th N. I. Field Pay Master, ..	Allahabad Azimgurh, Banda, Secrole, (Benares,) Buxar, Chunar, Dinapore, Goruckpore, Ghazeepore, Indore, Jubbulpore, Juanpore, Sultanpore, (Benares,) Mirzapore, Nursingpore, Nepaul, Mehidpore, Sehore, Segowlie, Sultanpore (Oude,) Sirdarpore, Saugor and Jubbulpore, ..	2 *Jan.*	55
Major R. J. Edgell, 53rd N. I., Benares Circle. ..		23 *Sep.*	58
Captain C. F. M. Mundy, 34th N. I., Sirhind Circle, ..	Deyrah Dhoon, Dugshai, Duttiah, Jutog, Kurnaul, Kussowlie, Loodianah, Mukho, Ferozepore, Simla, Subathoo and Umballah, ..	3 *July*	58
Captain F. N. Edmonstone, 3rd E. L. C., Rawul Pindee Circle ..	Attock, Bunno, Dera Ghazee Khan, Dera Ishmael Khan, Deenah, Fort Barrah, Fort Mackeson, Fort Michnee, Fort Shubkudder, Hazarah, Jhelum, Kohat, Liea Murdan, Murree, Murgullah, Nowshera Peshawur, Rawul Pindee, Shumshabad, Sulhud and Shahpore, ..	25 *Feb.*	58
Lieut. H. P. Williams, 72nd N. I.—Lahore Circle, ..	Govindgurh, Leia, Lahore, Mooltan, Mittankote, and the Four Seikh Local Infantry Regts., ..	29 *Jan.*	58

Pay Masters and Superintendents of Native Pensioners.

Name	Stations	Date	Year
Capt. W. W. Aubert, Invalid Establishment.—Barrackpore Pension Circle, ..	Arracan, Bancoorah, Beerbhoom, Bullooah, Burdwan, Cachar, Chittagong, Cuttack, Dacca, Goalparah, Kamroop, Luckimpore, Midnapore, Sandoway, Rungpore and Sylhet, ..	2 *Mar.*	57
Capt. D. Stansbury, 60th N. I., .. Allahabad Pension Circle, (Offg.) ..	Allahabad, Jubbulpore and Saugor, ..	21 *Apl.*	59
Captain Octavius Hamilton, 2nd E. Lt. Cavy., Haupper Pension Circle,	Agra, Delhi, Meerut, Kemaoon, Moradabad, Muttra, Mynpoorie, Rohtuck, and Subathoo, ..	31 *May*	55
Capt. M. J. Slater, 5th En. Regt.—Lucknow Pension Circle, (with his regt.,) ..	Cawnpore, Lucknow and Furruckabad, ..	21 *July*	58
Capt. G. G. Anderson, 15th N. I., ..	Officiating. ..	14 *Feb.*	59
Capt. C. L. Brown, 46th N.I.—Dinapore Pension Circle, ..	Benares, Bhaugulpore, Gyah, Ghazeepore, Hazareebaugh, Monghyr, Patna, Purneah, Sarun and Shahabad,	20 *Mar.*	55

SURVEYOR GENERAL'S DEPARTMENT.

Name	Office	Date	Year
Lieut. Colonel A. S. Waugh, Engineers, ..	Surveyor Genl. of India and Supdt., Great Trigonometrical Survey, Deyrah Dhoon, ..	16 *Dec.*	43
Major H. E. L. Thuillier, Artillery, ..	Deputy and Revenue Surveyor General, Supdt. Mathematical Instrument Maker's Department, and in charge of the Surveyor General's office at the Presidency, ..	13 *Apl.*	49

Great Trigonometrical Survey of India.

Lieut. Col. A. S. Waugh, Engrs.,	.. Superintendent, ..	16 *Dec.*	43
Major A. Strange, 7th Madras L.C.,	.. Astronomical Assist. G. T. Survey of India, coast Series, Vizagapatam—Leave S. C. 10 Oct. ..	24 *Dec.*	47
Lt. J. T. Walker, Bombay Engineers,	.. First Assist., G. T. Survey, in charge of Trigonometrical Survey operations on the Indus—Murree, ..	24 *Mar.*	54
Lieut. D. J. Nasmyth, Bombay Engrs.,	.. First Assistant, Bombay branch, Great Trigonometrical Survey of India, Bhooj, ..	24 *Mar.*	54
Capt. T. G. Montgomerie, Engineers,	.. First Assistant, G. T. Survey, Kashmir Series, Dehra Dhoon. ..	24 *Mar.*	54
Lieut. J. P. Basevi, Engrs.,	.. First Assist. G. T. Survey attached to Indus Series, Dehra Ishmael Khan (Punjaub,) ..	1 *Jan.*	58
Lieut. B. R. Branfill, 5th En. L. C.,	.. Second Asst. G. T. Survey, ..	4 *Oct.*	58
Lieut. H. R. Thuillier, Engineers,	.. Second Assist. G. T. Survey, ..	21 *May*	59
" J. Herschel Engineers	ditto - ditto	Nov.	59

Topographical Survey.

Capt. D. G. Robinson, Engineers,	.. In charge Topographical Survey, No. 1, Bengal Establishment, Rawul Pindee District, Dehra Dhoon. ..	25 *Oct.*	47
Capt. G. H. Saxton, 38th M. N. I.	.. Assist. Surveyor General, in charge of No. 1, party Ganjam Topographical Survey, Cuttack, ..	20 *Oct.*	54
Capt. G. C. Depree, Artillery,	.. Assistant Surveyor, Genl. No. 2, party Ganjam Topographical Survey, Cuttack,—Fur. S. C. 5th Jan. 59. ..	20 *Oct.*	54

Bengal Revenue Survey.

Major H. E. L. Thuillier, Artillery,	.. Superintendent, ..	9 *Feb.*	47
Captain W. S. Sherwill, 66th N. I.,	.. Surveyor 2nd or South Divn. Dinagepore (on Civil employ,) ..	15 *Oct,*	58
Capt. J. L. Sherwill, 39th N. I.	.. Officiating, ...	3 *Jan.*	59
Captain J. E. Gastrell, 13th N. I.	Surveyor, 4th or Western Division, Furreedpore, ..	15 *Oct.*	58
Capt. G. H. Thompson, 6th En. Regt.	.. Surveyor, Hazareebaugh Division, ..	14 *Jan.*	59
Captain W. S. Row, 33rd N. I.,	.. Assistant Surveyor,—Fur. S. C. 17 Jan. 59, ..	21 *Aug.*	55
Lieut. J. Sconce. Artillery.			

North-West Revenue Survey.

Capt. D. C. Vanrenen, Artillery,	.. Surveyor, 1st Division. Nagpore,—Fur. S. C. 29 Mar. 59. ..	3 *Oct.*	46
Capt. E. H. Willoughby, Artillery,	Surveyor, 2nd Division, Nagpore.—Fur. S. C. 30 Apl. 58, ..	9 *Feb.*	58
Lieut. A. D. Vanrenen, 71st N. I.,	.. Surveyor, Jhansie, at Agra, ..	26 *Nov.*	58
Capt. J. H. Grant, Artillery,	Assistant Surveyor, 2nd Division, Nagpore, in charge, ..	8 *July*	56
Lieut. R. E. Oakes, 52nd N. I.,	.. Assist. Surveyor 1st Division, Nagpore In charge, ..	8 *Apl.*	58

Punjaub Revenue Survey.

Lieut. J. Macdonald, 18th N. I.	.. Surveyor, Sindh, ..	10 *Sep.*	52
Lieut. F. C. Anderson, 71st N. I.	.. Surveyor Sind Saugor Dooab, at Murree,	19 *Nov.*	57
Capt. H. C. Johnstone, 5th En. Regt.,	.. Surveyor, Derajat, at Murree, ..	27 *May*	53
Lieut. P. Thompson, Artillery,	.. Assist. Surveyor, Sind Saugor Doab, ...	6 *Oct.*	58
Lieut. C. J. Griffiths, 72nd N. I.	.. Assistant Surveyor, Derajat, ..	25 *Feb.*	59

Employed in the Surveyor Generals' Department.

Capt. H. H. Godwin-Austen, H.M. 24th Foot,	Kashmir Survey, ..	8 *May*	57
Lieut A. B. Melville, 67th N. I., ..	Kashmir Survey, ..	8 *May*	57
Lieut. W. G. Murray, 68th N. I. ..	Kashmir Survey, ..	8 *May*	57

Pegu Survey.

Lieut. W. H. Edgecome, Madras Engrs.,	.. Superintendent, ..	26 *Sep.*	56
Lieut. R. C. Stewart, 84th Foot,	.. Assistant, ..	12 *Nov.*	54
Lieut. F. Fitzroy, Bengal Artillery,	.. Ditto, ..	26 *Sep.*	56
Lieut. G. Blair, Madras Artillery,	.. Ditto, ..	1 *Aug.*	56
Capt. D. Scott, 8th M. N. I.,	.. Ditto, ..	10 *Dec.*	57

ARMY COMMISSARIAT DEPARTMENT.

Rank and Names.	*Date of Appointment to present grade.*	*Where stationed or employed.*	REMARKS.
COMMISSARY GENERAL.			
Col. W. B. Thomson, C. B., 3rd En. Regt.	9 *Nov.* 58	Presidency,	
DEPY. COMMY. GENERALS.			
Major J. C. Scott, 20th N. I. ..	.. ..	Umballah, ..	Upper Circle.
Major G. B. Reddie, 29th N.I. ...	29 *Nov.* 58	Lucknow, ..	Central Circle.
Major T. F. Hobday, 72nd N I. ..	11 *May* 59	Presidency,	Lower Circle.
ASST. COMMY. GENLS.			
1st Class.			
Capt C.M.FitzGerald,31stNI.	20 *Oct.* 54	Kussowlie,	
Capt.R.C.Wroughton,12thNI	15 *Apl.* 56	.. ..	Furlough, S. C. 11th Jan. 59.
Capt.E.J. Simpson, 69th N I.	21 *June* 58	Presidency.	
Major R.S.Simpson, 27thN.I.	30 *Oct.* 58	Allahabad.	
Capt. J. I. Willes, 69th N.I.	29 *Nov.* 58	.. ..	Fur S. C. 28 Dec. 58.
Capt.R.D.Macpherson15thNI	11 *Maay* 59	.. ..	Furlough, S. C. 13 Apl. 1858.
2nd Class.			
Major T. H. Sibley, 62nd N.I.	2 *June* 57	Mean Meer (Lahore,)	Offg. Asst. Commy. Genl. 1st class.
Capt.L.R.Christopher,71stNI.	21 *June* 58	.. ..	Fur. S. C. 21 May 58.
Major G.S. Macbean, 74thN.I.	20 *Oct.* 54	.. ..	Furlough.
Major A.D. Dickens, 38th L. I.	15 *Apl.* 56	Lucknow,	Offg. Asst. Commy. Genl. 1st class.
Lieut. H. B. Chalmers, 27th N.I., ..	29 *Nov.* 58	Meerut.	
Capt. R. Davidson, 64th N. I.	11 *May* 59	.. ..	Furlough S. C. 14th July 58.
DEPTY. ASST. COMMY. GENLS.			
1st Class.			
Capt.M.J. Brander, 40th N.I.	30 *Nov.* 52	Cawnpore,	Offg. Assist. Commy. Genl. 2nd [class.
Lieut. J. Leven, 62nd N.I...	21 *July* 54	Fyzabad. ..	
Lieut. C. S. W. Ogilvie, 5th En. Regt.,	22 *Dec.* 58	Dinapore, ..	Offg. Asst. Commy. Genl. 2nd class
Capt. J. R. A. S. Lowe, 56th N. I. ..	14 *Sep.* 54	Benares, ..	Ditto, Ditto.
Capt. W. C. R. Mylne, 74th N. I. ..	28 *Oct.* 57	Agra, ..	Ditto, Ditto.
Lieut. J. Keer, 60th N. I. ..	10 *Feb.* 54	.. ..	
Lieut. J.H. Jenkins, 44thN.I.	29 *Nov.* 58	Rawul Pindee, ..	
Lieut. A. McKenzie, 9th N.I.	11 *May* 59	Peshawur.	
2nd Class.			
Lieut. J. S. Ogilvie,48th N.I.	30 *Oct.* 58	Saugor. ..	Offg. Depy. Asst. Commy. Genl. 1st [class.
Major T. James, 2nd N. I. (Grendrs.) ..	30 *Oct.* 58	Umballah,	Ditto, Ditto.
Lieut. J. Graham, 14th N. I.	30 *Oct.* 58	Bareilly, ..	Ditto, Ditto.
Capt. S. Chalmers, 53rd N.I.	30 *Oct.* 58	.. ..	Fur. S. C. 15th July 58.
Lieut. J. Sykes, 66th N. I. ..	22 *Dec.* 58	Ghazeepore,	Offg. Depy. Asst. Commy. Genl. 1st [class.
Lieut. Fitz. T. Goldsworthy, 72nd N. I. ..	30 *Oct.* 58	Head Qrs. Camp, ..	Ditto, Ditto.
Lieut. W. D. Hogg, 41st N.I.	22 *Dec.* 58	Seetapore,	
Capt. G.R. Roberts, 41st N.I.	11 *May* 59	Shahjehanpore. ..	
SUB-ASST. COMMY. GENLS.			
Lieut. C. S. Lane, 56th N. I., ...	30 *Oct.* 58	Gwalior, ..	Offg. Depy. Asst. Commy. Genl. 2nd [class.
Lieut. O. R. Newmarch, 44th N. I., ..	30 *Oct.* 58	Cawnpore,	Ditto, Ditto.
Capt. H R. Wroughton, 40th N. I., ..	30 *Oct.* 58	Gondah,..	Ditto, Ditto.
Captain W. Briggs, 71st N. I., ..	30 *Oct.* 58	Lucknow.	
Captain T. W. Holland, 38th N. I. ..	10 *Nov.* 58	Benares. ..	
Captain H. Mills, 2nd N. I. (Grs.) ..	30 *Oct.* 58	Allahabad,	Offg. Depy. Asst. Commy. Genl. [2nd class.
Captain H. A. Taylor, 74th N. I. ..	30 *Oct.* 58	Jullundur.	
Captain E. M. Martineau, 10th N. I. ..	30 *Oct.* 58	Ferozepore.	
Captain A. Macqueen, 42nd L. I. ..	30 *Oct.* 58	Fyzabad. ..	
Captain J E. Thomson, 62nd N. I. ..	30 *Oct,* 58	Mooltan.	

The Upper Circle consists of Umballah, Ferozepore, Lahore, Jullundur, Sealkote, Rawul Pindee, Peshawur, Kussowlie and Mooltan.

The Central Circle consists of Allahabad, Bundelkund, Agra, Futtehpore, Cawnpore, Rohilkund, Jhansie, Allyghur, Oude, Gwalior, Meerut and Mynpoorie.

The Lower Circle consists of Presidency, Dacca, Dinapore, Benares, Saugor, Mhow, Jubbulpore, Berhampore, Raneegunge, Assam, Midnapore and Sasseram.

ARMY COMMISSARIAT DEPARTMENT.—*Continued.*

Rank and Names.		Date of Appointment to present grade.	Where stationed or employed.	REMARKS.
SUB-ASST. COMMY. GENLS.—*Continued.*				
Capt. J. S. Dunbar, 64th N. I.	..	30 *Oct.* 58	Sealkote.	
Lieut. R. Ouseley, 48th N. I.,	..	30 *Oct.* 58	Futtehgurh	
Lieut. J. V. Hunt, 45th N. I.,	..	30 *Oct.* 58	Delhi.	
Lieut. N. R. Burlton, 40th N. I.,	..	10 *Nov.* 58	Goruckpore.	
Lieut. E. T. FitzGerald, 66th N. I.	..	30 *Oct.* 58	Umballah.	
Lieut. G. L. Keir, 41st N. I.	..	5 *Jan.* 59	RoyBareilly.	
OFFG. SUB.-ASST. COMMY. GENLS.				
Lieut. A. W. Bolton, 50th N. I.	..	19 *Nov.* 57	Goruckpore.	
Lieut. O. M. Graham, 6th En. Regt.,	..	29 *Jan.* 58	Toolseepore.	
Lieut. F. Allen, 42nd L. I.	..	25 *Sep.* 58	Dinapore.	
Captain A. S. Haig, 55th N. I.	..	29 *Sep.* 58	Fyzabad.	
Captain E. N. Perkins, 14th N. I.	..	11 *Oct.* 58	Mean Meer (Lahore.)	
Captain W. Forbes, 27th N. I.	..	13 *Oct.* 58	Benares.	
Captain J. A. Vanrenen, 54th N. I.	..	27 *Dec.* 58	Lucknow.	

SUBORDINATE OFFICERS OF THE ARMY COMMISSARIAT DEPARTMENT.

Rank and Names.		Date of appointment.	Where stationed or employed.	REMARKS.
JUNIOR COMMISSARIES. (4)				
Isham Baggs, (*a*)	..	5 *Nov.* 58	Campbellpore.	
William May, (*b*)	..	*do*	Dacca.	
J. Burnell, (*c*)	..	*do*	Presidency.	Asst. to Ex. Officer, 7 Mar. 59
S. Murray, (*d*)	..	*do*	Futtehgurh.	
DEPTY. COMMISSARIES. (6)				
Mr. A. E. Madras,	..	5 *Nov.* 58	Mhow.	
,, Robt. Kelly,	..	*do*	Nawabgunge.	
,, Philip Rubie,	..	*do*	Presidency.	
,, W. Lilly,	..	*do*	Landour.	
,, J. Pembroke,	..	*do*	Lucknow.	
,, A. B. Fox,	..	*do*	Murree,	
ASSIST. COMMISSARIES. (8)				
Mr. Jas. Atkin,	..	5 *Nov.* 58	Futtehpore.	
,, M. Gahan,	..	*do*	Dum-Dum.	
,, C. Hunter,	..	*do*	Agra.	
,, James Macdougal Hamilton,	..	*do*	Nynee Tal.	
,, William Norris,	..	*do*	Lucknow.	
,, Horatio Boardman Steward,	..	*do*	Lucknow.	
,, James Gillmon,	..	*do*	Umritsur.	
DEPUTY ASST. COMMISSARIES. (8)				
Mr. Michael Donnelly,	..	5 *Nov.* 58	Lahore,	
,, Joseph Cheers,	..	*do*	Sealkote.	
,, John Oliver,	..	*do*		
,, George Duncan,	..	*do*	Raneegunge.	
,, Daniel Ryan,	..	*do*	Jullundur.	
,, Thomas Johnston,	..	*do*	Agra.	
,, Robert Saunders,	..	*do*	Meerut.	
,, Mathew Cooper,	..	*do*	Attock.	
,, James Duncan,	..	*do*	Ferozepore.	
CONDUCTORS.				
Mr. Thomas Thrall,	..	21 *May* 58	Dugshaie.	
,, George Fredk. Knight,	..	*do*	Umballah.	
,, A. Duggan,	..	*do*	Agra.	

(*a*) Lieutenant on the Veteran Establishment, 2 February 1852.
(*b*) Lieutenant on the Veteran Establishment, 3 February 1857.
(*c*) Lieutenant on the Veteran Establishment, 3 January 1859.
(*d*) Ensign (unattached) 11th June 1858.

SUBORDINATE OFFICERS OF THE ARMY COMMISSARIAT DEPARTMENT.—(*Continued.*)

Rank and Names.	*Date of Appointment.*	*Where Stationed or employed.*	REMARKS.
CONDUCTORS. (*Contd.*)			
Mr. John Ritchson, ..	21 *May* 58	Mooltan.	
,, John Collins, ..	7 *Sep.* 58	Shahjehanpore	
,, C. Stokes, ..	5 *Nov.* 58	Rawul Pindee.	
,, John A. Schruder, ..	*do*	Peshawur.	
,, Henry Gardiner, ..	*do*	Dinapore.	
,, John Whelton, ..	*do*	Sealkote.	
,, W. Hardinge, ..	*do*	Hazareebaugh.	
,, George Rogers, ..	*do*	Allahabad.	
,, John Woodroffe. ..	*do*	Allyghur,	
,, James Paterson, ..	*do*	Presidency.	
,, Michael, O'Loughlin, ..	*do*	Presidency.	
,, George Briggs, ..	*do*	Roy Bareilly (Oude.)	
,, James Dwyer, ..	*do*	Peshawur.	
,, James Wilks, ..	*do*		
,, Alfred Simmons, ..	*do*	Lahore.	
,, Thomas Gill, ..	*do*	Campbellpore,	
,, William King, ..	*do*	Umballah.	
,, D. Johnson, ..	*do*	Lahore.	
,, Joseph Senior, ..	*do*	Nawabgunge.	
,, D. Hitchins, ..	*do*	Allahabad.	
SUB-CONDUCTORS (25.)			
Mr. J Black, ...	5 *Nov.* 58	Ferozepore.	
,, T. O'Donnell, ..	*do*		
,, J. Kelly, ..	*do*	Ferozepore.	
,, P. Carr, ..	*do*	Arrah.	
,, J. H. Sharpe, ..	*do*	Benares.	
,, T. Gibney, ..	*do*	Dacca.	
,, R. A. Dawson, ..	*do*	Bareilly.	
,, R. Tear, ...	*do*	Nowshera.	
,, W. Neal, ..	*do*	Berhampore.	
,, G. Smith, ..	*do*	Mynpoory.	
,, P. Leahy, ..	*do*	Cawnpore.	
,, M. Brien, ..	*do*	Lahore.	
,, C. O. Gorman, ..	*do*	Delhi.	
,, W. Asher, ..	*do*	Sealkote.	
,, J. O. Leary, ..	*do*	Lucknow.	
,, R. G. Davies, ..	*do*	Kalka.	
,, J. Williams, ..	*do*	Rawul Pindee.	
,, M. Dundan, ..	*do*	Peshawur.	
,, W. L. Smith, ..	*do*	Mooltan.	
,, S. Parkhouse, ..	*do*	Peshawur.	
,, W. Collar, ..	*do*	Umballah.	
,, R. Avice, ..	*do*	Peshawur.	
,, D. Nicol, ..	*do*	Lucknow.	
,, M. Carew, ...	*do*	Bareilly.	
,, A. Torrance, ..	*do*	Attock.	
SUPERNUMERARY.			
Mr. W. Higgins, ..	18 *Nov.* 58	Thaytmew.	

KEDDAH ESTABLISHMENTS.

Major E. F. Smith, 23rd N. I.,	.. Superintendent at Dacca,	.. 14 *June* 53
Major F. W. Baugh, 26th L. I.	.. Superintendent at Kemaoon,	.. 27 *May* 54
Mr. John MacDonald,	.. Asst. Supdt. at Kemaoon,	.. 5 *Sep,* 58

AUDITOR OF COMMISSARIAT AND STUD ACCOUNTS.

Major G. Newbolt, 31st N. I.	.. Presidency,	.. { 1 *May* 53 1 *May* 54

STUD DEPARTMENT.

CENTRAL PROVINCES.
Depôts at Ghazeepore, Buxar, Kurruntadhee and Poosah.
NORTH-WESTERN PROVINCES.
Depôts at Haupper and Seharunpore.

SUPERINTENDENT OF STUD.

Col. E. J. Dickey, 27th N. I.	.. Meerut,	.. 19 *May* 54

DEPUTY SUPERINTENDENTS.

Major W. W. Apperley, 3d E.L.C.	.. Central Provinces, Kurruntadhee,—On duty at the Cape of Good Hope,..	19 *May* 54
Major R. Thatcher, 9th N.I.,	.. N. W. P., Haupper,	.. 24 *Mar.* 55

FIRST CLASS ASSISTANTS.

Capt. J. K. Couper, 2nd Grs.	Buxar, (Offg. Depy. Supdt. Central Provinces,) ..	2 *June* 54
Capt. C. W. D'Oyly, 58th N. I.,	Haupper,—Fur. S. C. 15 Mar. 59.	.. 24 *Mar.* 55

SECOND CLASS ASSISTANTS.

Captain A. A. Macdonell, 40th N. I.	.. Poosah,	.. 31 *Dec.* 57
Lieut. W. C. MacDougall, 72nd N. I.,	.. Seharunpore,	.. 20 *Dec.* 58

SUB-ASSISTANTS.

Capt. B. Parrott, 37th N. I.,	.. Haupper,	.. 31 *Dec.* 57
Lieut. E. S. Jackson, 12th N. I.,	.. Buxar,—Fur. S. C. 15 Apl. 59.	.. 26 *Aug.* 58
Capt. W. B. Irwin, 10th N. I.	..	.. 12 *Nov.* 58
Capt. G. C. Lloyd, 56th N. I.,	.. Offg.	.. 26 *July* 58
Lieut. H. H. Lyster, 72nd N. I.	.. Offg.	.. 12 *Nov.* 58
Mr. John Taylor,	.. In charge of the Ord. Cattle Farm, Hissar,	20 *May* 50

ASSISTANT SURGEONS.

J. L. Bryden, M. D.,	.. In Medical charge Buxar and Kurruntadhee Studs	.. 21 *Apl.* 59
G. M. Govan, M. D.,	.. Haupper Stud,	.. 17 *May* 59
A. R. Waghorn,	.. In Medical charge of the Ordnance Cattle Farm, Hissar, ..	2 *June* 56

VETERINARY SURGEONS.

J. Siddall,	.. Kurrantadhee,	.. 24 *Dec.* 52
J. W. Garrad,	.. Haupper,	.. 20 *May* 58
J. S. Woods,	.. Seharunpore,	.. 30 *Mar.* 59

ORDNANCE DEPARTMENT.

COMMISSIONED AND WARRANT OFFICERS

Inspector Genl. of Ordnance & Magazines.

Lt. Col. E. W. S. Scott, Artillery,	.. Calcutta,	.. 18 *Jan.* 58

Principal Commissary of Ordnance.

Captain H. Lewis, Artillery,	.. Meerut,—Fur. P. A. 10 May 59,	.. 18 *Jan.* 58
Captain G. E. Voyle, Artillery,	.. Officiating,	.. 10 *May* 59

Commissaries.

1st Class,	Major C. Douglas, Artillery,	.. Offg. Civil employ,	.. 22 *Apl.* 53
	Capt. M. E. Currie, Artillery,	.. Fur. S. C. 30th July 1858,	.. 12 *Aug.* 57
	Capt. G. E. Voyle, Artillery,	.. (Offg. Principal Commy. of Ordnance,)	12 *Feb.* 58
2nd Class,	Capt. W. C. Russell, Artillery,	.. Arsenal, Fort William,	.. 28 *Nov.* 56
	Capt. L. Machell, Artillery,	.. Agra,	.. 12 *Aug.* 57
	Capt. T. Nicholl, Artillery,	.. Saugor,	.. 12 *Feb.* 58

Deputy Commissaries.

Capt. H. R. Brownlow, Artillery,	.. Ferozepore,	.. 28 *Nov.* 56
Capt. J. C. Griffith, Artillery,	.. Delhi,	.. 24 *Mar.* 57
Capt. J. G. Hathorn, Artillery,	.. Asst. to the Inspector General of Ordnance and Magazines,	.. 24 *Mar.* 57
Major W. T. Brown, Artillery,	.. Cawnpore,	.. 9 *Dec.* 56
Capt. T. N. Harward, Artillery,	.. Fur. S. C. 23 July 1858,	.. 7 *Apl.* 57
Lieut. John Stewart, Artillery,	.. Allahabad,	.. 18 *Sep.* 57
Lieut. J. R. Pearson, Artillery,	.. Fur.S.C.1 Apl.59.	.. 23 *Nov.* 57
Capt. E. Tierney, Artillery,	.. Fur. S. C. 14 Feb. 1859,	.. 31 *July* 58
Lieut. C. V. Arbuckle, Artillery,	.. Peshawur,	.. 1 *Feb.* 59
Lieut. D. J. Welsh, Artillery,	.. Allahabad,	.. 14 *Apl* 59
Capt. A. Darling, Artillery,	.. Offg., Phillour,	.. 20 *Nov.* 57
Lieut. H. A. Mallock, Artillery,	.. Offg. Mhow,	.. 17 *Feb.* 59
William Raynor,†	.. Ferozepore,	.. 10 *July* 55

† Captain on the Veteran Establishment.

ORDNANCE DEPARTMENT.—*Continued.*

Assistant Commissaries.

Name	Station	Date
Thomas Spencer,†	.. Mooltan,	.. 22 *Nov.* 52
George Forrest,†	.. Delhi, Lv. S. C. 15 Sep.	.. 22 *Feb.* 53
Joseph Green,*	.. Jhelum,	.. 6 *Jan.* 54
H. Michell,†	.. Arsenal, Fort William,	.. 10 *July* 55
Sylvester Fox,*	.. Dum-Dum,	.. 1 *May* 56
William Kelly,*	.. Peshawur,	.. *do*
William Parry,*	.. Agra, Lv. S. C. 13 April 1860.	.. 1 *May* 56
James Lamb,*	.. Attock,	.. 24 *Sep.* 58
Deputy Assistant Commissaries.		
Joseph Vyall,	.. Ferozepore,	.. 6 *Jan.* 54
Isaac James Corcoran,*	.. (Actg. Asst. Commy.,) Arsenal,	.. 17 *July* 56
Charles Sheridan,*	.. Asst. Director of the Arty. School of Instruction at Meerut,	.. 19 *Aug.* 56
John Buckley,*	.. Delhi,—Fur. S. C. 10th May 1858,	.. 11 *May* 57
John Borthwick,	.. Lahore,	.. 30 *May* 57
James Stone,	.. Saugor,	.. 15 *Feb.* 58
James Leonard, *(Supernumerary,)*	.. Military Auditor General's Office,	.. 15 *Feb.* 58
John Stotesbury,*	.. Phillour,	.. 15 *Feb.* 58
Wm. Harris,	.. Cawnpore,	.. 24 *Sep.* 58
Conductors.		
Enoch Postance,	.. Permanent Mhow,	.. 26 *Mar.* 47
James Cooper,	.. Govindgurh Depôt,	.. 14 *Apl.* 49
James Ross,	.. Allahabad,	.. 13 *Oct.* 49
Thomas Newbold,	.. Permanent, Ferozepore.	. 11 *Apl* 50
Andrew Stoney,	.. Permanent, Dera Ishmael Khan,	.. 1 *Sep.* 50
William Haslam,	.. Permanent, Arsenal, Fort William,	.. 4 *Apl.* 51
George Faichnie,	.. Phillour, (Offg. Permanent Conductor),	2 *May* 51
Michael Halpin,	.. Permanent, Arsenal, Fort William.—Fur. S. C. 23rd Feb. 1858,	.. 4 *Oct.* 51
Michael McGrath,*	.. Permanent, Allahabad, (Offg. extra Dep. Asst. Commy.)	.. 19 *Mar.* 52
George Padgham,	.. Dum-Dum,	.. 22 *Nov.* 52
Richard Vaughan,	.. Office of the Prinpl. Comy. of Ordnance,	29 *Dec.* 52
Martin Byrne,	.. Permanent, Delhi,	.. 22 *Feb.* 53
William Fitzgibbon,	.. Permanent, Arsenal, Fort William,	.. 4 *Mar.* 53
Thomas Fay,	.. Permanent, Attock,	.. 25 *Mar.* 53
William Morrison,	.. Permanent, Chunar,	.. 18 *Aug.* 53
Edward Quin,	.. Permanent, Allahabad,	. 27 *Aug.* 53
John Doyle,	.. Permanent, Agra,	. 28 *Dec.* 53
Thomas White,	.. Arsenal,	.. 20 *Apl.* 54
Patrick Sharkey,	.. Phillour,	.. 16 *Sep.* 54
James Hurley,	.. Permanent, Ferozepore,	.. 8 *Mar.* 55
Richd. Clarke,	.. Arsenal,	.. 11 *Nov.* 55
Joseph Upton,	.. Allahabad,	.. 21 *Dec.* 55
John Courtney,	.. Permanent, Allahabad,	.. 21 *Dec.* 55
J. C. Palphreyman,	.. Permanent Saugor,	.. 21 *Dec.* 55
James Lynch,	.. Military Auditor General's Office,	.. 1 *May* 56
James Smith,	.. Permanent, Attock,	.. *do*
Michl. Shannahan,	.. Allahabad,	.. *do*
Wm. Murray,	.. Mooltan,	.. *do*
Phillip Godby,	.. Permanent, Allahabad,—Lv.S.C.15 Nov.	*do*
Michael McHatton,	.. Permanent, Agra,	.. *do*
John Stiles,	.. Permanent, Agra,	.. *do*
Thomas Branigan,	.. Lucknow,	.. *do*
Patrick O'Keeffe,	.. Permanent, Saugor,	.. *do*
Thomas Ryan,	.. Permanent, Lucknow,	.. *do*
J. Hill,	.. Permanent, Allahabad,	.. *do*
J. Tanner,	.. Permanent, Phillour,	.. *do*
Alexander Heffernan,	.. Agra,	.. *do*
Henry Telfer,	.. Permanent, Arsenal, Fort William,	.. *do*
Thomas Wilkins,	.. Permanent, Arsenal, Fort William,	.. *do*
Daniel McSweeney,	.. Offg. Arsenal, Fort William,	.. *do*
James Byrne,	.. Allahabad,	.. *do*
Thomas Stevenson,	.. Allahabad,	.. *do*

*Lieutenants on the Veteran Establishment. † Captains on the Veteran Establishment.

Ordnance Department—*Continued.*

Name	Station	Date
Conductors.—Continued.		
Wm. Carroll,	.. Delhi,	.. 1 *May* 56
Wm. Prosser,	.. Allahabad,	.. *do*
John Byrne,	.. Permanent, Ferozepore,	.. 29 *June* 56
Thomas H. Hill,	. Arsenal,	.. 6 *July* 56
J. McDermot,	.. Attock,	.. 18 *do*
Pat. McDermot,	.. Lucknow,	.. 20 *Aug.* 56
Patrick Mallon,	.. Arsenal, Fort William,	.. 7 *Sep.* 56
Wm. Webb,	.. Allahabad,	.. 28 *Oct.* 56
Henry Shaw,	.. Arsenal, Fort William,	.. *do*
William Skeaf.	.. Benares,	.. 3 *Feb.* 57
John Ford,	.. Arsenal, Fort William,	.. 11 *May* 57
John Minahan,	.. Agra,	.. 14 *do*
James Parker,	.. Agra,	.. 30 *do*
Henry Franklin,	.. Cawnpore,	.. 22 *June* 57
James Smith,	.. Offg. Permanent, Ferozepore,	.. 11 *July* 57
John Doran,	.. Agra,	.. 11 *Sep.* 57
John Baker,	.. Peshawur,	.. 30 *do*
James Johnstone,	.. Ferozepore,	.. 30 *Sep.* 57
James Miller,	.. Permanent, Lucknow, (In charge of the Depôt at Bareilly,)	.. 1 *Oct.* 57
E. Lovegrove,	.. Allahabad,	.. 11 *Dec.* 57
Michael Rourke,	.. Lucknow,	.. 15 *Feb.* 58
R. W. Sharpe,	.. Mooltan,	.. 17 *Apl.* 58
Simon Vandrass,	.. Lucknow,	.. 24 *Sep.* 58
Andrew Walker,	.. Delhi,	.. 28 *do*
James Rogers,	.. Cawnpore,	.. *do*
T. H. M. Marchant,	.. Arsenal,	.. *do*
James Copley,	.. Cawnpore,	.. *do*
Miles McCarthy,	.. Arsenal, Fort William,	.. *do*
Sub-Conductors.		
~~Charles Rossiter~~,	.. Ferozepore,—(Offg. Condr.,)	.. 21 *Apl.* 54
*William Holroyd Bradbury,	.. Umballah,	.. 28 *May* 57
*J. Comber,	.. Mooltan,	.. 20 *Oct.* 57
*W. Barker,	.. Delhi,	.. 18 *Nov.* 57
J. Warburton,	.. Arsenal, (Offg. Condr.)	.. 27 *Dec.* 57
James Goulder,	.. Delhi,	.. *do*
*Thomas Heathcoate,	.. Ferozepore	.. *do*
Michael Flood,	... Lucknow,	.. 12 *Apl.* 58
*J. Bateman,	..	.. 19 *do* 58
James Harrison Bewsey,	.. Lucknow,	.. 27 *do* 58
*Patrick Quaid,	.. Allahabad,	.. 13 *May* 58
*Thomas Faxton,	... Allahabad,	.. *do*
* R. J. Baldwin,	... Agra,	.. *do*
*Henry Mann,	... Ferozepore,	.. *do*
Thomas Yeldham,	.. Delhi,	.. 16 *June* 58
Charles H. Crutcher,	.. Allahabad,	.. 12 *Aug.* 58
Lawrence Lesmond,	.. Phillour,	.. *do*
William Doherty,	.. Delhi,	.. *do*
William Swinnerton,	.. Allahabad,	.. *do*
Daniel McKay,	.. Arsenal,	.. *do*
Alexander Wilson,	.. Dinapore,	.. *do*
Edward Wilsey,	.. Arsenal, Fort William,	.. *do*
J. T. Hewson,	.. Arsenal, Fort William,	.. *do*
P. Riordan,	.. Saugor,	.. *do*
James Hand,	..	.. *do*
Thomas Thornton,	.. Delhi,	.. *do*
F. L. Tucker,	.. Agra,	.. *do*
G. B. Bleazby,	.. Mhow,	.. *do*
William Devine,	.. Allahabad,	.. *do*
Daniel Flynn,	.. Raneegunge,	.. *do*
Denis Desmond,	.. Arsenal,	.. *do*

* Officiating Sub-Conductors.

ORDNANCE DEPARTMENT.—(*Continued.*)

Sub-Conductors—(Continued.)		
Richard Monks,	.. Phillour,	.. 12 *Aug* 58
G. Leonard,	.. Bareilly,	.. *do*
P. Potter,	.. Agra,	.. *do*
E. W. Allum,	.. Ferozepore,	.. *do*
*W. Barker,	.. Ferozepore,	.. 12 *Oct.* 58
Nilus Peter Thompson,	.. Peshawur,	.. ———
*James Stagg,	.. Ferozepore,	.. 3 *Dec.* 58
*William Rawson,	.. Saugor,	.. 6 *do*
*C. Glover,	.. Agra,	.. 15 *do*
*H. Hobery,	.. Peshawur,	.. *do*
Q. S. Griffith,	...	.. 8 *Jan.* 59
J. Copeland,	.. Offg. Barrack Master at Bareilly and Shahjehanpore.	*do*

SUPERINTENDENT OF THE COSSIPORE FOUNDRY.

Lieut. Col. A. Broome, Artillery,	.. Cossipore,	.. 16 *Nov.* 46

AGENT FOR THE MANUFACTURE OF GUNPOWDER.

Col. V. Eyre, C. B. Artillery,	.. Ishapore,	.. 18 *Jan.* 58

AGENT FOR GUN CARRIAGES.

Col. F. Turner, C. B. Artillery,	.. Futtehgurh,	.. 18 *Jan.* 58

WARRANT OFFICERS ATTACHED TO DIFFERENT DEPARTMENTS.

Conductors.		
J. Crohan,	.. Gun Powder Agency, Ishapore,	.. 18 *Dec.* 54
J. Forbes,	.. Percn. Cap Manufactory, Dum-Dum,..	2 *Aug.* 55
J. Holman,	.. Artillery School of Instruction, Meerut,	7 *Aug.* 56
G. Leach,	.. Town Major's Office, Fort William, ..	28 *Aug.* 57
John Matthews,	.. 2nd Divn. Army Clothing Agency,	.. 4 *Dec.* 57
William Allsopp,	.. Governor Genl's. Stables, Presidency,..	1 *Aug.* 58
Sub-Conductors.		
John Wood,	.. Gun Powder Agency, Ishapore,	.. 19 *Dec.* 54
Edward Finlay,	.. 1st Divn. Army Clothing Agency,	.. 12 *May* 57
William Croydon,	.. Arty. School of Instruction, Meerut, ..	1 *Dec.* 58
John Connors,	.. Cossipore Gun Foundry,	.. 24 *Jan.* 59

* Officiating Sub-Conductors.

Department of Public Works.

SECRETARY TO THE GOVERNMENT OF INDIA IN THE DEPARTMENT OF PUBLIC WORKS.

Lieut. Col. H. Yule, Engrs., .. Secy. to the Govt. of India, Dep. of P. Works, 5 *Jan.* 59
Capt. A. Fraser, Engrs., .. Under Secy. to the Govt. of India, D. P. W., 9 *Mar.* 59
Mr. A. B. Sampson, B. A., .. Assistant Secy. to the Govt. of India D.P.W., 30 *May* 59

RAILWAY DEPARTMENT.

Major R. Strachey, Engrs., .. Consulting Engineer, to the Govt. of India, Lv. S. C. 31 Dec., .. 13 *Sep.* 58
Major W. W. H. Greathed, Engrs., .. Consulting Engr., N. W. P. .. 14 *June* 59
Capt. C. J. Hodgson, Engrs., .. Offg. ditto, Bengal, .. 6 *Apl.* 58
Capt. G. Sim, Engrs., .. Depy. Consulting Engr. N. W.P .. 5 *July* 58
Major J. G. Medley, Engrs. .. Ditto ditto ditto, Punjaub, .. 21 *Sep.* 58
Capt. E. Davidson, Engineers, .. Ditto ditto ditto, Bengal, .. 6 *Dec.* 58

LOWER PROVINCES.

The First Circle, comprises Presidency Division, Iron Bridge Yard, Garrison of Fort William, Circular and Eastern Canals, with the Suburban Roads, Barrackpore Division, Sylhet Division, Dacca Division, Upper Assam Division, Lower Assam Division, and Arracan Division.

Divisions.	*Names and Rank.*	*When appointed*	DUTY.
Calcutta, ..	Col. H. Goodwyn, Engrs., ..	1 *May* 54	[C. 9 Apl. 57. Chief Engineer.—Fur. S.
	Capt. R. DeBourbel, Engrs., ...	5 *Jan.* 57	Asst. to Chief Engr.
		18 *Sep.* 58	Offg. Ex. Engr. Dum-Dum.
	Captain C. B. Young, Engrs. ..	27 *Mar.* 57	Suptg. Engr. 1st Circle.
		14 *Aug.* 57	Offg. Chief Engr., L. P.
R	~~Lieut. Col. T. H. Sale, Engrs.~~, ...	27 *Apl.* 58	Offg. Supdg. Engr., 1st Circle.
Presidency Division, ..	Capt. G. Price, 1st En. B. F., ..	27 *Mar.* 57	Civil Architect.—Fur. S. C. 4 Sep. 58. [S. C.
	Capt. A. Impey, Engrs.	14 *Sep.* 58	Offg. Civil Architect,—Lv.
	Mr. T. Isaac, ..	.. ..	Offg. Civil Architect.
	Mr. F. R. Boyce, ..	23 *May* 56	Asst. to Civil Architect.
		5 *June* 57	Offg. Asst. to Chief Engr. L. P.,
	Mr. L. F. Byrne, ..	23 *June* 59	Special Asst. Engineer.
Iron Bridge Yard at Allipore, ..	Mr. R. S. Sterling, ..	11 *July* 54	Superintendent.
Garrison of Fort William,	Major J. J. McL. Innes, Engrs.,	6 *Apl.* 58	Garrison Engineer.
	Lieut. J. P. Westmorland, Engrs..	6 *May* 59	Assistant Engineer.
	Ensign W. Bird, (unattached,) ..	14 *June* 59	Barrack-Master.
Circular and Eastern Canals and the Suburban Roads, ..	Mr. H. Leonard, ..	.. ..	Superintendent.
	Mr. F. Bilderbeck, ..	25 *Sep.* 58	Asst. Supdt. [Apl. 58.
Barrackpore Division, Barrackpore, ..	Captain J. Eliot, Artillery, ..	20 *Sep.* 54	Ex. Officer.—Fur. S. C. 7
	Lieut. J. M. Heywood, Engrs., ..	28 *Mar.* 59	Asst. Engineer.
	Assistant Commy. J. Brooke, ..	13 *Dec,* 58	Barrack Master,—Fur. S. C. 5 Apl. 59.
	Mr. A. J. L. Perrier, ..	23 *June* 59	Special Asst. Engr.,
Dum-Dum Division, ..	Capt. R. De Bourbel, Engrs. ..	18 *Sep.* 58	Ex. Engineer.
Dacca Division, ..	Capt. A. F. Baird, 18th N. I. ..	26 *Oct.* 58	Asst. Engineer.
Lower Assam Division, Gowahatty, ..	Capt. W. E. Marshall 48th N. I.	5 *Jan.* 57	Executive Officer.
Arracan Divn., Akyab,..	Lieut. E. J. L. Twynam. 25th N.I.	14 *Mar.* 55	Ex. Officer.

ARRACAN ROAD.

1st Division, ...	Mr. W. Boate, ..	... ..	Superintendent.

D

DEPARTMENT OF PUBLIC WORKS.—*Continued.*

Divisions.	*Names and Rank.*	*When appointed.*	DUTY.
	ARRACAN ROAD—(*Continued.*)		
2nd Division, ..	Mr. G. Munro, ..	30 *May* 54	Ex. Engineer.
3rd Division, ..	Mr. C. B. Neild, ..	30 *May* 54	Ex. Engineer.
3rd Division, ..	Mr. R. Patterson, ..	25 *Feb.* 56	Ex. Engineer.

The Second Circle, comprises Dinapore Division, Nuddea Rivers, and the 2nd Division Grand Trunk Road, also the Road from the Ganges towards Darjeeling, Berhampore Division, Purneah Division, Raepore Road, Cuttack and Ungool Road, 1st Division Grand Trunk Road, and the Patna Branch Road.

Divisions.	*Names and Rank.*	*When appointed.*	DUTY.
Calcutta,	Lt. Col. E. L. Ommanney, Engrs.,	3 *May* 54	Suptg. Engr. 2nd Circle.
		14 *Apl.* 57	Offg. Chief Engr. Punjab.
Calcutta,	Capt. W. Maxwell, Artillery, ..	24 *Apl.* 57	Offg. Supdg. Engr. 2nd Circle.
Dinapore Division, Dinapore, ..	Capt. F. Alexander, Artillery, ..	30 *May* 54	Ex. Officer.
Dinapore Division, Dinapore, ..	Mr. G. J. Hardy, ..	13 *Dec.* 58	Barrack Master.
Dinapore Division, Dinapore, ..	Mr. F. C. Marshall, ..	8 *Jan.* 58	Asst. Engineer.
Patna Division, Patna, ..	Capt. C. J. Mead, Artillery, ..	25 *Mar.* 59	Ex. Engineer.
Patna Division, Patna, ..	Baboo Moheschunder Bose, ..	24 *June* 59	Asst. Engineer.
Patna Division, Patna, ..	Baboo Gopaulchunder Mookerjea,	*do*	Ditto.
Nuddea Rivers, Kishnagurh, ..	Mr T. W. Armstrong, ..	26 *July* 58	Superintendent.
Nuddea Rivers, Kishnagurh, ..	Baboo Tincowrie Ghose, ..	24 *June* 59	Asst. Engineer.
Nuddea Rivers, Kishnagurh, ..	Baboo Radhicanarain Ghose, ..	*do*	Ditto.
2nd Division G. T. Road Sheergotty, ..	Capt. F. S. Stanton, Engrs., ..	11 *Nov.* 53	Ex. Engineer.
		12 *May* 57	Offg. Ex. Engr. Patna Branch Road.
2nd Division G. T. Road Sheergotty, ..	Lieut. C. N. Judge, Engrs., ...	28 *Mar.* 59	Asst. Engineer.
2nd Division G. T. Road Sheergotty, ..	Lieut. R. C. Danbuz, Engrs., ..	28 *Mar.* 59	Ditto.
2nd Division G. T. Road Sheergotty, ..	Mr. G. Nolan, ...	16 *June* 59	Ditto.
2nd Division G. T. Road Sheergotty, ..	Mr. W. O'Neill ..	23 *June* 59	Special Asst. Engineer.
Road from the Ganges towards Darjeeling,	Mr. T. Login, ..	6 *Nov.* 57	Ex. Engineer.
Darjeeling, Division, ..	Capt. W. S. Trevor, Engrs., ..	2 *Oct.* 57	Ex. Engineer.
Santal Country, ..	Capt. H. T. Forbes, Artillery, ..	6 *Aug* 58	Ex. Engineer,
Berhampore Division, Berhampore, ..	Capt. F. P. Layard, 19th N. I. ..	18 *Dec.* 46	Ex. Engineer.
Berhampore Division, Berhampore, ..	Conductor. W. Craig, ..	13 *Dec.* 58	Barrack Master.
Purneah Division, Dinagepore, ..	Capt. C. Murray, 70th N. I., ..	11 *July* 54	Offg. Asst. Engineer, Darjeeling.
1st Divn. Grand T. Road, Hooghly, ..	Asst. Commy. E. Rooke,	6 *Oct.* 54	Executive Engineer.
Patna Branch Road, Patna,	Lieut. W C. Mackinnon, H. M. 87th Foot,	19 *Mar.* 56	Asst. Engineer,
Cuttack Division, ..	Lieut. H. Dixon, 22nd M. N. I.,	30 *Mar.* 55	Ex. Engineer.
Raepore Road, ...	Mr. F. Bond, ..	18 *Apl.* 56	Executive Engineer.
Ramghur Division, ..	Capt. J. Dawson, 43rd L. I., ..	21 *Sep.* 58	Executive Engineer.
	Nagpore Territory.		
Nagpore, ..	Col. A. H. E. Boileau, Engrs.,	1 *Apl.* 56	Chief Engineer.
Nagpore, ..	Capt. F. Applegath, 33rd M.N.I.	1 *June* 59	Ex. Officer, Bhandara Divn.
Nagpore, ..	Lt. E. A. Saunders, 7th M.N.I.	4 *Feb.* 56	Ex. Officer, Chundwara Divn.
Nagpore, ..	*		Ex. Officer, Chanda Divn.
Nagpore, ..	Lt. H. D. B. Smith, 2nd M.E.R.	14 *May* 59	Ex. Engr., Nagpore Divn.
Nagpore, ..	Capt. G. O. Rybot, Arty., ..	2 *Apl.* 56	Ex. Officer, Raepore Divn.

Department of Public Works.—(*Continued.*)

Divisions.	*Names and Rank.*	*When appointed.*	Duty.
	EMBANKMENT CIRCLE, HEAD QUARTERS MIDNAPORE.		
	Comprises Midnapore Division, Cuttack Division, Burdwan Division, Culmeejole Division, Southern Hidgellee Division, Northern Hidgellee Division, 24-Pergunnahs, Balasore Division, and Gunduck Embankments.		
Midnapore, ..	Capt. J. P. Beadle, Engrs., ..	27 *Oct.* 54	Supt. of Embankments.
Midnapore Division — Midnapore, ..	Capt. W. D. A. R. Short, Engrs.	6 *Oct.* 54	Ex. Engineer.
	Baboo Rampersaud Doss, ..	6 *Oct.* 54	Asst. Engineer.
	Baboo Jodoonauth Seal, ..	24 *June* 59	Asst. Engineer.
Cuttack Division, ..	Capt. J. C. Harris, Engrs., ..	5 *Dec.* 54	Executive Engineer.
	Sergeant G. Rayner, ..	28 *Oct.* 53	Asst. Engineer.
Burdwan Div. Burdwan,	Mr. W. Smith, ..	3 *July* 57	Ex. Engineer.
	Mr. W. Chisholm, ..	.. ..	Asst. Engineer.
	Mr. P. Neuville, ..	24 *June* 59	Asst. Engineer.
	Baboo Gopalchunder Coondoo, ..	24 *June* 59	Asst. Engineer.
Culmeejole Division, Culmeejole, ..	Sergeant T. H. Harper, ..	29 *Sep.* 57	Ex. Engineer.
	Mr. C. Mayne, ..	5 *May* 59	Ex. Engineer.
Southern Hidgellee Division, Contai, ..	Baboo Khetter Nath Bhuttacharjea, ..	24 *June* 59	Asst. Engineer.
Northern Hidgellee Division, Kedgeree, ..	Mr. T. Fennessy, ..	.. ..	Executive Engineer.
	Lieut. H. W. Garnault, Engrs., ..	1 *Nov.* 58	Asst. Engineer.
	Mr. W. Brown, ..	19 *Jan.* 57	Asst. Engineer.
	Baboo Rammessur Nath, ..	24 *June* 59	Asst. Engineer.
24-Perghs. Div., Allypore,	Segt. J. H. Harper, ..	28 *Dec.* 55	Ex. Officer.
Balasore Divn., Balasore, ..	Mr. C. Gilbert, ..	6 *Oct.* 54	Supervisor.
Gunduck River, Sarun, ..	Lieut. J. M. McNeile, Engrs., ..	11 *Oct.* 58	Asst, Engineer.
	PEGU.		
Rangoon Division,	Major A. G. Goodwyn, Engrs., ..	13 *Sep.* 58	Chief Engineer.—Leave S. C. to 31 May 60.
	Capt. C. D. Newmarch, Engrs.,	23 *Jan.* 57 14 *June* 59	Assist. to Chief Engr. Offg. Chief Engineer.
	Lieut. S. T. Trevor, Engrs., ..	18 *June* 59	Offg. Asst. to Chief Engr.
Thayat Mew „ ..	Lt. G. de P. Falconnett, M. Engrs.,	13 *June* 56	Ex. Engr.
„ „ ..	Sergt. J. W. Watt, ..	29 *Oct.* 58	Barrack Master.
Meeaday „ ..	Lieut. T. J. Geldart, 65th Bl. N. I,	.. ..	Asst. Engineer.
Rangoon Cantonment, ..	Capt. W. R. Fitzgerald, Artillery,	.. ..	Ex. Engineer.
Rangoon Town, ..	Lieut. S. T. Trevor, Engrs., ..	.. ..	Ex. Engineer (Offg. Asst. to Chief Engr.)
„ „ ..	Lieut. F. T. Pollok, 8th M. N. I.,	18 *June* 59	Offg. Executive Engr.
„ „ ..	Mr. J. James, ..	.. ..	Asst. Ex. Engineer.
„ „ ..	Sergt. C. McCarthy, ..	29 *Oct.* 58	Barrack Master.
Bassein, ..	Capt. E. Leeds, 47th N. I., ..	.. ..	Ex. Engineer.
Shoay Gyeen & Sittang Division, ..	Lieut. J. M. Williams, 1st M. F.	15 *Dec.* 57	Ex. Engineer.
Tounghoo, ..	Lieut. F. T. Pollok, 8th M.N.I.	17 *May* 59 18 *June* 59	Ex. Engineer. Offg. Ex. Engr. Rangoon [Town.
Tounghoop Road, ..	Lt. J. S. Ingram, 1st En. B. F.,	1 *Nov.* 53	Ex. Engineer.
Tounghoo and Thyat Mew Road, ..	Lieut. B. Wyld, 3rd M. E. Regt.,	20 *Nov.* 57	Ex. Engineer. In charge of the Henzadah Divn.
Henzadah Division, ..	Lieut. B. Wyld, 3rd M. E. Regt.	11 *Nov.* 58	Ex. Engineer.

DEPARTMENT OF PUBLIC WORKS.—*Continued.*

Divisions.	*Names and Rank.*	*When appointed.*	DUTY.
	NORTH-WESTERN PROVINCES.		
	First Circle.		
Agra, ..	Lt. Col. A. Cunningham, Engrs,	13 *Sep.* 58	Chief Engineer.
	Capt. J. E. T. Nicolls, Engrs., ..	13 *June* 56	Asst. to Chief Engr.
		15 *May* 58	Offg. Ex. Engr. Upper Sirhind Divn.
	Mr. T. Moss, ..	17 *Feb.* 58	Offg. Asst. to Chief Engr.
Meerut, ..	Col. J. Glasfurd, Engrs., ..	28 *Oct.* 56	Supdg. Engineer.
Agra, ..	Captain J. D. Campbell, Engrs.,	9 *Nov.* 58	Ex. Engineer. (Offg. Ex. Engr. Meerut Division.)
	Lieut. J. L. Watts, Engrs., ..	18 *Dec.* 56	Ex. Engineer.
Allyghur, ..	Mr. R. J. Clarke, ..	5 *May* 59	Ex. Engineer.
	Mr. R. Elliott, ..	1 *Nov* 56	Sub-Engineer.
Muttra, ..	Captain E. Smalley 36th N. I., ..	18 *June* 55	Ex. Engineer.
Bareilly, ..	Capt. J. J. Hume, 48th N.I., ..	18 *Nov.* 56	Ex. Engineer.
Mooradabad, ..	Mr. F. W. Mann, ..	1 *Nov.* 56	Offg. Ex. Engineer.
Gwalior, ..	Major J. H. Maxwell, Engrs., ..	3 *Jan.* 59	Ex. Engr.—On leave.
	Capt. W. S. Oliphant, Engrs. ..	17 *May* 59	Offg. Ex. Engineer.
	Capt. R. D. Dansey, 3rd Madras En. Regt., ..	4 *Jan.* 59	Asst. Engineer.
	Mr. T. Johnstone, ..	26 *Dec.* 58	Asst. Supervisor.
Seepree, ..	Lieut. C. Fraser, H. M.'s 86th Foot, ..	27 *Jan.* 59	Asst. Engineer.
Sironj, ..	Lieut. R. Anderson, H. M.'s 95th Regiment, ..	8 *Mar.* 59	Asst. Engineer.
Meerut, ..	Capt. J. D. Campbell, Engrs, ..	9 *Nov.* 58	Ex. Engineer.
	Condr. F. Rose, Arty., ..	1 *Nov.* 56	Sub Engineer.
Haupper, ..	Capt. A. W. Owen, 11th N. I., ..	20 *Apl.* 58	Asst. Engineer.
Nynee Tal. ..	Capt. T. G. Glover, Engrs., ..	19 *Apl.* 58	Ex. Engineer.
	Sub-Condr. E. Gillis, Arty. ..	3 *July* 51	Sub Engineer.
Shahjehanpore, ..	Capt. L. Russell, Engineers, ..	25 *May* 58	Ex. Engineer.
5th Divn. G. T. Road, Agra	Mr. R. J. Clarke, ..	21 *Feb.* 59	Ex. Engineer.
	Mr. C. Polites, ..	21 *Sep.* 58	Sub Engineer.
6th Dn. G.T. Road, Meerut	Capt. C. B. Stuart, 4th En. Regt.	19 *Apl.* 58	Ex. Engineer.
Kumaon, ..	Mr. W. W. Clarke, ..	15 *June* 56	Ex. Engineer.
	Second Circle.		
Allahabad, ..	Lt. Col. N. C. Macleod, Engrs...	20 *Aug.* 58	Supdg. Engineer.
	Capt. G. E. Watson, Engrs. ..	26 *Dec.* 58	Offg. Asst. to Supdg. Engr.
	Captain F. W. Peile, Engineers,	10 *Sept.* 57	Ex Engineer.
	Lieut. G. S. Hills, Engineers, ..	6 *Nov.* 57	Asst Engineer.
Azimgurh, ..	Lieut. R. H. Tulloh, 16th N. I.,	2 *Nov.* 55	Asst. Engineer.
Ghazeepore, ..	Capt. J. Dawson, 43rd N. I., ..	8 *Dec.* 57	Special Asst. Engr. [Divn.
		1 *Oct.* 58	Offg. Ex. Engr. Ramghur.
Benares, ..	Lieut. W. R. Tucker, Engineers,	9 *Oct.* 57	Ex. Engineer.
Ghazeepore, ..	Capt. J. R. Martin, Artillery, ..	26 *May* 57	Asst. Engineer.
Cawnpore, ..	Capt D. Limond, Engrs., ..	5 *July* 58	Ex. Engineer.
	Lieut. E. D. Malcolm, Royal Engineers, ..	25 *Feb.* 59	Asst. Engineer.
	Mr. T. H. Corrigan,, ..	17 *Apl.* 58	Sub-Engineer.
	Mr. J. J. Morgan, ..	11 *Aug.* 58	Barrack Master.
Jhansie, ..	Capt. J. Baillie, 26th N. I., ..	13 *Apl.* 58	Ex. Engineer.
Lullutpoor, ..	Lieut. E. Swetenham, 45th N. I.,	9 *Feb.* 59	Asst. Engineer.
Ooraie, ..	Lieut. A. H. B. Bruce, 43rd N. I.	19 *Apl.* 58	Ex. Engr.
Banda, ..	Lt. J. G. Lindsay, Madras Engrs.	10 *Mar.* 59	Offg. Ex. Engr.
3rd Divn. G. T. Road, Benares, ..	Capt. A. G. Priestley, 41st N. I.,	27 *May* 56	Ex. Engineer.
	Condr. D. McLeod, ..	10 *June* 59	Asst. Ex. Engineer.
4th Divn. G. T. Road, Futtehghur, ..	Lieut. H. Z. Darrah, 41st N. I.,	29 *May* 58	Ex. Engineer.
	Mr. W. D. Brockman, ..	28 *April* 58	Asst. Engineer.

Department of Public Works.—*Continued.*

Divisions.	*Names and Rank.*	*When appointed.*	Duty.
	OUDE.		
	Major W. A. Crommelin, C.B. Engrs.	6 *Apl.* 58	Chief Engineer, Oude.
	Lieut. A. M. Lang, Engrs., ..	1 *June* 58	Asst. to Chief Engineer.
	Lieut. A. Tulloch, 58th N. I., ..	27 *May* 56	Ex. Officer, Road Department.
	Capt. G. A. Craster, Engrs, ..	3 *Sep.* 58	Ex. Engineer, Lucknow.
	Lieut. R. G. Smyth, Engrs., ..	24 *June* 59	Offg. Garrison Engineer Lucknow.
	Lieut. G. Swetenham, Royal Engrs.,	17 *Feb.* 59	Asst. Engr. Lucknow.
	Capt. A. Cadell, Engineers, ..	17 *Feb.* 59	Ex. Engr. Fyzabad.
	Lieut. F. E. B. Beaumont, Royal Engineers, ..	17 *Feb.* 59	Asst. Engr. Fyzabad.
Oude, ..	Lieut. D. Ward, Engineers, ..	17 *Feb.* 59	Asst. Engr. Fyzabad.
	Lieut. M. Hall, 1st En. B. F. ..	17 *Feb.* 59	Ex. Engr. Barraitch.
	Lieut. R. C. B. Pemberton, Engrs.,	17 *Feb.* 59	Ex. Engr. Seetapore.
	Lieut. C. C. S. Moncrieff, Engrs., ..	17 *Feb.* 59	Asst. Engr Seetapore.
	* ..		Ex. Engr. Roy Bareilly.
	Lieut. J. U. Champain, Engineers,	17 *Feb.* 59	Ex. Engr. Gonda.
	Lieut. E. T. Thackeray, Engrs., ..	18 *Mar.* 59	Asst. Engineer Gonda.
	Lieut. M. G. Clerk, 4th En. Regt.,	17 *Feb.* 59	Asst. Engr. Gonda.
	Mr. W. B. Harington, ..	17 *Feb.* 59	Ex. Engr. Sultanpore.
	Ens. H. J. Nuthall, H. M. 56th Foot,	18 *Mar.* 59	Asst. Engr. Sultanpore.
	Mr. James McRae, ..	29 *May* 56	Road Surveyor.—Fur. S. C. 9th April 58.
	PUNJAUB.		
Lahore, ..	Col. R. Napier, C. B., Engrs., ..	1 *May* 54	Chief Engineer, (on Field service.)
	Lt. Col. E. L. Ommanney, Engrs.,	14 *Apl.* 57	Offg. Chief Engineer.
	Major F. M. Baker, 65th N. I., ..	.. ..	Assistant to Chief Engineer.
Madhopore, ..	Capt. J. H. Dyas, Engineers, ..	21 *Dec.* 49	Director of Canals.—Lv. py. to Fur.
	Major H. Drummond, Engrs., ..	.. ..	Offg. Director.
	First Circle.		
Lahore, Division, ..	Lt. Col. H. Rigby, Engrs. ..	14 *Apl.* 57	Suptg. Engr. 1st Circle.
	Capt. H. Hyde, Engrs. ..	5 *Apl.* 59	Executive Engr.
Sealkote, ,, ..	Capt. A. H. Heath, Arty., ..	24 *Apl.* 57	Ex. Engr.—Fur. S.C. 11th Jan. 59.
	Capt. J.T.N. O'Brien, H. M. 20th Foot, ..	23 *May* 59	Offg. Ex. Engineer.
	Depy. Asst. Commy. E. Smith, ..	20 *July* 58	Barrack Master.
Rawul Pindee,	Capt. S. H. J. Davies 51st N. I.,	10 *Oct.* 54	Ex Engineer.
	Depy. Commy J. Symms, ..	20 *July* 58	Barrack Master.
Murree, ..	*		Ex Engineer.
Peshawur Divn. ..	Capt. C. Pollard, Engrs., ..	.. ..	Executive Engr.
	Lieut. W. Jackson, 53rd N. I. ..	6 *Feb.* 56	Assist. Engineer.
	Mr. W. H. Manners, ..	20 *July* 58	Barrack Master.
Kohat Divn. ..	Lieut. C. M. Browne, Bo. Engrs.,	16 *June* 59	Ex. Engineer.
Attock, ..	Ensign A. Monies.(unattached,) ..	23 *May* 59	Asst. Engineer.
Mooltan, ..	Capt. H. Rose, 4th En. Regt. ..	1 *May* 59	Ex. Engineer.
	Mr. J. Lynch, ..	20 *July* 58	Barrack Master.
	Second Circle.		
Lahore, ..	Capt. C. W. Hutchinson, Engrs, ..	11 *Feb.* 59	Supdg. Engineer.
	Mr. S. S. Marriott, ..	20 *July* 58	Barrack Master.
Upper Sirhind Divn.,	~~Capt. G. F. Atkinson~~ Engrs. ..	8 *Oct.* 56	Ex. Engr.—Fur. S. C. 30 Apl. 58.
	Capt. J. E. T. Nicolls, Engrs. ..	15 *May* 58	~~Offg.~~ Ex. Engineer.
Lower Sirhind Divn. ..	Capt. A. K. Moffat, 58th N. I. ..	5 *July* 58	Executive Engr.
Khewra Salt Mines ..	Capt. D. Thomson, Artillery, ..	15 *May* 57	Ex. Engineer.
Western Sirhind Divn. Ferozepore, ..	Mr. C. J. Hopper, ..	20 *July* 58	Barrack Master.
Jullundur Dooab, ..	Capt. C. W. Nightingale, 18th N.I.	27 *Nov.* 57	Ex. Officer.
	Asst. Commy. J. Wallace, ..	20 *July* 58	Barrack Master.
Sutledge and Beas Road, ..	Sub-Conductor W. Smallman, ..	30 *Sep.* 53	Ex. Engineer.
Delhi Division, ..	Lieut. G. Newmarch, Engrs. ..	19 *Apl.* 58	Ex. Engineer.
7th Division, G. T. Road, ..	Mr. G. Robertson, ..	.. ..	Ex. Engineer.
Hindoostan and Thibet Road, Simlah, ..	Capt. D. Briggs, 17th N. I. ..	1 *Dec.* 54	Supdt.—Fur. S.C. 9 Nov. 58.
	Capt. G. A. F. Houchen, 10th N.I.	21 *Dec.* 55	Assist. Superintendent.
		8 *Nov.* 58	Offg. Superintendent.
	Capt. A. L Elderton, 2nd En. B.F.	20 *May* 59	Asst. Engineer.

Department of Public Works.—*Continued.*

Lahore and Peshawur Road.

Rank, Names and Corps.	*When appointed to the Dept.*	*Rank or Designation in the Dept.*	*Station where.*
Lt. Col. A. Taylor, C.B. Engrs.,	21 *Dec*, 49	Supt. Lahore and Peshawur Road,	Rawul Pindee.—Fur. S.C. 8 Mar 59.
Major A. Robertson, 48th M. N. I., ..	.. ..	Offg. Supdt. Ditto, ..	Rawul Pindee.
Capt. F. J. Davies, 58th N. I.	23 *May* 59	Ex. Engr. 1st Division, ..	Goojerat.
Mr. C. Knowles, ..	.. ..	Asst. Engr. Ditto, ..	
Capt. A. R. Bayly, H. M. 8th Foot, ..	20 *Dec.* 58	Ex. Engr. 2nd Divn.,	Jhelum.
Mr. H. Scott, ..	.. ...	Asst. Engr., ..	Jhelum.
Major A. Robertson, 48th M. N. I. ..	.. ..	Ex. Engr. 3rd Divn. (Offg. Supdt. Lahore and Peshawur Road,)..	Rawul Pindee.
Capt. J. T. Tovey, H. M. 24th Foot, ..	... ...	Offg. Ex. Engr., ..	Rawul Pindee.
~~Capt. W. Henderson, Engrs.~~		Ex. Engr. 4th Divn., ..	Fur. S. C. 29 Mar. 59.
Capt. E. N. Sandilands, H. M. 8th Foot. ..	.. ...	Offg. Ditto, ..	Attock.
Mr. L. Bean, ..	... ...	Asst. Engr., ..	Attock.

BAREE DOAB CANALS.

Capt. J. Crofton, Engrs., ..	21 *Dec.* 49	Supt. Baree Doab Canals ..	Upper Derajat.—Fur. S. C. 21st June 59.
Lt. J. G. Forbes, Engrs. ..	21 *June* 58	Asst. Engr. 1st Divn. Baree Doab Canals, ..	Attock.—Lv. S. C. 4 [Nov.
Lieut. R. Home, Engrs. ..	26 *Oct.* 58	Offg. Ex. Engr. 1st Divn. Baree Doab Canals, ..	Umritsir.
Lieut. J. Eckford, Engrs. ...	.. ..	Asst. Engr. 1st Divn. Ditto, ..	
Capt. H. W. Gulliver, Engrs.	28 *Mar.* 54	Ex. Engr. 2nd Divn. Baree Doab Canals, ..	Kohat.
Lieut. A. C. Padday, Engrs.,	12 *Apl.* 59	Asst. Engr. Ditto, ..	
	17 *May* 59	Offg. Asst. Engr. 1st Divn. Baree Doab Canals, ..	Attock.
Mr. A. G. Crommelin, ..	.. ..	Ex. Engr. 4th Division Baree Doab Canals, ..	Fur. S. C. 8 Dec. 58.
Mr. E. C. Palmer, ..	19 *Mar.* 59	Officiating Ditto, ..	
Capt. A. W. Garnett, Engrs.,	31 *May* 50	Executive Engineer, ..	Kohat.
Mr. Wilson, ..	23 *May* 59	Offg. Ex. Engineer, ..	Hazara.
Mr. J. D. Smithe, ..	.. ..	Supdt. Baree Doab Canal Workshops, ..	Madhopore.

CANAL DEPARTMENT.—NORTH-WESTERN PROVINCES.

Station, Designation and Division.		*Names and Rank.*	*When appointed.*	Duty.
Roorkee,	Superintendent General of Canals N. W. P.	Capt. A. D. Turnbull, Engrs.	22 *Nov.* 58	
Ditto,	Personal Assistant to ditto,	Mr. Harry Marten, ..	31 *Oct.* 54	
Ditto,	Deputy Supdt. Genl. of Canals, ..	Capt. W. E. Morton, Engrs	20 *Aug.* 58	
*	..	~~Lieut. W. H. Oliver, Engrs.~~	17 *May* 59	Asst. Engr.

CANAL DEPARTMENT.—NORTH-WESTERN PROVINCES.—*Continued.*

Divisions.		*Names and Rank.*	*When appointed.*	DUTY.
Roorkee, ..	Ganges Canal, ...	Capt. A. D. Turnbull, Engineers, ..	.. ..	Director.
Ditto, ..	Assistant Surveyor Ganges Canal, ..	Mr. W. T. Dodsworth, ..	21 *Nov.* 43	And Supervisor of Land Measurements.
Ditto, ..	Ditto, ..	Mr. T. W. Hunt, ..	16 *Nov.* 52	
Ditto, ..	Supdt. 1st or Northern Division Ganges Canal Works, ..	Major H. Drummond, Engineers, ..	2 *June* 56	Officiating Director of Canals, Punjaub.
Ditto, ..	Officiating Supdt...	Lieut. C. S. Thomason, Engineers, ..	27 *July* 55	
Ditto, ..	Ex. Officer 1st or Northern Divn. Ganges Canal Works (Material Department,) ..	Depy. Asst. Commy. James Finn,	4 *Sep.* 47	And Superintendent of Navigation.
Ditto, ..	Deputy Supdt. 1st or Northern Divn. Ganges Canal Works, ..	Mr. W. Kay, ..	25 *July* 45	Fur. S. C. 19 Nov. 57.
Meerut, ..	Supdt. Upper Central Divn. Ganges Canal Works, ..	Capt. T. C. Merrick, 4th En. Regt. ..	13 *Oct.* 54	
	Depy. Supdt. ditto, ..	Mr. W. B. Macrone, ..	18 *Apl.* 56	
	Superintendent of Lower Central Divn. Ganges Canal Works, ..	Mr. James Parker, ..	14 *Apl.* 57	
Cawnpore, ..	Supdt. 4th Division or Cawnpore Terminal line of Ganges C. Works,	Mr. C. C. Anderson, ..	25 *Feb.* 58	Officiating.
Ditto, ..	Depy. Supdt. ditto,	*		
Mynpoorie,	Supdt. Etawah Terminal Division Ganges Canal Works, ..	Lieut. H. E. Whish, 26th L. I., ..	12 *Feb.* 58	
Ditto, ..	Depy. Supt. ditto,	Lieut. C. H. Luard, Engrs.		
Delhi, ..	Supt. of the Western Jumna Canal, ..	Capt. C. T. Stewart, Engrs.,	9 *Mar.* 55	
Ditto, ..	Depy. Supt. ditto, ..	Lieut. W. Jeffreys, Engrs.	1 *May* 57	
Seharunpore,	Supt. of the Eastern Jumna Canals, ..	Major H. A. Brownlow, Engrs. ..		
Ditto, ..	Depy. ditto, ..	Lieut. J. Birney, Engrs. ..	21 *Oct.* 58	
Ditto, ..	Deputy ditto, ..	Ensign W. Willcocks, *(Unattached,)* ..		
Ditto, ..	Assistant Supt. ditto,	Lt. R. Home, Engrs. ..	11 *Sep.* 56	Offg. Ex. Engineer 1st Division Baree Doab Canals.
Deyrah, ..	Supt. of the Dhoon Canals,	Mr. R. E. Forrest, ..	28 *Apl.* 58	

CANAL DEPARTMENT.—NORTH-WESTERN PROVINCES.—*Continued.*

Divisions.		*Names and Rank.*	*When appointed.*	DUTY.
Delhi, ..	Asst. Supt. Delhi and Goorgaon Irrigation Works, ..	*		
Nynee Tal,	Works of Irrigation in Rohilkund, ..	Major W. Maxwell, Arty.	23 *Dec.* 54	Supdt. [Circle; L.P.
			24 *Apl.* 57	Offg. Supdg. Engr. 2d
		Mr. F. Read, ..	1 *Mar.* 58	Officiating.
		Mr. J. Norman, ..	— *Dec.* 58	Asst. Superintendent.
Agra, ..	Irrigation works in the district of Agra,	Sergt. E. Battie, ..	13 *Feb.* 57	Ex. Engineer.
Nowgong, ..	Irrigation works in Bundelcund, ..	*		Superintendent.
Roorkee, ..	Roorkee Work Shop, ..	Capt. A. Allen, 55th N. I.	1 *Nov.* 52	Superintendent.
		Capt. G. Baillie, Arty. ..	4 *Apl.* 55	Deputy Supt.
		Mr. J. L. Watson, ..	1 *Apl.* 52	Practical Engr.
		Mr W. Mason, ..	4 *Dec.* 56	Assist. Mathematical Instrument Maker.
Bijnour, ..	Deyrah and Patlee Dhoon Forests,	*		Superintendent.
		*		Assistant Engineer.

WARRANT OFFICERS OF THE DEPARTMENT OF PUBLIC WORKS.

Deputy Commissary.		
John Symms, ..	Barrack Master, Rawul Pindee, ..	1 *Nov.* 58
Assistant Commissaries.		
John Wallace, ..	Barrack Master, Jullunder, ..	1 *Nov.* 58
Edward Rooke, ..	Ex. Officer, 1st Division Grand Trunk Road, 2nd Circle, 2nd Class, L. P., ..	1 *Nov.* 58
John Brooke, ..	Barrack Master, Barrackpore Divn.,..	1 *Nov.* 58
Deputy Asst. Commissaries.		
James Finn, ..	In charge of the Manufacture of Materials for the works on the Ganges Canals, and Supdt. of Navigation, ..	1 *Nov.* 58
Edward Smith, ..	Barrack Master, (Sealkote,) ..	1 *Nov.* 58
David Gair,(*a*) ..	Furlough S. C. 23 December 58, ..	1 *Nov.* 58
Conductors.		
Conductor Francis Rose, ..	Meerut, ..	1 *Nov.* 56
Conductor W. Willcocks,(*b*) ..	Canal Dept., N. W. P. ..	1 *Nov.* 56
Conductor W. Smallman, ...	..	26 *June* 57
Condr. Alex. O'Berne, ...	..	2 *Dec.* 57
Conductor E. J. Gillis, ...	..	1 *Nov.* 58
Conductor A. B. Bremner, ...	..	*do*
Conductor J. McArthur, ...	..	*do*
Conductor D. Oliver, ...	..	*do*
Conductor W. Craig, ..	Barrack Master, Berhampore, ..	29 *do*
Conductor T. Marten, ...	..	3 *Jan.* 59
Conductor P. Stephens, ...	..	17 *Mar.* 59
Conductor D. McLeod, ...	Asst. Ex. Engr., 3 Division, Grand Trunk Road, ..	6 *Apl.* 59
Conductor C. B. Goode, ..	Landour, ..	9 *Apl.* 59
Conductor M. Cunningham, ...	..	20 *Apl.* 59
Sub-Conductors.		
Sub-Conductor M. Ogle, ...	..	25 *July* 57

(*a*) Lieut. on the Veteran Establishment.
(*b*) Ensign (Unattached.)

SUPERINTENDENT OF ARMY CLOTHING AND AUDITOR OF CLOTHING ACCOUNTS.

Name	Appointment	Date
Col. H. P. Burn, 4th En. Regt., ..	Presidency, ..	1 *June* 54
	Member of a special Committee at Bombay. ...	21 *June* 59

ARMY CLOTHING AGENTS.

Name	Appointment	Date
Capt. P. R. Innes, Invalid Estabt. ..	1st Divn., Allahabad,—Fur. S.C. 6 Sep. 58	25 *Feb.* 58
Major M. F. Kemble, 41st N. I. ..	Offg. 1st Division, Allahabad, ..	21 *Aug.* 58
Capt. M. J. Turnbull, 2nd E. Lt. Cavy. ..	2nd Division, Fort William, ..	31 *Dec.* 51
	In charge of the Office of Superintendent of Army Clothing, ..	21 *June* 59

GENERAL OFFICERS COMMANDING DIVISIONS.

Name	Appointment	Date
Maj. Genl. *Sir* J. B. Hearsey, K.C.B., 3rd E.L.C.,	Presidency Division, (Barrackpore,) ..	1 *Aug.* 56
Maj. Genl. C. A. Windham, C.B. H.M. Service,	Lahore Division, ..	9 *Oct.* 57
Maj. Genl. *Sir* R. Garrett, K.C.B. H.M. Service,	Sirhind Division, (Umballah,) ..	1 *Jan.* 58
Maj. Genl. *Sir* S. J. Cotton, K.C.B., M.H. Service,	Peshawur Division, ..	5 *June* 57
Brigr. Genl. N. B. Chamberlain, C.B. 16th N.I. Grs.	Punjaub Irregular Force, ..	15 *Dec.* 57
Major Genl. J. F. Bradford, C.B. 2nd E. L. C.,	Meerut Division, ..	14 *May* 58
Brigr. Genl. R. Walpole, 2nd Bat. Rifle Brigade,	Rohilcund and Kemaon, ..	29 *June* 58
Major Genl. G. Campbell, Arty., ..	Dinapore Division, ..	6 *July* 58
Brigr. Genl. *Sir* R. Napier, K.C.B. Engrs., ..	Gwalior Division, ..	7 *July* 58
Major Genl. *Sir* J. E. W. Inglis, K.C.B. H.M. Service, ..	Cawnpore Division, ..	26 *Feb.* 58

Assistant Adjutant Generals of Divisions

Name	Appointment	Date
Major W. Lydiard, 11th N.I., ..	Dinapore, ..	8 *Nov* 45
Major A. H. Ross, 42nd L. I., ..	Presidency, (Barrackpore,) ..	24 *Mar.* 54
Major W. Lamb, 51st N.I., ..	Lahore Division, ..	14 *Aug.* 57
Capt. T. Wright, 46th N. I., ..	Peshawur Division, ..	9 *Sep.* 58

Deputy Assistant Adjutant Generals of Divisions.

Name	Appointment	Date
Major D. S. Dodgson, 30th N. I. ..	Sirhind Divn. (Umballah,) ..	14 *Aug.* 57
Capt. R. G. Simeon, 4th E. L. C. ..	Meerut Divn., ..	14 *Aug.* 57
Major T. F. Wilson, C. B., 13th N. I. ..	Cawnpore,—Fur. S. C. 21st Feb. 59. ..	9 *Sep.* 58
Capt. G. S. Young, H. M. 80th Foot, ..	Offg. Cawnpore, ..	4 *Mar.* 59

Aides-de-Camp to General Officers Commanding Divisions.

Name	Appointment	Date
Lieut. J. Hearsey, 38th N. I. ..	To Maj. Genl. *Sir* J. B. Hearsey, K.C.B.,	30 *Jan.* 57
Capt. R. Swire, H. M.'s Service, ..	To Major Genl. C. A. Windham, C.B., ..	23 *Oct.* 57
Major A. R. Garrett, H.M.'s 46th Foot, ..	To Major Genl. *Sir* R. Garrett, K.C.B., ..	1 *Jan.* 58
Lieut. L. S. Cotton, H. M. 22nd Foot, ..	To Major Genl. *Sir* S. J. Cotton, K. C. B.,	6 *Mar.* 58
Capt. A. H. Bogle, Artillery, ..	To Major Genl. G. Campbell, ..	15 *Sep.* 58
Capt. W. J. Bradford, Madras Artillery, ..	To Maj. Genl. J. F. Bradford, C.B., ..	28 *Mar.* 59
Lieut. C. W. Fletcher, 48th N. I. ..	To Major Genl. *Sir* J. E. W. Inglis, K.C.B.	27 *Jan.* 59

BRIGADIERS COMMANDING DISTRICTS OR STATIONS.

First Class.

Name	Station	Date
Brigadier F. Wheler, 1st E. L. C. ..	Saugor, ..	29 *Oct.* 57
Brigadier St. G.D. Showers, C.B. 2nd En.B.F.,	Agra, ..	22 *Jan.* 58
Brigadier T. J. Galloway, H. M. 70th Foot, ..	Peshawur, ..	14 *May* 58
Brigadier M. Smith, H. M. 81st Foot ..	Fort William and Calcutta, ..	6 *July* 59

Second Class.

Name	Station	Date
D ~~Brigadier J. MacKenzie, 5th E. L. C.~~, ..	Ferozepore, ..	13 *Oct.* 57
Brigadier J. Christie, 1st E. L. C., ..	Barrackpore. ..	29 *Oct.* 57
Brigadier P. Gordon, 11th N. I. ..	Dinapore. (Benares,) ..	15 *Dec.* 57
Brigadier W. R. Corfield, 22nd N. I., ..	Native Infy. Brigade in China, ..	5 *Mar.* 58
Brigr. J. K. McCausland, C. B., 66th N. I. ..	Sealkote, ..	14 *May* 58
Brigr. R. Horsford, Artillery, ..	Meerut. ..	28 *May* 58
Brigr. C. Troup, 68th N. I., ..	Mooltan. ..	9 *June* 58
Brigr. T. Chute, H. M. 70th Foot, ..	Lucknow. ..	6 *July* 58
Brigr. W. G. Brown, H. M. 24th Foot, ..	Lahore, ..	28 *July* 58
Brigr. E. C. W. M. Milman, H. M. 37th Foot,	Jullundur, ..	23 *Aug.* 58
Brigr. A. H. Horsford, C. B., H. M. 3rd Battalion Rifle Brigade, ...	Trans-Gogra, ...	9 *May* 59
Brigr. M. G. Dennis, H. M., 1st Bn. 60th Foot, ..	Allahabad, ..	13 *May* 59
Brigr. H. Troup, 6th En. Regiment, ..	Delhi, ..	17 *May* 59
Brigr. A. H. Ferryman, C. B., H. M. 89th Foot, ..	Sind Saugor district, (Rawul Pindee,) ..	19 *May* 59

BRIGADE MAJORS.

Officer	Station	Date
Captain S. B. Cookson, 73rd N. I.,	.. Sind Sagur District, (Rawul Pindee,) ..	3 *Jan.* 53
Capt. G. E. Holmes, 72nd N. I.	.. Jullundur, ..	6 *Feb.* 56
Capt. W. Gordon, 49th N.I.	.. Mooltan, ..	22 *July* 53
Capt. C. E. Mills, 28th N. I.	.. Lahore, ..	29 *July* 53
Capt. J. Ross, 71st N. I.	.. Sealkote, ..	15 *Nov.* 53
Major H. Nicoll, 50th N. I.	.. Delhi,—Fur. S. C 29 April 59, ..	27 *June* 54
Capt. J. Woods, H. M. 81st Foot,	.. Offg. Delhi, ...	19 *May* 59
Major C. St. G. Brownlow, 15th N. I.	.. Umballah,—Lv. S. C. 1 Nov., ..	7 *Jan.* 55
Lt. C. M. Pym, H. M. 75th Foot,	.. Offg. Umballah, ..	18 *May* 59
Lt. Col. G. P. Whish, 60th N. I.,	.. Meerut, ..	28 *Sep.* 55
Capt. S. Richards, 55th N. I.,	.. Barrackpore. ..	24 *July* 57
Major W. Birch, 6th En. Regt.	.. Ferozepore, ..	14 *Aug.* 57
Captain F. J. Nelson, 65th N. I.,	.. Dinapore (Benares.)—(With his Regt.)	14 *Aug.* 57
Lieut. E. K. O. Gilbert, 27th N. I.,	.. Offg. Dinapore (Benares,) ..	3 *July* 58
Captain A. H. Bamfield, 56th N. I.,	.. Peshawur.—Fur. S. C. 18 June 1858, ..	16 *Apl.* 58
Capt. H. E. Iremonger, 21st N. I.,	.. Offg. Peshawur, ..	14 *June* 58
Major A. B. Johnson, 5th En. Regt.	.. Cawnpore, Fur. S. C. 30 Dec. 58. ..	6 *Oct.* 58
~~Lieut. C. A. McDougall,~~ 4th En. Regt.	.. Offg. Cawnpore, ..	31 *Dec.* 58
Lieut. F. J. Gully, 74th N. I.,	.. Saugor, ..	22 *Oct.* 58
Capt. J. Hudson, H. M. 15th Foot,	.. Allahabad, ..	23 *Oct.* 58
Capt. R. Patton, 3rd En. Regt.	.. Agra, ..	8 *Apl.* 59
Capt. E. J. N. Burton, H, M. 37th Foot,	.. Offg. Lucknow, ..	28 *Mar.* 59
Major M. Dillon, 2nd Battn. Rifle Brigade,	Trans-Gogra, ..	9 *May* 59

Officer	Station	Date
Captain S. Black, 37th N. I.,	.. Staff Officer Punjaub Irr. Force, ..	16 *Jan.* 57

FORT ADJUTANTS.

Officer	Station	Date
Lieut. G. Weld, 14th N. I.	.. Chunar, ..	10 *Apl.* 51
Capt. M. R. Nightingale, 2nd En. B. F.	.. Fort William,* ..	9 *Nov.* 53
Capt. T. M. Cameron, 55th N. I.,	.. Attock,—(Leave.) ..	29 *Mar.* 58
Capt. M. Batt, H. M. 98th Foot,	.. Offg. Attock, ..	19 *May* 59

* Also Supdt. Gentlemen Cadets, Fort William.

Embodied, 23rd July 1857. | **Bengal Yeomanry Cavalry.** | Serving in the Goruckpore district.

Uniform, *French Grey*—**Facings,** *Dark Blue*—**Lace**—*Black.*

Names.	*Date of Rank in Yeomanry Cavalry.*	Remarks.
Commandant.		
Major J. F. Richardson, c.b. 8th Irr. Cavy		
2nd in Command.		
Captain R. T. P. Stapleton, 1st E. L. C.	7 *Dec.* 58	
Adjutant.		
Cornet W. G. V. O. Bridgeman, ..	30 *Mar.* 58	Appointed Adjutant 10 Aug. 1858.
Quarter Master.		
Cornet H. Kloer, ..	5 *Oct.* 57	Appointed Qr. Master 14 Nov. 1857.
Assistant Surgeon.		
A. Garden, m. d. ..		
Veterinary Surgeon.		
F. Kight, ..	15 *Feb.* 58	
Lieutenants.		
Charles de Hoxar, ..	14 *Aug.* 57	
A. R. L. Ellis, ..	5 *Oct.* 57	
W. P. Davis, ..	5 *Oct.* 57	2nd in Comd. and Offg. Adjt. of the 10th [Bengal Police Battn
L. C. Percivall, ..	10 *Dec* 57	
Cornets.		
J. Scott,† ..	5 *Oct.* 57	
R. Palin, ..	5 *Oct.* 57	
H. Walkis, ..	5 *Oct* 57	
R. T. Little,† ..	10 *Dec* 57	
W. E. Phillot, ..	26 *Jan.* 58	
W. J. Burnell, ..	2 *Feb.* 59	
W. Barton, ..	2 *Feb.* 59	
G. Dorrett, ..	30 *Apl.* 59	
Doing Duty.		
Lt. F. B. Prinsep, 3rd E. L. C., ..		
Lt. C. A. Copland, 30th N. I. ..		
Lt. A. J. Macqueen, 18th N. I. ..		
Lt. J. G. Barlow, 54th N. I. ..		

The Regiment Consists of 1 Commandant—1 2nd in Command—1 Adjutant—1 Quarter Master—1 Assistant Surgeon—1 Veterinary Surgeon—1 Riding Master (non-commissioned) 1 Regimental Sergeant Major—1 Quarter Master Sergeant—1 Pay Master Sergeant—4 Troop Sergeant Majors—16 Sergeants—32 Corporals—4 Trumpeters—192 Troopers.

Calcutta Volunteer Guards.

CAVALRY.

Troop.	NAMES.	Date of Rank in Cal. Vol. Guards.	REMARKS.
	Major M. J. Turnbull, 2nd E. L. C.	.. ..	Commandant.
	*	.. ..	Adjutant.
	CAPTAINS.		
1	E D. Kilburn, ..	20 *June* 57	
2	J. Parry, ..	20 *June* 57	
3	T. Browne, ...	20 *June* 57	
4	G. Brown, ..	20 *June* 57	
5	C. B. Stewart, ..	20 *June* 57	
	LIEUTENANTS.		
2	J. Wallace, ..	20 *June* 57	
4	— Stack, ..	20 *June* 57	
5	— Lightfoot, ..	20 *June* 57	
1	*Sir* A. de H. Larpent, *Bart,* ..	20 *June* 57	
3	— Paterson. ..	16 *Sep.* 57	

ARTILLERY.

NAMES.	Date of Rank	REMARKS.
Captain C. H. Dickens, Arty. ..	14 *Aug.* 57	Commandant.
Lieut. J. Leonard, ..	14 *Aug.* 57	

INFANTRY.

Company.	NAMES.	Date of Rank	REMARKS.
	Major G. Holroyd, 43 L. I. ..	.. ..	Commandant of Infantry.
	*	.. ..	Adjutant.
	CAPTAINS.		
4	R. Ross, ..	26 *June* 57	
5	F. A. Goodenough, ..	26 *June* 57	
3	G. E. Evans, ..	7 *Sep.* 57	
Gren.	A. Stewart, ..	16 *Jan.* 58	
1	W. Kinnock, ..	16 *Jan* 58	
Rifle.	J. Rose, ..	1 *Apl.* 58	
2	A. S. Llewellyn, ..	5 *May* 58	
	LIEUTENANTS.		
4	H. G. Oxborough, ..	26 *June* 57	
Gren.	M. Balfour, ..	16 *Jan.* 58	
1	J. Morrison, ..	16 *Jan.* 58	
Rifle.	P. M. Tait, ..	1 *Apl.* 58	
5	A. Watson, ..	5 *May* 58	
3	H. Ronaldson, ..	16 *Aug.* 58	

GRADATION LIST

OF THE

GENERAL AND FIELD OFFICERS

OF

HER MAJESTY'S AND THE HON'BLE COMPANY'S

ARMY,

Serving on the Bengal Establishment.

GENERALS.

Names.	*Army Rank.*		*Corps.*	REMARKS.
Ulysses Lord Downes, K.C.B., ..	20 *June*	54	H. M. 29th Foot,	Europe.
Sir Robert Houstoun, K. C. B., ..	do		4th E. L. C.	Europe.
John Alexander Paul Macgregor,	do		54th N.I.	Europe.
Sir William Richards, K. C. B., ..	do		26th L.I.	India.
Thomas Evans, C. B., ..	18 *May*	55	H. M. 81st Foot,	Europe.
Sir Archibald Maclaine, K. C. B.,	5 *June*	55	H. M. 52nd Foot,	Europe.
Sir James Simpson, G. C. B., ..	8 *Sep.*	55	H. M. 87th Foot,	Europe.
James Ahmuty, ..	15 *Sep.*	55	Artillery.	Europe.
Mossom Boyd, ..	9 *Apl.*	56	53rd N.I.	Europe.
The Right Hon. Lord Clyde, G.C.B.,	11 *July*	57	H. M.'s Service, ..	India—Commander-in-Chief
Sir Robert Henry Cunliffe, *Bt.* and C. B., ..	13 *Oct.*	57	4th N.I.	Europe.
John Truscott, ..	27 *Jan.*	58	74th N.I.	Europe.

LIEUTENANT GENERALS.

George Swiney, ..	11 *Nov.* 1851	Artillery.	Europe.
Sir George Pollock, G. C. B., ..	do	Artillery.	Europe.
Alexander Lindsay, C. B., ..	do	Artillery.	Europe.
Suetonius Henry Tod, ..	do	60th N.I.	Europe.
Harry Thomson, ..	do	1st E.L.C.	Europe.
John Reeve, ..	do	H. M. 61st Regt.	Europe.
James Kennedy, C. B., ..	do	5th E.L.C.	Europe.
Charles William Hamilton, ..	do	40th N.I.	Europe.

LIEUTENANT GENERALS—*Continued.*

Names.		*Army Rank.*	*Corps.*		REMARKS.
Edmund Fredk. Waters, C. B.,	..	11 *Nov.* 1851	68th N.I.		Europe.
Richard Collyer Andree,	..	do	69th N.I.		Europe.
Thomas Shubrick,	..	do	2nd E.L.C.		Europe.
D ~~William Henry Komm~~,	..	do	25th N.I.		Europe.
D ~~William Vincent~~,	..	do	6th En. Regt.		India.
Thomas Henry Paul,	..	do	20th N.I.		Europe
E. Fleming, C. B.,	..	20 *June* 1854	H. M. 27th Foot,		Europe.
George W. Paty, C. B.,	..	do	H. M. 70th Foot,		Europe.
Rodrick McNeil,	..	do	H. M. 8th Foot,		Europe.
William Sutherland,	..	do	H. M. 53rd Foot,		Europe.
Hon'ble John Finch, C. B.,	..	20 *Feb.* 1855	H. M. 24th Foot,		Europe.
Samuel Swinhoe,	..	15 *Sep.* 1855	73rd N.I.	..	Europe.
John Anderson,	..	5 *Dec.* 1855	61st N.I.	..	Europe.
Firederick Young,	..	18 *Feb.* 1856	66th N.I.	..	Europe.
Thomas Monteath Douglas, C. B.,		18 *Mar.*	35th L.I.	..	Europe.
William Robert Clayton Costley,		2 *Apl.* ..	9th N.I.	.	Europe.
Sir George Petre Wymer, K. C. B.		8 *June* ..	38th L.I.	..	Europe.
Alexandr Dick,	..	4 *July* ..	71st N.I.	..	India.
William Pattle, C. B.,	..	18 do	3rd E. L.C.	..	Europe.
Thomas Fiddes,	..	15 *Sep.* ..	42nd N.I.	..	Europe.
Abraham Roberts, C. B.,	.	13 *Oct.* 1857	1st En. B. F.	..	Europe.
Chas. A. Grenado Wallington,	..	4 *Mar.* 1858	18th N.I.	..	Europe.
Thomas Oliver,	..	4 *May* 1858	37th N.I.	..	Europe.
Duncan Gordon Scott,	..	23 *July* 1858	30th N. I.	..	Europe.
Joseph Paterson,	..	11 *Aug* 1858	H. M.'s 60th Foot,		Europe.
Henry Hall, C. B.,	..	24 Oct. 1858	21st N. I.	..	Europe.
Samuel Shaw,	..	5 *Mar.* 1859	Artillery,	..	Europe.

MAJOR GENERALS.

Names		Army Rank	Corps		Remarks
Lt. Gen. { Mathew Coombs Paul,	..	20 *June* 1854	29th N. I.	..	Europe.
Sir John Cheap, K. C. B.,	..	do	Engineers,	..	Europe.
Joseph Harris,	..	do	4th En. Regt.	...	Europe.
John Tulloch, C. B.,	..	do	51st N. I.	..	Europe.
Richard Powney, }	..	do	Artillery,	..	Europe.
George Edward Gowan, C. B.,	..	do	Artillery,	..	Europe.
~~James Stuart, C. B.~~,	..	do	34th N.I.	..	Europe.
William Henry Hewitt,	..	do	27th N.I.	..	Europe.
John Home,	..	do	57th N.I.	..	Europe.
Geo. Wm. Aylmer Lloyd, C. B.,	..	de	28th N.I.	..	India.
Robert Blackall,	..	do	2nd En. B. F.	..	Europe.
James Eckford, C. B.,	..	28 *Nov.* 1854	65th N.I.	..	India.
Andrew Hervey, C. B.,	..	do	52nd N.I.	..	India.
Chas. Montabin Carmichael, C. B.,		do	5th E.L.C.	..	Europe.
Henry Lechmeme Worrall,	..	do	4th E.L.C.	..	Europe.
Sir John Bennett Hearsey, K. C. B.,		do	3rd E.LC.	..	Comdg. Presidency Division.
George Richard Pemberton,	..	do	62nd N.I.	..	Europe.
Stephen Davis Riley,	..	do	47th N.I.	..	India.
Christopher Godby, C. B.,	..	do	55th N.I.	..	Europe.
James Parsons, C. B.,	..	do	50th N.I.	..	India.

MAJOR GENERALS—*Continued.*

Names.	*Army Rank.*	*Corps.*	REMARKS.
George Warren,	28 *Nov.* 1854.	13th N. I.	India.
Henry Fisher Salter, C. B,	do	5th E. L. C.	Lv. S. C. to the Cape of G. H.
Thomas Mathew Taylor,	do	1st E. L. C.	Europe.
Robert Hawkes,	do	L. C.	Europe.
Archibald Fullerton Richmond, C.B.,	do	24th N.I.	Europe.
†*Sir* Patrick Grant, K. C. B.,	do	6th En. Regt.	C.-in-C. at Madras.
Christopher Dixon Wilkinson, C.B.,	do	6th En. Regt.	India.
William Henry Marshall,	do	32nd N.I.	Europe.
Francis Spencer Hawkins, C. B.,	do	2nd N.I. (Grs.)	Europe.
John Graham,	do	67th N.I.	Europe.
Edward Garstin,	do	Engineers,	India.
Richard Home,	do	43rd L.I.	Europe.
Alexander Carnegy, C.B.,	do	15th N.I.	Europe.
George Tomkyns,	do	19th N.I.	Europe.
Charles Richd. Wm. Lane, C. B.,	do	5th En. Regt.	Europe.
William John Gairdner, C. B.,	do	63rd N.I.	Europe.
George Brooke, C. B.,	do	Artillery,	Europe.
Thomas Dickinson,	do	10th N.I.	Europe.
Henry Chambers Murray Cox,	do	58th N.I.	Europe.
John Hoggan, C. B.,	do	45th N.I.	India.
George Huyshe, C. B.,	do	3rd B. E. Regt.	Europe.
Charles Hamilton, C. B.,	do	59th N.I.	Europe.
Philip Francis Story, C. B.,	13 *Apl.* 1855	3rd E. Lt. Cavy.	India.
C. A. Windham, C. B.	8 *Sep.*	H. M.'s Service,	Comdg. Lahore Division.
Henry Lawrence,	5 *Dec.*	72nd N. I.	Europe.
George Hicks, C. B.	18 *Feb.* 1856	70th N. I.	Europe.
Henry Francis Caley,	18 *Mar.*	64th Native Infy.	India.
Hope Dick,	2 *Apl.*	4th En. Regt.	Europe.
Joseph Nash, C. B.	9 *Apl.*	46th N.I.	India.
James Alexander, C. B.,	18 *May*	Artillery.	Europe.
John Theophilus Lane, C. B.,	8 *June*	Artillery.	India.
Sir R. Garrett, K. C. B.,	24 *July*	H. M.'s Service,	Comdg. Sirhind Division.
Robert Stewart,	15 *Sep.*	41st N. I.	Europe.
Edward Pettingal,	4 *Nov.*	12th N. I.	Europe.
Edward Huthwaite, C. B.,	14 *Mar.* 1857	Artillery,	Nainee Tâl.
Sir W. R. Mansfield, K. C. B.,	7 *Aug.*	H. M.'s Service,	Chief of the Staff.
Fredk. Geo. Lister,	22 *Aug.*	31st N. I.	Europe.
Sir A. Wilson, *Bt.* K. C. B.,	14 *Sep.*	Artillery.	Europe.
David Downing,	15 *Sep.*	39th N. I.	Europe.
Fredk. Hervey Sandys,	15 *Oct.*	36th N. I.	Europe.
John Moule,	27 *Jan.* 1858	33rd N. I.	Europe.
Louis Saunders Bird,	4 *Mar.*	23rd N. I.	Europe.
David Birrell,	25 *April*	71st N. I.	Europe.
Thomas Polwhele,	1 *May*	17th N. I.	Europe.
Richard Jas. Holwell Birch, C. B.,	4 *May*	2nd En. B. F.,	Secy. to Govt. Mily. Dept.
George Campbell,	4 *July*	Artillery.	Comdg. Dinapore Division.
Peter Innes,	13 do	14th N.I.	India.
John Fowler Bradford, C. B.,	23 do	2nd E. L. C.	Comdg. Meerut Division.
Harry Meggs Graves,	27 *Aug.*	13th N. I.	Europe.
Charles Grant, C. B.	14 *Oct.*	Artillery.	Europe.
Stuart Corbett, C. B.	4 *Feb.* 1859	16th N. I.	Europe.
William Sage,	13 *Mar.*	22nd N. I.	Europe.

† Lieut. Genl. in the East Indies, 25th Jan. 1856.

COLONELS.

Names.	*Army Rank.*	*Corps.*	REMARKS.
**George Congreve*, C. B., ..	20 *June* 1854	H. M. 29th Foot,	Quarter Master General, Queen's Troops.
**John Longfield*, ..	do	H. M. 8th Foot.	Europe.
**E. B. Brooke*, ..	do	H. M. 67th Foot, ..	Europe.
Sir Justin Sheil, K.C.B., & L.K.S., ..	28 *Nov.*	17th N. I., ..	Furlough.
James Manson, ..	do	44th N.I. ..	Furlough.
George Twemlow, ..	do	Artillery, ..	Furlough.
Nathaniel Jones, ..	do	49th N.I.	Furlough.
James Clarke Charnock Gray, ..	do	48th N.I. ..	Leave S. C. to Mussoorie.
Augustus Abbott, C. B., ..	do	Artillery, ..	Brigadier Comdt. of Artillery, and H. A. D. C. to the Govr. Genl., Furlough.
R. Walpole, C. B., ..	do	H. M. 2nd Battn., Rifle Brigade,	
Claud Douglas, ..	do	65th N.I. ..	Furlough.
*Henry Goodwyn, ..	do	Engineers. ..	Chief Engineer L. Provinces —Furlough.
~~James Steel, C. B~~, ..	do	67th N. I., ..	Furlough.
Charles Haldane, ..	do	44th N. I.	
**Thomas James Galloway*, ..	do	H. M. 70th Foot.	Brigadier Commanding at Peshawur.
**William Jones*, C. B., ..	do	H. M. 61st Foot.	Furlough.
Alex. Hy. Edmonstone Boileau, ..	do	Engineers. ..	Chief Engr. Nagpore Territory.
*George Connolly Ponsonby, ..	do	2nd E. L. C. ..	Furlough.
*~~Alexander Jardine~~, ..	do	H. M. 75th Foot.	
Frederick Brooke Corfield, ..	do	5th En. Regt. ..	Furlough.
*George Farquharson, ..	do	46th N.I.	
*William Robert Corfield, ..	do	22nd N.I. ..	Comdg. Native Infy. Brigade in China
**Matthew Smith*, ..	do	H. M. 81st Foot.	Brigr. Commanding at Fort William.
**Maurice Griffin Dennis*, ..	do	H. M. 60th Foot.	Brigr. Comdg. at Allahabad.
*Richard Horsford, ..	do	Artillery. ..	Brigadier Acting Comdt. of Arty. and Commdg. the Station of Meerut.
*John Christie, ..	do	1st E. L. C. ..	A.D.C. to the Queen.—Brigr. Comdg. at Barrackpore.
**Sir* Robert Napier, K. C. B., ..	do	Engineers. ..	Brigr. Genl. Comdg. a Divn. on Field Service Gwalior.
*Arthur Mitford Becher, C. B., ..	do	61st N.I. ..	Quarter Master Genl. of the Army.—On Furlough.
*John Fordyce, ..	do	Artillery, ..	Furlough.
*Thomas Fergusson Flemyng, ..	do	36th N.I. ..	Furlough.
*Francis Wheler, ..	do	1st E. L. C. ..	Brigadier Commanding at Saugor.
*John Studholme Hodgson, ..	do	12th N.I. ..	Furlough.
*John Kennedy McCausland, C B,	do	66th N. I.	Brigadier Commanding at Sealkote.
*~~James Mackenzie~~, ..	do	5th E. L.C.	Brigadier Commanding at Ferozepore.
*George St. Patrick Lawrence, ..	do	2nd E. L. C., ..	Civil employ.

* Brevet.

COLONELS.—*Continued.*

Names.	*Army Rank.*	*Corps.*	REMARKS.
**Sir* Richmond Campbell Shakespear, *Kt.*, ..	28 *Nov.* 1854	Artillery, ..	Civil employ.
Francis Rowcroft, C. B., ..	do	62nd N.I. ..	
**Trevor Chute,* ..	do	H. M. 70th Foot...	Brigr. Comdg. at Lucknow.
**William Gustavus Brown,* ..	do	H. M. 24th Foot...	Brigr. Comdg. at Lahore
*James Matthie, ..	do	21st N.I. ..	
**John Leslie Dennis,* ..	do	H. M. 52nd Foot.	
*Hugh Troup, ..	do	6th En. Regt. ..	Brigadier Comdg at Delhi
*William Maule Ramsay, ..	do	35th N. I. ..	Furlough.
**Sir* Archibald Bogle, *Kt.*, ..	do	42nd L. I., ..	Civil employ.—Furlough.
*David Simpson, ..	do	54th N. I. ..	Furlough.
*John Anderson Barstow, ..	do	58th N.I.	
*Edward Altham Cumberlege, ..	do	40th N.I. ..	Furlough.
*John Macdonald, ..	do	39th N.I.	
*Thomas Henry Shuldham, ..	do	15th N.I. ..	Furlough.
**Henry Richmond Jones,* ..	do	H. M. 6th Carabineers.	
*John Butler, ..	do	11th N. I.	
*Thomas Sewell, ..	do	25th N.I. ...	Lv. S C to the Cape of G H
*Francis Jenkins, ..	do	61st N.I. ..	Civil employ.
*Geo. Monro Carmichael Smyth,	do	1st En L C ..	
*George Burney, ..	do	65th N I ..	
*Edmund Wintle, ..	do	24th N I ..	Furlough.
*James Don Kennedy, ..	do	70th N I ..	
*Robert Turnbull Sandeman, ..	do	33rd N I ..	
*William Swatman, ..	do	3rd En Regt ..	Furlough.
*St. George Daniell Showers, C.B.	do	2nd En B F ..	Brigr Comdg at Agra
**Augustus George Blachford,* ..	do	H. M. 24th Foot.	
**Henry Renny,* ..	do	H. M. 81st Foot.	
**George Campbell,* ..	do	H. M. 52nd Foot.	
*Colin Troup, ..	do	68th N I ..	Brigr Comdg at Mooltan
*George Moyle Sherer, ..	do	73rd N I ..	
*William George Lennox, ..	do	63rd N I ..	
*John Welchman, C.B., ..	do	1st En B F ..	Furlough.
*Arthur Wheatley, ..	do	4th En L C ..	Furlough.
*William Ferguson Beatson, ..	do	4th En Regt ..	Furlough.
*Bulstrode Bygrave, ..	do	31st N I ..	Furlough.
*Richmond Houghton, ..	do	16th N I (Grs) ..	
*Charles Samuel Reid, ..	do	Artillery ..	
*John Edmonstoune Landers, ..	do	9th N I ..	Furlough
*Edward John Dickey, ..	do	27th N I ..	Supdt of Studs
*~~Henry Templer~~, ..	do	6th En Regt ..	Furlough
*Henry Pelham Burn, ..	1 *May* 1855	4th En Regt ..	Supdt of Army clothing
*E Rowland Mainwaring, ..	7 do	16th N. I. (Grs.)	Furlough.
*Astley Geo. F. J. Younghusband,	3 *Aug.*	35th L I ..	Furlough.
*John Craigie Halkett, C. B., ...	15 *Sep.*	20th N I ..	
*William Riddell, ..	5 *Dec.*	3rd En Regt ..	
*Auchmuty Tucker, C. B., ..	2 *Apl.* 1856	4th En L C ..	
*Henry Clayton, ..	18 *May*	3rd En L C ..	Furlough.
*Philip Harris, ..	8 *June*	70th N. I.	Furlough.
*James Travers, ..	6 *Dec.*	2nd N. I. (Grs)..	Furlough.
**John Hamilton Stewart,* ..	8 *Mar.* 1857	H. M. 29th Foot.	

* Brevet.

COLONELS.—*Continued.*

Names.	*Army Rank.*	*Corps.*	REMARKS.
William Erskine Baker, ..	10 *Mar.* 1857	Engineers, ..	Furlough.
*John Lewis Taylor, ..	14 do	26th N I ..	Furlough
*W. Reveridge Thomson, C B ..	29 *May*	3rd B E R ..	Commissary General
*Henry Forster, C. B.,	20 *June*	Shekhawattee Battalion.	Furlough.
*Patrick Gordon, ..	do	11th N I ..	Brigr Comdg at Dinapore
*John Liptrap, ..	do	45th N I ..	
*Robert Garrett, ..	do	64th N. I. ..	Furlough.
*Simon F Hannay, ..	do	43rd L I ..	Assam L Infy
*Edward Darvall, ..	do	57th N I ..	
*Peter Abbott, ..	do	72nd N I ..	
*Francis Burton Boileau, ..	do	Artillery ..	
*~~Edward Hely Hutchinson,~~ ..	do	H. M. 35th Foot..	
*George Henry Swinley. ..	27 do	Artillery ..	
*Henry Palmer, ..	29 *July*	48th N I ..	
*David Pott, ..	22 *Aug*	47th N I ..	
*Archibald Lorne Campbell, ..	15 *Sep.*	3rd En L C ..	
*Thomas Lowth Harington, ..	12 *Oct.*	5th En L C ..	Furlough.
*Douglas Seaton, ..	15 do	1st En B F ..	Furlough.
*~~Usher Williamson,~~ ..	26 *Nov.*	H. M. 27 Foot,	[Irr. Force.
*Neville Bowles Chamberlain, C.B..	27 do	16th N.I. (Grs.)	Brigr. Genl. Comdg. Punjaub
*James Abbott, ..	28 *Nov.*	Artillery ..	
*James W H Jamieson, ..	do	52nd N I ..	
*~~John Glasfurd,~~ ..	do	Engineers ..	
*William Pitt Robbins, ..	do	15th N I ..	
*Charles Hogge, C B, ..	do	Artillery ..	
*Hugh Boyd, ..	do	59th N. I. ..	Furlough.
*William E Mulcaster, ..	do	64th N I ..	
*Orfeur Cavenagh, ..	do	32nd N. I. ..	
*John Stafford Paton, ..	do	14th N I ..	Depy Qr Mr Genl of the Army.
*James M. B. F. Tytler, C. B., ..	19 *Jan.* 1858	37th N. I.	Furlough.
**E. H. Greathed,* C. B., ..	do	H. M. 8th Foot. ..	Deputy Adjt. Genl. Q. T. Bombay.
**Sir John Jones,* K. C. B., ..	do	H. M. 60th Foot,	
*John William Hicks, ..	15 *Feb.*	69th N. I. ..	
*Vincent Eyre, C. B., ..	24 *Mar.*	Artillery. ..	Gun-Powder Agent, Ishapore.
*Frank Turner, C. B., ..	24 *Mar.*	Artillery. ..	Gun Carriage Agent, Futtehghur.
*James D. McPherson, C.B.,	5 *Apl.*	22nd N. I.	Mily. Secy. to the Lt. Govr. of the Punjaub
*Henry Tombs, C. B., ..	20 *July*	Artillery. ..	Furlough.
*Henry Marion Durand, C. B, ..	20 *July*	Engineers, ..	Furlough.
*John Coke, C. B., ..	20 *July*	10th N. I. ..	Furlough.
*Arthur Cole Spottiswoode, ..	23 *July*	37th N. I. ..	
**Charles Herbert,* C. B., ..	19 *Aug.*	H. M. 75th Foot.	
*Joseph Graham, ..	27 *Aug.*	29th N. I. ..	
*Christopher ~~Simson Maling,~~ ..	24 *Oct.*	18th N. I. ..	Furlough.
*~~Edward L'Estrange,~~ ..	12 *Nov.*	H. M. 70th Foot.	

* Brevet.

LIEUTENANT COLONELS.

Names.	*Army Rank.*	*Corps.*	REMARKS.
Frederick Gaitskell, C. B., ..	17 *May.* 1854	Artillery,	
*Henry Drummond, ..	20 *June*	1st E.L.C.	
William Binfield Wemyss, ..	do	4th E.L.C. ..	Furlough.
Richard Drought, C. B., ..	do	60th N. I.,	
Archibald Little, ..	do	H. M. 9th Lancers,	
*Thomas Moore, ..	28 *Nov.*	5th E. L. C.	
*Charles Campbell, ..	do	42nd L.I. ..	Furlough.
Robert Augustus Master, C. B., ..	do	2nd E.L. C. ..	Furlough.
*George Cautley, ..	do	5th E.L.C.	
Robert Raikes Kinleside, ..	do	Artillery. ..	Furlough.
Alfred Huyshe, ..	do	Artillery.	
*John Clarke, ..	do	25th N.I. ..	Furlough.
*George Palmer Whish, ..	do	60th N.I.	
*Markham Eeles Sherwill, ..	do	2nd En. B. F.	
~~*John Abercrombie,~~ ..	do	Artillery. ..	Furlough.
Alexander Cunningham, ..	do	Engineers.	
William St. Leger Mitchell, ..	do	56th N. I.	
*Herbert B. Edwardes, C. B., ..	do	1st En. B. F.	
*Henry James Stannus, ..	do	5th E. L. C.	
*Henry F. Dunsford, C. B , ..	do	59th N. I.	
*Charles Cheape, ..	do	51st N. I.	
William Chas. Campbell, ..	do	30th N. I	
*Saunders A. Abbott, ..	do	51st N. I.	
John Caulfeild Hannyngton, ..	do	34th N. I.	
~~William Robert Dunmore,~~ ..	do	60th N. I. ..	Furlough.
Charles Clement Deacon, ..	11 *May* 1855	H. M. 61st Foot.	
Andrew Scott Waugh, ..	3 *Aug.*	Engineers, ..	Surveyor Genl. of India.
Wm. J. Baptist Knyvett, ..	15 *Sep.*	38th L.I.	
Alexander Murray, ..	2 *Nov.*	H. M. 87th Foot.	
B. O'Brien, ..	9 do	H. M. 87th Foot.	
*Nathl. Dunbar Barton, ..	18 *Mar.* 1856	63rd E. L. C. ..	Furlough.
Edward L. Ommanney, ..	15 *Apl.*	Engineers.	
Arthur Hall, ..	5 *May,*	5th E. L. C. ..	Furlough.
James Brind, C. B., ..	26 do	Artillery,	
William Neville Custance, ..	1 *Aug.*	H.M. 6th Dn. Gds.	
**Henry Garner Rainey,* ..	22 *Aug.*	H. M. 61st Foot.	Furlough.
John McNeill Walter, ..	17 *Oct.*	H. M. 35th Foot.	
John Laughton, ..	10 *Mar.* 1857	Engineers.	
**Jas. C. Brooke,* ..	14 *Apl.*	H. M. 8th Foot.	
Hamilton Vetch, ..	29 *May*	54th N. I.	
Arthur Sanders, ..	do	53rd N. I.	
Cuthbert Davidson, ..	31 do	49th N. I.	
George William Bishop, ..	do	23rd N. I.	
John Powell, ..	27 *June*	55th N. I. ..	Furlough.
Francis Claude Burnett, ..	do	Artillery,	
George Ramsay, ..	do	10th N. I.	
Edward G. J. Champneys, ..	1 *July*	5th En. Regt., ...	Military Auditor General.
Richard Y. B. Bush, ..	15 do	32nd N. I. ..	Furlough.
James G. A. Rice, ..	29 do	4th B. E. Regt.	
Joseph H. Hampton, ..	22 *Aug.*	50th N. I.	
William A. Cooke, ..	3 *Sep.*	2nd N.I. (Grs.)	
Arthur Broome, ..	14 do	Artillery.	
Henry Righy, ..	20 do	Engineers.	
Reginald E. Knatchbull, ..	28 do	Artillery, ..	Furlough.
~~Thomas Henry Sale,~~ ..	1 *Oct.*	Engineers.	
*Keith Young, C. B., ..	12 do	50th N. I ...	Judge Adv. Genl. of the Army.
Thomas Percival Touzel, ..	do	H. M. 27th Foot.	
~~*Archd. R. J. Swinton,~~ ..	15 do	32nd N.I.	
Frederick English, C. B., ..	2 *Nov.*	H. M. 53rd Foot.	
~~Robert Ramsay,~~ ..	18 do	74th N. I. ..	Furlough.

* Brevet.

LIEUTENANT COLONELS.—*Continued.*

Names.	*Army Rank.*	*Corps.*	REMARKS.
Henry William Matthews,	3 *Dec.* 1857	43rd L.I.	
**Edmund Wodehouse,*	12 do	H. M. 24th Foot.	
*Henry Alan Olpherts,	15 *Jan.* 1858	Artillery,	
*Edward Kaye,	1 do	Artillery.	
*Charles Reid, C. B.,	do	10th N.I.	
*Richard Baird Smith, C. B.,	do	Engineers,	Master of the Calcutta Mint.
*Richard S. Ewart,	do	30th N.I.	[Magazines.
Edward W. S. Scott,	do	Artillery,	Inspr. Genl. of Ordnance and
Norman C. MacLeod,	do	Engineers.	
*Edwin Beaumont Johnson, C. B.,	do	Artillery.	
Henry Aime Ouvry C. B.,	do	H. M. 9th Light Dragoons.	
**C. E. P. Gordon,*	do	H. M. 75th Foot.	
~~*Charles Apthorp,~~	24 *Mar.*	41st N.I.	
*Thomas Simpson,	do	57th N.I.	
*George James Montgomery,	do	15th N.I.	
Gravenor Kirby.	do	Artillery.	
~~T. J. W. Hungerford C. B.,~~	do	Artillery.	
*H. H. Maxwell,	do	Artillery.	
*J H. Smyth,	do	Artillery.	Furlough.
*G. Bouchier. C. B.,	do	Artillery.	
*W. Olpherts, C. B.,	do	Artillery.	
*G. W. G. Green, C. B.,	do	2nd En. B. F.	Furlough.
*F. F. Remmington, C. B.	do	Artillery.	
*James Metcalfe,	do	4th En. Regt.	
*C. H. Blunt, C. B.,	do	Artillery.	
**George Bryan Milman,*	do	H. M. 5th Foot.	
Charles Prior,	25 *Apl.*	64th N. I.	Furlough.
David Wilkie,	26 do	4th N.I.	
*W. Wynne Apperley,	1 *May*	3rd E. L. C.	
George William Hamilton,	19 do	17th N. I.	
Francis Roger Palmer, C. B.,	22 *June*	H. M 60th Foot.	
*Charles Cooper,	4 *July*	23rd N. I.	
William Payn,	13 do	H. M. 53rd Foot.	
Henry Alex. Carleton, C. B.,	20 do	Artillery	
*Alexander Taylor, C. B.,	do	Engineers.	
*Jeremiah Brasyer, C. B.,	do	Unattached.	
*John DeW. C. J. Moir,	do	28th N. I.	
*George Gordon,	do	50th N. I.	
*D. M. Stewart,	do	9th N. I.	
**William Campbell Mollan,*	20 do	H. M. 75th Foot.	
Ronald Macdonell,	23 do	4th E. L. C.	
**Legendre Charles Bourchier,*	9 *Aug.*	H. M. 75th Foot.	
William Barr,	18 do	Artillery.	
Herbert, E. S. Abbott,	22 do	74th N. I.	
~~John Butler,~~	27 do	55th N. I.	
~~Thomas Martin,~~	do	20th N. I.	
E. W. D. Lowe, C. B.,	26 *Sep.*	H. M. 32nd Foot.	
**A. T. Allan,*	12 *Nov.*	H. M. 81st Foot,	
**Charles Beamish,*	do	H. M. 35th Foot.	
*Fredk. W. Burroughs,	14 do	17th N. I.	
William Henry, Delamain,	14 do	Artillery. [neers.	
**Charles Sawyer,*	16 do	H. M. 6th Carabi-	
**W. C. Master,* C. B.,	do	H. M. 5th Foot.	
*George Timins,	23 do	34th N. I.	Furlongh.
David Reid,	23 *Dec.*	Artillery.	
Arthur Purves Phayre,	22 *Jan.* 59	6th En. Regt.	
*~~Henry A. Shuckburgh,~~	4 *Feb.*	40th N. I.	
Brooke Boyd,	15 *May*	68th N. I.	
Francis Elliot Voyle,	4th *June*	39th N. I.	
William A. J. Mayhew,	*Official,*	6th En. Regt.	Adjutant Genl. of the Army.
George W. Williams,	do	29th N. I.	
Henry Yule,	do	Engineers.	Secy. to Govt. D. P. W.

* Brevet.

MAJORS.

Names.	*Army Rank.*	*Corps.*	REMARKS.
~~Edward Knollys~~, ..	11 *Nov* 1851	H. M. 75th Foot.	
Archibald F. Macpherson, ..	do	43rd L.I.	
John Minshull Drake, ..	do	46th N.I.	
Andrew Henry Duncan, ..	do	3rd Bl. European [Regt.	
*Richard R. W. Ellis, ..	do	23rd N.I.	
Lionel P. D. Eld, ..	do	9th N.I.	
Charles Pattenson, ..	do	4th N.I.	
Edwin Marriott, ..	do	57th N.I.	
*Reynell G. Taylor, .	16 *Dec.*	2nd E. L. Cavy.	
*Crawford T. Chamberlain, ..	2 *May* 1852	28th N.I.	
*Arthur W. C. Plowden, ..	22 *Oct.*	1st E. L. Cavy.	
*Charles Vyvyan Cox, ..	4 *Mar.* 1853	Artillery.	
~~*Peter Christie~~, ..	do	do	
William Augustin John Mayhew,	9 *Dec.*	6th E. Regt. (*Offl. Lieut. Col.*)	Adjutant General of the [Army.
William Frost Nuthall, ..	do	18th N.I.	
*Albert Fytche, ..	do	70th N.I.	
*Harry Burnett Lumsden, ..	6 *Feb.* 1854	59th N.I.	
*Richard Strachey, ..	16 do	Engineers.	
George Warren Stokes, ..	20 *June*	59th N.I.	
*William Lamb, ..	do	51st N.I.	
*Edward F. Smith, ..	do	23rd N. I.	
~~*Hugh Mackenzie~~, ..	do	2nd E. B. F.	
*William Lydiard, ..	do	11th N.I.	
*George Burd Reddie, ..	do	29th N.I.	
George W. Williams, ..	do	29th N.I. (*Offl. Lt. Col.*)	
*James Knox Spence, ..	do	20th N.I.	
*George Mytton Hill, ..	do	17th N.I.	
James Corse Scott, ..	do	20th N.I.	
Theodore F. B. Beatson, ..	do	4th E. L. C.	
*Henry Stockley Grimes, ..	do	46th N.I.	
~~*Charles Henry Burt~~, ..	do	64th N.I.	
John Bontein, ..	do	37th N.I.	
Frederick Maitland, ..	do	5th En. Regt.	
*John Barrett, ..	do	37th N.I.	
~~James Sleeman~~, ..	do	73rd N.I.	
Francis Stuart Paterson, ..	do	54th N.I.	
Robert Morrieson, ..	do	52nd N.I.	
*David Gaussen, ..	do	43rd L.I.	
Clement Reade Browne, ..	do	60th N.I.	
*William Baker, ..	do	4th E, L. C.	
Robert Troup, ..	do	63rd N.I.	
Charles D. G. Walsh, ..	do	14th N.I.	
*William Richardson, ..	do	73rd N.I.	
Henry M. Nation, ..	do	3rd B.E.R.	
*John Hennessy, ..	do	70th N. I.	
~~*Frederick Joseph Harriott~~, ..	do	4th E. L. C.	
William P. Hampton, ..	do	31st N.I.	
*Walter C. Erskine, ..	do	73rd N.I.	
Richard S. Simpson, ..	do	27th N.I.	
James Charles Innes, ..	do	61st N.I.	
*William B. Legard, ..	do	31st N.I.	
*Wright W. Davidson, ..	do	32nd N.I.	
*George Jackson, ..	do	3rd E. L. C.	
*James Edward Verner, ..	do	60th N.I.	
Robert J. Hawthorne, ..	do	2nd E. L. C.	
*Philip A. P. Bouverie, ..	11 *July*	35th L. I.	
*Alexander Bagot, ..	24 do	15th N. I.	
*Alfred George Goodwyn, ..	2 *Aug.*	Engineers.	
*John Harley Maxwell, ..	do	Engineers.	
*John Reid Becher, ..	do	Engineers.	

* Brevet.

MAJORS—*Continued.*

Names.	*Army Rank.*	*Corps.*	REMARKS.
*Edward John Lake, ..	22 *Aug.* 1854	Engineers.	
*George Newbolt, ..	28 *Nov.*	31st N. I.	
James Townshend Daniell, ..	do	47thN. I.	
*John Liptrott, ..	do	2nd En. B. F.	
*Edward King Elliot, ..	do	43rd L. I.	
*Thomas Scott Horsbrugh, ..	do	32nd N. I.	
Henry Milne, ..	do	21st N, I.	
*William Henry Ryves, ..	do	61st N. I.	
*Stephen F. Macmullen, ..	do	3rd E. L. C.	
*Robert Thatcher, ..	do	9th N. I.	
John Smith, ..	do	49th N. I.	
*Samuel Richard Tickell, ..	do	31st N. I.	
Robert Napier Raikes, ..	do	67th N. I.	
Anthony Martin, ..	do	33rd N. I.	
*Andrew Hunter Ross, ..	do	42nd N. I.	
William Kelly Wollen, ..	do	19th N, I.	
James Gandy Gaitskell, ..	do	26th L. I.	
Christopher Hasell, ..	do	48th N. I.	
*John Morrieson, ..	do	30th N. I.	
*Edward Harvey, ..	do	4th E. L. C.	
Peter William Luard, ..	do	55th N. I.	
*Henry Lewis Bird, ..	do	48th N. I.	
*Thomas G. St. George, ..	do	17th N. I.	
*Charles Herbert, ..	2 *Jan.* 1855	18th N. I.	
*Charles James Robarts, ..	8 *Mar.*	43rd L. I.	
John Patrick Redmond, ..	11 *May*	H. M. 61st Foot.	
**Louis H. Hamilton,* ..	20 *July*	H. M. 87th Foot.	
**Alexander Hugh Cobbe,* ..	2 *Nov.*	H. M. 87th Foot.	
*Sydney Joseph Hire, ..	2 *Dec.*	22nd N. I.	
*Charles Vincent Bowie, ..	22 *Jan.* 1856	Artillery.	
**John Arthur Gildea,* ..	9 *Apl.*	H. M. 81st Foot.	
*George Verner, ..	18 *May*	9th N. I.	
*James Grant Stephen, ..	6 *June*	6th En. Regt.	
*John L. Vaughan, ..	do	21st N. I.	
*Roland Richardson, ..	do	1st E. L. C.	
*William A. A. Thomson, ..	13 *July*	4th E. L. C. [Gds.	
**Herman Stapylton.* ..	9 *Oct.*	H M. 27th Foot.	
Patrick W. Sydenham Ross, ..	17 *Oct.*	H. M. 35th Foot.	
*Charles T. E. Hinde, ..	24 *Nov.*	65th N. I.	
*John C. Phillips, ..	28 *Nov.*	3rd En. Regt.	
**Robert Stuart Baynes,* ..	26 *Dec.*	H. M. 8th Foot.	
**William Francis Ring,* ..	do	H. M. 87th Foot.	
John T. Shakespear, ..	1 *May* 1857	24th N. I,	
Samuel B. Faddy, ..	31 do	36th N. I.	
James Lumsdaine Walker, ..	do	71st N. I.	
Charles N. North, ..	19 *June*	H. M. 60th Foot.	
Charles V. Jenkins, ..	1 *July*	1st E. L. C.	
Edmund Sissmore, ..	11 do	69th N. I,	
Fred. Moffat Baker, ..	15 do	65th N. I.	
William C. Gott, ..	do	56th N. I.	
Henry Ramsay, ..	do	53rd N. I.	
Edward Dayot Watson, ..	21 do	44th N. I.	
D ~~Abraham Meyer,~~ ..	22 *Aug.*	58th N. I.	[Lower circle
T. F. Hobday, ..	28 do	72nd N. I. ..	Deputy Commissary General,
Wm. McCulloch, ..	4 *Sep.*	13th N. I.	
George G. Denniss, ..	14 do	1st En. B. F.	
William Henry Oakes, ..	7 *Nov.*	45th N. I.	
Frederick Johnston, ..	18 *Dec.*	62nd N. I.	
*E. K. Money, ..	19 *Jan.* 1858	Artillery.	
*A. Boyd, ..	do	2nd En. B. F.	
*R. C. Lawrence, ..	do	73rd N. I.	

* Brevet.

MAJORS—*Continued.*

Names.		*Army Rank.*	*Corps.*	REMARKS.
*H. Nicoll,	..	19 *Jan.* 1858	50th N. I.	
*D. C. Shute,	..	do	19th N. I.	
*R. A. Ramsay,	..	do	35th L. I.	
*H. R. Grindlay,	..	do	3rd E. L. C.	
*O. E. Rothney,	..	do	45th N. I.	
*J. Young,	..	do	Artillery.	
*H. M. Garstin,	..	do	36th N. I.	
*C. H. Barchard, C. B.,	..	do	20th N. I.	
*S. Greville,	..	do	1st En. B. F.	
*W. D. Harris,	..	do	2nd En. B. F.	
*J. C. Hay,	..	do	60th N. I.	
*E. Brown,	..	do	1st En. B. F.	
*G W. M. Hall,,	..	do	26th L. I.	
*H. F. M. Boisragon,	..	do	1st En. B. F.	
*D. Kemp,	..	do	5th En. Regt.	
*Thomas Edward Kennion,	..	do	Artillery	
*A. Light,	..	do	Artillery.	
*Thomas H. Sibley,	..	do	62nd N. I.	
*W. Maxwell,	..	24 *Mar.*	Artillery.	
*J. W. Carnegie,	..	do	15th N. I.	
*Francis G. Crossman,	..	do	45th N, I.	
*D. S. Dodgson,	..	do	30th N. I.	
*T. F. Wilson, C. B.,	..	do	13th N. I.	
*F. W. Baugh,	..	do	26th N. I.	
*H. Dinning,	..	do	71st N. I.	
*Chas St. G. Brownlow,	..	do	15th N. I.	
*M. F. Kemble,	..	do	41st N. I.	
*H. Hammond,	..	do	Artillery.	
*R. C. Germon,	..	do	13th N. I.	
*J. W. Sanders,	..	do	41st N. I.	
*T. T. Boileau,	..	do	2nd E. L. C.	
*R. J. Edgell,	..	do	53rd N. I.	
*E. Oakes,	..	do	6th En. Regt.	
*W. A. Crommelin, C. B.,	..	do	Engineers.	
*Henry Lane,	..	do	5th En. L. C.	
*T. A. Carey,	..	do	17th N. I.	
*R. P. Anderson,	..	do	25th N. I.	
*H. LeGeyt Bruce,	..	do	Artillery.	
*A. D. Dickens,	..	do	38th N. I.	
*G. S. Macbean,	..	do	74th N. I.	
*C. A. Barwell,	..	do	71st N. I.	
*D. M. Probyn, C. B.,	..	do	3rd E. L. C.	
*W. T. Hughes,	..	do	48th N. I.	
*T. James,	..	do	2nd N. I. (Grs.)	
*G. C. Hatch,	..	do	57th N. I.	
*H. M. Wilson,	..	do	6th En. Regt.	
*F. C. Maisey,	..	do	67th N. I.	
W. S. Ferris,	..	25 *Apl.*	12th N. I.	
*C. J. Richards,	..	1 *May*	25th N. I.	
R. C. Tytler,	..	16 do	38th L. I.	
*R. Larkins,	..	20 *July*	49th N. I.	
*R. J. Meade,	..	do	65th N. I.	
*C. Douglas,	..	do	Artillery,	
*J. W. Carter,	..	do	54th N. I.	
*John Hood,	..	do	49th N. I.	
*J. F. Richardson, C. B.,	..	do	49th N. I.	
*John Gordon,	..	do	5th En. Regt.	
*Alex Hume,	..	do	1st En. B. F.	
*R. C. Barclay,	..	do	68th N. I.	
*C. S. Weston,	..	do	36th N. I.	
*J. H. Brooks,	..	do	1st En. L. C.	

* Brevet.

Majors—*Continued*.

Names.		*Army Rank.*	*Corps.*		**Remarks.**
*F. O. Salusbury,	..	20 *July* 1858	1st En. B. F.		
*George Moir, C. B.,	..	do	Artillery.		
*A. G. Austen,	..	do	Artillery.		
*G. W. Boileau,	..	do	34th N. I.		
*S. J. Browne,	..	do	46th N. I.		
*W. D. Morgan,	..	do	22nd N. I.		
*A. L. McMullin,	..	do	23rd N. I.		
*W. A. Mackinnon, C. B.,	..	do	Artillery.		
*R. L. Thompson,	..	do	10th N. I.		
*J. H. Balmain,	..	do	4th En. L. C.		
*J. I. Murray,	..	do	71st N. I.		
*H. Forbes,	..	do	1st E. L. C.		
*H. C. Anderson,	..	do	54th N. I.		
*C. Cureton,	..	do	38th N I.		
*C. Cookworthy,	..	do	Artillery.		
*F. W. Lambert,	..	do	56th N. I.		
*C. J. S. Gough,	..	do	5th E. L. C.		
*H. Drummond,	..	do	Engineers.		
*A. B. Johnson,	..	do	5th En. Regt.		
*A. Pearson,	..	do	Artillery,		
*A. Bunny,	..	do	Artillery.		
*G. A. Renny,	..	do	Artillery.		
*G. Hutchinson,	..	do	Engineers.		
*O. Wilkinson,	..	do	4th En. L. C.		
George Ryley,	..	22 *Aug.*	74th N. I.		
*E. W. E. Walker,	..	28 do	Artillery.		
*H. P. Bishop,	..	do	Artillery.		
*J. S. Frith,	..	do	Artillery.		
*W. W. H. Greathed,	..	do	Engineers.		
*W. T. Brown,	..	do	Artillery.		
*J. S. Gibb,	..	do	Artillery.		
*W. Wilson,	..	do	Artillery.		
*F. R. Maunsell,	..	do	Engineers.		
*G. E. Watson,	..	do	Engineers.		
*J. F. Tennant,	..	do	Engineers.		
*J. G. Medley,	..	do	Engineers.		
*J. J. Mc L. Innes,	..	do	Engineers.		
*G. T. Chesney,	..	do	Engineers.		
*W. E. Warrand,	..	do	Engineers.		
*H. A. Brownlow,	..	do	Engineers.		
*P. Stewart,	..	do	Engineers.		
*J. St. J. Hovenden,	..	do	Engineers.		
G. A. Fisher,	..	13 *Nov.*	4th En. R.		
T. J. Gardiner,	..	23 do	16th N. I. (Grs.)		
*H. R. Garden,	..	26 *Dec.*	2nd N. I. (Grs.)		
Walter Birch,	..	22 *Jan.* 1859	6th. En. Regt.		
*R. H. Sale,	..	5 *Mar.*	9th N. I.		
*R. Warburton,	..	13 do	Artillery.		
*T. Rattray,	..	1 *Apl.*	64th N. I.		
P. A. Roberton,	..	15 *May*	68th N I.		
T. Pownall,	..	4 *June*	39th N. I.		
Fredk. Dayot, Atkinson,	..	*Official*, ..	2nd En. B. F.	..	Depy. Secretary to Govt [Mily. Dept.
Henry E. L. Thuillier,	..	do ..	Artillery,	..	Supt. of Revenue Surveys and Depy. Surveyor General.
H. W. Norman, *Lt. Col. C.B*	..	do ..	31st N. I.	..	Depy. Adjt. Genl. of the Army

Brevet.

GRADATION LIST

OF THE

OFFICERS

OF

THE BENGAL ARMY

His Excellency General the Right Hon'ble LORD CLYDE, G. C. B., Commander-in-Chief of Her Majesty's Forces in India, 13th August 1857.

GENERALS.

Season.	Names.	Army Rank.	Corps.	Remarks.
1794	*Sir* Robert Houstoun, K. C. B.,	20 *June* 1854	4 E. L. C.	Europe.
95	John Alex. Paul Macgregor,	ditto ..	54 N.I. ..	Europe.
93	*Sir* William Richards, K. C. B.,	ditto ..	26 L.I. ..	India.
90	James A'hmuty, ..	15 *Sep.* 1855	Artillery, ..	Europe.
95	Mossom Boyd, ..	9 *Apl.* 1856	53 N.I. ..	Europe.
98	*Sir* Robert Henry Cunliffe, Bart. and C. B., ..	13 *Oct.* 1857	4 N.I. ..	Europe.
98	John Truscott, ..	27 *Jan.* 1858	74 N.I. ..	Europe.

LIEUTENANT GENERALS.

Season.	Names.	Army Rank.	Corps.	Remarks.
1702	George Swiney, ..	11 *Nov.* 1851	Artillery, ..	Europe.
03	*Sir* George Pollock, G. C. B., ..	ditto ..	Artillery, ..	Europe.
04	Alexander Lindsay, C. B., ..	ditto ..	Artillery, ..	Europe.
98	Suetonius Henry Tod, ..	ditto ..	60 N.I. ..	Europe.
98	Harry Thomson, ..	ditto ..	1 E.L.C. ..	Europe.
97	James Kennedy, C. B., ..	ditto ..	5 E.L.C. ..	Europe.
99	Charles William Hamilton, ..	ditto ..	40 N.I. ..	Europe.
99	Edmund Fredk. Waters, C. B.,	ditto ..	68 N.I. ..	Europe.
99	Richard Collyer Andree, ..	ditto ..	69 N.I. ..	Europe.
96	Thomas Shubrick, ..	ditto ..	2 E.L.C. ..	Europe.

Lieutenant Generals—*Continued.*

Season.	Names.	Army Rank.	Corps.	Remarks.
1799	~~William Henry Komm~~, ..	11 *Nov.* 1851	25 N.I. ..	Europe.
01	~~William Vincent~~, ..	ditto ..	6 En. Regt.	India.
00	Thomas Henry Paul, ..	ditto ..	20 N.I. ..	Europe.
03	Samuel Swinhoe, ..	15 *Sep.* 1855	73 N.I. ..	Europe
00	John Anderson, ..	5 *Dec.* ..	61 N.I. ..	Europe.
01	Frederick Young, ..	18 *Feb.* 1856	66 N.I. ..	Europe.
05	Thos. Monteath Douglas, C.B.,	18 *Mar.* ..	35 L.I. ..	Europe.
01	Wm. Robert Clayton Costley,	2 *Apl.* ..	9 N.I. ..	Europe.
03	*Sir* Geo. Petre Wymer, K.C.B.,	8 *June* ..	38 L.I. ..	Europe.
03	Alexander Dick, ..	4 *July* ..	71 N.I. ..	India.
98	William Pattle, C. B., ..	18 ditto ..	3 E.L.C. ..	Europe.
04	Thomas Fiddes, ..	15 *Sep.* ..	42 N. I. ..	Europe.
03	Abraham Roberts, C. B., ..	13 *Oct.* 1857	1 En. B. F.	Europe.
02	Chas. A. Grenado Wallington,	4 *Mar.* 1858	18 N.I. ..	Europe.
03	Thomas Oliver, ..	4 *May* ..	37 N.I. ..	Europe.
04	Duncan Gordon Scott, ..	23 *July* ..	30 N.I. ..	Europe.
04	Henry Hall, C. B., ..	24 *Oct.* ..	21 N.I. ..	Europe.
04	Samuel Shaw, ..	5 *Mar.* 1859	Artillery, ..	Europe.

MAJOR GENERALS.

Season.	Names.	Army Rank.	Corps.	Remarks.
1804	Matthew Coombs Paul, ..	20 *June* 1854	29 N.I. ..	Europe.
09	*Sir* John Cheape, K. C. B., ..	ditto	Engineers, ..	Europe.
03	Joseph Harris, ..	ditto ..	4 En. Regt.	Europe.
04	John Tulloch, C B., ..	ditto ..	51 N.I. ..	Europe.
05	Richard Powney, ..	ditto ..	Artillery, ..	Europe.
05	George Edward Gowan, C.B.,	ditto ..	Artillery, ..	Europe.
05	~~James Stuart, C. B.~~, ..	ditto ..	34 N.I. ..	Europe.
06	William Henry Hewitt, ..	ditto ..	27 N.I. ..	Europe.
03	~~John Home~~, ..	ditto ..	57 N.I. ..	Europe.
04	Geo. Wm. Aylmer Lloyd, C.B.,	ditto ..	28 N.I. ..	India.
05	Robert Blackall, ..	ditto ..	2 En. B. F.	Europe.
04	James Eckford, C. B., ..	28 *Nov.*	56 N.I. ..	India.
05	Andrew Hervey, ..	ditto	52 N.I. ..	India.
05	Chas. M. Carmichael, C. B., ..	ditto ..	5 E.L.C. ..	Europe.
18	Henry Lechmere Worrall, ..	ditto ..	4 E. L. C. ..	Europe.
07	*Sir* John Bennett Hearsey, K. C. B., ..	ditto ..	3 E.L.C. ..	Comdg. Presidency Division.
05	George Richd. Pemberton, ..	ditto ..	62 N.I. ..	Europe.
04	Stephen Davis Riley, ..	ditto ..	47 N.I. ..	India.
05	Christopher Godby, C. B., ..	ditto ..	55 N.I. ..	Europe.
05	James Parsons, C. B., ..	ditto ..	50 N.I. ..	India.
18	George Warren, ..	ditto ..	13 N.I. ..	India.
07	Henry Fisher Salter, C. B.,	ditto ..	5 E.L.C. ..	Leave S. C. to the Cape of Good Hope.
07	Thomas Mathew Taylor, ..	ditto ..	1 E. L.C. ..	Europe.
05	Robert Hawkes, ..	ditto ..	L.C. ..	Europe.
08	Archibald F. Richmond, C. B.,	ditto ..	24 N.I. ..	Europe.
19	†*Sir* Patrick Grant, K. C. B.,	ditto ..	6 En. Regt.	Commander-in-Chief at Madras.
10	Chris. Dixon Wilkinson, C.B.,	ditto ..	6 En. Regt.	India.
10	William Henry Marshall, ..	ditto ..	32 N.I. ..	Europe.

† Lieut. Genl. in the East Indies, 25th Jan. 1856.

MAJOR GENERALS—*Continued.*

Season.	Names.	Army Rank.	Corps.	REMARKS.
1817	Francis S. Hawkins, C. B., ..	28 *Nov.* 1854	2nd N.I. (Grs)	Europe.
D 04	~~John Graham,~~ ..	ditto ..	67 N.I. ..	Europe.
11	Edward Garstin, ..	ditto ..	Engineers.	India.
04	Richard Home, ..	ditto ..	43 L.I. ..	Europe.
10	Alexander Carnegy, C. B., ..	ditto ..	15 N.I. ..	Europe.
06	George Tomkyns, ..	ditto ..	19 N.I. ..	Europe.
06	Charles R. W. Lane, C. B., ..	ditto ..	5 En. Regt.	Europe.
07	William John Gairdner, C. B.,	ditto ..	63 N.I. ..	Europe.
08	George Brooke, C. B., ..	ditto ..	Artillery. ..	Europe.
D 05	~~Thomas Dickinson,~~	ditto ..	10 N.I. ..	Europe.
05	Henry Chambers M. Cox, ..	ditto ..	58 N.I. ..	Europe.
07	John Hoggan, C. B., ..	ditto ..	45 N.I.	India.
19	George Huyshe, C. B., ..	ditto ..	3 B.E. Reg.	Europe.
17	Charles Hamilton, C. B., ..	ditto ..	59 N.I. ..	Europe.
24	Philip Francis Story, C. B.,	13 *Apl.* 1855	3 E. L.C...	India.
09	Henry Lawrence, ..	5 *Dec.* ..	72 N. I. ..	Europe.
07	George Hicks, C. B., ..	18 *Feb.* 1856	70 N. I. ..	Europe.
06	Henry Francis Caley, ..	18 *Mar.* ..	64 N.I. ..	India.
07	Hope Dick, ..	2 *April* ..	4 En. Regt.	Europe.
12	Joseph Nash, C. B., ..	9 *April* ..	46 N.I., ..	India.
20	James Alexander, C. B., ..	18 *May* ..	Artillery, ..	Europe.
20	John Theophilus Lane, C. B.,	8 *June* ..	Artillery, .	India.
05	Robert Stewart, ..	15 *Sep.* ..	41 N.I. ..	Europe.
04	Edward Pettingal, ..	4 *Nov.* ..	12 N.I. ..	Europe.
10	Edward Huthwaite, C. B., ...	14 *Mar.* 1857	Artillery. ..	Nainee Tal.
05	Frederick George Lister, ..	22 *Aug.* ..	31 N.I. ..	Europe.
19	*Sir* A. Wilson, *Bt.* K, C. B., ..	14 *Sep.* ..	Artillery, ..	Europe.
18	David Downing, ..	15 *Sep.* ..	39 N.I. ..	Europe.
08	Frederick Hervey Sandys, ..	15 *Oct.* ..	36 N.I. ..	Europe.
09	John Moule, ..	27 *Jan.* 1858	33rd N. I. ..	Europe.
07	Louis Saunders Bird, ..	4 *Mar.* ..	23rd N. I ..	Europe.
17	David Birrell, ..	25 *Apl.* ..	71st N. I. ..	Europe.
14	Thomas Polwhele, ..	1 *May* ..	17th N.I. ..	Europe.
20	Richard J. H. Birch, C. B.,	4 *May* ...	2nd En. B.F.	Secy. to Govt. Mily. Dept.
22	George Campbell, ..	4 *July* ..	Artillery. ..	Comdg. Dinapore Division.
23	Peter Innes, ..	13 ditto ..	14 N.I. ..	India.
20	John Fowler Bradford, C. B.,	23 ditto ..	2 E.L.C. ..	Commanding Meerut Division.
21	Harry Meggs Graves, ..	27 *Aug.* ..	13 N. I. ..	Europe.
19	Charles Grant, C. B., ..	14 *Oct.* ..	Artillery. ..	Europe
18	Stuart Corbett, C. B., ..	4 *Feb.* 59	16 N.I. ..	Europe.
08	William Sage, ..	13 *Mar.* 59	22 N.I. ..	Europe.

COLONELS.

1819	*Sir* Justin Sheil, K. C. B. and K. L. S., ..	28 *Nov.* 1854	17 N.I. ..	Furlough.
07	James Manson, ..	ditto ..	44 N.I.	Furlough.
11	George Twemlow, ..	ditto ..	Artillery, ..	Furlough.
15	Nathaniel Jones, ..	ditto ..	49 N.I.	Furlough.
11	James Clarke Charnock Gray, ..	ditto ..	48 N.I. ..	Leave S. C. to Mussoorie.

Maj. Genl. Brevet.

COLONELS—*Continued.*

Season.	Names.	Army Rank.	Corps.	REMARKS.
1819	Augustus Abbott, C. B., ..	28 *Nov.* 1854	Artillery, ..	Brigadier Commandant of Artillery and H. A. D. C. to the Governor General, Furlough.
18	Claud Douglas, ..	ditto ..	65 N.I. ..	Furlough.
23	*Henry Goodwyn, ..	ditto ..	Engineers, ..	Chief Engr., L. Provinces.—Furlough.
D 06	~~James Steel, C. B.,~~ ..	ditto ..	67 N.I. ..	Brigadier Commanding at Umballah.
18	Charles Haldane, ..	ditto ..	44 N.I.	
23	Alex. Henry E. Boileau, ..	ditto ..	Engineers, ..	Chief Engineer, Nagpore Territory.
19	~~*George Connolly Ponsonby,~~	ditto ..	2 E. L. C...	Furlough.
19	Frederick Brooke Corfield, ..	ditto ..	5 En. Regt.	Furlough.
18	*George Farquharson, ..	ditto ...	46 N.I.	
21	*William Robert Corfield, ..	ditto ..	22 N.I. ..	Comdg. Native I. Brigade in China.
19	*Richard Horsford, ..	ditto ..	Artillery,	Brigr. Acting Comdt. of Arty. and Comdg. the station of Meerut.
22	*John Christie, ..	ditto ..	1 E. L.C...	A. D. C. to the Queen.—Brigadier Commandng at Barrackpore.
27	**Sir* Robert Napier, K. C. B.,	ditto ..	Engineers, ..	Brigr. Genl. Comdg. a Divn. on Field Service, Gwalior.
32	*Arthur Mitford Becher, C.B.,	ditto ..	61 N.I. ..	Qr. Mr. Genl. of the Army, and H. A. D. C. to the Governor General.—Furlough.
21	*John Fordyce, ..	ditto ..	Artillery, ..	Furlough.
23	*Thomas Fergusson Flemyng,	ditto ..	36 N.I. ..	Furlough.
18	*Francis Wheler, ..	ditto ..	1 E. L. C...	Brigadier Comdg. at Saugor.
21	*John Studholme Hodgson, ..	ditto ..	12 N.I. ..	Furlough.
18	*John K. McCausland, C.B., .	ditto ..	66 N.I. ..	Brigadier Comdg. at Sealkote.
D 20	~~*James Mackenzie,~~ ..	ditto ..	5 E.L.C...	Brigadier Commanding at Ferozepore.
20	*George St. P. Lawrence, ..	ditto ..	2 E. L.C...	Civil employ and H.A.D.C. to the Governor General.
27	**Sir* Rd. C. Shakespear, *Kt.*,	ditto ..	Artillery, ..	Civil employ.
18	Francis Rowcroft C. B., ..	ditto ..	62 N.I.	
20	*James Matthie, ..	ditto ..	21 N. I. ..	
19	*Hugh Troup, ..	ditto ..	6 En. Regt.	Brigadier Comdg. at Delhi.
20	*William Maule Ramsay, ..	ditto ..	35 N.I. ...	Furlough.
21	**Sir* Archibald Bogle, *Kt.*, ..	ditto ..	42 L.I. ..	Civil employ.—Furlough.
18	*David Simpson, ..	ditto ..	54 N.I. ..	Furlough.
11	*John Anderson Barstow, ..	ditto ..	58 N.I.	
19	*Edward Altham Cumberlege,	ditto ..	40 N.I. ..	Furlough.
20	*John Macdonald, ..	ditto ..	39 N.I.	
22	*Thomas Henry Shuldham,	ditto ..	15 N.I. ..	Furlongh.
20	*John Butler, ..	ditto ..	11 N.I.	
18	*Thomas Sewell, ..	ditto ..	25 N. I.	Lv. S. C. to the Cape of G. H.
09	*Francis Jenkins, ..	ditto ..	61 N.I. ..	Civil employ.
19	*George M. C. Smyth, ..	ditto ..	1st E. L. C...	
18	*George Burney, ..	ditto ..	65 N.I. ...	
18	*Edmund Wintle, ..	ditto ..	24 N.I. ..	Furlough,
27	*James Don Kennedy, ..	ditto ..	70 N.I. ..	
24	*Robert T Sandeman, ..	ditto ..	33 N. I.	
26	*William Swatman, ..	ditto ..	3rd En. Regt.	Furlough.
24	*St George D Showers, C B.,	ditto ..	2 En. B. F.	Brigadier Comdg. at Agra.
19	*Colin Troup, ..	ditto ..	68 N.I. ..	Brigadier Comdg. at Mooltan.
21	*George Moyle Sherer, ..	ditto ..	73 N. I. ..	
17	*William George Lennox, ..	ditto ..	63 N.I. ..	
20	*John Welchman, C B ..	ditto ..	1 En. B. F.	Furlough.
23	*Arthur Wheatley, ..	ditto ..	4 E. L.C...	Furlough.
20	*William Ferguson Beatson,	ditto ..	4 En. Regt.	Furlough.

* Brevet.

COLONELS—*Continued.*

Season.	Names.	Army Rank.	Corps.	REMARKS.
1821	*Bulstrode Bygrave, ..	28 *Nov.* 1854	31st N. I. ..	Furlough.
19	*Richmond Houghton, ..	do	16 N I (Grs.)	
24	*Charles Samuel Reid, ..	do	Artillery.	
19	*John Edmonstoune Landers	do	9th N, I.	Furlough.
22	*Edward John Dickey, ..	do	27th N. I,	Supdt. of Studs.
~~13~~	~~*Henry Templer~~, ..	do	6thEn Regt	Furlough.
23	*Henry Pelham Burn, ..	1 *May* 1855	4th En. R.	Supt. of Army Clothing.
23	*Edward R Mainwaring, ..	7 do	16N.I.(Grds)	Furlough.
23	*A. G. F. J. Younghusband,	3 *Aug*	35th L. I...	Furlough.
21	*John Craigie Halkett, C.B...	15 *Sep.*	20th N.I.	
22	*William Riddell, ..	5 *Dec.*	3rd En. Regt	
25	*Auchmuty Tucker, C B ..	2 *Apl.* 1856	4th E. L.C.	
21	*Henry Clayton, ..	18 *May*	3rd E. L.C.	Furlough.
23	*Philip Harris, ..	8 *June*	70th N. I...	Furlough.
38	*James Travers, ..	6 *Dec.*	2dN.I. (Grs.)	Furlough.
27	*William Erskine Baker, ..	10 *Mar.* 1857	Engineers.	Furlough.
24	*John Lewis Taylor, ..	14 do	26th N. I...	Furlough.
25	*William B Thomson, C B. ..	29 *May*	3rd B. E. R.	Commissary General.
28	*Patrick Gordon, ..	20 *June*	11th N. I.	Brigadier Comdg. at Dinapore.
28	*John Liptrap, ..	do	45 N. I. ..	
18	*Robert Garrett, ..	do	64 N.I. ..	Furlough.
19	*Simon Fraser Hannay, ..	do	43rd L. I...	Assam Lt. Infy.
22	*Edward Darvall, ..	do	57th N I. ..	
25	*Peter Abbott, ..	do	72nd N. I...	
22	*Francis Burton Boileau, ..	do	Artillery. ..	
22	*George Henry Swinley, ..	27 do	Artillery. ..	
25	*Henry Palmer, ..	29 *July*	48th N.I. ..	
28	*David Pott, ..	22 *Aug.*	47th N.I. ..	
25	*Archibald Lorne Campbell,	15 *Sep.*	3rd En. L.C.	
~~20~~	~~*Thomas L. Harington~~, ..	12 *Oct.*	5th En. L.C.	Furlough.
26	*Douglas Seaton, ..	15 *Oct.*	1st En.B. F.	Furlough.
37	*N. B. Chamberlain, C. B., ..	27 *Nov.*	16N.I.(Grs.)	Brigr. Genl. Comdg. Punjaub Irr [Force
22	*James Abbott, ..	28 do	Artillery.	
23	*James W. H. Jamieson, ..	do	52nd N. I.	
~~27~~	~~*John Glasfurd~~, ..	do	Engineers.	
26	*William Pitt Robbins, ..	do	15th N. I.	
29	*Charles Hogge C. B., ..	do	Artillery.	
23	*Hugh Boyd, ..	do	59th N. I...	Furlough.
37	*William E. Mulcaster, ..	do	64th N. I.	
37	*Orfeur Cavenagh, ..	do	32nd N. I.	
37	*John Stafford Paton, ..	do	14th N. I...	Depy. Qr. Master Genl. of the Army.
41	*James M. B. F. Tytler, C.B.,	19 *Jan.* 1858	37th N. I...	Furlough.
23	*John William Hicks, ..	15 *Feb.*	69th N. I.	
28	*Vincent Eyre, C. B., ..	24 *Mar.*	Artillery. ..	Gun Powder Agent, Ishapore.
29	*Frank Turner, C B., ..	do	Artillery. ..	Gun carriage Agent, Futtehghur.
28	*James D. McPherson, C. B.,	5 *Apl.*	22nd N. I...	Mily. Secy. to the Lt. Govr., Punjaub.
41	*Henry Tombs, C. B., ...	20 *July*	Artillery. ..	Furlough.
29	*Henry M. Durand, C. B.,..	do	Engineers...	Furlough.
27	*John Coke, C. B., ...	do	10th N. I...	Furlough.
17	*Arthur Cole Spottiswoode,	23 do	37th N.I.	
23	*Joseph Graham, ..	27 *Aug.*	29th N.I.	
~~18~~	~~*Chris. Simson Maling~~, ..	24 *Oct.*	18th N.I. ..	Furlough.

* Brevet.

LIEUTENANT COLONELS.

Season.	Names.	Army Rank.	Corps.	REMARKS.
1823	Frederick Gaitskell, C. B., ..	17 *May* 1854	Artillery.	
20	*Henry Drummond, ..	20 *June*	1st E. L.C.	Civil employ.
25	Wm. Binfield Wemyss, ..	do	4th E. L.C.	Furlough.
23	Richard Drought, C. B., ..	do	60th N.I.	
24	*Thomas Moore, ..	28 *Nov.*	5th E.L.C.	
23	*Charles Campbell, ..	do	42nd L. I.	Furlough.
Col. 24	Robert A. Master, C. B., ..	do	2nd E.L.C.	Furlough.
25	*George Cautley, ..	do	5th E. L.C.	
26	Robert R. Kinleside, ..	do	Artillery. ..	Furlough.
27	Alfred Huyshe, ..	do	Artillery.	
27	*John Clarke, ..	do	25th N. I...	Furlough.
29	*George P. Whish, ..	do	60th N. I.	
29	*Markham E. Sherwill, ..	do	2nd En.B.F.	
D ~~30~~	~~*John Abercrombie,~~ ..	do	Artillery. ..	Furlough.
31	Alex. Cunningham, ..	do	Engineers.	
25	William St. Leger Mitchell,	do	56th N. I.,	
40	Herbert B. Edwardes, C. B.,	do	1st En. B.F.	
41	*Henry J. Stannus, ..	do	5th E. L. C.	
35	*Henry, F. Dunsford, C. B,	do	59th N. I.	
22	*Charles Cheape, ..	do	51st N. I.	
Col. 24	William C. Campbell, ..	do	30th N. I.	
27	*Saunders A. Abbott, ..	do	51st N. I.	
24	John C. Hannyngton, ..	do	34th N. I.	
R ~~25~~	~~Wm. Robert Dunmore,~~ ..	do	60th N. I ..	Furlough.
28	Andrew Scott Waugh, ...	3 *Aug.* 1855	Engineers. ..	Surveyor Genl. of India and Supdt. of the Great Trigonometrical Survey.
21	Wm. J. B. Knyvett, ..	15 *Sep.*	38th L. I.	
21	*Nathl. Dunbar Barton, ..	18 *Mar.* 1856	3rd E. L. C.	Furlough.
28	Edward L. Ommanney, ..	15 *Apl.*	Engineers.	
21	Arthur Hall, ..	5 *May*	5th E.L.C...	Furlough.
Col. 26	James Brind, C. B., ..	26 *June*	Artillery.	
29	John Laughton, ..	10 *Mar.* 1857	Engineers.	
22	Hamilton Vetch, ..	29 *May*	54th N. I.	
30	Arthur Sanders, ..	do	53rd N. I.	
27	Cuthbert Davidson, ..	31 do	49th N.I.	
25	George Wm. Bishop, ..	do	23rd N.I.	
23	John Powell, ..	27 *June*	55th N. I...	Furlough.
27	Francis Claude Burnett, ..	do	Artillery.	
29	George Ramsay, ..	do	10th N.I.	
28	Ed. G. J. Champneys, ..	1 *July*	5th En. Regt.	Military Auditor General.
27	Richard Y. B. Bush, ..	15 do	32nd N.I. ..	Furlough.
25	James G. A. Rice, ..	29 do	4thB.E.Regt.	
22	Joseph H. Hampton, ..	22 *Aug.*	50th N. I.	
28	William Augustus Cooke, ..	3 *Sep.*	2ndN.I(Grs.)	
27	Arthur Broome, ..	14 do	Artillery.	
29	Henry Rigby, ..	20 do	Engineers.	
27	Reginald E. Knatchbull, ..	28 do	Artillery.	
R ~~31~~	~~Thomas Henry Sale,~~ ..	1 *Oct.*	Engineers.	
23	*Keith Young, C. B., ..	12 do	50th N. I...	Judge Adv. Genl. of the Army.
R ~~23~~	~~*Archd. R. J. Swinton,~~ ..	15 do	32nd N. I.	
D ~~20~~	~~Robert Ramsay,~~ ..	18 *Nov.*	74th N. I...	Furlough.
24	Henry William Matthews, ..	3 *Dec.*	43rd L. I.	
39	*Henry A. Olpherts, ..	15 *Jan.* 1858	Artillery.	
35	*Edward Kaye, ..	19 do	Artillery.	
Col. 35	*Charles Reid, C. B., ..	do	10th N. I.	
do 37	*Richard Baird Smith, C. B.,	do	Engineers...	Master of the Calcutta Mint.
25	*Richard S. Ewart, ..	do	30th N. I.	
28	Edward W. S. Scott, ..	do	Artillery. ..	Inspector Genl. of Ordnace and Magazines.

* Brevet.

LIEUTENANT COLONELS.—*Continued.*

Season.	Names.	Army Rank.	Corps.	REMARKS.
1832	Norman C. MacLeod, ..	19 *Jan.* 1858	Engineers.	
42	*E. Beaumont Johnson, C. B.,	do	Artillery.	
~~24~~	~~*Charles Apthorp~~, ..	24 *Mar.*	41st N. I.	
27	*Thomas Simpson, ..	do	57th N. I.	
28	*George J. Montgomery, ..	do	15th N. I.	
30	*Gravenor Kirby, ..	do	Artillery.	
~~30~~	~~Townsend J. W. Hungerford, C. B.~~, ..	do	Artillery.	
42	*Henry Hamilton Maxwell,	do	Artillery.	
30	*John Hall Smyth, ..	do	Artillery.	Furlough.
39	*G. Bourchier, C. B., ...	do	Artillery.	
39	*William Olpherts, C. B., ..	do	Artillery.	
41	*G. W. G. Green, C. B., ..	do	2nd En. B. F.	Furlough.
41	*Fredk. F. Remmington, C. B.,	do	Artillery.	
36	*James Metcalfe, ..	do	4 En. Regt.	
42	*Charles, Harris Blunt, C. B.,	do	Artillery.	
23	*Charles Prior, ..	25 *Apl.*	64th N. I...	Furlough.
25	David Wilkie, ..	26 do	4th N. I.	
23	*William Wynne, Apperley,	1 *May*	3rd E. L. C.	
23	George William Hamilton, ..	19 do	17th N. I.	
23	*Charles Cooper, ..	4 *July*	23rd N. I.	
29	Henry Alex. Carleton, C. B.,	20 do	Artillery.	
44	*Alexander Taylor, C. B., ..	do	Engineers.	
	*Jeremiah Brasyer, C B., ..	do	Unattached.	
23	*J. DeW. C. J. Moir, ..	do	28th N. I.	
~~25~~	~~*George Gordon~~, ..	do	50th N. I.	
40	*Donald M. Stewart, ..	do	9th N. I.	
25	Ronald Macdonell, ..	23 do	4th E. L. C.	
29	William Barr, ..	18 *Aug.*	Artillery.	
31	Herbert E. S. Abbott, ..	22 do	74th N. I.	
~~26~~	~~John Butler~~, ..	27 do	55th N. I.	
~~25~~	~~Thomas Martin~~, ..	do	20th N. I.	
24	*Fredk. W. Burroughs, ..	14 *Nov.*	17th N. I.	
29	William H. Delamain, ..	14 do	Artillery.	
24	*George Timins, ..	23 do	34th N. I,	Furlough.
30	David Reid, ..	23 *Dec.*	Artillery.	
27	Arthur Purves Phayre, ..	22 *Jan,* 1859	6th En. Regt.	
~~24~~	~~*Henry A. Shuckburgh~~, ..	4 *Feb.*	40th N. I...	
35	Brooke Boyd, ..	15 *May*	68th N. I.	
30	Francis Elliot Voyle, ..	4 *June*	39th N. I.,	
25	Wm. Augustin J. Mayhew,	*Official*, ..	6th En. Regt.	Adjutant General of the Army.
25	George W. Williams, ..	do	29th N. I.	
40	Henry Yule, ..	do	Engineers.	Secy. to Govt., D. P. W.

MAJORS.

[1851.]

1825 Archd. F. Macpherson, 43rd L. I. .. 11 *Nov.*
25 John Minshull Drake, 46th N. I. do
25 Andrew Henry Duncan, 3rd B. E. Regt. .. do
25 *Richard R. W. Ellis, 23rd N. I. do
25 Lionel P. D. Eld, 9th N.I. .. do
25 Charles Pattenson, 4th N.I. .. do
25 Edwin Marriott, 57th N.I. .. do
40 *Reynell G. Taylor, 2nd En. L.C. 16 *Dec.*

[1852.]

1833 *C T. Chamberlain, 28th N. I... 2 *May*
32 *Arthur W. C. Plowden, 1st En. L. Cavy., .. 22 *Oct.*

[1853.]

1838 *Charles V. Cox, Artillery, .. 4 *Marc*
~~39 *Peter Christie,~~ Artillery, .. do
25 Wm. Augustin John Mayhew, 6 En. Regt. (Offl. Lt. Col.) 9 *Dec.*
37 William Frost Nuthall, 18th N.I. do
39 *Albert Fytche, 70th N.I. .. do

* Brevet.

[1854.]

1838	*Harry B. Lumsden, 59th N.I.	6	*Feb.*
37	*Richard Strachey, Engrs. ..	16	do
25	George Warren Stokes, 59th N. I., ..	20	*June*
25	*William Lamb, 51st N.I. ..		do
25	*Edward F. Smith, 23rd N.I. ..		do
25	*Hugh Mackenzie, 2nd En.B.F.		do
25	*William Lydiard, 11th N.I. ..		do
25	*George Burd Reddie, 29th N. I.		do
25	George W. Williams, 29th N. I. (Offl. Lt. Col.) ..		do
25	*James Knox Spence, 20th N.I.		do
25	*George Mytton Hill, 17th N. I. ..		do
25	James Corse Scott, 20th N.I. ..		do
25	Theodore F. B. Beatson, 4th En. L. Cavy.		do
25	*Henry Stockley Grimes, 46th N. I.,		do
25	*Charles Henry Burt, 64th N. I. ..		do
25	John Bontein, 37th N.I. ..		do
25	Frederick Maitland, 5th En. Regt.		do
25	*John Barrett, 37th N.I. ..		do
26	James Sleeman, 73rd N.I. ..		do
35	Francis Stuart Paterson, 54th N.I. ..		do
26	Robert Morrieson, 52nd N.I. ..		do
26	*David Gaussen, 42nd L.I. ..		do
26	Clement Read Browne, 60th N.I.		do
26	*William Baker, 4th En. L. Cavy.		do
26	Robert Troup, 63rd N.I. ..		do
27	Charles G. Walsh, 14th N.I. ..		do
27	*William Richardson, 73rd N. I. ..		do
27	Henry M. Nation, 3rd B.E. Regt.		do
27	*John Hennessy, 70th N. I. ..		do
27	*Frederick Joseph Harriott, 4th En. L. Cavy.		do
27	William P. Hampton, 31st N.I.		do
27	*Walter C. Erskine, 73rd N.I...		do
27	Richard S. Simpson, 27th N.I...		do
27	James Charles Innes, 61st N.I.		do
27	*William B. Legard, 31st N I...		do
27	*Wright W. Davidson, 32nd N.I.		do
27	*George Jackson, 3rd En. L. C.		do
27	*James Edward Verner, 60th N. I.		do
27	Robt. J. Hawthorne, 2nd En.L.C.		do
40	*Philip A. P. Bouverie, 35th L. I.	11	*July*
40	*Alexander Bagot, 15th N. I. ..	24	do
39	*Alfred G. Goodwyn, Engineers,	2	*Aug.*
41	*John Harley Maxwell, Engineers, ..		do
39	*John Reid Becher, Engineers, ..		do
41	*Edward John Lake, Engrs., ..	22	do
28	*George Newbolt, 31st N.I. ..	28	*Nov.*
28	J. Townshend Daniell, 47th N.I.		do

[1854]. *Continued.*

1828	John Liptrott, 2nd En. B. F. ..	28	*Nov.*
28	*Edward King Elliot, 43rd L.I.		do
28	*T. Scott Horsbrugh, 32nd N.I.		do
28	Henry Milne, 21st N. I.		do
28	*William Henry Ryves, 61st N. I. ..		do
28	*Stephen F. Macmullen, 3rd En. L. C. ..		do
28	*Robert Thatcher, 9th N.I. ..		do
28	John Smith, 49th N.I. ..		do
28	*Samuel Richard Tickell, 31st N.I.		do
29	Robert Napier Raikes, 67th N. I.		do
29	Anthony Martin, 33rd N.I. ..		do
29	*Andrew Hunter Ross, 42nd L. I.		do
33	Wm. Kelly Wollen, 19th N.I. .		do
29	James Gandy Gaitskell, 26th L.I		do
33	Christopher Hasell, 48th N.I. ..		do
29	*John Morrieson, 30th N.I. ..		do
29	*Edward Harvey, 4th En. L. C.		do
33	Peter William Luard, 55th N.I.		do
35	*Henry Lewis Bird, 48th N.I...		do
29	*Thomas G. St. George, 17th N. I. ..		do

[1855.]

1841	*Charles Herbert, 18th N.I. ..	2	*Jan.*
39	*Chas. James Robarts, 43rd L. I.	8	*Mar.*
41	*Sydney Joseph Hire, 22nd N.I.	2	*Dec.*

[1856.

1841	*Charles Vincent Bowie, Artillery,	22	*Jan.*
29	*George Verner, 9th N.I. ..	18	*May*
37	*Js. Grant Stephen, 6th En. R.,	6	*June*
40	*John L. Vaughan, 21st N.I.		do
39	*Roland Richardson, 1st En.L.C.		do
41	*Wm.A.A.Thomson, 4th En.L.C.	13	*July*
40	*Charles T. E. Hinde, 65th N. I.	24	*Nov.*
29	*John C. Phillips, 3rd En. Regt.	28	do

[1857.]

1840	John T. Shakespear, 24th N. I.	1	*May*
35	Samuel B. Faddy, 36th N. I., ..	31	do
34	James Lumsdaine Walker, 71st N. I., ..		do
39	Charles V. Jenkins, 1st En.L.C.,	1	*July*
34	Edmund Sissmore, 69th N. I.,...	11	do
36	Fredk. Moffat Baker, 65th N. I.	15	do
42	William C. Gott, 56th N. I., ..		do
34	Henry Ramsay, 53rd N. I., ..		do
37	Edward Dayot Watson, 44th N.I.	21	do
40	Abraham Meyer, 58th N. I.	22	*Aug.*
37	Thomas F. Hobday, 72nd N. I.	28	do
35	William McCulloch, 13th N. I.,	4	*Sep.*
40	George G. Denniss, 1st En. B.F.	14	do
37	William Henry Oakes, 45th N.I.	7	*Nov.*
41	Frederick Johnston, 62nd N. I.,	18	*Dec.*

* Brevet.

MAJORS—*Continued.*

[1858.]

1831 *Ernle Kyrle Money, Artillery, 19 *Jan.*
35 *Alexander Boyd, 2nd En. B. F. do
34 *Richard C. Lawrenc, 73rd N.I. do
35 *Henry Nicoll, 50th N. I. .. do
37 *Deane C. Shute, 19th N.I. .. do
37 *Robert A. Ramsay, 35th L.I... do
37 *Henry R. Grindlay, 3rd En.L.C. do
41 *Octavius E. Rothney, 45th N. I. do
39 *James Young, Artillery, .. do
42 *Hry. Murray Garstin, 36th N. I. do
45 *Chas. H. Barchard, C.B. 20thN.I. do
40 *Southwell Greville, 1st En B.F. do
41 *Webber D. Harris, 2nd En. B.F. do
~~41 *John Charles Hay, 60th N. I.~~ do
45 *Edward Brown, 1st En. B. F. do
41 *Geo. Whittle M. Hall, 26th L.I. do
45 *H. F. M. Boisragon, 1st En. B.F. do
46 *David Kemp, 5th En. Regt., .. do
42 *Thomas Edward Kennion, Arty. do
42 *Alfred Light, Artillery, .. do
43 *Thomas H. Sibley 62nd N. I. do
31 *William Maxwell, Artillery .. 24 *Mar.*
33 *John Wm. Carnegie, 15th N. I. do
38 *Francis G. Crossman, 45th N. I. do
38 *David S. Dodgson, 30th N.I... do
38 *Thomas F. Wilson, C.B. 13thN.I. do
29 *Folliott Walker Baugh, 26thN.I. do
39 *Henry Dinning, 71st N. I. .. do
40 *Chas. St. G. Brownlow, 15th N.I. do
41 *Matthew F. Kemble, 41st N. I. do
38 *Henry Hammond, Artillery, .. do
39 *Richard C. Germon, 13th N. I. do
42 *John Wm. Sanders, 41st N. I. do
41 *Thos. T. Boileau, 2nd En.L.C. do
41 *Richard J. Edgell, 53rd N. I. do
41 *Edward Oakes, 6th En. Regt. do
43 *W. A. Crommelin, C.B. Engrs. do
44 *Henry Lane, 5th E. L. C. .. do
43 *Thomas A. Carey, 17th N.I. do
43 *Robert P. Anderson, 25th N. I. do
42 Henry LeGeyt Bruce, Arty. ... do
42 *Arthur D. Dickens, 38th N.I. do
43 *George S. Macbean, 74th N.I. do
43 *Charles A. Barwell, 71st N.I. do
50 *Dighton M. Probyn, C.B. 3rd En. L. C. .. do
43 *Wm. T. Hughes, 48th N. I... do
45 *Thomas James, 2nd N.I., (Grs.) do
39 *George Cliffe Hatch, 57th N.I. do
39 *Henry Mein Wilson, 6th En. R. do
42 *Fred. C. Maisey, 67th N. I... do
38 *William S. Ferris, 12th N.I... 25 *April*
31 *Chas. Jas. Richards, 25th N. I. 1 *May*
35 *Robert C. Tytler, 38th L.I... 16 do
40 *Robertson Larkins, 49th N.I. 20 *July*
38 *Richard John Meade, 65thN.I, do
33 *Charles Douglas, Artillery, .. do
35 *John William Carter, 54th N.I. do
40 *John Hood, 49th N. I. .. do
41 *Joseph F. Richardson, C.B. 49th N. I. .. do
37 *John Gordon. 5th En. Regt... do
41 *Alex. Hume, 1st En. B. F. .. do
~~40 *Robert C. Barclay, 68th N.I.~~ do

1858.—*Continued.*

1840 *Chas. Samuel Weston, 36th N.I. 20 *July*
43 *J. Hatfield Brooks, 1st E. L. C. do
43 *Fredk. O. Salusbury 1st En.B.F. do
39 *George Moir, C.B. Artillery .. do
41 *Albert George Austen Arty... do
39 *George W. Boileau, 34th N.I., do
41 *Samuel J. Browne, 46th N. I. do
41 *Wm. Domett Morgan, 22nd N.I. do
41 *Alex. L. McMullin, 23rd N.I., do
41 *Wm. A. Mackinnon, C.B. Arty. do
40 *R. L. Thompson, 10th N.I. .. do
42 *John H. Balmain, 4th E. L. C. do
42 *John Irvine Murray, 71st N.I. do
45 *Hamilton Forbes, 1st E L. C. do
42 *Harry C Anderson, 54th N. I. do
43 *Charles Cureton, 38th N. I... do
42 *Colin Cookworthy, Artillery,.. do
43 *Fred. W. Lambert, 56th N.I. do
43 *Chas J S Gough, 5th E. L C. do
45 *Henry Drummond, Engineers, do
46 *Allen Bayard Johnson, 5th E.R. do
42 *Alfred Pearson, Artillery, .. do
43 *Arthur Bunny Artillery, .. do
44 *George Alex. Renny Artillery, bo
46 *George Hutchinson, Engrs. .. do
44 *Osborn Wilkinson, 4thEn. L.C do
36 George Ryley, 74th N. I. ... 22 *Aug.*
45 *Edward W. Ellis Walker, Arty. 28 do
45 *Henry Parlett, Bishop, Arty. .. do
45 *John Sabatier Firth, Arty. .. do
46 *William W.H. Greathed, Engrs. do
46 William, Tod Brown Artillery,.. do
47 *James Shaw Gibb Artillery, ... do
48 *William Wilson, Artillery, .. do
48 *Frederick R. Maunsell, Engrs. do
48 *George Edward Watson, Engrs. do
49 *James F. Tennant, Engrs. .. do
49 *Julius G. Medley, Engrs. .. do
49 *J. John McLeod Innes, Engrs. do
49 *George Tomkyns Chesney, Engineers. .. do
51 *William Edmond Warrand, Engineers. .. do
51 *Henry Alex Brownlow, Engrs. do
50 *Patrick Stewart, Engrs. .. do
50 *Julian St. John Hovenden, Engrs. do
30 G. A. Fisher, 4th En. Regt. .. 13 *Nov.*
30 Thomas J. Gardiner, 16th N. I. (Grs.) .. 23 do
45 *Huntly R. Garden, 2nd N I. (Grs.) 26 *Dec.*

[1859.]

1837 Walter Birch, 6th En. Regt. ... 22 *Jan.*
30 *Robert Henry Sale, 9th N.I. 5 *Mar.*
30 *Robert Warburton, Artillery, 13 do
40 *Thomas Rattray, 64th N. I... 1 *Apl.*
38 *Peter A. Roberton, 68th N.I. 15 *May*
35 Thomas Pownall, 39th N.I. .. 4 *June*

Official.

1832 Fred. D. Atkinson, 2nd En.B.F.,
32 Henry E. L. Thuillier, Arty.
44 H. W. Norman, 31st N. I., ..

* Brevet.

[1846.]

1834 Septimus H. Becher, 61st N.I. 1 *Dec.*
31 George Nuttall Greene, 70th N.I. 8 do
33 Henry J.C. Shakespear, 25th N.I. 26 do
35 Collingwood F. Fenwick, 30th N.I. do

[1847.]

1834 Henry James Piercy, 49th N.I.. 22 *Jan.*
36 Solomon Richards, 55th N.I. .. 15 *Feb.*
Major 32 Walter S. Sherwill, 66th N.I.. 22 do
35 Charles Harris, 27th N.I. .. 3 *May*
Major 38 Fredk. T. Wroughton, 6th En.R. 2 *June*
31 John S. D. Tulloch, 17th N.I... 14 do
Major 32 Fred. Dayot Atkinson, 2nd En. B. F.—(*Official Major*,) .. 12 *July*
Major 33 Joseph Chambers, 21st N.I. .. 27 *Aug.*
Lt. Col. 33 Stephen Pott, Engineers, .. 14 *Dec.*
32 Henry E. L. Thuillier, Artillery, (*Official Major*,) .. do
38 Thos. Mouat Cameron, 55th N.I. 30 do
32 Clare Sewell Salmon, 57th N.I.. 31 do

[1848.]

1834 Samuel John Becher, 11th N.I. 13 *May*
40 John D'Oyly Baring, 55th N.I. 15 *June*
38 George R. Cookson, 4th N.I. .. 7 *July*
35 Henry Strachey, 66th N.I. .. 19 do
39 Robert N. Tronson, 2nd En. B. F. 30 do
36 Edward Hall, 52nd N.I. .. 5 *Aug*
35 Charles L. Showers, 14th N.I... 27 *Oct.*
35 Charles F. M. Mundy, 34th N.I. 21 *Nov.*
37 Joseph P. P. T. Hawkey, 74th N.I. 1 *Dec.*

[1849.]

1842 William M. Cafe, 56th N.I. .. 27 *Jan.*
38 Wm. F. N. Wallace, 74th N.I. .. 1 *Feb.*
40 George Gaynor, 2nd En. B. F... 8 *Mar*
33 Robt. A. Trotter, 43rd L.I. .. 10 do
36 James Eardley Gastrell, 13th N. I. .. 19 do
Major 41 Robert Duffin, 58th N.I. .. 10 *Apl.*
Do 36 John Fras. D'Evereux Williams Hall, 22nd N.I. .. 23 do
37 Byam Martin Loveday 15th N. I. 12 *May*

[1849.]—*Continued.*

1837 Peter Drummond, 22nd N.I. .. 22 *May*
34 Augustus Turner, 4th En. Regt. 13 *June*
41 William Forbes, 27th N.I. .. 5 *July*
42 Augustus Kay Moffat, 58th N.I. 16 do
39 Edward James Simpson, 69th N. I. .. 31 do
36 William Wyld, 3rd En. L. Cavy. 1 *Aug.*
35 Henry Currey James, 32nd N.I. .. 16 do
38 George Strangways, 71st N.I. .. 21 do
40 George G. Anderson, 15th N.I... 20 *Sep.*
36 John Nelson Thomas, 39th N.I.. 1 *Nov.*
41 Joseph Bleaymire, 2nd En. B. F. 15 do
38 Robert H. D. Tulloh, 39th N.I. 28 do
39 Edwin Alex. Rowlatt, 21st N.I... 1 *Dec.*
35 Daniel Stansbury, 60th N.I. .. 12 do

[1850.]

R ~~1835 William C. Alexander, 4th~~ En.L.C. 21 *Jan.*
37 Peter H. K. Dewaal, 34th N.I... 1 *Feb.*
Maj. 35 Arthur Walton Onslow, 41st N.I. . 13 do
39 Charles Jackson, 39th N.I. .. 21 do
35 Robert Renny, 47th N.I. .. 22 *Mar.*
35 Gordon Caulfeild, 46th N.I. .. 23 do
36 Robert Andrew Smith, 19th N.I. 28 do
36 Thomas C. Blagrave, 26th L. I. 1 *Apl.*
41 Edwin S. Denniss, 62nd N.I. .. 1 *June*
35 Edward W. Hicks, 67th N.I... 12 do
Maj 35 John Cheap Brooke, 63rd N.I. do
35 Ewd. T. Dalton, 3rd B. E. R.,.. 13 do
36 Montagu J. Turnbull, 2nd E. L. Cavy. .. 10 *Aug.*
39 John Nisbett, 69th N.I. .. 15 do
40 John Matthew Cripps, 26th N.I. 1 *Sep.*
41 Geo. M. Waddilove, 24th N.I... 6 *Oct.*
40 John Scott Phillpotts, 66th N.I. 28 do
39 Theophilus Green, 48th N.I. .. 7 *Nov.*
40 Benjamin Parrott, 37th N.I. .. 8 *Dec.*
36 Henry Charles Roberts, 31st N.I. 11 do
Lt. Col. 37 Charles Becher Young, Engineers, do
36 Thomas Brougham, Artillery, .. do
36 Thomas Watson, 33rd N.I. .. 12 do
39 Henry L. Robertson, 65th N.I. 13 *Dec.*
37 Alexander Robinson, 19th N.I.. 31 do

[1851.]

1837 Fredk. N. Edmonstone, 3rd E. L. Cavy. Maj. .. 1 *Jan.*
Maj 36 Robert Patton, 3rd B. E. R.,.. 3 do
36 George Nicolson Oakes, 46th N.I. do

[1851.]—*Continued.*

1840 Nicholas C. Boswell, 2nd Gredrs. 17 *Feb.*
37 Martin Boileau Whish, 29th N.I. 15 *Mar.*
38 George Edward Ford, 72nd N.I. 17 do
39 Alex. S. O. Donaldson, 45thN.I. 17 *Apl.*
39 T. Whittaker Seager, 27th N.I. 18 do
38 Fredk. P. Layard, 19th N.I. .. 30 do
36 Samuel H. Jas. Davies, 51st N.I. 28 *June*
39 Charles Holroyd, 36th N.I. .. 1 *July*
37 Colin C. Robertson, 11th N.I... 1 *Aug.*
40 James Price Clarkson, 44th N.I. 2 do
40 Roderick B. Macleod, 3rd E. L Cavy. .. 6 *Sep.*
39 H. Richard Shelton, 38th L.I... 28 do
38 John Palmer Caulfeild, 4rh En.R. 3 *Oct.*
39 James W. Lewis Bird, 11th N.I. 13 do
37 John Eliot, Artillery, .. 9 *Dec.*
39 Octavius Hamilton, 2nd E. L. C. 20 do

[1852.]

1840 Julius Bentall Dennys, 38th L. I. 6 *Jan.*
37 Alex.B. Fenwick, 5th En. Regt. 10 do
— H. Skinner, *(Unattached,)* .. 16 do
37 Wm. R. Cunningham, 5th En.R., 31 *Jan.*
40 Olaus J. McL.Farrington, 4th N.I. 14 *Feb.*
37 John C. Haughton, 54th N.I. .. 15 do
39 Reginald Ouseley, 34th N.I. .. 21 do
37 Frederick C. Tombs, 10th N.I. .. 24 do
40 William Russell Eliott, 6thEn.R., 25 do
40 Hugh Rees James, 44th N.I. .. 29 do
42 Lestock Boileau Jones, 56th N.I. 9 *Mar.*
40 Henry Mills, 2nd Grenadiers, .. 22 do
37 Thomas Tulloh, 33rd N.I. .. 4 *Apl.*
37 Trevor Henry Shum, 33rd N.I... do
38 Rowland R. Mainwaring, 6th European Regt. .. 10 do
40 John William Bristow, 19th N.I 26 do
41 Campbell C. Grant Ross, 66thN.I. 10 *May*
41 Henry Borlase Stevens, 41st N.I. 25 do
37 Fras. W. Drummond, 5th E.L.C. 2 *June*
37 Cecil Plowden Trower, 23d N.I. 12 do
37 Henry Lewis, Artillery, .. do
39 Alex.David Turnbull, Engineers, do
37 Alfred C. Plowden, 50th N.I. .. 13 do
37 Edward Close, 32nd N.I. .. do
— Wm.Robt. Forster, *(Unattached,)* 29 *July*
41 Henry D. Maunsell, 62nd N.I... 3 *Oct.*
38 Robert Campbell, 47th N.I. .. 3 *Nov*
40 *Baron* F.A. Von Meyern, 53d N. I. 15 do
40 Edward Tulloch, 69th N. I. .. 17 do
40 Alexander A. Macdonell, 40th N.I. 19 do
38 Charles S. J. Terrot, 29th N. I. 11 *Dec.*
38 Henry Price deTeissier, Artillery, do
38 Henry Hopkinson, 70th N I. .. 12 do

[1853.]

1839 Chas. Browne Stuart, 4th En. R., 7 *Jan.*
39 Theodore Gordon, 65th N.I. .. 12 do

[1853.]—*Continued.*

1841 William Gordon, 49th N.I. .. 15 *Jan.*
40 Wm. Fitzmaurice Stafford, 36thN.I. 15 *Feb.*
38 Langston Peter Faddy, 29th N.I. 1 *Mar.*
38 George Holroyd, 43rd N. Lt. I... do
38 John R. McMullin, 50th N.I. .. do
38 Craven Hildesley Dickens, Arty. 3 do
38 Robt. C. Stevenson, 3rd B. E. R., 8 do
38 Ed. John Rickards, 5th En. Regt. 27 do
40 Donald C. Vanrenen, Artillery,.. 28 *Apl.*
40 Geo. Edward Holmes, 72nd N. I. 10 *May*
39 Wm. Alexander Shaw, 4th E.L. C. 27 do
41 Benjamin Henderson, 48th N.I... 5 *June*
42 Godfrey C. Bloomfield, 45th N. I. 10 do
38 Thomas P. Waterman, 13th N.I. 11 do
38 Basil Ebenezer Bacon, 50th N.I 22 do
40 Frederick W. Swinhoe, Artillery, 1 *July*
41 Charles B. Basden, 61st N.I. .. 6 do
39 Nathaniel Robert Sneyd, 57thN.I. 11 do
40 James Tickell, 73rd N.I. .. 19 do
39 Edward L. Dennys, 11th N.I. .. 26 do
38 William John Hicks, 22nd N.I... 29 do
40 Charles Need, 6th En. Regt. .. 1 *Aug*
40 Ewd. Moody Ryan, 20th N.I. .. 14 do
39 Robert C. Wroughton, 12th N.I. 28 do
40 Robert Roy Adams, 40th N.I... 3 *Sep.*
41 George Faithfull, 68th N.I. .. 13 do
39 William Fullerton, 14th N.I. .. 14 do
41 George Elliot Voyle, Artillery, .. 15 do
39 Augustus H.Ternan, 4th En.Regt. 20 do
40 Henry Duncan Twysden, 33rdN.I. 3 *Oct.*
42 Frederick J. Davies, 58th N.I... 19 do
40 Wm. Robert Wallace, 51st N.I. 1 *Nov.*
41 Amyand P. C. Elliot, 5th E. L. C. 14 do
39 H. E. Young, 64th N. I. .. 15 do
41 Mortimer J. Slater, 5th En. Regt. do
41 John Elphinstone Fraser, 4th N.I. do
40 Richard G. Simeon, 4th E. L. C. 27 do
43 Chas. C. Nicholetts, 1st E. Lt. C. 30 do
39 William Charles Clifton, 67th N. I. 8 *Dec.*
40 Henry Yule, Engrs, (*Offl. Lt. Col*) 11 do
39 Hastings B. Impey, 70th N.I. .. 12 do
39 Wredenhall Q. Pogson, 43rd L.I. do
39 William Claye Watson, 47th N.I. 15 do
41 L. R. Christopher, 71st N. I. .. 28 do

[1854.]

1839 Henry C. Adlam, 42nd L. I. .. 13 *Jan.*
39 William Agnew, 29th N. I. .. 14 do
41 William Poole Waddy, Artillery, 23 do
39 T. Hunter Smalpage, 31st N.I. 24 do
39 Joseph Lind Sherwill, 39th N.I. do
40 John Robertson Pughe, 47th N.I. 31 do
40 Hugh Lowman Pester, 63rd N. I. 12 *Feb.*
41 Alfred Wintle, Artillery, .. 10 *Mar.*
43 Conolly O'B. Palmer, 1st En. B.F., 20 do
40 Lenox J. Farquharson, 3rd E. L. Cavy. .. 21 do

CAPTAINS—*Continued.*

[1854.]—*Continued.*

1842	Andrew Simpson Smith, 24th N.I.	26	*Mar.*
39	Evelyn Bradford, 23rd N.I. ..	1	*April*
40	Archibald Oliver Wood, 14th N.I.	15	do
41	Edward C. Warner, 2nd E. L. C.	2	*May*
40	Robert T. Leigh, 6th En. Regt.	7	do
42	~~George F. D'Oyly,~~ 67th N.I. ..	17	do
39	Andrew Hunter, 25th N. I. ..	11	*June*
41	William Elliot Morton, Engrs.		do
39	Edwin Thomas, 3rd B. E. R., ..	12	do
39	William Graydon, 16th Gredrs...		do
39	Thos. Rochfort Snow, 4th E. L. Cavy. ..	18	do
39	Andrew Macqueen, 42nd L.I. ..		do
40	George Gill Moxon, 52nd N.I...	24	do
9	Charles P. St. J. Law, 11th N.I.	10	*July*
39	Henry Earl Read, 50th N.I. ..		do
41	Robert Maclagan, Engineers, ..	1	*Aug.*
41	John Douglas Campbell, Engrs.		do
41	John S. Douglas White, 40th N.I.	6	do
39	Hugh M. Davidson, 29th N.I. ..	21	do
43	Richard M. J. Tozer, 45th N.I...		do
41	James William Smith, 22nd N. I.	15	*Sep.*
39	James Snow Davies, 23rd N.I...	18	do
41	James Charles Curtis, 72nd N. I.	9	*Oct.*
41	John Jas. Hamilton, 2nd Gredrs.	24	do
42	Felix V. Richard Jervis, 56th N. I.	7	*Nov.*
42	Augustine Allen, 55th N. I. ..	14	do
42	Manners R. Nightingale, 2nd En. B. F. ..	22	do
41	John Wedderburn, 69th N. I. ..	28	do
43	Edmund W. E. Howard, 3rd E. L. Cavy. ..	5	*Dec*
40	Gould Read Weston, 65th N. I...	10	do
40	William T. Garstin, 70th N.I.	11	do
42	John Ross, 71st N.I. ..	30	do
41	John T. S. Hall, 12th N.I. ..	31	do
44	Wm. Fraser Stephens, 5th E.L. C.		do
41	Robert Mercer Paton, Artillery,		do

[1855.]

1842	John Doran, 24th N.I. ..	1	*Jan.*
40	Richard Nicholas, 64th N.I. ..	3	do
40	Banastre Pryce Lloyd, 11th N. I.		do
42	George Swiney, 6th En. Regt. ..	9	do
43	George H. Thompson, 6th En, R.,	10	do
41	Augustus Fraser Baird, 18th N.I.	15	do
40	John Ward, 4th En. Regt, ..	16	do
42	~~James Gordon Phillips,~~ 63rd N.I.	19	do
40	Jas. B. Y. Matheson, 52nd N.I.	26	do
41	Charles F. G. Lamb, 62nd N. I..	11	*Feb.*
40	Archibald Blackwood, 59th N. I.	15	do
41	Samuel C. Woodcock, Artillery,	20	do
48	Charles W. D'Oyly, 58th N. I. ..	28	do
40	Henry C. Johnstone, 5th En. R.,		do
41	~~Charles Wm. Timbrell, Artillery,~~	24	*Mar.*
41	Henley Thomas Bartlett, 21st N.I.	13	*April*

[1855.]—*Continued.*

1840	Charles Curtis Drury, 34th N.I.	14	*Apl.*
44	~~George Sinclair, 63rd N.I.~~ ..	17	do
41	Adrian Hugh Paterson, 68th N.I.	20	do
42	Wm. R. E. Alexander, 53rd N.I.	24	do
42	George F. Carnegie, 44th N.I...	1	*May*
42	James Pattle Beadle, Engineers,		do
41	John Smith, 51st N.I. ..	13	do
40	Robert Unwin, 16th Grenadiers,	11	*June*
40	John Allen Wright, 28th N.I.	12	do
40	*Lionel R. Newhouse, 19th N.I.		do
41	Marcus R. Somerville, 61st N.I.	3	*July*
40	François Mackenzie, 26th N.I.	8	do
40	Charles Dumbleton, 4th E. L. C.	9	do
40	Richard F. Grindall, 6th En. R.,	18	do
41	David Briggs, 17th N. I. ..	27	do
40	John MacDougall, 19th N.I. ..	31	do
40	Robert G. Mayne, 59th N.I. ..	3	*Aug.*
42	Archibald Impey, Engineers, ..		do
40	Stuart Fredk. Graham, 5th En.R.,	4	do
40	William Metcalf, 35th L.I. ..	7	do
40	Henry Finch, 31st N.I. ..	19	do
40	James Nowell Young, 3rd E.B.R.,	21	do
40	Francis Justin Nelson, 65th N.I.		do
40	George A. St. P. Fooks, 50th N.I		do
40	William H. Lowther, 52nd N. I.		do
40	*Arthur W. Owen, 11th N.I. ..		do
40	William Dunn Bishop, 30th N. I.	31	do
41	John Anstruther Angus, 9th N. I.	7	*Sep.*
40	Henry Le Poer Trench, 35th L.I.	17	do
40	Herbert Raban, 36th N.I. ..		do
40	Thomas E. B. Lees, 43rd L.I.	18	do
40	Percy F. Gardiner, 29th N. I. ..	27	do
40	Charles Frederic Smith, 39th N.I.		do
40	*Albert B. Beatson, 56th N.I...		do
40	Albert L. Nicholson, 64th N.I.	12	*Oct.*
41	William B. Marshall, Artillery, ..	15	do
41	Walker King Fooks, Artillery, ..	30	do
42	~~George F. Atkinson,~~ Engineers,	19	*Nov.*
42	William D. A. R. Short, Engrs...	3	*Dec.*
41	William Boyd Irwin, 10th N.I.	12	do
41	Henry Rawlins Drew, 6th En. R.,	22	do
41	George D'Aguilar, 4th N.I. ..		do
42	Peter Hy. Peck Gill, 37th N.I...	23	do
43	George Delane, 3rd E. L. Cavy...	24	do
41	Henry Arthur Dwyer, 59th N.I.	25	do
41	Fras. George Stainforth, 61st N.I.	29	do
41	James D. MacDonald, 39th N.I.	31	do
45	Robert T. H. Barber, 63rd N.I.		do

[1856.]

1842	James Anthony Steel, 17th N.I.	15	*Jan.*
41	William McNeile, 5th En. Regt.,	25	do
45	George C. Lambert, 1st En. B. F.	1	*Feb.*
41	William Clarke Green, 60th N.I.	4	do
41	James Marquis, 4th En. Regt.,..	17	do
41	George Noble Cave, 21st N.I. ..	27	do

* Brevet.

[1856.]—*Continued.*

Year	Name and Corps	Day	Month
1842	Henry E. Iremonger, 21st N.I.	28	*Feb.*
45	Trevor Wheler 1st En. B. Fus...	5	*Mar.*
41	Philip Roe Hockin, 48th N.I. ..	8	do
41	Robert Murray Nott, 64th N.I.		do.
41	Edward R. Wiggins, 35th L.I.		do
41	George McAndrew, 47th N.I. ..		do
41	Francis C. Wiggins, 70th N.I.		do
41	John Louis Nation, 57th N.I...		do
41	Frederick H. Smith, 34th N. I.	2	*Apl.*
42	James E. Thomson, 62nd N. I.	9	do
42	Edmund A. Grubb, 24th N.I. ..		do
42	Thomas Wright, 46th N.I. ..	17	do
42	William Irwin, 49th N.I. ..	18	*May*
41	Chas. B. G. Bacon, 3rd B. E. R.,	24	do
43	James E. T. Nicolls, Engineers,	8	*June*
41	Henry Reginald Courtenay, Arty. ..		do
41	Frederick Alexander, Artillery,..		do
41	Henry Stuart Bivar, 18th N.I...	11	do
41	Alfred Gyllett Nedham, 74th N. I. ..	12	do
41	*Marcus A. Garstin, 73rd N.I...		do
41	Robt. Knight Gordon, 72d N. I.		do
41	Chas. L. Montgomery, 65th N.I. ..		do
41	Blair Thos. Reid, 3rd B. E. R.,..		do
41	Rodk. D. Macpherson, 15th N.I.		do
41	Fredk. Wm. Ripley, 22nd N.I.		do
41	*Richard W. Chambers, 11th N.I.		do
41	*Fredk. G. Thellusson, 29th N.I.		do
42	Francis John Eagar, 25th N.I...	16	do
41	*Holled W. H. Coxe, 70th N. I.	21	do
41	Henry John B. Macleod, Arty.	26	do
41	Thos. Henry Wilson, 57th N.I.	27	do
45	Richard Jenkins, 5th E. L. C. ..	22	*July*
~~42~~	~~Benjamin Hawes, 2nd En. B. F.~~	10	*Aug.*
41	*Dormer Augs. Chase, 64th N.I.	12	do
43	Charles J. Hodgson, Engineers,	17	do
41	Archibald H. Campbell, 9th N. I.	25	do
~~43~~	~~Robert R. Harris~~, 67th N.I. ..	31	do
43	George Ward, 5th E. L. C. ..	12	*Sep.*
41	*Thomas Wm. Hilton, 65th N.I.	27	do
42	Geo. B. Mainwaring, 16th N.I. (Grenadiers,) ..	1	*Oct.*
41	Samuel Stallard, Artillery, ..	17	*Nov.*
46	John P. A. Theobald, 3rd E.L.C.	20	do
44	Daniel George Robinson, Engrs,	21	do
42	Henry D. Manning, 19th N.I...	23	do
42	Thos. Charles Darnell, 51st N.I.		do
42	John Innis Gibbs, 68th N.I. ..		do
42	Andrew L. Busk, 66th N.I. ..		do
41	Felix A. V. Thurburn, 14th N.I.		do
42	George A. Black, 69th N.I. ..		do
42	Edmund H. C. Wintle, 61st N.I.		do
42	John Patrick Briggs, 40th N.I.		do
42	William Landon Jones, 42nd L.I.		do
42	Samuel Rogers, 73rd N.I. ..		do
42	Thos. H. Chamberlain, 3rd B.E.R.,		do
42	William Elwyn, 58th N.I. ..		do
42	John J. Farrington, 2nd En. B. F.		do
42	Robert Alex. Napper, 55th N.I.		do
1842	Patrick George Scot, 12th N.I...	23	*Nov.*
43	John F. Campbell, 2nd En. B. F.		do
42	Henry Joseph Hughes, 62nd N.I.		do
42	John March Earle, 24th N.I. ..		do
42	Erskine G. Langmore, 27th N.I.		do
42	John P. W. Campbell, 47th N.I.		do
42	William Skene Row, 33rd N.I...		do
45	Etienne St. George, 1st En. B. F.		do
44	George R. Roberts, 41st N.I. ..		do
42	Chs. McC. Cotton, 2nd E. L. Cavy.		do
44	Frederick R. Pollock, 49th N.I.		do
43	John James Dansey, 16th N. I. Grenadiers, ..		do
42	James Reid, 37th N.I. ..		do
43	Wm. Henry S Earle, 20th N.I.		do
45	Archibald Cumine, 4th N.I. ..		do
42	Edward Thompson, 4th En. R.,		do
45	William J. P. Barlow, 63rd N.I.		do
44	Angelo E. Osborn, 45th N.I. ..		do
42	E. A. M. MacGregor, 4th E. L. C.		do
43	Arthur V. Dumbleton, 3rd E.L.C.		do
46	Henry White Best, 5th E. L. C.		do
46	Charles Powlett Lane, 3rd E. L.C.		do
44	Frederic Procter Bailey, 6th En. R.		do
44	John Fendall, 17th N.I. ..		do
44	Edgar J. Spilsbury, 67th N.I ..		do
48	Robert Alexander, 2nd E. Lt. C.		do
48	Henry C. Craigie, 1st E. L. C.		do
45	Fredk. C. J. Brownlow, 1st E.L.C.		do
42	Shakespear Sage, 30th N.I. ..		do
41	John Dawson, 43rd N.I. ..	10	*Dec*
41	George Holland, Artillery, ..	11	do
~~41~~	~~William L. Reynolds~~, 4th En. R.,		do
41	*John S. Dunbar, 64th N.I. ..		do
43	Melville Francis Evatt, 36th N.I.	26	do

[1857.]

Year	Name and Corps	Day	Month
1843	Alex. G. Forsyth, 3rd E. Regt.,..	1	*Jan*
50	*Sir* John Hill, *Bart.*, 1st E. L. Cavy., ..		do
42	Henry Francis, Artillery, ..	8	do
42	Fleming M. Martin, 52nd N. I.		do
42	Edward N. Perkins, 14th N. I.		do
46	William H. Hawes, 63rd N.I. ..	15	do
42	Phillip Rubie, 40th N.I. ..	20	do
43	Edmund D. R. Ross, 3rd E. Regt.	21	do
42	Wm. Thurlow Baker, 60th N. I.	24	do
42	Edward Atlay, Artillery, ..	30	do
44	Alexander Irvine, 24th N.I. ..	31	do
42	Alexander S. Allen, 34th N. I.	23	*Feb.*
44	Charles W. Hutchinson, Engrs.,	10	*Mar.*
51	George A. Galloway, 1st E. L. C.		do
45	Samuel Black, 37th N. I. ..	20	do
49	Henry Melvill, 2nd E. L. Cavy.	23	do
43	Henry Ruxton Corfield, 9th N.I.	4	*April*
42	John C. Dickson, 33rd N. I. ..	7	do
45	Edward Pryse Lloyd, 24th N. I.	1	*May*

* Brevet.

[1857.]—*Continued.*

Year	Name	Day	Month
1847	Hector Mackenzie, 20th N.I. ..	10	*May*
42	Henry Swinhoe, 30th N. I. ..	11	do
46	Danvers H. Osborn, 54th N.I. ..	13	do
43	Alex. P. S. Moncrieff, 44thN. I.	29	do
42	Julius Joseph Hockley, 66th N. I.	31	do
43	William Briggs, 71st N.I. ..		do
43	Edward Smalley, 36th N.I. ..		do
45	Charles Edward Mills, 28th N. I.		do
45	Arthur Gore Priestly, 41st N. I.	1	*June*
43	Francis J. Sidebottom, 62nd N. I.		do
45	William Paske, 28th N.I. ..	4	do
42	James Mansfield Nuttall, 5th En. Regt. ..	6	do
44	Henry K. Burne, 2nd N. I. (Grs.)		do
42	William Davis, 31st N. I. ..		do
42	James Young Gowan, 18thN.I...		do
44	Chas. W. Nightingale, 18th N. I.		do
46	Augustus K. Comber, 18th N.I.		do
45	Robert J. F. Hickey, 1st En.B.F.	7	do
44	Wm. Edward Cahill, 40th N. I.	8	do
48	Albert Henry Bamfield, 56th N.I.		do
43	Charles Warde, 68th N. I. ..		do
46	William Henry Paget, 54th N.I.		do
42	Donald McNeill, Artillery, ..	10	do
51	Geo. Augustus Graham, 28th N.I.		do
51	Henry Wm. Chapman, 28th N.I.		do
44	Thomas W. Holland, 38th N.I...		do
44	Thomas Warren Mercer, 46th N.I.	11	do
42	*Harry Smith Obbard, 61st N.I.		do
42	Tyrwhitt Pulman, Artillery, ..		do
42	George Maister, Artillery, ..		do
42	William Carmichael Russell, Arty.		do
42	Alexander Simpson, A. M., Arty.		do
42	John Ramsay Sladen Artillery,..		do
42	Robt. Dwarris Gibney, 59th N.I.		do
42	George Huntly Gordon, 39thN.I.		do
42	*Francis R. Thomson, 29th N. I.		do
42	William Henry Stubbs, 33rd N.I.		do
42	Hugh Rose, 4th En. Regt. ..		do
42	George B. Malleson, 33rd N.I....		do
42	*Fredk. Augustus Sage, 11th N.I.		do
42	Robert Maxwell, 35th L.I. ..	12	do
42	*Charles H. Byers, 70th N.I. ..		do
48	John Adrian Vanrenen, 54th N. I. ..	15	do
42	Henry C. Cuppage, 15th N.I. ..	23	do
42	Jeffery E. L. Willows, 10th N.I.		do
52	Hugh Ley Millett, 28th N. I. ..	27	do
42	Edward Robert Blair, 51st N.I.		do
44	Horatio Nelson Davies, 25th N.I.		do
43	H. F. Waddington, 52nd,N. I. ..		do
44	George Sim, Engineers, ..		do
49	William S. Graham, 2nd E. L. C.		do
~~54~~	~~E. Bertram DesVoeux,~~ 2ndE.L.C.		do
45	John Ruggles, 41st N. I. ..		do
49	George Charles Lloyd, 56th N. I.		do
47	Richard Sanderson Simonds, 4th En. Regt., ..		do
46	Herbert J. Hawes, 4th En. Regt.,		do
47	Leveson G. A. Campbell, 53rd N. I. ..		do

[1857.]—*Continued.*

Year	Name	Day	Month
1850	H. Edward Ellice, 1st E. L. C.,	1	*July*
42	Charles Andrews, 72nd N. I. ..		do
43	Charles William Miles, 23rd N.I.		do
42	Charles Stirling Dundas, Arty.	8	do
43	Alex. R.E. Hutchinson, 13th N.I.		do
42	Edmund Smyth, 13th N.I. ..	10	do
42	John Edward Cracroft, 69th N.I.		do
42	*Edmund Tyrwhitt, 51st N.I...		do
42	*Henry B. A. Poulton, 64th N.I.		do
42	*Bempde H. Baugh, 34th N.I.		do
43	Ed. M. Martineau, 10th N. I. ..	11	do
43	John Irwin Willes, 69th N. I...		do
44	Herbert L. Campbell, 52nd N. I.	13	do
44	Alfred LeGallais, 46th N.I. ..	14	do
51	Henry Alex. Cockburn, 53rd N.I.	15	do
50	Henry Doveton Battye, 56th N.I.		do
49	Horace Durrant, 5th E. L. C. ..	17	do
50	Wm. H. Macnaghten, 1st E.L.C.	19	do
43	J. S. Rawlins, 44th N. I. ..	21	do
42	Martin G. Brabazon, 60th N. I.	23	do
44	Nathl. W. Trenchard, 10th N.I.		do
42	*Toovey A. Corbett, 61st N.I.	25	do
42	Edward Van H. Holt, 42nd L. I.		do
42	Charles F. Hicks,* 5th En. Regt,		do
42	*William John Ward, 51st N.I..		do
42	James Emerson, 26th L. I. ..	30	do
43	Alexander Pond, 3rd En. Regt.	4	*Aug.*
45	Joseph Henry Dyas, Engineers,	11	do
45	John Francis Stafford, 4th N. I.		do
~~42~~	~~Richard Meacham, Artillery,~~ ..	12	do
42	James Adeane Law, 66th N.I.,	20	do
45	Duncan K. Presgrave, 59th N I.	21	do
43	Daniel Mocatta, 26th L. I. ..	27	do
44	Clemens T. Hallett, 72nd N. I.	28	do
43	John W. F. Bean, 1[illegible]th N. I. ..	4	*Sep.*
42	Charles Reay, 32nd N.I. ..	9	do
43	Archibald Swiney Haig, 55th N.I.	14	do
45	Alexander Fraser, Engineers, ..		do
	†Simon Budd, *Riding Master 1st Brigade Horse Artillery,*	14	do
43	Hugh Grant, 74th N. I. ..	18	do
43	George William Fraser, 27th N.I.	23	do
42	*Chas. Stephen Fowle, 22nd N.I.	24	do
53	A. Cromwell Warner, 2nd E. L. C.	1	*Oct.*
45	John Charles Harris, Engineers,		do
43	John James Hume, 48th N. I. ..	4	do
44	Henry Alex. Taylor, 74th N. I.	6	do
45	Mangles J. Brander, 40th N. I.	9	do
45	Henry R. Wroughton, 40th N. I.	15	do
47	Addington Taylor, 25th N. I. ..	17	do
52	Sidney Chalmers, 53rd N. I. ..	23	do
46	Charles Batchelor 3rd E. L. C...	7	*Nov.*
50	Charles P. Hildebrand, 10th N. I.	18	do
44	John Collings Bonamy, 32nd N. I. ..	21	do
46	Wm. B. Girdlestone, 67th N.I...	28	do
54	Digby Compton, 2nd E. L. C. ..	6	*Dec.*
42	Charles Metcalfe Young, Arty:,	9	do
42	*Alexander M. Mackenzie, 56th N. I. ..		do

* Brevet. † Unattached.

[1857.]—*Continued.*

1842 *Robert M. S. Annesley, 65th N. I. .. 9 *Dec*
42 *Charles Irvine, 51st N. I. .. do
42 *Henry King, 39th N. I. .. 10 do
42 Charles P. Lucas, 47th N. I. .. do
42 Thomas C. Merrick, 4th En. Regt. do
43 Samuel Briggs Cookson, 73rd N. I. .. 28 do
R ~~43 *Robert William Gibbs, 28th N.I.~~ do
43 Hugh T. Pollock, 35th N. I. .. do
43 *Charles Murray, 70th N. I. .. do

[1858]

1846 George Bushby, 4th E. L. C. .. 2 *Jan.*
51 Robert Baring, 1st E. L. C. 9 do
43 John J. Eckford, 5th En. Regt... 29 do
48 Charles Auguste Reid, 20th N. I. .. 6 *Feb.*
43 John Guyse Sparke, 21st N. I. 17 do
43 *William H. Walcot, 47th N. I. 22 do
43 *John Baillie, 26th L. I. .. 25 do
52 Melville Clarke, 1st E. L. C .. 10 *Mar.*
49 William B. Peile, 38th L. I. .. 11 do
45 Nedham T. Parsons, 1st En. B. F. 12 do
49 William F. Stewart, 45th N. I... 16 do
45 Wm. Elliot Marshall, 48th N. I. 21 do
43 Hungerford M. Boddam, Arty... 27 do
45 Patrick Maxwell 37th N. I. .. 1 *Apl.*
43 William D. Hoste, 55th N. I... 4 do
43 *William G. Ellice, 15th N. I... 4 do
47 W. T. Fagan, 44th N.I. .. 18 do
43 Charles Baldwin, 2nd En. B. F... 22 do
R ~~45 Henry Stokes, 12th N. I.~~ .. 25 do
45 Frederick R. Aikman, 4th N. I... 26 do
43 John Anthony Angelo, Artillery, 27 do
43 David J. F. Newall Arty. .. do
43 John Edmund Watson, Arty .. do
43 William Morton Gowan, Arty... do
43 William John Gray, Arty. .. do
43 John Stewart Tulloh, Arty. .. do
44 George Rodney Brown, Arty. .. do
44 William R. Fitzgerald, Arty. .. do
44 Edward Harrison, Artillery, .. do
44 William Frederick Cox, Arty., do
46 Thomas G. Glover, Engrs. .. do
46 Henry Hyde, Engineers, .. do
46 Ralph Young, Engineers, .. do
46 Charles D. Newmarch, Engineers, do
44 Robert W. Clifford, 2nd E.L. C. 30 do
43 Alex. Paterson, 2nd En. B. Fus. 1 *May*
44 Robert F. Webster, 3rd. En. R.,.. 15 do
53 Mowbray Thomson, 53rd N. I... 17 do
44 Harry Vince Timbrell, Artillery 21 do
43 Neil E. Boileau, 27th N.I. .. 26 do
49 William S. Pierson, 54th N. I. 6 *June*
43 George F. F. Vincent, 30th N. I. 9 do

[1858].—*Continued.*

D ~~1843 *Thomas John Geldart, 65th~~ N.I. 9 *June*
43 *Hy. Prevost Babbage, 55th N. I. .. 10 do
43 *William Henry Binny, 9th N. I. do
47 Charles H. E. Græme, 5th En. R. 17 do
43 *Charles M. Fitz Gerald, 31st N.I. .. 20 do
43 *Samuel R. J. Owen, 19th N.I. do
49 *Sir* C. W. A. Oakeley *Bt*, 5th E.L.C. 23 do
44 Joseph C. Griffith, Artillery, .. 4 *July*
43 *Henry J. Templer, 5th En. R., 10 do
45 Cooper M. N. Fellowes, 3rd En. R. 13 do
46 Thomas B. Harrison 4th E. L. C. 23 do
45 George M. Battye, 1st En. B. F. 2 *Aug.*
46 William C. L. Ryves, 12th N. I, .. 4 do
47 John T. Watson, 12th N. I. .. 6 do
46 James Crofton, Engineers, .. 13 do
44 Elliott Hyndman, 27th N.I. .. 21 do
45 William C. R. Mylne, 74th N. I. .. 22 do
45 Alex. T. Armstrong, 72nd N.I. 24 do
D ~~45 William Aitchison Mylne, Arty.~~ 27 do
45 Charles Henry Cookes, Artillery, do
45 John A. R. Mead, Artillery, .. do
45 John Fraser Raper, Artillery, ... do
45 Alfred Hales Heath, Artillery,.. do
45 William D. Couchman, Artillery, do
45 Frederic Day Urquhart, Arty... do
45 James G. Hathorn, Artillery, .. do
45 Frederick R. DeBude, Artillery, do
45 Charles S. Lemarchand, Artillery, do
45 Abraham R. Fuller, Artillery, .. do
45 Lancelot Machell, Artillery, .. do
45 Mark E. Currie, Artillery, .. do
45 John Hunter, Artillery, .. do
45 Augustus Darling, Artillery, .. do
45 William Hawtayne Parish, Arty. do
45 George Baillie, Artillery, .. do
45 John Fulton, Artillery, .. do
45 Thomas Henry Salt, Artillery, .. do
45 Robert Murray, Artillery, .. do
45 Peter Macfarlane Syme, Artillery, do
45 William Alex Ross, Artillery,.. do
45 William Dickson, Artillery, .. do
45 George Oliver Rybot, Artillery, do
46 Affleck Fraser, Arillery, .. do
46 Henry Montaguet Smith, Arty. do
46 James Edward Cordner, Artillery, do
46 Walter Delane, Artillery, .. do
46 Edward Simeon, Artillery, .. do
45 Arthur Watts Pixley, Artillery, do
45 Thomas Presant, Artillery, .. do
46 Alfred Digby Denniss, Artillery, do
R ~~46 Francis C. Simons, Artillery,~~ ... do
46 Charles McW. Mercer, Artillery, do
46 David Thomson, Artillery, .. do
Maj 46 Wallis Dowell, Artillery, .. do
46 Morgan Crofton Sankey, Arty... do
47 Jonathan Y. Worthington, Arty. do
47 Henry R. Brownlow, Artillery,.. do

* Brevet.

CAPTAINS—*Continued.*

[1858.]—*Continued.*

1847 Francis William Stubbs, Artillery, 27 *Aug.*
48 Alexander Gillespie, Artillery, .. do
48 John Hayes Grant, Artillery, .. do
48 Frederick E. Smalpage, Artillery, do
48 Thomas Alex. Dirom, Artillery, do
46 Thomas N. Harward, Artillery, do
48 Andrew H. Bogle, Artillery, .. do
49 Francis H. McLeod, Artillery, .. do
49 Sir William Hamilton Bart, Arty. do
46 Alexander Cadell, Engineers, .. do
47 William S. Oliphant, Engineers, do
47 Henry W. Gulliver, Engineers, do
47 Charles Pollard, Engineers, .. do
48 Charles T. Stewart, Engineers, .. do
48 Arthur W. Garnett, Engineers, do
~~49 Henry John Evans,~~ Artillery, .. do
49 De Vic Francis Carey, Artillery, do
49 Thomas Elliott Hughes, Artillery, do
49 Henry Murray, Artillery, .. do
49 William Brown, Artillery, .. do
49 James Ranald Martin, Artillery, do
48 Frederick Weston Peile, Engrs., do
48 Arthur Innes Shuldham, 20th N.I. do
~~49 William Henderson, Engineers,~~ do
49 Frederic S. Taylor, Engineers, do
49 Edward Davidson, Engineers, .. do
50 Lindsay Russell, Engineers, .. do
50 Ed. C. S. Williams, Engineers, do
51 T. George Montgomerie, Engrs. do
51 George Ayton Craster, Engineers, do
51 Wm. Spottiswoode Trevor, Engrs. do
50 David Limond, Engineers, .. do
50 Raoul de Bourbel, Engineers, .. do
49 Thomas Nicholl, Artillery, .. do
50 Fred. Smith Stanton, Engineers, do
49 Chas. Walsham Maynard, Arty. do
50 Edward Tierney, Artillery, .. do
50 Alexander H. Lindsay, Artillery, do
50 William Hichens, Engineers, .. do
50 Henry T. Forbes, Artillery, .. do
50 Francis R. Butt, Artillery, .. do
50 Thomas P. Smith, Artillery, .. do
50 Arthur Rotton, Artillery, .. do
50 Edward L. Earle, Artillery, .. do
50 Edward H. Willoughby, Artillery, do
50 George Charles Depree, Artillery, do

[1858.]—*Continued*

1850 George Miller Dobbin, Arty.. .. 27 *Aug.*
43 Robert Havard Price, 31st N. I.. 1 *Sep.*
43 Spencer C. D. Ryder, 14 N.I... 4 do
44 Thomas Staples, 58th N.I. .. do
49 *Hon'ble* Francis Algernon James Chichester, 5th E. L. C. .. 16 do
48 C. Henry Brownlow, 4thE.Regt. 3 *Nov.*
47 George James D. Hay. 57th N. I. 21 do
43 J. J. O'Bryen, 16th N. I.(Grs) 22 do
43 *George C. Hankin, 28th N.I... 8 *Dec.*
43 *George Hamilton, 51st N. I. .. 9 do
45 *John R. A. S. Lowe, 56th N.I. do
45 Frederick J. Ellis, 58th N.I. .. 26 do
44 *George A. F. Houchen, 10th N.I. 30 do
44 *James T. Norgate, 69th N.I... do
44 *John Jerdan, 43rd L.I. .. do

[1859.]

44 *Charles L. Brown, 46th N.I. .. 1 *Jan.*
44 *Abraham C. Bunbury, 34th N.I. do
44 *William H. Phillips, 59th N. I., do
46 John Mitchell Evans, 6th En. Regt. .. 22 do
44 *Arthur L. Elderton, 2nd European B. F. .. 27 do
44 *Arthur Crawford, 9th N.I. .. do
44 *John Lamb, 29th N.I. .. 3 *Feb.*
45 James K. Couper, 2nd N.I (Grs.) 16 do
46 William Robert Gordon, 68th N.I. 19 do
46 George Price, 1st En. B. F. .. 21 do
44 *John R. Auldjo, 36th N.I. .. 28 do
44 * Henry Wylie Norman, (Offl. Maj.) 31st N.I. .. 1 *Mar.*
44 *Robert H. Shebbeare, 60th N.I. do
44 *Robert Davidson, 64th N. I. ., do
~~48 John S. Bennett, 4th En. Regt.~~ .. 13 do
44 *Brooking Soady, 24th N. I. 1 *Apl,*
49 John I. Robinson, 5th En. L. C. 3 do
44 *George V. Balderston. 23rd N. I. 21 do
47 Alfred Francis, 68th N. I. 15 *May*
44 *Chas. C. Johnson, 33rd N. I... 7 *June*
44 *Edward Leeds, 47th N.I.. .. do
44 *John Hanning Speke, 46th N.I. 8 do
44 *Robert Cony Whiting. 70th N.I. do
50 *Hon.* William M. Fraser, 44th N.I. 19 do
44 *Robert W. T. Russell, 43rd L.I. 25 do

LIEUTENANTS.

[1847.]

1845 Montagu James White, 26th L.I. 7 *June*
45 Campbell Clark, 2nd En. B. F... 15 *Aug*
45 Richard J. D. Ferris, 55th N.I.. 30 do

[1848.]

1845 Charles C. Dandridge, 49th N.I. 13 *Mar.*
45 James Williamson, 49th N.I. .. 13 *Apl.*
45 John Adam Tytler, 66th N.I. .. 19 *July*
45 Wm. C. Hamilton, 2nd En. B. F. 21 *July*
45 John M. Mackenzie, 58th N.I. .. 10 *Aug.*

[1848.]—*Continued.*

1847 George Allgood, 49th N.I. .. 14 *Sep.*
45 Robert Stothert, 4th N.I. .. 20 *Oct.*
44 George Weld, 14th N.I. .. 27 do
45 Edmd. K. Otho Gilbert, 27th N.I. 3 *Nov.*

[1849.]

~~1845 John M. Bayley 50th N.I.~~ .. 4 *Jan.*
45 Thomas Pierce, 30th N.I. .. 13 do
45 Alex. D. Towgood, 2nd En. B.F. 21 *Feb.*
46 Wemyss Smith, 28th N.I. .. 10 *Apl.*

* Brevet.

[1849.]—*Continued.*

1846 Charles M. L. Clarke, 37th N.I. 26 *Apl.*
45 Joseph Hind, 26th L.I. .. 1 *May*
46 Walter Henry Smith, 56th N.I. 12 do
45 Richard C. Lindsey, 24th N.I... 20 *May*
45 Gordon Cavenagh, 39th N.I. .. 10 *June*
47 William Carnell, 3rd B. E. R.,.. 15 do
47 Shadwell S. Boulderson, 37th N.I. 30 do
47 Edward Hanson Paske, 53rd N.I. 16 *July*
45 Charles Armstrong, 10th N.I. .. 29 do
48 Wm. C. S. Clarke, 3rd E. L. C. 30 do
44 Hugh Hayley, 69th N.I. .. 31 do
48 John Cockerell, 2nd E. L. C. .. 1 *Aug.*
45 Edward H. Langmore, 71st N.I. 21 do
47 John Robert Currie, 4th N.I. .. 15 *Sep.*
46 Andrew A. Munro, 50th N.I. .. 22 *Oct.*
46 Decimus W. Becher, 2nd En.B.F. 15 *Nov.*
46 Thomas F. Forster, 39th N.I. .. 28 do
48 Alfred Tulloch, 58th N.I. .. 2 *Dec.*
45 John Perkins, 71st N.I. .. 7 do

[1850.]

1844 Hugh Norris Hodgson, 9th N.I. 5 *Jan.*
47 Robert E. Anderson, 3rd B. E. Regt., .. 1 *Feb.*
46 Thomas F. O. Scott, 41st N.I.. 13 do
49 Henry A. Prinsep, 3rd B. E. R.,.. 21 do
46 Richard C. Birch, 1st En. B. F. 1 *Mar.*
46 Thomas Taylor, 14th N.I. .. 5 do
46 Frederick C. Anderson, 71st N.I. 18 do
45 George A. Williams, 26th L.I... 1 *Apl.*
45 John Leven, 62nd N.I. .. 1 *June*
46 *Baron* F. Von Andlau, 28th N. I. 18 do
41 George G. Cunliffe, 41st N.I. .. 16 *July*
45 Edward Bertie Clay, 66th N.I... 24 do
46 Henry L. Gleig, 32nd N.I. .. 10 *Aug.*
45 James Sykes, 66th or Goorkha R., 13 do
47 T. W. R. Boisragon, 69th N. I. 15 do
48 Chas. Stewart Lane, 56th N.I. .. 1 *Sep*
45 James Spence Ogilvie, 48th N. I. 29 do
46 George C. Huxham, 48th N.I. .. do
49 Augustus Arthur Currie, 45th N.I. 26 *Oct.*
48 Augustus W. Bolton, 50th N.I. 27 do
47 Frederic N. Miles, 53rd N.I. .. 28 do
49 J. F. Lane Fisher, 19th N.I. .. 1 *Nov.*
46 Browne William Ryall, 63rd N.I. 6 do
47 Octavius L. Smith, 48th N.I. .. 7 do
45 John C. Millar, 29th N.I. .. 10 do
48 Charles Frederick Packe, 4th N. I. .. 12 do
46 James Burnie Lind, 24th N.I. .. 18 do
45 William Nembhard, 55th N.I. .. 19 do
48 Clements Robert Shaw, 37th N. I., .. 8 *Dec.*

[1850.] *Continued.*

1850 Clement John Mead, Artillery, . 9 *Dec.*
50 John Percivall, Artillery, .. do
50 Patrick Charles Anderson, Arty, do
50 Mordaunt M. FitzGerald, Arty., do

[1851.]

1849 Charles C. Ekins, 20th N.I. .. 1 *Jan.*
49 Dacres William Wise, 3rd E. L. C. do
48 Joseph Ford Sherer, 49th N.I... 24 do
48 James A. M. Biggs, 10th N.I. .. 8 *Feb.*
45 Hugh Pigot Williams, 72nd N. I. .. 20 do
45 Frederick C. Innes, 60th N.I. .. 1 *Mar.*
45 John Beresford Smyly, 29th N. I. .. 15 do
46 William C. Mac Dougall, 72nd N.I. .. 17 do
48 Orlando Manley Glubb 37th N. I. .. do
45 Arthur Ellis, 31st N.I. .. 31 do
45 Frek. R. N. Fortescue, 73d N. I. 7 *Apl.*
47 John Moore Graham, 27th N.I. 18 do
47 George Augustus Brown, 21st N.I. .. 21 do
46 Isaac F. MacAndrew, 19th N. I. 30 do
47 George A. H. Lillie, 13th N.I. .. do
45 Chas. Stuart W. Ogilvie, 5th En. Regt. .. 5 *May*
46 Francis A. Dickins, 31st N.I. .. 21 do
47 John Brenton Cox, 62nd N.I. .. 28 do
51 William R. Tucker, Engrs., ... 13 *June*
51 George Rennie Manderson, Artillery, .. do
46 James Burn, 40th N.I. .. 1 *July*
46 Walter Davison, 1st En. B.F. .. 6 do
46 Charles J. Nicholson, 54th N.I. 27 do
45 Henry Champion-Moller, 11th N. I. .. 1 *Aug.*
47 Henry B. Urmston, 62nd N.I... 15 do
46 William H. Jackson, 52nd N.I. 15 *Sep.*
47 Thomas E. Webster, 63rd N.I... 21 do
45 George A. Cuyler, 4th En. Regt. 3 *Oct.*
50 Guy A. Prendergast, 5th E. L, Cavy. .. 10 do
46 James Dowell Swayne, 11th N. I. 13 do
48 Charles V. Jenkins, 47th N.I. .. 16 do
46 James Augustus Grant, 6th En.R. 22 do
* Stephen Douglas, .. 3 *Nov.*
46 Francis John Gully, 74th N.I... 5 do
49 H. Paul W. Wynch, 59th N.I.. 10 do
45 Bejn. G. Vander Gucht, 2 Grs... 1 *Dec*
45 James C. Wood, 30th N.I. .. 11 do
51 James P. Basevi, Engineers, .. 12 do
51 Æneas Perkins, Engineers, .. do
46 Francis D. Ogilvie, 46th N.I... 31 do

* Unattached Lieutenant.

[1852.]

D ~~1846 Go. Henry Griffiths, 6th En. R.~~, 1 *Feb.*
45 Nicolai W. Elphinstone, 4th N.I. 14 do
45 Francis H. Hanmer, 34th N.I... 21 do
47 James C. Hamilton, 6th En. R., 25 do
46 Charles R. Blair, 2nd En. B.F. 1 *Mar.*
47 Thomas Lamb, 16th Grs. .. 12 do
46 Charles M. Longmore, 33rd N.I. 14 do
46 Jocelyn P. Cambridge, 2nd Gredrs. .. 22 do
50 Henry Macdonald, 19th N. I... 26 *Apl.*
50 William Gordon, 47th N.I. .. 11 *May*
49 John William Hoggan, 45th N. I. .. 15 do
49 Henry Zouch Darrah, 41st N.I. 25 do
52 Arthur Moffat Lang, Engrs, ... 12 *June*
52 Edward Wood Humphry, Engrs. do
52 Chas. Simeon Thomason, Engrs, do
45 Christopher J. Godby, 36th N.I. 10 *July*
49 Wm. George Davies, 71st N. I., do
46 Edward John Wild, 40th N.I.,.. 26 do
48 Hamilton Maxwell, 1st En. B. F. 7 *Aug.*
47 Lionel J. Trotter, 2nd En. B. F. 20 do
48 David B. Lockhart, 6th En. R., 21 do
49 Robert G. Rogers, 5th En. Regt. 28 do
46 Edward Dandridge, 73rd N.I... 7 *Sep.*
49 Robert Chalmers, 45th N.I., .. 10 do
47 Ralph Ouseley, 48th N.I. 1 *Oct.*
50 Thos. Gilbert Kennedy, 62nd N.I. 3 do
50 Thomas Buttanshaw, 28th N.I... 3 *Nov.*
49 Ralph Bristow Dundas, 38th L.I. 16 do
47 Arthur H. Millett, 69th N.I. .. 17 do
46 Thomas C. Hamilton, 35th N.I. do
*William Sheffield, .. 6 *Dec.*
49 Geo. Cleland Rowcroft, 41st N.I. 8 do
52 Salusbury Thomas Trevor, Engrs. 9 do
52 George Newmarch, Engineers, .. do
52 John Lidstone Watts, Engrs., .. do
46 J. Alfered Brereton, 33rd N. I. 30 do

[1853.]

1850 Edward Gresley Stone, 40th N. I. .. 2 *Jan.*
45 Edmund G. Higgins, 4th En. R., 7 do
45 William Reveley, 65th N.I. .. 12 do
46 Montgomery Hunter, 18th N.I. 31 do
48 Henry Richard Bradford, 36th. N. I. .. 15 *Feb.*
51 Cunliffe Martin, 1st E. L. C. .. 20 do
48 George J. Reeves, 50th N.I. .. 3 *Mar.*
45 Frederick E. Laing, 17th N.I... 18 do
49 Edward P. W. Ripley, 51stN. I do
49 Edward Thompson, 67th N.I. .. 21 do

[1853.]—*Continued.*

1850 Lawrence H. Williams 5th En. R. 10 *Apl.*
49 Henry M. Wemyss, 1st En. B. F. .. do
51 Charles Peter Hunter, 5th En. R. 18 do
47 Jas. J. E. Howard, 24th N.I. .. 1 *May*
50 John Angelo, 59th N.I. .. 8 do
48 Lachlan Forbes, 2nd Gredrs. .. 17 *May*
45 Alworth Merewether, 61st N.I. 18 do
47 R. D'Oyly C. Bracken, 52nd N.I. 20 do
48 Frederick W. Dunbar, 37th N. I. do
47 Calvert D. S. Clarke, 73rd N.I, 21 do
47 John Macdonald, 18th N.I. .. 24 do
48 Henry G. Jenkins, 4th E. L. C... 27 do
50 Charles William Fletcher, 48th N. I. .. 5 *June*
45 George Leith Fraser, 23rd N.I. 7 do
50 William Winson, 45th N.I. .. 10 do
53 John Underwood Champain, Engineers, .. 11 do
53 Robert C. Boileau Pemberton Engineers, .. do
53 Robert Home, Engineers, .. do
48 Samuel A. Hunter, 34th N.I. .. 29 do
48 Charles Shaw, 57th N.I. .. 11 *July*
46 Alexander F. Corbett, 43rd N.I. 14 do
D ~~48 John Parks Jervois~~, 73rd N.I. .. 19 do
46 Alfred Combe, 65th N.I. .. 24 do
45 William Nassau Lees, L. L. D. 42nd N. I. .. 25 do
45 Francis K. Bacon, 22nd N.I. .. 29 do
49 John C. Horne, 6th European Regiment .. 1 *Aug.*
47 Charles W. Peter, 42nd N.I. .. 3 do
49 Boyle T. Stafford, 18th N.I. .. 12 do
49 Robert Cadell, 20th N.I. .. 14 do
48 Alfred W. Montagu, 68th N.I... 13 *Sept.*
48 Roger Wolley Glasse, 14th N. I. 14 do
47 Joseph W. Orchard, 33rd N.I. .. 1 *Oct.*
47 John Arthur H. Moore, 23rd N. I. .. 10 do
51 George Herbert Hale, 57th N.I. 31 do
47 William P. Conolly, 46th N.I. .. 1 *Nov.*
50 William Jackson, 53rd N.I. .. do
48 John Grant Sombre Matheson, 2nd En. B. F. .. 12 do
51 W. John J. Richardes, 3rd E.L.C. 14 do
45 Samuel D. White, 3rd B. En. R. 15 do
45 Chas. Henry Hall, 64th N. I. .. do
45 Robert Cogan Cross, 17th N.I.. do
45 Henry John Allan, 9th N.I. .. do
45 Charles Baily, 17th N.I. .. do
45 Jonathan Keer, 60th N.I. .. do
46 Alexander H. B. Bruce, 43rd L.I. do
46 Robert Stewart, 22nd N. I. do
D ~~45 Robert Creighton, 55th N.I.~~ .. do
46 Edward C. Rawstorne, 9th N.I... do
46 Alexander A. Bruce, 4th En. R. do
47 Charles H. Palliser, 63rd N.I... do
47 Robt. H. M. Aitken, 13th N.I... do
48 Edgar Gibson Clark, 21st N.I. .. do

* Unattached Lieutenant.

Lieutenants—*Continued.*

[1853.]—*Continued.*

1848 Fredk. M. H. Forbes, 39th N.I. 15 *Nov.*
47 Henry B. Chalmers, 27th N.I. do
48 Wm. F. Leicester, 30th N.I. .. do
48 William G. B. Tyler, 42nd L.I. do
~~48 John Eales Caunter,~~ 15th N.I... do
48 Ewd. L. Clogstoun, 10th N.I... do
48 Chas. N. McMullin, 73rd N I. do
49 William M. Grierson, 70th N.I. do
49 James E. B. Parsons, 5th En. R. do
49 Robert F. Godby, 35th L.I. .. do
49 John Fredk. Orchard, 4th N.I.,.. do
50 George R. Westmacott, 23rd N.I. do
46 Eugene C. Impey, 5th En. Regt. do
51 Francis Howell Jenkins, 57th N.I. do
49 *Hon.* Fred. B. Best, 2nd En. B. F. 24 do
50 A. D. Jennings, 2nd E. L. C. 27 do
52 Fred. P. Luard, 1st E. Lt. Cavy. 30 do
48 Joseph Reay, 63d N. I. .. 5 *Dec.*
51 B. Haliburton Smith, 67th N. I. 8 do
53 Patrick Murray, Engineers, ... 9 do
53 Alexander McNeill, Engrs. .. do
50 Thomas W. Evans, 47th N. I... 15 do
47 Alex. McKenzie, 9th N. I. .. 24 do
49 Adrian D. Vanrenen, 71st N. I. 28 do

[1854.]

1850 John Hearsey, 38th N. I .. 1 *Jan.*
52 Edwin E. Brutton Bond, 57th N.I. do
51 John Gillespie, 61st N. I. .. 29 do
51 William Phaire, 54th N. I. .. 31 do
48 Robert Durie Griffin, 64th N. I. 1 *Feb.*
48 R. H. Tulloh, 16th N. I. (Grs.) do
50 William L. Randall, 59th N. I. 5 do
50 Henri Campbell, 63rd N.I. .. 12 do
50 John Morland, 1st E. B. F. .. 5 *Mar.*
~~47 Thomas E. Powell, 43rd L.I.~~ .. 6 do
51 Henry Foord Bamford, 38th L.I. 7 do
~~48 Henry D. Magniac,~~ 15th N. I. .. 10 do
50 Jas. Scott Ingram, 1st B. E. F. .. 20 do
50 Geo. B. C. Simpson, 23rd N. I. 1 *Apl.*
52 Henry Tindall, 61st N. I. .. 12 do
49 Francis Booth Norman, 14th N. I. 15 do
50 Gilbert James Pasley, 6th En. R. 26 do
51 E. J. L. Twynam, 25th N. I. .. 2 *May*
51 Brook S. B. Parlby, 6th En, R. 7 do
52 Walter Foggo Ireland, 25th N. I. do
51 Chas. McFarlane, 1st E. B. F. .. 10 do
52 J. Thornhill Bushby, 67th N. I. 17 do
~~51 Arthur H. Carter,~~ 74th N. I. 22 do
48 Peter Stark Lumsden, 60th N. I. 23 do
48 Ed. Richard Oakes, 52nd N. I. 1 *June*
49 Chas. A. McDougall, 4th En. R. do
54 William Jeffreys, Engrs. .. 8 do
50 Henry F. Newmarch, 24th N. I. 12 do
48 Newton Barton, 52nd N. I., .. 24 do
48 George Wheeler, 29th N. I. .. 3 *July*
51 John Pringle Sherriff, 35th N. I. 10 do
46 C. Gibbs Thorp, 69th N. I. 17 do
49 Henry Phillpotts, 15th N. I. .. 23 do
50 George Wm. Manson, 34th N.I. 5 *Aug.*

[1854.]—*Continued.*

1851 Horatio Phillips, 40th N.I. .. 6 *Aug.*
52 Frederick Allen, 42nd N.I. .. 9 do
50 Thos. E. Vander Gucht, 5th En.R. do
50 Henry Vincent Mathias, 50th N.I. do
50 William Cadogan Mitchel, 4th N.I. 14 do
45 F. J. Stephenson, 3rd B. En.R 19 do
50 William C. B. Ryan, 45th N.I. 21 do
50 James Trevenen, 24th N. I., .. 29 do
45 Frederick Duffin, 22nd N. I., .. 30 do
50 Frank Barnard Foote, 71st N.I., 1 *Sep.*
51 G. Cadogan Thomson, 51st N. I. 7 do
54 David Ward, Engineers, .. 7 do
49 R. Stannus Graves, 66th N.I. 15 do
48 Henry Albany Wyndham Waterfield, 27th N.I. .. 28 do
47 FitzThos. Goldsworthy, 72nd N.I. 9 *Oct.*
45 Henry B. Blake, 3rd En. R. .. 15 do
49 Thomas Quin, 22nd N.I. .. 17 do
50 A. C. Grant, 5th E.L. Cavalry, 1 *Nov.*
49 James T. Harris, 2nd En. B. F. 13 do
48 Harry H. Lyster, 72nd N. I. .. do
47 E. H. Woodcock, 55th N. I. .. 14 do
50 Augustus Willes, 2nd En. B. F. 22 do
50 Francis W. Russell, 3rd E. L. C. 28 do
50 John Boyd Saunders, 4th E. L. C. 4 do
49 Alfred Blunt, 13th N.I. .. do
52 George Alexander, 35th L. I. .. 30 do
46 John F. Templer, 3rd B. E. Regt. 9 *Dec.*
~~54 H. Alex. L. Carnegie, Engineers,~~ do
54 Edwd. Talbot Thackeray, Engrs., do
54 John Greenlaw Forbes, Engrs do
49 Arthur Cory, 16th N. I. (Greds.) 13 do
49 Hugh Henry Christian, 68th N.I. 16 do
50 Stannus W. Fraser, 28th N. I. .. 30 do
49 Thomas C. Anderson, 12th N. I. 31 do
~~50 Charlton~~ N. Tucker, 2nd E. L. C. do
54 J. C. Lockwood, 2nd E. L. Cavy. do

[1855.]

1850 George H. E. Howard, 24th N.I. 1 *Jan.*
51 Gavin Dring Crawfurd, 18th N.I. do
~~52 Reginald Travers, 6th En. Regt.~~ 9 do
~~53 Kennett Dixon, 4th E. Lt. Cavy.~~ 13 do
49 Wm. Butler Shawe, 60th N. I. .. 15 do
~~49 James D. Lance, 6th En. Regt.~~ .. 16 do
50 Robert D. Campbell, 63rd N.I... 19 do
~~50 Douglas Reid,~~ 2nd Greds. .. 1 *Feb.*
49 Bruce N. Smith, 46th N. I. .. 10 do
50 Clarence C. Taylor, 56th N.I. .. 25 do
49 William B. Thomson, 13th N. I. 28 do
48 Alexander Callander, 58th N.I... do
~~49 William A. Bettine, 53rd N.I. 9 Mar.~~
50 Brooke R. Chambers, 13th N. I. 10 do
50 Wm. Dinwiddie Hogg, 41st N. I. 26 do
51 Mansfeldt Geo. Smith, 59th N. I. 5 *Apl.*
49 Francis J. Craigie, 21st N.I. .. 13 do
51 Dashwood Ross, 10th N. I. .. 17 do
50 John H. Jenkins, 44th N.I. .. 1 *May*

[1855.]—*Continued.*

1853	J. Edmond D'Wilson, 42nd N. I.	7	*May*
50	William Cabell, 62nd N.I. ..	29	do
51	C. Tatham Hitchins, 54th N. I.	31	do
53	Burke Cuppage, 3rd E. L. C., ..	1	*June*
50	Wm. Alex. Garden, 39th N.I. ..	4	do
57	Charles Henry Luard, Engrs.. ..	8	do
57	John Birny, Engineers, ..		do
57	George Swinton, Engineers, ..		do
57	Chas. Neave Judge, Engineers, ..		do
57	George Scott Hills, Engineers, ..		do
51	L. Baines Magniac, 1st En. B. F.	17	do
52	C. Fredk. Middleton, 40th N. I.		do
53	George B. Stainforth, 61st N. I.,	3	*July*
50	Algar Bowdoin Temple, 49th N. I.	18	do
54	*Sir* M. Barlow, *Bart.* 4th E.L.Cvy.	18	do
51	Wm. Siddons Young, 59th N. I.	3	*Aug.*
53	Hugh Henry Gough, 1st E. L. C.	9	do
50	John C. McNeill, 12th N. I. ..	13	do
54	C. T. Otway Mayne, 15th N. I.	23	do
50	Beau. C. Urquhart, 39th N.I. ..	26	do
~~53~~	~~James Becher Tudor, 5th En. R.~~	1	*Sep.*
54	George Fergus Graham, 5th En. R.		do
48	Boyce W. D. Morton, 30th N. I.		do
48	R. O. H. Forbes, 3rd B. En. R.		do
50	Henry T. Oldfield, 9th N. I. ..	7	do
50	Richard H. Wall, 16th N.I. (Grs.)	9	do
50	Henry L. C. Bernard, 4th En. Regt.	10	do
52	R. T. P. Stapleton, 1st E. Lt. Cvy.	17	do
54	Robert Cunliffe Low, 4th E. L. C.	29	do
47	Robert Yeld Chambers, 65th N. I.	1	*Oct.*
51	K. J. W. Coghill, 2nd En. B. F.		do
50	Hy. S. Vincent Fisher, 30th N.I.	13	do
51	Wm. Pemberton Fisher, 4th En. R.	14	do
45	W. Ogilvie Rannie, 32nd N. I...	17	do
51	Welby Wroughton Boddam, 16th N. I. (Grs.) ..	22	do
51	James Cornwall Miller, 52nd N.I.	5	*Nov.*
53	John Gore Campbell, 42nd L.I.	9	do
52	Spencer Alfred T. Judge, 67th N.I.	10	do
49	Thos. H. Maddock, 3d B. En. Regt.	15	do
53	Alexander Kinkaid Johnston Canning Mackenzie, 5th E. Lt. C.	24	do
51	James W. Daniell, 1st En. B. Fus.	5	*Dec.*
48	C. L. Richardson, 58th N. I. ..	7	do
57	John Eckford, Engineers, ..	7	do
57	Ashton Milness Brandreth, Engrs.		do
57	Henry William Garnault, Engrs.,		do
57	H. Thomas Gordon, Engineers,		do
57	Ralph Graham Smyth, Engrs., ..		do
58	Parry Lambert, Engineers, ..		do
58	John Philip Steel, Engineers, ..		do
50	M. A. D. Orchard, 3rd B. En. R.	17	do
49	John L. Sawers, 37th N. I. ..	23	do
53	Richard J. Walker, 61st N. I...	29	do
51	Cornelius Richardes, 63rd N.I...	31	do

[1856.]

1849	John Paton Martin, 4th En. Regt.	4	*Jan.*
51	Charles E. Orman, 29th N. I. ..	14	do
51	Edwin A. C. Lambert, 1st E. B.F.		do
53	Robt. Geo. Armstrong, 17th N.I.	16	do

[1856.]—*Continued.*

1853	Donald Macdonald, 25th N.I.	18	*Jan.*
50	Thomas P. Harrison, 69th N.I...	28	do
52	Montagu Hall, 1st En. B.F. ..	1	*Feb.*
49	John P. Turton, 26th L.I. ..	10	do
50	Quintin Dick Parsons, 6th En. R.	20	do
50	Arthur U. F. Ruxton, 66th N.I.	23	do
52	Chas. K. M Walter, 73rd N. I.	26	do
50	Thomas Gally Ross, 21st N.I ..	27	do
51	L. H. P. DeH. Larpent, 21st N.I.	28	do
53	Gerard Noel Money, 1st En. B. F.	5	*Mar.*
53	Wm. Macdonald, 25th N. I. ..		do
52	Edmd. Yeamans Walcott, 57th N.I.	16	do
54	John Peter Harris, 21st N. I., ..	28	do
54	Henry Doyle Metcalfe, 25th N. I.	31	do
50	William Playfair, 4th N. I. ..	1	*April*
48	Robert S. Moseley, 65th N.I. ..		do
47	George Edward Hill, 32nd N.I. ..	2	do
53	Hy. Lumsden Hawkins, 30th N.I.	8	do
51	Thomas W. Rutherfurd, 33rd N.I.	10	do
55	Charles Wm. Grey, 3rd E. L. C.,	14	do
50	Henry Inglis, 41st N.I ..	15	do
50	James John Russell, 46th N.I. ..	17	do
53	E. B. Wake, 3rd E.L. Cavy., ..	26	do
54	Jas. A. M. Patton, 1st E.L. Cavy	3	*May*
54	Brydges R. Branfill, 5th E. L. C.	5	do
51	~~Wm. C. D. Campbell, 6th En. Regt.~~	6	do
47	Edward Holmes Scott, 55th N.I.	10	do
52	Mark Kerr St. John, 49th N.I...	18	do
50	Fredk. A. Buckley, 37th N.I. ..	22	do
50	Wm. E. R. Roberts, 54th N. I...	1	*June*
54	W. Henry Buttanshaw, 5th En. R.	11	do
58	John Magee McNeill, Engrs., ..	13	do
~~58~~	~~William Henzey Oliver, Engrs.,~~		do
58	C. C. Scott Moncrieff, Engrs.,..		do
58	William Burvill Holmes, Engrs.,.		do
58	Henry Francis Blair, Engineers,		do
58	John Magee Heywood, Engrs.,..		do
54	Philip Ward, 25th N.I. ..	16	do
54	A. R. D. Mackenzie, 1st E. L. Cvy.	22	do
52	George Archd. Bishop, 2nd E.B.F.	2	*July*
48	Willliam W. Clark, 36th N.I. ..	3	do
53	Robert Clifford, 74th N.I. ..	12	do
53	A. W. J. Montgomerie, 2nd E. L. Cavy. ..		do
52	E. R. C. Wilcox, 4th En. Regt. ..	18	do
~~54~~	~~Wm. Herbert Selly, 2nd E. L. C.~~	22	do
54	Edmund Ward, 22nd N. I. ..	10	*Aug.*
~~50~~	~~James Vallings, 19th N.I.~~ ..	14	do
50	Edward T. Sadler, 19th N.I. ..	26	do
52	Alexr. Brodie Melville, 67th N. I.	31	do
50	James V. Hunt, 45th N.I. ..	6	*Sep.*
54	Jas. N. Brutton Hewett, 17th N. I	9	do
55	Chas. M.S. Fair brother, 5th E.L.C.	12	do
53	J Skynner Walters, 28th N. I...	14	do
55	Francis H. Conolly, 49th N.I. ..	20	do
55	Anthony Stewart, 16th N.I. (Grs.)	1	*Oct.*
55	Harry Style Ruxton, 56th N.I. ..	8	do
55	Henry M. Caulfeild, 4th E. L. C.	9	do
55	Robert Dougal, 53rd N. I. ..	10	do
47	Frederick W. Graham, 11th N.I.	12	do
55	John Liston 10th N. I. ..	17	do
53	G. Nicholson Saunders, 24th N. I.	19	do

[1856.]—*Continued.*

1854 R. Wilkinson Dent, 1st E. L. C. 25 *Oct.*
50 Henry R. Buttanshaw, 47th N.I. 27 do
50 Frederick A. Lawford, 50th N. I. 28 do
48 Geo. Henry Basevi, 27th N.I. .. 11 *Nov.*
55 Geo. Farquhar Smith, 3rd E. L.C. 20 do
51 Henry Moubray Cadell, Arty., .. do
48 William Henry Wise, 64th N.I. 23 do
49 Edwd. O'B. Horsford, 46th N. I. do
49 David S. Buist, 27th N.I. .. do
49 Hanry Coape Smith, 9th N.I. .. do
49 James Graham, 14th N.I. .. do
49 James Thompson, 58th N.I. .. do
49 Henry Edward Whish, 26th L.I. do
49 Thomas Norris Baker, 31st N. I. do
50 John Hobart Tyler, 20th N.I... do
50 Augustus Wm. Cripps, 26th N. I. do
50 Ralph A. Nowell, 32nd N.I. .. do
50 Charles W. R. Chester, 19th N.I. do
50 Donald Macintyre, 66th N.I. .. do
50 Henry Roche Osborn, 74th N.I. do
50 Edward H. C. Simpson, 39th N.I. do
50 Charles F. Sharpe, 72nd N. I. .. do
50 Philip H. F. Harris, 70th N.I... do
51 Halford Fellowes, 31st N.I. .. do
51 Thomas Martin Shelley, 11th N.I. do
51 Fredk. M. Armstrong, 4th En. R. do
51 Alex. Howe Bramley, 44th N.I. do
51 Thomas James Watson, 46th N.I. do
51 James Thos. Liscombe, 34th N.I. do
51 Edward Stevenson, 3rd E. R. .. do
51 Ed. Samuel Jackson, 12th N. I. do
51 Henry Chad Cattley, 62nd N.I. do
51 W. C. S. Clarke, 37th N. I... do
51 Wm. Minto Gibbon, 44th N.I... do
51 Willoughby H. Garton, 50th N.I. do
51 T. Dennehy, 2nd N. I. (Grs.) .. do
51 John Paton Davidson, 4th N.I. do
51 William Fredk. Shaw, 43rd L. I. do
51 James Thomson, 34th N.I. do
51 Fredk. Jervis Ripley, 70th N.I... do
51 Fras. Ingram Conway Gordon, 5th En. Regiment. do
51 Richd. Manuel Sewell, 71st N.I.. do
52 Fredk. T. Bainbridge, 64th, N.I. do
52 E. Pulteney Gurdon, 33rd N. I. do
R ~~52 James Thos. Stanton, 60th N.I.~~ do
52 *Hon.* James Hay Fraser, 4th En. R. do
52 F. Hallowell Inglefield, 38th N.I. do
52 Douglas G. Manning, 52nd N. I. do
52 H. Albert Browne, 10th N. I. .. do
52 H. R. B. Worsley, 47th N.I. .. do
52 George Sale Dysart, 23rd N.I. .. do
52 John R. McPherson, 3rd En. R., do
52 John James Boswell, 69th N.I... do
52 J. Wemyss Campbell, 51st N. I. do
52 Alfred Whiting, 59th N.I. .. do
52 Rowland Smith, 59th N.I. .. do
52 M. Mitchell Procter, 38th N. I. do
52 William Wroughton, 54th N.I... do
52 John Roberts, 40th N.I., .. do
52 Wm. Ganor Waterfield, 23rd N.I. do
52 Alexander Bruce, 28th N.I. .. do
52 Wm. Fredk. Edwards, 45th N.I. do

[1856.]—*Continued.*

52 James C. P. Baillie, 35th L. I. .. 23 *Nov.*
52 J. Wm. H. Johnstone, 18th N. I. do
52 Hardress E. Waller, 40th N.I... do
53 Lancaster B. J. Davies, 5th En. R. do
53 Archibald G. Remington, 12th N.I. do
53 Charles Ward Hawes, 43rd L. I. do
53 Wm. George Keppel, 6th En. Regt. do
53 John Power Burton, 62nd N.I.... do
53 Philip Crampton Rynd, 73rd N.I. do
53 H. Mountford Bromley, 52nd N.I. do
53 Eric Stanhope Fox, 72nd N.I. .. do
53 S. G. Warde, 11th N.I. .. do
53 James Stevenson, 33rd N.I. .. do
53 William George Cubitt, 13th N.I. do
53 Richard Barton Hill, 60th N.I... do
53 Henry McDonnell De Wendt Douglas, 67th N.I. .. do
53 C. Adolphus de Kantzow, 48th N.I. do
53 Charles Kinloch Mylne, 35th L.I. do
53 F. Frederick Rowcroft, 2nd N. I. (Grenadiers,) .. do
53 Harry De Brett, 57th N.I. .. do
53 William Owen, 61st N. I. .. do
53 Chas. Smith Maclean, 10th N.I. do
53 H. L. Alex. Tottenham, 67th N.I. do
53 H. Chippindale P. Rice, 73d N.I. do
53 T. Boldero Boileau, 4th En. R., do
54 M. Mark Prendergast, 4th E. L.C. do
54 Alexander Copland, 4th N. I. .. do
54 Henry Benson Stuart, 18th N. I. do
54 R. Stanwix Robertson, 6th En. R., do
54 H. D. E. W. Chester, 36th N. I. do
54 Alexander Shand Thain, 13th N.I. do
54 Alex. Haldane Eckford, 69th N.I. do
54 T. Nicholls Walker, 2nd En. B. F. do
54 G. Ward C. Plowden, 3rd E.L.C., do
54 Wynyard Battye, 65th N.I. .. do
54 Thomas Cadell, 2nd E. B. F. .. do
54 Henry Wilson Gordon, 63rd N.I. do
54 *Sir* Atwell K. Lake, *Bt.*, 2nd E.B.F. do
54 Brudenell Rogers, 68th N.I. .. do
54 William Lumley Louis, 42d L. I. do
54 Geo. Ed. J. Maidman, 24th N.I. do
54 Thos. Adair Butler, 1st En. B. F. do
54 Fredk. A. C. Knyvett, 24th N.I. do
54 Robert Alexr. Dobbin, 6th En. R., do
54 Geo. F. Marrie Phillips, 30th N.I. do
54 Ed. Francis Browne, 15th N I. .. do
54 T. Chadwick Graham, 4th E.L.C., do
54 Henry Geo. Delafosse, 53rd N. I., do
54 Newton H. Wallace, 1st E. B. F., do
54 Stanhope Cary, 37th N. I., .. do
54 Fredk. D. Harington, 12th N. I... do
54 Mark Henry Heathcote, 19th N. I. do
55 Richard F. Angelo, 41st N.I. .. do
55 Percy Wm. Powlett, 58th N.I. .. do
55 Henry St. Geo. Tucker, 29th N.I. do
55 George Lewellin Smith, 29th N.I. do
55 Chas. Augustus Munro, 25th N.I. do
55 Henry C. Evelyn Ward, 5th En. R. do
55 Archibald L. Douglas, 2nd E.B.F. do
55 Charles Grant, 45th N.I. .. do
55 Andrew Wm. Hearsey, 57th N. I. do

[1856.]—*Continued.*

Year	Name	Day	Month
1855	H. M. Barton Burlton, 5th En. R.,	23	*Nov.*
55	Lionel Francis Wells, 2nd E.L.C.		do
55	Charles Hay Fairlie, 1st E. L. C.		do
55	Alfred Fitz Hugh, 21st N.I. ..		do
~~55~~	~~W. W. Frewen Hay~~, 17th N. I.		do
55	Alexr. Graham Owen, 1st E. B. F.		do
56	C. L. Brown Constable, 17th N. I.		do
56	Thomas Reid Davidson, 49th N. I.		do
56	Hamilton Chapman, 49th N.I...		do
55	Fras. W. Boileau, 16th N.I.(Grs.)		do
55	A. F. P. Harcourt, 30th N. I.		do
55	Swinton John Browne, 55th N. I.		do
56	Geo. G. Young, 16th N. I. (Grs.)		do
56	Charles Ellison Bates, 36th N. I.		do
56	H. P. P. Nash, 25th N. I., ..		do
54	Ed. D. Hamilton Vibart, 54th N.I.	26	do
51	Fras. Henry M. Sitwell, 31st I. N.	28	do
55	Edmund F. Litchfield, 42nd N. I.	8	*Dec.*
59	John Herschel, Engineers,	12	do
59	Robert Claude Danbuz, Engineers,		do
59	Hastings Macsween, Engineers, ..		do
59	Isaac Pratt Westmorland, Engrs...		do
59	Arthur Charles Padday, Engrs...		do
59	O. B. C. St. John, Engineers. ..		do
59	A. H. Bagge, Engineers. ..		do
56	Edward Temple, 25th N. I., ..	17	do
56	Ayrton Pullan, 36th N.I. ..	26	do
55	William Wells Lee, 3rd En. Regt.	31	do

[1857]

Year	Name	Day	Month
1854	Alex. H. Thomson, 3rd En. Regt.	1	*Jan*
56	Elliot H. Macnaghten, 2nd E.L.C.	9	do
56	Hy. Phipson Peacock, 3rd E.L.C.		do
56	Fras. Hill Macnaghten, 5th E.L.C.		do
56	Abel Henry Chapman, 1st E.L.C.		do
56	Alexander Shepherd, 5th E L. C.		do
56	C. Whiteman Thomas, 3rd E.L.C.		do
55	Frederic John Mackeson, 74th N.I	15	do
53	Walter Forbes Belli, 40th N.I.	20	do
55	Hy. Geo. Saunders, 3rd En. Regt.	21	do
56	A. H. and Prinsep, 4th E.L. Cvy.	23	do
56	J. H. T. Farquhar, 2nd E.L. Cavy.		do
56	C. Elliot Farquharson, 3rd E.L.C.		do
56	Cecil Clarke Jervoise, 1st E.L.C.		do
56	Samuel Boulderson, 5th E. L. C.		do
56	Richard Graham Birch, 1st E.L.C.		do
54	Geo. A. Aufrere Baker, 60th N.I.	24	do
54	Wm. Gordon Chalmers, 51st N.I.	27	do
54	Aylmer Vivian, 20th N.I., ..	31	do
54	Wm. Wheler Hume, 11th N.I...	1	*Feb.*
51	C. Vaughan Arbuckle, Arty., ..		do
55	Robert O. Wauchope, 57th N. I.	17	do
54	Bernard Cracroft, 50th N. I. ..	21	do
56	Arthur Geo. Webster, 1st E.L.C.	10	*Mar.*
52	Alex. McLeod Stewart, 64th N.I.	18	do
55	Alfred B. E. Thomas, 4th En. R.,	20	do
50	F. E. A. Chamier, 34th N. I...	8	*April*
57	Jardine Scott Robinson, 1st E.L.C.	27	do
55	Wm. George Murray, 68th N.I...	1	*May*
53	W. L. P. Drummond, 38th N.I.	9	do
53	Arthur Tulloch, 20th N.I. ..	10	do
53	Alexander Cockburn, 52nd N. I...		do
~~53~~	~~Tho. George Blackburne, 20th N.I.~~		do
55	Hugh Arthur Lewes, 20th N. I.		do
53	Arthur Parker Mew, 74th N.I...	11	do
54	Herbert Sconce, 74th N.I.		do
54	Henry Wm. Studdy, 32nd N.I.,		do

[1857.]—*Continued.*

Year	Name	Day	Month
1855	Jonathan Cape, 30th N.I. ..	11	*May*
56	Henry Algernon Shaw, 3rd E. R.		do
55	Robarts William Elton 74th N. I.		do
54	Benjamin Williams, 51st N.I. ..	19	do
50	Edward Chapman, 14th N.I. ..	21	do
53	Horatio Nelson Noble, 44th N. I.	29	do
55	Andrew R. Loughnan, 13th N. I.		do
54	Herbert Mills Repton, 67th N. I.	30	do
51	David James Welsh, Artv., ..		do
54	Frdk. Macdonald Birch, 71st N. I.	31	do
55	Marmaduke Ramsay, 36th N.I...		do
54	Jas. Henry Worsley, 71st N. I...		do
53	John Bartleman, 23rd N.I. ..		do
51	Fredk. Sleigh Roberts, Arty., ..		do
54	Patrick Robert Crolly, 62nd N. I.	1	*June*
55	Geo. Lawrence Keir, 41st N. I...		do
55	R. Horace Hudleston, 69th N. I.		do
56	W. E. M. Bruce Ramsay, 17th N. I.	3	do
54	Frederick John Keen, 35th L. C.	4	do
54	John Withers McQueen, 27th N.I.		do
55	W. V. Fitz. Jacob, 6th E. R.		do
51	A. Eds. Campbell, 31st N. I. ..	6	do
53	Hy. Octavius Currie, 5th En. Regt.		do
~~54~~	~~Alfred Bird Allen, 2nd N.I.~~ (Grs.)		do
56	Robert Cecil Clifford. 58th N. I.		do
55	Philip Sydney Yorke, 12th N. I.		do
55	Patrick Wheeler, 15th N.I. ..		do
55	Wm. Blunt Barwell, 18th N.I...		do
54	F. Dempster Hawkins, 32nd N. I.		do
55	F. D. Millet Brown, 1st En. B. F.	7	do
56	John B. Chatterton, 41st N.I. ..		do
54	Newton Robt. Burlton, 40th N.I.	8	do
56	H. Bristow Sanderson, 22nd N.I.		do
53	W. R. M. Holroyd, 23rd N.I...		do
51	Horatio Otto Hitchins, Arty., ..		do
51	John Stewart, Arty., ..		do
54	John Matthew Glubb, 38th N. I.,	10	do
56	Edward Knatchbull, 18th N. I.	12	do
56	J. C. Partridge, 1st E. B. F. ..		do
56	E. Burroughes Ward, 48th N. I.		do
36	Lionel Smith, 36th N. I. ..		do
59	H. R. Thuillier, Engineers, ..		do
59	A. J. W. Cumming, Engrs, ..		do
59	T. C. Manderson, Engineers, ..		do
55	Robt. Francis Firth, 65th N.I. ..	14	do
54	Frederick Wheeler, 39th N.I. ..	15	do
55	Russell Morland Skinner, 56th N.I.		do
51	George Cracklow, Arty., ..		do
55	William Astell Franks, 12th N. I.	19	do
54	Owen Ivon Chalmers, 4th En. R.,		do
54	Francis K. Hawkins, 44th N. I.,	21	do
51	Edward Lindsay Hawkins, Arty.,	25	do
~~56~~	William Robert Boyd, 2nd En. B. F.	27	do
55	Fras. Jas. N. Mackenzie, 52nd N.I.		do
56	Charles Case, 67th N. I. ..		do
55	Malcolm George Clerk, 4th En. R.,		do
54	Oswald Menzies, 35th N. I. ..		do
55	Henry Collett, 53rd N. I. ..		do
56	Arthur Donald Butter, 13th N.I.		do
56	George Charles Unny, 5th En. R.,		do
52	Hastings E. Harington, Arty., ..		do
52	John Richard Pearson, Arty., ..		do
56	Connel O'Donel, 48th N. I. ..	29	do
54	C. W. Campbell, 10th N. I., ..	30	do
52	Geo. Vincent Fosbery, 4th En. R.,	1	*July*
55	Fred. Richard Turner, 33rd N.I...		do

[1857.]—*Continued.*

~~1855~~	~~William Brodnax Knight~~, 72nd N.I.	1	*July*
57	Robt. Wm. Henderson, 72nd N.I.	4	do
52	Wm. Bentick Cumberland, Arty.,		do
52	Charles Hunter, Arty , ..	6	do
54	John Upperton, 46th N. I., ..	9	do
56	R. Boyd Mackenzie, 12th N. I.	10	do
54	Chs. David Peter Nott, 4th En. R.,		do
52	Hungerford Deedes Jackson, Arty		do
56	Henry Sullivan Jarrett, 3rd E. R.	11	do
55	Alfred Abercby. Dick, 52nd N. I.	13	do
54	R. Elphinistone Boyle, 46th N.I.	14	do
~~55~~	~~Joseph Park, 65th N. I.~~ ..	15	do
~~56~~	~~Robert Allen Stevens 56th N.I.~~,..		do
55	Robert Blair, 32nd N. I., ..	16	do
52	J. C. Campbell Daunt, 70th N.I.	20	do
55	OliverRichd. Newmarch, 44th N.I.	21	do
55	Charles Forbes Battye, 33rd N.I.		do
55	Geo, C. H. Armstrong, 59th N.I.	23	do
52	Ferdinand FitzRoy, Arty., ..	26	do
52	George Balfour Traill, Arty., ..	27	do
53	R. Durie Osborn, 26th L. I., ..	30	do
55	Otway Mayne Graham, 6th En.R.,		do
56	George Battye Fisher, 32nd N. I.	2	*Aug.*
55	E. Balfour Wimberley, 3rd En. R.	4	do
56	R. Groves Sandeman, 14th N. I.	6	do
56	Fredk. Hammond, 62nd N. I., ..	8	do
54	G. W. Henry Hogan, 4th N.I. ..	11	do
57	T. Alex. Hunter, 2nd En. B. F.,..	14	do
54	James Wm. O'Dowda, 50th N. I.	21	do
55	E. Lacon Ommanney, 59th N. I.		do
52	Christopher H. Barnes Arty., ..	24	do
56	Llewellyn Wavell, 45th N. I., ..	25	do
54	Hanson C. T. Jarrett, 26th L. I.	27	do
56	George Stewart, 17th N. I. ..	1	*Sep.*
52	John Bonham, Arty., ..		do
55	R. Byng P. P. Campbell, 54th N.I.	2	do
54	W. D. Shaw, 2nd N. I. (Grs.,)..	3	do
55	Montague P. Ricketts, 4th E. R.,	4	do
56	H. Christopher Fagan, 36th N. I.	5	do
52	James Alexander. Arty., ..	7	do
53	James Hills, Arty., ..	8	do
53	Minto Elliot, Arty., ..		do
53	David MacFarlan, Arty,, ..	12	do
56	Nelson Ellis, 1st En. B. F. ..	14	do
56	S. S. Sutherland, 42nd L. I., ..		do
56	Frederick Lance, 55th N. I. ..		do
53	James C. G. Price, Arty., ..		do
56	L. J. H. Grey, 16th N. I. (Grs.,)	15	do
57	*The Hon'ble* H.H. Hare, 17th N.I	16	do
56	Charles Richard Cock, 20th N. I.	18	do
56	Wm. D. Palmer, 74th N. I. ..		do
55	James Miller, 27th N.I. ..	23	do
53	James Sconce, Arty., ..		do
56	A. R. Chapman, 1st En. B. F...	24	do
~~54~~	~~Charles J. Anderson~~, 6thEn. Regt.	25	do
53	Henry Archibald Mallock, Arty.,		do
53	Edward C. W. Raynsford, Arty.,		do
54	John Watson, 35th N. I., ..	26	do
56	G. F. Irving Graham 4th En. R.,	27	do
56	E. C. Codrington, 57th N. I., ..	28	do
53	Robert Roche Franks, Arty., ..		do
54	Rawson Aislabie, Arty., ..		do
56	F. Van Hagen Sperling 5thEn.R.,	5	*Oct.*

[1857.]—*Continued.*

1854	Charles Gilbert Robinson, Arty.,	5	*Oct.*
57	Edwin Venour, 40th N. I. ..	9	do
56	Patk. Carfrae Dalmahoy, 60th N.I.		do
56	W. E. D. Broughton, 6th En. R.,	10	do
49	J. Donovan, (Unattached Lieut.)	17	do
54	Chas. Somner S. Taylor, Arty. ..	29	do
56	Archibald Lewis Playfair, 6th En.R.	7	*Nov.*
56	Edmund Swetenham, 45th N. I.,.		do
54	George Grant Gordon, Arty , ..	14	do
56	C. Metcalfe MacGregor, 68th N.I.	17	do
56	Francis Gellie, 9th N. I., ..		do
56	W. C. Anderson, 22nd N. I., ...		do
55	Fredk. Henry Hood, 30th N. I.		do
54	Penton Thompson, Arty., ..		do
56	Henry Hamer Stansfeld, 6th En.R.	19	do
54	G. Robertson Hennessy, 34th N.I.	11	*Dec.*
58	Edward Draper Elliott, Arty., ..	11	do
58	Charles Edward Delafosse, Arty.,		do
58	Francis William Ward, Arty., ..		do
58	G. F. Blackwood, Artillery, ..		do
58	William Clephane Brown, Arty.,		do
58	C. A. M. Warde, Artillery, ..		do
58	George Algernon Russell, Arty.,		do
58	George F. Hamilton, Arty., ..		do
58	Montague W. Ommanney, Arty.,		
58	John Arthur Tillard, Arty., ..	12	do
58	John Alves Low, Artillery, ..		do
58	Christison Syme Jackson, Arty.,		do
58	W. A. Beaver Gillies, Artillery,		do
58	Henry Stephenson Clarke, Arty.,		do
58	Robert James Abbott, Arty., ..		do
58	Alexander Samuel Heyland, Arty.,		do
58	Newson Dunnell Garrett, Arty.,		do
58	William Henry Wilkins, Arty., ..		do
58	Hugh Hildyard Murray, Arty.,..		do
58	T. J. C. A. Studdy, Arty., ..		do
58	Wilby Albony Liot, Arty.,.. ..		do
58	G. H. W. Ewbank, Artillery, ..		do
58	Alfred Richard T. Chilton, Arty.,		do
58	Hugh I. E. Ford, Arty., ...		do
58	Montague George Browne, Arty.,		do
58	Robert Henry Palmer, Arty., ..		do
58	John Harvey Annand, Arty., ..		do
58	William Bedford Troup, Arty.,..		do
58	George Gott Nelson, Arty., ..		do
58	James Vere Wylie, Arty., ..		do
58	Thomas Arnoll Davis, Arty., ..		do
58	Anthony Hepburn Murray, Arty.,		do

[1858.]

1854	Howell Locke Jones. Arty., ..	1	*Jan.*
57	Walter Albert Stirling, 4thE.L.C.	2	do
54	Edward Christian Griffin, Arty.,	8	do
57	Arthur Battye, 19th N. I. ..	22	do
56	Geo. Mitchell, 2nd En. B. F. ..	28	do
54	Alfred James Wake Arty. ..	10	*Feb.*
55	Robert C. Money, 32nd N. I., ...	12	do
55	Ed. Trower Fitzgerald, 66th N.I.		do
55	Fredk. Vincent Eyre, Arty., ..	14	do
57	Alfred Ollivant, 9th N. I., ..	1	*Mar.*
56	W. H. Warner, 1st En. B. F. ..	12	do
55	George Augustus Way, 58th N.I.	14	do

[1858.]—*Continued.*

Year	Name	Day	Month
1856	John George Campbell, 15th N.I.	22	*Mar.*
56	Robert Gunning, 14th N.I. ..	23	do
55	Alexander Henry Davidson, Arty.	27	do
56	John Boulton Brander, 37th N.I.,	1	*Apl.*
56	Rowley Sale Hill, 66th N.I. ..	12	do
55	Edward Fraser, Arty., ..	14	do
56	Richard Beadon, 4th E L. C. ..	16	do
55	John Chalmers, 39th N. I. ..	21	do
55	Fredk. Eustace Lewes, Arty., ..		do
56	Edward J. McNair, 2nd E. B. F.,	22	do
56	Benjamin J. Parsons, 23rd N. I.,	26	do
55	Hamilton Smithett, Arty., ..	27	do
55	Andrew Douie, Arty. ..		do
55	Richard Thomas Hare, Arty., ..		do
55	Chas. Edward Nairne, Arty., ..		do
55	Hector Munro, Arty., ..		do
55	William Gully, Arty.. ..		do
56	*Sir* R. de L. St. George, *Bart* Arty.		do
56	H. Chichester, Arty., ..		do
56	Duncan Scott Pemberton, Arty..		do
56	William Robert Craster, Arty., ..		do
56	Edward Trevor Hume, Arty., ..		do
56	Thaddeus Ryan, Arty., ..		do
56	Wm. O'Brien, Arty., ..		do
56	Alexander Walker, Arty., ..		do
56	Henry Girardot Arty , ..		do
57	William Jackson Stewart, Arty.,		do
57	Alfred Dixon, Arty.. ..		do
57	Fitzherbert Coddington, Arty.,		do
57	Edward Hart Dyke, Arty., ..		do
57	James Ronald Macleay Arty., ...		do
57	Richard Swanne Robinson, Arty.,		do
57	Anson Swinton, Arty., ...		do
57	Henry DeGrey Warter, Arty., ...		do
57	Edward Henry Ryan, Arty., ..		do
54	Chas. Metcalfe Bushby, 70th N.I.	30	do
55	Chs. Richard Matthews, 56th N.I.		do
55	Fredk. P. W. Freeman, 53rd N.I.		do
55	Robert Wheeler, 61st N. I.		do
55	Henry Morton, 5th En. Regt. ..		do
55	Thomas Myles Sandys, 73rd N. I.		do
55	R. C. Wm. Mitford, 3rd En. Regt.		do
56	R. Newcomen Evans, 53rd N. I.,		do
56	William Snow, 63rd N. I. ..		do
56	Trewren Hutton Scott, 26th N.I.		do
56	C. James Griffiths, 72nd N. I. ..		do
56	E. Charles Garstin, 29th N. I.		do
56	R. Blackall Graham, 13th N. I.		do
56	Joseph Barnard Smith, 5th E. R.		do
56	George Soden Goad, 49th N. I.		do
56	H. L. Ramsbotham, 47th N. I...		do
56	H. Howard Chapman, 6th E. R.,		do
56	Geo. Dukinfield Astley Younghusband, 66th N.I. ..		do
~~56~~	~~Alexander Shaw, 24th N. I.~~ ..		do
56	Henry Marsh Pratt, 51st N.I. ..		do
56	G. W. Holdsworth, 3rd En. Regt.		do
56	D. de-la-Garde Birkett, 3rd En. R.		do
56	James Jenkins Blair, 31st N.I. ..		do
56	William James Forlong, 55th N.I.		do
56	Leopold Exxel Evans, 15th N. I.		do
56	Henry Goschen, 3rd En. Regt., ..		do
56	John Williams Grant, 42nd L. I.,		do

[1858.]—*Continued.*

Year	Name	Day	Month
1856	Charles James Garstin, 29th N.I.	30	*Apl.*
56	James Frederic Elton, 37th N. I.		do
56	Alan Murray, 60th N. I. ..		do
56	George Atkins, 21st N. I. ..		do
56	Alfred Goldney, 50th N. I., ..		do
57	Charles Henry Ewart, 25th N. I.		do
57	Henry Russell Wintle, 28th N I.,		do
57	John Richdn. Pearson, 27th N. I.		do
57	R. H. de Montmorency, 65th N.I.		do
57	James Stuart Oliphant 5th E. R.,		do
57	Thomas Dayrell, 58th N. I. ..		do
57	John Lowis Loch, 2nd E.L. C. ..		do
57	Fredk. Trench, 2nd E.L. C. ..		do
57	William Tweedie, 4th En. Regt.,		do
57	F. Chassereau Bewsher, 47th N.I.		do
57	Geo. Constable Gregory, 58th N.I.		do
~~57~~	~~Francis Wetherell, 39th N. I.~~ ..		do
57	Frs. Fraser John Toke, 63rd N. I.		do
57	W. Swynfen Jervis, 1st En. B. F.		do
57	James Forsyth, 49th N. I. ..		do
57	W. Ewbank Chambers, 19th N. I.		do
57	Francis Hy. Woodgate, 11th N. I.		do
57	Arthur Power Palmer, 5th En. R.		do
57	Wellesley Campbell, 71st N. I.		do
57	Arthur Ed. Downing, 51st N. I.		do
57	F. Sale Sowley Brind, 44th N. I ,		do
57	Wm. Fairlie Fergusson, 5th E.L.C.		do
57	G. L. K. Hewitt, 41st N. I. ..		do
56	Chas. Henry Cantor, 2nd E. B. F.	1	*May*
54	Montague C. Perreau, 47th N. I.,		do
56	C. Patton Chambers, 48th N. I.,	15	do
57	T. F. Cosby Rochford, 4th E.L. C.	18	do
57	Fredk. Bruce Prinsep, 3rd E.L. C.		do
57	Harold Cooper Sitwell, 5th E.L.C.,		do
~~57~~	~~William Goodie, 4th E. L. C.~~, ..		do
57	Henry Charles Kemble, 3d E.L.C.		do
~~57~~	~~W. H. John Jennings, 2nd E.L.C.~~		do
57	A. Westby Brodhurst, 2nd E.L. C.		do
57	Robert Morris, 1st E. L. C.,		do
57	Langford C. Alexander, 5th E.L.C.,		do
57	Alfred Waterfield, 4th E. L. C.,..		do
57	George Clayton Swiney, 5th E.L.C.,		do
57	Fletcher Hayes Grant, 3rd E. L. C.,		do
57	Hamilton B. Webster, 4th E.L.C.,		do
57	Theodore W. Hogg, 2nd E. L. C.,		do
57	J. Shakespear, Irvine, 2d E. L. C.,		do
57	Anthony W. Twyford, 3rd E.L.C.,		do
57	Edward S. R. Carnac, 1st E. L.C.,		do
57	John Biddulph, 5th E. L. C., ..		do
57	G. C. B. Taylor, 1st E. L. C., ..		do
57	H. Boileau Lockwood, 4th E. L.C.		do
57	Edwin Beddy, 53rd N. I.		do
57	L. C. de Lorentz Daniell, 14th N.I.		do
57	Henry Isham Wheler, 38th N. I.,		do
57	John Goodeve Barlow, 54th N. I.		do
57	Frederic Arthur Bertie, 74th N. I.,		do
57	W. Francis Badgley, 20th N. I.,		do
57	Frederic Henderson, 16th N.I. (Grs)		do
57	William Reid Martin, 43rd L. I.,		do
57	Alexander Lindsay, 68th N. I.,..		do
57	William Hamilton, 61st N. I.,..		do
57	Francis William Grant, 22nd N.I.		do
57	Francis N.M. Maynard, 21st N. I.,		do

[1858.]—*Continued.*

1857 Philip H. M. Wynter, 32nd N. I., 18 *May*
57 Ed. Colnett Corbyn, 46th N. I., do
57 Lorne Macdonald, 73rd N. I., .. do
57 F. A. Douglas Cox, 17th N. I.,.. do
57 Thomas Herbert Lewin, 31stN. I., do
~~57 George Molyneux Hand,~~ 9thN. I. do
57 Robert Brown, 24th N. I., .. do
57 Harry Paynter Evans, 52nd N. I., do
57 Charles Albert Copland, 30th N.I. do
57 Thomas Pearson, 66th N. I., .. do
57 Fredk. L. Stoll Dyce, 71st N. I., do
57 *Sir* G. L. M. Parker, Bart, 36th N. I., .. do
57 M. Pritchard Moriarty, 41st N.I., do
57 A. J. Macqueen, 18th N. I., .. do
57 Henry Charles Anthony Szezepanshi, 40th N. I.. .. do
57 C. Martyn Boswell, 23rd N. I.,.. do
57 Stephen Beckett, 25th N. I., .. do
57 Thomas A. Scott, 28th N. I., do
57 William Feilden Mosley, 35thL.I. do
57 T. Dodgson Madden, 64th N. I., do
57 F. S. Goad, 69th N. I., .. do
57 Richard Stainforth, 56th N. I.,.. do
57 John Henry Tulloch, 53rd N. I., do
57 John L. G. O'Brien, 44th N. I... do
57 Edward George Wace, 33rd N. I. do
57 Ernest Lightfoot, 59th N. I., .. do
57 W. L. Dickens, 26th L. I., .. do
57 Geo. GariochThain, 2ndN.I.(Grs.) do
57 Henry W. Pitcher, 13th N. I., do
57 Henry Collingwood, 48th N. I., do
57 Henry Warde Webster, 45th N.I., do
57 Henry Campbell Garden, 57th N. I., .. do
57 John Allatt Drake, 10th N. I.,.. do
57 Burnard Edward Reade, 67th N.I. do
57 Robert John Foley, 62nd N. I., do
57 Francis T Ripley, 47th N. I., .. do
57 Charles J. Durand, 14th N. I.,.. do
57 George Scott Hills, 38th N. I.,.. do
57 Hugh Arthur Pakenham, 55th N.I. do
57 D. T. Heatley Sampson, 20th N.I. do
58 Reginald W. Sartorius, 72nd N.I. do
57 Chs. Richard Pennington, 32d N.I. do
57 Montague Millett, 43rd L.I., .. do
57 H. Gordon Waterfield, 34th N. I. 19 do
57 T. B. M Glascock, 50th N. I., do
56 Clement Pigou, 4th En. Regt ... 20 do
58 Chas Allan Baylay, Arty., .. 21 do
58 N. M. T. Horsford, 27th N. I.,... 26 do
~~57 Frank Cunliffe,~~ 73rd N. I. .. 2 *June*
57 Linley Blathwayt, 54th N. I., .. 6 do
58 Robert Atkins, 48th N. I. .. 7 do
58 Ross Fendall Lowis, Artillery, .. 11 do
58 John Henry Alexander, Artillery, do
58 P. T. Henry Taylor, Artillery, .. 12 do
58 Edward R. Conolly, Artillery, .. do
58 Thomas W. Bridges, Artillery, .. do
58 D. W. G. Fairfield, Artillery, .. do
58 Spencer Cargill, Artillery, .. do

[1858.]—*Continued.*

1858 Hugh Latham, Artillery, .. 12 *June*
58 H. J. Kinsman, Artillery, .. do
58 C. P. Elderton, Artillery, .. do
58 Alfred Edward Garnault, Artillery, do
58 Henry Grant Young, Artillery,.. do
58 Henry Cotton, Artillery, .. do
58 James Charles, Artillery, .. do
58 J. A. O. Hampton, Artillery, .. do
58 Harry Maxwell Mackenzie, Arty., do
58 Harry Lancelot Nicholas, Artillery, do
58 George William Thomson, Arty., do
58 E. H. Hugh Elliot, Artillery, .. do
58 Charles Henry Reilly, Artillery, do
58 William Stuart Alexander, Arty., do
58 John Chriton Greene, Artillery, do
58 Edward Francis Chapman, Arty., do
58 Thomas Graham, Artillery, .. do
58 Crombie Cowie, Artillery, .. do
58 Clarence Macpherson, Artillery, do
58 James Loch, Artillery, ... do
58 Benjamin V. Arbuckle, Artillery, do
58 George Lamb, Artillery, ... do
58 A. E. L. Kaye, Artillery, .. do
58 J. R. J. Dewar, Artillery, ... do
58 John Mylne Young, Artillery, ... do
58 Lewis Williams Taylor, Artillery, do
58 John Frederick Free, Artillery, do
56 James FitzGerald, 10th N. I. .. 17 do
58 Charles John Prinsep, 1st E.L.C. 21 do
58 R. Collinson D'E. Spottisoode, 3rd E L. C., ... do
58 D. C. S. L. Carnegie, 4th E.L.C., do
58 J. R. Glover Sweeny, 2nd E. L.C. do
58 Percy Bury Raikes, Arty., ... 4 *July*
58 Chas. Edward Armstrong, Arty., 27 do
58 Harry Alfred Rooke, 12th N. I., 4 *Aug.*
58 Edward Kitson, 64th N. I., .. 13 do
57 J. F. FitzGerald Cologan, 22nd N. I. .. 15 do
58 K. W. S. M Cameron Arty., .. 18 do
58 Alexander Andrew 27th N. I. .. 21 do
57 W. H. Barry FitzGerald, 74th N.I. 22 do
58 Ed. Andrew Phillips, 12th N. I. 24 do
58 G. A. P. Arbuthnot, 4th E. L. C. do
58 W. Hay Macnaghten, 5th E.L. C. do
58 Harvey Young Murray, 4th E.L.C. do
58 William Howey, 42nd L. I., .. 25 do
58 Hy. Whitmore Franks, 20th N.I., 27 do
58 Clarence Henry Palmer, 55th N. I. do
57 David Pringle, 58th N. I., .. 4 *Sep.*
~~58 Fredk. Hope Carleton, 62nd N. I.~~, 19 do
57 John Everard Whittiug, 68th N.I., 5 *Oct.*
53 †J. Hopkins, .. 19 do
58 W. Leycester Samuells, 11th N.I., 22 do
58 Gerveys Richard Grylls, 18th N.I. do
58 William Henry Brind, 28th N. I., do
58 H. Cunliffe Marsh, 67th N. I.,.. do
57 Henry Rowland, 63rd N. I., .. do
58 F. R. A. B. Constable, 69th N.I., do
58 William Pickard, 4th N. I., .. do
~~58 S. Wyndham Wyndham,~~ 12th N.I. do

[1858.]—*Continued.*

1858 Montagu C Smith, 38th N. I. .. 22 *Oct.*
58 John K. McCausland, 34th N. I. do
58 George M. Richmond, 54th N. I. do
58 C. Lorrain Woodruffe, 68th N. I. do
58 Richard M. Clifford, 60th N. I. do
58 Robert Hastie Inglis, 43rd L. I., do
58 Richard Worsley, 15th N. I. .. 30 do
57 Richard Hudson Dyas, 4th E. R. 3 *Nov.*
57 John Frederic Trevanion, 21st N.I. 6 do
58 St.Geo. Meadows Bishop, 66th N.I. 8 do
58 Alexander England, 44th N. I.,.. 9 do
58 Francis Hibbert 35th N. I., .. 12 do
58 F. C. W. Drummond, 70th N. I., 20 do
58 John McNair, 57th N. I. .. 21 do
57 Richard Percival Davis, 16th N.I. (Grs.) .. 25 do
58 †Patrick Roddy. ... 3 *Dec.*
59 John William Taylor, Artillery- 10 do
59 James Andrew S. Colquhoun, Artillery, .. do
59 Walter Ernest Forbes, Arty., .. do
59 John Forbes Meiklejohn, Arty., do
59 William Barron, Arty., .. 11 do
59 William James W. Muir, Arty.. do
59 Lionel Henry Septimus James, Arty., .. do
59 Palmer Boyd, Arty., .. do
59 Albert Berwick Cunningham, Arty., .. do
59 Edward John Machell, Arty. .. do
59 Fredk. Lindsay, Arty., .. do
59 Francis Arthur Stubbs, Arty., .. do
59 Guilbert Edward W. Malet, Arty. do
59 John Phillips Cottam, Arty., .. do
59 Horace George Willis, Arty., .. do
59 Vincent Carne Fisher, Arty., .. do
59 Murray William Daniell, Arty. .. do
59 Edward Albert Anderson, Arty., do

[1858.]—*Continued.*

1858 G. Bernard Johnston, 54th N. I. 21 *Dec.*
58 J. H. W. Osborne, 44th N. I... 23 do
58 William Brereton Birch, 21st N.I., do
58 A. D. C. Inglis, 18th N. I., .. do
58 J. Richard Marett, 2nd N.I.(Grs.) 25 do
~~58 Thos. Tudor Tucker, 58th N. I.,~~ 26 do

[1859.]

1857 Ninian Lowis, 61st N. I. .. 17 *Jan.*
57 James Calder Stewart, 6th En. R. 22 do
59 Arthur William Capel, 5th E.L.C. 5 *Feb.*
59 A. L. C. Littledale, 5th E. L. C. do
59 George C. Jackson, 2nd E. L. C. do
59 Robert Gordon Loch, 2nd E. L.C. do
59 Arthur Henry Taylor, 3rd E.L. C do
58 James Johnstone, 68th N. I., .. 19 do
58 W. Lynd Noverre, 1st En. B. F. 21 do
59 Thomas Dawes 72nd N. I. .. 1 *Mar.*
59 M. W. Gataker, 2nd N. I.(Grs.) do
59 C. Simeon Noble, 72nd N. I., .. 6 do
58 Fredk. Wm. Leman, 4th En, Regt. 13 do
58 H. Moule Evans, 6th En. Regt., 15 do
58 C. Herbert Bergman, 60th N. I., 17 do
59 Albert Hearsey, 5th En. L. C.,.. 29 do
59 V. James Hodson, 4th En. L. C , do
59 H. Alex. Shakespear, 5th En.L.C., do
59 Fendall Currie, 1st En. L. C., .. do
59 G. Thomas Halliday, 4th En.L.C., do
59 Francis William Collis, 30th N. I. do
59 Cecil George Millett, 70th N. I , do
59 James Barry Slater. 22nd N. I.,.. 1 *Apl.*
59 H. Montagu Buller, 5th En. L C., 3 do
58 M. Graham Taylor, 14th N. I.,.. 13 do
59 George Quin, 43rd L. I. .. 26 do
59 Henry Vansittart Riddell, 68th N.I. 15 *May*
59 Nathaniel James Jones. 15th N.I. 28 do
57 Woodburn F. Bartleman, 39th N.I. 4 *June*
59 William Stephen A. Lockhart, 44th N. I. .. 19 do

CORNETS AND ENSIGNS.

[1854.]

1854 G. Welland Hy. Hoggan, 4th N.I. 4 *Apl.*

[1857.]

1857 Hugh Bedford Troup, N. I. .. 4 *May*
57 Albert William Money, 3rd E. R. 15 *Aug.*
57 Herbert William Irons, N. I., .. 16 *Sep.*
57 Henry Utterton Smith, 46th N.I., 4 *Oct.*
57 Charles Albert Dodd, 74th N.I... do
57 John Harvey Blunt, 49th N.I. .. do
58 W. Lee Steere Harrison, 2d E.B.F. 4 *Nov.*
58 C. St. J. B. Barnett, 19th N.I ,... do
58 Alexander George Ross, 17th N.I., do
58 Hugh Thomas Jones, 31st N. I., 20 do
58 John Sutton Bagshaw, 5th E. R. 4 *Dec.*
58 Edward Packe, 37th N. I., .. 11 do
58 Edward Bell Cox, 3rd European Regiment, .. do
58 George B. P. Alcock, 24th N. I., do

[1857.]—*Continued.*

1858 Philip Story, 66th N. I., .. 11 *Dec.*
58 Angus Pulteney Martin, 71st N.I., 12 do
58 Robert Milne, 36th N. I., .. do
58 George Peter Cumming, 4th En. R. do
58 Arthur Irwin Iles, 40th N. I., .. do
58 Chas. Edward Macaulay, 23rd N.I., do
58 John Finnis, 5th En. Regt. .. do
58 George Stanley Byng, 25th N. I., do
58 Henry A. Plowden, 51st N. I., do
58 James D. Macpherson, 65th N.I. 19 do
58 W. Heathcote Unwin, 56th N.I. 20 do
58 F. Macnaghten Leslie, 53rd N. I., do

[1858.]

1858 Alfred James Wallace, 33rd N.I., 4 *Jan.*
58 Charles Handyside, 5th En. Regt. 20 do
58 Alexander F. Gerard, 3rd En. R. do
58 John Bruce Hay, 59th N. I., .. do
58 William Robert Birney, 26th N.I., do

† Unattached Lieutenants.

Cornets and Ensigns—(*Continued.*)

[1858.]—*Continued.*

1858	J. R. McK. Homfray, N. I. ...	20	*Jan.*
58	A. H. F. Campbell, 4th En. Regt.	4	*Feb.*
58	Edward F. Fortescue, 1st En. B. F.		do
58	William J. Cochrane, 45th N. I.,	20	do
58	Bailby Porteus Hodgson, 10th N.I.		do
58	Henry Spalding, 2nd E. B. F. ..		do
58	George Prince Nash, 2nd E. B.F.		do
58	George Welby Eaton, 73rd N. I.,	25	do
58	C. J. Farquharson, 48th N. I.	4	*Mar.*
58	T. Truman Oliphant, 5th En. R.	4	*April*
58	Archibald D. Campbell, 3rd E. R.		do
58	J. W. H. Michell, 10th N. I., ..		do
58	P. Louis N. Cavagnari, 1st E.B.F.	9	do
58	George Arthur Owen, 3rd En. R.	20	do
58	Frederick Cardew, 50th N. I. ..	12	*June*
58	George Hunt Holley, 1st En.B.F.		do
58	James E. Kennedy, 74th N. I. ..		do
58	Charles Leonard Money, 4th En. Regiment, ..	20	do
58	Chas. Kenneth Mackinnon, 63rd N. I.	20	*July*
58	George Logan, 4th En. Regt. ..	4	*Aug.*
58	William Pooley Onslow, 11th N.I.		do
58	H. H. Birch, 27th N. I. ..		do
58	George Buchanan Lee, 52nd N.I.	7	do
58	George Young, 66th N. I. ..	20	do
58	Griffith T. Jones, 35th N. I. ..	26	do
58	William D. Macturk, 64th N.I...		do
58	E. W. de Lousada, 69th N. I. ..		do
59	Alexr. Dunlop Anderson, 61st N.I	4	*Sept.*
59	Archibald Buchan Hepburn, 32nd N. I.		do
59	Adolphus Vallings, 41st N. I. ..	20	do
59	Hy. Archibald McNair, 29th N.I,		do
59	Walter E. Rutherfurd, 28th N.I.	4	*Oct.*
59	Rowland Erule K. Money, 13 N.I.	9	do
59	Robert Horatio Eades, 42nd N. I.	20	do
59	John Mackie Stewart, 57th N.I.		do
59	Henry Hugh Oldham, 67th N. I.	4	*Nov.*
59	Robert Cecil Beavan, 62nd N. I.		do
59	William C. Chowne, 12th N. I.		do
59	W. J. Parker, 4th N.I. ..		do
59	Arthur Noel Phillips, 19th N.I.,	8	*Dec.*
59	Charles S. de F. Roche, 47th N.I.,	11	do
59	George Buckley Stevens, 38th N.I.		do
59	Fredk. Henry Alexander, 34th N.I		do
59	Charles Stewart Pratt, 54th N. I.		do
59	Harvey Woodhouse, 30th N.I. ..		do
59	David Ross Clarke, 55th N. I. ..		do
59	John Munro Sym, N.I. ..		do
59	Charles A. E. S. Carter, 20th N.I.,		do
59	Francis Henry Goold, 1st En. B.F.		do
59	Clayton Turner Lane, 16th N. I.,		do
59	W. Saurin Brooke, 2nd N. I. (Grs.)		do
59	Edward Newbery, 6th En. Regt.,		do
59	Charles McNeile, 60th N. I., ..		do
59	Arthur Gore Handcock, 43rd N.I.		do
59	John Henry Baldwin, 68th N. I.,	20	do
59	Wm. George Maitland, 39th N. I.,		do

[1859.]

1859	David Adamson, 61st N. I. ..	5	*Jan.*
59	Andrew W. Christian, 22nd N. I.,	6	do
59	A. Fergusson Lindsay, 63rd N.I.,		do
59	Malcolm McNeill Rind, 21st N. I.		do
59	Alex. James D. Hawes, 32nd N.I.,		do
59	R. Mosely B. Thomas, 46th N.I...		do
59	Wigram Battye, 6th En. Regt., ..		do
59	E. Pipon Ommanney, 49th N. I.,		do
59	Henry George Becher, 73rd N. I.,		do
59	Irvine Low, 3rd En. L. C. ..	20	do
59	A. Manaton, Ommanney, 1st E.B.F.		do
59	John Edward Harden, 1st En. B.F.		do
59	Donald Darroch, 27th N. I. ..		do
59	Henry Roberts Young, 31st N.I...		do
59	Charles Harley Bridges, N. I. ...	4	*Feb.*
59	Hugh Gilliat Oldham, N. I. ...		do
59	Stuart Colquhoin MacTier, N. I.,..		do
59	Ives Maclean Urquhart, N. I. ...		do
59	Arthur Wm. Roberts, 5th E. L. C.,	20	do
59	Clement Ed. Benthall, 4th E. L. C.		do
59	Adam Wilson Graham, N. I. ...		do
59	Edward M. Bethune, N. I. ...		do
59	Hugh Wilson Williams, N. I. ...		do
59	Astell Harrison, N. I. ...		do
59	J. May, N.I. (F.S.C 15th June 59)		do
59	W. H. Becket, N. I. ...		do
59	John Watson Munro, N. I. ...	26	do
59	F. Elliott Farquharson, 2d E. L. C.	4	*Mar.*
59	H. C. Creak, 2nd E. L. C. ...		do
59	Francis Monro Newberry, N. I. ..		do
59	Charles Mercer, N. I. ...		do
59	Thomas James Quin, N. I. ...		do
59	F. J. Wheeler, N. I. ..		do
59	W. H. Senior, N. I. ..		do
59	J. L. Ferris, N. I. ..		do
59	A. B. Chalmers, N. I. ...		do
59	Christopher Middlemass, N. I. ..	9	*Apl.*
59	Neville Fraser Parker, N. I. ..		do
59	Charles William Riggs, N. I. ...	20	do
59	Charles Nesbit Hodgson, N. I. ..		do
59	Thomas Fraser Bruce, N. I. ..		do
59	A. B. Douglas, N. I. ...		do
59	Walter Robert Hamilton, N. I. ...	27	do
59	Arthur Cortlandt Anderson, N. I.	4	*May*
	Alexander Robertson Hutton, N. I.		
	Vincent William Tregear, N. I...		
	J. S. Tait, N. I. ..		
	H. B. Hanna N. I. ..		
	St. George Kirke, N. I. ..		
	Henry Forester Leighton, N.I. ..		
	Pearson Boyd, N. I. ..		
	Charles Walter Babington, N. I.,		
	Robert Melvill Jennings, L. C. ..		
	M. W. Balfe, N. I. ...		
	F. G. Hearn, N. I. ...		
	E. C. O'B. Horseford, N. I. ..		
	R. N. McNair, N. I ..		
	F. H. B. Marsh, N. I. ...		
	J. H. Campbell, N. I ..		

LOCAL RANK.

Lieutenant Colonel in Persia.

Col. *Sir* Justin Sheil, K. C. B. and K. L. S., 17th N. I., ... 2 June 1837

Major in Persia.

Major John Laughton, Engrs., ... 2 June 1837

Major in the Lahore Territories.

Lieut. Col. H. B. Edwardes, C. B., 1st En. B. F., ... 12 Sep. 1848

Majors in the Punjaub.

Major Reynell G. Taylor, 2nd E. L. C., ... 7 June 1849
Major Edward J. Lake, Engrs., ... do
Major Charles Herbert, 18th N. I., ... do

UNATTACHED OFFICERS.

Rank and Names.	*Date of Rank.*	REMARKS.
☞ [1] Brevet Major, 19 January 58. Lieut. Col. 20 July 58.		
Captains.		
Hercules Skinner, ..	16 *Jan.* 1852	Comdg. the 14th Irr. Cavy.—Fur. S. C., [3rd Jan. 1857.
William Robert Forster, ..	29 *July* 1852	2nd in Command of the Shekawattee Battn.
Jeremiah Brasyer, C. B., *PH*,[1] *l. c.* ..	6 *June.* 1857	Commandant of the Regt. of Ferozepore.
Simon Budd, ..	14 *Sep.* 1857	Riding Master of the 1st Brigade Horse Arty.
H. Bingham, ..	3 *Jan.* 1859	Offg. Intr. and Qr. Master.—Sappers and Miners.
Lieutenants.		
Stephen Douglas, ..	3 *Nov.* 1851	2nd in Command, of the Allahabad Levy.
William Sheffield, P C H, ..	6 *Dec.* 1852	Adjutant Goruckpore Recruit depot.
John Donovan, ..	17 *Oct.* 1857	Offg. Barrack Master at Dugshaie, Subathoo, and Kussowlee.
John Hopkins, ..	19 *Oct.* 1858	
Patrick Roddy, V. C. ..	3 *Dec.* 1858	Divl. Adjutant Mily. Police Oude.
Ensigns.		
Henry Holford, ..	20 *Sep.* 1857	Adjutant of the Bareilly Levy.
William Cliff, ..	do	Adjutant Arty. Recruit Depôt, Meerut.
Charles Stroud, ..	do	Offg. Barrack Master, Mean-Meer.
George Bradley, ..	do	
Jeremiah O'Brien, ..	do	Riding Master, 3rd Brigade of Horse Arty.
James Baxter, ..	do	Doing duty 4th En. L. C.
William Bird, ..	24 *Feb.* 1858	Barrack Master, Fort William.
J. S. Melville,† ..	do	Doing duty at Agra.
P. Gill, ..	16 *April* 1858	Adjutant of the Moradabad Levy.
M. Rosamond, ..	do	Barrack Master, Benares, Dehree and Chunar.
John Bray, ..	11 *May* 1858	
Michael Lyne, ..	10 *June* 1858	Mynpoorie Infantry Levy.
Stephen Murray, ..	11 do	Junior Commy. Army Commt. Dept.
Peter Gibson, ..	do	Offg. Barrack Master at Agra and Muttra.
Thomas McCarthy, ..	23 *July* 1858	Offg. Barrack Master, Allahabad.
Thomas Bird, ..	16 *Aug.* 1858	
John Norris, ..	do	
Thomas Doyle, ..	28 *Sep.* 1858	Offg. Barrack Master, Lucknow.
John McNamara, ..	9 *Oct.*	Qr. Mr. Arty. Recruit Depot, Meerut.
John McNally, ..	do	
Thomas Kinahan, ..	do	
George Masters, ..	do	Offg. Barrack Master, Cawnpore.
James Milrick, ..	do	
Amos Stratton, ..	do	Offg. Barrack Master, Futtehgurh.
Thomas Hardy, ..	29 *Nov.* 1858	Doing duty Bareilly Levy.
Richard Richardson, ...	do	
Henry Murray, ..	do	
——— Thompson, ..	do	
W. Willcocks, ..	30 *Dec.* 1858	Canal Dept. N. W. P.
A. Monies, ..	do	Asst. Engineer, Attock.
T. P. Stevens, ..	8 *Jan.* 1859	Adjutant 24th Punjaub Infantry.

REGIMENTAL GRADATION LIST.

COLONELS.

Names.	*Date of Rank.*
Artillery.	
James A'hmuty, ..	29 *Aug.* 24
George Swiney, ..	1 *Dec.* 34
Sir George Pollock, G. C. B., ..	3 *Mar.* 35
Alexander Lindsay, C. B., ..	2 *July* 35
Samuel Shaw, ..	25 *Mar.* 40
Richard Powney, ..	12 *July* 44
George Edward Gowan, C. B., ..	3 *July* 45
George Brooke, C. B., ..	21 *July* 51
Edward Huthwaite, C. B., ..	23 *Jan.* 54
George Twemlow, ..	6 *Mar.* 54
Sir Archdale Wilson Bart, K. C. B.	14 *Oct.* 58
Augustus Abbott, C. B. ..	14 *Nov.* 58
Engineers.	
Sir John Cheape, K. C. B., ..	19 *Feb.* 44
Edward Garstin, ..	5 *Dec.* 48
Henry Goodwyn, ..	3 *Aug.* 55
Alex. Henry Edmonstone Boileau, ..	8 *June* 56
William Erskine Baker, ..	10 *Mar.* 57
Cavalry.	
R	
4 *Sir* Robert Houstoun, K. C. B., ..	1 *May* 24
1 Harry Thomson, ..	1 *Dec.* 29
~~5 James Kennedy, C. B.~~, ..	26 *Dec.* 32
2 Thomas Shubrick, ..	19 *Apl.* 36
3 William Pattle, C. B., ..	5 *Jan.* 44
5 Chas. Montabin Carmichael, C. B.	6 *Sep.* 51
4 Henry Lechmere Worrall, ..	21 *Oct.* 52
3 *Sir* John Bennett Hearsey, K. C. B., .	4 *Nov.* 52
1 Thomas Mathew Taylor, ..	22 *Aug.* 55
4 Robert Hawkes, ..	4 *Feb.* 59

Names.	*Date of Rank.*
Infantry.	
54 John Alex. Paul Macgregor, ..	1 *May* 24
26 *Sir* William Richards, K. C. B., ..	1 *May* 24
53 Mossom Boyd, ..	13 *May* 25
~~4 *Sir* Robert Henry Cunliffe, Bt. and C. B.~~,	~~30 *May* 28~~
74 John Truscott, ..	4 *Mar.* 30
60 Suetonius Henry Tod, ..	5 *Apl.* 34
40 Charles William Hamilton, ..	6 *Aug.* 35
68 Edmund Frederick Waters, C. B., ..	16 *Nov.* 35
69 Richard Collyer Andree, ..	20 *June* 36
~~25 William Henry Kemm,~~ ..	~~11 *Nov.* 37~~
~~6 E William Vincent,~~ ..	~~8 *Oct.* 39~~
20 Thomas Henry Paul, ..	9 *July* 40
73 Samuel Swinhoe, ..	23 *June* 42
61 John Anderson, ..	7 *July* 42
66 Frederick Young, ..	3 *Oct.* 42
9 William Robt. Clay. Costley, ..	22 *Oct.* 42
1 Alexander Dick, ..	8 *Feb.* 43
42 Thomas Fiddes, ..	9 *Aug.* 43
1 E Abraham Roberts, C. B., ..	10 *Nov.* 43
18 Charles Arth. G. Wallington, ..	20 *Dec.* 43
37 Thomas Oliver, ..	13 *Mar.* 44
30 Duncan Gordon Scott, ..	7 *May* 44
21 Henry Hall, C. B., ..	21 *Dec.* 44
29 Matthew Coombs Paul, ..	2 *Feb.* 45
38 *Sir* George Petre Wymer, K. C. B., ..	10 *June* 45
35 Thomas Monteath Douglas, C. B., ..	7 *Sep.* 45
4 E Joseph Harris, ..	30 *Sep.* 45
51 John Tulloch, C. B., ..	23 *Oct.* 45
~~34 James Stuart, C. B.,~~ ..	~~26 *Dec.* 46~~
27 William Henry Hewitt,	11 *Mar.* 47
57 John Home, ..	19 *Mar.* 47
28 George William Aylmer Lloyd, C. B., ..	27 *Aug.* 47

COLONELS—*Continued.*

Names.	Date of Rank.	Names.	Date of Rank.
Infantry.		*Infantry.*	
R		R	
2*E* Robert Blackall, ..	18 *July* 48	70 George Hicks, C. B., ..	7 *May* 54
56 James Eckford, C. B., ..	27 *Oct.* 48	64 Henry Francis Caley, ..	7 *Nov.* 54
52 Andrew Hervey, C. B., ..	8 *Mar.* 49	41 Robert Stewart, ..	16 *Dec.* 54
62 George Richard Pemberton, ..	19 *Mar.* 49	4*E* Hope Dick, ..	16 *Jan.* 55
47 Stephen Davis Riley, ..	9 *Apl.* 49	12 Edward Pettingal, ..	25 *Feb.* 55
24 Archd. Fullerton Richmond, C. B,	28 *Mar.* 50	31 Frederick George Lister, ..	13 *Apl.* 55
55 Christopher Godby, C. B. ..	6 *Apl.* 50	39 David Downing, ..	7 *May* 55
6*E* Christopher Dix. Wilkinson, C.B,	28 *Sep.* 50	36 Frederick Hervey Sandys, ..	10 *Feb.* 56
32 William Henry Marshall, ..	15 *Mar.* 51	2 Fras. S. Hawkins, C.B., ..	18 *Feb.* 56
67 John Graham, ..	17 *Mar.* 51	33 John Moule, ..	9 *Apl.* 56
43 Richard Home, ..	7 *Apl.* 51	23 Louis Saunders Bird, ..	17 *Apl.* 56
15 Alexander Carnegy, C. B., ..	15 *Sep.* 51	16 Stuart Corbett, C. B., ..	18 *May* 56
19 George Tomkyns, ..	16 *Oct.* 51	22 William Sage, ..	18 *July* 56
5*E* Charles Rd. William Lane, ..	25 *May* 52	17 *Sir* Justin Sheil, K.C.B. and K.L.S.,	28 *Nov.* 56
63 William John Gairdner, C. B., ..	10 *Sep.* 52	44 James Manson, ..	29 *May* 57
50 James Parsons, C. B., ..	31 *Mar.* 53	49 Nathaniel Jones, ..	31 *May* 57
~~10 Thomas Dickinson,~~ ..	~~10 *May* 53~~	48 James Clarke Charnock Gray, ..	27 *June* 57
58 Henry Chambers Murray Cox,	5 *June* 53	46 Joseph Nash, C. B., ..	15 *July* 57
45 John Hoggan, C. B., ..	11 *July* 53	65 Claud Douglas, ..	1 *May* 58
59 Charles Hamilton, C. B., ..	14 *July* 53	~~67 James Steel, C. B.,~~ ..	~~9 *Oct.* 58~~
3 *E* George Huyshe, C. B., ..	15 *Nov.* 53	44 Charles Haldane, ..	13 *Mar.* 59
13 George Warren, ..	5 *Dec.* 53	5 E. Frederick Brooke Corfield, ..	26 *Apl.* 59
72 Henry Lawrence, ..	15 *Apl.* 54	62 Francis Rowcroft, C. B., ..	15 *May* 59

LIEUTENANT-COLONELS.

Names.	Date of Rank.	Names.	Date of Rank.
Artillery.		*Artillery.*	
Charles Grant, C. B., (*Supy.*) ..	5 *July* 46	Frank Turner, C. B., ..	11 *Oct.* 58
Richard Horsford, ..	31 *Mar.* 47	Henry Alex. Carleton, C. B., ..	14 *Oct.* 58
James Alexander, C. B., (*Supy.*) ..	1 *July* 47	William Henry Delamain, ..	14 *Nov.* 58
John Theophilus Lane, C.B., (*Supy.*)	10 *Feb.* 49	Gravenor Kirby, ..	21 *Nov.* 58
John Fordyce, ..	2 *Feb.* 51	David Reid, ..	23 *Dec* 58
George Campbell, (*Supy.*) ..	21 *July* 51	~~T J W Hungerford, C. B.,~~ ..	2 *Jan* 59
George Henry Swinley, ..	1 *July* 53		
James Abbott, ..	6 *Mar* 54		
Francis Burton Boileau, ..	10 *Mar.* 54		
Fredk. Gaitskell, C. B., ..	17 *May* 54		
Charles Samuel Reid, ..	31 *Dec.* 54		
James Brind, C. B., ..	26 *June* 56	*Engineers.*	
Robert Raikes Kinleside, ..	25 *June* 57	*Sir* Robert Napier, K. C. B., ..	1 *Aug.* 54
Francis Claude Burnett, ..	27 *June* 57	~~John Glasfurd,~~ ..	1 do 54
Arthur Broome, ..	14 *Sep.* 57	Andrew Scott Waugh, ..	3 do 55
Alfred Huyshe, ..	25 *Sep.* 57	Edward Lacon Ommanney, ..	15 *Apl.* 56
Reginald Edward Knatchbull, ..	28 *Sep.* 57	Henry Marion Durand, C. B., ..	8 *June* 56
Sir Richmond C. Shakespear, *Kt.*, ..	14 *Jan.* 58	John Laughton, ..	10 *Mar.* 57
Edward W. S. Scott, ..	10 *Feb.* 58	Henry Rigby, ..	20 *Sep.* 57
Vincent Eyre, C. B., ..	4 *July* 58	~~Thomas Henry Sale,~~ ..	~~1 *Oct.* 57~~
William Barr, ..	18 *Aug.* 58	Alexander Cunningham, ..	13 *Aug.* 58
Charles Hogge, C. B. ..	27 *Sep.* 58	Norman Chester MacLeod, ..	1 *Jan.* 59

Lieutenant-Colonels—*Continued.*

Names.	Date of Rank.
R *Cavalry.*	
Henry F. Salter, C.B., (*Supy.*) ..	5 *Jan.* 44
Philip Francis Story, C.B., (*Supy.*)	12 *Oct.* 51
2 John Fowler Bradford, C. B., ..	20 *Oct.* 52
4 Arthur Wheatley, ..	14 *Nov.* 53
~~5 James Mackenzie,~~ ..	1 *Apl.* 54
3 Henry Clayton, ..	28 *Nov.* 54
4 William Binfield Wemyss, ..	28 *Nov.* 54
1 Francis Wheler, ..	28 *Nov.* 54
2 Robert A. Master, C. B., ..	13 *Apl.* 55
3 Archibald Lorne Campbell, ..	17 *Sep.* 55
1 George M. Carmichael Smyth, ..	3 *May* 56
5 Arthur Hall, ..	5 *May* 56
4 Ronald Macdonell, ..	23 *July* 58
R *Infantry.*	
17 Thomas Polwhele, ..	17 *Feb.* 50
71 David Birrell, ..	1 *Mar.* 50
21 James Matthie, ..	1 *Mar.* 50
46 George Farquharson, ..	21 *June* 50
6*E* Hugh Troup, ..	13 *Aug.* 50
35 William Maule Ramsay, ..	28 *Sep.* 50
42 *Sir* Archibald Bogle, *Kt.*, ..	17 *Feb.* 51
54 David Simpson, ..	15 *Mar.* 51
58 John Anderson Barstow, ..	17 *Mar.* 51
22 William Robert Corfield, ..	31 *Mar.* 51
40 Edward Altham Cumberlege, ..	7 *Apl.* 51
39 John Macdonald, ..	11 *Apl.* 51
6*E* *Sir* Patrick Grant, K.C.B. (*Supy.*)	29 *Aug.* 51
15 Thomas Henry Shuldham, ..	15 *Sep.* 51
11 John Butler, ..	3 *Oct.* 51
25 Thomas Sewell, .	13 *Oct.* 51
61 Francis Jenkins, ..	16 *Oct.* 51
65 George Burney, ..	6 *Jan.* 52
24 Edmund Wintle, ..	10 *July* 52
70 James Don Kennedy, ..	10 *Sep.* 52
33 Robert Turnbull Sandeman, ..	27 *Oct.* 52
3*E* William Swatman, ..	12 *Jan.* 53
66 John Kennedy McCausland, C B.	31 *Mar.* 53
2*E* St. George Daniel Showers, C. B.,	10 *May* 53
68 Colin Troup, ..	5 *June* 53
73 George Moyle Sherer, ..	11 *July* 53
63 William George Lennox, ..	14 *July* 53
1*E* John Welchman, C. B., ..	14 *July* 53
31 Bulstrode Bygrave, ..	15 *Nov.* 53
4*E* William Fergusson Beatson, ..	15 *Nov.* 53
16 Richmond Houghton, ..	5 *Dec.* 53
9 John Edmondstoune Landers, ..	24 *Dec.* 53
27 Edward John Dickey, ..	15 *Apl.* 54
~~6*E* Henry Templer,~~	7 *May* 54
29 Joseph Graham, ..	9 *Aug.* 54
56 William St. Leger Mitchell, ..	28 *Nov.* 54

Names.	Date of Rank.
R *Infantry.*	
64 Robert Garrett, ..	28 *Nov.* 54
20 John Craigie Halkett, C. B., ..	28 *Nov.* 54
59 Hugh Boyd, ..	28 *Nov.* 54
2*E* Richard Jas. Howell Birch, C. B., (*Supy*) ..	10 *Dec.* 54
13 Harry Meggs Graves, (*Supy*) ..	13 *Dec.* 54
18 Christopher Simson Maling, ..	16 *Dec.* 54
3*E* William Riddell, ..	25 *Feb.* 55
45 John Liptrap, ..	7 *May* 55
69 John William Hicks, ..	10 *Nov.* 55
26 John L. Taylor, ..	10 *Feb.* 56
34 John C. Hannyngton, ..	9 *April* 56
37 Arthnr Cole Spottiswoode, ..	22 *May* 56
~~60 William R. Dunmore,~~	~~28 *Nov.* 56~~
52 James W. H. Jamieson, ..	10 *May* 57
30 William C. Campbell, ..	11 *May* 57
38 William J. B. Knyvett, ..	25 *May* 57
53 Arthur Sanders, ..	29 *May* 57
49 Cuthbert Davidson, ..	31 *May* 57
23 George William Bishop, ..	31 *May* 57
36 Thomas Fergusson Flemyng, ..	31 *May* 57
43 Simon Fraser Hannay, ..	8 *June* 57
10 George Ramsay, ..	27 *June* 57
55 John Powell, ..	27 *June* 57
5*E* Edward G. J. Champneys, ..	1 *July* 57
32 Richard Y. B. Bush, ..	15 *July* 57
4*E* James G. A. Rice, ..	29 *July* 57
72 Peter Abbott, ..	28 *Aug.* 57
2 William Augustus Cooke, ..	3 *Sep.* 57
48 Henry Palmer, ..	4 *Oct.* 57
57 Edward Darvall, ..	17 *Nov.* 57
~~74 Robert Ramsay,~~	~~18 *Nov.* 57~~
12 John Studholme Hodgson, ..	25 *April* 58
4 David Wilkie, ..	26 *Apl.* 58
47 David Pott, ..	1 *May* 58
14 Peter Innes, ..	4 *May* 58
17 George William Hamilton, ..	19 *May* 58
50 Joseph H. Hampton, ..	19 *May* 58
54 Hamilton Vetch, ..	6 *June* 58
3*E* Wm. Beveridge Thomson, C. B.,	13 *July* 58
74 Herbert E. S. Abbott, ..	22 *Aug.* 58
~~55 John Butler,~~	~~27 *Aug.* 58~~
~~20 Thomas Martin,~~	~~27 *Aug.* 58~~
15 William Pitt Robbins, ..	9 *Oct.* 58
16 Edward Rowland Mainwaring, ..	25 *Nov.* 58
6*E* A P Phayre, ..	22 *Jan.* 59
4*E* H P Burn, ..	13 *Mar* 59
60 R Drought, C B, ...	17 *Mar.* 59
43 Henry Wm. Matthews, ..	26 *Apl.* 59
68 Brooke Boyd, ..	15 *May* 59
39 Francis Elliot Voyle, ..	4 *June* 59

MAJORS.

Names.	Date of Rank.
Cavalry.	
5 Thomas Moore, ..	1 *Apl.* 54
3 Wm. Wynne Apperley, ..	28 *Nov.* 54
4 Auchmuty Tucker, C. B., ..	28 *Nov.* 54
2 George C. Ponsonby, ..	28 *Nov.* 54
2 Robert John Hawthorne, ..	13 *Apl.* 55

Names.	Date of Rank.
Cavalry.	
3 Nathaniel Dunbar Barton, ..	24 *Dec.* 55
1 Henry Drummond, ..	3 *May* 56
5 Thomas Lowth Harington, ..	5 *May* 65
1 Charles V. Jenkins, ..	1 *July* 57
4 T. F. B. Beatson, ..	23 *July* 58

Majors—*Continued.*

Names.	*Date of Rank.*	*Names.*	*Date of Rank.*
Infantry.		*Infantry.*	
R		R	
61 James Charles Innes, ..	3 *July* 55	33 Anthony Martin, ..	21 *July* 57
22 James Duncan McPherson, C.B.,	1 *Dec.* 55	3*E* A. H. Duncan, ..	4 *Aug.* 57
63 Robert Troup, ..	31 do	59 George Warren Stokes, ..	21 *Aug.* 57
21 Henry Milne, ..	28 *Feb.* 56	26 J. G. Gaitskell, ..	27 *Aug.* 57
32 Archibald Robt. John Swinton,	2 *Apl.* 56	72 T. F. Hobday, ..	28 *Aug.* 57
46 John Minshull Drake, ..	17 do	13 William McCulloch, ..	4 *Sep.* 57
6*E* Wm. Augustin John Mayhew,	6 *May* 56	1*E* G. G. Denniss, ..	14 *Sep.* 57
49 John Smith, ..	18 do	42 C. Campbell, ..	18 *Sep.* 57
73 James Sleeman, ..	18 *July* 56	48 Christopher Hasell, ..	4 *Oct.* 57
2*E* John Liptrott, ..	10 *Aug.* 56	45 William Henry, Oakes, ..	7 *Nov.* 57
19 W. K. Wollen, ..	26 *Aug.* 56	57 Edwin Marriott, ..	17 *Nov.* 57
17 Fredk. Wm. Burroughs, ..	9 *Sep.* 56	10 J. Coke, C. B., ..	18 *Nov.* 57
1*E* D. Seaton, ..	14 *Sep.* 56	67 Robert Napier Raikes, ..	28 *Nov.* 57
11 Patrick Gordon, ..	12 *Oct.* 56	62 Fred. Johnston, ..	18 *Dec.* 57
27 Richard Salisbury Simpson, ..	11 *Nov.* 56	4*E* James Metcalfe, ..	1 *Feb.* 58
31 William Philip Hampton, ..	28 do	12 W. S. Ferris, ..	25 *Apl.* 58
5*E*. F. Maitland, ..	31 *Dec.* 56	4 Charles Pattenson, ..	26 *Apl.* 58
9 L. P. D. Eld, ..	4 *Apl.* 57	2*E* M. E. Sherwill, ..	1 *May* 58
37 John Bontein, ..	20 *Mar.* 57	47 J. T. Daniell, ..	1 *May* 58
24 John Talbot Shakespear, ..	1 *May* 57	38 R. C. Tytler, ..	6 *May* 58
52 Robert Morrieson, ..	10 *May* 57	34 George Timins, ..	9 *May* 58
71 James Lumsdaine Walker, ..	31 *May* 57	50 Keith Young, C.B., ..	19 *May* 58
36 Samuel Brougham Faddy, ..	31 *May* 57	54 Francis Stuart Paterson, ..	16 *June* 58
R ~~41 C. Apthorp,~~ ..	1 *June* 57	30 R. S. Ewart, ..	19 *June* 58
18 William Frost Nuthall, ..	6 *June* 57	3*E* Henry M. Nation, ..	13 *July* 58
23 Charles Cooper, ..	8 *June* 57	74 George Ryley, ..	22 *Aug.* 58
R ~~40 H. A. Shuckburgh,~~ ..	8 *June* 57	55 Peter William Luard, ..	27 *Aug.* 58
29 G. W. Williams, ..	15 *June* 57	20 J. C. Scott, ..	27 *Aug.* 58
25 John Clarke, ..	27 *June* 57	~~58 A. Meyer,~~ D ..	4 *Sep.* 58
51 Charles Cheape, ..	27 *June* 57	15 G. J. Montgomery, ..	9 *Oct.* 58
28 John DeW. C. J. Moir, ..	27 *June* 57	16 Thomas James Gardiner, ..	25 *Nov.* 58
35 A. G. F. J. Younghusband, ..	27 *June* 57	6*E* Walter Birch, ..	22 *Jan.* 59
64 Charles Prior, ..	10 *July* 57	2 James Travers, ..	16 *Feb.* 59
69 E. Sissmore, ..	11 *July* 57	4*E* G. A. Fisher, ..	13 *Mar.* 59
65 Fred. Moffat Baker, ..	15 *July* 57	60 C. R. Browne, ..	17 do
56 William Charles Gott, ..	15 *July* 57	14 C. G. Walsh, ..	13 *Apl.* 59
53 Henry Ramsay, ..	15 *July* 57	43 A. F. Macpherson, ..	26 *Apl.* 59
70 Philip Harris, ..	20 *July* 57	68 P. A. Roberton, ..	15 *May* 59
44 Edward Dayot Watson, ..	21 *July* 57	39 T. Pownall, ..	4 *June* 59

HONORARY DISTINCTIONS

CONFERRED ON

THE REGIMENT OF ARTILLERY.

HORSE ARTILLERY.

The Sphinx, with the words "*Egypt*," "*Ava*," *and* "*Bhurtpore*."

1ST BRIGADE, head-quarters, "*Bhurtpore*," "*Moodkee*," "*Ferozeshuhur*," "*Subraon*," "*Punjaub*," "*Chillianwalla*," "*Goojerat*."

1st Troop, "*Egypt*," "*Deig*," "*Ava*," "*Moodkee*," "*Ferozeshuhur*," "*Alliwal*."

2nd Troop, "*Bhurtpore*," "*Moodkee*," "*Ferozeshuhur*," "*Sobraon*," "*Punjaub*,"

3rd Troop, "*Cabool*, 1842," "*Moodkee*," "*Ferozeshuhur*," "*Sobraon*," "*Punjaub*."

4th Troop, "*Bhurtpore*," "*Punjaub*," "*Mooltan*," "*Goojerat*."

5th Troop, "*Candahar*," "*Ghuznee*," "*Cabool*, 1842," "*Ferozeshuhur*," "*Sobraon*."

2ND BRIGADE, head-quarters, "*Bhurtpore*," "*Alliwal*," "*Sobraon*," "*Punjaub*," "*Chillanwalla*," "*Goojerat*,"

1st Troop, "*Bhurtpore*," "*Alliwal*," "*Sobraon*," "*Punjaub*," "*Chillianwalla*," "*Goojerat*."

2nd Troop, "*Bhurtpore*," "*Ava*," "*Ghuznee*," "*Affghanistan*," "*Maharajpore*," "*Sobraon*," "*Punjaub*," "*Chillianwalla*," "*Goojerat*."

3rd Troop, "*Bhurtpore*," "*Cabool*, 1842," "*Maharajpore*," "*Alliwal*," "*Sobraon*," "*Punjaub*," "*Chillianwalla*," "*Goojerat*."

4th Troop, "*Punjaub*," "*Chillianwalla*," "*Goojerat*."

3RD BRIGADE, head-quarters, "*Bhurtpore*," "*Ferozeshuhur*," "*Sobraon*," "*Punjaub*," "*Chillanwalla*," "*Goojerat*."

1st Troop, "*Bhurtpore*," "*Punniar*," "*Moodkee*," "*Ferozeshuhur*," "*Sobraon*," "*Punjaub*," "*Chillianwalla*," "*Goojerat*."

2nd Troop, "*Bhurtpore*," "*Maharajpore*," 2 guns, G. G. escort, "*Moodkee*," 2 guns, G. G. escort, "*Ferozeshuhur*," "*Alliwal*," "*Sobraon*," "*Punjaub*," "*Chillianwalla*," "*Goojerat*."

3rd Troop, "*Punniar*," "*Ferozeshuhur*," "*Sobraon*," "*Punjaub*."

4th Troop, "*Bhurtpore*," "*Affghanistan*," "*Moodkee*," "*Ferozeshuhur*," "*Punjaub*," "*Mooltan*," "*Goojerat*."

FOOT ARTILLERY.

A Gun, superscribed with *Bengal Artillery*, surrounded by a *Laurel Wreath*, and surmounted by a *Crown*: the word "*Ubique*," below.

1ST BATTALION, head-quarters, "*Bhurtpore*."

1st Company, "*Seringapatam*," "*Maharajpore*," "*Punjaub*," "*Chillianwalla*," "*Goojerat*."

2nd Company, "*Carnatic*," "*Allighur*," "*Delhi*," "*Laswarrie*," "*Deig*," "*Bhurtpore*."

3rd Company, "*Bhurtpore*," "*Punjaub*," "*Chillianwalla*," "*Goojerat*."

4th Company, "*Seringapatam*," "*Bhurtpore*."

2ND BATTALION.

2nd Company, "*Carnatic*," "*Mysore*," "*Seringapatam*," "*Cabool*, 1842," "*Ferozeshuhur*," "*Sobraon*," "*Punjaub*," "*Mooltan*," "*Goojerat*."

3rd Company, "*Arracan*," "*Cabool*, 1842," "*Ghuznee*, 1842."

4th Company, "*Arracan*," "*Affghanistan*," "*Candahar*," "*Kelat-i-Ghilzie*."

3RD BATTALION, head-quarters, "*Bhurtpore*."

1st Company, "*Mysore*," "*Allighur*," "*Delhi*," "*Laswarrie*," "*Deig*," "*Java*," "*Bhurtpore*."

2nd Company, "*Bhurtpore*."

3rd Company, "*Sobraon*," "*Punjaub*," "*Mooltan*," "*Goojerat*."

4th Company, "*Java*," "*Bhurtpore*," "*Sobraon*," "*Punjaub*," "*Mooltan*," "*Goojerat*."

4TH BATTALION, head-quarters, "*Bhurtpore*," "*Ferozeshuhur*," "*Sobraon*," "*Punjaub*," "*Chillianwalla*," "*Goojerat*."

1st Company, "*Plassey*," "*Buxar*," "*Allighur*," "*Delhi*," "*Laswarrie*," "*Deig*," "*Maharajpore*," "*Sobraon*," "*Punjaub*," "*Chillianwalla*," "*Goojerat*."

2nd Company, "*Carnatic*," "*Mysore*," "*Bhurtpore*," "*Ferozeshuhur*," "*Sobraon*," "*Punjaub*," "*Chillianwalla*," "*Goojerat*."

3rd Company, "*Bhurtpore*," "*Moodkee*," "*Ferozeshuhur*," "*Sobraon*," "*Chillianwalla*," "*Goojerat*."

4th Company, "*Arracan*," "*Ferozeshuhur*," "*Sobraon*," "*Punjaub*."

4th Company, Detachment, "*Chillianwalla*," "*Goojerat*."

5TH BATTALION.

1ST Company, "*Punjaub*."

2nd Company, "*Seringapatam*," "*Allyghur*," "*Delhi*," "*Laswarrie*," "*Deig*," "*Pegu*."

3rd Company, "*Ava*," "*Pegu*."

4th Company, "*Ava*."

6TH BATTALION, head-quarters, "*Sobraon*," "*Punjaub*."

1st Company, "*Sobraon*," "*Punjaub*."

2nd Company, "*Moodkee*," "*Ferozeshhuur*," "*Sobraon*."

3d Company, "*Sobraon*," "*Punjaub*."

4th Company, "*Ferozeshuhur*," "*Sobraon*," "*Punjaub*."

7TH BATTALION, head-quarters, "*Bhurtpore*."

2nd Company, "*Ghuznee*," *Affghanistan*, "*Jellalabad*," "*Cabool*, 1842," "*Ferozeshuhur*," "*Alliwal*," "*Punjaub*," Detachment, "*Goojerat*."

The 2nd Company 7th Battalion, in addition, bears a *Mural Crown*, with the word "*Jellalabad*."

3rd Company, "*Bhurtpore*," "*Punjaub*," "*Chillianwalla*," "*Goojerat*."

4th Company, "*Bhurtpore*," "*Cabool* 1842."

5th Company, "*Bhurtpore*."

6th Company, "*Punniar*," "*Punjaub*," *Mooltan*," "*Gooierat*."

8TH BATTALION.

4th Company, "*Java*," "*Punjaub*."

6th Company, "*Punjaub*."

9TH BATTALION.

1st, 5th and 6th Companies, "*Pegu*."

2nd Company, "*Bhurtpore*."

Regiment of Artillery.—*Head Quarters*, Meerut.

Uniform—*Blue.* Facings—*Scarlet.* Lace—*Gold.*

Regimental Staff
- Brigadier A. Abbott, c. b. .... *Commandant of Artillery*, 18th Jan. 1858.—Fur. S. C. 27th May 1858.
- Brigadier R. Horsford, ... *Offg. Commandant of Artillery*, 28th May 1858.
- Lt.-Col. E. B. Johnson, c. b. .... *Assistant Adjutant General*, 1st Jan. 1856.
- Col. C. Hogge, c. b. .... *Director Artillery Depôt of Instruction*, 3rd October 1853.

Each Brigade of Horse Artillery consists of—3 European and 1 Native Troops, with 1 Sergeant Major—1 Quarter Master Sergeant—1 Drill Sergeant—1 School Sergeant—1 Hospital Sergeant—1 Farrier Major—1 Trumpet Major—1 Rough Rider Sergeant—1 Drill Corporal—4 Native Doctors, as Brigade effective non-commissioned staff.

3 *European Troops*, each with 1 Staff Sergeant—6 Sergeants—6 Corporals—10 Bombardiers—2 Farriers—1 Native Farrier—2 Rough Riders—2 Trumpeters—2 half-pay Trumpeters—80 Gunners—169 Horses—169 Syces and 169 Grasscutters.

1 *Native Troop*, with 1 European Staff Sergeant—1 European Farrier Sergeant—1 Subadar—1 Jemadar—6 Havildars—6 Naicks—2 Native Farriers—2 Rough Riders—2 Trumpeters—90 Troopers, 170 Horses.

——*Lascar detail attached* to each Brigade: 4 Havildars—8 Naicks—96 Privates.

Each European Battalion consists of 4 companies, with 1 Sergeant Major—1 Quarter Master Sergeant—1 Drill Sergeant—1 Hospital Sergeant—1 School Sergeant—1 Bugle Major—1 Drill Corporal—1 Native Doctor, as Battalion effective non-commissioned staff, 4 Company Staff Sergeants—24 Sergeants—24 Corporals—24 Bombardiers—8 Buglers—8 half-pay Buglers—240 Gunners.

N. B.—The gun lascar detail attached to companies with horse batteries, consists of 1 Havildar, 2 Naicks, and 24 Privates—that attached to all other European companies consists of 1 native officer (Subadar and Jemadar alternately), 2 Havildars, 2 Naicks, and 31 Privates.

Each Native Battalion consists of 6 companies, with 1 Sergeant Major—1 Quarter Master Sergeant—1 Drill Sergeant—2 Bugle Majors—1 Havildar Major—1 Quarter Master Havildar—1 Drill Havildar—1 Drill Naick—1 Native Doctor, as Battalion non-commissioned staff, 6 Subadars—12 Jemadars 36 Havildars—36 Naicks—12 Buglers—528 Privates.

The peace establishment of a Horse field battery:—1 Rough Rider and Farrier Sergeant—1 Assistant Farrier and Saddler Sergeant—2 Havildars—2 Naicks—54 Syce Drivers—44 Syces—98 Grasscutters—98 Horses—1 Native Farrier.

The war establishment of a Horse field battery:—3 Havildars—3 Naicks—60 Syce Drivers—70 Syces—130 Grasscutters—130 Horses.

Note—Three additional Horses, with 3 Syces and 3 Grasscutters, are allowed for the Native Officers, when a battery is attached to a Native company of artillery.

Establishment of a Bullock field battery:—1 Bullock Sergeant, 4 Sirdars—59 Drivers—106 Bullocks.

Ser. Y	Ser. M	Rank and Names.	Battn.	Brigd.	Second Lieut.	First Lieut.	Brevet Captain.	Captain.	Brevet Major.	Major.	Brevet Lt. Col.	Lieut. Colonel.	Colonel	Major General.	Lieut. General.
		Colonels, 12.													
~~67~~	~~10~~	~~James Ahmuty~~, ..	1	..	7 *Sep.* 91	6 *Sep.* 99	.. ..	16 *May* 07	.. ..	15 *Feb.* 18	.. ..	14 *Jan.* 21	29 *Aug.* 24	28 *June* 38	11 *Nov.* 51 *gl* 15 *Sep.* 55
57	..	George Swiney, ..	4	..	19 *July* 02	20 *Aug.* 02	.. ..	23 *Oct.* 11	.. ..	2 *Aug.* 19	.. ..	1 *May* 24	1 *Dec.* 34	28 *June* 38	11 *Nov.* 51
~~56~~	~~9~~	~~Sir G. Pollock, G. C. B.~~	9	..	.. ..	14 *Dec.* 03	.. ..	26 *Mar.* 13	.. ..	12 *Aug.* 19	.. ..	1 *May* 24	3 *Mar.* 35	28 *June* 38	11 *Nov.* 51
54	11	Alex. Lindsay, c. b.,	2	..	.. ..	14 *Aug.* 04	.. ..	22 *Mar.* 13	.. ..	12 *Aug.* 19	.. ..	1 *May* 24	2 *July* 35	28 *June* 38	11 *Nov.* 51
~~54~~	~~10~~	~~Samuel Shaw~~, ..	3	..	.. ..	25 *Aug.* 04	.. ..	6 *May* 17	.. ..	1 *May* 24	.. ..	31 *May* 33	25 *Mar.* 40	20 *June* 54	5 *Mar.* 59
~~54~~	~~2~~	~~Richard Powney~~, ..	7	..	.. ..	7 *May* 05	.. ..	7 *Oct.* 17	.. ..	25 *May* 26	.. ..	3 *Mar.* 35	12 *July* 44	20 *June* 54	
53	3	Geo. Ed. Gowan, c. b.,	5	..	.. ..	28 *Mar.* 06	.. ..	1 *Sep.* 18	.. ..	16 *Sep.* 29	.. ..	2 *July* 35	3 *July* 45	20 *June* 54	
50	10	George Brooke, c. b.,	..	1	14 *Sep.* 08	21 *Feb.* 10	.. ..	25 *Aug.* 21	10 *Jan.* 37	27 *Jan.* 37	.. ..	28 *Feb.* 42	21 *July* 51	28 *Nov.* 54	
~~48~~	~~8~~	~~Ed. Huthwaite, c. b.~~,	..	2	12 *Nov.* 10	25 *Sep.* 17	12 *Nov.* 25	30 *Aug.* 26	28 *June* 38	20 *Jan.* 42	.. ..	3 *July* 45	*regl.* 23 *Jan.* 54 20 *June* 54	14 *Mar.* 57	
46	11	George Twemlow, ..	8	..	6 *Aug.* 12	1 *Aug.* 18	6 *Aug.* 27	16 *Sep.* 29	.. ..	15 *Jan.* 44	..	1 *July* 47	*regl.* 6 *Mar.* 54 28 *Nov.* 54		
40	3	*Sir* Archdale Wilson, Bart, k. c. b. ..	..	3	10 *Apl.* 19	7 *July* 20	10 *Apl.* 34	13 *Oct.* 34	.. ..	.. ...	.. ..	3 *July* 45	*regl.* 14 *Oct.* 58 28 *Nov.* 54	14 *Sep* 57	
40	3	Augustus Abbott, c. b.	6	..	16 *Apl.* 19	7 *Aug.* 21	16 *Apl.* 34	10 *May* 35	4 *Oct.* 42	.. ..	.. ..	3 *July* 45	*regl.* 14 *Nov.* 58 28 *Nov.* 54		

REGIMENT OF ARTILLERY—*Continued.*

Service Ys.	Service Ms.	Rank and Nanes.	Battn.	Brigd.	2nd Lieut.	1st Lieut.	Bt. Capt.	Captain.	Bt. Major.	Bt. Lt. Col.	Lt. Col.	Bt. Col.	Major. General.
		Lt. Colonels, 24.											
40	3	Charles Grant, c. b.,(a) ..	..	2	22 *Apl.* 19	2 *Aug.* 22	22 *Apl.* 34	17 *Jan.* 36	30 *Apl.* 44	19 *June* 46	5 *July* 46	20 *June* 54	14 *Oct.* 58
40	3	Richard Horsford, ...	3	..	29 *Apl.* 19	27 *Sep.* 23	29 *Apl.* 34	7 *Oct.* 36	3 *Apl.* 46	.. ..	31 *Mar.* 47	28 *Nov.* 54	
39	1	Js. Alexander, c. b.,(a) ..	1	..	16 *June* 20	6 *Apl.* 24	16 *June* 35	21 *Dec.* 36	23 *Dec.* 42	30 *Apl.* 44	1 *July* 47	20 *June* 54	18 *May* 56
38	1	J. Theos. Lane, c. b. (a) ...	2	..	9 *June* 21	1 *May* 24	9 *June* 36	22 *Aug.* 38	23 *Dec.* 42	30 *Apl.* 44	10 *Feb.* 49	20 *June* 54	8 *June* 56
~~37~~	~~2~~	~~John Fordyce~~, ...	6	..	10 *May* 22	25 *Mar.* 26	10 *May* 37	29 *Apl.* 40	19 *June* 46	7 *June* 49	2 *Feb.* 51	28 *Nov.* 54	
36	1	George Campbell,(a) ..	5	..	6 *June* 23	30 *Aug.* 26	6 *June* 38	10 *July* 40	30 *Apl.* 44	3 *Apl.* 46	21 *July* 51	20 *June* 54	4 *July* 58
~~36~~	~~1~~	~~George Henry Swinley~~, ..	3	..	6 *June* 23	28 *Sep.* 27	6 *June* 38	23 *Dec.* 40	3 *Apl.* 46	.. ..	1 *July* 53	27 *June* 57	
36	1	James Abbott, ...	1	..	6 *June* 23	28 *Sep.* 27	6 *June* 38	4 *Aug.* 41	7 *June* 49	.. ..	6 *Mar.* 54	28 *Nov.* 57	
36	1	Fras. Burton Boileau, ..	4	..	6 *June* 23	28 *Sep.* 27	6 *June* 38	12 *Aug.* 41	19 *June* 46	.. ..	10 *Mar.* 54	20 *June* 57	
~~35~~	~~7~~	~~Fredk. Gaitskell, c. b.~~ *P* ..	8	..	18 *Dec.* 23	28 *Sep.* 27	18 *Dec.* 38	23 *Nov.* 41	11 *Nov.* 51	.. ..	17 *May* 54		
~~34~~	~~7~~	~~Charles Samuel Reid~~, ..	9	..	16 *Dec.* 24	4 *Apl.* 29	16 *Dec.* 39	16 *Dec.* 43	11 *Nov.* 51	9 *Dec.* 53	31 *Dec.* 54	28 *Nov.* 54	
32	0	James Brind, c. b., ..	..	3	3 *July* 27	15 *Oct.* 33	23 *July* 42	3 *July* 45	20 *June* 54	... ...	26 *June* 56		
31	10	Robert Raikes Kinleside,	..	2	28 *Sep.* 27	25 *Sep.* 34	28 *Sep.* 42	3 *July* 45	7 *June* 49	28 *Nov.* 54	25 *June* 57		
~~31~~	~~8~~	~~Francis Claude Burnett~~, ..	6	..	4 *Nov.* 27	15 *Oct.* 34	4 *Nov.* 42	3 *July* 45	20 *June* 54	.. ..	27 *June* 57		
~~31~~	~~7~~	~~Arthur Broome~~, ..	4	..	13 *Dec.* 27	9 *July* 35	13 *Dec.* 42	3 *July* 45	20 *June* 54	.. ...	14 *Sep.* 57		
31	7	Alfred Huyshe, ..	..	1	13 *Dec.* 27	28 *Sep.* 35	13 *Dec.* 42	5 *Sep.* 45	7 *June* 49	28 *Nov.* 54	25 *Sep.* 57		
31	1	Reginald Ed. Knatchbull,	9	..	12 *June* 28	17 *Jan.* 36	12 *June* 43	21 *Dec.* 45	20 *June* 54	.. ...	28 *Sep.* 57		
31	1	*Sir* R. C. Shakespear, *Kt.*,	..	1	12 *June* 28	14 *May* 36	12 *June* 43	1 *May* 46	1 *Dec.* 48	7 *June* 49	14 *Jan.* 58	28 *Nov.* 54	
~~30~~	~~7~~	~~Ed. William S. Scott~~,† ..	1	..	12 *Dec.* 28	18 *Jan.* 37	12 *Dec.* 43	5 *July* 46	20 *June* 54	19 *Jan.* 58	10 *Feb.* 58		
~~30~~	~~7~~	~~Vincent Eyre~~, c. b., ..	7	..	12 *Dec.* 28	28 *Apl.* 37	12 *Dec.* 43	19 *Sep.* 46	20 *June* 54	11 *Dec.* 57	4 *July* 58	24 *Mar.* 58	
~~30~~	~~7~~	~~William Barr~~, ..	5	..	11 *Dec.* 29	1 *Aug.* 38	11 *Dec.* 44	9 *Aug.* 47	28 *Nov.* 54	.. ...	18 *Aug.* 58		
29	7	Charles Hogge, c. b. *PC*,..	7	..	11 *Dec.* 29	1 *Dec.* 38	11 *Dec* 44	1 *Jan.* 48	7 *June* 49	28 *Nov.* 54	27 *Sep.* 58	28 *Nov.* 57	
29	1	Frank Turner, c. b., ..	..	3	11 *June* 30	11 *Mar.* 39	11 *June* 45	7 *Jan.* 48	22 *Aug.* 55	19 *Jan.* 58	11 *Oct.* 58	24 *Mar.* 58	
29	1	Henry Alex. Carleton, c. b.,†	8	..	11 *June* 30	12 *Sep.* 39	11 *June* 45	6 *Feb.* 48	5 *Dec.* 55	20 *July* 58	14 *Oct.* 58		
29	1	William H. Delamain, ..	2	..	11 *June* 30	20 *Dec.* 39	11 *June* 45	16 *June* 48	18 *Feb.* 56	... ...	14 *Nov.* 58		
~~28~~	~~7~~	~~Gravenor Kirby, PC~~, ..	5	..	10 *Dec.* 30	6 *Dec.* 39	10 *Dec.* 45	1 *Sep.* 48	3 *Oct.* 57	24 *Mar.* 58	21 *Nov.* 58		
~~28~~	~~7~~	~~David Reid~~, ..	2	..	10 *Dec.* 30	12 *Dec.* 39	10 *Dec.* 45	26 *Oct.* 48	12 *Oct.* 57	.. ..	23 *Dec.* 58		
~~28~~	~~7~~	~~Townsend James William Hungerford, PC, c. b.~~ ..	..	2	10 *Dec.* 30	31 *Dec.* 39	10 *Dec.* 45	15 *Jan.* 49	12 *Oct.* 57	24 *Mar.* 58	2 *Jan.* 59		

(*a*) Supernumeraries.

REGIMENT OF ARTILLERY—*Continued.*

Ser. Y	Ser. M	Rank and Names.	Battn.	Brigade.	2nd Lieut.	1st Lieut.	Captain. Brevet.	Captain. Regl.	Bt. Major.
		Captains (72.)							
28	7	John Abercrombie,(1) - - -	8	..	10 *Dec.* 30	10 *Feb.* 40	10 *Dec.* 45	10 *Feb.* 49	7 *June* 49
28	1	Robert Warburton,*P*, - - -	7	..	9 *June* 31	18 *Mar.* 40	9 *June* 46	21 *Feb.* 49	13 *Mar.* 59
28	1	John Hall Smyth, (5) - -	..	1	9 *June* 31	11 *Apl.* 40	9 *June* 46	5 *May* 49	19 *Jan.* 58
27	7	Ernle Kyrle Money,*P*, - -	..	3	8 *Dec.* 31	29 *Apl.* 40	8 *Dec.* 46	5 *May* 49	19 *Jan.* 58
27	7	William Maxwell,†- - - -	6	..	8 *Dec.* 31	9 *June* 40	8 *Dec.* 46	20 *June* 49	24 *Mar.* 58
26	7	Henry E. Landor Thuillier,(2)	9	..	14 *Dec.* 32	1 *Sep.* 40	14 *Dec.* 47	2 *Feb.* 51	
25	7	Charles Douglas,† - - - -	1	..	13 *Dec.* 33	12 *Jan.* 41	13 *Dec.* 48	20 *May* 51	20 *July* 58
24	1	Edward Kaye,† (4) - -	..	2	12 *June* 35	1 *Apl.* 41	12 *June* 50	1 *Jan.* 52	2 *Jan.* 52
23	7	Thomas Brougham,† - - -	2	..	11 *Dec.* 35	12 *Aug.* 41	11 *Dec.* 50	18 *Mar.* 52	
22	7	John Eliot,*PH*,- - - -	7	..	9 *Dec.* 36	17 *Aug.* 41	9 *Dec.* 51	25 *Feb.* 53	
22	1	Henry Lewis,*PC*, - - -	4	..	12 *June* 37	17 *Aug.* 41	12 *June* 52	3 *Mar.* 53	
21	7	Henry Price de Teissier,*P*, -	5	..	11 *Dec.* 37	17 *Aug.* 41	11 *Dec.* 52	3 *Mar.* 53	
21	1	Charles Vyvyan Cox,†- - -	..	2	11 *June* 38	17 *Aug.* 41	.. ..	3 *Mar.* 53	4 *Mar.* 53
21	1	Craven Hildesley Dickens,*P*,-	2	..	11 *June* 38	17 *Aug.* 41	.. ..	3 *Mar.* 53	
21	1	Henry Hammond,*P*, - - -	3	..	11 *June* 38	17 *Aug.* 41	.. ..	3 *Mar.* 53	24 *Mar.* 58
20	7	George Bourchier, C. B. *P*,(5)-	..	2	11 *Dec.* 38	17 *Aug.* 41	19 *Jan.* 58	3 *Mar.* 53	19 *Jan.* 58
20	7	George Moir, C. B. *PH*, -	..	1	11 *Dec.* 38	17 *Aug.* 41	.. ..	3 *Mar.* 53	20 *July* 58
20	4	Peter Christie,†- - - -	1	..	12 *Mar.* 39	17 *Aug.* 41	.. ..	3 *Mar.* 53	4 *Mar.* 53
20	1	James Young,*PH*,- - - -	2	..	11 *June* 39	17 *Aug.* 41	.. ..	3 *Mar.* 53	19 *Jan.* 58
20	1	William Olpherts,*P*,C.B.V.C.(5)	..	2	11 *June* 39	17 *Aug.* 41	.. ...	3 *Mar.* 53	19 *Jan.* 58
20	1	Henry Alan Olpherts, *PC*, (7)	..	1	11 *June* 39	15 *Nov.* 41	.. ..	6 *Mar.* 53	7 *Mar.* 53
19	7	Donald Campl. Vanrenen,*PH*,	3	..	10 *Dec.* 39	13 *Jan.* 42	.. ..	28 *Apl.* 53	
19	1	Frederick William Swinhoe,*P*,	5	..	11 *June* 40	13 *Jan.* 42	.. ..	1 *July* 53	
18	7	George Elliot Voyle,*PH*, - -	2	..	11 *Dec.* 40	24 *Aug.* 42	.. ..	15 *Sep.* 53	
[illegible]	7	William Poole Waddy,† - -	1	..	11 *Dec.* 40	3 *Nov.* 42	.. ..	23 *Jan.* 54	
18	1	Alfred Wintle,*PH*, - - -	4	..	11 *June* 41	6 *June* 43	.. ..	10 *Mar.* 54	
18	1	Henry Tombs, C.B.V.C.,*PH*,(9)	..	1	11 *June* 41	15 *Jan.* 44	.. ..	25 *July* 54	1 *Aug.* 54
18	1	Albert George Austen,† - -	1	..	11 *June* 41	2 *Feb.* 44	.. ..	31 *July* 54	20 *July* 58
17	7	Robert Mercer Paton,*P*, - -	..	3	10 *Dec.* 41	20 *Feb.* 44	.. ..	31 *Dec.* 54	
17	7	Samuel Chs. Woodcock,*PH*, -	6	..	10 *Dec.* 41	1 *Mar.* 44	.. ..	20 *Feb.* 55	
17	7	Charles William Timbrell,*PH*,	5	..	10 *Dec.* 41	12 *July* 44	.. ..	24 *Mar.* 55	
17	7	William Alex. Mackinnon, C.B. *PH*, - - - - - - - -	1	..	10 *Dec.* 41	1 *July* 45	.. ..	22 *Aug.* 55	20 *July* 58
17	7	Wm. Bainbrigge Marshall,*PH*,	3	..	10 *Dec.* 41	3 *July* 45	.. ..	15 *Oct.* 55	
17	7	Walker King Fooks,*PH*, - -	7	..	10 *Dec.* 41	3 *July* 45	.. ..	30 *Oct.* 55	
17	7	Charles Vincent Bowie,*PH*, -	9	..	10 *Dec.* 41	3 *July* 45	.. ..	21 *Jan.* 56	22 *Jan.* 56
17	7	Fred. F. Remmington,C.B.,†(5)	..	3	11 *Dec.* 41	3 *July* 45	... ...	18 *May* 56	19 *Jan.* 58
17	7	Henry R. Courtenay,*PH*, -	4	..	11 *Dec.* 41	3 *July* 45	.. ..	8 *June* 56	
17	7	Frederick Alexander,*P*, -	4	..	11 *Dec.* 41	3 *July* 45	.. ..	8 *June* 56	
17	7	Henry J. Bannatyne Macleod,†	1	..	11 *Dec.* 41	3 *July* 45	.. ..	26 *June* 56	
17	7	Samuel Stallard,*PH*, - -	2	..	11 *Dec.* 41	3 *July* 45	.. ..	17 *Nov.* 56	
17	6	Henry Francis,*PH*,† - - -	1	..	8 *Jan.* 42	3 *July* 45	8 *Jan.* 57	1 *Feb.* 57	
17	5	Edward Atlay,*PH*,- - - -	7	..	30 *Jan.* 42	3 *July* 45	30 *Jan.* 57	30 *May* 57	
17	4	Henry LeGeyt Bruce,*PH*, -	3	..	15 *Feb.* 42	3 *July* 45	15 *Feb.* 57	8 *June* 57	24 *Mar.* 58
17	1	Donald McNeill,*P*, - - - -	2	..	11 *June* 42	3 *July* 45	10 *June* 57	15 *June* 57	
17	1	Edwin B. Johnson,C.B.,*PH*, (4)	..	1	11 *June* 42	3 *July* 45	10 *June* 57	25 *June* 57	5 *July* 57
17	1	Hy. Hamilton Maxwell,*PH*,(5)	6	..	11 *June* 42	3 *July* 45	10 *June* 57	27 *June* 57	27 *June* 57
17	1	Tyrwhitt [illegible], - - - -	2	..	11 *June* 42	3 *July* 45	11 *June* 57	4 *July* 57	
17	1	Thomas Edward Kennion, *P*, -	8	..	11 *June* 42	3 *July* 45	11 *June* 57	6 *July* 57	19 *Jan.* 58
17	1	Alfred Light,*PH*, - - - -	5	..	11 *June* 42	3 *July* 45	11 *June* 57	10 *July* 57	19 *Jan.* 58

(1) Brevet Lieut. Col. 28 Nov. 1854.
(2) Official Major.
(4) Brevet Lieut. Cols. 19 Jan. 1858.
(5) Brevet Lieut. Cols. 24 Mar. 1858.
(7) Brevet Lieut. Col. 15 Jan. 1858.
(9) Brevet Lieut. Col. 19 Jan. 1858. Brevet Colonel 20 July 1858.

REGIMENT OF ARTILLERY—*Continued.*

Ser. Y	Ser. M	Rank and Names.	Battn.	Brigade.	2nd Lieut.	1st Lieut.	Captain. Brevet.	Captain. Regl.	Bt. Major
		Captains.—*(Contd.)*							
17	1	Chas. Harris Blunt, C.B., *PH*, (1)	..	3	11 *June* 42	3 *July* 45	11 *June* 57	7 *Sep.* 57	24 *Mar.* 58
17	1	Colin Cookworthy, *PH*, - -	6	..	11 *June* 42	3 *July* 45	11 *June* 57	12 *Sep.* 57	20 *July* 58
17	1	George Maister, *PH*, - - -	8	..	11 *June* 42	3 *July* 45	11 *June* 57	14 *Sep.* 57	
17	1	William C. Russell, *PC*, - -	9	..	11 *June* 42	3 *July* 45	11 *June* 57	18 *Sep.* 57	
17	1	Alexander Simpson, A. M., *P*, -	9	..	11 *June* 42	3 *July* 45	11 *June* 57	25 *Sep.* 57	
17	1	John Ramsay Sladen, *PH*, - -	7	..	11 *June* 42	3 *July* 45	11 *June* 57	25 *Sep.* 57	
17	..	Charles Stirling Dundas, † -	3	..	8 *July* 42	3 *July* 45	8 *July* 57	28 *Sep.* 57	
16	11	Richard Meecham, *PH*, - -	2	..	12 *Aug.* 42	3 *July* 45	12 *Aug.* 57	5 *Oct.* 57	
16	7	Alfred Pearson, *PH*, - - -	5	..	9 *Dec.* 42	3 *July* 45	9 *Dec.* 57	1 *Jan.* 58	20 *July* 58
16	7	Charles Metcalfe Young, *P*, -	9	..	9 *Dec.* 42	3 *July* 45	9 *Dec.* 57	14 *Jan.* 58	
17	7	George Holland, *PH*, - - -	8	..	11 *Dec.* 41	3 *July* 45	11 *Dec.* 56	10 *Feb.* 58	
16	1	Hungerford M. Boddam, *PH*, -	7	..	9 *June* 43	3 *July* 45	.. ..	27 *Mar.* 58	
16	1	John Anthony Angelo, *PH*, -	8	..	9 *June* 43	26 *Sep.* 45	.. ..	27 *Apl.* 58	
15	7	David J. Falconer Newall, *PH*,	2	..	8 *Dec.* 43	3 *Oct.* 45	.. ..	27 *Apl.* 58	
15	7	John Edmund Watson, *PH*, -	6	..	8 *Dec.* 43	19 *Dec.* 45	.. ..	27 *Apl.* 58	
15	7	Arthur Bunny, *PH*, - - -	2	..	8 *Dec.* 43	21 *Dec.* 45	.. ..	27 *Apl.* 58	20 *July* 58
15	7	William Morton Gowan, *PH*, -	..	2	8 *Dec.* 43	22 *Dec.* 45	.. ..	27 *Apl.* 58	
15	7	William John Gray, *PH*, - -	4	..	8 *Dec.* 43	22 *Dec.* 45	.. ..	27 *Apl.* 58	
15	7	John Stewart Tulloh, *PH*, -	9	..	8 *Dec.* 43	23 *Jan.* 46	.. ..	27 *Apl.* 58	
15	1	George Rodney Brown, *PH*, -	4	..	7 *June* 44	13 *May* 46	.. ..	27 *Apl.* 58	
15	1	Wm. Robert Fitzgerald, *PH*,	9	..	7 *June* 44	5 *July* 46	.. ..	27 *Apl.* 58	
15	1	Edward Harrison, *PH*, - -	5	..	7 *June* 44	12 *Aug.* 46	.. ..	27 *Apl.* 58	
15	1	William Frederick Cox, † -	4	..	7 *June* 44	19 *Sep.* 46	.. ..	27 *Apl.* 58	
15	1	*Go. Alexander Renny *V. C.*†	..	1	7 *June* 44	6 *Oct.* 46	... ..	27 *Apl.* 58	20 *July* 58
15	1	*Harry Vince Timbrell, † - -	1	..	7 *June* 44	29 *Dec.* 46	.. ..	21 *May* 58	
14	7	*Joseph Carncross Griffith, *PH*,	8	..	9 *Dec.* 44	31 *Mar.* 47	.. ..	4 *July* 58	
14	7	*Edward W. Ellis Walker, *PH*,	7	..	9 *Dec.* 44	1 *July* 47	.. ..	18 *Aug.* 58	28 *Aug.* 58
		2nd Captains. (72.)					*2nd Capt.*	*Captain.*	
14	7	William Aitchison Mylne, *P*, -	9	..	9 *Dec.* 44	3 *July* 47	27 *Aug.* 58		
14	7	Charles Henry Cookes, *PH*, -	..	2	9 *Dec.* 44	1 *Dec.* 47	do		
14	7	John A. Richmond Mead, † -	4	..	9 *Dec.* 44	1 *Jan.* 48	do		
14	7	John Fraser Raper, † - - -	1	..	9 *Dec.* 44	7 *Jan.* 48	do		
14	7	Alfred Hales Heath, *PH*, - -	1	..	9 *Dec.* 44	6 *Feb.* 48	do		
14	7	Wm. Dundas Couchman, *PH*, -	..	1	9 *Dec.* 44	16 *June* 48	do		
14	1	Henry Parlett Bishop, *PH*, -	..	3	13 *June* 45	30 *June* 48	do	.. ..	28 *Aug.* 58
14	1	Frederic Day Urquhart, *PH*, -	6	..	13 *June* 45	19 *July* 48	do		
14	1	James George Hathorn, *PH*, -	5	..	13 *June* 45	1 *Sep.* 48	do		
14	1	Frederick Royle DeBudé, *PH*,	1	..	13 *June* 45	3 *Sep.* 48	do		
14	1	Charles S. Lemarchand, *PH*, -	6	..	13 *June* 45	13 *Jan.* 49	do		
14	1	Abraham Richard Fuller, *P*, -	8	..	14 *June* 45	15 *Jan.* 49	do		
14	1	Launcelot Machell, *PH*, - -	9	..	14 *June* 45	21 *Jan.* 49	do		
14	1	Mark Edward Currie, *PH*, -	9	..	14 *June* 45	10 *Feb.* 49	do		
14	1	John Hunter, *PH*, - - -	5	..	14 *June* 45	21 *Feb.* 49	do		
14	1	Augustus Darling, *P*, - - -	7	..	14 *June* 45	10 *Mar.* 49	do		
14	1	John Sabatier Frith, *PH*, - -	..	1	14 *June* 45	25 *Mar.* 49	do	.. ..	28 *Aug.* 58
14	1	William Hawtayne Parish, † -	8	..	14 *June* 45	17 *Apl.* 49	do		
14	1	George Baillie, *PH*, - - -	6	..	14 *June* 45	5 *May* 49	do		
14	1	John Fulton, *PH*, - - - -	7	..	14 *June* 45	5 *May* 49	do		
14	1	Thomas Henry Salt, *PH*, - -	3	..	14 *June* 45	1 *Oct.* 49	do		
14	1	Robert Murray, *PH*, - - -	9	..	14 *June* 45	4 *Dec.* 49	do		
14	1	Peter Macfarlane Syme, † -	1	..	14 *June* 45	21 *June* 50	do		
14	1	William Alexander Ross, -	2	..	14 *June* 45	23 *Sep.* 50	do		
14	1	William Dickson, *PH*, - - -	8	..	14 *June* 45	2 *Feb.* 51	do		
14	1	George Oliver Rybot, *PH*, -	7	..	14 *June* 45	20 *May* 51	do		
13	7	Affleck Fraser, † - - - - -	..	1	12 *Dec.* 45	1 *July* 51	do		
13	7	Henry Montague Smith, *PH*, -	2	..	12 *Dec.* 45	21 *July* 51	do		
13	7	James Edward Cordner, *PH*, -	6	..	13 *Dec.* 45	1 *Jan.* 52	do		
13	7	Walter Delane, *PH*, - - -	..	2	13 *Dec.* 45	18 *Mar.* 52	do		

(1) Brevet Lieut. Col. 24th March 1858.
* Supernumeraries.

REGIMENT OF ARTILLERY—*Continued.*

Ser. Y	Ser. M	Rank and Names.	Battn.	Brigade.	2nd Lieut.	1st Lieut.	2nd Capt.	Captain.	Bt. Major.
		2nd Captains.—*(Contd.)*							
13	7	Edward Simeon, - - - -	1	..	13 *Dec.* 45	16 *May.* 52	27 *Aug.* 58		
13	7	Arthur Watt Pixley, *PH*, - -	9	..	13 *Dec.* 45	25 *Feb.* 53	do		
13	7	Thomas Presant, † - - - -	6	..	13 *Dec.* 45	3 *Mar.* 53	do		
13	7	Alfred Digby Denniss, *PH*, -	2	..	13 *Dec.* 45	3 *Mar.* 53	do		
~~13~~	~~1~~	~~Francis C. Simons, *PH*,~~ - -	5	..	12 *June* 46	3 *Mar.* 53	do		
13	1	William Tod Brown, *PH*, -	7	..	12 *June* 46	3 *Mar.* 53	do	.. ..	28 *Aug.* 58
13	1	Charles McW. Mercer, *PH*, -	..	3	12 *June* 46	3 *Mar.* 53	do		
13	1	David Thomson, *PH*, - - -	6	..	12 *June* 46	3 *Mar.* 53	do		
13	1	Wallis Dowell, *PCH*, - - -	8	..	12 *June* 46	3 *Mar.* 53	do		
~~13~~	~~1~~	~~Morgan Crofton Sankey, *PH*,~~	..	1	12 *June* 46	3 *Mar.* 53	do		
12	7	Jonathan Y. Worthington, *PH*,	6	..	11 *Dec.* 46	3 *Mar.* 53	do		
12	1	Henry Rhd. Brownlow, *P*, -	4	..	11 *June* 47	3 *Mar.* 53	do		
12	1	James Shaw Gibb, *P*, - - -	5	..	11 *June* 47	3 *Mar.* 53	do	.. ..	28 *Aug.* 58
12	1	Francis William Stubbs, *PH*, -	..	2	11 *June* 47	3 *Mar.* 53	do		
11	7	Alexander Gillespie, † - - -	8	..	10 *Dec.* 47	3 *Mar.* 53	do		
11	7	John Hayes Grant, *PH*, - -	8	:	10 *Dec.* 47	3 *Mar.* 53	do		
11	7	William Wilson, - - - -	5	..	10 *Dec.* 47	3 *Mar.* 53	do	.. ..	28 *Aug.* 58
11	1	Fredk. E. Smalpage, - *HP*-	4	..	9 *June* 48	3 *Mar.* 53	do		
11	1	Thomas Alex. Dirom, *PH*, -	2	..	9 *June* 48	3 *Mar.* 53	do		
10	7	Thomas N. Harward, *PH*, -	9	..	8 *Dec.* 48	6 *Mar.* 53	do		
10	7	Andrew Hugh Bogle, *PH*, -	9	..	8 *Dec.* 48	28 *Apl.* 53	do		
10	7	Francis H. McLeod, *PH*, - -	..	3	8 *Dec.* 48	7 *July* 53	do		
10	7	*Sir* Wm. Hamilton, *Bart.*, *PH*,	2	..	8 *Dec.* 48	3 *Sep.* 53	do		
~~10~~	~~7~~	~~Henry John Evans,~~ † - -	..	1	8 *Dec.* 48	6 *Mar.* 54	do		
10	7	DeVic Francis Carey, † - -	..	3	8 *Dec.* 48	10 *Mar.* 54	do		
10	1	Thomas E. Hughes, *PCH*, -	9	..	8 *June* 49	17 *May* 54	do		
10	1	Henry Murray, - - -	..	2	8 *June* 49	21 *May* 54	do		
10	1	William Brown, *PH*, - - -	4	..	8 *June* 49	25 *July* 54	do		
10	1	James Ranald Martin, *PH*, -	7	..	8 *June* 49	31 *July* 54	do		
10	1	Thomas Nicholl, *PH*, - - -	3	..	8 *June* 49	20 *Feb.* 55	do		
10	1	Charles W. Maynard, *PH*, - -	3	..	8 *June* 49	28 *May* 55	do		
9	7	Edward Tierney, *PH*, - - -	9	..	11 *Dec.* 49	24 *June* 55	do		
9	7	Alex. Hadden Lindsay, *PH*, -	9	..	11 *Dec.* 49	12 *July* 55	do		
9	7	Henry T. Forbes, *PCH*, - -	7	..	11 *Dec.* 49	22 *Aug.* 55	do		
9	7	Francis Robt. Butt, *P*, - -	7	..	11 *Dec.* 49	2 *Oct.* 55	do		
9	7	Thomas Parkyns Smith, *PH* -	..	2	11 *Dec.* 49	15 *Oct.* 55	do		
9	1	Arthur Rotton, *PCH*, - - -	..	3	14 *June* 50	28 *Oct.* 55	do		
9	1	Edward L. Earle, *PCH*, - -	4	..	.. ..	14 *June* 50	do		
9	1	Edward H. Willoughby, *PCH*,	4	..	.. ..	14 *June* 50	do		
8	7	Geo. Charles Depree, *PCH*, -	7	..	... ..	9 *Dec.* 50	do		
8	7	Geo. Miller Dobbin, *PH*, - -	1	..	.. ..	9 *Dec.* 50	do		
8	7	Clement John Mead, - - -	7	..	.. ..	9 *Dec.* 50	14 *Nov.* 58		
		Lieutenants.—(168.)							
~~8~~	~~7~~	~~John Percivall,~~ † - - - - -	..	2	.. ..	9 *Dec.* 50			
8	7	Patrick C. Anderson, *PH*, - -	5	..	.. ..	9 *Dec.* 50			
8	7	Mordt. M. FitzGerald, *PH*, -	8	..	.. ..	9 *Dec.* 50			
8	1	G. Rennie, Manderson, *PH*, -	..	1	.. ..	13 *June* 51			
8	1	H. Moubray Cadell, *PH*, - -	..	1	.. ..	20 *Nov.* 56			
8	1	Chas. Vaughan Arbuckle, - -	9	..	.. ..	1 *Feb.* 57			
8	1	David James Welsh, *PCH*, - -	7	..	.. ..	30 *May* 57			
7	7	Fredk. Sleigh Roberts, *PH*, - -	5	..	.. ..	31 *May* 57			
7	7	Horatio Otto Hitchins, *PH*, - -	4	..	.. ..	8 *June* 57			
7	7	John Stewart, *PCH*, - -	8	..	.. ..	8 *June* 57			
7	7	George Cracklow, † - - -	..	3	.. ..	15 *June* 57			
7	7	Edwd. Lindsay Hawkins, - -	..	3	.. ..	25 *June* 57			
7	1	H. E. Harington, *PCH*, - -	9	..	.. ...	27 *June* 57			
7	1	J. Richard Pearson, *PCH*, - -	2	..	.. ..	27 *June* 57			
7	1	W. B. Cumberland, *PH*, - -	9	..	.. ..	4 *July* 57			
7	1	Charles Hunter, *PH*, - -	8	..	.. ..	6 *July* 57			
6	7	Hungerford D. Jackson, - -	4	..	.. ..	10 *July* 57			
6	7	Ferdinand Fitzroy, - - -	5	..	.. ..	26 *July* 57			
6	7	Geo. Balfour Traill, *PCH*, - -	..	3	.. ..	27 *July* 57			
6	7	Christopher H. Barnes, *PH*, -	..	1	.. ..	24 *Aug.* 57			
6	7	John Bonham, *PH*, - - -	8	..	.. ..	1 *Sep.* 57			
6	7	James Alexander, - - - -	7	..	.. ..	7 *Sep.* 57			

REGIMENT OF ARTILLERY—*Continued.*

Ser Y	Ser M	Rank and Names.	Battn.	Brigade.	Lieut.	2nd Capt.	Captain.	Bt. Major.
		Lieutenants.—(Contd.)						
6	1	James Hills, *PCH*, V. C. - -	..	1	8 *Sep.* 57			
6	1	Minto Elliot, - - - - -	..	1	8 *Sep.* 57			
6	1	David MacFarlan, *PH*, - - -	4	..	12 *Sep.* 57			
6	1	James C. G. Price, - - - -	1	..	14 *Sep.* 57			
5	7	James Sconce, *PH*, - - -	..	2	23 *Sep.* 57			
5	7	Henry Archibald Mallock, - -	6	..	25 *Sep.* 57			
5	7	Ed. C. Wm. Raynsford, - -	..	2	25 *Sep.* 57			
5	7	Robert Roche Franks, - -	..	2	28 *Sep.* 57			
5	1	Rawson Aislabie, *PH*, - - -	..	2	28 *Sep.* 57			
5	1	Chas. Gilbert Robinson, *PH*, -	..	1	5 *Oct.* 57			
D 5	1	~~Chas. S. Sedley Taylor,~~ - -	..	3	29 *Oct.* 57			
5	1	George Grant Gordon,† - -	6	..	14 *Nov.* 57			
5	1	Penton Thomson, *PH*, - -	9	..	17 *Nov.* 57			
4	7	Howell Locke Jones, *PH*, -	..	2	1 *Jan.* 58			
4	7	Edward Christian Griffin, *PH*, -	..	3	8 *Jan.* 58			
4	7	Alfred James Wake, - - -	..	3	10 *Feb.* 58			
4	1	Frederick Vincent Eyre, -	..	3	14 *Feb.* 58			
4	1	A. H. Davidson, - - - - -	..	3	27 *Mar.* 58			
4	1	Edward Fraser, - - - - -	..	1	14 *Apl.* 58			
4	1	Fredk. Eustace Lewes,† - -	9	..	21 *Apl.* 58			
4	1	Hamilton Smithett, - - - -	9	..	27 *Apl.* 58			
D 3	7	~~Andrew Dowie,~~ - - - -	..	2	do			
3	7	Richard Thomas Hare, - - -	..	3	do			
3	7	Charles Edward Nairne, - -	7	..	do			
D 3	7	~~Hector Munro,~~ - - - - -	6	..	do			
3	7	William Gully, - - - - - -	..	2	do			
D 3	1	~~*Sir* Richd. de L. St. George, *Bt.*~~	..	2	do			
3	1	Hugh Chichester, -	..	1	do			
3	1	Duncan S. Pemberton, - -	2	..	do			
3	1	William Robert Craster, -	..	2	do			
2	7	Edward Trevor Hume, -	..	3	do			
2	7	Thaddeus Ryan,†	..	..	do			
2	7	William O'Brien,† -	1	..	do			
2	7	Alexander Walker, -	6	..	do			
D 2	7	~~Henry Girardot,~~ -	..	2	do			
2	1	William Jackson Stewart,† -	1	..	do			
2	1	Alfred Dixon,† -	..	1	do			
2	1	Fitzherbert Coddington, -	..	2	do			
2	1	Edward Hart Dyke, -	..	2	do			
D 2	1	~~James Ronald Macleay,~~ -	..	1	do			
2	1	Richard Swanne Robinson, -	5	..	do			
2	1	Anson Swinton, -	3	..	do			
2	1	Henry DeGrey Warter, -	..	3	do			
2	1	Edward Henry Ryan, -	6	..	do			
1	7	Charles Allan Baylay, -	1	..	21 *May* 58			
1	7	Percy Bury Raikes, -	1	..	4 *July* 58			
1	7	Chas. Edward Armstrong, -	3	..	27 *July* 58			
1	7	K. W. S. M. Cameron, -	3	..	18 *Aug.* 58			
1	7	Edward Draper Elliott, -	5	..				
D 1	7	~~Chas. Edward Delafosse,~~ -	3	..				
1	7	Francis William Ward, -	..	1				
1	7	G. F. Blackwood, -	3	..				
1	7	W. Clephane Brown, -	3	..				
1	7	C. A. Madan Warde, -	2	..				
1	7	Geo. Algernon Russell, -	6	..				
1	7	G. F. Hamilton, -	5	..				
1	7	M. W. Ommanney, -	1	..				
1	7	John Arthur Tillard, -	..	1				
1	7	John Alves Low, -	1	..				
1	7	Christison Syme Jackson, -	..	3				
Killed 1	7	~~Wm. A. Beaver Gillies,~~ -	6	..	in Sittana Campaign Nov. 63.			
1	7	H. Stephenson Clarke, -	8	..				
1	7	Robert James Abbott,† -	1	..				
1	7	Alex. Samuel Heyland, -	3	..				
1	7	Newson Dunnell Garrett, -	5	..				
1	7	William Henry Wilkins, -	5	..				

Ser. Y	Ser. M	Rank and Names.	Battn.	Brigd.	Lieut.	2nd Capt.	Captain.	Bt. Major.
		LIEUTENANTS.—(*Contd.*)						
1	7	Hugh Hildyard Murray,	4	..				
1	7	T. J. C. A. Studdy,	2	..				
1	7	William Albony Liot,	5	..				
1	7	G. H. W. Ewbank,	3	..				
1	7	A. R. T. Chilton,	6	..				
1	7	H. I. E. Ford,†	1	..				
1	7	Montague Geo. Browne,	3	..				
1	7	Robert Henry Palmer,†	2	..				
1	7	John Harvey Annand,	2	..				
1	7	Wm. Bedford Troup,	4	..				
1	7	George Gott Nelson,	4	..				
1	7	James Vere Wylie,	1	..				
1	7	Thomas Arnoll Davis,	6	..				
1	7	A. Hepburn Murray,	2	..				
1	1	Ross Fendall Lowis,	5	..				
1	1	John Henry Alexander,	5	..				
1	1	Pierce Thomas Henry Taylor,	5	..				
1	1	Edward Robert Conolly,	2	..				
1	1	Thomas Walker Bridges,	2	..				
1	1	Digby W. C. Fairfield,	2	..				
1	1	Spencer Cargill,	3	..				
1	1	Hugh Latham,	5	...				
1	1	Harold John Kinsman,	3	..				
1	1	Charles Pitt Elderton,	8	..				
1	1	Alfred Edward Garnault,	5	..				
1	1	Henry Grant Young,	8	..				
1	1	Henry Cotton,	6	..				
1	1	James Charles,	6	...				
1	1	Joseph A. O. Hampton,	1	..				
1	1	Harry Maxwell Mackenzie,	2	..				
1	1	Harry Lancelot Nicholas,	1	..				
1	1	George William Thomson,	4	..				
1	1	Edward Hardy Hugh Elliot,	4	..				
1	1	Charles Henry Reilly,†	6	..				
1	1	William Stuart Alexander	6	..				
1	1	John Clinton Greene,	3	..				
1	1	Edward Francis Chapman,	3	..				
1	1	Thomas Graham,	1					
1	1	Crombie Cowie,	4	..				
1	1	Clarence Macpherson,	1	..				
1	1	James Loch,	3	..				
1	1	Benjamin Vaughan Arbuckle	6	...				
1	1	George Lamb,	2	..				
1	1	Astley Edward Lindsay Kaye	3	..				
1	1	James Raymond J. Dewar,	1	..				
1	1	John Mylne Young,	6	...				
1	1	Lewis Williams Taylor,	2	...				
1	1	John Frederick Free,	3	..				
..	7	John William Taylor,	..	..	10 Dec. 58			
..	7	Jas. A. Sutherland Colquhoun,	..	..	do			
..	7	Walter Ernest Forbes,	..	..	do			
..	7	John Forbes Meiklejohn,	..	..	do			
..	7	William Barron,	..	..	11 do			
..	7	William J. Wemyss Muir,	1	..	do			
..	7	Lionel Henry Septimus James,	..	..	do			
..	7	Palmer Boyd,	6	..	do			
..	7	Albert Berwick Cunningham,	2	..	do			
..	7	Edward John Machell,	..	..	do			
..	7	Frederick Lindsay,	4	..	do			
..	7	Francis Arthur Stubbs,	5	..	do			
..	7	G. E. W. Malet,	..	..	do			
..	7	John Phillips Cottam,	..	..	do			
..	7	Horace George Willis,	1	..	do			
..	7	Vincent Carne Fisher	..	..	do			
..	7	Murray William Daniell,	4	..	do			
..	7	Edward Albert Anderson,	..	..	do			

14 Vacancies.

Batteries of Horse Artillery.

Troop and Brigade to which attached.		Number and Calibre of Guns attached to each Battery.				Stations.	Commanded by
Troop.	Brigade.	Guns.		Howitzers.			
		6-Pr.	9-Pr.	12-Pr.	24-Pr.		
1stEuropean,	1	5	..	1	..	Lucknow, ..	Bt. Lt. Col. H. A. Olpherts.
2nd ditto, - -	1	5	..	1	..	Meerut, ..	Bt. Col. H. Tombs, C.B. & V. C.
3rd ditto, -	1	5	..	1	..	Trans Gogra,	Bt. Major G. Moir. C. B,
4th Native, -	1	5	..	1	..	Mutinied,	
5th ditto, - -	1	5	..	1	..	Phillibheet, ..	Bt. Lt. Col. J. H. Smyth.
1st European,	2	5	..	1	..	Lahore, ..	Bt. Lt. Col. G. Bourchier, C. B.
2nd ditto, - -	2	..	4	..	2	Allahabad, ..	Bt. Lt. Col. E. Kaye.
3rd ditto, - -	2	5	..	1	..	Peshawur, ..	Bt. Lt. Col. W. Olpherts, C.B.& V.C.
4th ditto, - -	2	5	..	1	..	Rawul Pindee.	Bt. Major C. V. Cox.
1st European,	3	5	..	1	..	Jullundur, ..	Capt. R. M. Paton.
2nd ditto, - -	3	5	..	1	..	Umballah, ..	Bt. Maj. E. K. Money.
3rd ditto, - -	3	..	5	..	1	Muttra. ..	Bt.Lt.Col. F.F. Remmington. C. B.,
4th ditto, - -	3	5	..	1	..	Camp Dera Ishmael Khan	Bt. Lt. Col. C. H. Blunt. C. B.,
13	3	55	9	11	3		

Mountain Train Battery.—(Nowshera.)

Capt. F. R. DeBude,	..	27 *Aug.* 58	29 *Apl.* 59	Commandant.
Lieut. F. E. Lewes,	..	21 *Apl.* 58	10 *Aug.* 58	Doing duty.

The Mountain Train Battery consists of four 12-Pounder M. T. Howitzers, and four 3-Pounder M. T. Guns—1 Subadar, 2 Jemadars, 2 Staff Sergeants, 1 Native Doctor, 6 Havildars, 6 Naicks. 2 Buglers, 88 Privates, 36 Sirdar Syces, 132 Syces, 2 Native Farriers, 120 Grasscutters, 168 mules.

Light Field Batteries, Foot Artillery.

No.	Company to which attached.	Drivers.	Ordnance.	Cattle.	Station.	Commanded by
1	2nd Co. 4th Battalion,	B	Each Lt. Fd. Baty., has 5-9-Pr. Guns and 1-24-Pr. Hr.	Horses,	Meerut, ..	Capt. A. Wintle.
2	2nd Co. 8th do ..	D		Bullocks,	Mutinied,	
3	Royal Artillery, ..	N		Horses,		
4	1st Co. 3rd Battalion.	M		Bullocks,	Meerut, ..	Capt. W. B. Marshall.
5	3rd Co. 7th do ..	A		Horses,	Mutinied,	
6	2nd Co. 7th do ..	F		Horses,	Mutinied,	
7	1st Co. 1st do ..	O		Horses,	Shahjehanpore, .	Bt. Maj. A. G. Austen.
8	2nd Co. 6th do ..	C		Horses,	Agra, ..	Bt. Lt. Col. H. H. Maxwell,
9	4th Co. 1st do ..	P		Horses,	Delhi, ..	Capt. H. Francis.
10	1st Co. 2nd do ..	Q		Horses,	Ferozepore, ..	Bt. Major A. Bunny.
11	4th Co. 5th do ..	L		Horses,	Dinapore, ..	Capt. F. W. Swinhoe.
12	2nd Co. 3rd do ..	I		Horses,	Cawnpore, ..	Bt. Maj. H. LeG. Bruce.
13	5th Co. 7th do ..	G		Horses,	Mutinied,	
14	3rd Co. 3rd do ..	R		Horses,	Bareilly, ..	Bt. Maj. H. Hammond.
15	6th Co. 8th do ..	K		Horses,	Mutinied,	
16	2nd Co. 1st do ..	V		Horses,	Umritsur, ..	Capt. W. P. Waddy.
17	3rd Co. 1st do ..	H		Horses,	Lucknow, ..	Bt. Maj. W. A. Mackinnon C. B.
18	4th Co. 9th do ..	S		Bullocks,	Mutinied,	
19	3rd Co. 6th do ..	T		Horses,	Peshawur, ..	Capt. S. C. Woodcock.
20	Royal Artillery, ..	U		Horses,		
21	2nd Co. 5th Battalion,	W		Horses,	Gwalior, ..	Bt. Maj. A. Light.
22	———					
23	4th Co. 2nd Battalion,			Horses,	Peshawur, ..	Capt. S. Stallard.
24	4th Co. 3rd do ..			Horses,	Jullundur, ..	Capt. C. S. Dundas.

Each Troop and Battery is allowed—1 Waggon per Gun in Cantonments and 2 on Service—1 spare. Howitzer Carriage, 2 Store Carts in Cantonments, 1 Extra on Service.

Proportion of Ammunition—6 Pr. Troop or Battery, 128 Rounds per Gun, 100 ditto per Howitzer, 9 Pr. Troop or Battery, 96 Rounds per Gun, 80 ditto per Howitzer.

1st Brigade of Horse Artillery.

Head-quarters, Meerut,

1st Troop,	Lucknow.	4th Troop,	(Native.) Mutinied.
2nd Troop,	Meerut.	5th Troop	Phillibheet.
3rd Troop,	Trans Gogra.		

Fur. Reg.	*Troop.*	RANK AND NAMES.	*Regl. Rank.*	*Date of Appointment to the Horse Artillery.*	REMARKS.
		Colonel.			
N.	..	G. Brooke, C. B., (*Major Genl.*)	28 *Nov.* 54	7 *Apl.* 54	Fur. S. C. 17th April 56.
		Lieut. Colonels.			
	..	A. Huyshe, - - - - - -	25 *Sep.* 57	5 *Dec.* 58	
	..	*Sir* R. C. Shakespear, *Kt.* (*Col.*)	14 *Jan.* 58	11 *May* 59	Political employ.
		Captains.			
N.	5	J. H. Smyth, (*Lt. Col.*) - - -	5 *May* 49	14 *Feb.* 53	Fur. P. A. 28th June 59.
	3	G. Moir, C. B. *PH,* (*Major*) - -	3 *Mar.* 53	17 *Mar.* 58	
	1	H. A. Olpherts, *P C,* (*Lt. Col.*) -	6 *Mar.* 53	19 *Nov.* 56	
N.	2	H. Tombs, C. B. V.C., (*Col.*) - -	25 *July* 54	27 *Nov.* 55	Fur. S. C. 7th Mar. 59.
	2	E. B. Johnson, C.B. *PH,* (*Lt. Col.*)	25 *June* 57	7 *Apl.* 54	Asst. Adjt. Genl. of Artillery.
	5	G. A. Renny, *V. C.*† (*Major*) -	27 *Apl.* 58	12 *Feb.* 58	Lv. P. A. 30th September.
		2nd Captains			
	1	W. D. Couchman, *PH,* - - -	27 *Aug.* 58	8 *May.* 56	
	..	J. S. Frith, *PH,* (*Major*) - - -	27 *Aug.* 58	11 *Oct.* 54	
	3	A. Fraser,† - - - - - - -	27 *Aug.* 58	1 *Dec.* 55	
	2	M. C. Sankey. *P.H.* - - -	27 *Aug* 58	30 *Sep.* 58	
	5	~~H. J. Evans,~~ † - - - - -	27 *Aug.* 58	5 *Dec.* 58	
		Lieutenants.			
	1	G. R. Manderson, *PH,* - - - -	13 *June* 51	28 *Jan.* 54	Lv. P. A. 15th Oct.
	5	H. M. Cadell, *PH,* - - - -	20 *Nov.* 56	26 *June* 58	
	1	C. H. Barnes, *PH.* - - - -	24 *Aug.* 57	30 *Sep.* 58	
	2	J. Hills, *PCH,* V.C., - - - -	8 *Sep.* 57	17 *June* 56	
	2	M. Elliot, - - - - - - -	8 *Sep.* 57	11 *May* 59	Survey Dept.
	3	C. G. Robinson, *PH,* - - - -	5 *Oct.* 57	11 *Feb.* 58	
	3	E. Fraser, - - - - - -	14 *Apl.* 58	30 *Sep.* 58	
	2	H. Chichester, - - - - - -	27 *Apl.* 58	10 *Aug.* 58	
	1	A. Dixon,† - - - - - -	27 *Apl.* 58	30 *Sep.* 58	
	5	J. R. Macleay, - - - - - -	27 *Apl.* 58	24 *Jan.* 59	
	3	F. W. Ward, - - - - - - -	.. ..	24 *Jan.* 59	
	2	J. A. Tillard, - - - - - -	12 *Dec.* 57	30 *Sep.* 58	
		Adjutant and Quarter Master.	*Army Rank.*	*Appointed.*	
		J. S. Frith, - - - - - - -	.. ..	30 *Sep.* 58	Adjutant Meerut Division of Arty.
		Surgeon.			
		W. F. Mactier, M. D. - - - -	16 *Apl.* 58	26 *Aug.* 58	
		Assistant Surgeons.			
	3	R. Bird, M. D. - - - - - -	29 *Sep.* 58	4 *Aug.* 55	On detached duty.
	3	J. A. P. Colles, M. D. - - - -	25 *Feb.* 59	27 *Jan.* 58	
	1	G. S. Sutherland, M. D. - - -	4 *Aug.* 57	27 *Apl.* 59	
		Veterinary Surgeons.			
		I. Bicknell, - - - - - - -	10 *May* 28	19 *Jan.* 56	
	1	G. Kettlewell, - - - - - - -	5 *Dec.* 54	18 *Mar.* 57	Fur. S. C. 17th July 58.
		Riding Master.			
		S. Budd, (*Unattached Capt.*) -	29 *Nov.* 54	14 *Sep.* 57	

2nd Brigade of Horse Artillery.

Head-quarters, Meean Meer, (Lahore,)

1st Troop, Meean Meer (Lahore.)
2nd Troop, Allahabad.
3rd Troop, Peshawur.
4th Troop, Rawul Pindee,

Fur. Reg.	Troop.	RANK AND NAMES.	*Regl. Rank.*	*Date of Appointment to the Horse Artillery.*	REMARKS.
		Colonel.			
		E. Huthwaite, C.B., *(Maj. Genl.)*	23 *Jan.* 54	24 *July* 45	Residing at Nainee Tal.
		Lieut. Colonels.			
N.		C. Grant, C. B., *(Maj. Genl.)* -	5 *July* 46	10 *June* 58	Fur. S. C. 5th Jan. 59.
N		R. R. Kinleside, - - - - -	25 *June* 57	23 *Apl.* 58	Fur. P. A. 24 June 59.
D ~~O.~~		~~T. J. W. Hungerford, C. B.~~ *PC, (a)*	2 *Jan.* 59	11 *May* 59	Fur. S. C. 15 Mar. 58.
		Captains.			
	2	Edward Kaye,† *(Lt. Col.)*- - -	1 *Jan.* 52	18 *Dec.* 57	
	4	C. V. Cox, *(Major)* - - - -	3 *Mar.* 53	19 *Dec.* 54	
	1	G. Bourchier, C. B. *P, (Lt. Col.)* -	3 *Mar.* 53	18 *Dec.* 57	
	3	W. Olpherts, C.B. & V.C. *P, (Lt. Col.)*	3 *Mar.* 53	5 *Dec.* 58	
		2nd Captains.			
	3	C. H. Cookes, *PH*, - - - - -	27 *Aug.* 58	19 *Jan.* 58	
	1	W. Delane, *PH*, - - - - -	27 *Aug.* 58	17 *Apl.* 55	
	4	F. W. Stubbs, *PH*, - - - - -	27 *Aug.* 58	24 *Jan.* 59	
	1	H. Murray, - - - - - -	27 *Aug.* 58	30 *Sep.* 58	
	2	T. P. Smith, *(b)* - - - - -	27 *Aug.* 58	11 *May* 59	
		Lieutenants.			
	1	J. Percivall, - - - - - - -	9 *Dec.* 50	26 *June* 58	
	1	J. Sconce, *PH*, - - - - -	23 *Sep.* 57	11 *Feb.* 58	
	4	E. C. W. Raynsford, - - - -	25 *Sep.* 57	21 *Jan.* 56	
	2	R. R. Franks, - - - - - -	28 *Sep.* 57	26 *Aug.* 57	
	2	Rawson Aislabie, - - - - -	28 *Sep.* 57	30 *Sep.* 58	
	3	H. L. Jones, *P.H.* - - - - -	1 *Jan.* 58	30 *Sep.* 58	
	4	A. Douie, - - - - - - -	27 *Apl.* 58	26 *June* 58	
	3	W. Gully, - - - - - - -	27 *Apl.* 58		
	2	*Sir* R. deL. St. George, *Bart.*, -	27 *Apl.* 58	11 *Feb.* 58	
	3	W. R. Craster, - - - - -	27 *Apl.* 58	30 *Sep.* 58	
	4	H. Girardot, - - - - - -	27 *Apl.* 58	30 *Sep.* 58	
	3	F. Coddington, - - - - - -	27 *Apl.* 58	30 *Sep.* 58	
	1	E. H. Dyke, - - - - - - -	27 *Apl.* 58	24 *Jan.* 59	
		Adjutant and QuarterMaster.	*Army Rank.*	*Appointed.*	
		W. Delane, - - - - - -	18 *Mar.* 52	30 *Sep.* 58	
		Surgeon			
		G. Harper, - - - - - - -	25 *Aug.* 53	17 *Feb.* 59	
		Assistant Surgeon.			
	1	H. W. Robinson, B.A., - - - -	7 *Sep.* 54	14 *Jan.* 56	
		Veterinary Surgeon.			
		M. J. Marshall, - - - - - -	22 *Dec.* 54	15 *Apl.* 56	
		Riding Master.			
		Richard Crux, - - - - - -	30 *Mar.* 53	8 *Apl.* 53	

(*a*) Received degrees of honor in the Oordoo and Hindee languages from the College of Fort William on the 23rd Nov. 1847, and 4 Oct. 1848.

(*b*) Has furnished Certificates of qualification in surveying and Civil Engineering.

3rd Brigade of Horse Artillery.

Head-quarters, Umballah.

1st Troop,,	½ at Jullundur. ½ at Sealkote	4th Troop, (Camp DeraIshmael Khan.)
2nd Troop	Umballah.	
3rd Troop,	Muttra.	

Fur. Reg.	Troop.	Rank and Names.	Regl. Rank.	Date of Appointment to the Horse Artillery.	Remarks.
		Colonel.			
O.		*Sir* A. Wilson, *Bt.* K.C.B. (*Major Genl.*) - - - - - - - -	14 *Oct.* 58	28 *Feb.* 59	Fur. S. C. 1st Apl. 58.
		Lieut. Colonels.			
		J. Brind, C. B., - - - - - - -	26 *June* 56	20 *June* 54	
		F. Turner, C. B. (*Col.*) - - - -	11 *Oct.* 58	2 *Dec.* 50	Agent for Gun-Carriages Futtehgurh.
		Captains.			
	2	E. K. Money, *P*, (*Major,*) - - -	5 *May* 49	30 *Nov.* 53	
	1	R- M. Paton, *P*, - - - - -	31 *Dec.* 54	28 *Feb.* 56	
	3	F. F. Remmington, CB.† (*Lt. Col.*)	18 *May* 56	17 *Mar.* 58	Lv. P. A. 25th September.
	4	C. H. Blunt, C. B. *PH*, (*Lt. Col.*)	7 *Sep.* 57		
		2nd Captains.			
		H. P. Bishop, *PH* (*Major.*) - -	27 *Aug.* 58	11 *Nov.* 53	
	3	C. McW. Mercer, *PH*, - - - -	27 *Aug.* 58	25 *Oct.* 58	
	2	F. H. McLeod, *PH*, - - - -	27 *Aug.* 58	17 *Jan.* 55	
	4	DeVic F. Carey,† - - - - -	27 *Aug.* 58	15 *Jan.* 53	
	1	A. Rotton, *PCH*, - - - - -	27 *Aug.* 58	20 *July* 53	
		Lieutenants.			
	2	G. Cracklow,† - - - - - -	15 *June* 57	11 *Feb.* 58	
	2	E. L. Hawkins, - - - - - -	25 *June* 57	30 *Sep.* 58	
	1	G. B. Traill, *PCH*, - - - -	27 *July* 57	26 *June* 58	
	3	C. S. S. Taylor, - - - - - -	29 *Oct.* 57	30 *Sep.* 58	
	4	E. C. Griffin, *PH*, - - - - -	8 *Jan.* 58	5 *Dec* 58	
	2	A. J. Wake, - - - - - -	10 *Feb* 58	26 *June* 58	
	4	F. V. Eyre, - - - - - -	14 *Feb.* 58	10 *Aug.* 58	
	1	A. H. Davidson, - - - - -	27 *Mar.* 58	14 *May.* 58	
	4	R. T. Hare, - - - - - - -	27 *Apl.* 58	26 *June* 58	
	3	E. T. Hume, - - - - - -	27 *Apl.* 58	5 *Dec.* 58	
	3	H. DeG. Warter, - - - - -	27 *Apl.* 58	24 *Jan.* 59	
	1	C. S. Jackson, - - - - - -	12 *Dec.* 57	30 *Sep.* 58	
		Adjutant and Quarter Master.	*Army Rank.*	*Appointed.*	
		H. P. Bishop, - - - - - - -	30 *June* 48	30 *Sep.* 58	
		Surgeon.			
		*			
		Assistant Surgeon.			
	3	J. F. N. Wise, M. D. - - - - -	16 *July* 56	31 *Jan.* 59	
		Veterinary Surgeons.			
		J. R. Hoey, - - - - - - -	1 *Apl.* 40	11 *Feb.* 56	Lv. S. C. 20 October.
		J. G. Bushman, - - - - - -	7 *Jan.* 58	9 *Dec.* 58	
		Riding Master.	*Unatt. Ens.*		
		J. O'Brien, - - - - - -	20 *Sep.* 57	27 *Aug.* 58	

1st Battalion of Foot Artillery.

(European.)

Head-quarters, Delhi,

1st Co., Shahjehanpore.
No. 7, Horse Battery attached.

2nd Co., Umritsir.
No. 16, Horse Battery attached.

3rd Co., Lucknow.
No. 17, Horse Battery attached.

4th Co., Delhi.
No. 9, Horse Battery attached.

Fur. Reg.	Compy.	Rank and Names.	Regl. Rank.	Army Rank.	Remarks.
		Colonel.			
		J. A'hmuty, - - - - - - -	29 *Aug.* 24	*g.* 15 *Sep.* 55	Europe, 5th Feb. 25.
		Lieut. Colonels.			
O.		J. Alexander, C.B., (*Supy*) - -	1 *July* 47	*m.g.* 18 *May* 56	Furlough, P. A. 14 April 57.
		J. Abbott, - - - - - -	6 *Mar.* 54	*col.* 28 *Nov.* 57	[Magazines.]
		E. W. S. Scott.† - - - - -	10 *Feb.* 58	19 *Jan.* 58	Inspector Genl. of Ordnance and
		Captains.			
	4	C. Douglas,† - - - - - -	20 *May* 51	*m* 20 *July* 58	Ordnance Dept.
	1	~~P. Christie,†~~ - - - - - -	3 *Mar.* 53	*m* 4 *Mar.* 53	Fur. S. C. 14th May 58.
	2	~~W. P. Waddy,†~~ - - - - -	23 *Jan.* 54		
	1	A. G. Austen,† - - - - -	31 *July* 54	*m* 20 *July* 58	
	3	W. A. Mackinnon, C. B. *PH*,	22 *Aug.* 55	*m* 20 *July* 58	
O.	2	H. J. B. Macleod, - - - -	26 *June* 56	... ...	Fur. S. C. 17th Aug. 58,
	4	Henry Francis, *PH*, - - - -	1 *Feb.* 57	8 *Jan.* 57	
	1	H. V. Timbrell,† - - - - -	21 *May* 58	.. ..	Doing duty with Recruit Depôt, Meerut.
		2nd Captains.			
	1	J. F. Raper † - - - - - -	27 Aug. 58		
N.	1	A. H. Heath, *PH*, (*a*) - - - -	27 *Aug.* 58	.. ..	Dept. P. W. Punjaub.
	2	F. R. DeBude, *PH*, - - - -	27 *Aug.* 58	.. ..	Comdg. mountain Train Battery.
	3	P. M. Syme,† - - - - - -	27 *Aug.* 58		
	4	E. Simeon, - - - - - -	27 *Aug.* 58		
		G. M. Dobbin, *PH*, - - - -	27 *Aug.* 58		
		Lieutenants.			[Native Christian Arty., Agra.]
	1	J. C. C. Price,† - - - - - -	14 *Sep.* 57	.. ..	Comdg. a company of Eurasian and
	2	W. O'Brien,† - - - - - -	27 *Apl.* 58	.. ..	Offg. Adjt. aud Qr. Mr. Arty. Division Govindghur.
	1	W. J. Stewart,† - - - - - -	27 *Apl.* 58		
	3	C. A. Baylay, - - - - - -	21 *May* 58		
	1	P. B. Raikes, - - - - - -	4 *July* 58		
	2	M W Ommanney, - - - - -	———		
	4	J. A. Low, - - - - - -	———		
	2	R. J. Abbott,† - - - - - -	———		
	2	H. I. E. Ford,† - - - - - -	12 *Dec.* 57		
	3	~~J. V. Wylie,~~ - - - - - -	12 *Dec.* 57		
	4	J. A. O. Hampton, - - - - -	———		
	4	H. L. Nicholas, - - - - -	———		
	4	T Graham, - - - - - -	———		
	3	C Macpherson, - - - - - -	———		
	1	J R J Dewar, - - - - - -	———		
	3	W. J. W. Muir, - - - - -	11 *Dec.* 58		
	1	H. G Willis, - - - - - - -	11 *Dec.* 58		
		Adjutant and Quarter Master	*Appointed.*		
		G. M. Dobbin, - - - - - -	30 *Sep.* 58		
		Surgeon.			
		*			
		Assistant Surgeon.			
		*			

(*a*) Has furnished certificates of qualification in Surveying and Civil Engineering.

2nd Battalion of Foot Artillery.

(European.)

Head-quarters, Ferozepore.

1st Co., Ferozepore.
No. 10, Horse Battery attached.
2nd Co., Phillour and Ferozepore.

3rd Co., Peshawur.
4th Co., Peshawur.
No. 23 Horse Battery attached.

Fur. Reg.	Compy.	Rank and Names.	Regl. Rank.	Army Rank.	Remarks.
		Colonel.			
		A. Lindsay, C. B., - - - - - -	2 *July* 35	*lg* 11 *Nov* 51	Europe, 5th Dec. 39.
		Lieut. Colonels.			
		J. T. Lane, C. B. (*Supy*) - - -	10 *Feb.* 49	*my* 8 *June* 56	Nynee Tal.
		W. H. Delamain,† - - - - -	14 *Nov.* 58		
		D. Reid, (*a*) - - - - -	23 *Dec.* 58		
		Captains.			
O.	..	T. Brougham,† - - - - - -	18 *Mar.* 52	11 *Dec.* 50	Fur. P. A. 12 April 59.
	4	C. H. Dickens, *P*, - - - - -	3 *Mar.* 53	.. ..	Supt. of Irrigation in Behar.
	3	James Young, *PH*, - - - - -	3 *Mar.* 53	*m* 19 *Jan.* 58	D. P. W. Jullundur Division.
	3	G. E. Voyle, *PH*, - - - - -	15 *Sep.* 53	.. ..	Ordnance Dept.
	4	S. Stallard, *PH*, - - - - -	17 *Nov.* 56		
	2	D. McNeill, *P* (*b*) - - - - -	15 *June* 57	10 *June* 57	
N.	3	Tyrwhitt Pulman, - - - - -	4 *July* 57	11 *June* 57	Fur. P. A. 1 April 59.
N.	~~1~~	~~R. Mecham, *PH*,~~ - - - - -	5 *Oct.* 57	12 *Aug* 57	Punjaub Irr. Force.
	3	D J F Newall, *P, H*, - - - -	27 *Apl* 58		
	1	A. Bunny, - - - - - -	27 *Apl.* 58	*m* 20 *July* 58	
		2nd Captains.			
O.	1	W. A. Ross, † - - - - - -	27 *Aug.* 58	... ..	Fur. S. C. 24th Jan. 59.
O.	2	H. M. Smith, *P,H*, - - - - -	27 *Aug.* 58	.. ..	Fur. S. C. 8th Dec. 54.
	4	A. D. Denniss, *PH*, - - - -	27 *Aug.* 58		
O.	3	T A. Dirom, *PH*, - - - - -	27 *Aug.* 58	.. ..	Fur. S. C. 21st Dec. 58.
	..	*Sir* W. Hamilton, *Bart.*, *PH*, (*c*).	27 *Aug.* 58		
		Lieutenants.			
N.	3	J. R. Pearson, *PCH*, (*c*) - - -	27 *June* 57	.. ..	Ordnance Department.
N.	2	D. S. Pemberton, - - - - -	27 *Apl.* 58	.. ..	Fur. S. C. 5th Nov. 58.
	4	C. A. M. Warde. - - - - - -	11 *Dec.* 57		
	1	T. J. C. A. Studdy, - - - - -	12 *Dec.* 57		
	2	R. H. Palmer,† - - - - - -	12 *Dec.* 57		
	4	J. H. Annand, - - - - - -	12 *Dec.* 57		
	1	A. H. Murray, - - - - - -	12 *Dec.* 57		
	1	E. R. Conolly, - - - - - -	12 *June* 58		
	3	T. W. Bridges, - - - - - -	12 *June* 58		
	2	D W G Fairfield - - - - -	———		
	4	H. M. Mackenzie, - - - - -	———		
	3	G Lamb, - - - - - -	———		
	1	L W Taylor, - - - - - -	———		
	4	A. B. Cunningham, - - - - -	11 *Dec.* 58		
		Adjutant and Quarter Master.	*Appointed.*		
		Sir W. Hamilton, *Bart.*, - - -	30 *Sep.* 58		
		Surgeon.			
		J. Ransford, - - - - - - - -	16 *Jan.* 55	12 *Jan.* 43	
		Assistant Surgeon.			
	2	L. H. J. Maclean, - - - - -	17 *Apl.* 59	14 *Jan.* 54	

(*a*) Passed a successful examination in the Assamese and Bengallee languges.
(*b*) Has passed examinations in the Persian, Turkish, Oordoo, Hindee and Punjaubee languages.
(*c*) Have furnished certificates of qualification in Surveying and Civil Engineering.

3rd Battalion of Foot Artillery.

(European.)
Head-quarters, Jullundur.

1st Co., Meerut.
No. 4, Bullock Batty. attached.
2nd Co. Cawnpore.
No. 12, Horse Battery attached.

3rd Co., Bareilly, Phillibheet and Moradabad.
No. 14 Horse Battery attached.
4th Co., Jullundur.
No. 24 Horse Battery attached.

Fur. Reg.	Compy.	Rank and Names.	Regl. Rank.	Army Rank.	Remarks.
		Colonel.			
N.		S. Shaw, - - - - - - - - -	25 *Mar.* 40	*lg* 5 *Mar.* 59	Furlough, S. C. 6th Jan. 55.
		Lieut. Colonels.			
		R. Horsford, - - - - - - -	31 *Mar.* 47	*col* 28 *Nov.* 54	Brigadier actg. Comdt. of Arty. & Comdg. the station of Meerut
		G. H. Swinley, - - - - - -	1 *July* 53	*col* 27 *June* 57	
		Captains.			
	3	H. Hammond, *P*, - - - - - -	3 *Mar.* 53	*m* 24 *Mar.* 58	
N.	4	D. C. Vanrenen, *PH*, - - - -	28 *Apl.* 53	.. ..	Survey Department.
	1	W. B. Marshall, *PH*, - - - -	15 *Oct.* 55		
	2	H. LeG. Bruce, *PH*, - - - -	8 *June* 57	*m* 24 *Mar.* 58	
	4	C. S. Dundas,† - - - - - -	28 *Sep.* 57	8 *July* 57	
		2nd Captains.			
		T. H. Salt, *PH*, - - - - - -	27 *Aug.* 58		
	4	Thomas Nicholl, *PH*, - - - -	27 *Aug.* 58	.. ..	Ordnance Department.
	3	C. W. Maynard *PH*, - - - -	27 *Aug.* 58		
		Lieutenants.			
	2	A. Swinton, - - - - - - -	27 *Apl.* 58		
	4	C. E. Armstrong, - - - - -	27 *July* 58		
	2	K. W. S. M. Cameron, - - - -	18 *Aug.* 58		
	1	C. E. Delafosse, - - - - - -	11 *Dec.* 57	.. ..	Leave S. C. 29th Oct.
	3	G. F. Blackwood, - - - - -	11 *Dec.* 57		
	3	W. C. Brown, - - - - - -	———		
	2	A. S. Heyland, - - - - - -	12 *Dec.* 57		
	4	G. H. W. Ewbank, - - - - -	12 *Dec.* 57		
	4	M. G. Browne, - - - - - -	12 *Dec.* 57		
	4	S. Cargill, - - - - - - -	———		
	3	H. J. Kinsman, - - - - - -	12 *June* 58		
	1	J. C. Greene, - - - - - - -	———		
	3	E. F. Chapman, - - - - - -	———		
	2	J. Loch, - - - - - - - -	———		
	1	A. E. L. Kaye, - - - - - -	———		
	1	J. F. Free, - - - - - - -	———		
		Adjutant and Quarter Master.	*Appointed.*		
		T. H. Salt, - - - - - - - -	30 *Sep.* 58		
		Surgeon.			
	..	S. A. Homan, - - - - - - -	17 *Mar.* 59	18 *July* 56	
		Assistant Surgeons.			
	1	J. Ince, M. D., - - - - - - -	26 *Nov.* 56	20 *Feb.* 56	
	2	A. D. Campbell, M. D., - - -	.. ..	27 *Jan.* 58	

4th Battalion of Foot Artillery.

(European.)

Head-quarters. Meean Meer, (Lahore.)

1st Co., Delhi.
2nd Co., Meerut.
No. 1 Horse Battery attached.

3rd Co., Meean Meer, (Lahore)
4th Co., Seetapore.

Fur. Reg.	Compy.	RANK AND NAMES.	Regl. Rank.	Army Rank.	REMARKS.
		Colonel.			
		G. Swiney,	1 *Dec.* 34	*lg* 11 *Nov.* 51	Europe, S.C., 10th Nov. 35.
		Lieut. Colonels.			
		F. B. Boileau,	10 *Mar.* 54	*c* 20 *June* 57	
		A. Broome,	14 *Sep.* 57	.. ..	Supdt., Cossipore Foundry.
		Captains.			
N.	3	H. Lewis, *PC,*	3 *Mar.* 53	12 *June* 52	Principal Commy. of Ordnance.
	2	A. Wintle, *PH,*	10 *Mar.* 54		
	3	H. R. Courtenay, *PH,*	8 *June* 56	.. ..	Lv. S. C. 20th November.
	2	F. Alexander,	8 *June* 56	.. ..	D. P. W. Lower Provinces.
	1	W. J. Gray,	27 *Apl.* 58	.. ..	In charge of Military Stores at Almorah.
O.	1	G. R. Brown,	27 *Apl.* 58	.. ..	Fur S C. 18 March 59.
	4	W. F. Cox,†	27 *April* 58		
		2nd Captains.			
	3	J. A. R. Mead,†	27 *Aug.* 58		
	1	H. R. Brownlow, *P,*	27 *Aug.* 58	.. ..	Ordnance Department.
O.		F. E. Smalpage, *PH*	27 *Aug.* 58	.. ..	Fur. S. C. 31st May 59.
N.	4	W. Brown, *PH,*	27 *Aug.* 58	.. ..	Fur. S. C. 13 Mar. 58.
	3	E. L. Earle, *PCH, (a)*	27 *Aug.* 58	.. ..	Civil employ.
N.	2	E. H. Willoughby. *PCH,*	27 *Aug.* 58	.. ..	Survey Dept.
		Lieutenants.			
	1	H. O. Hitchins, *PH,*	8 *June* 57		
N.	2	Hungerford D. Jackson,	10 *July* 57	.. ..	Fur. S. C. 16th June 59.
N.	1	D. MacFarlan, *PH,*	12 *Sep.* 57	.. ..	Fur. S. C. 23rd December 57.
	1	H. H. Murray,	12 *Dec.* 57	.. ..	Leave S. C. 26th Oct.
	3	W. B. Troup,	12 *Dec.* 57	.. ..	Leave P. A. 31st July.
	4	G. G. Nelson,	12 *Dec.* 57		
	2	G. W. Thomson,	———		
	2	E. H. H. Elliot,	———		
	2	C. Cowie,	———		
	4	F. Lindsay,	11 *Dec.* 58		
	3	M. W. Daniell,	11 *Dec.* 58		
		———	*Appointed.*		
		Adjutant and Quarter Master.			
		F. E. Smalpage,	30 *Sep.* 58	.. .	Fur. S. C. 31st May 59.
		Surgeon.			
		J. Barber,	11 *Dec.* 50	18 *Apl.* 43	
		Assistant Surgeon.			
		*			

(*a*) Has furnished certificates of qualification in Surveying and Civil Engineering.

5th Battalion of Foot Artillery.

(European.)
Head-quarters, Agra.

1st Co., Bareilly.
2nd Co., Gwalior.
No. 21, Horse Battery attached.

3rd Compy., Cawnpore.
4th Co., Dinapore.
No. 11, Horse Battery attached.

Fur. Reg.	Compy.	Rank and Names.	Regl. Rank.	Army Rank.	Remarks.
		Colonel.			
O.		G. E. Gowan, C. B., - - - -	3 *July* 45	*mg.* 20 *June* 54	Fur. P. A. 22 January 58.
		Lieut. Colonels.			
		G. Campbell, *(Supy)* - - - -	21 *July* 51	*mg.* 4 *July* 58	Comg. Dinapore Division.
		W. Barr, - - - - - - -	18 *Aug.* 58		
		G. Kirby, *P. C.* - - - - -	21 *Nov.* 58	24 *Mar.* 58	Commdg. Arty. Division, Cawnpore.
		Captains.			
	1	H. P. DeTeissier, *P*, - - - -	3 *Mar.* 53	11 *Dec.* 52	
	4	F. W. Swinhoe, *P.* - - - -	1 *July* 53		
O.	3	C. W. Timbrell, *PH*, - - -	24 *Mar.* 55	.. ..	Fur. S C. 4 Mar. 59.
	2	A. Light, *PH*, - - - - - -	10 *July* 57	*m* 19 *Jan.* 58	
	3	A. Pearson, *PH*, - - - -	1 *Jan.* 58	*m* 20 *July* 58	
	1	E. Harrison, *PH*, - - - - -	27 *Apl.* 58	.. ..	Doing duty with 4th Troop 2nd Bde. H. Arty.
		2nd Captains.			
	3	J. G. Hathorn, *PH*, - - - -	27 *Aug.* 58	.. ..	Ordnance Department.
	2	J. Hunter, *PH*, - - - - - -	27 *Aug.* 58		
R		~~F. C. Simons, *PH*,~~ - - - -	27 *Aug.* 58	*m* 28 *Aug.* 58	Comdg. Assam Local Arty.
	4	J. S. Gibb, *P*, - - - - - -	27 *Aug.* 58	*m* 28 *Aug.* 58	Fur. S. C., 17th Sep. 58.
N.	1	W. Wilson, - - - - - -	27 *Aug.* 58		
		Lieutenants.			
	3	P. C. Anderson, *PH*, - - - -	9 *Dec.* 50	.. ..	Adjt. Arty. Divn. Cawnpore.
	1	F. S. Roberts, v.c *PH*, - - -	31 *May* 57	.. ..	Quarter Mr. Genl.'s Dept.
N.	4	Ferdinand Fitzroy, - - - -	26 *July* 57	.. ..	Survey Dept., Pegu.
	2	R. S. Robinson, - - - - - -	27 *Apl.* 58		
	2	E. D. Elliott, - - - - - -	11 *Dec.* 57		
	4	G. F. Hamilton, - - - - -	11 *Dec.* 57		
	4	N. D. Garrett, - - - - - -	12 *Dec.* 57		
	1	W. H. Wilkins, - - - - - -	12 *Dec.* 57		
	1	W. A. Liot, - - - - - - -			
	4	R. F. Lowis, - - - - - -	———		
	2	J. H. Alexander, - - - - -	———		
	2	P. T. H. Taylor, - - - - -	12 *June* 58		
	3	H. Latham, - - - - - - -	12 *June* 58		
	4	A. E. Garnault, - - - - - -			
	1	F. A. Stubbs, - - - - - -	11 *Dec.* 58		
			Appointed.		
		Adjutant and Quarter Master.			
		J. Hunter, - - - - - - - -	30 *Sep.* 58		
		Surgeons.			
		R. Whittall, - - - - - - -	14 *Feb.* 59	31 *Dec.* 54	
	4	John Squire, - - - - - -	26 *Mar.* 59	24 *Apl.* 59	
		Assistant Surgeon.			
		*			
		Veterinary Surgeon.			
		*			

6th Battalion of Foot Artillery.

(*European.*)

Head-quarters, Peshawur.

1st Co., Lucknow.
2nd Co., Agra.
No. 8, Horse Battery attached.

3rd Co., Peshawur.
No. 19, Horse Battery attached.
4th Co., Shahjehanpore.

Fur. Reg.	Compy.	Rank and Names.	Regl. Rank.	Army Rank.	Remarks.
		Colonel.			
N.		A. Abbott, C. B., - - - - - -	14 Nov. 58	28 *Nov.* 54	Brigadier Comdt. of Arty. and H. A. D C. to the Govr. Genl. Fur. S. C. 27 May 58.
		Lieut. Colonels.			
O.		J. Fordyce, - - - - - - -	2 *Feb.* 51		
		F. C. Burnett, - - - - - - -	27 *June* 57	*c* 28 *Nov.* 54	Fur. S. C. 6th Feb. 57.
		Captains.			
	1	W. Maxwell,†- - - - - - -	20 *June* 49	*m* 24 *Mar.* 58	Canal Dept. N. W. P.
	3	S. C. Woodcock, *PH*, - - - -	20 *Feb.* 55		
	2	H. H. Maxwell, *PH*, - - - -	27 *June* 57	*lc.* 24 *Mar.* 58	
	4	C. Cookworthy, *PH*, - - - -	12 *Sep.* 57	*m* 20 *July* 58	
	1	J. E. Watson, *P.H*, - - - -	27 *Apl.* 58		
		2nd Captains.			
	2	F. D. Urquhart, *PH*, - - - -	27 *Aug.* 58	.. ..	Audit Department.
	2	C. S. Lemarchand,- (*a*) - -	27 *Aug.* 58		
	1	G. Baillie, *PH*, (*a*) - - - -	27 *Aug.* 58		
N.		J. E. Cordner, *PH*, - - - -	27 *Aug.* 58	.. ..	Depy. Supt. Roorkee Work Shops.
	4	T. Presant,† - - - - - -	27 *Aug.* 58	.. ..	Fur- P. A. 29 Mar. 59.
	3	D. Thomson, *PH*, (*a*) - - - -	27 *Aug.* 58	.. ..	Ex. Engineer Khewra Salt mines.
O.	4	J. Y. Worthington, *P.H*, - - -	27 *Aug.* 58	.. ...	Fur. S. C. 2 Feb. 58.
		Lieutenants.			
	2	H. A. Mallock, (*b*) - - - - -	25 *Sep.* 57		Offg. Ordnance Dept.
N.	4	George Grant Gordon,† - - -	14 *Nov.* 57	.. ..	Furlo. S. C. 24th April 57.
	2	H. Munro, - - - - - - -	27 *Apl.* 58		
	3	A. Walker, - - - - - - -	27 *Apl.* 58		
	3	E. H. Ryan, - - - - - - -	27 *Apl.* 58	.. ..	Punjaub Irr. Force.
	3	G. A. Russell, - - - - - -	11 *Dec.* 57		
	3	W. A. B. Gillies, - - - - -	12 *Dec.* 57		
	3	A. R. T. Chilton, - - - - -			
	2	T. A. Davis, - - - - - -	12 *Dec.* 57		
	3	H. Cotton, - - - - - - -			
	2	J. Charles, - - - - - - -			
	1	C. H. Reilly, - - - - - -	———		
	2	W. S. Alexander, - - - - -	———		
	4	B. V. Arbuckle, - - - - -	———		
	1	J. M. Young, - - - - - -	———		
	4	P. Boyd, - - - - - - - -	11 *Dec.* 58		
			Appointed.		
		Adjt. and Qr. Mr., J. E. Cordner,	30 *Sep.* 58	.. ..	Fur. P. A. 29 Mar. 59.
		Surgeon.			
	*				
		Assistant Surgeon.			
	*				

(*a*) Have furnished certificates of qualification in Surveyingand Civil Engineering.
(*b*) Has furnished the certificate of qualification in Surveying.

7th Battalion of Foot Artillery.

(*Native.*)

Head-quarters, Umballah.

1st Co., Umballa,
Has a 6 Pounder battery, attached.
2nd Co., Nusseerabad.—(Mutinied.)
3rd Co, Delhi.—(Mutinied.)
4th Co., Lahore.—(Disarmed.)
5th Co., Oude (Fyzabad.)—(Mutinied.)
6th Co., Cawnpore.—(Mutinied.)

Fur. Reg.	Compy.	Rank and Names.	Regl. Rank.	Army Rank.	Remarks.
		Colonel.			
		R. Powney, - - - - - - - -	12 *July* 44	*m.g.* 20 *June* 54	Europe, 18th Feb. 47.
		Lieut. Colonels.			
		V. Eyre, C. B. - - - - - - -	4 *July* 58	*c.* 24 *Mar.* 58	Gun-Powder Agent, Ishapore.
		C. Hogge, C. B., *PC*, - - - -	27 *Sep.* 58	*c.* 28 *Nov.* 57	Director Arty. Depot of Instruction.
		Captains.			
N.	2	R. Warburton, *P*, - - - - - -	21 *Feb.* 49	*m.* 13 *Mar.* 59	Fur. S, C. 14th April 57.
N.	6	J. Eliot, *PH*, - - - - - -	25 *Feb.* 53	9 *Dec.* 51	Dept. of Public Works, L. P.
	1	W. K. Fooks, *PH*, - - - - -	30 *Oct.* 55		
	5	Edward Atlay, *PH*, - - - - -	30 *May* 57	30 *Jan.* 57	Comdg. Recruit Depôt, Meerut.
N.	6	J. R. Sladen, *PH*, - - - - - -	25 *Sep.* 57	11 *June* 57	Punjaub Irr. Force.—Fur. S. C. 7th May 1858.
	1	H. M. Boddam,, *PH*, - - - -	27 *Mar.* 58	.. ..	Civil employ.
	3	E. W. E. Walker, *PH*, (*a*) - -	18 *Aug.* 58	*m.* 28 *Aug.* 58	
		2nd Captains.			
	6	A. Darling, *P*, - - - - - -	27 *Aug.* 58	.. ..	Offg. Ordnance Dept.
N.	1	J. Fulton,† - - - - - - -	27 *Aug* 58	.. ..	Fur S. C. 30th Nov. 58.
	4	G. O. Rybot, *PH*, (*a*) - - -	27 *Aug.* 58	.. ..	Executive Officer Nagpore Provinces.
	2	W. T. Brown, *PH*, - - - -	27 *Aug.* 58	*m.* 28 *Aug.* 58	Ordnance Department.
	6	J. R. Martin, *PH*, (*a*) - - - -	27 *Aug.* 58		
	4	H. T. Forbes, *PCH*, - - - -	27 *Aug.* 58	.. ..	Ex. Engineer, Santal Pergunnahs.
	5	F. R. Butt, *P*, - - - - - -	27 *Aug.* 58	.. ..	In charge of the Huzara Mountain Train.
N.	1	G. C. Depree, (*b*) - - - - -	27 *Aug.* 58	.. ..	Surveyor Generals' Department.
	3	C. J. Mead, - - - - - - -	14 *Nov.* 58	.. ..	Ex. Engineer, Patna Division .
		Lieutenvnts.			
	1	D. J. Welsh, *PCH*, - - - - -	30 *May* 57	.. ..	Ordnance Department.
N.	4	J. Alexander, - - - - - -	7 *Sep.* 57	.. ..	Fur. S. C. 19th Jan. 59.
N.	1	C. E. Nairne, - - - - - -	27 *April* 58	.. ..	Fur. S. C. 28th Sept. 58.
		———	*Appointed.*		
		*Adjutant,**			
		*Intr. and Qr. Mr.,**			
		Surgeon.			
		*			
		Assistant Surgeon.			
		*			

(*a*) Have furnished Certificates of qualification in Civil Engineering and Surveying.

(*b*) Has furnished the Certificate of qualification in Surveying.

8th Battalion of Foot Artillery.

(Native.)

Head-quarters, Bareilly.

1st Co., Cawnpore—(Mutinied.)
2nd Co., Bareilly.—(Disarmed.)
3rd Co., Almorah.—(Mutinied.)
4th Co., Lahore.—(Disarmed.)
5th Co., Umritsir.—(Disarmed.)
6th Co., Bareilly.—(Mutinied.)

Fur. Reg.	Compy.	Rank and Names.	Regl. Rank.	Army Rank.	Remarks.
		Colonel.			
		G. Twemlow,	6 *Mar.* 54	28 *Nov.* 54	Furlough, S. C. 22d Feb. 53.
		Lieut. Colonels.			
		F. Gaitskell, C. B., *P*,	17 *May* 54		
		H. A. Carleton, C. B., †	14 *Oct.* 58	20 *July.* 58	Leave S. C. to 15th Dec.
		Captains.			
D O.	2	J. Abercrombie,	10 *Feb.* 49	*lc* 28 *Nov.* 54	Furlough, S. C. 5th Nov. 58.
N.	1	T. E. Kennion, *P*,	6 *July* 57	*m.* 19 *Jan.* 58	Fur. S. C 5th Feb. 58.
	4	G. Maister, *PH*,	14 *Sep.* 57	11 *June* 57	Punjaub Irr. Force.
	2	G. Holland, *PH*,	10 *Feb.* 58	11 *Dec.* 56	
	5	J. A. Angelo, *PH*,	27 *April* 58		
	5	J. C. Griffith, *PH*,	4 *July.* 58	.. ..	Ordnance Department.
		2nd Captains			
N.	4	A. R. Fuller, *P*, (*a*)	27 *Aug*, 58	.. ..	Civil employ..
O.	5	W. H. Parish, †	27 *Aug.* 58	.. ..	Furlough, S. C. 16th July 58.
O.	6	W. Dickson, *PH*,	27 *Aug.* 58	.. ..	Fur. S. C. 18th Feb. 59.
	5	W. Dowell, *PCH*,	27 *Aug.* 58	.. ..	Adjutant of the Bengal Arty. at Lucknow.
	2	A. Gillespie, † (*b*)	27 *Aug.* 58	.. ..	In charge of the Derajat Field Magazine.
	3	J. H. Grant, *PH*, (*b*)	27 *Aug.* 58	.. ..	Survey Department.
		Lieutenants.			
N.	5	M. M. FitzGerald, (*b*)	9 *Dec.* 50	.. ..	Fur. S. C. 11th Jan. 59.
	5	J. Stewart, *PCH*,	8 *June* 57	.. ..	Ordnance Department.
..		C. Hunter, *PH*, (*c*)	6 *July* 57		
O.	4	J. Bonham, *PH*,	1 *Sep.* 57	.. ..	Fur S. C. 15th Jan, 58.
N.	2	H. S. Clarke,	——	.. ..	Fur. S. C. 4 Mar. 59.
	5	C. P. Elderton,	12 *June* 58		
N.	5	H. G. Young,	.. ..	.. ..	Fur. S. C. 14 May 59.
			Appointed.		
		Adjutant, C. Hunter,	10 *Aug.* 58	——	Adjutant Artv. Divn. Bareillv.
		Intr. and Qr. Master,*			
		Surgeon.			
		*			
		Assistant Surgeon.			
		*			

(*a*) Has attained the standard of proficiency in the Oordoo and Hindee languages prescribed by G. O. Govr. of Bengal 9th March 1852, and received a certificate of high proficiency in the Persian language, G. O. 31st Aug. 1854.

(*b*) Have furnished certificates of qualification in Surveying and Civil Engineering.

(*c*) Has furnished certificates of qualification in Surveying.

9th Battalion of Foot Artillery.

(Native.)

Head-quarters, Dum-Dum.

1st Co., Dum-Dum, .. (Disarmed.)
2nd Co., Dum-Dum,.. (Disarmed.)
3rd Co., Dum-Dum, .. (Disarmed.)
4th Co., Nowgong. (Mutinied.)
5th Co., Dum-Dum. (Disarmed.)
6th Co., Cawnpore.

Fur. Reg.	Compy.	Rank and Names.	Regl. Rank.	Army Rank.	Remarks.
		Colonel.			
		Sir G. Pollock, G. C. B., - - -	3 *Mar.* 35	*lg.* 11 *Nov.* 51	Europe, S.C. 21st Feb. 1847.
		Lieut. Colonels.			
		C. St Reid, - - - - - - - -	31 *Dec.* 54	*col* 28 *Nov.* 54	
N.	..	R. E. Knatchbull, - - - - -	28 *Sep.* 57	.. ..	Fur. S. C. 26th Feb. 58
		Captains.			
	3	H. E. L. Thuillier, *- - - - - -	2 *Feb.* 51	14 *Dec.* 47	Surveyor General's Department.
N	6	C. V. Bowie, *PH,* - - - - -	21 *Jan.* 56	*m* 22 *Jan.* 56	~~A. D. C. to G. G. and~~ Political employ.
	6	W. C. Russell, *PH,* - - - - -	18 *Sep.* 57	11 *June* 57	Ordnance Dept.
	2	Alex. Simpson, A. M., *P,* - - -	25 *Sep.* 57	11 *June* 57	
N.	3	C. M. Young, *P.(a)* - - -	14 *Jan.* 58	9 *Dec.* 57	Fur. P A 25th Apl 59
N.	1	J. S. Tulloh, *PH,* - - - - -	27 *Apl.* 58	.. ..	Fur. S. C. 23 Mar. 58.
	5	W. R. Fitzgerald, *PH,* - - - -	27 *Apl.* 58	.. ..	Dept. P. Works, Pegu Circle.
		2nd Captains.			
D ~~N.~~	~~4~~	~~W. A. Mylne, P,~~ - - - - - -	27 *Aug.* 58	.. ..	Fur. S. C. 30th Apl. 58.
	3	L. Machell, *PH,* - - - - -	27 *Aug.* 58	.. ..	Ordnance Dept.
N.	2	M. E. Currie, *PH,* - - - -	27 *Aug.* 58	.. ..	Ordnance Dept.
N.	1	R. Murray, *PH,* - - - - -	27 *Aug.* 58	.. ..	Civil employ.
	..	A. W. Pixley, *PH,* - - - - -	27 *Aug.* 58		
N.	6	T. N. Harward, *PH,* - - - -	27 *Aug.* 58	.. ..	Ordnance Department.
	5	A. H. Bogle, *PH.(b)* - - - -	27 *Aug.* 58	.. ..	A.D.C. to Maj. Genl. G. Campbell.
	3	T. E. Hughes, *PCH,* - - -	27 *Aug.* 58	.. ..	Punjaub, Irr. Force.
N.	6	E. Tierney, *P,H,* - - - - -	27 *Aug.* 58	.. ..	Ordnance Department.
O.	1	A. H. Lindsay, *PH,* - - - -	27 *Aug.* 58	.. ..	Fur. S. C. 4 May 58.
		Lieutenants.			
	1	C. V. Arbuckle, *P.C.H.*† - -	1 *Feb.* 57	.. ...	Ordnance Dept.
N.	6	H. E. Harington, V. C. *P.H.,* -	27 *June* 57	.. ..	Fur. S. C. 3 Dec. 58.
	2	W. B. Cumberland, *P.H.* - -	4 *July* 57	.. ..	Punjaub Irr. Force.
	3	P. Thompson, *PH,* - - - -	17 *Nov.* 57	.. ..	Revenue Survey Dept.
	5	F. E. Lewes,† - - - - - -	21 *Apl.* 58	.. ..	Doing duty Mountain Train Baty.
N.	3	H. Smithett, - - - - - -	27 *Apl.* 58	.. ..	Fur. S. C. 19 Nov. 58.
			Appointed.		
		Adjutant, A. W. Pixley, - - -	30 *Sep.* 58	.. ..	Station and Arty. Divn. Staff Officer, Dum-Dum.
		Intr. & Qr. Mr., A. Simpson, A. M.,	11 *June* 52	.. ..	Officiating.
		Surgeon.			
		*			
		Assistant Surgeon.			
		*			

* Official Major.

(*a*) Attained the standard of proficiency in the Punjaubee language prescribed by G. O. G. G. 14 Oct. 1851.

(*b*) Received degrees of honor in the Oordoo and Hindee languages from the College of Fort William, on the 23 Nov. 1847 and 4 Oct. 1848.

Corps of Engineers.

Fort William.

Uniform—*Scarlet.* **Facings**—*Garter Blue Velvet.* **Lace**—*Gold.*

Fur. Reg.	ER. Y	ER. M	Names.	*Second Lieutenant.*	*First Lieutenant.*	*Captain.*	*Brevet Major.*	*Lieutenant Colonel.*	*Colonel.*	*Major Genl.*	*Lieut. Genl.*	Remarks.
			Colonels (5.)									
N.	49	7	Sir John Cheape, K. C. B.,	3 *Nov.* 09	29 *Dec.* 16	1 *Mar.* 21	25 *June* 30	19 *Feb.* 44	10 *June* 45 *Regimental* 19 *Feb.* 44	20 *June* 54	... ...	Fur. P. A. 12 Feb. 1857.
	11	2	Edward Garstin,	6 *May* 15	1 *Sep.* 18	5 *July* 22	20 *Apl.* 35	5 *Dec.* 48	17 *Mar.* 51	28 *Nov.* 54		
N.	35	7	Henry Goodwyn,	18 *Dec.* 23	1 *Jan.* 26	*Bt.* 18 *Dec.* 38 *Regimental* 20 *May* 39	11 *Nov.* 46	5 *Dec.* 48	*Bt.* 28 *Nov.* 54 *Regimental* 3 *Aug.* 55	... ...	... ...	Chief Engineer Lower Provinces and Comdt. Corps of Engrs.—Fur. S. C. 9 April 1857.
	[illegible]	1	Alex. Henry E[illegible],	17 *June* 24	7 *Feb.* 27	20 *May* 39	19 *Aug.* 47	1 *May* 49	*Brevet* 28 *Nov.* 54 *Regimental* 8 *June* 56			Chief Engr. in the Nagpore Territories and Offg. Comdt. Corps of Engrs.
N.	32	7	William Erskine Baker,	15 *Dec.* 26	28 *Sep.* 27	31 *Mar.* 40	*Brevet* 19 *June* 46 *Regimental* 15 *Jan.* 51	*Brevet* 20 *June* 54 *Regimental* 21 *Aug.* 54	10 *Mar.* 57	... ...	... ...	Military Secretary to the Secretary of State for India in Council, (Europe.)
			Lieutenant Colonels (10.)									
	32	7	*Sir* Robert Napier, K. C. B.,	15 *Dec.* 26	28 *Sep.* 27	25 *Jan.* 41	3 *April* 46	*Bt.* 7 *June* 49 *Regimental* 1 *Aug.* 54	*Brevet* 28 *Nov.* 54	... ...	... ...	Chief Engineer, Punjaub and Offg. Chief Engineer, L. Provinces.
	32	1	John Glasfurd,	15 *June* 27	28 *Sep.* 27	28 *Aug.* 41	7 *June* 49	1 *Aug.* 54	*Brevet* 28 *Nov.* 57	... ...	... ...	Superintending Engr. 1st Circle N.W.P.
N.	31	7	Andrew Scott Waugh,	13 *Dec.* 27	13 *Dec.* 27	*Bt.* 13 *Dec.* 42 *Regimental* 19 *Feb.* 44	20 *June* 54	3 *Aug.* 55	... ...			Surveyor General of India and Supdt. of the Great Trigonometrical Survey.
	31	7	Edward Lacon Ommanney,	13 *Dec.* 27	22 *Jan.* 34	*Bt.* 13 *Dec.* 42 *Regimental* 5 *April* 44	20 *June* 54	15 *Apl.* 56	... ...			Superintending Engineer 2nd Circle Lower Provinces and Offg. Chief Engineer, Punjaub.
	31	1	Henry Marion Durand, C. B.,	12 *June* 28	20 *April* 35	*Brevet* 12 *June* 43 *Regimental* 30 *Nov.* 44	7 *June* 49	*Brevet* 28 *Nov.* 54 *Regimental* 8 *June* 56	20 *July* 58	... ...	... ...	Member of the Council of India, (Europe.)
	31	1	John Laughton,	12 *June* 28	3 *Feb.* 39	*Bt.* 12 *June* 43 *Regimental* 11 *Nov.* 46	20 *June* 54	10 *Mar.* 57	... ...			Leave S. C. 14 October.
	30	1	Henry Rigby,	12 *June* 29	20 *May* 39	*Bt.* 12 *June* 44 *Regimental* 1 *Dec.* 47	28 *Nov.* 54	20 *Sep.* 57	... ...	... ...	... ...	Suptg. Engr. 1st Circle, Punjaub,
	26	7	Thomas Henry Sale,	10 *Dec.* 30	20 *May* 39	*Bt.* 10 *Dec.* 45 *Regimental* 26 *Feb.* 50	... ...	1 *Oct.* 57	... ...	... ...	... ...	Offg. Supdg. Engineer 1st Circle, Lower Provinces.
	23	1	Alexander Cunningham,	9 *June* 31	20 *May* 39	*Bt.* 9 *June* 46 *Regimental* 15 *Jan.* 51	7 *June* 49	*Brevet* 28 *Nov.* 54 13 *Aug.* 58			...	Chief Engineer N. W. P.
	27	7	Norman Chester MacLeod, ...	8 *Dec.* 31	20 *May* 39	*Bt.* 8 *Dec.* 46 *Regimental* 28 *Feb.* 51	29 *Apl.* 56	*Brevet* 19 *Jan.* 58 *Regimental* 1 *Jan.* 59	... ...	... ...	... ...	Supdg. Engr. 2nd Circle N. W. Provinces.

Corps of Engineers—*Continued.*

Fur. Reg.	Ser. Y	Ser. M	Names.	Second Lieut.	First Lieut.	2nd Capt.	Captain.	Bt. Major.	Bt. Lt. Col.	Remarks.
			Captains. (30).							
N.	26	1	Stephen Bott, - - - - -	14 *Dec.* 32	31 *Mar.* 40	14 *Dec.* 47	15 *Feb.* 54	.. ..	.. ..	Fur S. C. 29 Dec. 58.
	23	6	Charles Becher Young, -	11 *Dec.* 35	25 *Jan.* 41	11 *Dec.* 50	15 *Feb.* 54	.. ..	.. ..	Suptg Engineer 1st Circle, L. P. Offg. Chief Engr. L. P.
	23	1	Richard Strachey, - - -	10 *June* 36	24 *Feb.* 41	10 *June* 51	15 *Feb.* 54	16 *Feb.* 54	.. ..	Consulting Engineer, to the Govt. of India—Railway Dept.
	22	1	Richard B. Smith, C.B., -	9 *Dec.* 36	28 *Aug.* 41	9 *Dec.* 51	15 *Feb.* 54	16 *Feb.* 54	19 *Jan.* 58	Master of the Calcutta Mint. [Lv. S. C. 31 Dec.
	22	1	Alex. D. Turnbull, *PH*, -	12 *June* 37	22 *Oct.* 41	12 *June* 52	1 *Aug.* 54	.. ..	.. ..	Supdt. General of Irrigation, N. W. P.
	22	1	Alfd. Geo. Goodwyn, *PH*, -	12 *June* 37	8 *Jan.* 42	12 *June* 52	ditto	2 *Aug.* 54	.. ..	Chief Engineer, Pegu.—Lv. S. C.
	21	4	John Reid Becher, *PH*, C.B.	6 *Mar.* 38	3 *Apl.* 42	6 *Mar.* 53	ditto	2 *Aug.* 54	.. ..	Deputy Commissioner Hazara. Punjaub.
	20	1	Henry Yule, *P* - - - -	11 *Dec.* 38	1 *Jan.* 43	1 *Dec.* 53	ditto	.. ..	*Offg. Lt. Col.*	Secy. to the Govt. of India, Pub. Works Department.
	20	1	William Elliot Morton, *P* -	11 *June* 39	8 *Nov.* 43	1 *June* 54	ditto	.. ..	.. ..	Deputy Supdt. Genl. of Irrigation N. W. P. [Roorkee.
	19	7	Robert Maclagan, *P*, - -	10 *Dec.* 39	29 *Dec.* 43	.. ..	ditto	.. ..	.. ..	Principal of the Thomason College of Civil Engineering at
	19	1	John Harley Maxwell, -	11 *June* 40	1 *Feb.* 44	.. ..	ditto	2 *Aug.* 54	.. ..	Ex. Engineer, Gwalior Division.—Lv. S. C.
	19	1	John Douglas Campbell, -	11 *June* 40	1 *Feb.* 44	.. ..	ditto		..	Ex. Engineer, Meerut Division.
	19	1	Edward John Lake, *PH*, -	11 *June* 40	1 *Feb.* 44	.. ..	21 *Aug.* 54	22 *Aug.* 54	.. ..	Commissioner Trans Sutlej States.
	18	7	James Pattle Beadle, - -	11 *Dec* 40	5 *Apl.* 44	.. ..	1 *May* 55	.. ..	.. ..	Superintendent of Embankments, Bengal.
O.	18	7	Archibald Impey, † - - -	11 *Dec.* 40	24 *Sep.* 44	.. ..	3 *Aug.* 55	.. ..	.. ..	Ex. Engr. Allahabad Divn. Offg. Civil Architect.
N.	18	7	George F. Atkinson, *PH*, -	11 *Dec.* 40	30 *Nov.* 44	.. ..	19 *Nov.* 55	.. ..	.. ..	Ditto Upper Sirhind Division.—Fur. S. C. 30 April 58.
	18	1	Wm. D. A. R. Short, † -	11 *June* 41	5 *May* 46	.. ..	3 *Dec.* 55			Ex. Engineer Midnapore Division of Embankments.
	17	7	Wm. Arden Crommelin, C.B.	10 *Dec.* 41	18 *Oct.* 46	.. ..	15 *Apl.* 56	24 *Mar.* 58	.. ..	Chief Engineer, Oude. [Sirhind Div.
	17	7	James E. T. Nicolls, *PH*, -	10 *Dec.* 41	11 *Nov.* 46	.. ..	8 *June* 56	.. ..	.. ..	Asst. to the Chief Engr. N. W. P. Offg. Ex. Engr. Upper
	17	1	Charles James Hodgson, † -	10 *June* 42	23 *May* 47	.. ..	17 *Aug.* 56	.. ..	.. ..	Offg. Consulting Engr., Railway Dept., Bengal.
	16	1	Daniel G. Robinson, *PH*, -	9 *June* 43	16 *June* 47	.. ..	21 *Nov.* 56	..	..	Great Trigonometrical Survey.
	16	1	Chas. W. Hutchinson, *PH*,	9 *June* 43	19 *Aug.* 47	.. ..	10 *Mar.* 57	.. ..	.. ..	Offg. Supdg. Engr. 2nd Circle, Punjaub.
N.	16	1	Alexander Taylor, C.B. † -	9 *June* 43	19 *Nov.* 47	... ..	16 *May* 57	19 *Jan.* 58	20 *July* 58	Supt. Lahore and Peshawur Road.—Fur.
	16	1	George Sim, † - - - -	9 *June* 43	1 *Dec.* 47	.. ..	27 *June* 57	.. ..	.. ..	Dep. Consulting Engr., Railway Dept., East India Railway
	15	7	Joseph Henry Dyas, † - -	8 *Dec.* 43	4 *Nov.* 48	.. ..	11 *Aug.* 57			Director of Canals, Punjaub.—Lv. p. to Fur. [N. W. P.
	15	7	Alexander Fraser, † - -	8 *Dec.* 43	9 *Nov.* 48	.. ..	14 *Sep.* 57	.. ..	.. ..	Under Secretary Public Works Dept. [jaub.
	15	7	Henry Drummond, † - -	8 *Dec.* 43	1 *May* 49	.. ..	20 *Sep.* 57	20 *July* 58		Supt. N. Div. Ganges Canal. Offg. Director of Canals, Pun-
	15	7	John Charles Harris, † -	8 *Dec.* 43	6 *Nov.* 49	.. ..	1 *Oct.* 57			Ex. Engineer, Cuttack Divn. Embankments.
	15	1	Thomas George Glover, † -	7 *June* 44	13 *Nov.* 49	.. ..	27 *Apl* 58	.. ..	.. ..	Ex. Engineer, Nynee Tal Div.
	15	1	Henry Hyde, - - - -	7 *June* 44	26 *Feb.* 50	.. ..	27 *Apl.* 58	.. ..	.. ..	Ex Engr. Lahore Div. [Hosheyarpore.
	15	1	*Ralph Young, *PH*, - - -	7 *June* 44	16 *June* 50	.. ..	27 *Apl.* 58	.. ..	.. ..	Depy. Commissioner of Jullundur, Offg. Deputy Commr.
	15	1	*George Hutchinson, † - -	7 *June* 44	15 *Jan.* 51		27 *Apl.* 58	20 *July* 58	. .	Milv. Secy. to the Chief Commr., Oude.
	14	7	*Chas. D. Newmarch, † -	9 *Dec.* 44	28 *Feb.* 51	.. ..	27 *Apl.* 58			Assistant to the Chief Engineer, Pegu. (Offg. Chief Engr.)
N.	14	7	*James Crofton, † - - -	9 *Dec.* 44	7 *Oct.* 51	.. ..	13 *Aug.* 58	.. ..	.. ..	Supt. Baree Doab Canal, Punjaub.—Fur. S. C. 21st June 59.

* Supernumeraries.

Corps of Engineers—*Continued.*

Fur. Reg.	Ser. Y	Ser. M	Names.	Second Lieut.	First Lieut.	2nd Capt.	Captain.	Bt. Major.	Bt. Lt. Col.	Remarks.
			2nd Captains, (30.)							
	14	7	Wm. W. H. Greathed, *PH,*	9 *Dec.* 44	14 *May* 52	27 *Aug.* 58	.. ..	28 *Aug.* 58	.. ..	Consulting Engineer, to Government N. W. P. (Railway Dept.)
	14	1	Alexander Cadell,† - -	13 *June* 45	1 *Jan.* 54	do	.. ..	.. ..	.. ..	Ex. Engr., Fyzabad (Oude.)
	13	7	William S. Oliphant, *PH,*	12 *Dec.* 45	15 *Feb.* 54	do	.. ..	.. ..	.. ..	Ex. Engr., Gwalior Division, N. W. P.
	13	7	Henry William Gulliver,†	12 *Dec.* 45	do	do	.. ..	.. ..	.. ..	Ex. Engr. 2nd Div. Baree Doab Canals.
	13	7	Charles Pollard, *PH,* - -	12 *Dec.* 45	do	do	.. ..	.. ..	.. ..	Ex. Engr. Peshawur Division.
	13	1	Chas. Thornton Stewart,†	12 *June* 46	do	do	.. ..	.. ..	.. ..	Supdt. Western Jumna Canals.
	13	1	Fredk. Richard Maunsell,†	12 *June* 46	do	do	.. ..	28 *Aug.* 58	.. ..	Comdt. Corps of Sappers and Miners.
	~~13~~	~~1~~	~~Arthur William Garnett,~~ -	12 *June* 46	do	do	.. ..	.. ..	.. ..	Ex. Engineer Kohat.
	12	7	Frederick Weston Peile, -	11 *Dec.* 46	1 *Aug.* 54	do	.. ..	.. ..	.. ..	Ex. Engr,, Ramghur Div. Offg. Ditto Allahabad Div.
	~~12~~	~~7~~	~~George Edward Watson,~~†	11 *Dec.* 46	do	do	.. ..	28 *Aug.* 58	.. ..	Asst. to Supt. Engr. 2nd Circle N. W. P.
	12	1	J. Francis Tennant, *PH,* -	11 *June* 47	do	do	.. ..	28 *Aug.* 58	.. ..	Astronomer to Government.
O.	~~12~~	~~1~~	~~William Henderson,~~† - -	11 *June* 47	do	do	.. ..	.. ..	.. ..	Ex. Engr. 4th Div. Lahore and Peshawur Road. Fur. S. C. [29 Mar. 59.
	12	1	Julius George Medley, *PH,*	11 *June* 47	do	do	.. ..	28 *Aug.* 58	.. ..	Deputy Consulting Engr., Mooltan and Lahore Railway.
N.	12	1	Fredk. Sherwood Taylor, -	11 *June* 47	do	do	.. ..	.. ..	.. ..	Furlough, S. C. 26 Mar. 59.
	12	1	Edward Davidson, *PH,* -	11 *June* 47	do	do	.. ..	.. ..	.. ..	Deputy Consulting Engr., Eastern Bengal Railway.
	11	7	Lindsay Russell, - - -	10 *Dec.* 47	do	do	.. ..	.. ..	.. ..	Ex. Engr., Shahjehanpore Divn.
N.	11	1	Ewd. C. S. Williams, *PCH,*	9 *June* 48	do	do	.. ..	.. ..	.. ..	Principal of the Civil Engineering College, Fort William.
	10	7	James J. McLeod Innes, vc†	8 *Dec.* 48	do	do	.. ..	28 *Aug.* 58	.. ..	Garrison Engineer, Fort William.
	10	7	George Tomkyns Chesney,	8 *Dec.* 48	do	do	.. ..	28 *Aug.* 58	.. ..	Offg. Principal Civil Engrg. College, Fort William.
	~~10~~	~~1~~	~~Thos. G. Montgomerie, *PH*~~	8 *June* 49	do	do	.. ..	.. ..	.. ..	Great Trigonometrical Survey, 1st Assistant.
N.	10	1	Wm. Ed. Warrand, *PH,* -	8 *June* 49	do	do	.. ..	28 *Aug.* 58	.. ..	Furlough S. C. 15 Apl. 58.
	9	7	George Ayton Craster, -	11 *Dec.* 49	do	do	.. ..	.. ..	.. ..	Ex. Engineer, Lucknow Divn.
	9	7	H. A. Brownlow, - - -	11 *Dec.* 49	do	do	.. ..	28 *Aug.* 58	.. ..	Supdt. Eastern Jumna Canals.
	9	7	Wm. Spottiswoode Trevor,	11 *Dec.* 49	do	do	.. ..	.. ..	.. ..	Ex. Engineer Darjeeling Divn.
N.	~~9~~	~~1~~	~~Patrick Stewart,~~ - - -	14 *June* 50	do	do	.. ..	28 *Aug.* 58	.. ..	Fur. S. C. 6 Apl. 58.
	9	1	David Limond, - - -	14 *June* 50	21 do	do	.. ..	.. ..	.. ..	Ex. Engineer, Cawnpore Divn.
	9	1	Raoul de Bourbel, - -	14 *June* 50	23 *Jan.* 55	do	.. ..	.. ..	.. ..	Ex. Engr. Dum-Dum.
	8	7	Fredk. Smith Stanton, -	9 *Dec.* 50	1 *May* 55	do	.. ..	.. ..	.. ..	Ex. Engr. 2nd Divn., Grand Trunk Road.
N.	~~8~~	~~7~~	~~William Hichens,~~† -	9 *Dec.* 50	3 *Aug.* 55	do	.. ..	.. ..	.. ..	~~Fur. S. C. 16th Dec. 56.~~
	~~8~~	~~7~~	~~Julian St. John Hovenden~~	9 *Dec.* 50	3 *Dec.* 55	do	.. ..	28 *Aug.* 58	.. ..	~~Commandant 24th Punjaub Infantry.~~
			Lieutenants, (60.)							
	~~8~~	~~1~~	~~Wm. Raffles Tucker, *PH,*~~	.. ..	13 *June* 51	.. ..	.. ..	.. ..	.. ..	Ex. Engineer Benares Divn.
	~~7~~	~~7~~	~~J. Palladio Basevi, *PH,*~~ -	.. ...	12 *Dec.* 51	.. ..	.. ..	.. ..	.. ..	Great Trigonometrical Survey, 1st Assistant
	7	7	Æneas Perkins,† - - -	.. ..	12 *Dec.* 51	.. ..	.. ..	.. ..	.. ..	Fur. S. C. 30 Apl. 58.
O.	7	1	Arthur Moffatt Lang,† -	.. ..	12 *June* 52	.. ..	.. ..	... ..	.. ..	Assist to the Chief Engr., Oude.
	~~7~~	~~1~~	~~Edward Wood Humphry,~~	.. ..	12 *June* 52	.. ..	.. ..	.. ..	.. ..	Adjutant, Sappers and Miners.
	7	1	Chas. Simeon Thomason,	.. ..	12 *June* 52	.. ..	.. ..	.. ..	.. ..	Asst. Supdt. N. Division Ganges Canal, Offg. Supdt.
	6	7	Salusbury Thomas Trevor,	.. ..	9 *Dec.* 52	.. ..	.. ..	.. ..	.. ..	Ex. Engr. Rangoon Divn. Offg. Asst. Chief Engr. Pegu.

CORPS OF ENGINEERS—*Continued.*

Fur. Reg.	Ser Y	Ser M	NAMES.	Second Lieut.	Lieut.	2nd Capt.	Captain	Bt. Major.	Bt. Lt. Col.	REMARKS.
			LIEUTENANTS.—(*Contd.*)							
	6	7	George Newmarch, *PCH*, -	.. ..	9 *Dec.* 52	.. ..	.. ..	.. ..	.. ..	Ex. Engineer, Delhi Division.
	6	7	John Lidstone Watts,† -	.. ..	do	.. ..	.. ..	.. ..	.. ..	Ex. Engineer, Agra Division.
	6	1	J. Underwood Champain,	.. ..	11 *June* 53	.. ..	.. ..	.. ..	.. ..	Ex. Engineer, Gondah Division.
	6	1	R. C. B. Pemberton, *PH*,	.. ..	do	.. ..	.. ..	.. ..	.. ..	Ex. Engineer, Seetapore Division.
	6	1	Robert Home,† - - -	.. ..	do	.. ..	.. ..	.. ..	.. ..	Offg. Ex. Engineer, 1st Division Baree Doab Canals.
	5	7	Patrick Murray, -† - - -		9 *Dec.* 53	.. ..	.. ..	.. ..	.. ..	Sappers and Miners.
	5	7	Alexander McNeill,†		9 *Dec.* 53	.. ..	.. ..	.. ..	.. ..	Asst. Engineer, Berhampore Division.
	5	1	William Jeffreys, *PCH*, -	.. ..	8 *June* 54	.. ..	.. ..	.. ..	.. ..	Depy. Supdt. Western Jumna Canals, Delhi.
	4	10	David Ward, *P. H.* -	.. ..	7 *Sep.* 54	.. ..	.. ..	.. ..	.. ..	Asst. Engineer Fyzabad (Oude).
	4	7	H. Alex. Lindsay Carnegie	.. ..	9 *Dec.* 54	.. ..	.. ..	.. ..	.. ..	Furlough P. A. 1st April 1859.
	4	7	Ed. Talbot Thackeray,† -	.. ..	do	.. ..	.. ..	.. ..	.. ..	Asst. Engr. Gondah Division.
	4	7	John Greenlaw Forbes,†	.. ..	do	.. ..	.. ..	.. ..	.. ..	Assist. Engr. 1st Divn. Baree Doab Canals.
	4	1	Charles Henry Luard, -	.. ..	8 *June* 55	.. ..	.. ..	.. ..	.. ..	Depy. Supdt. Etawah Division Ganges Canal.
	4	1	John Birny, - - - -	.. ..	do	.. ..	.. ..	.. ..	.. ..	Depy. Supdt. Eastern Jumna Canal.
	4	1	George Swinton,† - - -	.. ..	do	.. ..	.. ..	.. ..	.. ..	Asst. Engineer, Ramghur Division.
	4	1	Charles Neave Judge, -	.. ..	do	.. ..	.. ..	.. ..	.. ..	Asst. Engineer, 2nd Division G. T. Road.
	4	1	Geo. Scott, Hills, - - -	.. ..	do	.. ..	.. ..	.. ..	.. ..	Assist. Engineer, Allahabad Division.
	3	7	John Eckford, - - -	.. ..	7 *Dec.* 55	.. ..	.. ..	.. ..	.. ..	Asst. Engineer, 1st Division Baree Doab Canals. [Roorkee.
	3	7	A. Milness Brandreth, -	.. ..	do	.. ..	.. ..	.. ..	.. ..	Offg. Asst. Principal of the Thomason Civil Engrg. College,
	3	7	Henry William Garnault,	.. ..	do	.. ..	.. ..	.. ..	.. ..	Asst. Engineer, Embankment Circle, L. P. [Presidency.
	3	7	Hamilton Thos. Gordon,†	.. ..	do	.. ..	.. ..	.. ..	.. ..	Professor of Constructive Design in the Civil Engrg. College
	3	7	Ralph Graham Smyth, -	.. ..	do	.. ..	.. ..	.. ..	.. ..	Offg. Garrison Engineer, Lucknow.
	3	7	Parry Lambert,† - - -	.. ..	do	.. ..	.. ..	.. ..	.. ..	Asst. Engineer, Oude.
	3	7	John Philip Steel, - - -	.. ..	do	.. ..	.. ..	.. ..	.. ..	
	3	1	John Magee McNeile, -	.. ..	13 *June* 56	.. ..	.. ..	.. ..	.. ..	Asst. Engineer, Embankment Circle, L. P.
	3	1	William Henzey Oliver,† -	.. ..	do	.. ..	.. ..	.. ..	.. ..	Irrigation Dept. N. W. P.
	3	1	C. C. Scott Moncrieff,† -	.. ..	do	.. ..	.. ..	.. ..	.. ..	Asst. Engineer, Seetapore Division.
	3	1	William Burvill Holmes,†	.. ..	do	.. ..	.. ..	.. ..	.. ..	Sappers and Miners.
	3	1	Henry Francis Blair,† -	.. ..	do	.. ..	.. ..	.. ..	.. ..	Asst. Engineer, Punjaub.
	3	1	John Magee Heywood, -	.. ..	do	.. ..	.. ..	.. ..	.. ..	Asst. Engr., Barrackpore Division.
	2	7	John Herschel, - - -	.. ..	12 *Dec.* 56	.. ..	.. ..	.. ..	.. ..	Sappers and Miners.
	2	7	Robert Claude Danbuz, -	.. ..	do	.. ..	.. ..	.. ..	.. ..	Asst. Engineer 2nd Division G. T. Road.
	2	7	Hastings Macsween, - -	.. ..	do	.. ..	.. ..	.. ..	.. ..	Sappers and Miners.
	2	7	Isaac Pratt Westmorland,	.. ..	do	.. ..	.. ..	.. ..	.. ..	Asst. Garrison Engineer, Fort William.
	2	7	Arthur Charles Padday, -	.. ..	do	.. ..	.. ..	.. ..	.. ..	Asst. Engineer, 2nd Division Baree Doab Canals.
	2	7	O. B. C. St. John, - -	.. ..	do	.. ..	.. ..	.. ..	.. ..	
	2	7	Arthur Herbert Bagge, -	.. ..	do	.. ..	.. ..	.. ..	.. ..	Sappers and Miners.
	2	1	Hry. Ravenshaw Thuillier,	.. ..	12 June 57	.. ..	.. ..	.. ..	.. ..	Great Trigonometrical Survey, 2nd Assistant.
	2	1	A. J. W. Cumming, -	.. ..	do	.. ..	.. ..	.. ..	.. ..	
	2	1	T. C. Manderson, - - -	.. ..	do	.. ..	.. ..	.. ..	.. ..	

Corps of Bengal Sappers and Miners.

Remodelled, and Designation changed by G. O. G. G., 20th March 1851.

Head-quarters, Roorkee, 7th Nov. 1853.

UNIFORM—*Scarlet.* FACINGS—*Dark-blue.* LACE, *Gold.*

" *Bhurtpore*"—" *Sobraon*"—" *Punjaub.*"

The 2nd and 3rd Companies, " *Affghanistan*"—" *Ghuznee.*"
The 2nd Company, " *Punjaub.*"—" *Mooltan*"—" *Goojerat.*"
The 3rd Company, " *Punjaub,*"—" *Mooltan.*"—Detachment, " *Goojerat.*"
The 7th and 8th Companies, " *Jellalabad.*"
The 4th, 5th, 7th and 8th Companies, and Detachment 2nd and 3rd Companies " *Cabool, 1842.*"
The Detachment of the 2nd and 3rd Companies, " *Candahar*" and " *Ghuznee.*"
The 3rd, 4th and 7th Companies, " *Maharajpoor.*"
The 1st Company, " *Punniar*"—" *Punjaub*"—" *Mooltan.*"
The 6th Company, " *Ferozeshuhur.*"
Late 1st Company Pioneers, now 4th Company, " *Punjaub*"
Late 2nd and 3rd Companies Pioneers, now 5th and 6th Companies, " *Punjaub*"—" *Mooltan*"—" *Goojerat.*"
Late 4th Company Pioneers, now 7th Company, " *Punjaub*"—" *Chillianwalla*"—" *Goojerat.*"
Late 5th Company Pioneers, now 8th Company, " *Punjaub.*" Detachment, " *Mooltan*" and " *Chillianwallah*"—" *Goojerat.*"
Late 6th Company Pioneers, now 9th Company, " *Punjaub*"—" *Chillianwalla*"—" *Goojerat.*"
Late 7th Company Pioneers, now 10th Company, " *Punjaub*"—" *Chillianwalla*"—" *Goojerat.*"

RANK, NAMES AND CORPS.	*Army Rank.*	*When Appointed.*	REMARKS.
Major.			
F. R. Maunsell, Engineers, - -	28 *Aug.* 58	7 *Sep.* 50	Commandant.
Captain.			
H. Bingham, (*unattached*), - -	3 *Jan.* 59	.. ..	Offg. Interpreter & Quarter Master.
Lieutenants.			
E. W. Humphry, Engineers, - -	12 *June* 52	.. ..	Adjutant.
P. Murray, Engrs., - - - - -	9 *Dec.* 53	23 *Jan.* 56	Doing duty.
W. B. Holmes, Engrs, - - - -	13 *June* 56	.. ...	~~Ditto.~~ D. P. W.
J. Herschel, Engrs, - - - - -	12 *Dec.* 56	26 *Feb.* 59	~~Ditto.~~ G. T. S.
H. Macsween, Engrs, - - - -	do	... ..	~~Ditto.~~ D. P. W. Railways
A. H. Bagge, Engrs., - - - -	do	... ...	~~Ditto.~~ do. Canals.
Surgeon.		*Appointed*	
F. Turnbull, M. D., - - - -	30 *Sep.* 58	26 *Apl.* 47	Fur. P. A. 28 April 59.
Deputy Asst. Commissary.			
James Smith, - - - - - - -	.. ..	6 *Jan.* 54	
Sub-Conductors.			
Q. S. Griffith, - - - - - - -	8 *Jan.* 59		
J. Copeland, - - - - - - - -	do		
J. Smith, - - - - - - - - -	1 *July* 59		

Strength—12 Companies, with 1 Sergeant Major—1 Quarter Master Sergeant—24 Sergeants—24 First Corporals—24 Second Corporals—2 Native Doctors—12 Subadars—12 Jemadars—48 Havildars—96 Naicks—24 Buglers—1200 Privates.

Governor General's Body-Guard.

"JAVA"—"AVA"—"MAHARAJPORE"—"MOODKEE"—"FEROZESHUHUR"—"ALLIWAL"—"SUBRAON."

Ballygunge.—Arrived 20th January 1852.

RANK, NAMES AND CORPS.	*Army Rank.*	*When Appointed.*	REMARKS.
Major W. A. A. Thomson, 4th En. L. C., - - -	13 *July* 56	12 *Apl.* 51	Commandant.
Capt. G. Delane, 3d En. Lt. C.,	24 *Dec.* 55	29 *Sept.* 52	2nd in Command, Offg. political employ.
*			Adjutant.
Asst. Surg. H. D. Jones, - -	20 *May.* 54	25 *Feb.* 59	In Medical charge.
Veterinary Surg. H. C. Hulse, -	23 *Aug.* 28	10 *Nov.* 52	

REGIMENTALS—*Jacket,* Scarlet—*Facings,* Dark-blue—*Lace,* Silver.

Strength—2 Troops, with 1 Sergeant Major—2 Pay Havildars—1 Drill Havildar—1 Quarter Master Havildar—1 Trumpeter Major—2 Native Doctors—1 Subadar Major—3 Subadars—4 Jemadars—12 Havildars—15 Naicks—4 Farriers—2 Rough Riders—3 Trumpeters—144 Troopers.

Raised in 1858. }

1st European Light Cavalry.

{ Allahabad.

RIGHT WING.

FACINGS.———

Fur. Reg	SER Y	SER M	
O.	50	3	*Colonel* Thos. Mathew Taylor. *Cornet* 27 Mar. 1809; *Lieut.* 1 Sep. 1818; *Bt. Capt.* 16 Sep. 1823; *Capt.* 13 May 1825; *Major* 1 Mar 1836; *Lt. Col.* 5 Aug 1839; *Bt. Col.* 14 Nov. 1849; *Col.* 22 Aug. 1855; *Major General* 28 Nov. 54.—Fur. S. C. 4 Jan. 55.
	39	11	*Lt. Col.* F. Wheler, *P.* *Cornet* 18 Aug. 1819; *Lieut.* 30 June 1821; *Capt.* 7 July 1833; *Bt. Maj.* 9 Nov. 1846; *Maj.* 15 Dec. 1851; *Bt. Lt. Col.* 7 June 1849; *Lt. Col.* 28 Nov. 1854; *Bt. Col.* 28 Nov. 1854.—Brigadier Comdg. at Saugor.
	20	7	*Major* C. V. Jenkins, *PH.* *Cornet* 24 Jan. 1839; *Lieut.* 1 Jan. 1844; *Capt.* 31 Jan. 1852; *Maj.* 1 July 1857.—

☞ *Brevet.* [1] Major 20 July 1858. [2] Major 20 July 1858.

Fur. Reg	Y	M		Remarks.	Cornet.	Lieut.	Captain. Brevet.	Captain. Regl.
			CAPTAINS. 14					
O.	16	6	J. H. Brooks, *PH*, [1]*m* - -	Fur. P. A. 28 Apl. 59	30 *Jan.* 43	16 *Oct.* 45	.. ..	20 *Feb.* 53
	16	5	C. H. Nicholetts, *P*, - -	.. ..	19 *Feb.* 43	23 *Oct.* 45	.. ..	30 *Nov.* 53
N.	14	9	H. Forbes, *PH*, [2]*m*, -	Fur. S.C. 27 May 58	3 *Oct.* 44	31 *Mar.* 51	.. ..	25 *Oct.* 56
N.	13	9	F. C. J. Brownlow, *PH*, -	Fur. S. C. 6 Jan. 57	1 *Oct* 45	1 *Jan.* 52	.. ..	23 *Nov.* 56
	9	9	*Sir* J. Hill, *Bart.*, *PH*, -	.. ..	20 *Oct.* 49	31 *Jan.* 52	.. ..	1 *Jan.* 57
	9	7	H. E. Ellice,† - - - -	.. ..	20 *Dec.* 49	18 *Aug.* 52	.. ..	1 *July* 57
	8	10	W. H. Macnaghten,† - -	.. ..	20 *Sept.* 50	20 *Oct.* 52	.. ..	19 *July* 57
			LIEUTENANTS. 18					
N.	7	8	C. Martin, *PC*, - - -	Fur. S. C. 3 Feb. 59	20 *Nov.* 51	20 *Feb.* 53		
N.	6	9	F. P. Luard, *PH*, - - -	Fur. S. C. 1 Sep. 58	12 *Oct.* 52	30 *Nov.* 53		
	6	8	R. T. P. Stapleton,† - -	Bengal Yeomanry Cavalry, ..	20 *Nov.* 52	17 *Sep.* 55		
	~~5~~	~~1~~	~~Robert Wilkinson Dent~~, -	.. ..	4 *June* 54	25 *Oct.* 56		
	2	10	A. H. Chapman, - - -	.. ..	20 *Sep.* 56	9 *Jan.* 57		
N.	2	8	Richard Graham Birch, -	Fur. S. C. 14 Feb. 58	20 *Nov.* 56	23 *Jan.* 57		
	2	6	J. S. Robinson,† - - -	.. ..	4 *Jan.* 57	27 *Apl.* 57		
	1	11	Robert Morris, - - - -	.. ..	4 *Aug.* 57	18 *May* 58		
	1	6	E.S.R.Carnac, - - - -	.. ..	4 *Jan.* 58	18 *May* 58		
	1	6	G. C. B. Taylor, - - -	.. ..	20 *Jan.* 58	18 *May* 58		
	..	8	F. Currie,	.. ..	20 *Nov.* 58	29 *Mar.* 59		
			CORNETS. 8					
			* E. C. B. Rawlinson					
			*					
			*					
			*					
			*					
			*					
			*					
			*					

LEFT WING.

Y	M	
59	10	*Colonel* Harry Thomson. *Cornet* 31 Aug. 1799; *Lieut.* 22 Dec. 1803; *Capt.* 15 April 1816; *Major* 27 Oct. 1818; *Lieut. Col.* 29 April 1825; *Col.* 1 Dec. 1829; *Major Genl.* 28 June 1838; *Lieut. Genl.* 11 Nov. 1851.—Europe, 22 Dec. 34.
38	11	*Lt. Col.* G. M. C. Smyth. *Cornet* 14 Aug. 1820; *Lieut.* 3 Oct. 1821; *Capt.* 24 July 1828; *Bt. Major* 23 Nov. 1841; *Bt. Lt. Col.* 11 Nov. 1851; *Major* 21 Oct. 1852; *Lieut. Col.* 3 May 1856; *Bt. Col.* 28 Nov. 1854.

Strength of 4 *Regiments of European Light Cavalry*—10 Troops, with 1 Sergeant Major—1 Quarter Master Sergeant—10 Troop Sergeant Majors—1 Saddler Sergeant—1 Farrier Sergeant—1 Hospital Sergeant—1 Orderly room Clerk—40 Sergeants—1 Trumpet Major—10 Trumpeters—40 Corporals—10 Farriers—1 Armourer Sergeant—700 Privates.

1st European Light Cavalry.

LEFT WING.—*Continued.*

Fur. Reg.	Ser. Y	Ser. M	
	38	2	*Major* Henry Drummond. *Cornet* 5 May 1821; *Lieut.* 1 May 1824; ***Bt. Capt.*** 5 May 1836; *Capt.* 16 Nov. 1845; ***Bt. Maj.*** 9 Nov. 1846; *Major* 3 May 1856; ***Bt. Lt. Col.*** 20 June 1854.—Civil employ. ☞ *Brevets.* [1] Maj. 3 Apl. 46. Lt. Col. 7 June 49. Bt. Col. 28 Nov. 1854. [2] Major 22 Oct. 52. [3] Major 6 June 56.

Fur. Reg.	Ser. Y	Ser. M	Captains.	Remarks.	Cornet.	Lieut.	Captain. Brevet.	Captain. Regl.
	36	6	J. Christie,[1] *c.* - - -	Brigr. Comdg. at [Barrackpore,	4 *Jan.* 23	28 *May* 24	4 *Jan.* 38	1 *Jan.* 46
	26	1	A. W. C. Plowden, *P*,[2]*m.* -	.. ..	19 *June* 33	23 *Dec.* 41	19 *June* 48	21 *Oct.* 52
	20	3	R. Richardson,†[3]*m*, - -	Lv. S. C. 1 Nov. ..	26 *Mar.* 39	1 *Jan.* 46	26 *Mar.* 54	20 *Sep.* 54
N.	10	10	H. C. Craigie, *PH*, - - -	Fur. S.C. 16 Mar. 58	20 *Aug.* 48	11 *Sep.* 51	.. ..	23 *Nov.* 56
	8	5	G. A. Galloway, *PCH*, - -	.. ..	20 *Feb.* 51	21 *Oct.* 52	.. ..	10 *Mar.* 57
	7	11	R. Baring, *PH*, - - - -	A.D.C. to the Govr. General, ..	25 *July* 51	20 *Sep.* 54	.. ..	9 *Jan.* 58
	6	11	M. Clarke, *PH*, - - - -	.. ..	28 *July* 52	28 *Sep.* 54	.. ..	10 *Mar.* 58
			Lieutenants.					
	5	10	Hugh Henry Gough, *V.C.*†	2d Mahrattah Horse,	4 *Sep.* 53	9 *Aug.* 55		
	5	3	J. Alex. Mountford Patton,†	.. ..	20 *Apl.* 54	3 *May* 56		
	4	7	A. R. Davidson Mackenzie,†	.. ..	30 *Dec.* 54	22 *June* 56		
N.	3	7	C. H. Fairlie,† - - - -	Fur. S. C. 30 Oct. 58	4 *Dec.* 55	23 *Nov.* 56		
N.	2	8	C. C. Jervoise, - - -	Fur. S. C. 8 Dec. 58	4 *Nov.* 56	23 *Jan.* 57		
	2	7	Arthur Geo. Webster, - -	Mooltanee Horse, ..	20 *Dec.* 56	10 *Mar.* 57		
	1	4	C. J. Prinsep, - - - -	.. ..	6 *Mar.* 58	21 *June* 58		
			*					
			*					
					Appointed.			
	..	..	*Adjt.* C. Martin, - - -	Fur. S. C. 3 Feb. 59	30 *June* 58			
	..	..	A. H. Chapman, - - -	Officiating. ..	2 *Feb.* 59			
	..	..	*Intr.* *					
	..	..	*Surg.* J. F. Beatson, M.D.A.B.	.. ..	3 *July* 58			
	..	..	*Asst. Surg.* W. E. Caird, -	.. ..	31 *Jan.* 59			
	..	..	*Vety. Surg.*, T. P. Page, -	.. ..	29 *Mar.* 53			
	..	..	*Riding Master*, W. Keily,*	.. ..	12 *Aug.* 58			

* Lieut. Veteran Establishment 31 May 1852.

Rised in 1858.

2nd European Light Cavalry. {Meerut.

RIGHT WING.

FACINGS.——

Fur. Reg.	Ser. Y	Ser. M	
	63	..	*Colonel* Thomas Shubrick. *Cadet* 1796; *Cornet* 22 Sept. 1798; *Lieut.* 29 May 1800; *Capt.* 18 Aug. 1814; *Major* 12 Aug. 1819; *Lieut. Col.* 26 June 1826; *Col.* 19 April 1836; *Major Genl.* 23 Nov. 1841; *Lieut. Genl.* 11 Nov. 1851.—Europe, 21 Jan. 38.
	37	10	*Lieut. Col.* John Fowler Bradford, C.B.*P.* *Cornet* 1 Sep. 1821; *Lieut.* 1 May 1824; *Capt.* 27 Apl. 1833; *Major* 4 April 1844; *Bt. Lt. Col.* 19 June 1846; *Lt. Col.* 20 Oct. 1852; *Bt. Col.* 20 June 54.—*Major Genl.* 23 July 1858.—Comdg. Meerut Division.
O.	38	8	Major G. C. Ponsonby. *Cornet* 1 Nov. 1820; *Lieut.* 14 Sept. 1822; *Capt.* 19 May 1838; *Bt. Major* 23 Dec. 1842; *Major* 28 Nov. 1854; *Bt. Lt. Col.* 7 June 1849; *Bt. Col.* 28 Nov. 1854.—Fur. S. C. 17 Aug. 1857.

☞ *Brevet.* [1] Maj. 9 Nov. 46. Lt. Col. 7 June 49. Col. 28 Nov. 54. [2] Maj. 16 Dec. 51.

Fur. Reg.	Y	M	CAPTAINS.	REMARKS.	*Cornet.*	*Lieut.*	CAPTAIN. *Brevet.*	CAPTAIN. *Regi.*
N.	38	2	G. St. P. Lawrence,[1]*c.* -	Political employ, and H. A. D. C. to G. G. ..	5 *May* 21	1 *May* 24	5 *May* 36	5 *Jan.* 44
	19	4	R. G. Taylor,*P*,[2]*m* - - -	Civil employ, ..	26 *Feb.* 40	5 *Jan.* 44	.. ..	15 *Dec.* 51
	18	5	E. C. Warner,† - - -	.. ..	25 *Jan.* 41	3 *June* 44	.. ..	2 *May* 54
O.	10	3	W. S. Graham,† - - -	Fur. S.C. 13 Mar. 58	14 *Apl.* 49	31 *May* 51	.. ..	27 *June* 57
N.	4	9	Ed. Bertram Desvoeux, -	Fur. S. C. 4 Aug. 56	20 *Oct.* 54	23 *Nov.* 56	.. ..	27 *June* 57
	17	4	C. Mc. C. Cotton,*PH*, -	.. ..	3 *Mar.* 42	17 *Oct.* 46	.. ..	23 *Nov.* 56
O.	14	10	R. W. Clifford,† - - -	Fur. S. C. 19 Jan. 57	3 *Sep.* 44	8 *May* 49	.. ..	30 *Apl.* 58
			LIEUTENANTS.					
	10	10	J. Cockerell,† - - - -	Comdg. Divisional Battn. Benares, ..	20 *Sep.* 48	1 *Aug.* 49		
O.	8	10	G. N. Tucker,*PCH*, - -	Fur. S. C. 4 May 58	20 *Sep.* 50	31 *Dec.* 54		
	5	9	A. W. J. Montgomerie,*PH*,	.. ..	4 *Oct.* 53	12 *July* 56		
	3	9	L. F. Wells,† - - - -	.. ..	20 *Oct.* 55	23 *Nov.* 56		
	2	6	J. L. Loch,† - - - -	.. ..	20 *Jan.* 57	30 *Apl.* 58		
	2	1	W. H. J. Jennings, - -	.. ..	20 *June* 57	18 *May* 58		
	2	1	A. W. Brodhurst, - - -	.. ..	24 *June* 57	18 *May* 58		
	1	7	T. W. Hogg, - - - -	.. ..	4 *Dec.* 57	18 *May* 58		
	1	7	J. S. Irvine, - - - -	.. ..	20 *Dec.* 57	18 *May* 58		
	1	3	J. R. G. Sweeny, - - -	.. ..	4 *Apl.* 58	21 *June* 58		
	..	9	G. C. Jackson, - - -	.. ..	20 *Oct.* 58	5 *Feb.* 59		
	..	8	R. G. Loch,† - - -	.. ..	4 *Nov.* 58	5 *Feb.* 59		
			CORNETS.					
		4	F. E. Farquharson, - -	.. ..	4 *Mar.* 59			
		4	H. C. Creak, - - -	.. ..	4 *Mar.* 59			
			*					
			*					
			*					
			*					
			*					
			*					

LEFT WING.

*Colonel**

2nd European Light Cavalry

LEFT WNIG.—*Continued.*

Fur. Reg.	Ser. Y	Ser. M	
N.	36	2	*Lt. Col.* Robert Augustus Master, C. B. *Cornet* 12 May 1823; *Lieut.* 13 May 1825; *Brevte Capt.* 12 May 1840; *Capt.* 10 March 1841; *Bt. Major* 7 June 1849, *Major* 20 Dec. 1851; *Bt. Lieut. Col.* 28 Nov. 1854; *Lieut. Col.* 13 April 1855.—Fur. S. C. 18 Jan. 58.
	30	10	*Major* R. J. Hawthorne. *Cornet* 12 Sep. 1828; *Lieut.* 13 April 1837; *Bt. Capt.* 12 Sep. 1843; *Capt.* 11 Dec. 48; *Bt. Major* 20 June 54; *Major* 13 Apl. 55.

☞ *Brevet.* [1] Major 24 Mar. 1858.

Fur. Reg.	Ser. Y	Ser. M	Captains.	Remarks.	Cornet.	Lieut.	Captain. Brevet.	Captain. Regl.
	23	1	M. J. Turnbull, *P*, - - -	Army Clothing Agent Fort William,	28 *June* 36	10 *Mar.* 41	.. ..	10 *Aug.* 50
	20	5	O. Hamilton, *P*, - - - -	Pay Department, ..	24 *Jan.* 39	28 *Sep.* 41	.. ..	20 *Dec.* 51
O.	17	11	T. T. Boileau, *PH*,[1]*m*, -	Fur. S. C. 2 Feb. 58	27 *July* 41	8 *May* 49	.. ..	13 *Apl.* 55
	10	7	R. Alexander, † - - - -	.. ..	20 *Dec.* 48	10 *Aug.* 50	.. ..	23 *Nov.* 56
	10	3	H. Melvill, *PH*, - - -	.. ..	12 *Apl.* 49	16 *Sep* 50	.. ..	23 *Mar.* 57
	5	9	A. Cromwell Warner, *PH*,	.. ..	4 *Oct.* 53	28 *Aug.* 54	.. ..	1 *Oct.* 57
	4	10	Digby Compton, † - - -	Lv. S. C. 15 Oct. ..	26 *Aug.* 54	13 *Apl.* 55	.. ..	6 *Dec.* 57
			Lieutenants.					
D N.	2	8	~~J. H. T. Farquhar,~~ - - -	Fur. S. C. 9 Mar. 58	4 *Nov.* 56	23 *Jan.* 57		
	5	6	John Cutts Lockwood, † -	.. ..	20 *Jan.* 54	31 *Dec.* 54		
	9	..	A. D. Jennings, † - - -	.. ..	4 *July* 50	27 *Nov.* 53		
D	5	3	~~William H. Solly,~~ † - - -	.. ..	17 *Apl.* 54	22 *July* 56		
N.	2	10	~~E. H. Macnaghten,~~ † - -	Fur. S. C. 6 Jan. 59	8 *Sep.* 56	9 *Jan.* 57		
	2	6	F. Trench, *P.C.H.* - -	.. ..	20 *Jan.* 57	30 *Apl.* 58		
			*					
			*					
					Appointed.			
	..	..	*Adjutant*, A. W. J. Montgomèrie, - - - - -	.. ..	3 *July* 58			
	..	..	*Intr*, *					
	..	..	*Surg.*, C. L. Cox, A. B., -	.. ..	3 *July* 58			
	..	..	*Asst. Surg.*, J.C. Dickinson,	.. ..	31 *Jan.* 59			
	..	..	*Vety. Surg.*, W. Johnson,	.. ..	5 *Nov.* 47			
	..	..	*Riding Mr.*, C. Loder, * -	.. ..	25 *July* 58			

* Lieut. on the Veteran Establishment 7th April 1856.

Raised in 1858.

3rd European Light-Cavalry. Lahore.

RIGHT WING.

FACINGS ———

Fur. Reg.	Ser. Y	Ser. M	
	58	7	*Colonel* William Pattle, C. B. *Cornet* 9 Dec. 1800; *Lieut.* 11 May 1805; *Capt.* 8 June 1816; *Major* 26 June 1826; *Lieut. Col.* 27 April 1838; *Bt. Col.* 4 July 1843; *Col.* 5 Jan. 1844; *Maj. Genl.* 20 June 1854; *Lt. Genl.* 18 July 1856.—Fur., S. C., 27 July 51.
O.	38	6	*Lieut. Col.* Henry Clayton. *Cornet* 16 Jan. 1821; *Lieut.* 6 Mar. 1823; *Capt.* 18 June 1835 *Bt. Major* 30 April 44; *Major* 6 Sep. 51; *Bt. Lt. Col.* 20 June 54; *Lt. Col.* 28 Nov. 54; *Bt. Colonel* 18th May 1856.—Fur. S. C. 12 March 58.
N.	35	3	*Major* W. W. Apperley. *Cornet* 14 April 24; *Lieut.* 13 May 25; *Bt. Capt.* 14 April 39. *Capt.* 1 Mar. 43; *Bt. Major* 11 Nov. 51; *Major* 28 Nov. 1854; *Bt. Lieut. Col.* 1 May 1858.—Stud Department.—Fur. S. C. 30 Apl. 1856.

☞ *Brevet.* [1] Major 20 June 54.

Fur. Reg.	Ser. Y	Ser. M	CAPTAINS.	REMARKS.	*Cornet.*	*Lieut.*	CAPTAIN. *Brevet.*	CAPTAIN. *Regl.*
	31	..	G. Jackson,†[1]*m*	2nd Irregular Cavy.	19 *July* 28	26 *Mar.* 38	19 *July* 43	30 *July* 49
	23	5	W. Wyld, *P*,	Civil employ, ..	9 *Feb.* 36	24 *Oct.* 39	.. ..	1 *Aug.* 49
	22	1	F. N. Edmonstone, *P*,	Pay Department, ..	2 *June* 37	1 *Mar.* 43	.. ..	1 *Jan.* 51
	19	6	R. B. Macleod, *PH*,	.. ..	4 *Jan.* 40	27 *Sep.* 43	.. ..	6 *Sep.* 51
	16	2	E. W. E. Howard, *P*, *(a)*	Cantonment Joint Magte., Umballah,	21 *May* 43	28 *Oct.* 48	.. ..	5 *Dec.* 54
	15	11	A. V. Dumbleton, *P*,	.. ..	26 *July* 43	8 *May* 49	.. ..	23 *Nov.* 56
O.	13	1	C. Batchelor, *PH*,	Fur. S.C. 30 Jan. 57,	10 *June* 46	20 *July* 49	.. ..	7 *Nov.* 57
			LIEUTENANTS.					
O.	11	8	W. C. S. Clarke, *PH*,	Fur. S.C. 22 Sep. 58	24 *Nov.* 47	30 *July* 49		
	10	3	D. W. Wise, *PH*,	.. ..	14 *Apl.* 49	1 *Jan.* 51		
	9	7	F. W. Russell, *PH*,	.. ..	20 *Dec.* 49	28 *Nov.* 54		
	5	3	G. W. Chicheley Plowden,†	2nd in Comd. Divnl. Battn., Allahabad,	4 *Apl.* 54	23 *Nov.* 56		
N.	2	9	C. W. Thomas,†	Fur. S. C. 17 Nov. 58	20 *Oct.* 56	9 *Jan.* 57		
	2	3	F. B. Prinsep,	.. ..	20 *Apl.* 57	18 *May* 58		
	2	1	H. C. Kemble,	.. ..	10 *June* 57	18 *May* 58		
	1	9	F. H. Grant,	.. ..	20 *Oct.* 57	18 *May* 58		
	1	7	A. W. Twyford,	.. ..	20 *Dec.* 57	18 *May* 58		
	..	8	A. H. Taylor,	.. ..	4 *Nov.* 58	5 *Feb.* 59		
			CORNETS.					
	..	6	I. Low,	.. ...	20 *Jan.* 59			
			*					
			*					
			*					
			*					
			*					
			*					
			*					

LEFT WING.

Fur. Reg.	Ser. Y	Ser. M	
	50	10	*Colonel Sir* John Bennett Hearsey, K. C. B. *Cornet* 14 Sep. 1808; *Lieut.* 1 Nov. 1809; *Capt.* 31 Aug. 1819; *Major* 19 Nov. 1835; *Lieut. Col.* 28 Dec. 1838; *Bt. Col.* 19 Mar. 1849; *Col.* 4 Nov. 1852; *Maj. Genl.* 28 Nov. 1854.—Commanding Presidency Division

(*a*) Passed an examination in the Punjaubee language.

3rd European Light Cavalry.

LEFT WING.—*Continued.*

Fur. Reg.	Ser. Y	Ser. M	
	33	9	*Col.* Philip Francis Story, C. B. *Cornet* 20 Oct. 1825; *Lieut.* 10 July 1826; *Capt.* 28 Oct. 1832; *Major* 28 Oct. 1842; *Bt. Lt. Col.* 4 July 1843; *Lt. Col.* 2 Oct. 1851; *Brevet Col.* 1 Feb. 54; *Maj. Genl.* 13 April 1855.—Cawnpore.
	38	..	*Lt. Col.* Archibald Lorne Campbell. *Cornet* 4 July 1821; *Lieut.* 13 May 1825; *Capt.* 12 Jan. 34; *Bt. Maj.* 19 June 46; *Maj.* 20 Oct. 52; *Bt. Lt. Col.* 20 June 54; *Lt. Col.* 17 Sep. 1855; *Bt. Col.* 15 Sep. 57.—Mussoorie.
O.	37	2	*Major* N. D. Barton, *P.* *Cornet* 1 May 22; *Lieut.* 1 May 24; *Bt. Capt.* 1 May 37; *Capt.* 30 Oct. 37; *Bt. Maj.* 11 Nov. 51; *Maj.* 24 Dec. 55; *Bt. Lt. Col.* 18 Mar. 56.—Fur. S.C. 7 Feb. 59.

☞ *Brevet.* [1] Maj. 28 Nov. 54. [2] Maj. 19 Jan. 58. [3] Major 24 Mar. 58.

Fur. Reg.	Ser. Y	Ser. M	Captains.	Remarks.	Cornet.	Lieut.	Captain. Brevet.	Captain. Regl.
	30	3	S. F. Macmullen, †[1]*m*	.. ..	28 *Mar.* 29	20 *Nov.* 41	28 *Mar.* 44	31 *Dec.* 51
	22	4	H. R. Grindlay, *P*, [2]*m*	Lv. S. C. 1 Nov. ..	24 *Feb.* 37	1 *Aug.* 42	24 *Feb.* 52	4 *Nov.* 52
	19	6	L. J. Farquharson, *PH*,	.. ..	3 *Jan.* 40	8 *May* 46	.. ..	21 *Mar.* 54
	16	4	G. Delane, *PH*,	G. G. Body Guard,	22 *Feb.* 43	29 *Oct.* 46	.. ..	24 *Dec.* 55
	13	7	J. P. A. Theobald, †	.. ..	27 *Dec.* 45	12 *Apl.* 49	.. ..	20 *Nov.* 56
O.	13	6	C. P. Lane, *P*,	Fur. P. A. 8 Apl. 59	20 *Jan.* 46	8 *May* 49	.. ..	23 *Nov.* 56
O.	9	9	D. M. Probyn, C.B. *PH*, [3]*m*.	1st Sikh Irr. Cavy.	20 *Oct.* 49	19 *Aug.* 53	.. ..	21 *Aug.* 57
			Lieutenants					
	8	2	W. J. S. Richardes,	.. ..	3 *May* 51	14 *Nov.* 53		
D	~~5~~	~~10~~	~~Burlas Cuppage, †~~	.. ..	~~4 Sep. 53~~	~~1 June 56~~	at Kerbalta July 1864	
	3	11	C. William Grey, †	... ..	25 *July* 55	14 *Apl.* 56		
	5	9	Edward Baldwin Wake,	.. ..	20 *Oct.* 53	26 *Apl.* 56		
	3	9	G. Farquhar Smith,	4th Sikh Irr. Cavy.	20 *Oct.* 55	20 *Nov.* 56		
	2	10	H. P. Peacock, †	.. ..	20 *Sep.* 56	9 *Jan.* 57		
	2	8	C. E. Farquharson, †	.. ..	4 *Nov.* 56	23 *Jan.* 57		
	1	4	R. C. D'E. Spottiswoode, *	.. ..	20 *Mar.* 58	21 *June* 58		
					Appointed.			
	..	..	*Adjt.*, D. W. Wise,	.. ..	30 *June* 58			
	..	..	*Intr.*, A. V. Dumbleton,	Officiating, ..	20 *Feb.* 57			
	..	..	*Surg.* J. H. Butler, F.R.C.S.	.. ..	30 *June* 58			
	..	..	*Asst. Surg.* S. C. Courtney, M. D.,	.. ...	31 *Jan.* 59			
	...	..	*Vety. Surg.*, J. Harris,	.. ..	29 *Mar.* 51			
	..	..	*Riding Master*, J. Boucher,	.. ..	13 *May.* 52			

Raised in 1858. } **4th European Light Cavalry.** { Lucknow.

RIGHT WING.

FACINGS ———

Fur. Reg.	Ser. Y	Ser. M	
	63	5	*Col. Sir* Robert Houstoun, K. C. B. *Cornet* 26 Feb. 1796; *Lieut.* 1 Nov. 1798; *Capt.* 22 Dec. 1803; *Major* 1 Nov. 1809; *Lieut. Col.* 13 Dec. 1818; *Col.* 1 May 1824; *Major Genl.* 10 Jan. 1837; *Lieut. Genl.* 9 Nov. 1846; *Genl.* 20 June 1854.—Europe, 20 Oct. 21.
	53	4	*Col.* Robert Hawkes. *Cornet* 29 March 1806; *Lieut.* 9 November 1811; *Bt. Capt.* 29 March 1821; *Capt.* 13 May 1825; *Major* 10 Oct. 1836; *Lieut. Col.* 23 Dec. 1839; *Bt. Col.* 28 March 1850; *Col.* 4 Feb. 1859; *Maj. Genl.* 28 Nov. 1854.—Furlough P. A. 6 Mar. 1854.
O.	35	6	*Lt. Col.* Arthur Wheatley. *Cornet* 9 Jan. 24; *Lt.* 13 May 25; *Capt.* 3 Dec. 1838; *Bt. Maj.* 7 June 1849; *Major* 16 Apl. 1850; *Lt. Col.* 14 Nov. 1853; *Bt. Col.* 28 Nov. 1854.—Fur. S C., 9 May 1856.
	32	5	*Major* A. Tucker, C. B. *Cornet* 4 Feb. 1827; *Lieut.* 9 Jan. 1829; *Capt.* 23 Dec. 1839 *Bt. Maj.* 4 July 43; *Maj.* 28 Nov. 54; *Bt. Lt. Col.* 20 June 54; *Bt. Col.* 2 Apl. 1856.

☞ *Brevet.* [1] Major 20 June 1854. [2] Major 20 June 1854. [3] Major 13 July 1856. [4] Major 20 July 1858.

Fur. Reg.	Ser. Y	Ser. M	CAPTAINS.	REMARKS.	Cornet.	Lieut.	CAPTAIN. Brevet.	CAPTAIN. Regl.
	32	1	~~W. Baker,~~ *P*,[1]*m*	.. ..	17 *June* 27	4 *Dec.* 32	17 *June* 42	8 *May* 49
~~N.~~	~~31~~	~~5~~	~~F. J. Harriott, *P*,[2]*m*~~	Fur. S. C. 3 Feb. 59	20 *Feb.* 28	23 *Dec.* 39	20 *Feb.* 43	2 *Oct.* 51
O.	20	1	T. R. Snow, *P*,	Fur. S. C. 15 Apl. 58	18 *June* 39	28 *Oct.* 42	18 *June* 54	13 *Jan.* 55
	18	2	W. A. A. Thomson, *PH*,[3]*m*	G. G.'s Body Guard,	21 *May* 41	24 *Mar.* 43	21 *May* 56	12 *July* 56
	17	2	J. H. Balmain, †[4]*m*	.. ..	21 *Apl.* 42	16 *Oct.* 46	.. ..	9 *Oct.* 56
	17	1	E. A. M. MacGregor, †	.. ..	8 *June* 42	8 *May* 49	.. ..	23 *Nov.* 56
	13	5	G. Bushby, †	Doing duty Lahore, Light Horse, ..	24 *Jan.* 46	10 *July* 52	.. ..	2 *Jan.* 58
			LIEUTENANTS.					
	9	7	J. B. Saunders, *PC*,	Fur. P.A, 4 Mar. 59	20 *Dec.* 49	28 *Nov.* 54		
	~~6~~	~~5~~	~~K. Dixon~~, †	.. ..	17 *Feb.* 53	13 *Jan.* 55		
	5	2	*Sir* Morison Barlow, *Bart.* †	.. ..	6 *May* 54	18 *July* 55		
	4	10	Robert Cunliffe Low, *PH*,	2nd in Comd. 4th Seikh Irr. Cavy.,	26 *Aug.* 54	29 *Sep.* 55		
	3	9	H. M. Caulfeild, †	Mooltanee Horse, ..	4 *Oct.* 55	9 *Oct.* 56		
N.	2	9	A. H. Prinsep,	Fur. S.C. 29 Oct. 58	20 *Oct.* 56	23 *Jan.* 57		
	2	6	W. A. Stirling,	.. ..	20 *Jan.* 57	2 *Jan.* 58		
	2	3	T. F. C. Rochford,	.. ..	4 *Apl.* 57	18 *May* 58		
	~~2~~	~~2~~	~~W. Condie~~,	.. ..	20 *May* 57	18 *May* 58		
	1	9	A. Waterfield,	.. ..	4 *Oct.* 57	18 *May* 58		
N.	1	7	H. B. Webster,	Fur. S.C. 21 Dec. 58	4 *Dec.* 57	18 *May* 58		
	1	5	H. B. Lockwood,	.. ..	20 *Feb.* 58	18 *May* 58		
	1	..	G A. P. Arbuthnot,	.. ..	25 *June* 58	24 *Aug.* 58		
	..	8	V. J. Hodson,	.. ..	20 *Nov.* 58	29 *Mar.* 59		
	..	8	G. T. Halliday,	.. ..	20 *Nov.* 58	29 *Mar.* 59		
			CORNETS.					
	..	5	~~C. E. Benthall~~,	.. ..	20 *Feb.* 59			
			*					
			*					
			*					
			*					
			*					
			*					
			*					

LEFT WING.

Fur. Reg.	Ser. Y	Ser. M	
	39	11	*Colonel* Henry Lechmere Worrall. *Cornet* 16 Aug. 1819; *Lieut.* 22 May 1822; *Capt.* 26 June 1826; *Major* 12 Jan. 1834; *Lieut. Col.* 12 Nov. 1838; *Bt. Col.* 19 March 1849; *Col.* 21 Oct. 1852; *Maj. Genl.* 28 Nov. 1854.—Europe, 21 January 1853.
O.	33	2	*Lieut. Col.* William Binfield Wemyss. *Cornet* 22 *May* 1826; *Lt.* 3 Dec. 1828; *Capt.* 10 Oct. 1836; *Bt. Maj.* 9 Nov. 46; *Maj.* 2 Oct. 1851; *Bt. Lt. Col,* 20 June 1854; *Lieut. Col,* 28 Nov. 1854.—Fur. S. C. 30 Dec. 56.

4th European Light Cavalry.

LEFT WING.—*Continued.*

Fur. Reg.	Ser. Y	Ser. M	
	33	4	*Lt. Col.* R. Macdonell. *Cornet* 2 Mar. 1826; *Lieut.* 3 May 1829; *Bt. Capt.* 2 Mar. 1841 *Captain* 10 June 1842; *Major* 27 Nov. 1853; *Lieut. Colonel* 23 July 1858.
	33	..	*Major* T. F. B. Beatson, *Cornet* 27 June 1826; *Lieut.* 29 Aug. 1832; *Bt Capt.* 27 June 1841; *Captain* 14 Oct. 1844; *Bt. Major* 20 June 1854; *Major* 23 July 1858.

☞ *Brevet.* [1] Major 28 Nov. 1854. [2] Major 20 July 1858.

Fur. Reg.	Y	M	Captains.	Remarks.	*Cornet.*	*Lieut.*	Captain. *Brevet.*	Captain. *Regl.*
	29	3	E. Harvey,[1]*m* †- - - -	.. ..	31 *Mar.* 30	4 *Nov.* 33	31 *Mar.* 45	8 *May* 49
	24	1	~~W. C. Alexander~~, - - -	.. ..	7 *June* 35	16 *June* 40	21 *Jan.* 50	9 *Oct.* 50
N.	20	2	~~W. Alexander Shaw~~, *PH*, -	Fur. P.A. 22 Mar. 59	26 *Mar.* 39	29 *July* 42	.. ..	27 *May* 53
	19	9	R. G. Simeon, *P*, - - -	Depy. Asst. Adjt. Genl., Meerut Divn.,	16 *Oct.* 39	14 *Oct.* 44	.. ..	27 *Nov.* 53
	19	..	C. Dumbleton, † - - -	.. ..	9 *July* 40	18 *Dec.* 45	9 *July* 55	20 *Sep.* 55
O.	15	5	O. Wilkinson, *PH*,[2]*m* - -	Fur. S. C. 19 April 1859. ..	27 *Jan.* 44	12 *Aug.* 48	.. ..	30 *Apl.* 58
	13	7	T. B. Harrison, *P*, - - -	Cantonment Jt. Magte. Lucknow.	20 *Dec.* 45	9 *Oct.* 50	.. ..	23 *July* 58
			Lieutenants.					
	11	..	H. G. Jenkins, † - - -	.. ..	26 *June* 48	27 *May* 53		
	5	6	M. Mark Prendergast, † -	.. ..	4 *Jan.* 54	23 *Nov* 56		
N.	4	7	Thos. Chadwick Graham, -	2nd Punjaub Cavy.	25 *Nov.* 54	23 *Nov.* 56		
	2	8	Richard Beadon, - - -	Cavalry Depôt, Hazáreebaugh, ..	20 *Nov.* 56	16 *Apl.* 58		
	1	4	D. C. S. L. Carnegie, - -	.. ..	20 *Mar.* 58	21 *June* 58		
	1	1	H. Y. Murray, - - -	.. ..	20 *June* 58	24 *Aug.* 58		
			*C. E. Benthall					
			*		*Appointed.*			
			*					
	..	..	*Adjt.*, *Sir* M. Barlow *Bart.*	Officiating, ..	19 *Jan.* 59			
	..	..	*Intr.*,					
	..	..	*Surg.*, F. Anderson, M. D.,	Offg. Supdg. Surgeon Barrackpore circle	30 *June* 58			
	..	..	*Asst. Surg.*					
	..	..	*Vety. Surg.*,*					
	..	..	*Riding Mr.* T. Bradshaw,*	.. ..	7 Nov. 46			

* Lieut. Veteran Establishment, 16th May 1854.

Raised in 1858.

5th European Light Cavalry.

Peshawur,

RIGHT WING.

FACINGS——

Fur. Reg.	Ser. Y	Ser. M	
O.	60	9	*Colonel* James Kennedy, C. B. *Cornet* 1 Nov. 1798; *Lieut.* 29 May 1800; *Capt.* 27 Feb. 1812; *Major* 1 Oct. 1819; *Lieut. Col.* 13 May 1825; *Bt. Col.* 18 June 1831; *Col.* 26 Dec. 1832; *Major Genl.* 23 Nov. 1841; *Lt. Genl.* 11 Nov. 1851.—Fur. P. A. 6 Oct. 1857.
O.	31	5	*Lieut. Col.* A. Hall. *Cornet* 9 Feb. 1828; *Lieut.* 1 Mar. 1836; *Capt.* 14 Jan. 1842; *Major* 14 Nov. 1853; *Lieut Col.* 5 May 1856.—Fur. S. C. 30 Dec. 1856.
O.	~~30~~	~~3~~	~~Major Thomas Lowth Harington~~, *P.* *Cornet* 6 April 1827; *Lieut.* 3 Dec. 1838; *Bt. Capt.* 6 April 1842; *Capt.* 6 March 1846; *Bt. Major* 19 June 1846; *Major* 5 May 1856; *Bt. Lieut. Col.* 20 June 1854. Bt. Colonel 12 Oct. 1857,—Fur. S. C. 15 April 58.

☞ *Bts.* [1] Maj. 17 April 50. Lt. Col. 28 Nov. 54. [2] Maj. 24 Mar. 58.

Fur. Reg.	Y	M	CAPTAINS.	REMARKS.	*Cornet.*	*Lieut.*	CAPTAIN. *Brevet.*	CAPTAIN. *Regl.*
	18	6	H. J. Stannus, *PCH*, [1]*lc.* -	Pay Dept,	31 *Dec.* 40	12 *Nov.* 42	.. ..	16 *Apl.* 50
~~N.~~	~~18~~	~~4~~	~~A. P. C. Elliot, *PH*~~, - -	Political employ,	8 *Mar.* 41	18 *Mar.* 48	.. ..	14 *Nov.* 53
	15	6	W. F. Stephens, *PH*, - -	Civil employ,	1 *Jan.* 44	4 *June* 48	.. ..	31 *Dec.* 54
	15	6	H. Lane, *PC*, [2] *m* - - -	.. ..	1 *Jan.* 44	1 *Dec.* 48	.. ..	5 *May* 56
O.	14	5	R. Jenkins, *PH*, - - -	Fur. S.C. 19 Apl. 58,	20 *Feb.* 45	8 *May* 49	.. ..	22 *July* 56
O.	10	6	H. Durrant, *P*, - - -	Fur. S.C. 24 Nov. 57,	20 *Jan.* 49	16 *Apl.* 50	.. ..	17 *July* 57
	9	11	J. I. Robinson, † - -	.. ..	9 *Aug.* 49	20 *Aug.* 51	.. ..	3 *Apl.* 59
			LIEUTENANTS.					
	9	4	G. A. Prendergast, † - -	.. ..	20 *Mar.* 50	10 *Oct.* 51		
	5	4	B. Robinson Branfill, *PH*, -	Great Trigonometrical Survey, ..	14 *Mar.* 54	5 *May* 56		
	2	10	F. H. Macnaghten, † - -	.. ..	20 *Sep.* 56	9 *Jan.* 57		
N.	2	8	Samuel Boulderson, - -	Fur. S. C. 7 Mar. 59	20 *Nov.* 56	23 *Jan.* 57		
	2	3	H. C. Sitwell, - - -	.. ..	20 *Apl.* 57	18 *May* 58		
N.	1	9	L. C. Alexander, - -	Fur. S.C. 8 Nov. 58,	4 *Oct.* 57	18 *May* 58		
	1	6	J. Biddulph, - - -	.. ..	20 *Jan.* 58	18 *May* 58		
	..	10	A. W. Capel, - - -	.. ..	4 *Sep.* 58	5 *Feb.* 59		
	..	9	A. L. C. Littledale, - -	.. ..	4 *Oct.* 58	5 *Feb.* 59		
	..	8	A. Hearsey, - - - -	.. ..	4 *Nov.* 58	29 *Mar.* 59		
	..	8	H. A. Shakespear, - -	.. ..	20 *Nov.* 58	29 *Mar.* 59		
	..	6	H. M. Buller, - - -	.. ..	4 *Jan.* 59	3 *Apl*, 59		
			CORNETS.					
	..	5	A. W. Roberts, - - - -	... ..	20 *Feb.* 59			
			*					
			*					
			*					
			*					
			*					
			*					
			*					

Raised in 1858.

5th European Light Cavalry.

Peshawur.

LEFT WING.

FACINGS,———.

Fur. Reg.	Ser. Y	Ser. M	
	53	3	*Col.* Charles Montabin Carmichael, C. B. *Cornet* 27 Mar. 1806; *Lt.* 12 Apl. 1810; *Bt. Capt.* 27 Mar. 1821; *Capt.* 8 May 1821; *Maj.* 30 Dec. 1833; *Lt. Col.* 1 Nov. 1838; *Bt. Col.* 19 March 1849; *Col.* 6th Sep. 1851; *Maj. Genl.* 28 Nov. 1854.—Furlough, 5 May 1849.
	51	2	*Lt. Col.* Henry Fisher Salter, C. B. *Cort.* 30 Apl. 1808; *Lt.* 1 Sept. 18; *Bt. Capt.* 30 Apl. 23; *Capt.* 1 May 24; *Maj.* 19 May 38; *Bt. Lt. Col.* 23 July 39; *Lit. Col.* 5 Jan. 44; *Bt. Col.* 16 July 49; *Maj. Genl.* 28 Nov. 54; Presidency.
D	~~38~~	~~6~~	~~*Lieut. Col.* James Mackenzie.~~ *Cornet* 13 Jan. 21; *Lt.* 13 May 25; *Brevet Capt.* 13 Jan. 1836; *Capt.* 5 Oct. 1836; *Bt. Maj.* 9 Nov. 1846; *Major* 10 *Aug.* 1850; *Brevet Lieut. Col.* 7 June 1849; *Lieut. Col.* 1 Apl. 1854; *Bt. Col.* 28 Nov. 1854.—Bridr. Comdg. at Ferozepore.
Lt. Col.	34	8	~~*Major*~~ T. Moore. *Cornet* 11 Dec. 1824; *Lieut.* 13 May 1825; *Capt.* 21 Jan. 1839; *Bt. Maj.* 7 June 1849; *Maj.* 1 Apl. 54; *Bt. Lt. Col.* 28 Nov. 1854.

☞ *Bts.* [1] Maj. 7 June 49; *Lt. Col.* 28 Nov. 54. [2] Maj. 20 July 1858.

Fur. Reg.	Y	M	CAPTAINS.	REMARKS.	*Cornet.*	*Lieut.*	CAPTAIN. *Brevet.*	CAPTAIN. *Regl.*
Maj O.	33	10	G. Cautley,[1] *lc* - - -	Fur. S. C. 10 Mar. 57	22 *Sep.* 25	17 *May* 29	22 *Sep.* 40	10 *July* 44
	22	1	F. W. Drummond, *PH*, -	.. ..	2 *June* 37	8 *Mar.* 42	2 *June* 52	1 *Nov.* 54
O.	15	7	G. Ward, *PH*, - - - -	Fur. S.C. 26 Mar. 58	1 *Dec.* 43	17 *Feb.* 49	.. ..	12 *Sep.* 56
O.	13	8	H. W. Best, *P*, - - -	Fur. S. C. 1 Apl 59				
O.	11	4	C. J. S. Gough, *P*, [2]*m.*	Fur. S. C. 8 Feb. 59	20 *Dec.* 45	8 *May* 49	.. ..	23 *Nov.* 56
O.	10	7	*Sir* C. W. A. Oakeley, *Bt.*,†	Fur. S. C. 23 Dec. 56	20 *Mar.* 48	1 *Sep.* 49	.. ..	23 *June* 57
	10	..	*Hon'ble* F. A. J. Chichester, *PH*,	.. ..	20 *Dec.* 48 / 20 *July* 49	19 *May* 50 / 10 *Aug.* 50	.. .. /	29 *June* 58 / 16 *Sep.* 58
			LIEUTENANTS.					
Capt.	9	8	A. C. Grant, *PH*, - - -	A. D.C to C.-in-C., Madras, ..	20 *Nov.* 49	1 *Nov.* 54		
	6	6	A. K. J. C. Mackenzie,† -		26 *Jan.* 53	24 *Nov.* 55		
N.	3	9	C. M. S. Fairbrother, -	Fur. S.C. 22 Apl. 58	20 *Oct.* 55	12 *Sep.* 56		
	2	10	Alex. Shepherd, - - -	.. ..	20 *Sep.* 56	9 *Jan.* 57		
	2	6	W. F. Fergusson, - - -	.. ..	4 *Jan.* 57	30 *Apl.* 58		
	1	9	G. C. Swiney, - - - -	.. ..	20 *Oct.* 57	18 *May* 58		
	1	1	W. H. Macnaghten, - -	.. ..	10 *June* 58	24 *Aug.* 58		
			*					
			*		*Appointed.*			
			Adjt. G. A. Prendergast, -	Officiating, ..	7 *Jan.* 59			
	..	..	*Interpreter*,*					
	..	..	*Surgeon*, D. McRae, - -	.. ..	3 *Dec.* 58			
	..	..	*Asst. Surg.*, H. Clark, M.D.	.. ..	31 *Jan.* 59			
	..	..	*Vety. Surg.* W. McDermott,	.. ..	27 *June* 44			
	..	..	*Riding Master* V. B. Cullen,	Lv. to 1 Dec. p. to regt., ..	16 *Jan.* 57			

Raised in 1754.

1st European Bengal Fusiliers.

Dugshaie.

"PLASSEY"—"BUXAR"—"GUZERAT"—"DEIG"—"BHURTPORE"—"AFFGHANISTAN"—"GHUZNEE"—"FEROZESHUHUR"—"SUBRAON"—"PEGU."

FACINGS—*Dark-blue*.

Fur. Reg.	Ser. Y	Ser. M	
N.	54	4	*Colonel* Abraham Roberts, C. B. *Ens.* 18 March 1805; *Lieut.* 19 March 1805; *Capt.* 27 Aug. 1822; *Major* 24 Sept. 1826; *Lieut. Col.* 28 Sept. 1831; *Col.* 10 Nov. 1843; *Maj. Genl.* 20 June 1854; *Lieut. Genl.* 13 Oct. 1857.—Fur. S. C. 3 March 1854.
N.	38	1	*Lieut. Colonel* John Welchman C. B. *Ens.* 1 June 1821; *Lieut.* 11 July 1823; *Capt.* 5 Mar. 1836; *Bt. Maj.* 9 Nov. 1846; *Maj.* 28 Mar. 1848; *Lt. Col.* 14 July 53. *Bt. Col.* 28 Nov. 54.—Fur. S. C. 13 Mar. 58.
N.	30	1	*Major* D. Seaton. *2nd Lt.* 5 June 1829; *1st Lt.* 29 July 1836; *Capt.* 6 Feb. 1846; *Bt. Maj.* 19 June 1846; *Maj.* 14 Sep. 1856; *Bt. Lt. Col.* 20 June 1854; *Bt. Col.* 15 Oct. 1857.—Fur. S.C. 27 May 59.
	19	5	*Major* G. G. Denniss. 2nd *Lieut.* 8 Feb. 1840; 1st *Lieut.* 1 Nov. 1842; *Capt.* 29 June 1849; *Maj.* 14 Sep. 1857.

☞ *Brevet.* [1] Maj. 19 Jan. 58. [2] Maj. 2 Mar. 50; Lt. Col. 28 Nov. 54. [3] Maj. 20 July 58; [4] Major 20 July 1858. [5] Maj. 19 Jan. 58. [6] Maj. 19 Jan. 58.

Fur. Reg.	Ser. Y	Ser. M	CAPTAINS 14.	REMARKS.	2nd Lieut.	1st Lieut.	Captain. Brevet.	Captain. Regl.
O.	18	11	Southwell Greville, [1] *m* -	Fur. S. C. 4 May 58	31 *July* 40	4 *Nov.* 43	.. ..	1 *Mar.* 50
	18	9	H. B. Edwardes, C. B., *P*, [2] *lc*	Civil employ, ..	26 *Sep.* 40	10 *Nov.* 43	.. ..	1 *Mar.* 50
	18	6	A. Hume, [3] *m* - - -	.. ..	22 *Dec.* 40	22 *Nov.* 43	.. ..	6 *July* 51
O.	16	1	F. O. Salusbury, [4] *m* - -	Fur., P. A. 4 Apl. 59	9 *June* 43	9 *Mar.* 45	.. ..	1 *Oct.* 53
	16	1	C. O'B. Palmer, *PH*, - -	.. ..	9 *June* 43	29 *Oct.* 45	.. ..	20 *Mar.* 54
O.	14	6	E. Brown, [5] *m* - - - -	Fur. S. C. 20 Dec. 58	29 *Dec.* 44	10 *Feb.* 46	.. ..	14 *Jan.* 56
	14	5	G. C. Lambert, - - -	Fur. S.C. 12 Dec. 56	20 *Feb.* 45	11 *Feb.* 46	.. ..	1 *Feb.* 56
	14	7	T. Wheler, *PH*, - - - -	Gwalior Contingent,	10 *Dec.* 44	4 *Mar.* 46	.. ..	5 *Mar.* 56
N.	14	1	E. St. George, *PC*, (*a*) -	Fur. S. C. 14 June 58	14 *June* 45	14 *May* 46	.. ..	23 *Nov.* 56
	14	1	H. F. M. Boisragon, *PH*, [6] *m*	25th Punjaub Infy...	14 *June* 45	13 *Oct.* 46	.. ..	23 *Nov.* 56
	14	1	R. J. F. Hickey, *PH*, (*b*) -	17th Regt. Irr. Cavy.,	13 *June* 45	17 *June* 48	.. ..	7 *June* 57
O.	13	11	N. T. Parsons, *PH*, - -	Fur. S. C. 9 Mar. 58	26 *July* 45	29 *June* 49	.. ..	12 *Mar.* 58
N.	13	10	G. M. Battye, *P*, (*b*) - -	Civil employ, ..	20 *Aug.* 45	23 *Jan.* 50	.. ..	2 *Aug.* 58
N.	13	7	G. Price, *PH*, - - - -	Civil Architect, ..	27 *Dec.* 45	1 *Mar.* 50	.. ..	21 *Feb.* 59
			1st LIEUTENANTS 22.					
	13	6	R. C. Birch, *P*, - - -	Civil employ, ..	14 *Jan.* 46	1 *Mar.* 50		
O.	13	3	W. Davison, *PH*, - - -	Fur. S. C. 13 Mar. 58	20 *Apl.* 46	6 *July* 51		
	14	1	H. Maxwell, *PH*, (*b*) - -	Adjutant, ..	9 *June* 45	7 *Aug.* 52		
O.	10	7	H. M. Wemyss, *PH*, - -	Fur. S. C. 21 Oct. 58	9 *Dec.* 48	18 *Apl* 53		
	9	7	John Morland, - - - -	Instr. of Musketry,	11 *Dec.* 49	5 *Mar.* 54		
	9	7	James Scott Ingram, *PH* (*b*)	Asst. Supt. Toongoop Pass Road, ..	12 *Dec.* 49	20 *Mar.* 54		
	8	6	C. McFarlane, *P*, - - -	.. ..	20 *Jan.* 51	10 *May* 54		
	8	5	Lane Baines Magniac, -	.. ..	20 *Feb.* 51	17 *June* 55		
	8	1	Jas. Williamson Daniell, -	.. ..	16 *June* 51	5 *Dec.* 55		
O.	7	7	Edwin A. C. Lambert, *PH*,	Fur. S. C. 19 Apl. 59	12 *Dec.* 51	14 *June* 56		
	7	4	Montagu Hall, - - - -	D. P. W. Oude, ..	1 *Mar.* 52	1 *Feb.* 56		
	6	4	Gerard Noel Money, † -	.. ..	4 *Mar.* 53	5 *Mar.* 56		
N.	5	1	Thomas Adair Butler, V. C.	Fur. S. C. 5 Jan. 59	9 *June* 54	23 *Nov.* 56		
	4	7	Newton H. Wallace, † - -	.. ..	9 *Dec.* 54	23 *Nov.* 56		–
	3	9	Alex. Grham Owen, - -	6th Irr. Cavy. ..	4 *Oct.* 55	23 *Nov.* 56		
	3	7	F. D. MaBrown, † - - -	.. ..	8 *Dec.* 55	7 *June* 57		
	3	6	N. Ellis, - - - - - - -	.. ..	20 *Jan.* 56	14 *Sep.* 57		
	3	6	A. R. Chapman, - - -	.. ..	4 *Jan.* 56	24 *Sep.* 57		
	2	5	W. S. Jervis, - - - -	.. ..	4 *Feb.* 57	30 *Apl.* 58		
	2	7	W. H. Warner, † -- - -	.. ..	13 *Dec.* 56	12 *Mar.* 58		
	2	10	J. C. Partridge, - - - -	.. ..	20 *Sep.* 57	12 *June* 57		
	1	8	W. L. Noverre, - - - -	.. ..	20 *Nov.* 57	21 *Feb.* 59		

(*a*) Has received certificates of high proficiency in the Oordoo and Hindee languages, from the College of Fort William, on the 27th April and 15th August 1850, also a degree of honor for his eminent attainments in the Oordoo language, 25th February 1851.
(*b*) Have furnished certificates of qualification in Surveying.

1st European Bengal Fusiliers—*Continued.*

Fur. Reg.	Ser. Y	Ser. M	2nd Lieutenants, 10.	Remarks.		2nd Lieut.
	1	5	E. F. Fortescue, - - -	..	..	4 *Feb.* 58
	1	3	P. L. N. Cavagnari, - -	..	..	9 *Apl.* 58
	1	1	G. H. Holley, - - - -	..	..	12 *June* 58
	..	7	F. H. Goold, - - - -	..	..	11 *Dec.* 58
	..	6	J. E. Harden, - - - -	..	..	20 *Jan.* 59
			Adjutant.			*Appointed.*
	..	..	H. Maxwell, - - - -	..	..	15 *Feb.* 52
			Interpreter.			
	..	..	C. McFarlane, - - - -	..	..	4 *Dec.* 58
			Surgeon.			
	..	..	J. B. Harrison, M. D. - -	..	..	8 *Oct.* 58
			Assistant Surgeon.			
	..	..	D. McAuley, M. D.,- - -	Left Wing,	..	4 *Aug.* 55
	..	..				

Strength—10 Companies, with 1 Sergeant Major—1 Quarter Master Sergeant—5 Staff Sergeants—50 Sergeants—50 Corporals—20 Drummers—30 Half-pay Drummers—820 Privates.

Raised in 1839. | **2nd European Bengal Fusiliers.** | Delhi.

"Punjaub"—"Chillianwalla"—"Goojerat"—"Pegu."

Facings—*Dark-blue.*

Fur. Reg.	Ser. Y	Ser. M	
	53	3	*Colonel* Robert Blackall. *Ens.* 27 Mar. 1806; *Lieut.* 4 Nov. 1807; *Bt. Capt.* 27 Mar. 1821; *Capt.* 11 July 1823; *Major* 21 June 1830; *Lieut. Col.* 22 April 1836; *Bt. Col.* 9 Nov. 1846; *Col.* 18 July 1848; *Maj. Genl.* 20 June 1854.—Furlough, 17 Jan. 1851.
	38	6	*Lt. Col.* Richard James Holwell Birch, C. B. *Ens.* 7 Jan. 1821; *Lieut.* 11 July 1823; *Bt. Capt.* 7 Jan. 1836; *Capt.* 20 March 1836; *Bt. Major* 30 April 1844; *Major* 31 Oct. 1849. *Bt. Lt. Col.* 3 April 1846; *Lieut. Col.* 10 Dec. 1854; *Bt. Col.* 20 June 1854; *Major Genl.* 4 May 1858.—Secretary to the Govt. of India, Mily. Department.
	34	6	*Lt. Col.* St. George Daniel Showers, C. B. *Ens.* 9 Jan. 1825; *Lieut.* 25 June 1826; *Capt.* 22 Feb. 1836; *Bt. Major* 9 Nov. 1846; *Major* 24 April 1847; *Lieut. Col.* 10 May 1853; *Bt. Col.* 28 Nov. 1854.—Brigadier Comdg. at Agra.
	30	5	*Major* John Liptrott. 2nd *Lieut.* 7 Feb. 29; 1st *Lt.* 25 Feb. 34; *Bt. Capt.* 7 Feb. 44; *Capt.* 30 April 46; *Bt. Maj.* 28 Nov. 54; *Maj.* 10 Aug. 56.—17 Irregular Cavalry.
	29	3	*Major* M. E. Sherwill, *PC.* 2nd *Lieut.* 7 April 1830; 1st *Lieut.* 3 Oct. 1840; *Bt. Capt.* 7 Apl. 1845; *Capt.* 12 June 1847; *Bt. Major* 7 June 1849; *Maj.* 1 May 1858. *Bt. Lieut. Col.* 28 Nov. 1854.

☞ *Brevet.* [1] Maj. 20 June 54. [2] Maj. 19 Jan. 58. [3] Maj. 19 Jan. 58; [4] Maj. 19 Jan. 58; Lt. Col. 24 Mar. 58.

Fur. Reg.	Y	M	Captains.	Remarks.	2nd Lieut.	1st Lieut.	Captain. Brevet.	Captain. Regl.
	33	4	Hugh Mackenzie, [1]*m*	.. ..	15 *Mar.* 26	28 *June* 27	15 *Mar.* 41	4 *Feb.* 45
	26	..	F. D. Atkinson, *PC*, *	Military Secretariat,	11 *June* 33	3 *Oct.* 40	.. ..	12 *July* 47
	24	6	A. Boyd, [2]*m*	.. ..	21 *Jan.* 35	27 *Dec.* 41	.. ..	15 *Aug.* 47
	19	11	R. N. Tronson, *PH*,	Civil employ, ..	24 *July* 39	15 *Aug.* 42	.. ..	30 *July* 48
O.	19	5	G. Gaynor, *PH*,	Civil employ, ..	29 *Jan.* 40	12 *Nov.* 42	.. ..	8 *Mar.* 49
	18	7	J. Bleaymire,	Lv. S. C. to Australia and New Zeland,	11 *Dec.* 40	12 *Nov.* 42	.. ..	15 *Nov.* 49
O.	18	5	W. D. Harris [3] *m*	Fur. S C. 5 Nov. 58	25 *Jan.* 41	26 *Dec.* 42	.. ..	1 *Mar.* 52
N.	18	..	G. W. G. Green, C. B., *PH.*[4]*lc*	2d Punjaub Infy.	12 *June* 41	26 *Aug.* 43	.. ..	24 *Nov.* 53
	17	1	M. R. Nightingale, *PH*,	Garrison Staff, Fort William, ..	11 *June* 42	10 *July* 44	.. ..	22 *Nov.* 54
	17	1	B. Hawes, *PCH*,	Offg. Political employ, ..	11 *June* 42	24 *Jan.* 45	.. ..	10 *Aug.* 56
	16	11	J. J. Farrington, *PH*, (*a*)	.. ..	28 *July* 42	24 *Jan.* 45	.. ..	23 *Nov.* 56
	16	4	J. F. Campbell,	.. ..	25 *Feb.* 43	23 *Oct.* 45	.. ..	23 *Nov.* 56
N.	16	..	Charles Baldwin, *PC*,	Civil employ, ..	10 *July* 43	8 *Jan.* 47	.. ..	22 *Apl.* 58
	15	7	A. Paterson, *PH*,	.. ..	9 *Dec.* 43	12 *June* 47	.. ..	1 *May* 58
			1st Lieutenants.					
	15	5	A. L. Elderton, †(*b*)	D. P. W. Punjab.	27 *Jan.* 44	12 *July* 47	27 *Jan.* 59	
O.	14	7	C. Clark, *PH*,	Fur. S. C. 9 Mar. 58	9 *Dec.* 44	15 *Aug.* 47		
	14	6	W. C. Hamilton, *P*,	Civil employ, ..	5 *Jan.* 45	21 *July* 48		
O.	14	6	A. D. Toogood, †	Fur. S. C. 23 Feb. 58	12 *Jan.* 45	21 *Feb.* 49		
N.	12	11	D. W. Becher, *PH*,	Fur. P. A. 28 Apl. 59	27 *July* 46	15 *Nov.* 49		
O.	12	5	L. J. Trotter,	Fur. S. C. 13 Mar. 58	20 *Feb.* 47	20 *Aug.* 52		
	12	11	C. R. Blair,	Lv. S. C. 31 Oct.	27 *July* 46	1 *Mar.* 52		
O.	11	7	J. G. S. Matheson, †(*c*)	Fur. S. C. 19 Feb. 56	20 *Dec.* 47	12 *Nov.* 53		
	10	5	*Hon'ble* F. B. Best,	.. ..	7 *Feb.* 49	24 *Nov.* 53		
	10	..	J. T. Harris,	15 Punjaub Infy.	27 *June* 49	13 *Nov.* 54		
	8	7	Augustus Willes,	.. ..	9 *Dec.* 50	22 *Nov.* 54		
	8	4	K. J. W. Coghill, *PH*,	.. ..	26 *Feb.* 51	1 *Oct.* 55		
	7	1	G. A. Bishop, (*d*)	.. ..	12 *June* 52	2 *July* 56		

(*a*) Has passed an examination in Field Engineering.

(*b*) Has furnished certificates of qualification in Surveying and Civil Engineering; passed the prescribed examination in Field Engineering and obtained a first class certificate in Musketry.

(*c*) Has passed an examination in the Burmese Language.

(*d*) Has furnished certificates of qualification in Surveying.

* Official Major.

2ND EUROPEAN BENGAL FUSILIERS—*Continued.*

Fur. Reg.	Ser. Y	Ser. M	1st Lieutenants.—*Continued.*	Remarks.	2nd Lieut.	1st Lieut.
	5	3	Thomas Cadell, *PCH*, - -	.. ..	17 *Apl.* 54	23 *Nov.* 56
	5	2	*Sir* A. King Lake, *Bart.*, -	.. ..	20 *May* 54	23 *Nov.* 56
	4	2	A. L. Douglas, - - - -	.. ..	20 *Apl.* 55	23 *Nov.* 56
R N.	3	5	~~William Robert Boyd~~, -	Fur. S.C. 24 Mar. 57	20 *Feb.* 56	27 *June* 57
	3	1	Thomas Alex. Hunter, -	.. ..	14 *June* 56	14 *Aug.* 57
	3	1	George Mitchell, - - -	Lv. S. C. 15 Oct.	26 *June* 56	28 *Jan.* 58
	3	..	E. J. McNair, - - - -	.. ..	26 *July* 56	22 *Apl.* 58
N.	2	7	C. H. Cantor, - - - -	Fur. S.C. 17 Nov. 58	13 *Dec.* 56	1 *May* 58
N.	5	4	T. N. Walker,† - - - -	Fur. S.C. 14 May 59	14 *Mar.* 54	23 *Nov.* 56
			2ND LIEUTENANTS.		*Appointed.*	
	1	8	W. L. S Harrison, - -	.. ..	4 *Nov.* 57	
	1	5	H. Spalding, - - - -	.. ..	20 *Feb.* 58	
R	1	5	~~G. P. Nash~~,† - - - -	.. ..	20 *Feb.* 58	
			Adjutant.			
	..	..	K. J. W. Coghill, - - -	.. ..	6 *Dec.* 56	
			Interprete.			
			*			
			Surgeons.			
	..	..	E. Hare, - - - - -	Lv, S. C. 15 Nov.	19 *Feb.* 57	
			Assistant Surgeon.			
			*			

Strength—10 Companies, with 1 Sergeant Major—1 Quarter Master Sergeant—5 Staff Sergeants —50 Sergeants—50 Corporals—20 Drummers—30 Half-pay Drummers and 820 Privates.

Raised 15 Nov. 1853.

3rd European Regiment.

Gwalior.

FACINGS—*White.*

Fur.Reg.	Ser. Y	Ser. M	
	39	3	*Colonel* George Huyshe, C. B. *Ens.* 22 March 1820; *Lieut.* 3 June 1822; *Capt.* 21 Jan 1829; *Major* 12 Jan. 1837; *Bt. Lieut. Col.* 23 Dec. 1842; *Lieut. Col.* 8 Feb. 1843; *Bt. Col.* 14 July 53; *Col.* 15 Nov. 53; *Major General* 28 Nov. 54.—Fur., S.C. 16 May 1853.
D O.	~~31~~	~~10~~	~~*Lieut. Col.* William Swatman~~, *P.* *Ens.* 24 Oct. 27; *Lt.* 24 Aug. 33; *Capt.* 17 Mar. 40; *Maj* 11 Mar 47; *Lieut. Col.* 12 Jan. 53; *Bt. Col.* 28 Nov. 1854.—Fur. S. C. 12 Dec. 1856.
	36	1	*Lieut. Col.* William Riddell. *Ens.* 28 May 1823; *Lieut.* 13 May 1825; *Capt.* 1 Dec. 36; *Bt. Maj.* 23 Dec. 42; *Maj.* 15 Nov. 49; *Bt. Lt. Col.* 20 June 54; *Lieut. Col.* 25 Feb. 1855; *Bt. Col.* 5 Dec. 1855.
	33	1	*Lieut. Col.* William Beveridge Thomson, C. B. *P.* *Ens.* 30 June 1826; *Lieut.* 8 Apl. 1828; *Capt.* 3 Aug. 1837; *Bt. Major* 3 Apl. 1846; *Major* 21 Sep. 1854; *Bt. Lt. Col.* 20 June 1854; *Lieut. Col.* 13 July 1858; *Bt. Col.* 29 May 1857.—Commissary General.
	33	9	*Major* A. H. Duncan. *Ens.* 28 Sep. 25; *Lieut.* 11 Apl. 28; *Bt. Capt.* 28 Sep. 40; *Capt.* 11 Nov. 1847; *Bt. Major* 11 Nov. 1851; *Major* 4 Aug. 1857.—Bhagulpore Hill Rangers.
N.	31	6	*Major* H. M. Nation, *Ens.* 19 Jan. 28; *Lieut.* 8 Oct. 39; *Bt. Capt.* 19 Jan. 43; *Capt.* 7 June 1853; *Bt. Major* 20 June 1854; *Major* 13 July 1858.—Civil employ, and Comg. Behar Station Guards.

☞ *Brevet.* [1] Maj. 28 Nov. 56.

Fur.Reg.	Y	M	CAPTAINS.	REMARKS.	*Ensign.*	*Lieut.*	CAPTAIN. *Brevet.*	CAPTAIN. *Regl.*
	28	10	J. C. Phillips, *P*,[1]*m* - -	1st Mahrattah Horse.	30 *Sep.* 30	2 *Dec.* 36	30 *Sep.* 45	1 *Mar.* 51
	24	1	E. T. Dalton, *(a)* - - -	Civil employ, ..	15 *June* 35	24 *Dec.* 41	13 *June* 50	15 *Nov.* 53
	23	6	Robert Patton, *P*, - - -	Brigade Staff, ..	3 *Jan.* 36	3 *Oct.* 40	3 *Jan.* 51	15 *Nov.* 53
	21	4	R. C. Stevenson, *PH*,- -	.. ..	8 *Mar.* 38	12 *Nov.* 42	8 *Mar.* 53	21 *Sep.* 54
	20	1	Edwin Thomas, *P*, - - -	.. ..	12 *June* 39	6 *Mar.* 41	12 *June* 54	15 *Oct.* 54
	18	10	J. N. Young, *P*, - - -	Judge Adv. Genl.'s Dept., ..	21 *Aug.* 40	16 *July* 42	21 *Aug.* 55	9 *Dec.* 54
N.	18	1	C. B. G. Bacon, *P*, - - -	Furlough, S. C. 26 Feb. 58, ..	24 *May* 41	24 *May* 43	24 *May* 56	1 *June* 56
N.	18	1	B. T. Reid, *P(b)* - - -	Civil employ,	12 *June* 41	24 *Jan.* 45	12 *June* 56	23 *Nov.* 56
	17	..	T. H. Chamberlain, *PH*, -	Political employ,	8 *July* 42	24 *Jan.* 45	.. ..	23 *Nov.* 56
O.	16	5	A. G. Forsyth, *PH*, - -	Fur. S.C. 18 Feb. 59	7 *Feb.* 43	29 *July* 45	.. ..	1 *Jan.* 57
	16	5	E. D. R. Ross, *PH*, - -	Offg. Political employ	22 *Feb.* 43	21 *Dec.* 45	.. ..	21 *Jan.* 57
	16	..	Alex. Pond, *PCH*, - - -	.. ..	11 *July* 43	26 *Dec.* 46	.. ..	4 *Aug.* 57
	15	6	R. F. Webster,† - - -	.. ..	30 *Dec.* 43	15 *Mar.* 48	.. ..	15 *May* 58
O.	14	6	C. M. N. Fellowes,† - -	Fur. S.C. 16 Feb. 58	12 *Jan.* 45	15 *June* 48	.. ..	13 *July* 58
			LIEUTENANTS.					
	12	7	William Carnell, *PH*, - -	Mhair. Regiment,	11 *Dec.* 46	15 *June* 49		
	12	1	R. E. Anderson,† - - -	.. ..	11 *June* 47	1 *Feb.* 50		
	10	8	H. A. Prinsep, *PH*, - -	Private Secy. and A. D. C. to the Lt. Govr. N. W. P.	20 *Dec.* 48	21 *Feb.* 50		

(a) Passed a successful examination in the Assamese and Bengallee languages.
(b) Passed an examination in the Punjaubee language, 10th December 1851.

3RD EUROPEAN REGIMENT.—*Continued.*

Fur. Reg.	Ser. Y	Ser. M	LIEUTENANTS.	REMARKS.	*Ensign.*	*Lieut.*
N.	14	7	F. J. Stephenson, *PC*, -	Fur. S. C. 30 Apl. 58	10 *Dec.* 44	19 *Aug.* 54
	14	7	S. Dewe White, *(a) PC*, -	.. ..	10 *Dec.* 44	15 *Nov.* 53
	14	..	H. B. Blake,† - - - -	.. ..	4 *July* 45	15 *Oct.* 54
O.	13	7	J. F. Templer,† - - -	Fur. S. C. 3 Mar. 57	13 *Dec.* 45	9 *Dec.* 54
	10	10	R. O. H. Forbes, *PCH*, -	Adjt. District Police, Azimgurh, ..	30 *Aug.* 48	1 *Sep.* 55
O.	9	11	T. H. Maddock, *PH*, -	Fur. S. C. 8 Oct. 58	28 *July* 49	15 *Nov.* 55
	9	5	M. A. D. Orchard,† - -	.. ..	21 *Jan.* 50	17 *Dec.* 55
O.	6	11	John Robt. McPherson,†	Fur. S. C. 30 Nov 58	22 *July* 52	23 *Nov.* 56
	8	5	Edward Stevenson, *PCH*,-	Lv. p. to Furlough.	20 *Feb.* 51	23 *Nov.* 56
	4	7	Alex. Henry Thomson, -	.. ..	10 *Dec.* 54	1 *Jan.* 57
	3	9	Henry George Saunders, -	.. ..	20 *Oct.* 55	21 *Jan.* 57
	3	9	E. B. Wimberley, B.A. *PH*,	.. ..	20 *Oct.* 55	4 *Aug.* 57
	3	11	R. C. W. Mitford, *PCH*, -	3rd Regt. Hodson's, Horse, ..	25 *July* 55	30 *Apl.* 58
	2	7	George W. Holdsworth, -	.. ..	13 *Dec.* 56	30 *Apl.* 58
	2	7	D. Dela-G. Birkett, - -	.. ..	13 *Dec.* 56	30 *Apl.* 58
	2	7	H. Goschen,† - - - -	23rd Punjaub Infy.	13 *Dec.* 56	30 *Apl*, 58
	4	..	W. W. Lee, - - - -	.. ..	3 *July* 55	31 *Dec.* 56
N.	2	7	H. A. Shaw, - - - - -	Fur. S. C. 21 Oct. 58	12 *Dec.* 56	11 *May* 57
	2	7	H. S. Jarrett, *PCH*, - -	.. ..	13 *Dec.* 56	11 *July* 57
			ENSIGNS.			
	1	11	A. W. Money, - - - -	Lv. S. C. 9 Oct. ..	15 *Aug.* 57	
	1	6	A. F. Gerard, - - - -	.. ..	20 *Jan.* 58	
	1	3	A. D. Campbell, - - - -	.. ..	4 *Apl.* 58	
	1	3	G. A. Owen,- - - - -	.. ..	20 *Apl.* 58	
	1	7	E. B. Cox, - - - - -	.. ..	11 *Dec.* 57	
			Adjutant.			
	..	..	E. B. Wimberley, B. A., -	.. ..	31 *Jan.* 59	
			Interpreter.			
	..	..	F. J. Stephenson, - - -	Fur. S. C. 30 Apl. 58	18 *Mar.* 56	
	..	..	H. G. Saunders, - - -	Offg. Qr. Master,		
	..	..	*Surg.* C. M. Henderson, M.D.	.. ..	27 *Apl.* 59	
	..	..	*Asst. Surg.* R. S. Bateson,	.. ..	5 *Feb.* 57	
			,, C. Hatchell, -	.. ..	———	
			,, P. M. Crosbie, B. A. M. B.	.. ..	———	

Strength—10 Companies, with 1 SergeantMajor—1 Quarter Master Sergeant—5 Staff Sergeants—50 Sergeants—50 Corporals—20 Drummers—30 Half-pay Drummers—820 Privates.

(a) Received a Certificate of High Proficiency in Hindee, 29th October 1851, and attained the standard of proficiency in the Oordoo and Hindee languages.

Raised in July 1858. }

4th European Regiment.

{ Allahabad.

RIGHT WING.

FACINGS———.

Fur. Reg.	Ser. Y	Ser. M	
O.	51	3	*Col.* Hope Dick. *Ens.* 9 April 1808; *Lieut.* 18 Oct. 1812; *Bt. Capt.* 9 Apl. 1823; *Capt.* 1 May 24; *Bt. Maj.* 28 June 38; *Maj.* 13 Feb. 39; *Bt. Lt. Col.* 30 April 1844; *Lt. Col.* 4 March 1845; *Bt. Col.* 20 June 1854; *Col.* 16 Jan. 55; *Major Genl.* 2 Apl. 1856—Fur. P. A. 28 Feb 1854.
N.	39	..	*Lieut. Col.* Wm. Fergusson Beatson. (*a*) *Ens.* 13 July 1820; *Lieut.* 11 July 11823; *Bt. Capt* 13 July 1853; *Capt.* 26 Jan. 1837; *Bt. Major* 9 Nov. 1846; *Major* 18 Juy 1848; *Lieut. Col.* 15 Nov. 1853; *Bt. Col.* 28 Nov. 1854.—Fur. P. A. 19 May 1859.
	33	5	*Lt. Col.* J. G. A. Rice. *Ens.* 5 Feb. 1826; *Lieut.* 9 July 1828; *Bt. Capt.* 5 Feb. 1841; *Capt.* 6 March 1846; *Major* 18 April 1853; *Lieut. Col.* 29 July 1857.
	34	11	*Lieut. Col.* H. P. Burn. *Ens.* 16 Aug. 24; *Lieut.* 13 May 25; *Capt.* 6 July 37; *Bt. Maj.* 4 Oct. 42; *Bt. Lieut. Col.* 20 June 54; *Major* 16 Jan. 55; *Lieut. Col.* 13 Mar. 59. *Bt. Col.* 1 May 55. Supt. of Army Clothing and Auditor of Clothing Accounts.
	27	6	*Major* G. A. Fisher†, *Ens.* 29 Dec. 1831; *Lieut.* 1 Feb. 1837; *Bt. Capt.* 9 June 1846; *Capt.* 31 Oct. 1848; *Bt. Major* 14 Nov. 1858; *Major* 13 Mar. 1859.

Fur. Reg.	Ser. Y	Ser. M		Remarks.	*Ensign.*	*Lieut.*	Captain. *Brevet.*	Captain. *Regl.*
			CAPTAINS.					
	25	1	Augustus Turner,† - -	Judge Ad. General's Dept., ..	13 *June* 34	28 *June* 37	13 *June* 49	14 *Nov.* 49
	18	11	J. Ward,† - - - - - -	.. ..	26 *July* 40	26 *May* 43	.. ..	16 *Jan.* 55
	16	9	E. Thompson, *PH*, - -	.. ..	24 *Sep.* 42	14 *July* 48	.. ..	23 *Nov.* 56
	12	1	R. S. Simonds,† - - -	.. ..	11 *June* 47	14 *Nov.* 49	.. ..	27 *June* 57
N.	13	4	H. J. Hawes, *P*, - -	Civil employ, ..	24 *Feb.* 46	1 *Feb.* 50	.. ..	27 *June* 57
	11	7	C. H. Brownlow, *PH*,- -	8th Punjaub Infy...	20 *Dec.* 47	10 *Sep.* 52	.. ..	3 *Nov.* 58
D	~~10~~	~~11~~	~~J. S. Bennett,†~~ - - -	Futtehgurh Infantry Levy., ..	27 *July* 48	16 *Jan.* 55	.. ..	13 *Mar.* 59
			LIEUTENANTS.					
N.	9	10	J. P. Martin, *P*, - -	Civil employ,	20 *Sep.* 49	4 *Jan.* 56		
	7	5	*Hon'ble* J. H. Fraser,† -	2nd Regt. Hodson's, Horse, ..	20 *Feb.* 52	23 *Nov.* 56		
	3	7	M. G. Clerk, † - - -	Dep. P. W. Oude,..	7 *Dec.* 55	27 *June* 57		
	10	1	C. A. McDougall, *PH*, -	Offg. Brigade Staff.	8 *June* 49	1 *June* 54		
	7	1	E. R. C. Wilcox, † - -	.. ..	13 *June* 52	18 *July* 56		
O.	7	5	F. M. Armstrong, † - -	Fur. S. C. 20 Oct. 58	20 *Jan.* 51	23 *Nov.* 56		
	4	5	Alfred B. E. Thomas, *PCH*,	Adjt. District, Police Mirzapore, ..	4 *Feb.* 55	20 *Mar.* 57		
	2	7	G. F. J. Graham, - - -	Adjt. District, Police Etawah, ..	20 *Dec.* 56	27 *Sep.* 57		
	4	5	M. P. Ricketts, *PC*, - -	.. ..	4 *Feb.* 55	4 *Sep.* 57		
	1	10	R. H. Dyas, - - -	.. ..	4 *Sep.* 57	3 *Nov.* 58		
	1	5	F. W. Leman, - - -	.. ..	20 *Feb.* 58	13 *Mar.* 59		
			ENSIGNS.					
	1	1	C. L. Money. - - -	.. ..	20 *June* 58			
	1	7	G. P. Cumming,† - -	.. ..	12 *Dec.* 57			
	1	5	A. H. F. Campbell, - -	.. ..	4 *Feb.* 58			
	..	11	G. Logan, - - - - -	.. ...	4 *Aug.* 58			
	..	..	*					
	..	..	*					
	..	..	*					
	..	..	*					
	..	..	*					
	..	..	*					

(*a*) Received a Cross of the first class of the National and Military Order of San Fernando of Spain.

Raised in July 1858. } **4th European Regiment.** { Allahabad.

LEFT WING.

Facings———

Fur. Reg.	Ser. Y	Ser. M	
	55	7	*Colonel* Joseph Harris. *Ens.* 1 Dec. 1803; *Lieut.* 13 Nov. 1804; *Capt.* 10 June 1819; *Major* 21 Jan. 1829; *Lieut. Col.* 5 April 1834; *Col.* 30 Sept. 1845; *Major General* 20 June 1854.—Europe, 18 Apl. 43.
			Lt. Col. *
	23	8	*Major* J. Metcalfe. *Ens.* 11 Dec. 1835; *Lieut.* 8 July 1839; *Capt.* 1 Jan. 1850; *Major* 1 Feb. 1858; *Bt. Lieut. Colonel.* 24 March 1858.

Fur. Reg.	Ser. Y	Ser. M	Captains.	Remarks.	Ensign.	Lieut.	Captain. Brevet.	Captain. Regl.
	21	8	J. P. Caulfeild, *PH*, - -	Comdg. district Police, Futteagurh	12 *Dec.* 37	3 *Oct.* 40	.. ..	3 *Oct.* 51
	20	8	C. B. Stuart, *P*, (*a*) - -	Dept. P. W. N. W. P.	11 *Dec.* 38	18 *Apl.* 41	.. ..	7 *Jan.* 53
	20	5	A. H. Ternan, *P*, - -	Civil employ, ..	24 *Jan.* 39	19 *Apl.* 42	.. ..	20 *Sep.* 53
	18	5	J. Marquis, † - - - -	Loyal Poorbeeah Regiment, ...	17 *Feb.* 41	5 *Feb.* 43	17 *Feb.* 56	23 *Nov.* 56
D	~~17~~	~~8~~	~~W. L. Reynolds~~, *PH*, - -	.. ..	11 *Dec.* 41	12 *Oct.* 45	11 *Dec.* 56	21 *Oct.* 57
	17	1	H. Rose, *P*, (*a*) - - -	D. P. W. Punjaub,	11 *June* 42	1 *Apl.* 47	11 *June* 57	15 *Nov.* 57
	16	8	T. C. Merrick, *PH*, -	Canal Dept. N. W. P., ..	10 *Dec.* 42	1 *Jan.* 50	10 *Dec.* 57	1 *Feb.* 58
			Lieutenants.					
	14	7	G. A. Cuyler, *P*, - -	.. ..	29 *Dec.* 44	3 *Oct.* 51		
	14	4	E. G. Higgins, † - - -	.. ..	19 *Mar.* 45	7 *Jan.* 53		
	12	11	A. A. Bruce, † - - - -	.. ..	15 *Aug.* 46	15 *Nov.* 53		
	9	7	H. L. C. Bernard, *PH*, -	25th Punjaub Infy.	11 *Dec.* 49	10 *Sep.* 55		
	8	1	W. P. Fisher, *PH*, - -	2nd Punjaub Infy.	13 *June* 51	14 *Oct* 55		
	5	6	T. B. Boileau, *PH*, - -	.. ..	28 *Dec.* 53	23 *Nov* 56		
N.	4	7	Owen Ivon Chalmers, † -	Fur. S.C. 30 Oct. 58,	10 *Dec.* 54	19 *June* 57		
O.	7	6	G. V. Fosbery, † - - -	Fur. S. C. 3 Jan. 57,	20 *Jan.* 52	1 *July* 57		
	4	9	C. D. P. Nott, - -	1st Seikh Infy. ..	27 *Sep.* 54	10 *July* 57		
	2	7	C. Pigou, - - - - -	.. ..	13 *Dec.* 56	20 *May* 58		
	2	6	W. Tweedie, - - - -	Hyderabad Contingent,	20 *Jan.* 57	30 *Apl.* 58		
					Appointed.			
	..	..	*Adjt.*, C. Pigou, - - -	Officiating, ..	7 *May* 59			
	..	..	*Intr.*, G. A. Cuyler, - -	.. ..	4 *Dec.* 58			
	..	..	*Surg.* T. C. Hutchinson, -	.. ..	27 *Apl.* 59			
	..	..	*Asst. Surg.* *					

(*a*) Have furnished certificates of qualification in surveying and civil Engineering.

Raised in July 1858

5th European Regiment.

Berhampore.

RIGHT WING.

FACINGS———

Fur. Reg.	Ser. Y	Ser. M	
			*Colonel**
	30	3	*Lieut. Col.* Edward Geoffry J. Champneys. *Ens.* 29 Mar. 1829; *Lieut.* 30 May 1834; *Bt. Capt.* 29 Mar. 1844; *Capt.* 24 Jan. 1845; *Major* 30 Dec. 1852; *Lieut. Col.* 1 July 1857.—Military Auditor General.
	32	11	*Major* F. Maitland, *P. Ens.* 17 Aug. 1826; *Lieut.* 21 Jan. 1838; *Bt. Captain* 17 Aug. 1841; *Capt.* 15 Feb. 1851; *Bt. Major* 20 June 1854; *Major* 31 Dec. 1856.

☞ *Brevet* [1] Major 19 Jan. 1858. [2] Major 20 July 1858.

Fur. Reg.	Ser. Y	Ser. M	CAPTAINS.	REMARKS.	*Ensign.*	*Lieut.*	CAPTAIN. *Brevet.*	CAPTAIN. *Regl.*
	18	6	M. J. Slater, *PC*,*	Pay Department. ..	22 *Dec.* 40	12 *Nov.* 42	.. ..	15 *Nov.* 53
	22	6	A. B. Fenwick, *PH*,	Qr. Mr. Genl's. Dept.	10 *Jan.* 37	16 *July* 42	10 *Jan.* 52	9 *Aug.* 54
	18	10	H. C. Johnstone, *PH*, *(a)*	Revenue Survey Dept.	31 *July* 40	1 *May* 46	.. ..	28 *Feb.* 55
	18	5	W. McNeile, *PC*, *(b)*	Civil employ, ..	25 *Jan.* 41	8 *July* 48	25 *Jan.* 56	11 *June* 56
O.	13	5	D. Kemp, † [1]*m*	Fur. S. C. 3 May 58	4 *Feb.* 46	15 *Feb.* 51	.. ..	31 *Dec.* 56
N.	12	11	A. B. Johnson, *PH*, [2]*m*	Brigade Staff, ..	27 *July* 46	26 *Feb.* 51	.. ..	5 *Oct.* 57
	12	4	C. H. E. Græme, *P*, *(c)*	.. ..	20 *Feb.* 47	31 *Mar.* 53	.. ..	17 *June* 58
			LIEUTENANTS.					
	10	7	J. E. B. Parsons, *P*,	Civil employ, ..	20 *Dec.* 48	15 *Nov.* 53		
	8	7	E. C. Impey, *P*,	Political employ, ..	10 *Dec.* 50	15 *Nov.* 53		
O.	8	7	T. E. VanderGucht, *PH*,	Fur. S.C. 10 Mar. 59	20 *Dec.* 50	9 *Aug.* 54		
	~~6~~	~~1~~	~~James Becher Tudor~~, †	1st Regt. Beatson's Horse, ..	12 *June* 53	1 *Sep.* 55		
	5	6	Geo. Fergus Graham, †	23 Punjaub Infy. ..	14 *Jan.* 54	1 *Sep.* 55		
	4	10	Wm. Henry Buttanshaw,	.. ..	4 *Sep.* 54	11 *June* 56		
	4	3	H. C. Evelyn Ward, *PH*,	Corps of Guides ..	20 *Apl.* 55	23 *Nov.* 56		
	4	1	H. M. Barton Burlton,	Meade's Horse, ..	12 *June* 55	23 *Nov.* 56		
	3	2	Fred. Van H. Sperling,	.. ..	15 *May* 56	5 *Oct.* 57		
	2	5	A. P. Palmer,	2nd Regt. Hodson's Horse, ..	20 *Feb.* 57	30 *Apl.* 58		
	3	1	J. B. Smith, †	.. ..	26 *June* 56	30 *Apl.* 58		
			ENSIGNS.					
	~~1~~	~~7~~	~~J. S. Bagshaw~~,	.. ..	4 *Dec.* 57			
	1	6	C. Handyside,	Fur. S.C. 14 Sep. 58	20 *Jan.* 58			
	1	3	T. T. Oliphant,	.. ..	4 *Apl.* 58			
	1	7	John Finnis,	.. ..	12 *Dec.* 57			
			*					
			*					
			*					
			*					
			*					
			*					

(a) Has furnished certificate of qualification as a Surveyor and Civil Engineer.
(b) Received a certificate of high proficiency in the Hindee language, on the 26th June 1847, from the College of Fort William.
(c) Has furnished certificate of qualification in Surveying and Civil Engineering. Has also attained a degree of proficiency in the Punjaubee language.

* With the Regiment.

Raised in July 1858.

5th European Regiment.

Berhampore.

LEFT WING.

FACINGS———

Fur. Reg.	Ser. Y	Ser. M	
	52	5	*Colonel* Charles Richard William Lane, C. B. *Ens.* 5 Feb. 1807; *Lieut.* 7 March 1813; *Bt. Capt.* 5 Feb. 1822; *Capt.* 30 Jan. 1824; *Major* 30 April 1835; *Lieut. Col.* 26 Dec. 1841; *Colonel* 25 May 1852; *Major General* 28 Nov. 54.—Furlough, P. A. 10 Sept. 51.
N.	39	3	*Colonel* Fredk. Brooke Corfield. *Ens.* 3 April 1820; *Lieut.* 11 July 1823; *Capt.* 22 April 1831; *Major* 14 March 1843; *Bt. Lt. Col.* 7 June 1849; *Lt. Col.* 3 Sept. 1849; *Bt. Col.* 28 Nov. 1854; *Col.* 26 April 1859.—Furlough. S. C. 23 July 1858.
			*Major**

☞ *Brevet.* [1] Maj. 20 July 58.

Fur. Reg.	Ser. Y	Ser. M	Captains.	Remarks.	*Ensign.*	*Lieut.*	Captain. *Brevet.*	Captain. *Regl.*
Maj. O.	22	7	John Gordon, *P*, [1] *m*, - -	Fur. S.C. 14 July 58	9 *Dec.* 36	16 *July* 42	.. ..	5 *May* 51
N.	22	5	W. R. Cunningham, *P*, -	Fur. S.C. 13 July 57	31 *Jan.* 37	12 *Nov.* 42	31 *Jan.* 52	15 *June* 52
	21	4	E. J. Rickards, *PH*, - -	Mhairwarrah Battn.	27 *Mar.* 38	20 *Dec.* 43	27 *Mar.* 53	18 *Apl.* 53
	18	11	S. Fredk. Graham, *P*, - -	Civil employ, ..	4 *Aug.* 40	1 *Mar.* 44	4 *Aug.* 55	23 *Nov.* 56
O.	17	1	J. M. Nuttall,† - - -	Fur. S.C. 31 July 57	10 *June* 42	24 *Jan.* 45	.. ..	6 *June* 57
O.	16	11	C. Fredk. Hicks,† - - -	Fur. S. C. 9 Oct. 57	25 *July* 42	6 *Mar.* 46	25 *July* 57	29 *July* 57
	16	1	J. J. Eckford, *PH*, (a) - -	Mynpoory Police, ..	9 *June* 43	6 *Apl.* 50	.. ..	29 *Jan.* 58
			Lieutenants.					
Capt.	16	..	H. J. Templer,† - - -	Camel Corps. ..	10 *July* 43	17 *Nov.* 50	10 *July* 58	
	13	10	C. S. W. Ogilvie, *P*, - -	Army Comt. Dept.	23 *Aug.* 45	5 *May* 51		
	10	7	R. Gordon Rogers, *PH*, -	Arracan Battn. ..	9 *Dec.* 48	28 *Aug.* 52		
N.	8	7	L. H. Williams,† - - -	Fur. S. C. 28 July 57	10 *Dec.* 50	10 *Apl.* 53		
	8	5	C. P. Hunter, *PH*, - -	1st Assam Light Infy. Battalion, ..	20 *Jan.* 51	18 *Apl.* 53		
	7	7	F. I. Conway-Gordon,† -	Instructor of Musketry, ..	20 *Dec.* 51	23 *Nov.* 56		
R	~~6~~	~~5~~	~~H. O. Currie~~,† - - - -	.. ..	4 *Feb.* 53	6 *June* 57		
	6	5	L. B. J. Davies,† - - -	.. ..	13 *Feb.* 53	23 *Nov.* 56		
N.	3	1	G. C. Udny,† - - - -	Fur. S.C. 21 Feb. 59	14 *June* 56	27 *June* 57		
	3	7	Henry Morton,† - - -	.. ..	20 *Dec.* 55	30 *Apl.* 58		
	2	6	J. S. Oliphant,† - - -	.. ..	4 *Jan.* 57	30 *Apl.* 58		
					Appointed.			
	..	..	*Adjutant*, T. E. Vander Gucht, - - - - -	Fur. S.C. 10 Mar. 59	18 *Jan.* 59			
	..	..	L. B. J. Davies, - - -	Officiating, ...	21 *Feb.* 59			
	..	..	*Intr.*, M. J. Slater, - -	Officiating, ..	18 *Mar.* 59			
	..	..	*Surgeon*, J. A. Dunbar, M.D.	.. ..	3 *Dec.* 58			
	..	..	*Asst. Surg.*, J. F. Tierney,	.. ..	27 *Jan.* 59			

(a) Has furnished the certificates of qualification in Surveying and Civil Engineering.

Raised in July 1858.

6th European Regiment.

Hazareebaugh.

RIGHT WING.

FACINGS———

Fur. Reg.	Ser. Y	Ser. M	
	47	11	*Colonel* Christopher Dixon Wilkinson, C.B. *Ens.* 16 August 1811; *Lieut.* 1 March 1816; *Capt.* 14 June 1825; *Major* 26 June 1833; *Lieut. Col.* 26 March 1840; *Col.* 28 Sep. 1850; *Major General* 28 Nov. 54.
R N.	~~44~~	~~7~~	~~*Lt. Colonel* Henry Templer.~~ *Ens.* 16 Dec. 1814; *Lieut.* 16 June 1816; *Bt. Capt.* 16 Dec. 1829; *Capt.* 2 Jan. 1831; *Bt. Major* 9 Nov. 1846; *Major* 6 Nov. 48; *Lt. Col.* 7 May 1854; *Bt. Colonel* 28 Nov. 1854.—Furlough S. C. 23 July 58.
	30	11	*Lieut. Col* A. P. Phayre.† *Ens.* 13 Aug. 1828; *Lieut.* 9 July 1838; *Bt. Capt.* 13 Aug. 1843; *Capt.* 16 May 49; *Bt. Major* 20 June 1854; *Major* 10 Jan. 55; *Lieut. Colonel* 22 Jan. 1859.—Civil employ.
	22	5	*Major* Walter Birch, *P*, *Ens.* 31 Jan. 1837; *Lieut.* 15 Jan. 1841; *Capt.* 1 Mar. 1851; *Major* 22 Jan. 1859.—Brigade Staff.

Fur. Reg.	Ser. Y	Ser. M	CAPTAINS.	REMARKS.	*Ensign.*	*Lieut.*	CAPTAIN. *Brevet.*	CAPTAIN. *Regl.*
O.	21	7	R. R. Mainwaring, *PH*, -	Fur. S.C. 14 *June* 59	31 *Dec.* 37	27 *Oct.* 41	.. ..	10 *Apl.* 52
	19	3	C. Need, *PH*, - - - -	Offg. Comdt. Landour Rangers, ..	14 *Apl.* 40	16 *July* 42	.. ..	1 *Aug.* 53
	18	7	R. T. Leigh, *PC,(a)* - -	Civil employ, ..	12 *Dec.* 40	13 *June* 44	.. ..	7 *May* 54
	17	5	George Swiney, *PH*, - -	Comdg. district Police, Jaloun, ..	30 *Jan.* 42	5 *Dec.* 45	.. ..	9 *Jan.* 55
	15	7	G. H. Thompson, *P*, - -	Rev. Survey Dept.	8 *Dec.* 43	6 *Nov.* 48	.. ..	10 *Jan.* 55
N.	15	5	F. P. Bailey, *PH*, - - -	Fur. S.C. 15 June 58	9 *Feb.* 44	16 *May* 49	.. ..	23 *Nov.* 56
O.	13	7	J. M. Evans, *PCH*, - -	Arracan Battalion, ..	13 *Dec.* 45	10 *Apl.* 52	.. ..	22 *Jan.* 59
			LIEUTENANTS.					
	11	1	D. B. Lockhart,† - - -	Fur. S.C. 12 Feb. 58	10 *June* 48	21 *Aug.* 52		
	10	7	J. C. Horne, *P*, - - -	Civil employ, ..	20 *Dec.* 48	1 *Aug.* 53		
	8	7	G. J. Pasley, *PH*, - -	Bhaugulpore Hill Rangers, ..	20 *Dec.* 50	26 *Apl.* 54		
	8	6	B. S. B. Parlby, *PH*, - -	6th Punjaub Infy. ..	11 *Jan.* 51	7 *May* 54		
	7	~~6~~	~~R. Travers, *PCH*,~~ - - -	Kamroop Regiment.	20 *Jan.* 52	9 *Jan.* 55		
N.	5	5	Robert Stanwix Robertson†	Fur. S.C. 12 Aug. 58	4 *Feb.* 54	23 *Nov.* 56		
	5	..	Robert Alexander Dobbin,	.. ..	6 *July* 54	23 *Nov.* 56		
	4	6	Otway Mayne Graham,,† -	Army Commt. Dept.	20 *Jan.* 55	30 *July* 57		
N.	2	11	A. L. Playfair,† - - -	Fur. S.C. 22 June 58	5 *Aug.* 56	7 *Nov.* 57		
	3	7	W V. F. Jacob, *PH*, - -	.. ..	8 *Dec.* 55	4 *June* 57		
	2	10	H. H. Chapman, - - -	.. ..	20 *Sep.* 56	30 *Apl.* 58		
	1	10	J. C. Stewart,† - - -	.. ..	4 *Sep.* 57	22 *Jan.* 59		
	1	1	H. M. Evans - - - -	.. ..	20 *June* 58	15 *Mar.* 59		
			ENSIGNS.					
	..	7	E. Newbery, - - - -	.. ..	11 *Dec.* 58			
	..	6	W. Battye, - - - -	.. ..	6 *Jan.* 59			
			*					
			*					
			*					
			*					
			*					
			*					
			*					
			*					

(a) Passed a successful examination in the Punjaubee Language.

Raised in July 1858. } **6th European Regiment.** Hazareebaugh.

LEFT WING.

FACINGS———

Fur. Reg.	Ser. Y	Ser. M	
D	57	..	~~*Col.* William Vincent.~~ *Ens.* 5 July 1802; *Lt.* 29 March 1804; *Bt. Capt.* 1 Oct. 15; *Capt.* 9 Apl. 1816; *Maj.* 2 Oct. 1824; *Lt. Col.* 30 May 28; *Bt. Col.* 23 Jan. 34; *Col.* 8 Oct. 1839; *Maj. Genl.* 23 Nov. 1841; *Lieut. Genl.* 11 Nov. 51.—In India.—Hills North of Deyrah.
	39	..	(*a*) *Col. Sir* Patrick Grant, K.C.B. *Ens.* 16 July 1820; *Lieut.* 11 July 1823; *Capt.* 14 May 1832; *Bt. Major* 30 Apl. 1844; *Major* 15 June 1845; *Bt. Lieut. Col.* 3 Apl. 1846; *Bt. Col.* 2 Aug. 1850; *Lieut. Col.* 29 Aug. 1851; *Maj. Genl.* 28 Nov. 54.—Commander-in-chief at Madras.
	39	0	*Lieut. Col.* Hugh Troup. *Ens.* 16 July 1820; *Lieut.* 11 July 1823; *Capt.* 27 June 1830; *Maj.* 16 May 44; *Lt. Col.* 13 Aug. 50; *Bt. Col.* 28 Nov. 54.—Brigadier Comdg. at Delhi.
N.	33	5	(*b*) *Major* W. A. John Mayhew. *Ens.* 16 Feb. 1826; *Lt.* 8 Oct. 1839; *Bt. Capt.* 16 Feb. 1841; *Capt.* 24 Jan. 1845; *Bt. Maj.* 9 Dec. 1853; *Maj.* 6 May 1856.—Adjt. Genl. of the Army.

☞ *Brevet.* [1] Major 6 June 56. [2] Major 24 Mar. 1858. [3] Major 24 Mar. 1858.

Fur. Reg.	Y	M	CAPTAINS.	REMARKS.	*Ensign.*	*Lieut.*	CAPTAIN. *Brevet.*	CAPTAIN. *Regl.*
	21	5	F. T. Wroughton, † - -	.. ..	18 *Feb.* 38	3 *Oct.* 40	.. ..	2 *June* 47
R O.	22	1	~~J. G. Stephen,~~ *PC*, (*c*)[1]*m* -	Fur. S.C. 18 Mar. 59	13 *June* 37	18 *Feb.* 41	.. ..	21 *June* 50
	20	..	H. M. Wilson, *P*, [2]*m* - -	Military Secretariat,	6 *July* 39	23 *Feb.* 42	.. ..	22 *Oct.* 51
	19	7	W. R. Eliott, *PCH*, - -	Civil employ, ..	10 *Dec.* 39	9 *Mar.* 42	.. ..	25 *Feb.* 52
	19	..	R. F. Grindall, *PH*, - -	.. ..	18 *July* 40	16 *July* 42	18 *July* 55	20 *Feb.* 56
	18	6	H. R. Drew, † - - - -	Kamroop Regt., ..	22 *Dec.* 40	16 *Aug.* 42	22 *Dec.* 55	6 *May* 56
O.	18	5	E. Oakes, †[3]*m* - - - -	Fur.S.C. 29 Dec. 58,	2 *Feb.* 41	13 *Mar.* 44	2 *Feb.* 56	23 *Nov.* 56

Fur. Reg.	Y	M	LIEUTENANTS.	REMARKS.	*Ensign.*	*Lieut.*
N.	13	5	J. A. Grant, *PH*, - - -	Fur. S. C. 12 Feb. 58	26 *Jan.* 46	22 *Oct.* 51
D	13	1	~~G. H. Griffiths, *PH*,~~ - -	10th Irregular Cavy.,	12 *June* 46	1 *Feb.* 52
	12	1	J. C. Hamilton, † - - -	.. ..	12 *June* 47	25 *Feb.* 52
R O.	10	7	~~J. D. Lance, *PH*,~~ - - -	Fur. S. C. 27 Aug. 58	8 *Dec.* 48	16 *Jan.* 55
	9	6	Q. D. Parsons, *PH*, - -	11th Irr. Cavalry...	20 *Jan.* 50	20 *Feb.* 56
D	8	1	~~W. C. D. Campbell,~~ † -	.. ..	13 *June* 51	6 *May* 56
	6	4	Wm. George Keppel, †-	Adjt. Ghazeepore District Police, ..	14 *Mar.* 53	23 *Nov.* 56
R N.	4	7	~~Charles Joseph Anderson,~~ -	Fur. S.C. 5 Dec. 56	9 *Dec.* 54	25 *Sep.* 57
	3	1	W. E. D. Broughton, † -	.. ..	13 *June* 56	10 *Oct.* 57
	2	7	H. H. Stansfeld, † - - -	.. ..	13 *Dec.* 56	19 *Nov.* 57

Y	M			*Appointed.*
..	..	*Adjutant*, H. H. Stansfeld,	Officiating, ...	29 *Jan.* 59
..	..	*Interpreter*,*		
..	..	*Surgeon*. G. E. Morton, M.D.	.. ..	3 *Dec.* 58
..	..	*Instructor of Musketry*, Lieut. F. F. Rowcroft, 2nd N. I. (Grs.) ..	.. ..	9 *Apl.* 59

(*a*) Lieut. Genl. in the East Indies 25th January 1856.

(*b*) Official Lieutenant Colonel.

(*c*) Received a degree of honor in Persian, on the 19th June 1843, from the College of Fort William, and certificates of high proficiency in the Hindee and Oordoo languages, 23rd December 1853.

R

Raised in 1762.

2nd (Grenadiers) Regiment of Native Infantry.

Disarmed Barrackpore.

"BUXAR"—"GUZERAT"—"CANDAHAR"—"GHUZNEE"—"CAUBUL 1842"—"MAHARAJPORE"—"MOODKEE"—FEROZESHUHUR."
Burdwan-ka-Pultun. Late 1st Battaliou 1st Regt. N I.
FACINGS—*Yellow.*

Fur. Reg.	Ser. Y	Ser. M	
	41	10	*Col.* Francis Spencer Hawkins, C. B. *Ens.* 5 Sept. 1817; *Lieut.* 1 Aug. 1818; *Capt.* 1 Dec. 1830; *Major* 18 Feb. 1840; *Bt. Lt. Col.* 26 May 1841; *Lt. Col.* 26 Feb 1846; *Bt. Col* 17 March 1851; *Col.* 18 Feb. 1856; *Maj. Genl.* 28 Nov. 1854.—Furlough S. C., 5 Oct. 1852.
O.	30	1	*Lieut. Col.* W. A. Cooke. *Ens.* 7 June 1829; *Lieut.* 30 April 1835; *Bt. Capt.* 7 June 1844; *Capt.* 18 Nov. 1844; *Major,* 17 May 1853; *Lieut. Col.* 3 Sep. 1857.—Fur. S. C. 16 Oct. 1857.
N.	21	1	*Major* J. Travers, *PH.* *Ens.* 11 June 1838; *Lieut.* 7 June 1841; *Capt.* 7 Jan. 1846; *Bt. Major* 8 Jan. 1846; *Major* 16 Feb. 1859; *Bt Lt. Col.* 20 June 1854; *Bt. Col.* 6 Dec. 1856.—Bhopal Contingent.

☞ *Brevet.* [1]Major 24 March 1858. [2]Major 26 Dec. 1858.

Fur. Reg.	Y	M	CAPTAINS.	REMARKS.	*Ensign.*	*Lieut.*	CAPTAIN. *Brevet.*	CAPTAIN. *Regl.*
	19	1	N. C. Boswell, †	.. ..	12 *June* 40	26 *Mar.* 42	.. ..	17 *Feb.* 51
	18	9	H. Mills, *P*, (*a*)	Army Commt. Dept.	20 *Oct.* 40	16 *July* 42	.. ..	22 *Mar.* 52
	17	11	J. J. Hamilton, *PH*,	Civil employ, ..	9 *Aug.* 41	4 *Oct.* 44	.. ..	24 *Oct.* 54
	15	7	H. K. Burne, *P*,	Military Secretariat,	30 *Dec.* 43	21 *Dec.* 45	.. ..	6 *June* 57
	14	7	Thomas James, *P*, [1]*m*	Army Comt. Dept.	10 *Dec.* 44	8 *Dec.* 48	.. ..	12 *Feb.* 58
N.	14	6	H. R. Garden, *P*, [2]*m*	Qr. Mr. Genl's. Dept.	20 *Jan.* 45	18 *July* 49	.. ..	25 *Dec.* 58
	14	1	J. K. Couper, *PH*,	Stud Department, ..	14 *June* 45	17 *Feb.* 51	.. ..	16 *Feb.* 59
			LIEUTENANTS.					
	13	10	B. G. VanderGucht, *PH*,	Comdg. district Police, Ghazeepore,	20 *Sep.* 45	1 *Dec.* 51		
	13	1	J. P. Cambridge, †	.. ..	12 *June* 46	22 *Mar.* 52		
	10	10	L. Forbes, *PH*,	Comdg. district Police, Etawah,	20 *Sep.* 48	17 *May* 53		
N.	9	1	D. Reid, *PH*,	Fur. S.C. 21 Mar. 59	14 *June* 50	1 *Feb.* 55		
	7	11	T. Dennehy, †	Comdg. Allahabad Police Battn., ..	20 *July* 51	23 *Nov.* 56		
	5	8	F. Frederick Rowcroft, †	Instr. of Musketry 6 En. Regt ..	10 *Dec.* 53	23 *Nov.* 56		
N.	5	3	Alfred Bird Allen, †	Fur. S. C. 4 May 58	4 *Apl.* 54	6 *June* 57		
	4	10	Wm. Dalrymple Shaw, †	Adjt. Divnl. Battn. Allahabad,	4 *Sep.* 54	3 *Sep.* 57		
N.	1	11	G. G. Thain,	Fur. S. C. 1 Feb. 59	25 *July* 57	18 *May* 58		
	1	5	J. R. Marett,	.. ..	4 *Feb.* 58	25 *Dec.* 58		
	..	10	M. W. Gataker,	.. ..	4 *Sep.* 58	1 *Mar.* 59		
			ENSIGNS.					
	..	7	W. S. Brooke,	.. ..	11 *Dec.* 58			
			*					
			*					
			*					
			*					
	..	..	*Adjt.*,		*Appointed.*			
	..	..	*Intr.*,					
	..	..	*Surg.*, *					
	..	..	*Ass. Surg.*, *					

N. B.—This Corps was made a Grenadier Regt. for its services at Candahar, under Genl. Nott, and has a third color, with the word "GHUZNEE" inscribed in English, Persian and Hindee.

(*a*) Has furnished certificate of qualification in Surveying and Civil Engineering.

Raised in 1763.

4th Regiment of Native Infantry.

Right Wing Noorpoore.—Left Wing Kangra, Disarmed,

"CARNATIC"—"MYSORE"—"PUNJAUB."

Bailun-ka-Pultun. Late 2nd Battalion 1st Regt. N.I.

On the Regtl. Color "A ROYAL TIGER *under a Banian Tree.*"

FACINGS—*Yellow.*

Fur. Reg.	Ser. Y	Ser. M	
D	59	9	~~*Col.* Sir R. Henry Cunliffe, *Bt.* and c. b.~~ *Ens.* 25 Sep. 1799; *Lieut.* 28 Oct. 1799; *Capt.* 1 May 1808; *Maj.* 17 Oct. 1818; *Lt. Col.* 30 Jan. 1824; *Col.* 30 May 1828; *Maj. Genl.* 28 June 1838; *Lieut. Genl.* 11 Nov. 1851; *Genl* 13 Oct. 1857.—Europe, 10 Jan. 33,
	33	9	*Lieut. Col.* D. Wilkie, *P. Ens.* 28 Sep. 25; *Lieut.* 22 Aug. 27; *Bt. Capt.* 28 Sep. 40; *Capt.* 31 Mar. 45; *Bt. Major* 11 Nov. 51; *Maj.* 15 Nov. 1853; *Lieut. Col.* 26 April 1858.
	33	7	*Major* C. Pattenson,† *Ens.* 4 Dec. 25; *Lieut.* 8 Oct. 39; *Bt. Capt.* 4 Dec. 40; *Capt.* 22 Aug. 47; *Bt. Major* 11 Nov. 51; *Major* 26 April 1858.—Lv. P. A. 15 October.

Fur. Reg.	Y	M	CAPTAINS.	REMARKS.	*Ensign.*	*Lieut.*	CAPTAIN. *Brevet.*	CAPTAIN. *Regl.*
	21	4	G. R. Cookson, *PH*, - -	Cantt. Joint Magte. Meerut. ..	1 *Mar.* 38	2 *Jan.* 42	.. ..	7 *July* 48
N.	19	5	O. J. McL. Farrington, *P*,	Civil employ, ..	15 *Feb.* 40	12 *Nov.* 42	.. ..	14 *Feb.* 52
	18	7	J. E. Fraser, *P*, - - - -	.. ..	11 *Dec.* 40	16 *Apl.* 44	.. ..	15 *Nov.* 53
	18	6	G. D'Aguilar, *P*, - - -	.. ..	22 *Dec.* 40	24 *Jan.* 45	22 Dec. 55	1 *Apl.* 56
	14	7	A. Cumine, *PH*, (*a*) - -	... ..	10 *Dec.* 44	16 *May* 48	.. ..	23 *Nov.* 56
	14	6	J. F. Stafford, *PH*, - -	7th Punjaub Infy.,	12 *Jan.* 45	1 *July* 48	.. ..	11 *Aug.* 57
N.	14	6	F. R. Aikman, *V.C.PH*, -	Fur., S. C 7 May 58	18 *Jan.* 45	7 *July* 48	.. ..	26 *Apl.* 58
			LIEUTENANTS.					
	14	6	R. Stothert, *PH*, - - -	.. ..	18 *Jan.* 45	20 *Oct.* 48		
	12	4	J. R. Currie,† - - -	19th Punjaub Infy.	26 *Jan.* 47	15 *Sep.* 49		
N.	11	7	C. F. Packe, *PH*, (*a*)† -	Fur. S.C. 2 Mar. 58	10 *Dec.* 47	12 *Nov.* 50		
	14	1	N. W. Elphinstone, *PC*, (*b*)	Civil employ, ..	14 *June* 45	14 *Feb.* 52		
	10	4	J. F. Orchard,† - - -	.. ..	3 *Mar.* 49	15 *Nov.* 53		
	9	6	W. C. Mitchel, *PH*, - -	Googaira Levy, ..	21 *Jan.* 50	14 *Aug.* 54		
O.	9	7	W. Playfair, *PH*, - - -	Fur. S. C. 4 Aug. 57	20 *Dec.* 49	1 *Apl.* 56		
	7	9	J. P. Davidson,† - - -	1st Punjaub Infy.,	20 *Oct.* 51	23 *Nov.* 56		
	5	6	Alexander Copland,† - -	.. ..	14 *Jan.* 54	23 *Nov.* 56		
	5	3	G. W. Henry Hoggan, *PH*,	Adjt. Divnl. Battn. Meerut, ..	4 *Apl.* 54	11 *Aug.* 57		
	1	5	W. Pickard, - - - -	Lv. S. C. 27 Aug.	20 *Feb.* 58	22 *Oct.* 58		
			ENSIGNS.					
	..	8	W. J. Parker. - - - -	.. ..	4 *Nov.* 58			
			*					
			*					
			*					
			*		*Appointed.*			
	..	..	*Adjutant*, R. Stothert, - -	.. ..	1 *Oct.* 57			
	..	..	*Intr.*, G. D'Aguilar, - -	Officiating, ..	8 *Feb.* 53			
	..	..	*Surgeon*, J. R. Withecombe, M.D., - - -	Fur. S.C. 15 Dec. 56	5 *Jan.* 57			
	..	..	*Asst. Surg.* J. J. T. Lawrence,	..	19 *Nov.* 55			

(*a*) Passed the examination in Field Engineering.

(*b*) Received a degree of Honor, for his eminent attainments in the Persian language, from the College of Fort William, on the 4th May 1850.

Raised in 1761. | **9th Regiment of Native Infantry.** | Mutinied, Allygurh.

(*Rifle Company.*)

"BUXAR"—"DEIG."

Jellasur-ka-Pultun. Late 1st Battalion 8th Regt. N. I.

FACINGS—*White.*

Fur. Reg.	Ser. Y	Ser. M	
	56	9	*Colonel* William Robert Clayton Costley. *Ens.* 16 October 1802; *Lieut.* 3 June 1804; *Capt.* 9 Dec. 1817; *Major* 27 Jan. 1826; *Lieut. Col.* 2 Jan. 1831; *Col.* 22 Oct. 1842; *Major General* 20 June 54; *Lieut. Genl.* 2 April 1856.—Furlough, P. A., 3 Feb. 53.
O.	39	6	*Lt. Col.* John Edmondstoune Landers. *Ens.* 10 Jan. 1820; *Lieut.* 11 July 1823; *Bt. Capt.* 10 Jan. 1835; *Capt.* 31 March 1835; *Bt. Major* 9 Nov. 1846; *Major* 3 Oct. 1848; *Lieut. Col.* 24 Dec. 1853. *Bt. Colonel* 28 *Nov.* 1854.—Fur. S. C. 20 Mar. 1857.
N.	33	8	*Major* L. P. D. Eld, *PC.* *Ens.* 5 Nov. 1825; *Lieut.* 15 Sep. 1833; *Bt. Captain* 5 Nov. 1840; *Capt.* 1 Jan. 1845; *Bt. Major* 11 Nov. 1851; *Major* 4 April 1857.—Fur. S. C 14 May 1858.

☞ *Brevet.* [1] Major 28 Nov. 54. [2] Major 18 May 56. [3] Major 5 Mar. 1859. [4] Major 19 Jan. 1858.—*Lt. Col.* 20 July 1858.

Fur. Reg.	Y	M	CAPTAINS.	REMARKS.	*Ensign.*	*Lieut.*	CAPTAIN. *Brevet.*	CAPTAIN. *Regl.*
	30	3	R. Thatcher,[1]*m* - - - -	Stud Department,	1 *Apl.* 29	31 *Mar.* 35	1 *Apl.* 44	24 *Jan.* 45
	28	4	G. Verner,[2]*m* - - - -	Political employ, .	24 *July* 30	20 *Apl.* 35	24 *July* 45	4 *Mar.* 48
	28	1	R. H. Sale,[3]*m* - - - -	.. ..	9 *June* 31	8 *Oct.* 39	9 *June* 46	3 *Oct.* 48
	18	9	D. M. Stewart, *P,*[4]*lc* -	Adjut. Genl.'s Dept.,	12 *Oct.* 40	3 *Jan.* 44	.. ..	1 *June* 54
O.	17	11	J. A. Angus, *PH,* - -	Lv. P. to Fur. ..	15 *July* 41	14 *Dec.* 44	.. ..	7 *Sep.* 55
	17	10	A. H. Campbell, *PH,* - -	.. ..	25 *Aug.* 41	1 *Jan.* 45	25 *Aug.* 56	23 *Nov.* 56
	16	1	H. R. Corfield,† - - -	Instr. H. M. 13 Lt. Infantry.	10 *June* 43	28 *Sep.* 45	.. ..	4 *Apl.* 57
			LIEUTENANTS.					
	16	1	W. H. Binny, *PH,(a)* - -	Offg. Comdt. Mily. Police, Banda, ..	10 *June* 43	4 *Mar.* 48	10 *June* 58	
	15	5	A. Crawford,† - - - -	.. ..	27 *Jan.* 44	3 *Oct.* 48	27 *Jan.* 59	
	14	11	H. N. Hodgson, *PH,* -	23rd Punjaub Infy.	27 *July* 44	5 *Jan.* 50		
	14	4	H. J. Allan,† - - - -	.. ..	19 *Mar.* 45	15 *Nov.* 53		
O.	13	1	E. C. Rawstorne,† - -	Fur. S.C. 20 Apl. 55	13 *June* 46	15 *Nov.* 53		
	12	1	A. McKenzie, *P,* - -	Army Comt. Dept.	12 *June* 47	24 *Dec.* 53		
	9	7	H. T. Oldfield, *PH,* - -	2nd in Command Agra Police Battn.	11 *Dec.* 49	7 *Sep.* 55		
O.	10	7	Henry Coape Smith, *P.H.* -	Lv. S. C. to New South Wales for 2 years, G. O. 13 Jan. 57. ..	20 *Dec.* 48	23 *Nov.* 56		
	2	9	Francis Gellie, A. M.† - -	Allyghurh Infy. Levy.	20 *Oct.* 56	17 *Nov.* 57		
	2	4	Alfred Ollivant, - - -	Adjt. District Police, Jhansie, ..	4 *Mar.* 57	1 *Mar.* 58		
	2	1	~~G. M. Hand,~~ - - - -	Fur. S. C 2 July, 58	12 *June* 57	18 *May* 58		
			ENSIGNS.					
			*					
			*					
			*		*Appointed.*			
			*					
			*					
	..	..	*Adjt.,*					
	..	..	*Intr.,**					
	..	..	*Surg.,**					
	..	..	*Asst. Srg.,**					

(*a*) Has furnished the certificate of qualification in surveying.

Raised in 1763.

10th Regiment of Native Infantry.

Mutinied, Futtehgurh.

"BUXAR"—"KORAH"—"PEGU."

Duffel-ka-Pultun. Late 2nd Battalion 7th Regt. N.I.

FACINGS—*Dark-green.*

Fur. Reg.	Ser. Y	Ser. M	
D.	53	1	~~Colonel Thomas Dickinson.~~ *Ens.* 24 May 1806; *Lieut.* 15 June 1808; *Bt. Capt.* 2 May 1821; *Capt.* 1 May 1824; *Major* 11 July 1836; *Lieut. Col.* 3 Oct. 1842; *Col.* 16 May 1853; *Major General* 28 Nov. 54.—Fur. P. A. 17 Mar. 56.
	28	9	*Lieut. Col.* George Ramsay, *P* *Ens.* 6 Oct. 1830; *Lieut.* 23 Aug. 1834; *Capt.* 5 May 1841; *Maj.* 10 Sep. 1852; *Lieut. Col.* 27 June 1857.—Political employ.
N.	31	7	*Major* J. Coke, C. B. *PC.* *Ens.* 3 Dec. 1827; *Lieut.* 29 Aug. 1835; *Bt. Capt.* 3 Dec. 1842; *Capt.* 28 Mar. 1848; *Bt. Major* 20 June 1854; *Major* 18 Nov. 1857; *Bt. Lieut. Col.* 19 Jan. 1858: *Bt. Colonel* 20 July 1858—1st Punjaub Infy.—Fur. S. C. 3 Jan. 59.

☞ *Brevet.* [1] Maj. 2 Oct. 52; Lieut. Col. 19 Jan. 1858. [2] Major 20 July 1858.

Fur. Reg.	Y	M	Captains.	Remarks.	Ensign.	Lieut.	Captain. Brevet.	Captain. Regl.
	24	1	C. Reid, C. B., [1] *l.c.*, - -	Sirmoor Battalion,	13 *June* 35	3 *Oct.* 40	13 *June* 50	1 *Oct.* 52
N.	18	10	R. L. Thompson, *PH*, [2] *m* -	Fur. S.C. 13 Apl. 58	18 *Sep.* 40	16 *July* 42	18 *Sep.* 55	18 *June* 57
	18	7	W. B. Irwin, *PH*, - - -	Stud Dept. ..	12 *Dec.* 40	24 *Jan.* 45	12 *Dec.* 55	18 *June* 57
	17	..	J. E. L. Willows, *PH*, -	23rd Punjaub Infy.	23 *June* 42	29 *Mar.* 50	23 *June* 57	11 *July* 57
	16	6	E. M. Martineau, *PC*, (*a*) -	Army Commt. Dept.	28 *Dec.* 42	1 *Jan.* 51	.. ..	11 *July* 57
	15	...	N. W. Trenchard, † - -	.. ..	8 *July* 44	25 *June* 52	.. ..	23 *July* 57
	9	7	C. P. Hildebrand, *PH*, (*b*) -	Civil employ, ..	12 *Dec.* 49	13 *Nov.* 55	.. ..	18 *Nov.* 57
			Lieutenant.					
	7	1	H. A. Browne, *P*, (*c*) - -	Civil employ, ..	13 *June* 52	23 *Nov.* 56		
	15	6	G. A. F. Houchen, *PH*, (*d*)	D. P. W. Punjaub,	30 *Dec.* 43	15 *Feb.* 47	30 *Dec.* 58	
O.	13	10	C. Armstrong, *P*(*a*) - -	Fur. S. C. 5 Nov. 58	22 *July* 45	29 *July* 49		
O.	11	6	J. A. M. Biggs, *PH*, - -	Fur. S. C. 2 Mar. 58	20 *Jan.* 48	8 *Feb.* 51		
O.	11	1	E. L. Clogstoun, *PH*, - -	Fur. S. C. 6 Sep. 58	10 *June* 48	15 *Nov.* 53		
	8	6	Dashwood Ross, *PH*, - -	.. ..	11 *Jan.* 51	17 *Apl.* 55		
	3	7	John Liston, - - - -	12 Punjaub Infy.	7 *Dec.* 55	17 *Oct.* 56		
N.	5	7	C. Smith Maclean, *PCH*, -	1 Punjaub Cavy.	14 *Dec.* 53	23 *Nov.* 56		
N.	4	6	Chas. W. Campbell, - -	Fur. S.C. 29 Dec. 57	20 *Dec.* 54	30 *June* 57		
	3	1	James Fitzgerald, - - -	.. ..	16 *June* 56	17 *June* 58		
	2	..	J. A. Drake, - - - -	.. ..	26 *July* 57	18 *May* 58		
			Ensigns.					
	1	5	B. P. Hodgson, - - -	.. ..	20 *Feb.* 58			
	1	3	J. W. H. Michell, - - -	.. ..	4 *Apl.* 58			
			*					
			*		*Appointed.*			
			*					
			Adjt.,*					
			Intr.,*					
			Surg.,*					
			Asst. Surg.,*					

N. B.—This Regiment has two honorary colors, and two extra Jemadars.

(*a*) Received a first class certificate Royal School of Musketry. Hythe.

(*b*) Has passed an examination in the Burmese Language, 8 June 1855.

(*c*) Has passed an examination in the Burmese Language, 9 September 1853; and received a Certificate of high Proficiency in Oordoo 1st November 1856.

(*d*) Has furnished certificates of qualification in surveying and civil engineering.

Raised in 1763.

11th Regiment of Native Infantry.

Mutinied, Meerut.

" GUZERAT"—" BHURTPORE."

Runseet-ka-Pultun. Late 1st Battalion 5th Regt. N.I.

FACINGS—*White.*

Fur. Reg.	Ser. Y	Ser. M	
			Colonel *
	38	6	*Lieut. Col.* John Butler. *Ens.* 12 Jan. 1821; *Lieut.* 11 July 1823; *Bt. Capt.* 12 Jan. 1836; *Capt.* 1 Jan. 1837; *Major* 12 Oct. 1845. *Lieut. Col.* 3 Oct. 1851; *Bt. Col.* 28 Nov. 1854.
	33	3	*Major* P. Gordon,† *Ens.* 26 Apl. 1826; *Lieut.* 7 Aug. 1833; *Bt. Capt.* 26 Apl. 1841; *Capt.* 20 Nov. 1845; *Bt. Maj.* 3 April 1846; *Major* 12 Oct. 1856; *Bt. Lieut. Col.* 20 June 1854; *Bt. Colonel* 20 June 1857.—Brigr. Comdg. at Dinapore. ☞ *Brevet.* [1] Maj. 20 June 54

Fur. Reg.	Y	M	CAPTAINS.	REMARKS.	*Ensign.*	*Lieut.*	CAPTAIN. *Brevet.*	CAPTAIN. *Regl.*
	33	4	W. Lydiard,†[1]*m* - - -	Asst. Adjutant Genl. Dinapore Divn.	15 *Mar.* 26	1 *Dec.* 36	15 *Mar.* 41	27 *Mar.* 46
	25		~~S. J. Becher,~~ - - - -	Agra Infy. Levy, ..	14 *June* 34	30 *July* 39	.. ..	13 *May* 48
	23	4	~~C. C. Robertson, P,~~ - -	Civil employ, ..	24 *Feb.* 37	16 *Dec.* 39	.. ..	1 *Aug.* 51
N.	20	9	J. W. L. Bird, *PCH*, - -	Fur. S. C. 8 Feb. 59	23 *Sep.* 38	3 *Oct.* 40	.. ..	13 *Oct.* 51
	20	7	E. L. Dennys, *PH*, (*a*) - -	Cantt. Jt. Magte., Delhi, ..	11 *Dec.* 38	20 *Jan.* 41	.. ..	26 *July* 53
N.	20	..	C. P. St. J. Law, *PH*, - -	10th Irregular Cavy.	10 *July* 39	16 *July* 42	10 *July* 54	12 *Oct.* 56
	19	6	B. P. Lloyd, *P*, - - -	Civil employ, ..	3 *Jan.* 40	24 *Jan.* 45	3 *Jan.* 55	23 *Nov.* 56
			LIEUTENANTS.					
	18	10	A. W. Owen, *PH*, - - -	D. P. W. N. W. P.	21 *Aug.* 40	7 *Apl.* 45	21 *Aug.* 55	
	18	1	R. W. Chambers, *PC*, - -	Comdt. districtpolice Mozuffernuggur,	12 *June* 41	27 *Mar.* 46	12 *June* 56	
	17	1	F. A. Sage, *PCH*, - - -	Comdt. Mily. Police, Shahjehanpore.	11 *June* 42	10 *Nov.* 47	11 *June* 57	
O.	14	6	H. Champion-Möller, *P*, -	Fur. S. C. 12 Mar. 58	20 *Jan.* 45	1 *Aug.* 51		
N.	13	7	J. D. Swayne, *PH*, - -	Fur. S. C. 5 Nov. 58	12 *Dec.* 45	13 *Oct.* 51		
N.	11	11	F. W. Graham, *PH*, - -	Fur. P. A. 5 Apl. 59	26 *July* 47	12 *Oct.* 56		
O.	8	6	T. M. Shelley,† - -	Fur. S.C. 19 Apl. 58	20 *Jan.* 51	23 *Nov.* 56		
	6	1	S. G. Warde,† - - -	Adjt. Hodson's Horse	12 *June* 53	23 *Nov.* 56		
	4	11	Wm. Wheler Hume,† - -	2nd in Command Landour Regiment, ..	5 *Aug.* 54	1 *Feb.* 57		
	2	5	F. H. Woodgate,† - - -	.. ..	20 *Feb.* 57	30 *Apl.* 58		
	1	8	W. L. Samuells, - - -	Fur. S.C. 16 July 58	20 *Nov.* 57	22 *Oct.* 58		
			ENSIGNS.					
	..	11	W. P. Onslow, - - - -	.. ..	4 *Aug* 58			
	..	..	*					
			*					
			*		*Appointed.*			
			*					
	..	..	*Adjt.*,*					
	..	..	*Intr.*,*					
	..	..	*Surg.*, D. J. O'Callaghan, -	Fur. S,C. 28 Sep. 58	18 *Oct.* 56			
	..	..	*Asst. Surg.*,*					

(*a*) Has furnished the certificate of qualification in Civil Engineering and Surveying.

Raised in 1763.

12th Regiment of Native Infantry.

Mutinied Right Wing at Nowgong, Left Wing at Jhansi

"CARNATIC"—"LASWARRIE"—"FEROZESHUHUR"—*5th Company*, "SUBRAON."
Hote-ka-Pultun. Late 1st Battalion 12th Regt. N.I
FACINGS—*White.*

Fur. Reg.	Ser. Y	Ser. M	
O.	55	6	*Col.* Edward Pettingal. *Ens.* 1 Jan. 04; *Lt.* 1 Feb. 07; *Bt. Capt.* 1 Jan. 19: *Capt.* 21 Oct. 21; *Bt. Maj.* 10 Jan. 37; *Maj.* 25 July 39; *Lt. Col.* 18 Mar. 45; *Bt. Col.* 20 June 54; *Col.* 25 Feb. 55; *Major General* 4 Nov. 1856.—Fur. P. A. 27 June 1856.
O.	37	5	*Lt. Col.* J. S. Hodgson. *Ens.* 3 Feb. 1822; *Lieut.* 1 May 1824; *Capt.* 21 June 1834; *Bt. Major* 9 Nov. 1846; *Major* 28 Aug. 1853; *Bt. Lieut. Col.* 7 June 1849; *Lieut. Col.* 25 Apl. 1858; *Bt. Col.* 28 *Nov.* 1854.—Fur. S. C. 16January 1855.
	21	7	*Major* W. S. Ferris,*P.* *Ens.* 11 Dec. 1837; *Lieut.* 16 July 1842; *Capt.* 1 Jan. 1851; *Major* 25 Apl. 1858.—Audit Dept.

Fur. Reg.	Y	M	CAPTAINS.	REMARKS.	*Ensign.*	*Lieut.*	CAPTAIN. *Brevet.*	CAPTAIN. *Regl.*
N.	20	6	R. C. Wroughton,*P,* - -	Army Comt. Dept.	13 *Jan.* 39	24 *Aug.* 42	.. ..	28 *Aug.* 53
	18	9	R. R. Adams,*P,* - - -	Civil employ, ..	26 *Sep.* 40	16 *Sep.* 42	.. ..	3 *Sept* 53
O.	18	7	J. T. S. Hall,† - - - -	Fur. P. A. 4 Oct. 56	12 *Dec.* 40	10 *Apl.* 43	.. ..	31 *Dec.* 54
N.	17	..	P. G. Scot,*P,* - - -	Fur., S. C. 26 July 58, ..	10 *June* 42	1 *Sep.* 45	.. ..	23 *Nov.* 56
N.	~~14~~	~~5~~	~~H. Stokes,*P,*~~ - - - -	Civil employ.—Fur. S. C. 10 Apl. 56.	11 *Feb.* 45	1 *Jan.* 51	.. ..	25 *Apl.* 58
	13	4	W. C. L. Ryves,† - - -	Regiment of Lucknow, ..	20 *Mar.* 46	28 *Aug.* 53	.. ..	4 *Aug.* 58
O.	12	7	J. T. Watson,*PH,* - -	Fur. S. C. 19 Feb. 58	20 *Dec.* 46	3 *Sep.* 53	.. ..	6 *Aug.* 58
			LIEUTENANTS.					
O.	9	10	T. C. Anderson,† -	Fur. S.C. 20 Feb. 57	27 *Aug.* 49	31 *Dec.* 54		
N.	8	7	J. C. McNeill,† - - -	Fur. S. C. 15 July 58	9 *Dec.* 50	13 *Aug.* 55		
N.	8	5	E. S. Jackson,*PH,* - -	Stud Dept. ..	26 *Feb.* 51	23 *Nov.* 56		
N.	6	5	A. G. Remington,† - -	Jhansie Police.	13 *Feb.* 53	23 *Nov.* 56		
N.	4	1	P. S. Yorke,† - - - -	Fur. S. C 14 Dec. 58, ..	9 *June* 55	6 *June* 57		
	3	9	Wm. Astell Franks, -	Adjt. district Police, Cawnpore, ..	4 *Oct.* 55	19 *June* 57		
	3	4	R. B. Mackenzie,† - -	.. ..	4 *Mar.* 56	10 *July* 57		
N.	4	7	F. D. Harington,*P.H.,* -	Fur. S.C. 29 Dec. 58	10 *Dec.* 54	23 *Nov.* 56		
	1	5	H. A. Rooke, - - - -	... ...	20 *Feb.* 58	4 *Aug.* 58		
	1	2	E. A. Phillips,† - - - -	.. ...	8 *May* 58	24 *Aug.* 58		
	~~1~~	~~2~~	~~S. W. Wyndham,~~ - - -	13 Punjaub Infy.,..	20 *May* 58	22 *Oct.* 58		
			ENSIGNS.					
	..	8	W. C. Chowne, - - - -	.. ..	4 *Nov.* 58			
			*					
			*					
			*					
			*		*Appointed.*			
	..	..	*Adjutant,**					
	..	..	*Interpreter,**					
	..	..	*Surg.,*					
	..	..	*Asst. Surg.,**					

Raised in 1764.

13th Regiment of Native Infantry.

Mutinied, Lucknow.

"GUZERAT"—"MYSORE"—"PUNJAUB."—"GOOJERAT"

Gaurud-ka-Pultun. Late 1st Battalion 7th Regt. N.I.

On the Regimental Color "A ROYAL TIGER *under a Banian Tree.*"

FACINGS—*Dark-green.*

Fur. Reg.	Ser. Y	Ser. M	
	40	9	*Colonel* George Warren. *Ens.* 6 Oct. 1818; *Lieut.* 30 Jan. 1820; *Capt.* 13 April 1830; *Major* 25 Feb. 1837; *Bt. Lt. Col.* 23 July 1839; *Lt. Col.* 6 Aug. 1843; *Bt. Col.* 16 July 1849; *Col.* 5 Dec. 1853; *Maj. Genl.* 28 Nov. 1854.
O.	37	..	*Lt. Col.* Harry Meggs Graves. *Ens.* 25 June 22; *Lt.* 15 Feb. 24; *Capt.* 3 May 33; *Bt. Maj.* 30 Apl. 44; *Maj.* 1 Nov. 49; *Bt. Lt. Col.* 19 June 46; *Lt. Col.* 13 Dec. 54; *Bt. Col.* 20 June 1854. *Major General* 27 Aug. 1858.—Fur. S. C. 28 Jan. 1859.
	24	7	*Major* W. McCulloch, *P. Ens.* 12 Dec. 1834; *Lieut.* 18 Feb. 1839; *Capt.* 30 June 1848; *Major* 4 Sep. 1857.—Political employ.

☞ *Brevet.* [1] Major 24 March 1858. [2] Major 24 March 1858.

Fur. Reg.	Ser. Y	Ser. M	CAPTAINS.	REMARKS.	*Ensign.*	*Lieut.*	CAPTAIN. *Brevet.*	CAPTAIN. *Regl.*
	23	7	J. E. Gastrell, *PC*, - -	Rev. Survey Dept.	11 *Dec.* 35	8 *Oct.* 39	.. ..	19 *Mar.* 49
N.	21	2	T. F. Wilson, C.B. *PCH*,[1]*m*	Depy. Asst. Adjt. Gl. Cawnpore Divn...	24 *Apl.* 38	1 *July* 42	.. ..	15 *June* 49
O.	21	1	T. P. Waterman, *P*, - -	Fur. S.C. 12 Feb. 58	11 *June* 38	16 *July* 42	11 *June* 53	28 *Nov.* 54
O.	20	1	R. C. Germon, *PH*,[2]*m* -	Fur. S.C. 12 Feb. 58	12 *June* 39	6 *Sep.* 42	12 *June* 54	28 *Feb.* 55
	17	..	E. Smyth, *P*, - - - -	Lv. P. A. 15 Oct. ..	10 *July* 42	15 *July* 45	10 *July* 57	18 *June* 57
	16	5	A. R. E. Hutchinson, *PH*,	Political employ, ..	30 *Jan.* 43	22 *July* 46	.. ..	8 *July* 57
	16	..	J. W. F. Bean, *PH*, - -	Cant. Jt. Magte., Rawul Pindee,	21 *June* 43	30 *June* 48	.. ..	4 *Sep.* 57
			LIEUTENANTS.					
O.	12	1	G. A. H. Lillie, *PH*, - -	Fur. S.C. 15 June 58	11 *June* 47	30 *Apl.* 51		
	11	11	R. H. M. Aitken, *P*, - -	Divl. Comdt. Mily. Police, Oude, ..	2 *Sep.* 47	15 *Nov.* 53		
	10	7	A. Blunt, *PH*, - - -	Commdt. 8th Bengal Police Battn. Cuttack,	9 *Dec.* 48	28 *Nov.* 54		
	10	1	W. B. Thomson, *PH*, -	Civil employ, ..	8 *June* 49	28 *Feb.* 55		
O.	8	6	B. R. Chambers, *PH*, - -	Fur. S. C. 19 Jan. 58	20 *Dec.* 50	10 *Mar.* 55		
N.	5	11	William George Cubitt,† -	Fur. S.C. 12 Feb. 58	26 *July* 53	23 *Nov.* 56		
	5	5	Alexander Shand Thain, †	Chundeyree Police,	20 *Feb.* 54	23 *Nov.* 56		
N.	4	6	Andrew Robert Loughnan,	Fur. S.C. 29 Apl. 58	4 *Jan.* 55	29 *May* 57		
	2	7	A. D Butter, - - - -	.. ..	12 *Dec.* 56	27 *June* 57		
	3	1	R. B. Graham, - - - -	Adjt. district Police, Muttra, ..	14 *June* 56	30 *Apl.* 58		
	2	..	H. W. Pitcher,† - - -	1st. Punjaub Infy.	26 *July* 57	18 *May* 58		
			ENSIGNS.					
	..	9	R. E. K. Money, - - -	.. ..	9 Oct. 58			
			*					
			*					
			*					
			*					
	..	..	*Adjutant*,*		*Appointed.*			
	..	..	*Intr.*,*					
	..	..	*Surg.**					
	..	..	*Asst. Surg.*,*					

Raised in 1764.

14th Regiment of Native Infantry.

Mutinied, Jhelum.

" SERINGAPATAM"—" MAHARAJPORE"—" FEROZESHUHUR."

On the Regimental Color an embroidered Star for Seringapatam.

Escotten-ka-Pultun. Late 1st Battalion 10th Regt. N.I.

FACINGS—*Light-buff.*

Fur. Reg.	Ser. Y	Ser. M	
	..	..	*Colonel**
	35	6	*Lieut. Col.* Peter Innes. *Ens.* 16 Jan. 1824; *Lt.* 28 Aug. 1825; *Bt. Capt.* 16 Jan. 1839; *Capt.* 12 Jan. 1842; *Bt. Major* 30 April 1844; *Major* 15 April 1854; *Bt. Lt. Col.* 3 April 1846; *Lieut. Col.* 4 May 1858; *Bt. Col.* 20 June 1854; *Major Genl.* 13 July 1858.
	31	6	*Major* C. G. Walsh, *PC*, *Ens.* 25 Dec. 27; *Lieut.* 8 Oct. 39; *Bt. Capt.* 25 Dec. 42; *Capt.* 10 Sep. 1848; *Bt. Major* 20 June 1854; *Major* 13 Apl. 1859.—Regt. of Loodianah.

☞ *Brevet.* [1] Major 9 Feb. 51. Lt. Col. 28 Nov. 54. Col. 28 Nov. 57.

Y	M	CAPTAINS.	REMARKS.	*Ensign.*	*Lieut.*	CAPTAIN. *Brevet.*	CAPTAIN. *Regl.*
24	5	C. L. Showers, *P*,	Political employ,	21 *Jan.* 35	8 *Oct.* 39	.. ..	27 *Oct.* 48
22	1	J. S. Paton, *PH*,[1] *c*	Qr. Mr. Genl.'s Dept.	12 *June* 37	3 *Oct.* 40	.. ..	8 *Feb.* 51
20	3	W. Fullerton, *P*,	Lv. S. C. 15 Oct.	26 *Mar.* 39	10 *June* 42	.. ..	14 *Sep.* 53
19	3	A. O. Wood, †	.. ..	14 *Apl.* 40	1 *Mar.* 44	.. ..	15 *Apl.* 54
17	7	F. A. V. Thurburn, *PH*,	Civil employ, ..	11 *Dec.* 41	24 *Jan.* 45	.. ..	23 *Nov.* 56
17	6	E. N. Perkins, *PH*,	Army Commt. Dept.	8 *Jan.* 42	16 *Feb.* 46	8 *Jan.* 57	4 *May* 58
15	10	S. C. D. Ryder, *P*,	Staff Officer to the Troops at Sasseram,	4 *Sep.* 43	10 *Sep.* 48	4 *Sep.* 58	13 *Apl.* 59
		LIEUTENANTS.					
14	10	G. Weld, *PH*,	Garrn. Staff Chunar,	27 *Aug.* 44	27 *Oct.* 48		
13	4	T. Taylor, *PH*,	.. ..	6 *Mar.* 46	5 *Mar.* 50		
11	1	R. W. Glasse, *PH*,	Regt. of Loodianah,	20 *May* 48	14 *Sep.* 53		
10	7	F. B. Norman, *PH*, (*a*)	Qr. Mr. Genl.'s Dept.	8 *Dec.* 48	15 *Apl.* 54		
10	5	J. Graham, *PC*,	Army Comt. Dept.	7 *Feb.* 49	23 *Nov.* 56		
8	7	E. Chapman, †	8 Punjaub Infy. ..	20 *Dec.* 50	21 *May* 57		
2	9	Robert Gunning,	10 Punjaub Infy. ..	20 *Oct.* 56	23 *Mar.* 58		
3	5	R. G. Sandeman, †	Civil employ, ..	8 *Feb.* 56	6 *Aug.* 57		
2	4	L. C. de L. Daniell,	.. ..	6 *Mar.* 57	18 *May* 58		
1	11	C. J. Durand, †	.. ..	4 *Aug.* 57	18 *May* 58		
1	1	M. G. Taylor,	.. ..	26 *May* 58	13 *Apl.* 59		
		ENSIGNS.					
		*					
		*					
		*					
		*					
		*		*Appointed.*			
..	..	*Adjutant,* T. Taylor,	.. ..	8 *May* 54			
..	..	*Intr.,**					
..	..	*Surg.*					
..	..	*Surg **					

(*a*) Has furnished certificate of qualification as a Civil Engineer and Surveyor.

Raised in 1764. — **15th Regiment of Native Infantry.** — Mutinied, Nusseerabad.

"BHURTPORE"—"PUNJAUB"—"CHILLIANWALLA"—"GOOJERAT."

Doo-ka-Pultun. Late 1st Battalion 11th Regt. N.I.

FACINGS—*French-grey.*

Fur. Reg.	Ser. Y	Ser. M	
	47	9	*Colonel* Alexander Carnegy, C. B. *Ens.* 13 Oct. 1811; *Lieut.* 1 Nov. 1815; *Capt.* 25 Jan. 1826; *Major* 25 Feb. 1835; *Lieut. Col.* 5 Nov. 1841; *Col.* 5 Sept. 1851; *Maj. Genl.* 28 Nov. 1854.—Fur., S.C., 29 Mar. 1853.
O.	35	9	*Lieut. Colonel* Thomas Henry Shuldham, *P. Ens.* 6 Oct. 1823; *Lieut.* 16 May 1824; *Capt.* 1 Jan. 37; *Major* 30 Sept. 45; *Lieut. Col.* 15 Sep. 1851.—*Bt. Col.* 28 Nov. 1854. —Fur. P. A. 15 Apl. 1859.
	32	..	*Lieut. Col.* Wm. Pitt Robbins. *Ens.* 20 June 1827; *Lieut.* 31 May 1834; *Bt. Capt.* 20 June 42; *Capt.* 1 Feb. 1843; *Bt. Maj.* 7 June 1849; *Maj.* 28 Nov. 1854; *Bt. Lt. Col.* 28 Nov. 1854; *Lt. Colonel* 9 Oct. 1858; *Bt. Col.* 28 Nov. 1857.—Ramghur Light Infy.
	30	6	*Major* G. J. Montgomery. *Ens.* 6 Jan. 1829; *Lieut.* 26 Feb. 1835; *Bt. Capt.* 6 Jan. 1844 *Capt.* 24 Jan. 45; *Bt. Major* 28 Nov. 54; *Major* 9 Oct. 1858.—*Bt. Lt. Col.* 24 Mar. 58

☞ *Brevet.* [1] Major 24 Mar. 1858. [2] Major 24 July 1854. [3] Major 24 Mar. 58.

Fur. Reg.	Y	M		Remarks.	*Ensign.*	*Lieut.*	Captain. *Brevet.*	Captain. *Regl.*
			CAPTAINS.					
N.	25	1	J. W. Carnegie, *PC*,[1]*m* -	Civil employ, ..	23 *May* 34	1 *Apl.* 38	.. ..	9 *Aug.* 48
	22	1	B. M. Loveday, *P.C*, - - -	.. ..	12 *June* 37	10 *Mar.* 41	.. ..	12 *May* 49
	19	7	G. G. Anderson, *PCH*,- -	Offg. Pay Dept. ..	10 *Dec.* 39	5 *Nov.* 41	.. ..	20 *Sep.* 49
	18	10	A. Bagot, *PH*,[2]*m* - - -	Nusseree Battn., ..	18 *Sep.* 40	16 *July* 42	.. ..	23 *July* 54
	18	9	C. St. G. Brownlow,[3]*m PH*,	Brigade Staff, ..	26 *Sep.* 40	28 *Sep.* 43	.. ..	28 *Nov.* 54
N	18	1	R. D. Macpherson, *P*, -	Army Comt. Dept.	12 *June* 41	24 *Jan.* 45	12 *June* 56	23 *Nov.* 56
	17	..	H. C. Cuppage,† - - -	Jat. Horse, ..	23 *June* 42	5 *Oct.* 46	23 *June* 57	9 Oct. 58
			LIEUTENANTS.					
	16	3	W. G. Ellice, *PH*, - - -	.. ..	4 *Apl.* 43	9 *Aug.* 48	4 *Apl.* 58	
	~~11~~	~~3~~	~~J. E. Caunter~~,† - - -	Mhairwarrah Battn.,	28 *Mar.* 48	15 *Nov.* 53		
O.	~~11~~	~~5~~	~~H. D. Magniac~~,† - - -	Fur. S.C. 27 Mar. 57	20 *Jan.* 48	10 *Mar.* 54		
	10	..	H. Phillpotts, *PH*, (*a*) -	Mhair Regiment, ..	9 *June* 49	23 *July* 54		
	4	10	Chas. Thos. Otway Mayne,	Civil employ,	22 *Aug.* 54	23 *Aug.* 55		
	4	8	Ed. Francis Browne, *PH*, -	Fur. P. A. 10 Mar. 59	4 *Nov.* 54	23 *Nov.* 56		
	4	..	Patrick Wheeler, *PH*, -	Lv. S. C. 7 Nov. ..	4 *July* 55	6 *June* 57		
	3	5	John George Campbell, -	Mhair Regiment, ..	20 *Feb.* 56	22 *Mar.* 58		
	2	7	L. E. Evans, - - - -	.. ..	13 *Dec.* 56	30 *Apl.* 58		
	1	1	R. Worsley, - - - -	.. ..	12 *June* 58	30 *Oct.* 58		
	..	7	N. J. Jones, - - - -	.. ..	11 *Dec.* 58	28 May 59		
			ENSIGNS.					
			*					
			*					
			*					
			*		*Appointed.*			
			*					
	..	..	*Adjutant*,*					
	..	..	*Intr.*,*					
	..	..	*Surg.*,*					
	..	..	*Asst. Surg.*,*					

(*a*) Has furnished certificate of qualification in Civil Engineering.

Raised in 1765.

16th (Grenadiers) Regiment of Native Infantry.

Disarmed. Mean Meer, (Lahore.)

"Mysore" — "Seringapatam" — "Affghanistan" — "Ghuznee"—(Candahar—Ghuznee—Cabool, 1842)—"Maharajpore"—"Moodkee"—"Ferozeshuhur"—"Subraon."

Has on its Colors an Embroidered Star for services at Seringapatam, and "a Royal Tiger *under a Banian Tree" for services in Mysore.*

Hoosainee-ka-Pultun. Late 2nd Battalion 10th Regt. N.I.—Facings—*Buff.*

Fur. Reg.	Ser. Y	Ser. M	
N.	39	10	*Colonel* Stuart Corbett, c.b. *Ens.* 7 Sep. 1819; *Lieut.* 9 Apl. 1822; *Capt.* 18 Aug. 1825; *Bt. Major* 28 June 1838; *Major* 19 Sept. 1840; *Lieut. Col.* 26 Dec. 1846; *Bt. Col.* 20 June 1854; *Col.* 18 May 1856; *Major Genl.* 4 Feb. 1859.—Fur. P. A. 27 May 1859.
	39	2	*Lt. Col.* Richmond Houghton. *Ens.* 21 April 1820; *Lieut.* 11 July 1823; *Capt.* 25 Sept. 1834; *Bt. Maj.* 3 April 1846; *Maj.* 1 Oct. 48; *Lt. Col.* 5 Dec. 53; *Bt. Col.* 28 Nov. 54; —Lv. P. A. 31 Oct.
O.	35	2	*Lieut. Col.* E. R. Mainwaring. *Ens.* 9 Jan. 1824; *Lieut.* 13 May 1825; *Capt.* 20 Feb. 1838; *Bt. Maj.* 4 Oct. 1842; *Major* 13 Dec. 1854; *Bt. Lieut. Col.* 20 June 1854; *Lt. Col.* 25 Nov. 1858; *Bt. Col.* 7 May 1855.—Fur. S. C. 19 Mar. 1858.
	28	1	*Major* T. J. Gardiner, *Ens.* 9 June 1831; *Lieut.* 30 June 1838; *Bt. Capt.* 9 June 1846; *Capt.* 2 Nov. 1848; *Bt. Major* 23 Nov. 1858; *Major* 25 Nov. 1858. ☞ *Brevet.* [1] Maj. 2 Nov. 49; Lt. Col. 28 Nov. 54; Col. 27 Nov. 57.

Fur. Reg.	Y	M	Captains.	Remarks.	Ensign.	Lieut.	Captain. Brevet.	Captain. Regl.
	22	4	N. B. Chamberlain, c. b., *PH*,[1]c - - - -	Brigdr. Genl. Comdg. Punjaub Irr. Force, & H.A.D.C. to the G.G.	24 *Feb.* 37	16 *July* 42	.. ..	1 *Nov.* 49
	20	7	W. Graydon, *PH*, - - -	4th Punjaub Infy...	12 *June* 39	12 *Nov.* 42	12 *June* 54	13 *Dec.* 54
	18	10	R. Unwin, *P*, - - - -	Cantt. Joint Magte. and Supdt. of the Abkarry mehal in Bareilly, ..	9 *Sep.* 40	29 *Dec.* 43	.. ..	11 *June* 55
	17	6	G. B. Mainwaring, *P,H*, -	.. ..	8 *Jan.* 42	21 *Dec.* 45	.. ..	1 *Oct.* 56
	16	..	J. J. Dansey,† - - - -	.. ..	10 *June* 43	10 *Oct.* 47	.. ..	23 *Nov.* 56
	15	7	J. J. O'Bryen, *PCH, (a)* -	.. ..	22 *Nov.* 43	2 *Nov.* 48	22 *Nov.* 58	25 *Nov.* 58
			Lieutenants.					
Capt O.	12	6	T. Lamb, *PCH, (b)* - -	Fur. P. A. 13 May 59	20 *Jan.* 47	12 *Mar.* 52		
	11	1	R. H. Tulloh, *PH*, - -	D.P. Works N. W.P.	9 *June* 48	1 *Feb.* 54		
	10	9	A. Cory, *PH*, - - - -	3rd Irr. Cavalry. ..	3 *Oct.* 48	13 *Dec.* 54		
	9	7	R. H. Wall, *PH*, - - -	.. ..	11 *Dec.* 49	9 *Sep.* 55		
	7	7	W. W. Boddam,† - - -	Civil employ, ..	12 *Dec.* 51	22 *Oct.* 55		
	4	5	Anthony Stewart, *P*, - -	.. ..	4 *Feb.* 55	1 *Oct.* 56		
	4	4	F. W. Boileau, *P* - - -	2nd Sikh Irr. Cavy.	20 *Mar.* 55	23 *Nov.* 56		
	3	1	Gee. Gordon Young, *PH*,	Civil employ, ..	13 *June* 56	23 *Nov.* 56		
	2	7	L. J. H. Grey,† - - -	.. ..	13 *Dec.* 56	15 *Sep.* 57		
N	2	3	F. Henderson, - - - -	Fur. S. C. 19 Apl. 59	4 *Apl.* 57	18 *May* 58		
	1	11	R. P. Davis, - - - -	.. ..	22 *Aug.* 57	25 *Nov.* 58		
			Ensigns.					
Lt.	..	7	C. T. Lane, - - - -	.. ..	11 *Dec.* 58			
			*					
			*					
			*					
			*		*Appointed.*			
	..	..	*Adjutant*, J. J. O'Bryen, -	Officiating, ..	28 *Sep.* 55			
	..	..	*Interpreter*, A. Stewart, -	Offg. Cantt. Joint Magte. Meean Meer.	20 *Oct.* 56			
	..	..	*Surg.*,*					
	..	..	*Assist. Surg.*, J. Hooper, -	.. ..	6 *Dec.* 56			

N. B.—This Corps was made a Grenadier Regiment for its services at Candahar under Genl. Nott.

(*a*) Has furnished certificate of qualification in Surveying.

(*b*) Passed a successful examination in the Vernacular Languages, 19th September 1851.

Raised in 1765.

17th Regiment of Native Infantry.

Mutinied, Azimghur.

Barkur-ka-Pultun. Late 2nd Battalion 11th Regt. N.I.

FACINGS—*Black.*

Fur. Reg.	SER. Y	M	
	39	4	*Colonel Sir* Justin Sheil, K.C.B. and K.L.S. *Ens.* 4 Mar. 1820; *Lieut.* 11 July 1823; *Capt.* 13 April 1830; *Major* 17 April 1841; *Lieut. Col.* 11 March 1847; *Bt. Col.* 28 Nov. 1854; *Colonel* 28 Nov. 1856.—On furlough.
O.	43	10	*Lt. Col.* Thomas Polwhele. *Ens.* 22 Aug. 1815; *Lt.* 1 Feb. 1818; *Capt.* 26 July 1830; *Bt. Maj.* 23 Dec. 1842; *Maj.* 21 Aug. 1843; *Bt. Lt. Col.* 3 April 1846; *Lt. Col.* 17 Feb. 1850; *Bt. Col.* 20 June 1854; *Major General* 1 May 1858.—Fur. S.C. 13 Apl. 1858.
	35	..	*Lt. Col.* G.W. Hamilton *Ens.* 20 June 24; *Lt.* 22 Aug. 26; *Bt. Capt.* 20 June 39; *Capt.* 17 Mar. 1844; *Bt. Maj.* 11 Nov. 1851; *Maj.* 5 Aug. 1854; *Lt. Col.* 19 May 1858.—Civil employ.
	34	6	*Maj.* Fred. Wm. Burroughs. *Ens.* 8 Jan. 25; *Lieut.* 19 Oct. 27; *Bt. Capt.* 8 Jan. 40; *Capt.* 1. Oct. 41; *Bt. Major* 11 Nov. 51; *Major* 9 Sep. 56; *Bt. Lieut. Col.* 14 Nov. 1858.—Comdt. Recruit depôt, Barrackpore.

☞ *Brevet.* [1] Major 20 June 1854. [2] Maj. 28 Nov. 1854. [3] Major 24 March 1858.

Fur. Reg.	Y	M	CAPTAINS.	REMARKS.	*Ensign.*	*Lieut.*	CAPTAIN. *Brevet.*	CAPTAIN. *Regl.*
	33	1	G. M. Hill, *P*, [1]*m* - - -	Pay Department, ..	13 *June* 26	28 *Aug.* 33	13 *June* 41	31 *Oct.* 49
	29	1	T. G. St. George, †[2]*m* - -	Offg. Pay Dept. ..	22 *May* 30	1 *Nov.* 38	22 *May* 45	18 *Mar.* 53
	27	1	J. S. D. Tulloch, *P*, *(a)* -	Jhansie Police. ..	14 *June* 32	9 *July* 40	14 *June* 47	15 *Nov.* 53
N.	18	1	D. Briggs, *PH*, - - - -	Supt. Hindostan and Thibet Road, ..	11 *June* 41	8 *Sep.* 43	.. ..	27 *July* 55
	17	1	J. A. Steel, *PH*, - - - -	Civil employ, ..	11 *June* 42	24 *Jan.* 45	.. ..	15 *Jan.* 56
	16	2	T. A. Carey, *PH*, [3]*m* -	.. ..	1 *May* 43	9 *Sep.* 49	.. ..	9 *Sep.* 56
	15	6	J. Fendall, *PH*, - - -	Civil employ, ..	30 *Dec.* 43	31 *Oct.* 49	.. ..	23 *Nov.* 56
			LIEUTENANTS.					
	14	7	F. E. Laing, † - - - -	.. ..	10 *Dec.* 44	18 *Mar.* 53		
	14	6	R. C. Cross, *PH*, - - -	Bhopal Levy. ..	18 *Jan.* 45	15 *Nov.* 53		
	14	1	C. Baily, *PH*, - - - -	Offg. Intr. H. M. 3rd Buffs, Dum-Dum,	14 *June* 45	15 *Nov.* 53		
	5	7	Robert Geo. Armstrong, † -	Allahabad Levy. ..	14 *Dec.* 53	16 *Jan.* 56		
	5	4	Jas. Nicholas Brutton Hewett, *PH*, - - -	Offg. Divl. Adjt. Mily. Police, Oude, ..	4 *Mar.* 54	9 *Sep.* 56		
	3	7	~~W. W. F. Hay~~, † - - -	Fur. P. A. 5th Jan. 59. ..	7 *Dec.* 55	23 *Nov.* 56		
	3	4	C. L. B. Constable, † - -	.. ..	4 *Mar.* 56	23 *Nov.* 56		
	3	1	W. E. M. B. Ramsay, -	On duty at Berhampore,	13 *June* 56	3 *June* 57		
	2	10	George Stewart, † - -	1st Sikh Irr. Cavy.	20 *Sep.* 56	1 *Sep.* 57		
	2	5	*Hon'ble* H. H. Hare, -	Regt. of Lucknow,	20 *Feb.* 57	16 *Sep.* 57		
	2	1	F. A. D. Cox, - - -	Fur. S. C. 25 May 58	26 *May* 57	18 *May* 58		
			ENSIGNS.					
	1	8	A. G. Ross, - - - - -	.. ..	4 *Nov.* 57			
	..	6	A. M. Ommanney, - -	.. ..	20 *Jan.* 59			
			*					
			*					
			*		*Appointed*			
	..	..	*Adjutant,*					
	..	..	*Intr.* *					
	..	..	*Surg.*, J. Naismith, M. D., -	.. ..	14 *Dec.* 54			
	..	..	*Asst. Surg.*, *					

(a) Passed an examination in the Punjaubee Language 10th Dec. 1851.

Raised in 1776.

18th Regiment of Native Infantry.

Mutinied, Bareilly.

"Bhurtpore"—"Punjaub."

Raje-ka-Pultan. Late 2nd Battalion 6th Regt. N.I.

Facings—*Bright-yellow.*

Fur. Reg.	Ser. Y	Ser. M	
	55	5	*Colonel* Charles Arthur Grenado Wallington. *Ens.* 13 February. 1804; *Lieut.* 3 June 1804; *Capt.* 1 Oct. 1815; *Major* 14 Dec. 1826; *Lieut. Col.* 4 April 1832; *Col.* 20 Dec. 1843; *Major General* 20 June 1854; *Lieut. Genl.* 4 Mar. 1858.—Europe, 1 April 1841.
~~N.~~	~~35~~	~~6~~	~~*Lt. Col.* Christopher Simson Maling. *Ens.*~~ 9 Jan. 1824; *Lieut.* 13 May 1825; *Capt.* 23 May 1834; *Bt. Major* 9 Nov. 1846; *Major* 1 Nov. 1849; *Bt. Lt. Col.* 20 June 1854; *Lieut. Col.* 16 Dec. 1854; *Bt. Colonel* 24 Oct. 1858.—Fur. S. C. 27 Feb. 1855.
N.	22	7	*Major* W. F. Nuthall.(a) *Ens.* 9 Dec. 1836; *Lieut.* 3 Oct. 1840; *Bt. Capt.* 9 Dec. 1851; *Capt.* 31 Jan. 1853; *Bt. Major* 9 Dec. 1853; *Major* 6 June 1857.—Pegu Levy.

☞ *Brevet.* [1] Major 2 Jan. 1855.

Fur. Reg.	Y	M	Captains.	Remarks.	*Ensign.*	*Lieut.*	Captain. *Brevet.*	Captain. *Regl.*
	22	4	F. C. Tombs, *PC*, - - -	Pay Department, ..	24 *Feb.* 37	12 *Apl.* 41	24 *Feb.* 52	24 *May* 53
	18	5	C Herbert, *P*,[1] *m* - - -	Calcutta Native Militia, ..	30 *Jan.* 41	21 *Dec.* 45	.. ..	1 *Jan.* 55
	18	5	A. F. Baird, *P*, - - -	Dep. P. W. L. P. ..	17 *Feb.* 41	1 *Mar.* 46	.. ..	15 *Jan.* 55
	18	1	H. S. Bivar, *P*, *(b)* - -	Civil employ, ..	11 *June* 41	3 *July* 46	11 *June* 56	23 *Nov.* 56
	17	1	J. Y. Gowan, *PH*, - - -	.. ..	11 *June* 42	1 *Aug.* 46	.. ..	6 *June* 57
	15	1	C. W. Nightingale, *PH*, *(c)*	Dept. Public Works, Punjaub, ..	8 *June* 44	12 *Nov.* 48	.. ..	6 *June* 57
	13	7	A. K. Comber, *PH*, *(d)* -	Civil employ, ..	12 *Dec.* 45	13 *Apl.* 52	.. ..	6 *June* 57
			Lieutenants.					
	13	7	M. Hunter, *PH*, *(c)* - -	2nd in Command Rohilkund Horse,	13 *Dec.* 45	31 *Jan.* 53		
	12	7	J. Macdonald, *PH*, - -	Survey Dept.	11 *Dec.* 46	24 *May* 53		
	10	7	B. T. Stafford, *PH*, - -	Agra Infy. Levy, ..	9 *Dec.* 48	12 *Aug.* 53		
	8	1	G. D. Crawfurd, *PH*, - -	.. ..	14 *June* 51	1 *Jan.* 55		
	6	6	Jas. W. H. Johnstone, *PH*,	Civil employ, ..	20 *Dec.* 52	23 *Nov.* 56		
N.	5	6	H. B. Stuart, - - - -	Fur. S. C. 22 Sep. 58	20 *Jan.* 54	23 *Nov.* 56		
	4	5	Wm. Blunt Barwell,† - -	Adjutant Rohilkund Horse, ..	4 *Feb.* 55	6 *June* 57		
	2	10	E. Knatchbull, - - - -	.. ..	1 *Sep.* 56	12 *June* 57		
	2	1	A J. Macqueen, - - -	.. ..	13 *June* 57	18 *May* 58		
	1	7	G. R. Grylls, - - - -	.. ..	12 *Dec.* 57	22 *Oct.* 58		
	..	11	A. D. C. Inglis, - - -	.. ..	7 *Aug.* 58	23 *Dec.* 58		
			Ensigns.					
			*					
			*					
			*					
			*					
			*		*Appointed.*			
			Adjutant,*					
			Intr. *					
			Surgeon, R. H. Oakley, -	.. ..	9 *July* 56			
			Asst. Surg.,*					

(a) Has passed an examination in the Burmese language.
(b) Has passed an examination in the Bengalee language.
(c) Have furnished certificates of qualification in Surveying and Civil Engineering.
(d) Has passed an examination in the Bengali language.

Raised in 1776.

19th Regiment of Native Infantry.

Disbanded, Barrackpore.

Ung-ka-Pultun. Late 2nd Battalion 3rd Regt. N.I.

FACINGS—*Dark-green.*

Fur. Reg.	SER. Y	SER. M	
O	52	4	*Colonel* George Tomkyns. *Ens.* 28 Feb. 1807; *Lieut.* 5 Jan. 1811; *Bt. Capt.* 28 Feb. 1822; *Capt.* 1 May 1824; *Major* 5 March 1835; *Lieut. Col.* 23 Nov. 1841; *Col.* 16 *Oct.* 1851; *Major General* 28 Nov. 54.—Fur. P. A. 16 Feb. 59.
			*Lieut. Colonel**
	25	6	*Major* W. K. Wollen.† *Ens.* 4 Jan. 1834; *Lieut.* 22 Sep. 1836; *Capt.* 24 Jan. 1845; *Bt. Major* 28 Nov. 1854; *Major* 26 Aug. 1856.
			☞ *Brevet.* [1] Major 19 Jan. 1858.

Fur. Reg.	Y	M	CAPTAINS.	REMARKS.	*Ensign.*	*Lieut.*	CAPTAIN. *Brevet.*	CAPTAIN. *Regl.*
	23	1	R. A. Smith,† - - - - -	.. ..	11 *June* 36	18 *June* 37	.. ..	28 *Mar.* 50
	22	1	D. C Shute, *PH*,[1]*m* -	Qr. Mr. General's Department, ..	12 *June* 37	29 *July* 40	.. ..	1 *Nov.* 50
	21	10	A. Robinson, *PH*, - -	.. ..	27 *Aug.* 37	3 *Oct.* 40	.. ..	31 *Dec.* 50
	21	4	F. P. Layard, *P*, - -	Dept. of P. W., L. P.	11 *Mar.* 38	16 *July* 42	.. ..	30 *Apl.* 51
	19	7	J. W. Bristow, *P*, *(a)* -	Civil employ, ..	11 *Dec.* 39	9 *Aug.* 43	.. ..	26 *Apl.* 52
	18	11	J. MacDougall,† - - -	Regt. of Lucknow,	31 *July* 40	22 *Nov.* 43	31 *July* 55	26 *Aug.* 56
	17	1	H. D. Manning, *PH*, *(b)* -	Commdt. district Police, Azimgurh,	10 *June* 42	31 *Jan.* 44	.. ..	23 *Nov.* 56
			LIEUTENANTS.					
O.	16	..	S. R. J. Owen, A.K.C.,† -	Fur. S.C. 19 Feb. 59	20 *June* 43	1 *Mar.* 50	20 *June* 58	
	19	1	L. R. Newhouse,† - -	.. ..	12 *June* 40	28 *Mar* 50	12 *June* 55	
	10	6	J. F. L. Fisher, *PH*, - -	Sirmoor Battalion,	20 *Dec.* 48	1 *Nov.* 50		
	13	4	I. F. MacAndrew, *P*, *(b)* -	Civil employ, ..	20 *Feb.* 46	30 *Apl.* 51		
	9	7	H. Macdonald,† - - -	Adjt. District Police, Deyra Dhoon, ..	20 *Dec.* 49	26 *Apl.* 52		
O.	9	1	James Vallings, *P*, -	Fur. S. C. 3 Aug. 57	15 *June* 50	14 *Aug.* 56		
	8	7	E. T. Sadler, - - -	Offg Qr. Mr. Genl's. Department, ..	10 *Dec.* 50	26 *Aug.* 56		
	9	4	C. W. R. Chester, *P*, -	Extra Goorkha Regt.	20 *Feb.* 50	23 *Nov.* 56		
	4	6	M. H. Heathcote,† - -	.. ..	20 *Dec.* 54	23 *Nov.* 56		
	2	6	Arthur Battye,† - -	Sirmoor Rifle Regt.	6 *Jan.* 57	22 *Jan.* 58		
	2	5	W. E. Chambers,† - - -	.. ..	20 *Feb.* 57	30 *Apl.* 58		
			ENSIGNS.					
	1	8	C. St. J. B. Barnett,† - -	.. ..	4 *Nov.* 57			
	..	7	A. N. Phillips, - - - -	.. ..	8 *Dec.* 58			
			*					
			*					
			*		*Appointed.*			
	..	..	*Adjt.* *					
	..	..	*Intr.* *					
	..	..	*Surgeon* *					
	..	..	*Asst. Surg.* *					

a) Attained the standard of proficiency in the Punjaubee language prescribed by G. O. G. G. 14th October 1851.
(b) Have furnished certificates of qualification in surveying and Civil Engineering.

Raised in 1776.

20th Regiment of Native Infantry.

Mutinied Meerut.

"PUNJAUB"—"CHILLIANWALLA"—"GOOJERAT."
Baillie-ka-Pultun. Late 2nd Battalion 5th Regt. N.I.
FACINGS—*White.*

Fur. Reg.	Ser. Y	Ser. M	
	57	10	*Colonel* Thomas Henry Paul. *Ens.* 4 Sept. 1801; *Lieut.* 30 Sept. 1803; *Capt.* 16 Dec. 1814; *Major* 7 Nov. 1824; *Lieut. Col.* 30 July 1828; *Bt. Col.* 22 Jan. 1834; *Col.* 9 July 1840; *Major Genl.* 23 Nov. 1841; *Lieut. Genl.* 11 Nov. 1851.—Europe, 28 Feb. 42.
	37	8	*Lieut. Col.* John Craigie Halkett, C. B. *Ens.* 22 Oct. 1822; *Lieut.* 22 Oct 1824; *Capt.* 6 Aug. 1834; *Bt. Major* 23 Dec. 1842; *Major* 3 Sept. 1849; *Bt. Lt. Col.* 20 June 1854; *Lieut. Col.* 28 Nov 1854; *Bt. Col.* 15 Sep. 1855.—Lv. S. C. 30 Nov.
O.	33	7	*Lieut. Col.* T. Martin. *Ens.* 18 Dec. 25; 8 Apl. 28; *Bt. Capt.* 18 Dec. 40; *Capt.* 14 Mar. 43; *Bt. Major* 11 Nov. 51; *Major* 28 Nov. 1854; *Lieut Col.* 27 Aug. 1858.—Leave S. C. 8 Oct.,
	33	..	*Major.* J. C. Scott, *P.* *Ens.* 27 June 1826; *Lieut.* 3 Oct. 1828; *Bt. Capt.* 27 June 1841; *Capt.* 24 Jan. 1845; *Bt.* Maj. 20 June 1854; *Maj.* 27 Aug. 1858.—Army Commt Dept.,

☞ *Brevet.* [1] Maj. 20 June 1854. [2] Maj. 19 Jan. 1858.

Fur. Reg.	Y	M	CAPTAINS.	REMARKS.	*Ensign.*	*Lieut.*	Captain *Brevet.*	Captain *Regl.*
	33	1	J. K. Spence,[1]*m* - - -	Civil employ, ..	21 *May* 26	6 *Aug.* 34	21 *May* 41	3 *Sep.* 49
	19	1	E. M. Ryan, *PCH*, - - -	Civil employ, ..	12 *June* 40	7 *Aug.* 42	.. ..	14 *Aug.* 53
	16	5	W. H. S. Earle, *PC*, - -	Comdg. Divisional Battn., Boolundshuhur, ..	17 *Feb.* 43	31 *Dec.* 47	.. ..	23 *Nov.* 56
	14	6	C. H. Barchard, C.B. *PH*,[2]*m*	.. ..	12 *Jan.* 45	3 *Sep.* 49	.. ..	10 *May* 57
	12	4	Hector Mackenzie, *P*, *(a)* -	Civil employ,	20 *Feb.* 47	20 *Sep.* 49	.. ..	10 *May* 57
	11	9	C. A. Reid,† - - - -	Meerut Infy. Levy,	25 *Sep.* 47	9 *Mar.* 50	.. ..	6 *Feb.* 58
O.	11	4	A. I. Shuldham,† - -	Fur. P. A. 25 Apl. 59	25 *Feb.* 48	25 *Mar.* 50	.. ..	27 *Aug.* 58
			LIEUTENANTS.					
O.	10	6	C. C. Ekins, *PH*, *(b)* -	Fur. S.C. 3 Aug. 58	20 *Dec.* 48	1 *Jan.* 51		
	10	1	R. Cadell, *PH*, - - -	Comdt. Munclah Police, ..	9 *June* 49	14 *Aug.* 53		
	9	6	J. H. Tyler,† - - -	12th Irr. Cavalry, ..	20 *Dec.* 49	23 *Nov.* 56		
	6	5	Arthur Tulloch, *P.C.H.* -	Adjt. District, Mily. Police, Oude, ..	20 *Jan.* 53	10 *May* 57		
	6	4	Thomas G. Blackburne,† -	8th Irregular Cavy,	20 *Feb.* 53	10 *May* 57		
	3	9	Hugh Arthur Lewes,† -	7th Punjaub Infy...	4 *Oct.* 55	10 *May* 57		
	4	7	Aylmer Vivian,† - - -	.. ..	9 *Dec.* 54	31 *Jan.* 57		
	2	10	C. R. Cock, - - - -	.. ..	4 *Sep.* 56	18 *Sep.* 57		
	2	3	W. F. Badgley, - - -	Doing duty Mily. Police, Oude. ..	4 *Apl.* 57	18 *May* 58		
	1	10	D. T. H. Sampson, - -	.. ..	20 *Aug.* 57	18 *May* 58		
	1	1	H. W. Franks, - - - -	.. ..	12 *June* 58	27 *Aug.* 58		
			ENSIGNS.					
	..	7	C. A. E. S. Carter, - -	.. ..	11 *Dec.* 58			
			*					
			*					
			*					
			*		*Appointed.*			
	..	..	*Adjt.*,*					
	..	..	*Intr.*,*					
	..	..	*Surg.*, R. Whittall, - -	.. ..	24 *Jan.* 57			
	..	..	*Asst. Surg.*,*					

(*a*) Passed an examination in the Punjaubee language, 10th December 1851.
(*b*) Passed an examination in FieldEngineering.

Raised in 1776. } **21st Regiment of Native Infantry.** } Peshawur.

"LASWARRIE"—"BHURTPORE."

Neelwur-ka-Pultun. Late 2nd Battalion 9th Regt. N.I.

FACINGS—*Yellow.*

Fur Reg.	Ser. Y	Ser. M	
	53	10	*Colonel* Henry Hall, C. B. *Ens.* 10 September 1805; *Lieut.* 13 March 1806; *Capt.* 5 Oct. 1821; *Major* 13 Jan. 1828; *Lieut. Col.* 9 Jan. 1833; *Col.* 21 Dec. 1844; *Major Genl.* 20 June 1854, Lieut. General 24 Oct. 1858.—Europe, 27 Jan. 42.
	37	8	~~*Lieut. Colonel*~~ James Matthie. *Ens.* 24 Oct. 1821; *Lieut.* 1 Jan. 1824; *Capt.* 8 Sep. 1835; *Major* 22 Nov. 1843; *Lieut. Col.* 1 March 1850; *Bt. Col.* 28 Nov. 1854.—Leave S. C. 1 November.
	30	4	~~*Major*~~ Henry Milne.† *Ens.* 7 March 1829; *Lieut.* 8 October 1839; *Bt. Capt.* 7 March 1844; *Capt.* 1 May 1846; *Bt. Major* 28 Nov. 1854; *Major* 28 Feb. 1856. ☞ *Brevet.* [1] Major 6 June 56.

Fur Reg.	Y	M	CAPTAINS.	REMARKS.	*Ensign.*	*Lieut.*	CAPTAIN. *Brevet.*	CAPTAIN. *Regl.*
	25	7	J. Chambers, *PC*, *(a)* -	Fur. S. C. 26 Feb. 58	13 *Dec.* 33	15 *Mar.* 41	.. ..	27 *Aug.* 47
	20	5	E. A. Rowlatt, *PH*, *(b)* -	Civil employ, ..	14 *Feb.* 39	1 *July* 41	.. ..	1 *Dec.* 49
	18	9	J. L. Vaughan, *PC*, [1]*m* -	5th Punjaub Infy.	12 *Oct.* 40	16 *July* 42	.. ..	30 *June* 50
	18	2	H. T. Bartlett, *PC*, *(c)* -	Cant. Joint Magte. Peshawur, ..	21 *Apl.* 41	23 *June* 43	.. ..	13 *Apl.* 55
	17	7	G. N. Cave, *PH*, - -	16th Punjaub Infy.	10 *Dec.* 41	22 *Mar.* 44	.. ..	27 *Feb.* 56
	17	..	H. E. Iremonger, *PCH*, -	Offg. Brigade Staff.	19 *June* 42	28 *June* 44	.. ..	28 *Feb.* 56
N.	16	5	J. G. Sparke, *PH*, - - -	Fur. S C. 24 Feb. 59	17 *Feb.* 43	24 *Jan.* 45	17 *Feb.* 58	7 *Sep.* 58
			LIEUTENANTS.					
	12	6	G. A. Brown, *P*, - - - -	.. ..	26 *Dec.* 46	21 *Apl.* 51		
	11	8	E. G. Clark, *P*, - -	Civil employ, ..	20 *Nov.* 47	15 *Nov.* 53		
	10	7	F. J. Craigie, *PH*, - - -	2nd Punjaub Cavy.,	8 *Dec.* 48	13 *Apl.* 55		
	9	3	T. G. Ross, † - - - -	Sylhet Light Infy. Battalion, ..	20 *Mar.* 50	27 *Feb.* 56		
	8	5	L. H. P. DeH. Larpent, †-	.. ..	20 *Jan.* 51	28 *Feb.* 56		
	5	1	John Peter Harris, *PH*, -	.. ..	8 *June* 54	28 *Mar.* 56		
	3	7	Alfred FitzHugh, *P. C-H.*	2nd Sikh Infantry,	7 *Dec.* 55	23 *Nov.* 56		
	2	7	G. Atkins, † - - - - -	.. ..	20 *Dec.* 56	30 *Apl.* 58		
	2	2	F. N. M. Maynard, - -	Adjt. district police, Oude. ..	20 *Apl.* 57	18 *May* 58		
	1	9	J. F. Trevanion, - - -	24 Punjaub Infy. ..	29 *Sep.* 57	6 *Nov.* 58		
	1	..	W. B. Birch, - - - -	.. ..	30 *July* 58	23 *Dec.* 58		
			ENSIGNS.					
	..	6	M. McN. Rind, - - -	.. ..	6 *Jan.* 59			
			*					
			*		*Appointed.*			
			*					
	..	..	*Adjt.*, *					
	..	..	*Interpreter*, G. A. Brown, -	.. ..	28 *Apl.* 56			
	..	..	*Surg.* J. S. Morrieson, M. D., - - - - - - -	.. ..	16 *Jan.* 55			
	..	..	*Asst. Surg.* J. White, M.D.,	Fur. P.A. 30 Mar. 59	1 *Jan.* 59			
	..	...	J. Mc. D. Stokes, - -	.. ..	9 *May* 59			

(a) Received a certificate for high proficiency in the Oordoo language from the College of Fort William and pased an examination in the Punjaubee language, 11th July 53.

(b) Passed a successful examination in the Assamese and Bengallee languages.

(c) Passed an examination in the Punjaubee language, 10th December 1851.

Raised in 1778.

22nd Regiment of Native Infantry.

Mutinied, Oude (Fyzabad.)

" CARNATIC"—" DEHLEE"—" PUNJAUB."

Bole-ka-Pultun. Late 2nd Battalion 2nd Regt. N.I.

FACINGS—*White.*

Fur. Reg.	Ser. Y	Ser. M	
N.	50	2	~~Col. Wm. Sage.~~ *Ens.* 24 Apl. 1809; *Lt.* 16 Dec. 14; *Bt. Capt.* 24 Apl. 24; *Capt.* 13 May 25; *Bt. Maj.* 28 June 1838; *Major* 1 Oct. 1840; *Lieut. Col.* 19 Feb. 1847; *Bt. Col.* 28 Nov. 1854; *Col.* 18 July 1856; Maj. Genl. 13 Mar. 1859.—Fur. S. C. 25 June 1858.
	37	7	*Lt.Col.* Wm. Rbt. Corfield. *Ens.* 3 Dec. 21; *Lt.* 11 Sept.23; *Capt.* 30 July 32; *Maj.* 2 Feb.45; *Bt. Lt. Col.* 7 June 49. *Lt. Col.* 31 Mar. 51; *Bt. Col.* 28 Nov. 54.—Comdg. Native Infy. Brigade in China.
	30	7	~~Major~~ J. D. McPherson, C. B., *P. Ens.* 4 Dec. 1828; *Lieut.* 26 Nov. 1836; *Bt. Capt.* 4 Dec. 1843; *Capt.* 1 Nov. 1848; *Bt. Majr* 7 June 1849; *Major* 1 Dec. 1855; *Bt. Lt. Col.* 28 Nov. 1854; *Bt. Col.* 5 April 1858.—Mily. Secy. to the Leiut. Govr. of the Punjaub.

☞ *Brevet.* [1] Major 20 July 1858. [2] Major 2 Dec. 1855.

Fur. Reg.	Ser. Y	Ser. M	CAPTAINS.	REMARKS.	*Ensign.*	*Lieut.*	CAPTAIN. *Brevet.*	CAPTAIN. *Regl.*
	23	3	J. F. D'E. W. Hall,(*a*) -	.. ..	16 *Apl.* 36	20 *July* 39	.. ..	23 *Apl.* 49
	22	6	P. Drummond,*P*, - - -	Bareilly Infy. Levy.,	13 *Jan.* 37	1 *Nov.* 41	.. ..	22 *May* 49
	20	10	W. J. Hicks,†- - - -	Comdg. district Police, Etah, ..	1 *Sep.* 38	27 *June* 42	.. ..	29 *July* 53
	18	7	J. W. Smith,*PH*, - - -	Cant. Jt. Mag. Ferozepore, ..	11 *Dec.* 40	16 *July* 42	.. ..	15 *Sep.* 55
	18	7	W. D. Morgan,*PH*,[1]*m*	.. ..	12 *Dec.* 40	19 *Jan.* 43	.. ..	15 *May* 55
N.	18	1	S. J. Hire,*PH*,[2]*m* - -	Fur. S.C. 19Aug.58,	12 *June* 41	22 *Mar.* 44	.. ..	1 *Dec.* 55
	18	1	F. W. Ripley,*PH*,-(*b*)	Civil employ, ..	12 *June* 41	24 *Jan.* 45	12 *June* 56	23 *Nov.* 56
			LIEUTENANTS.					
N.	16	9	C. S. Fowle,† - - -	Fur. S.C. 7 Sep. 58,	24 *Sep.* 42	3 *June* 45	24 *Sep.* 57	
O.	14	4	F. K. Bacon,*P*, - - -	Furlough S.C. 1 December 1855, ..	19 *Mar.* 45	29 *July* 53		
	13	1	R. Stewart, *PH*, - - -	Political employ, ..	12 *June* 46	15 *Nov.* 53		
	10	4	Thomas Quin,*PH*,- -	6th Punjaub, Infy.	20 *Feb.* 49	17 *Oct.* 54		
O.	14	6	F. Duffin, *PH*, - - -	Fur.P,A.13 June 59	29 *Dec.* 43	30 *Aug.* 54		
N.	5	5	E. Ward, - - - - -	Fur. S. C. 30 Apl. 58	20 *Feb.* 54	10 *Aug.* 56		
	2	7	H. B. Sanderson, - - -	9th Punjaub Infy...	20 *Dec.* 56	8 *June* 57		
	2	7	W. C. Anderson, - - -	1st Punjaub Cavy.	13 *Dec.* 56	17 *Nov.* 57		
N.	2	2	F. W. Grant,† - - - -	Fur. S. C. 11 Feb. 59	20 *Apl.* 57	18 *May.* 58		
	1	9	J F. F. Cologan,† - - -	Ju d. ..	20. *Sep* 57	15 Aug. 58		
		10	J. B. Slater, - - - -	.. ..	4 Sep. 58	1 *Apl.* 59		
			ENSIGNS.					
		6	A. W. Christian, - - -	.. ..	6 *Jan.* 59			
			*					
			*					
			*		*Appointed.*			
			*					
	..	..	*Adjutant,* *					
	..	..	*Intr.,* *					
	..	..	*Surg.* *					
	..	..	*Asst. Surg.* *					

(*a*) Has furnished certificate of qualification in Surveying.
(*b*) Has passed an examination in the Burmese language.

N. B.—This Regiment has an honorary standard and extra Jemadar for Allygurh and Delhi. On the Standard are inscribed the words " Lake and Victory."

Raised in 1788. | **23rd Regiment of Native Infantry.** | Mutinied, Mhow.

"ALLYGURH"—"DEHLEE"—"BHURTPORE."
Chota Crawfurd-ka-Pultun. Late 2nd Battalion 4th Regt. N.I.

FACINGS—*Dark-green.*

Fur. Reg.	Ser. Y	Ser. M	
O.	51	1	*Colonel* Louis Saunders Bird. *Ens.* 4 June 1808; *Lieut.* 16 Dec. 1814; *Bt. Capt.* 4 June 1823; *Capt.* 5 April 1825; *Bt. Major* 28 June 1838; *Major* 18 June 1840; *Bt. Lt. Col.* 3 April 1846; *Lt. Col.* 12 Sept. 1846; *Bt. Col.* 20 June 1854; *Col.* 17 Apl. 1856; *Major General* 4 March 1858.—Furlough, P. A. 10 Jan. 1857.
	33	2	*Lt. Col.* George William Bishop. *Ens.* 26 Apl. 1826; *Lieut.* 20 June 1828; *Bt. Capt.* 26 Apl. 1841; *Capt.* 28 May 1843; *Major* 10 July 1852; *Lt. Col.* 31 May 1857.
O.	35	2	*Major* C. Cooper. *Ens.* 4 May 1824; *Lt.* 12 Apl. 1826; *Bt. Capt.* 4 May 1839; *Capt.* 30 June 1840; *Bt. Major* 11 Nov. 1851; *Major* 8 June 1857; *Bt. Lieut. Col.* 4 July 1858.—Fur. S. C. 13 Mar. 58.

☞ [1] Maj. 11 Nov. 51. [2] Maj. 20 June 54 [3] Major 20 July 58.

Fur. Reg.	Y	M		Remarks.	Ensign.	Lieut.	Captain. Brevet.	Captain. Regl.
			CAPTAINS.					
N.	33	8	R. R. W. Ellis, *P*, [1]*m*	Political employ, ..	5 *Nov.* 25	17 *Dec.* 32	5 *Nov.* 40	10 *Feb.* 46
	33	5	E. F. Smith, [2]*m*	Supdt. Dacca Elephant Keddahs,	16 *Feb.* 26	28 *July* 33	16 *Feb.* 41	1 *Apl.* 46
	22	1	C. P. Trower, *PH*,	Judge Advte. Genl's Dept., ..	12 *June* 37	3 *Oct.* 40	12 *June* 52	15 *Nov.* 53
	20	1	E. Bradford, *P*,	Lv. S.C. 25 Sept. ..	11 *June* 39	16 *July* 42	.. ..	1 *Apl* 54
	19	10	J. S. Davies, *P*,	Political employ, ..	18 *Sep.* 39	2 *May* 43	18 *Sep.* 54	23 *Nov.* 56
	18	5	A. L. McMullin, *P*, [3]*m*	Offg Civil employ.	17 *Feb.* 41	24 *Jan.* 45	17 *Feb.* 56	12 *June* 57
	15	10	C. W. Miles, *PH*,	Comdg a Police Battalion at Burdwan,	4 *Sep.* 43	8 *Aug.* 47	.. ..	1 *July* 57
			LIEUTENANTS.					
	15	2	G. V. Balderston, †	Regt. of Lucknow,	21 *Apl.* 44	6 *Mar.* 53	21 *Apl* 59	
	14	..	G. L. Fraser, *P*,	Offg. Adjt. Genl's. Dept., ..	4 *July* 45	7 *June* 53		
	12	7	J. A. H. Moore, *PH*, (*a*)	Shekhawattee Battn.	11 *Dec.* 46	10 *Oct.* 53		
	9	5	G. R. Westmacott, *PH*,	Hyderabad Congt...	20 *Jan.* 50	15 *Nov.* 53		
O.	8	7	G. B. C. Simpson, *PH*,	Fur. S. C. 30 June 58	9 *Dec.* 50	1 *Apl.* 54		
	7	1	G. S. Dysart, *PH*,	Political employ, ..	13 *June* 52	23 *Nov.* 56		
	6	9	W. G. Waterfield, *P*,	Civil employ, ..	3 *Oct.* 52	23 *Nov.* 56		
	5	8	John Bartleman, †	Sikh Police Regt.,..	20 *Oct.* 53	31 *May* 57		
	5	7	W. Rice M. Holroyd, *P*,	Civil employ, ..	10 *Dec.* 53	8 *June* 57		
	3	2	B. J. Parsons, †	Leave to 1 Nov. ..	15 *May* 56	26 *Apl.* 58		
	2	1	C. M. Boswell,	.. ..	13 *June* 57	18 *May* 58		
			ENSIGNS.					
	1	7	C. E. Macaulay, †	1st Sikh Irr. Cavy.	12 *Dec.* 57			
			*					
			*					
			*					
			*					
					Appointed.			
..	..		*Adjt.*,*					
..	..		*Intr.**					
..	..		*Surg.*					
..	..		*Asst. Surg.*,*					

N.B.—This Regiment has an honorary standard and extra Jemadar for Allygurh and Delhi. On the Standard are inscribed the words "Lake and Victory."

(*a*) Has furnished the certificate of qualification in surveying.

24th Regiment of Native Infantry.

Raised in 1779.

Disarmed, Peshawur.

"Laswarrie"—"Moodkee"—"Ferozeshuhur"—"Alliwal."

Dabie-ka-Pultun. Late 2nd Battalion 8th Regt. N.I.

Facings—*White.*

Fur.Reg.	Ser. Y	Ser. M	
	49	8	*Colonel* Archibald Fullerton Richmond, c. b. *Ensign* 27 Oct. 1809; *Lieut.* 16 Dec. 1814; *Capt.* 1 May 1824; *Major* 13 May 1833; *Lieut. Col.* 24 Jan. 1840; *Col.* 28 March 1850; *Maj. Genl.* 28 Nov. 1854.—Furlo' S. C., 10 Feb. 49.
O.	39	10	*Lieut. Col.* Edmund Wintle. *Ens.* 20 Sept. 1819; *Lieut.* 25 April 1822; *Bt. Capt.* 20 Sept. 1834; *Capt.* 5 Feb. 1835; *Major* 9 July 1846; *Lt. Col.* 10 July 1852; *Bt. Col.* 28 Nov. 1854.—Fur. P. A. 12 Apl. 59.
O.	19	5	*Major* J. T. Shakespear, *PH*, *Ens.* 8 Feb. 1840; *Lieut.* 13 Aug. 1842; *Capt.* 5 Dec. 1849 *Major* 1 May 1857.—Fur. P. A. 14 June 1859.

Fur.Reg.	Y	M		Remarks.	*Ensign.*	*Lieut.*	Captain. *Brevet.*	Captain. *Regl.*
			Captains.					
	18	5	G. M. Waddilove, *PH*,	Lv. P A 15 Oct. ..	17 *Feb.* 41	11 *Oct.* 43	.. ..	6 *Oct.* 50
	17	4	A. S. Smith, *P*,	.. ..	3 *Mar.* 42	1 *Apl.* 45	.. ..	26 *Mar.* 54
	17	1	J. Doran, *PH*,	19th Punjaub Infy.,	11 *June* 42	20 *Sep.* 45	.. ..	1 *Jan.* 55
D	~~16~~	~~7~~	~~E. A. Grubb, *P*,~~	.. ..	20 *Dec.* 42	30 *Oct.* 45	Oct '62	9 *Apl.* 56
	16	7	J. M. Earle, *PH*,	... ..	9 *Dec.* 42	18 *Dec.* 45	.. ..	23 *Nov.* 56
N.	15	1	A. Irvine, †	Fur. P A 25 Apl. 59	8 *June* 44	21 *Dec.* 45	.. ..	31 *Jan.* 57
	14	6	E. P. Lloyd, *PH*, (a)	Civil employ. ..	29 *Dec.* 44	12 *Sep.* 46	.. ..	1 *May* 57
			Lieutenants.					
	14	5	R. C. Lindsey, †	.. ..	11 *Feb.* 45	20 *May* 49		
	15	3	B. Soady, *PH*,	.. ..	1 *Apl.* 44	6 *Oct.* 50	1 *Apl.* 59	
	13	1	J. B. Lind, *P*,	5th Punjaub Infy., ..	26 *May* 46	18 *Nov.* 50		
	9	3	H. F. Newmarch, *PH*,	Civil employ, ..	25 *Mar.* 50	12 *June* 54		
	9	1	J. Trevenen, †	14th Punjaub Infy.	14 *June* 50	29 *Aug.* 54		
	8	7	G. H. E. Howard, †	.. ..	10 *Dec.* 50	1 *Jan.* 55		
	5	6	Geo. Nicholson Saunders, †	6th Punjaub Infy...	20 *Dec.* 53	19 *Oct.* 56		
	5	1	F. A. Currie Knyvett, *PH*,	Mirzapore Police,	10 *June* 54	23 *Nov.* 56		
	5	1	G. Ed. John Maidman, *PH*,	18th Punjaub Infy.,	9 *June* 54	23 *Nov.* 56		
D	~~2~~	~~7~~	~~Alexander Shaw,~~	14th Punjaub Infy.,	12 *Dec.* 56	30 *Apl.* 58		
	2	1	R. Brown,	.. ..	12 *June* 57	18 *May* 58		
			Ensigns.					
Z	1	7	G. B P. Alcock,	.. ..	11 *Dec.* 57			
			*					
			*					
			*					
			*		*Appointed.*			
	..	..	*Adjutant,*					
	..	..	*Intr.*, A. S. Smith,	Officiating. ..	9 *Apl.* 57			
	..	..	*Surg.*,*					
	..	..	*Assistant Surg.*,*					

(a) Passed a successful examination in the vernacular Languages.

Raised in 1795.

25th Regiment of Native Infantry, (Volunteers.)

Disarmed, Benares.

(Rifle Company.)

"JAVA"—"PUNJAUB"—"CHILLIANWALLA"—"GOOJERAT."

Murriam-ka-Pultun. Late 1st Battalion 20th Regt. N.I.

FACINGS—*Blue.*

Fur. Reg.	Ser. Y	M	
D	58	6	~~Colonel William Henry Kemm~~. *Ens.* 15 Jan. 1801; *Lieut.* 20 July 1801; *Capt.* 17 April 1814; *Major* 1 May 1824; *Lieut. Col.* 23 Feb. 1827; *Bt. Col.* 18 June 1831; *Col.* 11 Nov. 1837; *Major Genl.* 23 Nov. 1841; *Lieut. Genl.* 11 Nov. 51.—Europe, 8 Sep. 36.
O	39	10	*Lt. Col.* Thomas Sewell. *Ens.* 3 Sept. 1819; *Lt.* 2 Dec. 1820; *Capt.* 7 Dec. 1827; *Bt. Maj.* 23 Nov. 1841; *Major* 20 Nov. 1845; *Lieut. Colonel* 13 Oct. 1851; *Bt. Col.* 28 Nov. 1854.—Lv. S. C. to the Cape of G. H.—G. O. 14 Apl. 59.
N	31	5	*Major* J. Clarke, *PC*. *Ens.* 21 Jan. 1828; *Lieut.* 5 Jan. 1837; *Brevet Capt.* 21 Jan. 1843; *Capt.* 15 Aug. 1844; *Bt. Major* 7 June 1849; *Maj.* 27 June 1857; *Bt. Lieut. Col.* 28 Nov. 1854.—Civil employ.

☞ *Brevet.* [1] Major 1 May 58. [2] Major 24 Mar. 58.

Fur. Reg.	Ser. Y	M	CAPTAINS.	REMARKS.	*Ensign.*	*Lieut.*	CAPTAIN. *Brevet.*	CAPTAIN. *Regl.*
N.	27	1	C. J Richards, [1]*m* - - -	Fur. S. C. 18 Sep. 57	14 *June* 32	15 *May* 37	.. ..	12 *Feb.* 46
	25	..	H. J. C. Shakespear, *PCH*,	Nagpore Irr Force,	7 *July* 34	5 *July* 37	.. ..	26 *Dec.* 46
	20	1	A. Hunter, *PH*, - - - -	.. ..	11 *June* 39	8 *Nov.* 41	11 *June* 54	5 *Mar.* 56
	17	4	F. J. Eagar, † - - - -	Offg. Intr. H. M 5th Foot. ..	3 *Mar.* 42	24 *Jan.* 45	.. ..	16 *June* 56
O.	16	6	R. P. Anderson, *PC*, [2]*m*	Fur. S. C. 12 Jan. 58	28 *Dec.* 42	13 *Jan.* 49	.. ..	23 *Nov.* 56
	15	1	H. N. Davies, *PCH*, - -	.. ..	8 *June* 44	9 *Sep.* 53	.. ..	27 *June* 57
O.	12	1	Addington Taylor, † - -	Fur. S. C. 5 Nov. 57	11 *June* 47	15 *Nov.* 53	.. ..	17 *Oct.* 57
			LIEUTENANTS.					
	7	10	E. J. L. Twynam, *PH*, (*a*) -	Dept. of P. W. Arracan Division,	20 *Aug.* 51	2 *May* 54		
	6	9	Walter Foggo Ireland, † -	Baghalcund Mily. Police,	27 *Sep.* 52	7 *May* 54		
N.	5	8	Donald Macdonald, *PH*, -	Fur. S C 10 May 59	20 *Oct.* 53	18 *Jan.* 56		
N.	5	7	William Macdonald, † - -	Fur. S. C. 16 July 58	10 *Dec.* 53	5 *Mar.* 56		
	5	6	Henry Doyle Metcalfe, † -	Offg. Intr. H. M. 20th Foot. ..	4 *Jan.* 54	31 *Mar.* 56		
	5	5	Philip Ward, † - - - -	.. ..	5 *Feb.* 54	16 *June* 56		
N.	4	4	Chs. Augustus Munro, *PH*,	Fur. S.C. 17 Feb. 58	17 *Mar.* 55	23 *Nov.* 56		
N.	3	4	H. P. P Nash, † - - -	Fur. S.C. 5 Mar. 58	4 *Mar.* 56	23 *Nov.* 56		
	3	2	Edward Temple, † - - -	Bhopal Levy, ..	15 *May* 56	17 *Dec.* 56		
	2	5	C. H. Ewart, † - - - -	.. ..	20 *Feb.* 57	30 *Apl.* 58		
	2	1	S. Beckett, † - - - -	Leave S. C. 15 Nov.	13 *June* 57	18 *May* 58		
			ENSIGNS.					
	1	7	G. S. Byng, - - - -	.. ..	12 *Dec.* 57			
			*					
			*					
			*					
			*		*Appointed.*			
..	..		*Adjutant*, D. Macdonald, -	Fur. S C 10 May 59	20 *Feb.* 58			
..	..		*Inter.*, *					
..	..		*Surg.*, J. Hilliard, M.D. F. R. C. S. L., ..	.. ..	19 *Feb.* 58			
..	..		*Asst. Surg.*, T. J. Duthoit, M. B., - - - - -	.. ..	13 *Sep.* 55			

(*a*) Has furnished the certificates of qualification in Surveying and Civil Engineering.

Raised in 1797.

26th Regiment of Native (Light) Infantry.

Disarmed, Lahore, (Meean Meer.)

(Rifle Company.)

"Arracan"—"Caubul 1842"—"Moodkee"—"Ferozeshuhur"—"Subraon."

Poel-ka-Pultun. Late 1st Battalion 13th Regt. N.I.

Facings—*Red.*

Fur. Reg.	Ser. Y	Ser. M	
	64	9	*Col. Sir* William Richards, K. C. B. *Ens.* 26 Sept. 1794; *Lieut.* 8 Jan. 1796; *Capt.* 21 Sept. 1804; *Major* 7 Aug. 1814; *Lieut. Col.* 3 Sept. 1818; *Col.* 1 May 1824; *Major Genl.* 10 Jan. 1837; *Lieut. Genl.* 9 Nov. 1846; *Genl.* 20 June 1854.—In India.
O.	34	5	*Lieut. Col.* John Lewis Taylor. *Ens.* 23 Jan. 1825; *Lieut.* 26 Dec. 1826; *Capt.* 12 Jan. 1837; *Bt. Maj.* 3 Apl. 1846; *Maj.* 18 June 1850; *Bt. Lt. Col.* 20 June 54; *Lt. Col.* 10 Feb. 1856; *Bt. Colonel* 14 Mar. 1857.—Fur. S. C. 13 Feb. 1857.
O.	28	11	*Major* J. G. Gaitskell. *Ens.* 7 Aug. 1830; *Lt.* 1 Jan. 1837; *Capt.* 24 Jan. 1845; *Bt. Major* 28 Nov. 1854; *Maj.* 27 Aug. 1857.—Fur. S.C. 4 Feb. 1856.

☞ *Brevet.* [1] Major 24 Mar. 1858. [2] Major 19 Jan. 1858.

Fur. Reg.	Y	M	Captains.	Remarks.	Ensign.	Lieut.	Captain. B.	Captain. Regl.
N.	23	6	T. C. Blagrave,† - - -	Furlough S. C. 4 Sep. 1858. ..	3 *Jan.* 36	3 *Oct.* 40	.. ..	1 *Apl.* 50
	20	6	F. W. Baugh,†-[1]*m* - -	Supt. Kemaoon Elephant Keddahs,..	13 *Jan.* 39	3 *Nov.* 41	.. ..	18 *June* 50
	19	7	J. M. Cripps,*P*, - - -	Civil employ. ..	11 *Dec.* 39	16 *July* 42	.. ..	1 *Sep.* 50
O.	19	..	François Mackenzie,*PH*, -	Fur. S. C. 5 Feb. 58	8 *July* 40	8 *Feb.* 43	8 *July* 55	10 *Feb.* 56
	18	1	G. W. M. Hall,*PH*,[2]*m* -	4th Irregular Cavy.	12 *June* 41	22 *Nov.* 43	12 *June* 56	23 *Nov.* 56
	16	9	J. Emerson,*PH*, - - -	Cant. Joint Magte. Dinapore, ..	24 *Sep.* 42	10 *June* 45	.. ..	30 *July* 57
O.	16	1	D. Mocatta,*P*, - - -	Fur. S.C. 20 Nov. 58	9 *June* 43	21 *Dec.* 45	.. ..	27 *Aug.* 57
			Lieutenants.					
	16	4	J. Baillie,*P*, - - -	D. P. W. N. W. P.	25 *Feb.* 43	1 *Dec.* 46	25 *Feb.* 58	
	14	7	M. J. White,*PCH*,(*a*) -	11th Punjaub Infy.	10 *Dec.* 44	7 *June* 47		
O.	14	5	J. Hind,† - - - -	Fur. P.A. 29 Mar. 59	20 *Jan.* 45	1 *May* 49		
N.	13	10	G. A. Williams,*PH*, - -	4th Seikh Local Infy.	23 *Aug.* 45	1 *Apl.* 50		
N.	10	7	J. P. Turton,*PH*, - - -	Fur. S. C. 9 Feb. 57	9 *Dec.* 48	10 *Feb.* 56		
	10	1	H. E. Whish,*P-TC*,(*b*) -	Canal Dept. N.W.P.,	9 *June* 49	23 *Nov.* 56		
	9	6	A. W. Cripps,*P*,(*a*) - -	17th Punjaub Infy.	26 *Dec.* 49	23 *Nov.* 56		
	5	6	Robert Durie Osborn,† -	2nd Sikh Irr. Cavy.	20 *Dec.* 53	30 *July* 57		
	5	1	Hanson C. Taylor Jarrett,†	20th Punjaub Infy.	10 *June* 54	27 *Aug.* 57		
	3	6	T. H. Scott, *PH*, - - -	13th Punjaub Infy.	20 *Jan.* 56	30 *Apl.* 58		
	2	..	W. L. Dickens, - - -	.. ..	20 *July.* 57	18 *May* 58		
			Ensigns.					
	1	6	W. R. Birney, - - -	.. ..	20 *Jan.* 58			
			*					
			*					
			*					
			*		*Appointed.*			
	..	..	*Adjutant*,					
	..	..	*Interpreter*,					
	..	..	*Surg.*,*					
	..	..	*Asst. Surg.*, A.P. Tomkyns,	.. ..	7 *June* 56			

This Corps was made Light Infantry for its services in Affghanistan under Genl. Pollock.

(*a*) Have attained a degree of proficiency in the Punjaubee language.

(*b*) Has furnished certificates of qualification in Civil Engineering and Surveying.

Raised in 1797.

27th Regiment of Native Infantry.

Disarmed; Peshawur.

Martdeel-ka-Pultun. Late 2nd Battalion 13th Regt. N.I.

FACINGS.—*Red.*

Fur. Reg.	SER. Y	SER. M	
O.	51	10	*Colonel* William Henry Hewitt. *Ens.* 4 Sep. 1807; *Lieut.* 23 Sep. 1812; *Bt. Capt.* 4 Sep. 1822; *Capt.* 23 May 1823; *Major* 13 April 1830; *Lieut. Col.* 11 Nov. 1835; *Bt. Col.* 9 Nov. 1846; *Col.* 11 March 1847; *Maj. Genl.* 20 June 1854.—Fur. S. C. 1 April 1858.
	36	..	*Lt. Col.* E. John Dickey. *Ens.* 11 July 23; *Lt.* 17 Aug. 24; *Capt.* 16 June 35; *Bt. Maj.* 9 Nov. 46; *Maj.* 27 Oct. 48; *Lt. Col.* 15 April 54; *Bt. Col.* 28 Nov. 1854.—Supdt. of Studs.
	31	2	*Major* R. S. Simpson, *P.* *Ens.* 1 May 1828; *Lieut.* 7 Feb. 1833; *Bt. Capt.* 1 May 1843; *Capt.* 24 Jan. 1845; *Bt. Maj.* 20 June 1854; *Major* 11 Nov. 1856.—Army Commt. Dept.

Fur. Reg.	Y	M	CAPTAINS.	REMARKS.	*Ensign.*	*Lieut.*	CAPTAIN. *Brevet.*	CAPTAIN. *Regl.*
	24	5	C. Harris, *P,*	Offg. Comdt. Bijnore Rajpoot Levy.	9 *Feb.* 35	8 *Oct.* 39	.. ..	3 *May* 47
	18	5	W. Forbes,†	Army Commt. Dept.	25 *Jan.* 41	16 *July* 42	.. ..	5 *July* 49
	19	11	T. W. Seager,†	.. ..	28 *July* 39	12 *Nov.* 42	.. ..	18 *Apl.* 51
	16	11	E. G. Langmore, *P,*	Offg. Barrack Master at Rawul Pindee, Murree & Campbellpore,	28 *July* 42	31 *Dec.* 45	.. ..	23 *Nov.* 56
	16	1	G. W. Fraser, *PH,*	14th Punjaub Infy.	9 *June* 43	3 *Nov.* 46	.. ..	23 *Sep.* 57
	16	..	N. E. Boileau, *PC,*		5 *July* 43	3 *May* 47		26 *May* 58
	15	1	E. Hyndman, *PH,*		7 *June* 44	10 *Aug.* 47		21 *Aug.* 58
			LIEUTENANTS.					
	13	9	~~E. K. O. Gilbert, *PH,(a)*~~	Offg. Brigade Staff,	20 *Sep.* 45	3 *Nov.* 48		
	12	1	J. M. Graham, *PC,*	Commdt. 5th Bengal Police Battn. ..	11 *June* 47	18 *Apl.* 51		
	11	7	~~H. B. Chalmers, *P,*~~	Army Comt. Dept.	11 *Dec.* 47	15 *Nov.* 53		
O.	11	2	H. A. W. Waterfield, *PH,*	On duty at Meanmeer. ..	10 *May* 48	28 *Sep.* 54		
	11	1	G. H. Basevi, *PH,(a)*	Fur. S.C. 26 Feb. 58,	9 *June* 48	11 *Nov.* 56		
	10	7	D. S. Buist, *PH,*	Sylhet Light Infy. Battalion, ..	20 *Dec.* 48	23 *Nov.* 56		
	5	3	John Withers McQueen,†	4th Punjaub Infy.	4 *Apl.* 54	4 *June* 57		
	4	1	James Miller,†	.. ..	8 *June* 55	23 *Sep.* 57		
	2	5	J. R. Pearson,	3rd Irr. Cavy.	20 *Feb.* 57	30 *Apl.* 58		
	1	8	N. M. T. Horsford,†	.. ..	20 *Nov.* 57	26 *May.* 58		
	1	4	A. Andrew,	Fur. S. C. 4 Sep. 58	4 *Mar.* 58	21 *Aug.* 58		
			ENSIGNS.					
	..	11	H. H. Birch,	.. ..	4 *Aug.* 58			
	..	6	D. Darroch,	.. ..	20 *Jan.* 59			
			*					
			*					
			*		*Appointed.*			
	..	..	*Adjutant,* E. Hyndman,	Officiating, ..	6 *Mar.* 58			
	..	..	*Intr.* *					
	..	..	*Surg.,**					
	..	..	*Asst. Surg,*	.. ..				

(*a*) Have furnished certificates of qualification in Surveying and Civil Engineering.

Raised in 1797.

28th Regiment of Native Infantry.

Mutinied, Shahjehanpore.

" DEHLEE."—*The Lt. Co.* " ARRACAN."

Stupper-ka-Pultun. Late 1st Battalion 14th Regt. N.I.

FACINGS—*Dark-green.*

Fur. Reg.	Ser. Y	Ser. M	
	55	6	*Colonel* George William Aylmer Lloyd, C. B. *Ens.* 1 Jan. 1804; *Lieut.* 17 Sept. 1806; *Bt Capt.* 1 Jan. 1819; *Capt.* 13 May 1825; *Major* 3 June 1830; *Lieut. Col.* 7 Jan. 1836. *Bt. Col.* 9 Nov. 1846; *Col.* 27 Aug. 1847; *Maj. Genl.* 20 June 1854.—Residing in the Dinapore Division.
	..	..	*Lieut. Col.**
	35	..	*Major* J. DeW. C. J. Moir. *Ens.* 21 June 1824; *Lt.* 28 Aug. 1826; *Bt. Capt.* 21 June 1839; *Capt.* 24 Jan. 1845; *Bt Maj.* 11 Nov. 1851; *Maj.* 27 June 1857; *Bt. Lt. Col.* 20 July 1858. ☞ [1] Maj. 2 May 52.

Fur. Reg.	Ser. Y	Ser. M	CAPTAINS.	REMARKS.	*Ensign.*	*Lieut.*	CAPTAIN. *Brevet.*	CAPTAIN. *Regl.*
	21	7	C. T. Chamberlain, *P*, [1]*m* -	1st Irregular Cavy.	12 *Dec.* 37	26 *Mar.* 40	.. ..	1 *May* 52
	14	6	C. E. Mills, *P*, - - - -	Brigade Staff. ..	18 *Jan.* 45	17 *Apl.* 52	.. ..	31 *May* 57
	14	5	W. Paske, *PH*, - - - -	Civil employ, ..	11 *Feb.* 45	1 *May* 52	.. ..	4 *June* 57
	7	7	G. A. Graham, *PH*, - -	Punjaub Irr. Force,	13 *Dec.* 51	19 *Oct.* 54	.. ..	10 *June* 57
	7	6	H. W. Chapman, *PCH*, -	Bareily Infy. Levy.	20 *Dec.* 51	20 *Dec.* 54	.. ..	10 *June* 57
	7	5	H. L. Millett, *PH*, - -	Punjaub Irr. Force,	20 *Jan.* 52	21 *July* 56	.. .	27 *June* 57
O.	19	1	J. A. Wright, *P.H* - -	Fur. S.C. 16 June 57	12 *June* 40	24 *Jan.* 45	12 *June* 55	30 *Apl.* 58
			LIEUTENANTS.					
	15	7	G. C. Hankin, *P (a)* -	6th Irregular Cavy.	8 *Dec.* 43	13 *Nov.* 45	8 *Dec.* 58	
R	~~16~~	~~6~~	~~R. W. Gibbs, *P.H.*~~, - -	.. ..	28 *Dec.* 42	6 *June* 45	28 *Dec.* 57	
N.	13	1	W. Smith, *P. H.*, - - -	Cantt. Joint Magte. and Supdt. of the Cant. Abkarry Mehal, Agra. Fur. S.C. 18 Feb. 59..	12 *June* 46	10 *Apl.* 49		
	13	7	Baron F. Von. Andlau, *PH.*	Kemaoon Battalion,	13 *Dec.* 45	18 *June* 50		
	9	7	T. Buttanshaw, *P. H.*, -	.. ..	12 *Dec.* 49	3 *Nov.* 52		
	9	5	S. W. Fraser.† - - - -	.. ..	16 *Feb.* 50	30 *Dec.* 54		
O.	5	7	John S. Walters, - - -	Fur. S. C. 2 Aug. 58	9 *Dec.* 53	14 *Sep.* 56		
	6	8	A. Bruce,† - - - -	Sikh Police Regt. ..	20 *Oct.* 52	23 *Nov.* 56		
	2	5	H. R. Wintle, - - - -	.. ..	20 *Feb.* 57	30 *Apl.* 58		
	2	1	T. A. Scott,† - - - -	Adjt. district police, Oude, ..	13 *June* 57	18 *May* 58		
	1	7	W. H. Brind, - - - -	.. ..	12 *Dec.* 57	22 *Oct.* 58		
			ENSIGNS.					
	..	9	W. E. Rutherfurd, - -	.. ..	4 *Oct.* 58			
			*					
			*					
			*					
			*					
	..	..	*Adjutant,*		*Appointed.*			
	..	..	*Intr.,**					
	..	..	*Surgeon,**					
	..	..	*Asst. Surg.,**					

N. B.—This Regiment has an honorary standard and extra Jemadar for Allygurh and Delhi. On the Standard are inscribed the words " Lake and Victory."

(*a*) Passed an examination in the Punjaubee language.

Raised in 1797. | **29th Regiment of Native Infantry.** | Mutinied, Moradabad.

"DEHLEE"—"PUNJAUB."

Cullenjun-ka-Pultun. Late 2nd Battalion 14th Regt. N.I.

FACINGS—*Dark-green.*

Fur. Reg.	Ser. Y	Ser. M	
	53	7	*Colonel* Matthew Coombs Paul. *Ens.* 23 Nov. 1805; *Lieut.* 23 Feb. 1807; *Capt.* 9 Oct. 1818; *Major* 11 April 1828; *Lieut. Col.* 15 Sept. 1833; *Col.* 2 Feb. 1845; *Maj. Genl.* 20 June 1854.—Europe, 22 Feb. 1844.
	40	..	*Lt. Col.* Joseph Graham. *Ens.* 20 July 1819; *Lieut.* 1 Dec. 1820; *Capt.* 12 Dec. 1833; *Bt. Major* 9 Nov. 1846; *Maj.* 4 Jan. 49; *Bt. Lt. Col.* 20 June 54; *Lt. Col.* 9 Aug. 1854; *Bt. Col.* 27 Aug. 1858.—Leave P. A. 15 Oct.
	33	2	(*a*) *Major* G. W. Williams, *P. Ens.* 15 May 1826; *Lieut.* 21 Aug. 1832; *Bt. Capt.* 15 May 1841; *Capt.* 24 Jan. 1845; *Bt. Maj.* 20 June 1854; *Maj.* 15 June 57.—Civil employ. ☞ *Brevet.* [1] Major 20 June 54.

Fur. Reg.	Y	M	CAPTAINS.	REMARKS.	*Ensign.*	*Lieut.*	CAPTAIN. *Brevet.*	CAPTAIN. *Regl.*
	33	3	G. B. Reddie, *P*, [1] *m* - -	Army Comt. Dept.	15 *Apl.* 26	24 *Apl.* 33	15 *Apl.* 41	6 *Dec.* 45
	22	1	M. B. Whish, † - - - -	.. ..	13 *June* 37	14 *Feb.* 40	.. ..	15 *Mar.* 51
	21	7	C. S. J. Terrot, *P*, - - -	.. ..	11 *Dec.* 37	3 *Oct.* 40	11 *Dec.* 52	27 *Aug.* 53
	21	4	L. P. Faddy, † - - - -	Civil employ, ..	1 *Mar.* 38	5 *Sep.* 41	1 *Mar.* 53	3 *July* 54
	20	6	W. Agnew, *PCH*, (*b*) - -	Civil employ,	14 *Jan.* 39	16 *July* 42	14 *Jan.* 54	9 *Mar.* 55
	19	10	H. M. Davidson, † - -	.. ..	21 *Aug.* 39	22 *Dec.* 44	21 *Aug.* 54	23 *Nov.* 56
	18	9	P. F. Gardiner, *PH*, - -	10th Punjaub Infy.,	27 *Sep.* 40	24 *Jan.* 45	27 *Sep.* 55	15 *June* 57
			LIEUTENANTS.					
R	~~18~~	~~2~~	~~E. G. Thellusson, †~~ (*c*) - -	.. ..	21 *Apl.* 41	29 *Mar.* 46	12 *June* 56	
O.	17	1	F. R. Thomson, † - - -	Fur. S.C. 19 Oct. 58	11 *June* 42	7 *Apl.* 46	11 *June* 57	
	15	5	J. Lamb, † - - - - -	Fur. P.A. 16 May 59	3 *Feb.* 44	1 *Oct.* 49	3 *Feb.* 59	
N.	14	6	J. C. Millar, *PH*, - -	Fur. S.C. 5 Nov. 58	29 *Dec.* 44	10 *Nov.* 50		
N.	14	1	J. B. Smyly, *P*, (*d*) - -	Civil employ,	14 *June* 45	15 *Mar.* 51		
	11	7	G. Wheeler, *PH*, - - -	Cant. Jt. Magte and Supdt. of the Cantt. Abkarry Mehal, Jhansie..	11 *Dec.* 47	3 *July* 54		
	8	6	C. E. Orman, *PH*, - -	Cant. Jt. Magte and Supdt. of the Cantt. Abkarry Mehal, Roorkee,	11 *Jan.* 51	14 *Jan.* 56		
N	4	5	Henry St. George Tucker, -	Fur. S. C. 5 Feb. 58	4 *Feb.* 55	23 *Nov.* 56		
	4	4	George Lewellin Smith, † -	Adjt. district police, Shahjehanpore, ..	5 *Mar.* 55	23 *Nov.* 56		
	3	1	Edward C. Garstin, † - -	Leave, to 1 Nov. ..	13 *June* 56	30 *Apl.* 58		
	2	7	C. J. Garstin, † - - - -	.. ..	20 *Dec.* 56	30 *Apl.* 58		
			ENSIGNS.					
	..	10	H. A. McNair, - - - -	.. ..	20 *Sep.* 58			
			*					
			*					
			*					
			*		*Appointed.*			
	..	..	*Adjutant,**					
	..	..	*Intr.**					
	..	..	*Surg.,**					
	..	..	*Asst. Surg.**					

(*a*) Official Lieutenant Colonel.
(*b*) Passed a successful examination in the Assamese and Bengallee languages.
(*c*) Has furnished certificate of qualification in Surveying and Civil Engineering.
(*d*) Attained the standard of proficiency in the Punjaubee language prescribed by G. O. G. G. 14th Oct. 1851

Raised in 1798.

30th Regiment of Native Infantry.

Mutinied, Nusseerabad.

"DEHLEE"—"LASWARRIE"—"DEIG"—"CABOOL 1842"—"ALLIWAL"—"PUNJAUB" —"CHILLIANWALLA"—"GOOJERAT."

For services under Lord Lake this Regiment has on its Colours "an Embroidered Star," and the words "Lake and Victory."

Mucdoon-ka-Pultun. Late 1st Battalion 15th Regt. N.I.

FACINGS—*Buff.*

Fur. Reg.	Ser. Y	Ser. M	
	53	10	*Col* Duncan Gordon Scott. *Ens.* 10 Sep. 05; *Lt.* 19 Dec. 05; *Capt.* 11 July 23; *Maj.* 7 Dec. 27; *Lt. Col.* 29 Oct. 32; *Col.* 7 May 44; *Maj. Genl.* 20 June 54; *Lieut. Genl.* 23 July 58. —Europe, 13 Dec. 1844.
	34	7	*Lt. Col.* William Charles Campbell. *Ens.* 7 Dec. 24; *Lt.* 27 Dec. 25; *Capt.* 13 Oct. 39; *Bt. Maj.* 2 Aug. 50; *Maj.* 11 Dec. 51; *Bt. Lt. Col.* 28 Nov. 54; *Lieut. Col.* 11 May 57. —Leave P. A. 15 Oct.
	32	8	*Major* R. S. Ewart, *Ens.* 14 Nov. 26; *Lieut.* 24 Apl. 32; *Bt. Capt.* 14 Nov. 41; *Capt.* 1 Feb. 44; *Bt. Major* 20 June 54; *Major* 9 June 58; *Bt. Lieut. Col.* 19 Jan. 58.

☞ *Brevet.* [1] Major 28 Nov. 1854. [2] Maj. 24 Mar. 1858.

Fur. Reg.	Ser. Y	Ser. M	CAPTAINS.	REMARKS.	*Ensign.*	*Lieut.*	CAPTAIN. *Brevet.*	CAPTAIN. *Regl.*
	29	5	J. Morrieson, *P*, [1]*m*	.. ..	5 *Feb.* 30	2 *Dec.* 38	5 *Feb.* 45	19 *Jan.* 46
	24	5	C. F. Fenwick, †	Lv. S. C. 15 Oct.	21 *Jan.* 35	13 *Oct.* 39	.. ..	26 *Dec.* 46
	21	..	D. S. Dodgson, *P*, [2]*m*	Dep. Asst. Adjt. Genl. Sirhind Division,	22 *June* 38	3 *Oct.* 40	.. ..	13 *Jan.* 49
	18	10	W. D. Bishop, *P*,	Cant. Jt. Magte. and Supt. of the Cant. Abkarry Mehal, Futtehgurh. ..	31 *Aug.* 40	3 *Nov.* 43	31 *Aug.* 55	8 *Apl.* 56
	17	1	S. Sage, †	Futtehgurh Infy. Levy. ..	11 *June* 42	1 *Feb.* 44	.. ..	23 *Nov.* 56
	16	11	H. Swinhoe, †	.. ..	4 *Aug.* 42	24 *Jan.* 45	.. ..	11 *May* 57
	16	..	G. F. F. Vincent, *P*, *(a)*	Offg. Intr. H. M. 99th Foot. ..	21 *June* 43	1 *Oct.* 46	.. ..	9 *June* 58
			LIEUTENANTS.					
	14	9	T. Pierce, *PC*,	Civil employ, ..	8 *Oct.* 44	13 *Jan.* 49		
	13	7	J. C. Wood, *P*,	Civil employ,	12 *Dec.* 45	11 *Dec.* 51		
N.	11	7	W. F. Leicester, *PH*, *(b)*	3rd Sikh Infy. ..	11 *Dec.* 47	15 *Nov.* 53		
N.	11	1	B. W. D. Morton, *P*, *(c)*	Civil employ, ..	9 *June* 48	1 *Sep.* 55		
	8	11	H. S. V. Fisher, *PCH*,	Civil employ, ..	28 *July* 50	13 *Oct.* 55		
	6	1	H. L. Hawkins, †	Adjt. Mayne's Irr. Horse. ..	11 *June* 53	8 *Apl.* 56		
	5	..	G. Fredk. M. Phillips, *PH*,	Mhairwarrah Battn.	15 *July* 54	23 *Nov.* 56		
N.	4	1	Alfred F. P. Harcourt,	Fur. S. C. 15 Oct. 58	8 *June* 55	23 *Nov.* 56		
D	~~4~~	~~1~~	~~Jonathan Cape,~~	.. ..	21 *June* 55	11 *May* 57		
	3	11	Fredk Henry Hood, *(d)*	1st Regt. Gwalior Infy	20 *Aug.* 55	17 *Nov.* 57		
	2	1	C. A. Copland, †	.. ..	13 *June* 57	18 *May* 58		
	..	7	F. W. Collis,	.. ..	10 *Dec.* 58	29 *Mar.* 59		
			ENSIGNS.					
	..	7	H. Woodhouse,	.. ..	11 *Dec.* 58			
			*					
			*					
			*		*Appointed.*			
			*					
	..	..	*Adjutant*, *					
	..	..	*Interpreter*, *					
	..	..	*Surgeon*, C. G. Andrews,	Fur. S.C. 19 Nov. 58	22 *Sep.* 56			
	..	..	*Asst. Surg.* *					

N. B.—This Regiment has an honorary standard and extra Jemadar for Allygurh and Delhi.

(a) Passed successful examinations in the Assamese and Bengallee languages.

(b) Passed an examination in Field Engineering. *(c)* Has passed an examination in the Bengali language.

(d) Received a Certificate as Assistant Instructor of Musketry from the Royal School of Musketry at Hythe on the 7th Aug. 1855, and a first class certificate from the Umballah School of Musketry.

Raised in 1798. | Calpee.

31st Regiment of Native (Light) Infantry.

(*Rifle Company.*)

"DEHLEE"—"LASWARRIE"—"DEIG"—"BHURTPORE"—"KHELAT"—"AFFGHANISTAN"—"MAHARAJPORE"—"PUNJAUB"—"CHILLIANWALLA"—"GOOJERAT."

For services under Lord Lake this Regt. has on its Colours "an Embroidered Star," and the words "Lake and Victory."

Broon-ka-Pultun. Late 2nd Battalion 15th Regt. N.I.

FACINGS—*Buff.*

Fur. Reg.	Ser. Y	Ser. M	
N	53	3	*Col.* Frederick Geo. Lister. *Ens.* 27 Mar. 1806; *Lt.* 9 Oct. 1808; *Bt. Capt.* 27 Mar. 21; *Capt.* 16 March 1824; *Bt. Major* 10 Jan. 1837; *Maj.* 4 Sept. 1839; *Lt. Col.* 30 Sept. 45; *Bt. Col.* 20 June 1854; *Col.* 13 Apl. 55; *Major Genl.* 22 Aug. 1857.—Fur. S. C. 12 Apl. 1854.
O	38	6	*Lieut. Col.* Bulstrode Bygrave. *Ens.* 16 Jan. 1821; *Lieut.* 23 July 1823; *Bt. Capt.* 16 Jan. 1836; *Capt.* 4 May 1837; *Bt. Major* 9 Nov. 1846; *Major* 8 July 1848; *Lieut. Col.* 15 Nov. 1853; *Bt. Col.* 28 Nov. 1854.—Fur. P. A. 18 April 1859.
	31	4	*Major* W. P. Hampton.† *Ens.* 3 March 1828; *Lieut.* 8 May 1834; *Bt. Capt.* 3 March 1843; *Capt.* 24 Jan. 1845; *Bt. Maj.* 20 June 1854; *Major* 28 Nov. 1856.

☞ *Brevet.* [1] Maj. 20 June 54. [2] Maj. 28 Nov. 54. [3] Maj. 28 Nov. 54.

Fur. Reg.	Y	M	CAPTAINS.	REMARKS.	*Ensign.*	*Lieut.*	CAPTAIN. *Brevet.*	CAPTAIN. *Regl.*
	30	1	W. B. Legard,[1]*m* - - -	.. ..	18 *June* 28	1 *June* 34	18 *June* 43	2 *Feb.* 45
	30	6	G. Newbolt,*PC*,[2]*m* -	Auditor Comt. and Stud Accts., ..	7 *Jan.* 29	15 *Feb.* 36	7 *Jan.* 44	10 *Feb.* 47
	30	1	S. R. Tickell,*PC*,[3]*m* -	Civil employ,	12 *June* 29	4 *Aug.* 36	12 *June* 44	25 *Dec.* 47
N.	23	7	H. C. Roberts,† - - -	Fur. S. C. 1 Feb. 59	11 *Dec.* 35	3 *Oct.* 40	11 *Dec.* 50	27 *July* 51
	~~30~~	~~5~~	~~T. H. Smalpage,†~~ - - -	.. ..	24 *Jan.* 39	3 *Apl.* 44	24 *Jan.* 54	23 *Nov.* 56
N.	18	11	H. Finch,*P*, - - -	Fur. S. C. 24 Jan. 59	19 *Aug.* 40	24 *Jan.* 45	19 *Aug.* 55	28 *Nov.* 56
	16	7	W. Davis, *P,H*, - -	Divl. Comdt. Jhansie,	9 *Dec.* 42	12 *Mar.* 46	.. ..	6 *June* 57
			LIEUTENANTS.					
	16	..	C. M. FitzGerald,*P*, -	Army Commt. Dept.	20 *June* 43	17 *Aug.* 46	20 *June* 58	
O.	15	10	R. H. Price,*PH*, - -	Fur. S .C. 14 Feb. 57	1 *Sep.* 43	10 *Feb.* 47	1 *Sep.* 58	
	15	4	H. W. Norman,*PH*,(*a*)	Adjt. Genl.'s Dept.,	1 *Mar.* 44	25 *Dec.* 47	1 *Mar* 59	
	14	6	A. Ellis,*P*, - - - -	Lv. S. C. 15 Nov. ..	29 *Dec.* 44	31 *Mar.* 51		
	13	7	F. A. Dickins,*P*,(*b*) -	Civil employ, ..	12 *Dec.* 45	21 *May* 51		
	9	9	T. N. Baker,† - - -	.. ..	20 *Sep.* 49	23 *Nov.* 56		
	8	6	H. Fellowes,*P.C.H.* -	.. ..	11 *Jan.* 51	23 *Nov.* 56		
O.	8	5	F. H. M. Sitwell,*PH*, -	Fu.r S. C. 2 Feb. 58	20 *Jan.* 51	28 *Nov.* 56		
O.	8	5	A. E. Campbell,† - -	Fur. S. C. 6 Jan. 59	20 *Jan.* 51	6 *June* 57		
	2	7	J. J. Blair,†- - - -	.. ..	13 *Dec.* 56	30 *Apl.* 58		
	2	1	T H. Lewin,† - - -	.. ..	12 *June* 57	18 *May* 58		
			ENSIGNS.					
	1	8	H. T. Jones, - - -	Fur. S. C. 8 May 58	20 *Nov.* 7			
	..	6	H. R. Young, - - -	.. ..	20 *Jan.* 59			
			*					
			*					
			*		*Appointed*			
	..	..	*Adjutant* H. Fellowes, -	.. ..	31 *July* 57			
	..	..	*Interpreter*, A. Ellis, -	Leave S. C. 15 Nov.	11 *Mar* 53			
	..	..	*Surg.*, E. B. Thring, -	Fur. S.C. 1 Feb. 59	8 *Dec.* 55			
	..	..	*Asst. Surg.*, E. Tayler, -	.. ..	28 *Mar.* 59			

N. B.—This Regiment has an honorary standard and extra Jemadar for Allygurh and Delhi.

(*a*) Official Major.

(*b*) Passed an examination in the Punjaubee language. Attained the standard of proficiency in Hindee 7 July 1856, and in Oordoo 10 Jan. 1857, Received the reward of 1000 Rupees for proficiency in the Native languages.

Raised in 1798.

32nd Regiment of Native Infantry.

"BHURTPORE."

Disarmed, Barrackpore

Guthrie-ka-Pultun. Late 1st Battalion 16th Regt. N. I.

FACINGS—*Black Velvet.*

Fur. Reg.	Ser. Y	Ser. M	
	47	11	*Colonel* William Henry Marshall. *Ens.* 16 Aug. 1811; *Lieut.* 1 Sep. 1816; *Capt.* 10 Oct. 1825; *Major* 2 April 1834; *Lieut. Col.* 4 Jan. 1841; *Col.* 15 Mar. 1851; *Maj. Genl.* 28 Nov. 1854.—Fur. S. C. 21 Feb. 52.
	31	2	*Lieut. Col.* Richard Y. B. Bush. *Ens.* 19 May 1828; *Lieut.* 18 Aug. 1834; *Capt.* 1 Feb. 1841; *Major* 12 Jan. 1853; *Lieut. Col.* 15 July 1857.—Fur. S. C. 10 Dec. 58.
	~~35~~	~~6~~	~~*Major* A. R. J. Swinton.~~ *Ens.* 16 Jan. 1824; *Lieut.* 9 July 1825; *Bt. Capt.* 16 Jan. 1839; *Capt.* 28 Oct. 39; *Bt. Maj.* 11 Nov. 1851; *Maj.* 2 Apl. 1856; *Bt. Lt. Col.* 15 Oct. 1857.

☞ *Brevet.* [1] Maj. 20 June 54. [2] Maj. 28 Nov. 54. [3] Maj. 10 Aug. 50. Lt. Col. 28 Nov. 54. Col. 28 Nov. 1857.

Fur. Reg.	Y	M		REMARKS.	*Ensign.*	*Lieut.*	CAPTAIN. *Brevet.*	CAPTAIN. *Regl.*
			CAPTAINS.					
	31	..	W. W. Davidson, *PH*,[1]*m*	16th Irregular Cavy.	19 *July* 28	3 *Apl.* 35	19 *July* 43	1 *Jan.* 49
O.	30	5	T. S. Horsbrugh, *PH*,[2]*m*	Fur. S.C. 11 May 58	17 *Feb.* 29	19 *Sep.* 36	17 *Feb.* 44	9 *Apl.* 49
O.	24	1	H. C. James, *PC*,	Fur. S.C. 16 Mar. 58	12 *June* 35	18 *July* 37	.. ..	16 *Aug.* 49
	22	1	Orfeur Cavenagh, *PC*,[3]*c*	.. ..	12 *June* 37	13 *Jan.* 42	.. ..	10 *Aug.* 50
	22	1	E. Close,†	.. ..	13 *June* 37	16 *July* 42	13 *June* 52	2 *Apl.* 56
	16	10	C. Reay, *P*,	Cantt. Jt. Magte. and Supdt. of Abkarry, Raneegunge,	9 *Sep.* 42	1 *Jan.* 49	9 *Sep.* 57	17 *Oct.* 57
	15	6	J. C. Bonamy, *P*,	.. ..	1 *Jan.* 44	16 *Aug.* 49	.. ..	21 *Nov.* 57
			LIEUTENANTS.					
	13	5	H. L. Gleig,†	.. ..	26 *Jan.* 46	10 *Aug.* 50		
	13	11	W. O. Rannie,†	.. ..	20 *July* 45	17 *Oct.* 55		
O.	12	..	G. E. Hill,†	Fur. S. C. 4 May 58	26 *June* 47	2 *Apl.* 56		
	9	5	R. A. Nowell, *PH*,	.. ..	20 *Jan.* 50	23 *Nov.* 56		
N.	4	9	Henry Wm. Studdy, *PH*,	Fur. S. C. 31 Aug. 58	12 *Oct.* 54	11 *May* 57		
	3	11	Robert Blair,†	Alexander's Horse.	7 *Aug.* 55	16 *July* 57		
	2	7	G. B. Fisher,†	Lv. S. C. 14 Oct. ..	20 *Dec.* 56	2 *Aug.* 57		
	4	7	F. D. Hawkins,†	Adjt. Mily. Police, Oudh, ..	10 *Dec.* 54	6 *June* 57		
	4	4	R. C. Money,	.. ..	20 *Mar.* 55	12 *Feb.* 58		
	2	2	P. H. M. Wynter,†	Regt. of Ferozepore,	4 *May* 57	18 *May* 58		
	1	9	C. R. Pennington,	.. ..	4 *Oct.* 57	18 *May* 58		
			ENSIGNS.					
	..	10	A. B. Hepburn.	.. ..	4 *Sep.* 58			
	..	6	A. J. D. Hawes,	.. ...	6 *Jan.* 59			
			*					
			*					
			*					
					Appointed.			
	..	..	*Adjt.* R. A. Nowell,	.. ..	6 *Dec.* 55			
	..	..	*Intr.*,*					
	..	..	*Surgeon*, H. N. Elton,	.. ..	4 *Apl.* 58			
	..	..	*Asst. Surg.*,*					

Raised in 1798.

33rd Regiment of Native Infantry.

(Volunteer Corps for general service.)

{ Jullundur.

"LASWARRIE"—"BHURTPORE"—"CAUBUL 1842"—"FEROZESHUHUR"—"SUBRAON."
Hilliard-ka-Pultun. Late 2nd Battalion 16th Regt. N.I.
FACINGS—*Black.*

Fur. Reg.	Ser. Y	Ser. M	
O.	48	7	*Colonel* John Moule. *Ens.* — Nov. 1810; *Lieut.* 19 Jan. 1816; *Capt.* 29 April 1826; *Maj.* 30 June 1840; *Lt. Col.* 1 Apl. 46; *Bt. Col.* 20 June 54; *Col.* 9 April 1856; *Major General* 27 Jan. 1858. Fur. S. C. 28 Dec. 58.
	34	5	*Lieut. Colonel* Robert Turnbull Sandeman, *P.* *Ens.* 9 Feb. 1825; *Lieut.* 8 April 1832; *Capt.* 12 Feb. 1838; *Bt. Major* 3 April 1846; *Major* 4 Jan. 1847; *Lieut. Col.* 27 Oct. 52; *Bt. Col.* 28 Nov. 1854.
N.	29	8	*Major* A. Martin. *Ens.* 19 Nov. 1829; *Lieut.* 14 Nov. 1837; *Bt. Capt.* 19 Nov. 1844; *Capt.* 11 May 1846; *Bt. Maj.* 28 Nov. 1854; *Major* 21 July 1857.—4th Irregular Cavy.

Fur. Reg.	Y	M	CAPTAINS.	REMARKS.	*Ensign.*	*Lieut.*	CAPTAIN. *Brevet.*	*Regl.*
	23	7	T. Watson,† - - - -	12th Irregular Cavy.	12 *Dec.* 35	24 *Jan.* 40	12 *Dec.* 50	14 *Mar.* 52
	22	3	T. Tulloh,† - - - -	21st Punjaub Infy.	4 *Apl.* 37	3 *Oct.* 40	4 *Apl.* 52	30 *Dec.* 52
O.	22	3	T. H. Shum,† - - -	Fur. S.C. 15 Apl. 58	4 *Apl.* 37	14 *July* 42	4 *Apl.* 52	1 *Oct.* 53
O.	18	10	H. D. Twysden,† - - -	Fur. S. C. 8 Mar. 59	9 *Sep.* 40	29 *Jan.* 46	.. ..	3 *Oct.* 53
N.	17	4	W. S. Row, *PC*, - - -	Rev. Survey Dept...	23 *Feb.* 42	10 *Feb.* 46	.. ..	23 *Nov.* 56
	17	3	J. C. Dickson,†- - - -	2nd in Command Mynpoory Levy...	7 *Apl.* 42	11 *May* 46	7 *April* 57	1 *July* 57
O.	17	1	W. H. Stubbs, *P*, - - -	Fur. S. C. 3 Aug. 58	11 *June* 42	7 *Sep.* 46	11 *June* 57	21 *July* 57
			LIEUTENANTS.					
	15	1	C. C. Johnson, *PH*, (*a*) - -	Quarter Mr. Genl.'s Dept. ..	7 *June* 44	4 *Jan.* 47	7 *June* 59	
	17	1	G. B Malleson, *P*, - -	Audit Department..	11 *June* 42	28 *Sep.* 47	11 *June* 57	
	13	7	C. M. Longmore, *PC*, - -	.. ..	12 *Dec.* 45	14 *Mar.* 52		
O.	13	1	J. A. Brereton, *PH*, - -	Fur. S. C. 6 Aug. 58	12 *June* 46	30 *Dec.* 52		
	12	6	J. W. Orchard,† - - -	.. ..	20 *Dec.* 46	1 *Oct.* 53		
	8	1	T. W. Rutherfurd, *P*, - -	.. ..	14 *June* 51	10 *Apl.* 56		
	7	5	E. P. Gurdon, *PH*, - -	Meerut Military police,, ..	20 *Jan.* 52	23 *Nov.* 56		
	6	1	J. Stevenson,† - - - -	24th Punjaub Infy.	18 *June* 53	23 *Nov.* 56		
D	~~4~~	~~1~~	~~Fred. Richard Turner~~, *PH*,	Adjt. district police, Chundeyree, ..	17 *Mar.* 55	1 *July* 57	2nd May 64	
	3	10	Charles Forbes Battye,† -	11th Punjaub Infy.	2 *Sep.* 55	21 *July* 57		
	2	..	E. G. Wace,† - - - -	... ..	1 *July* 57	18 *May* 58		
			ENSIGNS.					
	1	6	A. J. Wallace, - - - -	.. ..	4 *Jan.* 58			
			*					
			*					
			*					
			*					
					Appointed.			
	..	..	*Adjt.*, C. M. Longmore, -	.. ..	22 *Feb.* 58			
	..	..	*Intr.*, T. W. Rutherfurd, -	.. ..	22 *Feb.* 58			
	..	..	*Surg.*,*					
	..	..	*Asst. Surg.**					

(*a*) Has passed an examination in Field Engineering.

Re-embodied, 4th July 1846.

34th Regiment of Native Infantry.

7 Companies disbanded Barrackpore and 3 Mutinied at Chittagong.

Brudshaw-ka-Pultun. Late 1st Battalion 17th Regt. N. I.

Facings—*White.*

Fur. Reg.	Ser. Y	Ser. M	
N.	53	3	~~Colonel James Stuart, C. B.~~ *Ens.* 27 March 1806; *Lt.* 15 Feb. 1808; *Bt. Capt.* 27 March 1821; *Capt.* 11 July 1823; *Major* 8 March 1830; *Lieut. Col.* 6 Aug. 1835; *Bt. Col.* 9 Nov. 1846; *Col.* 26 Dec. 1846; *Major Genl.* 20 June 1854.—Fur. S. C. 31 Mar. 1854.
	34	6	*Lt. Col.* John C. Hannyngton, *PC. Ens.* 8 Jan. 1825; *Lieut.* 20 July 1825; *Bt. Capt.* 8 Jan. 1840; *Capt.* 11 Oct. 1843; *Major* 6 Oct. 1850; *Bt. Lt. Col.* 28 Nov. 1854; *Lt. Col.* 9 April 1856.—Deputy Mily. Auditor General.
N.	34	5	*Major* G. Timins, *Ens.* 25 Jan. 1825; *Lieut.* 7 Apl. 1828; *Bt. Capt.* 25 Jan. 1840; *Capt.* 10 Jan. 1845; *Bt. Major* 11 Nov. 1851; *Major* 19 May 1858; *Bt. Lt. Col.* 23 Nov. 1858. —Fur. S. C. 21 June 59.

☞ *Brevet.* [1] Major 20 July 1858.

Fur. Reg.	Y	M	Captains.	Remarks.	*Ensign.*	*Lieut.*	Captain. *Brevet.*	Captain. *Regl.*
	24	3	C. F. M. Mundy,† - -	Pay Department, ..	23 *Mar.* 35	1 *July* 40	.. ..	21 *Nov.* 48
	22	1	P. H. K. Dewaal,† - -	.. ..	13 *June* 37	3 *Oct.* 40	.. ..	1 *Feb.* 50
	19	11	R. Ouseley, *P*, - - -	Cantt. Jt. Magte. and Supdt. of the Abkary Mehal Saugor,	29 *July* 39	1 *Aug.* 41	.. ..	21 *Feb.* 52
	19	7	G. W. Boileau, *PH*, [1]*m* -	Comdt. Mily. Police, Oudh, ..	10 *Dec.* 39	23 *June* 42	.. ..	5 *Aug.* 54
	19	3	C. C. Drury, *PH.* - - -	.. ..	14 *Apl.* 40	16 *July* 42	14 *Apl.* 55	23 *Nov.* 56
	18	3	F. H. Smith, *PH*, - - -	2d Mahrattah Horse,	2 *Apl.* 41	10 *Jan.* 45	2 *Apl.* 56	11 *Dec.* 57
	17	4	A. S. Allen, *PH*, - - -	.. ..	23 *Feb.* 42	24 *June* 47	23 *Feb.* 57	19 *May* 58
			Lieutenants.					
	17	..	B. H. Baugh, *P*, - - -	Cantt. Jt. Magte and Supdt. of Abkarry, Barrackpore, ..	10 *July* 42	21 *Nov.* 48	10 *July* 57	
	15	6	A. C. Bunbury,† - - -	.. ..	1 *Jan.* 44	1 *Feb.* 50	1 *Jan.* 59	
O.	14	7	F. H. Hanmer,† - - -	Fur. S.C. 24 June 59	9 *Dec.* 44	21 *Feb.* 52		
	11	7	S. A. Hunter,† - - - -	.. ..	20 *Dec.* 47	29 *June* 53		
	9	7	G. W. Manson, *PH.* - -	Lv. S. C. 20 Sep.	11 *Dec.* 49	5 *Aug.* 54		
O.	8	4	J. T. Liscombe,† - - -	Fur. S.C. 16 Mar. 59	20 *Feb.* 51	23 *Nov.* 56		
	7	7	J. Thomson, *PH*, - - -	.. ..	12 *Dec.* 51	23 *Nov.* 56		
	9	4	F. E. A. Chamier, *P*, - -	Civil employ, ..	20 *Feb.* 50	8 *April* 57		
	5	5	G. R. Hennessy, *PH*, - -	Adjt. District Police, Futtehgurh, ..	4 *Feb.* 54	11 *Dec.* 57		
	1	11	H. G. Waterfield,† - -	Sylhet Lt. Infy. Battn.	4 *Aug.* 57	19 *May* 58		
	1	1	J. K. McCausland, - -	.. ..	11 *June* 58	22 *Oct.* 58		
			Ensigns.					
	..	7	F. H. Alexander, - -	.. ..	11 *Dec.* 58			
			*					
			*					
			*					
			*					
					Appointed.			
	..	..	*Adjutant*,*					
	..	..	*Intr.*,*					
	..	..	*Surg.*,*					
	..	..	*Surg.*, J. Allan, F. R. C. S.,	.. ..	21 *Feb.* 57			

Raised in 1798. | **35th Regiment of Native (Light) Infantry.** | Disarmed, Umritsir.

(Rifle Company.)

"ALLYGURH"—"DEHLEE"—"BHURTPORE"—"AFFGHANISTAN"—"GHUZNEE"
Mural Crown, superscibed "JELLALABAD."—"CAUBUL 1842."
On the Colours and Appointments a "MURAL CROWN" *superscribed* "JELLALABAD."
On the Honorary Colour the Motto "LAKE *and* VICTORY."
Noke-ka-Pultun. Late 2nd Battalion 17th Regt. N. I.
FACINGS—*White.*

Fur. Reg.	SER. Y	SER. M	
	52	7	*Colonel* Thomas Monteath Douglas, C. B. *Ens.* 4 Dec. 1806; *Lieut.* 9 Sept. 1808; *Capt.* 1 May 1824; *Major* 17 Jan. 1829; *Lieut. Col.* 2 April 1834; *Bt. Col.* 4 Oct. 1842; *Col.* 7 Sept. 1845; *Maj. Genl.* 20 June 54; *Lt. Genl.* 18 March 56.—Fur. P. A., 9 March 51.
O.	38	3	*Lt. Col.* William Maule Ramsay, *P.* *Ens.* 21 March 1821; *Lieut.* 21 July 1823; *Capt.* 1 Jan. 1836; *Major* 5 July 1844; *Lieut. Col.* 28 Sept. 1850; *Bt. Col.* 28 Nov. 1854.—Fur. S. C. 12 March 1858.
R N.	~~35~~	~~6~~	~~*Major* A. G. F. J. Younghusband.~~ *Ens.* 16 Jan. 1824; *Lieut.* 21 Apl. 1825; *Bt. Capt.* 16 Jan. 1839; *Capt.* 13 Oct. 1839; *Bt. Major* 4 Oct. 1842; *Major* 27 June 1857; *Bt. Lieut. Col.* 20 June 1854; *Bt. Colonel* 3 Aug. 1855.—Fur. S. C. 6 Sep. 1858.

☞ *Brevet.* [1] Maj. 19 Jan. 58. [2] Maj. 11 July 1854.

Fur. Reg.	Y	M	CAPTAINS.	REMARKS.	*Ensign.*	*Lieut.*	CAPTAIN. *Brevet.*	CAPTAIN. *Regl.*
	22	6	R. A. Ramsay, *P*, [1]*m*	Kemaoon Battalion,	18 *Dec.* 36	3 *Oct.* 40	18 *Dec* 51	17 *Nov.* 52
	19	1	P. A. P. Bouverie, *PH*, [2]*m*	Political employ, ..	12 *June* 40	29 *Oct.* 41	.. ..	10 *July* 54
O.	18	10	H. LeP. Trench, *PH*, *(a)*	Fur. S.C. 4 June 58,	17 *Sep.* 40	13 *Jan.* 42	17 *Sep.* 55	23 *Nov.* 56
	18	4	E. R. Wiggins, †	.. ..	8 *Mar.* 41	24 *Jan.* 45	8 *Mar.* 56	4 *June* 57
O.	18	11	W. Metcalf, †	Fur. S.C 21 Apl. 59,	7 *Aug.* 40	11 *Mar.* 47	7 *Aug.* 55	27 *June* 57
	17	1	R. Maxwell, †	.. ..	12 *June* 42	28 *Aug.* 47	12 *June* 57	1 *Mar.* 58
N.	16	6	H. T. Pollock, †	Fur. S.C. 26 Feb. 58,	28 *Dec.* 42	1 *Apl.* 51	28 *Dec.* 57	12 *Nov.* 58
			LIEUTENANTS.					
	13	1	T. C. Hamilton, *PH*,	Arracan Battalion,	13 *June* 46	17 *Nov.* 52		
	10	5	R. F. Godby, *PH*,	1st Seikh Irr. Cavy.,	20 *Feb.* 49	15 *Nov.* 53		
	8	5	J. P. Sherriff, †	2nd Seikh Infantry.	20 *Jan.* 51	10 *July* 54		
	7	6	G. Alexander, *PH*,	Nusseree Battalion,	1 *Jan.* 52	30 *Nov.* 54		
	6	6	J. C. P. Baillie, *P*, *(b)*	7th Punjaub Infy.	20 *Dec.* 52	23 *Nov.* 56		
	5	7	Charles Kinloch Mylne, †	.. ..	10 *Dec.* 53	23 *Nov.* 56		
	4	11	Frederick John Keen, †	2nd Punjaub Infy.	4 *Aug.* 54	4 *June* 57		
	4	10	Oswald Menzies, *PH*,	9th Punjaub Infy...	26 *Aug.* 54	27 *June* 57		
N.	4	11	J. Watson, *PH*,	Fur. S. C. 6 Feb. 58	1 *Aug.* 54	26 *Sep.* 57		
	2	1	W. F. Mosley,	Regt. of Ferozepore,	13 *June* 57	18 *May* 58		
	1	7	F. Hibbert,	.. ..	12 *Dec.* 57	12 *Nov.* 58		
			ENSIGNS.					
		10	G. T. Jones,	.. ..	26 *Aug.* 58			
			*					
			*					
			*					
			*		*Appointed.*			
			Adjt.					
			Intr., *					
			Surg., *					
			Asst. Surg. *					

N. B.—This Regiment has an honorary standard and extra Jemadar for Allygurh and Delhi, and was made Light Infantry, the first on the Bengal Presidency, for its services at Jellalabad.
(a) Has furnished certificates of qualification in Surveying and Civil Engineering.
(b) Passed an examination in the Punjaubee language.

Raised in 1800.

36th Reg. of Nat. Infy. (Bengal Volunteers.)

Mutinied, Jullundur.

"Seringapatam"—"Bhurtpore"—"Alliwal"—"Punjaub"—"Chillianwalla"—"Goojerat."

This Regt. has on its Colours "an Embroidered Star" *for services at Seringapatam Markum-ka-Pultun.* Late 1st Battalion 18th Regt. N.I.

Facings—*Lemon-yellow.*

Fur. Reg.	Ser. Y	Ser. M	
O.	52	5	*Col.* Frederick Hervey Sandys. *Ens.* 11 Feb. 1807; *Lieut.* 22 March 1811; *Capt* 1 May 1824; *Bt. Major* 10 Jan. 1837; *Major* 1 Oct. 1840; *Lieut. Col.* 30 Jan. 1846; *Bt. Col.* 20 June 1854; *Col* 10 Feb. 56; *Maj. Genl.* 15 Oct. 1857.—Fur. P.A. 20 Mar. 56.
N.	35	6	*Lt. Col.* Thos. Fergusson Flemyng. *Ens.* 14 Jan. 1824; *Lieut.* 6 May 1825; *Bt. Capt.* 14 Jan. 1839; *Capt.* 12 Jan. 1841; *Bt. Major* 19 June 1846; *Bt. Lt. Col.* 7 June 1849; *Major* 10 July 1852; *Lt. Col.* 31 May 1857; *Bt. Col.* 28 Nov. 1854.—Fur. S. C. 9 Feb. 58.
	24	4	*Major* S. B. Faddy, *P*, *Ens.* 24 Feb. 1835; *Lieut.* 1 Feb. 1840; *Capt.* 14 Nov. 1846; *Major* 31 May 1857.

☞ Brevet [1] Major 20 July 1858. [2] Major 19 Jan. 1858.

Fur. Reg.	Ser. Y	Ser. M	Captains.	Remarks.	*Ensign.*	*Lieut.*	Captain. *Brevet.*	Captain. *Regl.*
	19	6	C. Holroyd, *PH*, *(a)* - -	Civil employ, ..	31 *Dec.* 39	12 *Jan.* 41	.. ..	1 *July* 51
O.	19	6	C. S. Weston, *PH*,[1]*m* -	Fur. S.C. 18 Mar. 58,	4 *Jan.* 40	9 *Dec.* 42	.. ..	10 *July* 52
	18	10	W. J. F. Stafford, *P*, -	11th Punjaub Infy.	9 *Sep.* 40	25 *July* 44	.. ..	15 *Feb.* 53
	18	10	H. Raban, *PH*, - - -	Comdt. 6th Bengal Police Battn., ..	17 *Sep.* 40	27 *Dec.* 44	17 *Sep.* 55	9 *Oct.* 56
	16	6	H. M. Garstin, *PH*,[2]*m* -	Arracan Battalion,..	20 *Dec.* 42	24 *Jan.* 45	.. ..	23 *Nov.* 56
	16	4	M. F. Evatt, *P*, - - -	.. ..	25 *Feb.* 43	30 *Jan.* 46	.. ..	26 *Dec.* 56
	16	4	E. Smalley, *PH*, - - -	D. P. W. N. W. P,	23 *Feb.* 43	14 *Nov.* 46	.. ..	31 *May* 57
			Lieutenants.					
	15	4	J. R. Auldjo,† - - -	.. ..	28 *Feb.* 44	22 *June* 47	28 *Feb.* 59	
	14	1	C. J. Godby, *PH*, - - -	4th Punjaub Cavy,..	13 *June* 45	10 *July* 52		
O.	11	7	H. R. Bradford, *P*, -	Fur. S. C. 17 Jan. 59	10 *Dec.* 47	15 *Feb.* 53		
	10	11	W. W. Clark,† - - -	1st Regt. Gwalior Infy. ..	10 *Aug.* 48	3 *July* 56		
	5	4	H. D. E. W. Chester, *PH*,	7th Irr. Cavalry, ..	20 *Feb.* 54	23 *Nov.* 56		
	3	3	C. E. Bates,- - - - -	.. ..	20 *Apl.* 56	23 *Nov.* 56		
	3	1	Ayrton Pullan,† - - -	Adjt. Seikh Police Corps, ..	14 *June* 56	26 *Dec.* 56		
	4	4	Marmaduke Ramsay, *PCH*,	Loyal Poorbeeah Regt. ..	20 *Mar.* 55	31 *May* 57		
	2	7	L. Smith,† - - - - -	.. ..	13 *Dec.* 56	12 *June* 57		
	2	7	H. C. Fagan, - - - -	19 Punjaub Infy. ..	20 *Dec.* 56	5 *Sep.* 57		
	2	1	*Sir* G. L. M. Parker, *Bart.*	Lv. S. C. 20 Oct...	13 *June* 57	18 *May* 58		
			Ensigns.					
	1	7	R. Milne, - - - - -	... ..	12 *Dec.* 57			
			*					
			*					
			*					
			*		*Appointed.*			
			Adjutant, J. R. Auldjo, -	Officiating, ..	11 *Sep.* 57			
			Intr.,*					
			Surg. C. Harland, - - -	.. ..	7 *June* 56			
			*Assist. Surg.**					

(a) Passed successful examinations in the Assamese and Bengallee languages.

Raised in 1800.

37th Regt. of Nat. Infy. (Bengal Volunteers.)

Mutinied, Benares.

" SERINGAPATAM"—" BHURTPORE"—" AFFGHANISTAN"—" PUNJAUB."

This Regt. has on its Colours " an EMBROIDERED STAR" *for services at Seringapatam.*

Ba'en Balunteer, Burral-ka-Pultun. Late 2nd Battalion 18th Regt. N.I.

FACINGS—*Lemon-yellow.*

Fur. Reg.	Ser. Y	Ser. M	
	55	8	*Colonel* Thomas Oliver. *Ens.* 16 Nov. 1803 ; *Lieut.* 18 May 1805 ; *Capt.* 16 Nov. 1818 ; *Major* 18 July 1827 ; *Lieut. Col.* 3 July 1832 ; *Col.* 13 March 1844 ; *Maj. Genl.* 20 June 1854 ; *Lieut. Genl.* 4 May 1858.—Europe, 14 Dec. 1843
O.	35	4	*Lt. Col.* A. C. Spottiswoode. *Ens.* 25 Feb. 1824 ; *Lieut.* 13 May 1825 ; *Capt.* 14 Nov. 1833 ; *Bt. Maj.* 9 Nov. 46 ; *Maj.* 17 Mar. 51 ; *Bt. Lt. Col.* 20 June 54 ; *Lt. Col.* 22 May 1856 ; *Bt. Col.* 23 July 1858.—Lv. S C. for 2 years, G. O. 20 Nov. 1858.
O.	32	11	*Major* J. Bontein. *Ens.* 17 Aug. 1826 ; *Lieut.* 7 Feb. 1837 ; *Bt. Capt.* 17 Aug. 1841 ; *Capt.* 27 June. 1846 ; *Bt. Major* 20 June 1854 ; *Maj.* 20 Mar. 1857.—Fur. S. C. 13 May 59.

☞ *Brevet.* [1] Maj. 20 June 54. [2] Maj. 18 Mar. 51 ; Lt. Col. 28 Nov. 54. Col. 19 Jan. 58.

Fur. Reg.	Y	M	CAPTAINS.	REMARKS.	*Ensign.*	*Lieut.*	CAPTAIN. *Brevet.*	CAPTAIN. *Regl.*
	32	9	J. Barrett,†[1]*m* - - - -	.. ..	30 *Sep.* 26	8 *Oct.* 39	30 *Sep.* 41	26 *Apl.* 49
	18	11	B. Parrott, *PH*, - - -	Stud Dept., ..	19 *Aug.* 40	16 *July* 42	.. ..	8 *Dec.* 50
N.	18	5	J.M.B.F. Tytler, C.B. *PH*,[2]*c*	9th Irregular Cavy.	17 *Feb.* 41	12 *Nov.* 42	.. ..	17 *Mar.* 51
	16	11	P H. P. Gill, *PC*, - - -	Cant. Jt. magte. and Supdt. of the Cant Abkarry mehal in Benares, ..	25 *July* 42	27 *June* 46	.. ..	23 *Dec.* 55
N.	16	9	J. Reid, *P*, (*a*) - - - -	Civil employ, ..	24 *Sep.* 42	30 *Dec.* 47	.. ..	23 *Nov.* 56
	14	6	S. Black, *PH*, - - - -	Staff Officer, Punjaub Irr. Force. ..	29 *Dec.* 44	13 *Apl.* 48	.. ..	20 *Mar.* 57
	14	5	P. Maxwell, *B.A.P.*(*b*) -	Civil employ, ..	11 *Feb.* 45	17 *Jan.* 49	.. ..	1 *Apl.* 58
			LIEUTENANTS.					
O.	13	7	C. M. L. Clarke, *PCH*, (*c*) -	Fur. S. C. 1 Apl. 59	13 *Dec.* 45	26 *Apl.* 49		
	12	7	S. S. Boulderson, *PCH*, -	Civil employ, ..	11 *Dec.* 46	30 *June* 49		
	11	7	C. R. Shaw, *PCH*, - - -	Civil employ, ..	10 *Dec.* 47	8 *Dec.* 50		
	11	7	O. M. Glubb, *P*, - - -	Cant. Jt. magte. and Supdt. of the Abkarry mehal in Allahabad ..	11 *Dec.* 47	17 *Mar.* 51		
N.	10	11	F. W. Dunbar, *PH*, - -	Fur. P. A. 25 Mar. 59, ..	1 *Aug.* 48	20 *May* 53		
	10	6	J. L. Sawers,† - - - -	Comdg. District, Police, Humeerpoor,	20 *Jan.* 49	23 *Dec.* 55		
	9	..	F. A. Buckley, *PC*, - -	.. ..	17 *July* 50	22 *May* 56		
O.	8	1	W. C. S. Clarke, *PH*, - -	Fur. S. C. 22 Oct. 57	13 *June* 51	23 *Nov.* 56		
N.	4	7	Stanhope Cary, *PH*, - -	Fur. S. C. 14 July 58	10 *Dec.* 54	23 *Nov.* 56		
N.	2	10	J. B. Brander, - - - -	Fur. S. C. 8 Dec. 58	10 *Sep.* 56	1 *Apl.* 58		
	2	7	J. F. Elton,† - - - -	.. ..	20 *Dec.* 56	30 *Apl.* 58		
			ENSIGNS.					
N.	1	7	E. Packe, - - - - -	Fur. S C. 13 Nov. 58	11 *Dec.* 57			
			*					
			*					
			*					
			*		*Appointed.*			
	..	..	*Adjutant*,*					
	..	..	*Intr.*,*					
	..	..	*Surg.*,*					
	..	..	*Assist. Surg.*, J. H. Thornton, B. A., B.M., - - -	.. ..	16 *Jan.* 57			

(*a*) Received a Certificate of High Proficiency in the Persian Language 21st Sep. 1852, a degree of Honor for eminent attainment in ditto, 29th Nov. 1852. Attained the standard of proficiency in the Oordoo and Hindee languages prescribed by G. O. 9th Mar. 52.

(*b*) Passed an examination in the Punjaubee Language also passed the Civil service examinations Lower and higher standards.

(*c*) Has furnished certificate of qualification in Surveying.

Raised in 1800. } **38th Regt. of Nat. Light Infy. (Bengal Volunteers.)** { Mutinied, Delhi.

(*Rifle Company.*)

"Seringapatam"—"Candahar"—"Ghuznee"—"Caubul 1842."

Balunteer, Titteelee-ka-Pultun. Late 1st Battalion 19th Regt. N.I.

Facings—*Dark-green.*

Fur. Reg.	Ser. Y	Ser. M	
	54	11	*Colonel Sir* George Petre Wymer, K. C. B. *Ens.* 15 Aug. 1804; *Lieut.* 21 Sept. 1804; *Capt.* 1 Aug. 1818; *Major* 11 July 1828; *Lt. Col.* 26 Sept. 1833; *Bt. Col.* 23 Dec. 1842; *Col.* 10 June 1845; *Maj. Genl.* 20 June 1854; *Lt. Genl.* 8 June 1856.—Europe, 10 Feb. 1848.
	37	3	*Lt. Col.* Wm. J. B. Knyvett. *Ens.* 28 Mar. 22; *Lt.* 13 May 25; *Bt. Capt.* 28 Mar. 37; *Capt.* 30 March 1837; *Bt. Major* 11 Nov. 1851; *Major* 6 Jan. 1852; *Bt. Lt. Col.* 15 Sep. 1855; *Lieut. Col.* 25 May 1857.—Leave. P. A. 1 Oct.
	24	5	*Major* R. C. Tytler, *P*, *Ens.* 16 Feb. 1835; *Lieut.* 25 Sep. 1837; *Captain* 26 Feb. 1846; *Major* 16 May 1858.

☞ *Brevet.* [1] Major 24 Mar. 58. [2] Major 20 July 58.

Fur. Reg.	Y	M	Captains.	Remarks.	*Ensign.*	*Lieut.*	Captain. *Brevet.*	Captain. *Regl.*
O.	20	6	H. R. Shelton, *PH*, - -	Fur. S.C. 31 May 58,	13 *Jan.* 39	12 *Nov.* 42	.. ..	28 *Sep.* 51
	19	6	J. B. Dennys, *PH*, - -	Political employ, ..	3 *Jan.* 40	12 *Nov.* 42	.. ..	6 *Jan.* 52
	~~17~~	~~1~~	~~A. D. Dickens, *P*, [1]*m*~~ - -	Army Comt. Dept.	11 *June* 42	8 *Oct.* 43	.. ..	9 *May* 57
	16	4	C. Cureton, *PH*, [2]*m* - -	2nd Irr. Cavy., ..	22 *Feb.* 43	26 *Feb.* 46	.. ..	25 *May* 57
	15	1	T. W. Holland, *PC*, - -	Army Comnt. Dept.	7 *June* 44	8 *Nov.* 49	.. ..	10 *June* 57
N.	10	5	W. B. Peile, † - - - -	Fur. S. C. 7 Apl. 58	7 *Feb.* 49	28 *Sep.* 51	.. ..	11 *Mar.* 58
			*					
			Lieutenants.					
	9	7	R. B. Dundas, *PCH*, - -	.. ..	12 *Dec.* 49	16 *Nov.* 52		
	9	..	J. Hearsey, *PC*, - - - -	A. D. C. to Major General *Sir* J. B. Hearsey, K. C. B.,	8 *July* 50	1 *Jan.* 54		
O.	8	2	H. F. Bamford, † - - -	Fur. S. C. 20 Sep. 56	3 *May* 51	7 *Mar.* 54		
	6	10	M. M. Procter, *PH*, - -	.. ..	31 *Aug.* 52	23 *Nov.* 56		
	5	7	W. L. P. Drummond, † (*a*)	Divl. 2nd in Comd Mily. Police, Oude.	9 *Dec.* 53	9 *May* 57		
N.	4	6	John Matthew Glubb, † ..	Fur. S. C. 1 Apl. 58	20 *Dec.* 54	10 *June* 57		
O.	7	4	F. H. Inglefield, † - - -	Fur. S. C. 2 Mar. 58	20 *Feb.* 52	23 *Nov.* 56		
	2	7	R. C. Clifford, - - - -	.. ..	13 *Dec* 56	6 *June* 57		
	2	4	Henry I. Wheler, - -	Fur. S. C. 1 Oct. 58	6 *Mar.* 57	18 *May* 58		
	1	11	G. S Hills, - - - -	.. ..	4 *Aug.* 57	18 *May* 58		
	1	1	M. C. Smith, - - - -	Doing duty with 1st En. B. F. ..	11 *June* 58	22 *Oct.* 58		
			Ensigns.					
	..	7	G. B. Stevens. - - -	.. ..	11 *Dec.* 58			
			*					
			*					
			*					
			*		*Appointed.*			
	..	..	*Adjt.**					
	..	..	*Interpreter,**					
	..	..	*Surg.*, J. Wood, - - -	Fur. S. C. 15 Dec. 58	11 *Dec.* 53			
	..	..	*Asst. Surg.**					

N. B.—This Corps was made Light Infantry for its services at Candahar under General Nott. It has also a third or honorary color for Seringapatam, Black, with Death's Head and Bayonets crossed, and the Persian word Hoormut حرمت (Honor) superscribed.

(*a*) Received a first class certificate from the Umballah School of Musketry.

Raised in 1800. } **39th Regt. of Nat. Infy. (Bengal Volunteers.)** { Disarmed, Sealkote.

"Seringapatam"—"Punniar." *The 6th Company,* "Maharajpore."
On the Regimental Color an embroidered radiant Star for Seringapatam
Balunteer, Burral-ka-Pultun. Late 2nd Battalion 19th Regt. N.I.

Facings—*Dark-green.*

Fur. Reg.	Ser. Y	Ser. M						
N.	39	11	*Colonel* David Downing. *Ens.* 16 Aug. 1819; *Lieut.* 2 March 1822; *Capt.* 3 July 1832; *Major* 15 Sept. 1839; *Lieut. Col.* 12 Oct. 1845; *Bt. Col.* 20 June 1854; *Col.* 7 May 55; *Major Genl.* 15 Sep. 1857.—Fur. S. C. 20 Mar. 1854.					
	38	3	*Lieut. Colonel* John Macdonald. *Ens.* 4 Apl. 1821; *Lieut.* 27 Aug. 1823; *Capt.* 26 Sep. 1833; *Major* 11 Apl. 1845; *Lieut. Col.* 11 Apl. 1851; *Bt. Col.* 28 Nov. 1854.					
	28	1	*Lt. Col.* F. E. Voyle, *P.* *Ens.* 9 June 1831; *Lieut.* 17 Oct. 1838; *Bt. Capt.* 9 June 1846; *Capt.* 18 Nov. 1846; *Major* 4 June 1855. *Lieut. Col.* 4 June 1859.—Civil employ.					
	24	1	*Major* T. Pownall, *Ens.* 13 June 35; *Lieut.* 1 July 39; *Capt.* 10 June 49; *Major* 4 June 59.					
			Captains.	**Remarks.**	***Ensign.***	***Lieut.***	**Captain.** *Brevet.*	**Captain.** *Regl.*
	23	5	J. N. Thomas,† - - -	.. ..	9 *Feb.* 36	25 *July* 39	.. ..	1 *Nov.* 49
	21	1	R. H. D. Tulloh, *P,* - -	Civil employ, ..	11 *June* 38	3 *Oct.* 40	.. ..	28 *Nov.* 49
	20	7	C. Jackson,† - - -	.. ..	11 *Dec.* 38	16 *July* 42	.. ..	21 *Feb.* 50
	20	5	J. L. Sherwill, *P,* (a) - -	Rev. Survey Dept.	24 *Jan.* 39	24 *Jan.* 45	24 *Jan.* 54	4 *June* 55
	18	9	C. Fredk. Smith,† - -	Civil employ, ..	27 *Sep.* 40	18 *Mar.* 45	27 *Sep.* 55	23 *Nov.* 56
	18	6	J. D. MacDonald, *PH,* -	Commanding district police, Humeerpore.	31 *Dec.* 40	15 *Aug.* 45	31 *Dec.* 55	21 *Apl.* 58
	17	1	G. H. Gordon,† - - -	10th Punjaub Infy.,	11 *June* 42	30 *Jan.* 46	11 *June* 57	4 *June* 59
			*					
			Lieutenants.					
	16	7	H. King, *PH,* - - - -	18th Punjaub Infy.	10 *Dec.* 42	18 *Nov.* 46	10 *Dec.* 57	
	14	6	G. Cavenagh,† - - - -	.. ..	18 *Jan.* 45	10 *June* 49		
	13	7	T. F. Forster, *P.,* - -	Civil employ, ..	13 *Dec.* 45	28 *Nov.* 49		
	11	7	F. M. H. Forbes, *PH,* -	Offg. Civil employ,	10 *Dec.* 47	15 *Nov.* 53		
	9	7	W. A. Garden, *PH,* -	2d Assam Light Infy Battn., ..	11 *Dec.* 49	4 *June* 55		
N.	9	7	B. C. Urquhart, *PH,* -	17th Irr. Cavy. ..	11 *Dec.* 49	26 *Aug.* 55		
	8	7	E. H. C. Simpson, *PH,* -	Benares Horse, ..	9 *Dec.* 50	23 *Nov.* 56		
	5	1	Frederick Wheeler, *P,* -	.. ..	9 *June* 54	15 *June* 57		
	3	11	John Chalmers, A. M., *PH,*	Civil employ, ..	6 *Aug.* 55	21 *Apl.* 58		
	2	6	Francis Wetherell, - -	.. ..	20 *Jan.* 57	30 *Apl.* 58		
	1	10	W. F. Bartleman, -	Fur. S.C. 30 June 58	16 *Sep.* 57	4 *June* 59		
			Ensigns.					
	..	7	W. G. Maitland, - -	.. ..	20 *Dec.* 58			
			*					
			*					
			*		*Appointed.*			
			*					
	..	..	*Adjutant,**					
	..	..	*Intr.,* F. Wheeler, - - -	Officiating, ..	4 *Nov.* 56			
	..	..	*Surgeon,*					
	..	..	*Asst. Surg.* A. R. Atkinson, M. D., - - - -	.. ..	16 *Nov.* 53			

N. B.—This Corps enjoys the privilege of wearing a feather and has a third or honorary color for Seringapatam Black, with Death's Head and Bayonets crossed, and the Persian word Hoormut حرمت (Honor) superscribed.

(a) Has furnished certificate of qualification in surveying.

Raised in 1820.

40th Regt. of Native Infantry, (Volunteers.)

Mutinied, Dinapore.

"JAVA"—"AVA"—"ARRACAN"—"PEGU."

Hamilteen-ka-Pultun. Late 2nd Battalion 20th Regt. N. I.

FACINGS—*Blue.*

Fur. Reg.	Ser. Y	Ser. M	
	58	9	*Colonel* Charles William Hamilton. *Ens.* 20 Sept. 1800; *Lieut.* 20 Sept. 1801; *Bt. Capt.* 15 June 1814; *Capt.* 16 Dec. 1814; *Major* 11 July 1823; *Lieut. Col.* 13 May 1825; *Bt. Col.* 18 June 1831; *Col.* 6 Aug 1835; *Major Genl.* 23 Nov. 1841; *Lieut. Genl.* 11 Nov. 51.—Furlough, P. A. 9 April 52.
N.	39	7	*Lieut. Colonel* Edward Altham Cumberlege. *Ens.* 19 Dec. 1819; *Lieut.* 11 July 1823; *Capt.* 29 Nov. 1834; *Major* 4 April 1845; *Lieut. Col.* 7 April 1851; *Bt. Col.* 28 Nov. 1854.—Fur. S. C. 17 July 58.
	34	5	*Major* H. A. Shuckburgh. *Ens.* 9 Feb. 1825; *Lt.* 18 Aug. 1825; *Bt. Capt.* 9 Feb. 1840; *Capt.* 1 Jan. 1844; *Bt. Maj.* 11 Nov. 1851; *Maj.* 8 June 1857; *Bt. Lt. Col.* 4 Feb. 1859.

Fur. Reg.	Y	M	CAPTAINS.	REMARKS.	*Ensign.*	*Lieut.*	CAPTAIN. *Brevet.*	CAPTAIN. *Regl.*
	18	7	A. A. Macdonell, *PH*, (*a*)	Stud Dept.	12 *Dec.* 40	1 *Jan.* 44	.. ..	19 *Nov.* 52
O.	18	1	J. S. D. White, *PH*,	Fur. S. C. 24 Jan. 59	11 *June* 41	12 *Sep.* 44	.. ..	6 *Aug.* 54
N.	17	5	J. P. Briggs, *PCH*, (*b*)	Civil employ,	30 *Jan.* 42	24 *Jan.* 45	.. ..	23 *Nov.* 56
	17	5	P. Rubie, †	.. ..	17 *Feb.* 42	14 *Apl.* 45	.. ..	20 *Jan.* 57
O.	15	6	W. E. Cahill, †	Fur. S. C. 14 Feb. 58	1 *Jan.* 44	15 *Oct.* 48	.. ..	8 *June* 57
	14	7	M. J. Brander, *PC*, (*c*)	Army Comt. Dept.	10 *Dec.* 44	18 *June* 50	.. ..	9 *Oct.* 57
	14	6	H. R. Wroughton, *PC*,	Army Comt. Dept.	20 *Jan.* 45	21 *Feb.* 51	.. ..	15 *Oct.* 57
			LIEUTENANTS.					
	13	7	J. Burn, *PH*,	.. ..	12 *Dec.* 45	1 *July* 51		
	13	1	E. J. Wild, *PH*,	Comdg. Mily. Police, Futtehpore, ..	13 *June* 46	26 *July* 52		
	9	5	Edgar G. Stone, *PH*,	2nd in Comd. Mynpoory Irr. Horse,	20 *Jan.* 50	2 *Jan.* 53		
	8	6	H. Phillips, †	.. ..	7 *Jan.* 51	6 *Aug.* 54		
N.	7	1	C. F. Middleton, *PH*,	Meerut Levy. ..	12 *June* 52	17 *June* 55		
	6	9	J. Roberts, †	Lv. S. C. 16 Oct. ..	27 *Sep.* 52	23 *Nov.* 56		
O.	6	11	H. E. Waller, †	Fur. S.C. 29 July 58	10 *Aug.* 52	23 *Nov.* 56		
	4	6	Newton Robt. Burlton,	Offg. Army Commt. Dept., ..	30 *Dec.* 54	8 *June* 57		
N.	2	4	Edwin Venour,	Fur. S.C. 9 Apl. 1858	4 *Mar.* 57	9 *Oct.* 57		
	2	1	H. C. A. Szezepanshi, †	.. ..	13 *June* 57	18 *May* 58		
	6	1	W. F. Belli, *PH*,	.. ..	11 *June* 53	20 *Jan.* 57		
			ENSIGNS.					
	1	7	A. I. Iles,	.. ..	12 *Dec.* 57			
			*					
			*					
			*					
			*		*Appointed.*			
	..	..	*Adjutant*, J. Burn,	Comdg. an East Indian Regt. at Raneegunge. ..	4 *Mar.* 53			
	..	..	*Intr.*, *					
	..	..	*Surg.*,					
	..	..	*Asst. Surg.*,					

(*a*) Passed a successful examination in the Assamese and Bengalee languages.

(*b*) Has passed a successful examination in the Burmese language.

(*c*) Received a certificate for high proficiency in the Oordoo language from the College of Fort William, on the 4t July 1849, and also one in the Hindee language, 18th September 1849.

Raised in 1803.

41st Regiment of Native Infantry.

Mutinied, Oude (Seetapore.)

(*Rifle Company.*)

"BHURTPORE"—"SUBRAON."

Doobye-ke-daheena-Pultun. Late 1st Battalion 21st Regt. N.I.

FACINGS—*Pale-yellow.*

Fur. Reg.	Ser. Y	Ser. M	
	53	3	*Colonel* Robert Stewart. *Ens.* 29 March 1806; *Lieut.* 31 Oct. 1808; *Bt. Capt.* 29 March 1821; *Capt.* 1 May 1824; *Bt. Major,* 10 Jan. 1837; *Major* 11 Oct. 1838; *Lieut. Col.* 26 Dec. 1844; *Bt. Col.* 20 June 1854; *Col.* 16 Dec. 1854; *Major Genl.* 15 Sep. 1856.—Fur., S.C. 12 Aug. 1853.
			*Lt. Col.**
R N.	34	6	~~*Major* C. Apthorp.~~ *Ens.* 9 Jan. 1825; *Lieut.* 20 May 1827; *Bt. Capt.* 9 Jan. 1840; *Capt* 27 Feb. 1846; *Bt. Major* 11 Nov. 51; *Major* 1 June 57; *Bt. Lt. Col.* 24 Mar. 1858.—Fur. S. C. 5 Nov. 1858.

☞ *Brevet.* [1] Major 24 Mar. 58. [2] Major 24 Mar. 58.

Fur. Reg.	Y	M	CAPTAINS.	REMARKS.	*Ensign.*	*Lieut.*	CAPTAIN. *Brevet.*	CAPTAIN. *Regl.*
Major O.	24	1	A. W. Onslow,† - - -	Fur. S.C. 16 Apl. 58	13 *June* 35	28 *Feb.* 40	.. ..	13 *Feb* 50
	18	5	M. F. Kemble,†[1]*m* - -	Offg. Army clothing Agent 1st Division Allahabad. ..	17 *Feb.* 41	29 *Sep.* 43	.. ..	16 *July* 50
	18	1	H. B. Stevens, *PH,* - -	Kelat-i-Ghilzie Regiment, ..	11 *June* 41	21 *June* 44	.. ..	25 *May* 52
O.	17	1	J. W. Sanders, *PH,*[2]*m* -	Fur. S. C. 5 Apl. 58	11 *June* 42	9 *Sep.* 44	.. ..	26 *Mar.* 55
	15	1	G. R. Roberts, *P,* - -	Army Commt. Dept.	7 *June* 44	1 *July* 46	.. ..	23 *Nov.* 56
	14	2	A. G. Priestley, *PH, (a)* -	Dept. P. W., N.W.P.	1 *May* 45	28 *Dec.* 47	.. ..	1 *June* 57
O.	14	1	J. Ruggles, *PH,(a)* -	Fur. S.C. 16 Feb. 58	13 *June* 45	28 *Sep.* 49	.. ..	27 *June* 57
			LIEUTENANTS.					
Capt.	13	7	T. F. O. Scott, *PH, (b)* -	Sylhet Light Infy. Battn. ..	13 *Dec.* 45	13 *Feb.* 50		
	12	4	G. G. Cunliffe,† - - -	.. ..	20 *Mar.* 47	16 *July* 50		
	10	1	H. Z. Darrah, *PH,(a)* -	D. P. W. N. W. P.	8 *June* 49	25 *May* 52		
	9	11	G. C. Rowcroft, *PH, (b)* -	Kelat-i-Ghilzie Regiment,	10 *Aug.* 49	8 *Dec.* 52		
	9	6	W. D. Hogg, *P,* - - -	Army Commt. Dept.	20 *Dec.* 49	26 *Mar.* 55		
N.	9	6	Henry Inglis,† - - -	Fur. S. C. 5 Apl. 58	20 *Jan.* 50	15 *Apl.* 56		
	4	6	Richard Fisher Angelo, *P* -	Lv. to 1st Nov. ..	4 *Jan.* 55	23 *Nov.* 56		
	4	4	George Lawrence Keir, -	Army Commt. Dept.	17 *Mar.* 55	1 *June* 57		
	2	10	J. B. Chatterton, -	Fur. S.C. 26 Feb. 58	4 *Sep.* 56	7 *June* 57		
N.	2	6	G. L. K. Hewett,† -	Bareilly Police, ..	20 *Jan.* 57	30 *Apl.* 58		
	2	1	M. P. Moriarty, - - -	.. ..	13 *June* 57	18 *May* 58		
			ENSIGNS.					
Lt.	..	10	A. Vallings, - - - -	.. ..	20 *Sep.* 58			
			*					
			*					
			*					
			*					
					Appointed.			
	..	..	*Adjutant,* *					
	..	..	*Intr.,**					
	..	..	*Surg.,**					
	..	..	*Asst. Surg.,* J. Lee, M.D., -	.. ..	9 *Dec.* 54			

(*a*) Have furnished certificates of qualification in Surveying and Civil Engineering.
(*b*) Have passed the examination in Field Engineering.

Raised in 1803. }

42nd Regiment of Native (Light) Infantry.

{ Mutinied, Saugor, (Camp. Malthone..)

(Rifle Company.)

"Arracan"—"Affghanistan"—"Candahar"—"Ghuznee"—"Caubul 1842"—"Moodkee"—"Ferozeshuhur"—"Subraon."

Jansin-ke-Pultun. Late 2nd Battalion 21st Regt. N.I.

Facings—*Yellow.*

Fur. Reg.	Ser. Y	Ser. M	
	54	4	*Colonel* Thomas Fiddes. *Ens.* 19 March 1805; *Lieut.* 12 April 1805; *Capt.* 1 Jan. 1819; *Maj.* 10 June 1826; *Lt. Col.* 19 June 1831; *Col.* 9 Aug. 1843; *Maj. Genl.* 20 June 1854; *Lieut. Genl.* 15 Sep. 1856.—Europe, 10 Feb. 45.
N.	36	4	*Lt. Col. Sir* Archibald Bogle, *Kt. Ens.* 13 March 1823; *Lieut.* 13 May 1825; *Capt.* 14 Aug. 32; *Major* 4 Oct. 1844; *Lieut. Col.* 17 Feb. 1851; *Bt. Col.* 28 Nov. 1854.—Civil employ.—Fur. S. C. 20 Mar. 57.
N.	35	1	*Major* C. Campbell. *Ens.* 23 May 1824; *Lt.* 14 July 1825; *Bt. Capt.* 23 May 1839; *Capt.* 21. Aug. 43; *Bt. Maj.* 7 June 49; *Maj.* 18 Sep. 57; *Bt. Lt. Col.* 28 Nov. 54.—Fur. S. C. 30 Nov. 58.

☞ *Brevet.* [1] Maj. 20 June 1854. [2] Maj. 28 Nov. 54.

Fur. Reg.	Y	M	Captains.	Remarks.	*Ensign.*	*Lieut.*	Captain. *Brevet.*	Captain. *Regl.*
	32	1	D. Gaussen,†[1]*m* - - -	.. ..	25 *May* 27	24 *July* 37	25 *May* 42	15 *Feb.* 48
	29	6	A. H. Ross,†[2]*m* - - -	Asst. Adjt. General Presy. Division, ..	20 *Jan.* 30	6 *Sep.* 39	20 *Jan.* 45	15 *Nov.* 53
	20	6	H. C. Adlam,*PH,* - - -	Comdt. of the Behar Irr. Horse, ...	13 *Jan.* 39	16 *July* 42	13 *Jan.* 54	9 *Aug.* 54
	20	1	A. Macqueen,*PCH,(a)* -	Army Commt. Dept.	18 *June* 39	21 *Aug.* 43	18 *June* 54	9 *Nov.* 55
N.	17	1	W. L. Jones,*PC,* - - -	Fur. S. C. 16 Feb. 58	10 *June* 42	24 *Jan.* 45	.. ..	23 *Nov.* 56
	16	11	E. V. H. Holt,† - - -	.. ..	25 *July* 42	2 *Mar.* 46	25 *July* 57	25 *Aug.* 58
			*					
			Lieutenants.					
Capt.	14	1	W. N. Lees, L.L.D.*PC,* *(b)*	Civil employ, ..	14 *June* 45	25 *July* 53		
D N.	~~10~~	~~6~~	~~C. W. Peter,~~ *P,* - - -	Fur. P. A. 15 Apl.59,	20 *Dec.* 46	3 *Aug.* 53	13th April 59	
	11	6	W. G. B. Tyler,*PCH,* *(c)*-	Civil employ, ..	20 *Jan.* 48	15 *Nov.* 53		
	6	9	F. Allen,*PH,* - - - -	Calcutta, N. Militia,	20 *Sep.* 52	9 *Aug.* 54		
O.	6	5	J. E. D. Wilson,† - - -	Fur. S.C. 25 May 58	20 *Jan.* 53	7 *May* 55		
	5	11	John Gore Campbell,† -	.. ..	20 *Aug.* 53	9 *Nov.* 55		
	5	1	William Lumley Louis,† -	.. ..	8 *June* 54	23 *Nov.* 56		
	4	3	Edmund F. Litchfield,† -	.. ..	20 *Mar.* 55	8 *Dec.* 56		
	3	1	S. S. Sutherland,† - -	Adjt. district police, Saugor. ..	13 *June* 56	14 *Sep.* 57		
	2	7	J. W. Grant,† - - - -	.. ..	13 *Dec.* 56	30 *Apl.* 58		
	1	5	W. Howey, - - - -	.. ..	4 *Feb.* 58	25 *Aug.* 58		
			Ensigns.					
Lt	..	9	R. H. Eades, - - - -	.. ..	20 *Oct.* 58			
			*					
			*					
			*					
			*					
					Appointed.			
	..	..	*Adjt.* C. W. Peter, - -	Fur. P. A. 15 Apl. 59	3 *July* 55			
	..	..	J. G. Campbell, - - -	Officiating, ..	9 *Mar.* 59			
	..	..	*Interpreter,**					
	..	..	*Surg.,** - - - - -					
	..	..	*Asst. Surg.**					

N. B.—This Corps was made Light Infantry for its services in Affghanistan under General Nott.

(a) Has furnished the certificate of qualification as Assay Master, 12th April 1856.

(b) Received Certificate of High Proficiency in the Arabic language, 3rd Sep., 1851, a Degree of Honor for his eminent attainments in the Persian language 29th Oct. 1851, a certificate of High Proficiency in the Oordoo language 15th Nov. 1851, Degree of Honor in Oordoo, 3rd April 1852, and a certificate of High Proficiency in Hindee 21 Dec. 52.—Received the reward of 1,000 Rs. for proficiency in the Native languages, G. O. 5th Jan. 1853.

(c) Has furnished certificate of qualification as a Surveyor.

Raied in 1803.

43rd Regiment of Native (Light) Infantry.

Disarmed, Barrackpore.

(*Rifle Company.*)

"AFFGHANISTAN"—"CANDAHAR"—"GHUZNEE"—"CAUBUL 1842"—"MAHARAJPORE"—"SUBRAON."

Kyne-ke-daheena-Pultun. Late 1st Battalion 22nd Regt. N.I.—FACINGS—*Pea-green.*

Fur. Reg.	Y	M	
N.	55	6	*Colonel* Richard Home. *Ens.* 1 Jan. 1804; *Lieut.* 29 Aug. 1805; *Bt. Capt.* 1 Jan. 1819; *Capt* 10 Nov. 1821; *Major* 29 Nov. 1834; *Lieut. Col.* 17 Sept. 1841; *Col.* 7 April 1851.; *Major General* 28 Nov. 54.—Fur. S. C. 10 Jan. 1855.
	39	3	*Lieut. Colonel* Simon Fraser Hannay. *Ens,* 3 Apl. 1820; *Lt.* 11 July 1823; *Capt.* 1 Apl. 1835; *Bt. Major* 9 Nov. 1846; *Major* 26 July 1852; *Bt. Lt. Col.* 20 June 1854; *Lieut. Col.* 8 June 1857; *Bt. Col.* 20 June 1857; 1st Assam Lt. Infy. Battalion.
	35	4	*Lt. Col.* H. W. Matthews. *Ens.* 3 Mar. 1824; *Lieut.* 9 Nov. 1826; *Bt. Capt.* 3 Mar. 39; *Capt.* 17 Nov. 1842; *Bt. Maj.* 11 Nov. 1851; *Major* 9 Mar. 1855; *Bt. Lt. Col.* 3 Dec. 57; *Lieut. Col.* 26 April 1859
N.	33	11	*Major* A. F. Macpherson, *Ens.* 9 Aug. 1825; *Lieut.* 23 Feb. 1827; *Bt. Capt,* 9 Ang. 40; *Capt.* 24 Jan. 45; *Bl. Maj.* 11 Nov, 51; *Maj.* 26 Apl. 59.—Fur. S.C. 11 June 1858.

☞ *Brevet.* [1] Maj. 28 Nov. 1854. [2] Maj. 8 Mar. 1855.

Y	M	CAPTAINS.	REMARKS.	*Ensign.*	*Lieut.*	CAPTAIN. *Brevet.*	CAPTAIN. *Regl.*
30	5	E. K. Elliot, *P*, [1]*m* -	Civil employ. ..	7 *Feb.* 29	2 *June* 39	7 *Feb.* 44	21 *Jan.* 52
25	4	R. A. Trotter,† - - -	.. ..	10 *Mar.* 34	10 *Oct.* 39	10 *Mar.* 49	14 *July* 53
21	4	G. Holroyd,(*c*)† - - -	.. ..	1 *Mar.* 38	26 *Sep.* 41	1 *Mar.* 53	15 *Nov.* 53
20	7	W. Q. Pogson, *P*, - -	.. ..	12 *Dec.* 38	16 *July* 42	12 *Dec.* 53	6 *Mar.* 54
20	1	C. J. Robarts, *PH*, [2]*m*,	14th Irregular Cavy.	12 *June* 39	17 *Nov.* 42	12 *June* 54	9 *Mar.* 55
18	10	T. E. B. Lees, *PH*, -	2nd Assam Light Infy. Battn. ..	18 *Sep.* 40	24 *Jan.* 45	18 *Sep.* 55	23 *Nov.* 56
17	7	J. Dawson, *P*,(*a*) - - -	Dept. P. W. L. P.	10 *Dec.* 41	10 *Mar.* 49	10 *Dec.* 56	26 *Apl.* 59
		LIEUTENANTS.					
15	6	J. Jerdan,† - - - - -	Doing duty Darjeeling Depot, ..	30 *Dec.* 43	25 *July* 50	30 *Dec.* 58	....
15		R. W. T. Russell,† - -	.. ..	25 *June* 44	21 *Jan.* 52	25 *June* 59	
13	1	A. F. Corbett, *P*,(*b*) -	Comdt. Mily. Police, Budaon District, ..	13 *June* 46	14 *July* 53		
13	3	A. H. B. Bruce, *PH*, - -	D. P. W, N. W. P.,	20 *Apl.* 46	15 *Nov.* 53		
~~13~~	~~1~~	~~T. E. Powell, *PH*,~~	.. ..	11 *June* 47	6 *Mar.* 54		
7	7	W. F. Shaw,† - - - -	.. ..	12 *Dec.* 51	23 *Nov.* 56		
6	5	C. W. Hawes, *PH*, - -	Guide Corps,	13 *Feb.* 53	23 *Nov.* 56		
2	3	W. R. Martin, - -	Fur. S.C. 4 Aug. 58,	4 *Apl.* 57	18 *May* 58		
1	10	M. Millett, - - - -	.. ..	4 *Sep.* 57	18 *May* 58		
1	..	R. H. Inglis, - - - -	.. ..	28 *June* 58	22 *Oct.* 58		
..	7	G. Quin, - - - -	.. ..	11 *Dec.* 58	26 *Apl.* 59		
		ENSIGNS.					
..	7	A. G. Handcock, - - -	.. ..	11 *Dec.* 58			
		*					
		*					
		*					
		*		*Appointed.*			
..	..	*Adjutant*, T. E. Powell, -	.. ..	20 *Apl.* 54			
..	..	*Interpreter*,*					
..	..	*Surg.*, T. C. Hutchinson, -	In charge of 4th European Regt.,	9 *July* 56			
..	..	*Asst. Surg.*,*					

N. B.—This Corps was made Light Infantry for its services in Affghanistan under General Nott.

(*a*) Has furnished certificates of qualification in Surveying and Civil Engineering.

(*b*) Attained the standard of proficiency in the Punjaubee language prescribed by G. O. G. G. 14th Oct. 1851.

Raised in 1803.

44th Regiment of Native Infantry.

Disarmed and Dispersed, Agra.

"DEIG"—"FEROZESHUHUR."

Kyne-ke-baean-Pultun. Late 2nd Battalion 22nd Regt. N.I.

FACINGS—*Pea-green.*

Fur. Reg.	Ser. Y	Ser. M	
N.	51	4	*Colonel* James Manson. *Ens.* 1 March 1808; *Lieut.* 16 Dec. 1814; *Bt. Capt.* 1 March 1823; *Capt.* 13 May 1825; *Bt. Major,* 28 June 1838; *Major,* 11 July 1841; *Lieut. Col.* 24 April 1847; *Bt. Col.* 28 Nov. 1854; *Col.* 29 May 57.—Fur. P. A. 24 Feb. 57.
	40	5	*Lieut. Colonel* Charles Haldane. *Ens.* 6 Feb. 1819; *Lieut.* 26 Aug. 1820; *Bt. Capt.* 6 Feb. 34; *Capt.* 25 Feb. 35; *Maj.* 19 Dec. 42; *Lieut. Col.* 9 April 49; *Bt. Col.* 28 Nov. 1854; —*Col.* 13 Mar. 1859.
	22	4	*Major* E. D. Watson, *P.* *Ens.* 7 Mar. 1837; *Lieut.* 26 June 1840; *Capt.* 13 June 1849; *Maj.* 21 July 1857 —Leave P. A. 15 Oct.

Fur. Reg.	Y	M	CAPTAINS.	REMARKS.	*Ensign.*	*Lieut.*	CAPTAIN. *Brevet.*	CAPTAIN. *Regl.*
O.	19	7	J. P. Clarkson, *PH*, - -	Fur. P. A. 28Apl.59	10 *Dec.* 39	16 *July* 42	.. ..	2 *Aug.* 51
	18	10	H. R. James, *P*, - - -	Civil employ, ..	21 *Aug.* 40	1 *Aug.* 43	.. ..	29 *Feb.* 52
N.	17	1	G. F. Carnegie, *P*, (*a*) - -	Fur. S.C. 19 Dec. 56	11 *June* 42	9 *Jan.* 44	.. ..	1 *May* 55
N.	16	4	A. P. S. Moncrieff, *PCH*, -	Civil employ, ..	22 *Feb.* 43	10 *Jan.* 46	.. ..	29 *May* 57
	16	1	J. S. Rawlins, *PCH*, - -	Seharunpore Police,	10 *June* 43	13 *June* 49	.. ..	21 *July* 57
	11	11	W. T. Fagan, *PCH*, - -	Comdt. 7th Bengal Police Battn. ..	28 *July* 47	9 *Feb.* 51	.. ..	18 *Apl.* 58
	9	7	*Hon'ble* W. M. Fraser, *PH*,	Comdg. district Police, Dehra Dhoon,	11 *Dec.* 49	30 *Mar.* 53	.. ..	19 *June* 59
			LIEUTENANTS.					
	8	7	J. H. Jenkins, *PC*, (*b*) - -	Army Commt. Dept.	10 *Dec.* 50	1 *May* 55		
	8	5	A. H. Bramley,† - - -	.. ..	20 *Jan.* 51	23 *Nov.* 56		
	8	1	W. M. Gibbon, *PH*, - -	Meades' Horse, ..	13 *June* 51	23 *Nov.* 56		
	5	7	Horatio Nelson Noble,† -	Adjt. Mily. Police Battn., Agra, ..	9 *Dec.* 53	29 *May* 57		
	4	7	F. Kellett Hawkins, *PH*, -	Civil employ, ..	20 *Dec.* 54	21 *June* 57		
	4	4	O. R. Newmarch, *P*, - -	Army Commt. Dept.	17 *Mar.* 55	21 *July* 57		
	2	4	F. S. S, Brind,† - - -	.. ..	4 *Mar.* 57	30 *Apl.* 58		
	2	..	J. L. G. O'Brien, - -	.. ..	24 *June* 57	18 *May* 58		
	1	6	A. England, - - - -	1st Sikh Infy. ..	4 *Jan.* 58	9 *Nov* 58		
	1	..	J. H. W. Osborne, - -	.. ..	4 *July* 58	23 *Dec.* 58		
	..	9	W. S. A. Lockhart, - -	Lv. S. C. 15 Oct.	4 *Oct.* 58	19 *June* 59		
			ENSIGNS.					
			*					
			*					
			*					
			*		*Appointed.*			
			*					
	..	..	*Adjt.*,*					
	..	..	*Intr.*,*					
	..	..	*Surg.* C. B. Chalmers, - -	.. ..	6 *Dec.* 56			
	..	..	*Asst. Surg.*, R.K. Buckell,	Offg. Civil Furruckabad, ..	2 *Apl.* 55			

(*a*) Passed an examination in Field Engineering; also, passed an examination in the Punjaubee language, 10th Dec. 1851.

(*b*) Received degrees of honor for his acquirements in the Oordoo and Hindee languages, from the College of Fort William, on the 2d September, 1850 and 5th February, 1851.

Raised in 1803.

45th Regiment of Native Infantry.

Mutinied, Ferozepore.

"MOODKEE"—"FEROZESHUHUR"—"PUNJAUB"—"CHILLIANWALLA"—"GOOJERAT."

Murreeroo-ke-daheena-Pultun. Late 1st Battalion 23rd Regt. N.I.

FACINGS—*Dark-green.*

Fur.	Ser. Y	Ser. M	
	51	4	*Colonel* John Hoggan, C. B. *Ens.* 1 March 1808; *Lieut.* 16 Dec. 1814; *Bt. Capt.* 1 March 1823; *Capt.* 1 May 1824; *Major* 8 Oct. 1836; *Lieut. Col.* 22 Dec. 1842; *Col.* 14 July 1853; *Maj. Genl.* 28 Nov. 1854.—Residing at Deyrah.
	40	10	*Lt. Col.* John Liptrap. *Ens.* 30 Aug. 1818; *Lieut.* 4 Nov. 1818; *Capt.* 19 June 1831; *Bt. Maj.* 9 Nov. 1846; *Major* 17 Feb. 1850; *Bt. Lt. Col.* 20 June 1854; *Lt. Col.* 7 May 1855; *Bt. Col.* 20 June 1857.
	22	1	*Major* W. H. Oakes, *PC.* *Ens.* 19 June 1837; *Lieut.* 27 Jan. 1839; *Capt.* 22 March 1849; *Major* 7 Nov. 1857.—Civil employ.

☞ *Brevet.* [1] Major 24 Mar. 1858; [2] Major 19 Jan. 1858.

Fur.	Y	M		Remarks.	Ensign.	Lieut.	Captain. Brevet.	Captain. Regl.
			Captains.					
	21	7	F. G. Crossman, *PH*,[1]*m* -	Rohilcund Horse, ..	11 *Dec.* 37	3 *Oct.* 40	.. ..	1 *July* 50
	19	6	A. S. O. Donaldson, † - -	.. ..	3 *Jan.* 40	21 *Apl.* 42	.. ..	17 *Apl.* 51
	18	..	O. E. Rothney, *P*,[2]*m*, - -	4th Seikh Infantry,	27 *June* 41	20 *July* 43	.. .	15 *May* 52
	16	11	G. C. Bloomfield, *PH*, - -	23rd Punjaub Infy.,	27 *July* 42	10 *July* 46	.. ..	10 *June* 53
	16	6	R. M. J. Tozer, † - - -	Lv. S. C. 1 Nov., ..	28 *Dec.* 42	8 *May* 47	.. ..	21 *Aug.* 54
O.	15	6	A. E. Osborn, *PH.* - -	Fur. S. C. 14 Sep. 58	30 *Dec.* 43	22 *Mar.* 49	.. ..	23 *Nov.* 56
	10	7	W. F. Stewart, *PH*, - -	Benares Horse, ..	8 *Dec* 48	28 *July* 50	.. ..	16 *Mar.* 58
			Lieutenants.					
O.	10	4	A. A. Currie, *PH*, - - -	Fur. P.A. 14 June 59	3 *Mar.* 49	26 *Oct.* 50		
	10	..	J. W. Hoggan, *P*, - -	17th Punjaub Infy.	27 *June* 49	15 *May* 52		
	9	10	R. Chalmers, *PH*, - - -	2nd in Comd. Murray's Jat. Horse,	7 *Sep.* 49	10 *Sep.* 52		
	9	4	W. Winson, *PH*, - - -	Kelat-i-Ghilzie Regiment, ..	3 *Mar.* 50	10 *June* 53		
	8	7	W. C. B. Ryan, *PH*, - -	Punjaub Irr. Force.	10 *Dec.* 50	21 *Aug.* 54		
	8	6	J. V. Hunt, *P*, - - -	Offg. Army Commt. Dept. ..	20 *Dec.* 50	6 *Sep.* 56		
	6	7	W. F. Edwards, † - - -	Malwah Bheel Corps,	9 *Dec.* 52	23 *Nov.* 56		
	4	1	Charles Grant, - - - -	.. ..	9 *June* 55	23 *Nov.* 56		
	3	1	Llewellyn Wavell, - - -	11th Punjaub Infy.	14 *June* 56	25 *Aug.* 57		
	2	7	E. Swetenham, (*a*) - -	Dept. P.W., N.W.P.	13 *Dec.* 56	7 *Nov.* 57		
	1	11	H. W. Webster, - - -	.. ..	26 *July* 57	18 *May* 58		
			Ensigns.					
	1	5	W. J. Cochrane, - - -	.. ..	20 *Feb.* 58			
			*					
			*					
			*					
			*					
					Appointed.			
	..	..	*Adjt.*,*					
	..	..	*Interpreter*, *					
	..	..	*Surg.*,*					
	..	..	*Asst. Surg.* M. B. Lamb, M. D., ..	.. ..	10 *Apl.* 56			

(*a*) Has furnished the certificate of qualification in Surveying and Civil Engineering.

Raised in 1803.

46th Regiment of Native Infantry.

Mutinied, Sealkote.

"ASSAM"—"PUNJAUB"—"CHILLIANWALLA"—"GOOJERAT."

Murreeroo-ke-baean-Pultun. Late 2nd Battalion 23rd Regt. N.I.

FACINGS—*Dark-green.*

Fur. Reg	Ser. Y	Ser. M	
	46	..	*Col.* Joseph Nash, C B. *Ens.* July 1813; *Lieut.* 25 Dec. 1817; *Capt.* 24 Jan. 1829; *Maj.* 26 Sept. 1841; *Bt. Lt. Col.* 30 April 1844; *Lt. Col.* 11 Nov. 1847; *Bt. Col.* 20 June 1854; *Col.* 15 July 1857; *Major Genl.* 9 April 1856.—Nynee Tal.
	39	11	*Lt. Col.* George Farquharson. *Ens.* 2 Aug. 1819; *Lieut.* 11 June 1820; *Capt.* 20 July 1832; *Major* 13 March 1844; *Bt. Lt. Col.* 7 June 1849; *Lieut. Col.* 21 June 1850; *Bt. Col.* 28 Nov. 1854.—Lv. P. A. for 6 months G. O. 26 Mar. 59.
	33	11	*Major* J. M. Drake, *P. Ens.* 14 Aug. 25; *Lieut.* 1 Apl. 28; *Bt. Capt.* 14 Aug. 40; *Capt.* 26 Oct. 44; *Bt. Maj.* 11 Nov. 51; *Maj.* 17 April 1856.

☞ *Brevet.* [1] Maj. 20 June 54. [2] Major 20 July 1858.

Fur. Reg	Y	M		Remarks.	Ensign.	Lieut.	Captain. Brevet.	Captain. Regl.
			Captains.					
	33	..	H. S. Grimes, *P*, [1]*m* - -	Offg. Pay Dept. ..	27 *June* 26	29 *Aug.* 33	27 *June* 41	21 *Apl.* 48
	24	3	G. Caulfeild, † - - - -	Sealkote Infy. Levy.	23 *Mar.* 35	3 *Oct.* 40	23 *Mar.* 50	8 *Oct.* 50
	23	6	G. N. Oakes, *PCH*, - -	Civil employ, ..	3 *Jan.* 36	1 *July* 42	3 *Jan.* 51	31 *Dec.* 51
N.	18	6	S. J. Browne, *PH*, [2]*m* - -	2nd Punjaub Cavy.	22 *Dec.* 40	26 *Oct.* 44	.. ..	10 *Feb.* 55
	17	6	T. Wright, *P—TC*, (*a*) - -	Asst. Adjutant Gl. PeshawurDivn. and Offg. Comdt. 2nd Sikh Cavy. ..	8 *Jan.* 42	15 *Dec.* 44	.. ..	17 *Apl.* 56
	17	1	T.W. Mercer, *P*, (*b*) - -	Civil employ, ..	11 *June* 42	24 *Jan.* 45	11 *June* 57	9 *July* 57
	15	6	A. Le Gallais, B A. *PH*, -	Cantonment Joint Magte. Sealkote...	1 *Jan.* 44	21 *Apl.* 48	.. ..	14 *July* 57
			Lieutenants.					
	15	6	C. L. Brown, *P*, - - -	Pay Dept. ..	1 *Jan.* 44	25 *July* 49	1 *Jan.* 59	
O.	15	1	J. H. Speke, *PH*, (*c*) -	Fur. S. C. 7 June 55,	8 *June* 44	8 *Oct.* 50	8 *June* 59	
O.	13	3	F. D. Ogilvie, *PH*, - -	Fur. P.A. 13 Jan. 57	20 *Apl.* 46	31 *Dec.* 51		
	11	11	W. P. Conolly, *P*, - -	Joudpore Legion,	11 *Aug.* 47	1 *Nov.* 53		
O.	10	6	B. N. Smith, *PH*, - - -	3rd Irr. Cavy. ..	20 *Jan.* 49	10 *Feb.* 55		
	9	4	J. J. Russell, † - - - -	.. ..	3 *Mar.* 50	17 *Apl.* 56		
	10	7	E. O'B. Horsford, † - -	2nd Infy. Gwalior Contingent,	9 *Dec.* 48	23 *Nov.* 56		
	8	4	T. J. Watson, *PH*, - - -	Adjt. Maj. Robert's Cavy, ..	20 *Feb.* 51	23 *Nov.* 56		
	5	1	John Upperton, *P*, - -	Regt. of Lucknow,	10 *June* 54	9 *July* 57		
	4	7	R. Elphinstone Boyle, *PCH*,	2nd Sikh Infy. ..	10 *Dec.* 54	14 *July* 57		
	2	2	E. C. Corbyn, † - - -	Adjt. Mily. Police Boolundshuhur district. ..	6 *May* 57	18 *May* 58		
			Ensigns.					
	1	9	H. U. Smith, † - - - -	.. ..	4 *Oct.* 57			
	..	6	R. M. B. Thomas, - - -	.. ..	6 *Jan.* 59			
			*					
			*		*Appointed.*			
			*					
	..	..	*Adjutant*, *					
	..	..	*Interpreter*, *					
	..	..	*Surg.* R. C. Guise, - - -	.. ..	5 *Jan.* 57			
	..	..	*Asst. Surg.*, *					

(*a*) Has passed an examination in Surveying at the Thomason College at Roorkee.
(*b*) Has passed an examination in Field Engineering; also passed the Civil Service examinations in the Punjaub lower and higher Standards
(*c*) Has passed an examination in the Turkish Language.

Raised in 1824. — **47th Regt. of Nat. Infy. (Volunteers.)** — On Service in China.

" MOODKEE"—" FEROZESHUHUR"—" ALLIWAL"—" SUBRAON."

Craum-ka-Pultun. Late 69th N. I.
FACINGS—*Yellow.*

Fur. Reg.	Ser. Y	Ser. M	
	55	6	*Colonel* Stephen Davis Riley. *Ens.* 1 Jan. 1804; *Lieut.* 2 July 1806; *Bt. Capt.* 1 Jan. 1819; *Capt.* 20 Aug. 1822; *Major* 3 July 1832; *Lieut. Col.* 19 April 1839; *Col.* 9 April 1849; *Major General* 28 Nov. 1854.—Presidency.
	30	6	*Lieut. Col.* D. Pott. *Ensign* 20 Jan. 1829; *Lieut.* 6 June 1833; *Capt.* 8 Oct. 1839; *Bt. Major* 3 April 1846; *Major* 31 Jan. 1854; *Bt. Lt. Col.* 20 *June* 1854; *Lieut. Col.* 1 May 1858; *Bt. Col.* 22 Aug. 1857.
O.	30	6	*Major* J. T. Daniell, *P.* *Ensign* 20 Jan. 1829; *Lieut.* 10 Feb. 1835; *Bt. Capt.* 20 Jan. 1844; *Captain* 24 Jan. 1845; *Bt Major* 28 Nov 1854; *Major* 1 May 1858.—Fur. P. A. 1st Mar. 1859.

Fur. Reg.	Y	M	CAPTAINS.	REMARKS.	*Ensign.*	*Lieut.*	CAPTAIN. *Brevet.*	CAPTAIN. *Regl.*
	24	3	R. Renny,† - - - -	3rd Seikh Infy.	31 *Mar.* 35	15 *Apl.* 38	.. ..	22 *Mar.* 50
	21	7	R. Campbell, *PH,* - - -	2nd Assam Lt. Infy.	11 *Dec.* 37	3 *Oct.* 40	.. ..	3 *Nov.* 52
	20	4	W. C. Watson, *PH,* - -	.. ..	24 *Feb.* 39	15 *Jan.* 42	.. ..	15 *Dec.* 53
	19	6	J. R. Pughe, *P,* - - -	Comdt. 3rd Bengal Police Battn. ..	3 *Jan.* 40	20 *July* 43	.. ..	31 *Jan.* 54
	18	4	G McAndrew, *P,* - -	22nd Punjaub Infy.,	8 *Mar.* 41	22 *Dec.* 45	8 *Mar.* 56	27 *Oct.* 56
	16	11	J. P. W. Campbell, *PH,* -	2nd Seikh Infy. ..	28 *July* 42	21 *Jan.* 46	.. ..	23 *Nov.* 56
	16	7	C. P. Lucas,† - - - -	.. ..	10 *Dec.* 42	19 *May* 47	10 *Dec.* 57	1 *May* 58
			LIEUTENANTS.					
D	~~16~~	~~4~~	~~W. H. Walcot, *PH,*~~ - -	.. ..	22 *Feb.* 43	3 *Aug.* 49	22 *Feb.* 58	
	15	1	E. Leeds, *PH,* - - -	Dept. of P. W. Pegu,	7 *June* 44	22 *Mar.* 50	7 *June* 59	
	11	6	C. V. Jenkins, *PH,* - - -	Civil employ, ..	20 *Jan.* 48	16 *Oct.* 51		
	9	7	W. Gordon,† - - - -	.. ..	12 *Dec.* 49	11 *May* 52		
	9	5	T. W. Evans,† - - - -	Doing duty Recruit Depot, Barrackpore.	16 *Feb.* 50	15 *Dec.* 53		
	8	6	H. R. Buttanshaw,† - -	.. ..	24 *Dec.* 50	27 *Oct.* 56		
N.	7	1	H. R. B. Worsley,† -	Fur. S.C. 12 Nov. 58	13 *June* 52	23 *Nov.* 56		
	5	5	M. C. Perreau,† - - -	.. ..	4 *Feb.* 54	1 *May* 58		
	2	10	H. L. Ramsbotham, - -	.. ..	4 *Sep.* 56	30 *Apl.* 58		
	2	6	F. C. Bewsher,† - - -	.. ..	20 *Jan.* 57	30 *Apl.* 58		
	1	11	F. T. Ripley, - - -	.. ..	4 *Aug.* 57	18 *May* 58		
			ENSIGNS.					
Lt.	..	7	C. S. de F. Roche, - - -	.. ..	11 *Dec.* 58			
			*					
			*					
			*					
			*					
					Appointed.			
	..	..	*Adjt.* W. H. Walcot, -	Officiating. ..	6 *Dec.* 58			
	..	..	*Intr.*,*					
	..	..	*Surg.*,*					
	..	..	*Asst. Surg.*					

Raised in 1804.

48th Regiment of Native Infantry.

Mutinied, Oude (Lucknow.)

(*Rifle Company.*)

"AFFGHANISTAN"—"GHUZNEE"—"MOODKEE"—"FEROZESHUHUR"—"ALLIWAL."

Mutees-ka-Pultun. Late 2nd Battalion 24th Regt. N.I.

FACINGS—*White.*

Fur. Reg.	Ser. Y	Ser. M	
O.	45	..	*Colonel* James Clarke Charnock Gray. *Ens.* 12 July 1814; *Lieut.* 5 June 1816; *Capt.* 1 Aug. 1828; *Major* 1 Sept. 1841; *Lieut. Col.* 27 Aug. 1847; *Bt. Col.* 28 Nov. 1854; *Col.* 27 June 1857.—Leave S. C. 15 November.
	33	5	*Lieut. Col.* H. Palmer, *PC.* *Ens.* 13 Feb. 1826; *Lieut.* 27 June 1835; *Capt.* 16 Oct. 1840; *Bt. Major* 3 Apl. 1846; *Major* 5 June 1853; *Bt. Lt. Col.* 20 June 1854; *Lieut. Col.* 4 Oct. 1857; *Brevet Col.* 29 July 1857.—Comdg. Regt. of Lucknow.
O.	25	1	*Major* C. Hasell. *Ens.* 13 Dec. 1833; *Lieut.* 22 June 1838; *Capt.* 24 Jan. 1845; *Bt. Maj.* 28 Nov. 1854; *Major* 4 Oct 1857.—Fur. S. C. 5 May 1859.

☞ *Brevet.* [1] Maj. 28 Nov. 54. [2] Maj. 24 March 58.

Fur. Reg.	Y	M	CAPTAINS.	REMARKS.	*Ensign.*	*Lieut.*	CAPTAIN. *Brevet.*	CAPTAIN. *Regl.*
O.	24	6	H. L. Bird,†[1]*m* - - - -	Fur. S. C. 16 Apl. 58	13 *Jan.* 35	30 *June* 38	.. ..	12 *May* 45
O.	19	11	T. Green,† - - - -	Fur. S. C. 24 Apl. 58	28 *July* 39	28 *Apl.* 41	.. ..	7 *Nov.* 50
N.	18	5	B. Henderson,*P,* - - -	3rd Punjaub Infy. and Civil employ,	4 *Feb.* 41	21 *Apl.* 44	.. ..	5 *June* 53
N.	18	4	P. R. Hockin,*P,* - - -	2nd Sikh Irr. Cavy.	8 *Mar.* 41	24 *Jan.* 45	8 *Mar.* 56	23 *Nov.* 56
	16	6	W. T. Hughes,*P,*[2]*m* - -	1st Punjaub Cavy.	28 *Dec.* 42	19 *Feb.* 47	.. ..	1 *June* 57
	15	10	J. J. Hume,*PH,* - - -	Dep. P. W. Grand Trunk Road,	4 *Sep.* 43	24 *July* 47	.. ..	4 *Oct.* 57
	14	7	W.E. Marshall,*PH(a)TC,*	Dept. P. Works, L. Provinces,	9 *Dec.* 44	2 *July* 49	.. ..	21 *Mar.* 58
			LIEUTENANTS.					
	14	1	J. S. Ogilvie,*PC,* - - -	Army Commt. Dept.	13 *June* 45	29 *Sep.* 50		
N.	13	1	G. C. Huxham,*PCH,* - -	Fur. S. C. 22 Apl. 58	13 *June* 46	29 *Sep.* 50		
	12	1	O. L. Smith,† - -	Oude Mily. Police.	12 *June* 47	7 *Nov.* 50		
	12	1	R. Ouseley,*PC,* - - -	Army Commt. Dept.	11 *June* 47	1 *Oct.* 52		
	9	4	C. W. Fletcher,*PH,* - -	A. D. C. to Major Genl. *Sir* J. E. W. Inglis, K. C. B. ..	20 *Feb.* 50	5 *June* 53		
	3	1	E. B. Ward,- - - - -	Divl. Adjt. Mily. Police, Oudh, ..	14 *June* 56	12 *June* 57		
	5	10	C. A.de Kantzow,†- - -	.. ..	14 *Sep.* 53	23 *Nov.* 56		
	2	7	C. O'Donel,† - - - -	Doing duty Recruit Depot,Barrackpore	20 *Dec.* 56	29 *June* 57		
	3	1	C. P. Chambers, - - -	.. ..	14 *June.* 56	15 *May* 58		
	1	11	H. Collingwood, - - -	.. ..	26 *July* 57	18 *May* 58		
	1	5	R. Atkins, - - - - -	.. ..	4 *Feb.* 58	7 *June* 58		
			ENSIGNS.					
	1	4	C. J. Farquharson, - - -	.. ..	4 *Mar.* 58			
			*					
			*					
			*					
			*		*Appointed.*			
	..	..	*Adjutant,**					
	..	..	*Intr.,* *					
	..	..	*Surg.,*W.W.Wells, F.R.C.S.	Fur. S. C. 23 Feb. 58	12 *Apl.* 54			
	..	..	*Asst. Surg.,**					

(*a*) Has furnished the certificates of qualification in civil Engineering and Surveying at Thomason College.

Raised in 1804.

49th Regiment of Native Infantry.

Disarmed, Meean Meer (Lahore,)

"ARRACAN"—"PUNJAUB"—"MOOLTAN."

Rayle-ka-Pultun. Late 1st Battalion 25th Regt. N. I.

FACINGS—*Buff.*

Fur. Reg.	Ser. Y	Ser. M	
O	41	10	*Colonel* Nathaniel Jones. *Ens.* 2 Sep. 1817; *Lieut.* 1 Aug. 1818; *Capt.* 21 Sept. 1828; *Major* 21 July 1841; *Lieut. Col.* 12 Aug. 1847; *Bt. Col.* 28 Nov. 1854; *Col.* 31 May 1857.—Fur. P. A. 27 May 1859.
	31	2	*Lieut. Col.* Cuthbert Davidson, *P.* *Ens.* 11 May 1828; *Lieut.* 4 Jan. 1832; *Capt.* 8 Sept. 1842; *Major* 10 May 1852; *Lieut. Col.* 31 May 1857.—Political employ.
	30	1	*Major* John Smith, *P.* *Ens.* 7 June 1829; *Lieut.* 8 Jan. 1835; *Bt. Capt.* 7 June 1844; *Capt.* 7 July 45; *Bt. Maj.* 28 Nov. 54. *Maj.* 18 May 1856.

☞ *Brevet*, [1] Major 20 July 1858. [2] Maj. 20 July 1858. [3] Major 20 July 1858.

Fur. Reg.	Y	M	CAPTAINS.	REMARKS.	*Ensign.*	*Lieut.*	CAPTAIN. *Brevet.*	CAPTAIN. *Regl.*
O.	25	1	H. J. Piercy, *P*,	Fur. S. C. 16 Mar. 58	13 *June* 34	17 *July* 37	.. ..	22 *Jan.* 47
	19	7	R. Larkins, *PH*, [1]*m*	17th Punjaub Infy.	10 *Dec.* 39	30 *Aug.* 41	.. ..	13 *Mar.* 48
O.	19	5	J. Hood, *PH*, [2]*m*	Fur. S C 17 July 58	29 *Jan.* 40	5 *Nov.* 41	.. ..	10 *June* 50
	18	2	J. F. Richardson, C.B. *PH*, (*a*)[3]*m*	Comdg. Volunteer Cavalry, ..	21 *Apl.* 41	24 *Jan.* 45	.. ..	24 *Jan.* 51
	18	1	W. Gordon, *PH*, (*b*)	Brigade Staff.	11 *June* 41	14 *Mar.* 45	.. ..	15 *Jan.* 53
	17	..	W. Irwin, †	Lv. P. A. 15 Oct. ...	8 *July* 42	22 *Jan.* 47	.. ..	18 *May* 56
	15	1	F. R. Pollock, *PH*,	Civil employ, ..	8 *June* 44	23 *June* 47	.. ..	23 *Nov.* 56
			LIEUTENANTS.					
	14	6	C. C. Dandridge, *PH*,	Futtehgurh Infantry Levy. ..	18 *Jan.* 45	13 *Mar.* 48		
	14	6	J. Williamson, *PH*,	9th Punjaub Infy.	20 *Jan.* 45	13 *Apl.* 48		
	12	7	G. Allgood, *PH*,	Qr. Mr. Genl.'s Dept.	20 *Dec.* 46	14 *Sep.* 48		
	11	7	J. F. Sherer, *PH*,	Comdt. Kookey Levy and Asst. Supdt. of Cachar, ..	10 *Dec.* 47	24 *Jan.* 51		
	9	6	Algar B. Temple, † *e*	Kemaoon Battn. ..	26 *Dec.* 49	18 *July* 55		
	7	4	M. K. St. John, †	Alexanders' Horse,	1 *Mar.* 52	18 *May* 56		
	4	4	Francis Henry Conolly, †	Offg. Adjt. Recruit depot, Barrackpore,	17 *Mar.* 55	20 *Sep.* 56		
	3	..	Thomas Reid Davidson,	16 Irr. Cavalry, ..	15 *July* 56	23 *Nov.* 56		
	3	..	Hamilton Chapman,	Alexanders' Horse,	15 *July* 56	23 *Nov.* 56		
	3	..	George Soden Goad, †	13 Punjaub Infy., ..	26 *July* 56	30 *Apl.* 58		
	2	5	James Forsyth,	.. ..	20 *Feb.* 57	30 *Apl.* 58		
			ENSIGNS.					
	1	9	J. H. Blunt,	.. ..	4 *Oct.* 57			
	..	6	E. P. Ommanney,	.. ..	6 *Jan.* 59			
			*					
			*					
			*		*Appointed.*			
	..	..	*Adjutant.*					
	..	..	*Intr.*,*					
	..	..	*Surg.*, M. McN. Rind,	.. ..	24 *Jan.* 57			
	..	..	*Asst. Surg.*, A. J. Dale, M.B.,	Fur. S. C. 9 Feb. 57,	13 *Sep.* 55			

(*a*) Honorary Rank of Major.

(*b*) Has furnished the certificates of qualification in surveying and Field Engineering and Received a first class certificate, as an Instructor of musketry from the Royal school of musketry, Hythe.

Raised in 1840.

50th Regiment of Native Infantry.

Mutinied, Sultanpore, (Benares.)

"PUNNIAR"—"PUNJAUB."

Cristeen-ka-Pultun. Late 2nd Battalion 25th Regt. N.I.

FACINGS—*Buff.*

Fur. Reg.	Ser. Y	Ser. M	
	53	1	*Colonel* James Parsons, C. B. *Ens.* 24 May 1806; *Lieut.* 13 Aug. 1812; *Bt. Capt.* 24 May 1821; *Major* 22 April 1836; *Bt. Lt. Col.* 23 July 1839; *Lt. Col.* 7 July 1842; *Bt. Col.* 16 July 1849; *Col.* 31 Mar. 1853; *Maj. Genl.* 28 Nov. 1854.—Bareilly.
	36	..	*Lt. Col.* Joseph Hampton Hampton. *Ens.* 11 July 23; *Lieut.* 18 Nov. 24; *Bt. Capt.* 11 July 38; *Capt.* 7 July 42; *Bt. Major* 11 Nov. 51; *Major* 9 Aug. 1854; *Bt. Lt. Col.* 22 Aug. 1857; *Lieut. Colonel* 19 May 1858.
	35	6	*Major* K. Young, C. B., *PC*, *Ens.* 16 Jan. 24; *Lieut.* 13 May 25; *Bt. Capt.* 16 Jan. 39; *Capt.* 14 June 44; *Bt. Major* 11 Nov. 1851; *Major* 19 May 1858; *Bt. Lieut. Col.* 12 Oct. 1857.—Judge Advocate General,

☞ *Brevet.* [1] Major 20 June 54. Lt. Col. 20 July 58. [2] Major 19 Jan. 1858.

Fur. Reg.	Y	M	CAPTAINS.	REMARKS.	*Ensign.*	*Lieut.*	CAPTAIN. *Brevet.*	CAPTAIN. *Regl.*
	~~33~~	~~4~~	~~G. Gordon, †[illegible]~~ - - -	1st Seikh Infantry,	15 *Mar.* 26	12 *Mar.* 29	15 *Mar.* 41	4 *Jan.* 49
N.	24	7	H. Nicoll, *P*, [2]*m* - - -	Brigade Staff,	12 *Dec.* 34	4 *Nov.* 38	.. ..	22 *Oct.* 49
	22	1	A. C. Plowden, *P*, - - -	Private Secretary and A. D. C. to the Lt. Governor, Bengal.	13 *June* 37	3 *Oct.* 40	13 *June* 52	3 *Mar.* 53
	21	4	J. R. McMullin, *P*, (*a*) - -	Comdt. Military Police, Goruckpore.	1 *Mar.* 38	7 *July* 42	1 *Mar.* 53	15 *Nov.* 53
	21	..	B. E. Bacon, *P*, - - -	Qr. Mr. Genl.'s Dept.	22 *June* 38	16 *July* 42	22 *June* 53	9 *Aug.* 54
O.	20	..	H. E. Read, *PH*, - - -	Lv. S C. 15 Oct. ..	10 *July* 39	14 *June* 44	10 *July* 54	23 *Nov.* 56
	18	11	G. A. St. P. Fooks, *PH* - -	Comdg. District Police, Jounpore,	21 *Aug.* 40	24 *Jan.* 45	21 *Aug.* 55	19 *May* 58
			LIEUTENANTS.					
	~~14~~	~~1~~	~~J. M. Bayley, †~~ - - -	.. ..	13 *June* 45	4 *Jan.* 49		
	13	2	A. A. Munro, *P*, (*b*) - -	Civil employ, ..	5 *May* 46	22 *Oct.* 49		
	11	..	A. W. Bolton, *P*, - - -	Offg. Army Commt. Dept., ..	20 *June* 48	27 *Oct.* 50		
	10	7	G. J. Reeves, *PH*, - - -	Comdt. 2nd Bengal Police Battn. Offg. Comdt. of the Irr. Cavy. in Chota Nagpore. ..	8 *Dec.* 48	3 *Mar.* 53		
	9	7	H. V. Mathias, *PCH*, (*c*) -	Baghalcund Military Police, ..	20 *Dec.* 49	9 *Aug.* 54		
	9	1	F. A. Lawford, *PH*, - -	3rd Regt. Hodson's Horse, ..	14 *June* 50	28 *Oct.* 56		
	8	1	W. H. Garton, † - - -	Adjutant Divisional Battn. Benares,	14 *June* 51	23 *Nov.* 56		
	5	2	Bernard Cracroft, *PH*, - -	Baghalcund Military Police, ..	15 *May* 54	21 *Feb.* 57		
	4	10	Jas. Wm. O'Dowda, *PH*, -	Adjutant District Police, Jounpore,	12 *Sep.* 54	21 *Aug.* 57		
	2	7	A. Goldney, - - - -	Seikh Police corps,	13 *Dec.* 56	30 *Apl.* 58		
	1	11	T. B. M. Glascock, † - -	.. ..	11 *Aug.* 57	19 *May* 58		
			ENSIGNS.					
	1	1	F. Cardew, - - - - -	.. ..	12 *June* 58			
			*					
			*					
			*					
			*		*Appointed.*			
	..	..	*Adjt.*,*					
	..	..	*Interpreter*,*					
	..	..	*Surg.*,*					
	..	..	*Asst. Surg.**					

(*a*) Has passed an examination in Field Engineering.
(*b*) Has passed the Civil service examinations in the Punjaub higher and lower standards.
(*c*) Has received a first class certificate from the school of Musketry at Umballah.

Raised in 1804.

51st Regiment of Native Infantry.

Mutinied, Peshawur.

" PUNNIAR"—" PUNJAUB"—" MOOLTAN"—" GOOJERAT."

Duberne-ka-Pultun. Late 1st Battalion 26th Regt. N.I.

FACINGS—*Dark-green.*

Fur. Reg.	Ser. Y	Ser. M	
	53	7	*Colonel* John Tulloch, C. B. *Ens.* 23 Nov. 1805 ; *Lt,* 2 Feb. 1807 ; *Capt.* 11 July 1821 ; *Major* 24 Jan. 1829 ; *Lieut. Col.* 30 April 1834 ; *Col.* 23 Oct. 1845 ; *Maj. Genl.* 20 June 1854.—Fur. 3 Mar. 50.
			*Lieut. Colonel,**
N.	36	..	*Major* C. Cheape. *Ens.* 11 July 1823 ; *Lieut.* 13 May 1825 ; *Bt. Capt.* 11 July 1838 ; *Capt.* 1 May 1843 ; *Bt. Major* 2 Aug. 1850 ; *Major* 27 June 1857 ; *Bt. Lieut. Col.* 28 Nov. 1854.—Fur. S. C. 26 Feb. 1856.

☞ *Brevet.* [1] Maj. 20 June 1854. [2] Maj. 3 Aug. 50 ; Lieut. Col. 28 Nov. 1854.

Fur. Reg.	Y	M		Remarks.	Ensign.	Lieut.	Captain. Brevet.	Captain. Regl.
			CAPTAINS.					
	33	5	W. Lamb, *P*, [1]*m* - - -	Asst. Adjt. Genl. Lahore Division.	4 *Feb.* 26	25 *Apl.* 36	4 *Feb.* 41	1 *July* 46
	31	1	S. A. Abbott, *P*, [2]*lc* -	Civil employ and H. A. D. C. to the G.G.	12 *June* 28	18 *Feb.* 38	12 *June* 43	2 *Aug.* 50
	23	..	S. H. J. Davies, *P*, (*a*) -	Offg. D. P. W. ..	28 *June* 36	30 *Jan.* 42	28 *June* 51	1 *Oct.* 52
	18	9	W. R. Wallace, † - - -	.. ..	27 *Sep.* 40	12 *Nov.* 42	.. ..	1 *Nov.* 53
O.	17	11	John Smith, *PH*, - -	Fur. S. C. 3 April 57	29 *July* 41	1 *May* 43	.. ..	13 *May* 55
	17	1	T. C. Darnell, *P*, - -	9th Punjaub Infy.	11 *June* 42	7 *May* 44	.. ..	23 *Nov.* 56
	17	..	E. R. Blair, † - - -	.. ..	10 *July* 42	24 *Jan.* 45	.. ..	27 *June* 57
			LIEUTENANTS.					
	17	..	E. Tyrwhitt, *PH*, - - -	Comdg. Police Battn. Meerut, ..	10 *July* 42	1 *July* 46	10 *July* 57	
	16	11	W. J. Ward, *P*, - - - -	4th Irr. Cavalry, ..	25 *July* 42	2 *Aug.* 50	25 *July* 57	
	16	7	C. Irvine, *PH*, (*b*) - - -	19th Punjaub Infy.,	9 *Dec.* 42	5 *Jan.* 52	9 *Dec.* 57	
	15	7	G. Hamilton, *PH*, - - -	.. ..	9 *Dec.* 43	1 *Oct.* 52	9 *Dec.* 58	
O.	10	..	E. P. W. Ripley, *PH.* -	Fur. S. C. 2 Feb. 58.	20 *July* 49	18 *Mar.* 53		
	8	1	G. C. Thomson, †- - -	1st Irr. Cavy., ..	9 *July* 51	7 *Sep.* 54		
	6	10	J. W. Campbell, *PH*, - -	Doing duty with the 5th Police Battn.,	20 *Aug.* 52	23 *Nov.* 56		
	5	3	Wm. Gordon Chalmers, † -	.. ..	4 *Apl.* 54	27 *Jan.* 57		
	4	9	Benjamin Williams, † - -	Mooltanee Regt. of Cavy. ..	27 *Sep.* 54	19 *May* 57		
	2	7	H. M. Pratt, † - - -	25 Punjaub Infy. ..	4 *Nov.* 56	30 *Apl.* 58		
	2	4	A. E. Downing, † - - -	.. ..	4 *Mar.* 57	30 *Apl.* 58		
			ENSIGNS.					
	1	7	H. A. Plowden, - - -	20 Punjaub Infy., ..	12 *Dec.* 57			
			*					
			*					
			*					
			*		*Appointed.*			
	..	..	*Adjutant,**					
	..	..	*Interpreter, **					
	..	..	*Surg.**					
	..	..	*Asst. Surg. **					

(*a*) Has furnished the certificate of qualification in Civil Engineering.
(*b*) Has passed an examination in Field Engineering

Raised in 1804.

52nd Regiment of Native Infantry.

Mutinied, Saugor.

"PUNJAUB"—"MOOLTAN"—"GOOJERAT

Hindree-ka-Pultun. Late 2nd Battalion 26th Regt. N.I.

FACINGS—*Dark-green.*

Fur. Reg.	Ser. Y	Ser. M	
	53	3	*Colonel* Andrew Hervey, C. B. *Ens.* 27 March 1806; *Lieut.* 2 Jan. 1811; *Bt. Capt.* 27 March 1821; *Capt.* 1 May 1824; *Major* 31 Jan. 1832; *Lieut. Col.* 16 March 1838; *Col.* 8 March 1849; *Maj. Genl.* 28 Nov. 1854.—Darjeeling.
	35	6	*Lt. Col.* James Wm. Henry Jamieson. *Ensign* 16 Jan. 1824; *Lieut.* 13 May 1825; *Bt. Capt.* 16 Jan. 1839; *Capt.* 4 Sep. 1839; *Bt. Maj.* 7 June 1849; *Maj.* 15 September 1851; *Bt. Lt. Col.* 28 Nov. 1854; *Lieut. Col.* 10 May 1857; *Bt. Col.* 28 Nov. 1857.
	32	4	*Major* R. Morrieson, *P. Ens.* 17 Mar. 1827; *Lieut.* 6 May 1829; *Bt. Capt.* 17 Mar. 1842; *Capt.* 24 Jan. 1845; *Bt. Major* 20 June 1854; *Major* 10 May 1857.—Political employ.

Fur. Reg.	Y	M	CAPTAINS.	REMARKS.	*Ensign.*	*Lieut.*	CAPTAIN. *Brevet.*	CAPTAIN. *Regl.*
	23	1	E. Hall, *P*, - - - -	Allygurh Levy. ..	10 *June* 36	20 *Nov.* 38	.. ..	5 *Aug.* 48
	19	6	G. G. Moxon, *P*, - - -	Civil employ. ..	3 *Jan.* 40	8 *Apl.* 42	.. ..	24 *June* 54
	19	5	J. B. Y. Matheson, *P*, - -	Benares Horse, ..	26 *Jan.* 40	16 *July* 42	26 *Jan.* 55	5 *Nov.* 55
	18	11	W. H. Lowther, *PH*, - -	.. ..	21 *Aug.* 40	24 *Jan.* 45	21 *Aug.* 55	23 *Nov.* 56
	17	6	F. M. Martin, † - - -	.. ..	8 *Jan.* 42	3 *Jan.* 46	8 *Jan.* 57	10 *May* 57
	15	7	H. F. Waddington, *P*, -	Civil employ, ..	8 *Dec.* 43	15 *July* 48	.. ..	27 *June* 57
	15	2	H. L. Campbell, *PH*, - -	9th Irregular Cavy.	21 *Apl.* 44	5 *Aug.* 48	.. ..	13 *July* 57
			LIEUTENANTS.					
N.	13	5	W. H. Jackson, † - -	Fur. S. C. 11 Feb. 59, ..	26 *Jan.* 46	15 *Sep.* 51		
	12	2	R. D'O. C. Bracken, *PH*, -	2d Seikh Local Infy.	26 *Apl.* 47	20 *May* 53		
	11	7	R. E. Oakes, *PH*, - - -	Revenue. Surv. Dept.	11 *Dec.* 47	1 *June* 54		
O.	11	1	N. Barton, † - - - -	Fur. P. A. 25 May 1859, ..	10 *June* 48	24 *June* 54		
	8	1	J. C. Miller, *PH*, - - -	.. ..	13 *June* 51	5 *Nov.* 55		
	7	1	D. G. Manning, † - - -	.. ..	12 *June* 52	23 *Nov.* 56		
N.	6	1	H. M. Bromley, † - - -	Jubbulpore Police,	11 *June* 53	23 *Nov.* 56		
	6	5	Alexander Cockburn, † -	Nagpore Irr. Force,	20 *Jan.* 53	10 *May* 57		
	4	4	F. J. N. Mackenzie, † -	9th Irr. Cavalry ..	17 *Mar.* 55	27 *June* 57		
	3	7	A. A. Dick, † - - - -	1st Regt. Sikh Irr. Cavy. ..	20 *Dec.* 55	13 *July* 57		
	2	1	H. P. Evans, - - - -	Lv. S. C. 24 Nov.,	12 *June* 57	18 *May* 58		
			ENSIGNS.					
	..	11	G. B. Lee, - - - - -	.. ..	7 *Aug.* 58			
			*					
			*					
			*					
			*		*Appointed.*			
	..	..	*Adjt.*, J. C. Miller, - -	.. ..	9 *Sep.* 56			
	..	..	*Inter.*,*					
	..	..	*Surgn.*,*					
	..	..	*Asst. Surg.*,*					

Raised in 1804. } **53rd Regiment of Native Infantry.** { Mutinied, Cawnpore.

"CAUBUL 1842"—"PUNJAUB."

Castor-ka-Pultun. Late 1st Battalion 27th Regt. N.I.

FACINGS—*Yellow*.

Fur. Reg.	Ser. Y	Ser. M	
	62	4	*Colonel* Mossom Boyd. *Ens.* 3 March 1797; *Lieut.* 30 Oct. 1797; *Capt.* 18 Oct. 1807; *Major* 21 May 1816; *Lieut. Col.* 11 June 1822; *Col.* 13 May 1825; *Major Genl.* 28. June 38; *Lieut. Genl.* 11 Nov. 1851; *Genl.* 9 April 1856.—Europe, 17 Jan. 43.
	~~28~~	~~2~~	~~*Lieut. Col.* Arthur Sanders.~~ *Ens.* 11 May 1831; *Lieut.* 12 March 1837; *Capt.* 24 Aug. 1843; *Major* 29 Feb. 1852; *Lieut. Col.* 29 May 1857. Comdg. Raneegunge Depot.
	25	1	*Major* H. Ramsay, *P*. *Ens.* 14 June 1834; *Lieut.* 8 Jan. 1840; *Bt. Capt.* 14 June 1849; *Capt.* 15 Dec. 1849; *Major* 15 July 1857.—Civil employ.

☞ *Brevet.* [1] Major 24 March 1858.

Fur. Reg.	Y	M	CAPTAINS.	REMARKS.	*Ensign.*	*Lieut.*	CAPTAIN. *Brevet.*	CAPTAIN. *Regl.*
N.	19	..	*Baron* F. A. VonMeyern, *PH*, - - - - - - -	Nagpore Irr. Force,	8 *July* 40	17 *June* 42	.. ..	15 *Nov.* 52
	18	7	R. J. Edgell, *PH*,[1]*m* -	Pay Department, ..	11 *Dec.* 40	16 *July* 42	.. ..	24 *Apl.* 55
	17	4	W. R. E. Alexander, *PH*,-	Alexander's Horse.	2 *Mar.* 42	1 *Oct.* 43	.. ..	24 *Apl.* 55
O.	12	7	L. G. A. Campbell, *PH*. -	Fur. S. C. 12 Nov. 58.	20 *Dec.* 46	12 *Oct.* 51	.. ..	27 *June* 57
	8	1	Henry A. Cockburn, *PCH*	Meades' Horse, ..	13 *June* 51	7 *Feb.* 55	.. ..	15 *July* 57
N.	6	7	S. Chalmers, *PC*, - - -	Army Commt. Dept.	9 *Dec.* 52	24 *Apl.* 55	.. ..	23 *Oct.* 57
N.	5	7	Mowbray Thomson, † - -	Cawnpore Police. ..	20 *Dec.* 53	4 *June* 55	.. ..	17 *May* 58
			LIEUTENANTS.					
N.	4	7	Henry George Delafosse, †-	Fur. S. C. 2 Feb. 58	9 *Dec.* 54	23 *Nov.* 56		
	12	6	E. H. Paske, *P*, - - -	Civil employ, ..	26 *Dec.* 46	16 *July* 49		
	12	7	F. N. Miles, † - - - -	Comdg. district police, Nursingpore,	11 *Dec.* 46	28 *Oct.* 50		
	9	7	W. Jackson, *PH*, - - -	D. P. W. Punjaub,	20 *Dec.* 49	1 *Nov.* 53		
N.	~~9~~	~~9~~	~~W. A. Battine, *PC*,~~ -	16th Irregular Cavy.	20 *Sep.* 49	9 *Mar.* 55		
	3	9	R. Dougall, - - - -	17th Punjaub Infy..	4 *Oct.* 55	10 *Oct.* 56		
	2	7	R. N. Evans, - - - -	.. ..	13 *Dec.* 56	30 *Apl.* 58		
	4	1	Henry Collett, - - - -	9th Punjaub Infy..	8 *June* 55	27 *June* 57		
	3	7	F. P. W. Freeman, † - -	.. ..	7 *Dec.* 55	30 *Apl.* 58		
	2	5	Edwin Beddy, - - - -	.. ..	20 *Feb.* 57	18 *May* 58		
	2	1	J. H. Tulloch, - - - -	.. ..	24 *June* 57	18 *May* 58		
			ENSIGNS.					
N.	1	7	F. M. Leslie. - - - -	Fur. S. C. 4 Dec. 58	20 *Dec* 57			
			*					
			*					
			*					
			*		*Appointed.*			
	..	..	*Adjutant*,*					
	..	..	*Interpreter*,*					
	..	...	*Surgeon*,*					
	..	..	*Asst. Surgeon.**					

Raised in 1804.

54th Regiment of Native Infantry.

Mutinied Delhi.

"FEROZESHUHUR."

Mapert-ka-Pultun. Late 2nd Battalion 27th Regt. N.I.

FACINGS—*Yellow.*

Fur Reg.	Y	M	
	62	5	*Colonel* John Alex. Paul Macgregor. *Ens.* 4 Feb. 1797; *Lieut.* 30 Oct. 1797; *Capt.* 1 May 1805; *Major* 12 June 1814; *Lieut. Col.* 1 Aug. 1818; *Col.* 1 May 1824; *Major Genl.* 10 Jan. 1837; *Lieut. Genl.* 9 Nov. 1846; *Genl.* 20 June 1854.—Europe, S. C., 10 Mar. 46.
O.	39	11	*Lieut. Colonel* David Simpson. *Ens.* 16 Aug. 1819; *Lieut.* 16 Aug. 1822; *Capt.* 24 April 1833; *Major* 22 *Dec.* 1844; *Lieut. Col.* 15 Mar. 1851; *Bt. Col.* 28 Nov. 1854.—Fur. S. C. 16 Apl. 1858.
O.	36	1	*Lt Col.* H. Vetch. *Ens.* 15 June 1823; *Lieut.* 13 May 1825; *Bt. Capt.* 15 June 1838; *Capt.* 13 June 1842; *Bt. Maj.* 11 Nov. 1851; *Maj.* 29 Aug. 1854; *Bt. Lt. Col.* 29 May 57; *Lieut. Colonel* 6 June 1858.—Fur. S. C. 17 Apl. 1857.
D	24	7	*Major* F. S. Paterson. *Ens.* 12 Dec. 1834; *Lieut.* 10 Sep. 1838; *Capt.* 13 Jan. 1842; *Bt. Major* 20 June 1854; *Major* 6 June 1858.

☞ *Brevet.* [1] Major 20 July 1858. [2] Major 20 July 1858.

Fur Reg.	Y	M	CAPTAINS.	REMARKS.	*Ensign.*	*Lieut.*	CAPTAIN. *Brevet.*	CAPTAIN. *Regl.*
	24	4	J. W. Carter,†[1]*m* - -	Comdt. Police Battn. Rohilkund Divn.,	24 *Feb.* 35	3 *Oct.* 40	24 *Feb.* 50	15 *Nov.* 53
	22	5	J. C. Haughton, *PCH*, - -	Civil employ, ..	15 *Feb.* 37	16 *July* 42	15 *Feb.* 52	15 *Nov.* 53
	16	10	H. C. Anderson, *P*,[2]*m* -	Cawnpore Infy. Levy.	2 *Sep.* 42	7 *Mar.* 47	.. ..	11 *May* 57
O.	13	6	D. H. Osborn, *PCH*, - -	Fur. S. C 17 July 58	27 *Dec.* 45	18 *July* 48	.. ..	13 *May* 57
N.	13	2	W. H. Paget, *PH*, (*a*) - -	5th Punjaub Cavy.	13 *June* 46	15 *Nov.* 53	.. ..	8 *June* 57
	11	7	J. A. Vanrenen, *PC*, - -	Offg. Army Commt. Dept., ..	10 *Dec.* 47	29 *Aug.* 54	.. ..	15 *June* 57
	10	1	W. S. Pierson, *PH*, - -	Comdt. Police Corps, Muttra, ..	8 *June* 49	14 *Feb.* 55	.. ..	6 *June* 58
			LIEUTENANTS.					
	8	6	C. T. Hitchins, *PH*, (*a*) -	Comdg. 7 Bengal Police Battn. Dacca	7 *Jan.* 51	31 *May* 55		
	6	10	W. Wroughton,† - - - -	.. ..	4 *Sep.* 52	23 *Nov.* 56		
	4	10	E. D. H. Vibart, *PH*, - -	1st Regt. Mahrattah Horse, ..	14 *Sep.* 54	26 *Nov.* 56		
N.	13	7	C. J. Nicholson, *P*, - -	Fur. S. C. 29 Jan. 58	3 *Dec.* 45	27 *July* 51		
	8	5	W. Phaire, *PCH*, - -	Offg. Civil employ,	20 *Jan.* 51	31 *Jan* 54		
	8	7	W. E. R. Roberts,† - -	.. ..	20 *Dec.* 50	1 *June* 56		
	3	10	R. B. P. P. Campbell,† -	.. ..	4 *Sept.* 55	2 *Sep.* 57		
	2	4	J. G. Barlow, - - - -	.. ..	6 *Mar.* 57	18 *May* 58		
	1	11	L. Blathwayt,† - - - -	.. ..	11 *Aug.* 57	6 *June* 58		
	1	1	G. M. Richmond,† - -	.. ..	12 *June* 58	22 *Oct.* 58		
	1	1	G. B. Johnston, - - -	.. ..	12 *June* 58	21 *Dec.* 58		
			ENSIGNS.					
	..	7	C. S. Pratt, - - - -	.. ..	11 *Dec.* 58			
			*					
			*					
			*					
			*		*Appointed.*			
	..	..	*Adjutant*,*					
	..	..	*Intr.*,*					
	..	..	*Surg.*,*					
	..	..	*Asst. Surg.*,*					

(*a*) Have furnished certificates of qualification in Surveying and Civil Engineering.

Raised in 1815.

55th Regiment of Native Infantry.

Mutinied, Nowshera.

Ockterlony-ka-dinah-Pultun. Late 1st Battalion 28th Regt. N.I.

FACINGS—*White.*

Fur Reg.	Ser. Y	Ser. M	
	53	3	*Colonel* Christopher Godby, C. B. *Ens.* 27 March 1806 ; *Lieut.* 14 June 1809 ; *Bt. Capt.* 27 March 1821 ; *Capt.* 11 July 1823 ; *Major* 14 June 1833 ; *Lieut. Col.* 1 Feb. 1840 ; *Bt. Col.* 7 June 1849 ; *Col.* 6 April 50 ; *Maj. Genl.* 28 Nov. 54.—Fur. S. C., 10 Feb. 50.
O.	35	6	*Lt. Col.* J. Powell. *Ens.* 16 Jan. 1824 ; *Lieut.* 9 July 1825 ; *Capt.* 30 Nov. 1840 ; *Bt. Major* 11 Nov. 1851 ; *Major* 15 Nov. 1852 ; *Lt. Col.* 27 June 1857.—Fur. S.C. 4 Feb. 59.
	~~33~~	~~4~~	~~*Lt. Col.* J. Butler, P.~~ *Ens.* 2 Mar. 1826 ; *Lieut.* 11 July 1826 ; *Bt. Capt.* 2 Mar. 1841 ; *Capt.* 2 Mar. 1845 ; *Bt. Major* 20 June 1854 ; *Major* 14 Nov. 1854 ; *Lt. Col.* 27 August 1858.
	25	7	*Major* P. W. Luard, *PH.* *Ens.* 13 Dec. 33 ; *Lt.* 1 Dec. 36 ; *Capt.* 3 May 45 ; *Bt. Maj.* 28 Nov. 54 ; *Major* 27 Aug. 58.—Lv. P. A. 15 Oct.

Fur Reg.	Y	M		Remarks.	Ensign.	Lieut.	Captain. Brevet.	Captain. Regl.
			CAPTAINS.					
	23	4	S. Richards, *PH,*	Brigade Staff, ..	8 *Mar.* 36	3 *Oct.* 40	.. ..	15 *Feb.* 47
	21	..	T. M. Cameron, *PH,*	Garrison Staff, Attock	15 *July* 38	3 *Oct.* 42	.. ..	30 *Dec.* 47
	19	..	J. D'O. Baring, †	.. ..	1 *July* 40	12 *Nov.* 42	.. ..	15 *June* 48
	17	1	A. Allen, *PH,*	Supdt. Workshops, Roorkee, ..	10 *June* 42	28 *June* 43	.. ..	14 *Nov.* 54
O.	16	10	R. A. Napper, *PH,*	Fur. S. C. 10 Aug. 58	9 *Sep.* 42	24 *Jan.* 45	.. ..	23 *Nov.* 56
	16	5	A. S. Haig, *PCH,*	Offg. Army Commt. Department, ..	30 *Jan.* 43	2 *May* 45	.. ..	14 *Sep.* 57
	16	3	W. D. Hoste, †	15th Punjaub Infy.,	4 *Apl.* 43	3 *May* 45	4 *Apl.* 58	27 *Aug.* 58
			LIEUTENANTS.					
	16	1	H. P. Babbage, *PC,* (a)	Civil employ, ..	10 *June* 43	28 *Jan.* 46	10 *June* 58	
	14	7	R. J. D. Ferris, *P,*	Civil employ, ..	10 *Dec.* 44	30 *Dec.* 47		
	14	1	W. Nembhard, *P,*	Civil employ, ..	14 *June* 45	19 *Nov.* 50		
	~~13~~	~~1~~	~~R. Creighton,~~ †	.. ..	12 *June* 46	15 *Nov.* 53		
	12	4	E. H. Woodcock, †	12th Irr. Cavalry, ..	1 *Mar.* 47	14 *Nov.* 54		
	11	10	E. H. Scott, *PH,*	16th Punjaub Infy.	2 *Sep.* 47	10 *May* 56		
	4	6	Swinton John Browne, †	5th Punjaub Infy.,	20 *Jan.* 55	23 *Nov.* 56		
	3	1	Frederick Lance, †	16th Punjaub Infy.	13 *June* 56	14 *Sep.* 57		
	2	7	W. J. Forlong, †	Doing duty 3rd Battn. Rifle Brigade, ..	13 *Dec.* 56	30 *Apl.* 58		
	1	11	H. A. Pakenham,	Offg. Benares Horse,	15 *Aug.* 57	18 *May* 58		
	1	1	C. H. Palmer,	Doing duty with H. M. 99th Foot, ..	12 *June* 58	27 *Aug.* 58		
			ENSIGNS.					
	..	7	D. R. Clarke,	.. ..	11 *Dec.* 58			
			*					
			*					
			*					
			*					
					Appointed.			
	..	..	*Adjutant,* *					
	..	..	*Intr.* *					
	..	..	*Surg.* *					
	..	..	*Asst. Surg.,* *					

(*a*) Has passed an examination in the Bengallee Language.

Raised in 1815.

56th Regiment of Native Infantry.

Mutinied, Cawnpore.

" MAHARAJPORE"—" PUNJAUB"—" CHILLIANWALLA"—" GOOJERAT."

Lambroon-ka-Pultun. Late 2nd Battalion 28th Regt. N.I.

FACINGS—*White.*

Fur.Reg.	Ser. Y	Ser. M	
	55	6	*Colonel* James Eckford, C. B. *Ens.* 1 Jan. 1804; *Lieut.* 17 Sept. 1806; *Bt. Capt.* 1 Jan. 1819; *Capt.* 20 July 1823; *Major* 18 July 1831; *Lieut. Col.* 11 March 1837; *Col.* 27 Oct. 48; *Major General* 28 Nov. 54.—Sirhind Circle.
	33	5	*Lt. Col.* Wm. St. Leger Mitchell. *Ens.* 5 Feb. 1826; *Lieut.* 6 May 1829; *Bt. Capt.* 5 Feb. 1841; *Captain* 5 Nov. 42; *Maj.* 15 June 49; *Lieut. Col.* 28 Nov. 54.
	17	5	*Major* W. C. Gott, *PH. Ens.* 2 Feb. 1842; *Lieut.* 11 Dec. 1842; *Capt.* 13 Jan. 1849; *Major* 15 July 1857.

☞ *Brevet.* [1] Major 20 July 1858.

Fur.Reg.	Y	M		Remarks.	Ensign.	Lieut.	Captain. Brevet.	Captain. Regl.
			CAPTAINS.					
N.	17	1	W. M. Cafe, *PH*, - - -	Fur. S. C. 29 July 58	11 *June* 42	12 *Apl.* 43	.. ..	27 *Jan.* 49
	17	..	L. B. Jones, *PH*, - - -	Judge Advo. G. Dept.	16 *July* 42	24 *Jan.* 45	.. ..	9 *Mar.* 52
	16	7	F. V. R. Jervis, *PCH*, -	Lv. S. C. 18 Nov. ...	10 *Dec.* 42	29 *June* 45	.. ..	7 *Nov.* 54
N.	11	4	A. H. Bamfield, *PH*, -	Brigade Staff, ..	20 *Mar.* 48	15 *Oct.* 49	.. ..	8 *June* 57
	11	1	F. W. Lambert, *PH*, [1]*m*	1st Punjaub Infy...	9 *June* 48	1 *Oct.* 50	.. ..	27 *June* 57
	10	1	G. C. Lloyd,† - - -	Stud. Dept. ..	9 *June* 49	5 *Sep.* 53	.. ..	27 *June* 57
	9	6	Henry D. Battye, *PH*, -	Civil employ, ..	7 *Jan.* 50	21 *June* 54	.. ..	15 *July* 57
			LIEUTENANTS.					
	18	9	A. B. Beatson,† - - -	On duty at Meerut,	27 *Sep.* 40	20 *Nov.* 45	27 *Sep.* 55	
N.	16	7	A. M. Mackenzie, *PH*, -	8th Irr. Cavy. ..	9 *Dec.* 42	1 *Dec.* 46	9 *Dec.* 57	
O.	13	7	W. H Smith, *PH*, -	Fur. S. C. 1 July 59	20 *Dec.* 45	12 *May* 49		
	10	7	C. S. Lane, *PC*, - - -	Army Commt. Dept.	9 *Dec.* 48	1 *Sep* 50		
	15	7	J. R. A. S. Lowe, *PC*, (*a*) -	Army Commt. Dept.	9 *Dec.* 43	26 *July* 53	9 *Dec.* 58	
O.	8	7	C. C. Taylor, *PH*, - -	Fur. S. C. 18 Aug. 57	20 *Dec.* 50	25 *Feb.* 55		
	4	..	H S. Ruxton, - - - -	13th Punjaub Infy.	20 *July* 55	8 *Oct.* 56		
	2	7	R. A. Stevens, - - - -	.. ..	13 *Dec.* 56	15 *July* 57		
	3	7	R. M. Skinner,† - - -	Allygurh Police, ..	7 *Dec.* 55	15 *June* 57		
	3	3	C. R. Mathews,† - - -	Doing duty Recruit depot, Barrackpore,	20 *Mar.* 55	30 *Apl.* 58		
	2	1	R. Stainforth,† - - - -	Adjt. district Police, Oude, ..	20 *June* 57	18 *May* 58		
			ENSIGNS.					
	1	7	W. H. Unwin, - - -	1st Sikh Infy., ..	20 *Dec.* 57			
			*					
			*					
			*					
			*		*Appointed.*			
	..	..	*Adjutant*, *					
	..	..	*Inter.*, *					
	..	..	*Surg.*, *					
	..	..	*Asst. Surg.*, *					

(*a*) Received certificates of high proficiency in Oordoo, 29th Oct. 1850, and Hindee, 23rd Dec. 1851 and attained the standard of proficiency, prescribed by G. G. O. 9th March 1852, in the Hindee language on the 16th Sep. 1852 and in the Oordoo language on the 4th Oct. 1852.

Raised in 1815.

57th Regiment of Native Infantry.

Mutinied, Ferozepore.

(*Rifle Company.*)
"ASSAM."

Lord Moira-ka-Pultun. Late 1st Battalion 29th Regt. N.I.

FACINGS—*Buff.*

Fur. Reg	SER. Y	SER. M	
	~~50~~	~~6~~	~~*Colonel* John Home.~~ *Ens.* 1 Jan. 1803; *Lieut.* 21 Sept. 1804; *Bt. Capt.* 1 Jan. 1818; *Capt.* 31 May 1820; *Major* 31 May 1830; *Lieut. Col.* 7 Jan. 1836; *Bt. Col.* 9 Nov. 1846; *Col.* 19 March 1847; *Major General* 20 June 1854.—Europe, 10 Feb. 47.
	~~36~~	~~2~~	~~*Lieut. Col.* Edward Darvall.~~ *Ens.* 1 May 1823; *Lieut.* 6 Jan. 1825; *Capt.* 4 Aug. 1836; *Bt. Maj.* 9 Nov. 1846; *Maj.* 11 July 1853; *Bt. Lt. Col.* 20 June 1854; *Lt. Col.* 17 Nov. 57 *Bt. Col.* 20 June 1857. ;
N.	33	6	*Major* E. Marriott. *Ens.* 26 Dec. 1825; *Lieut.* 21 Sep. 1828; *Bt. Capt.* 26 Dec. 1840; *Capt.* 21 July 1841; *Bt. Major* 11 Nov. 1851; *Major* 17 Nov. 1857.—Fur. S. C. 9 Mar. 58.

☞ *Brevet.* [1] Maj. 20 June 54. Lt. Col. 24 Mar. 1858. [2] Major 24 Mar. 1858.

Fur. Reg	Y	M	CAPTAINS.	REMARKS.	*Ensign.*	*Lieut.*	CAPTAIN. *Brevet.*	CAPTAIN. *Regl.*
	31	6	T. Simpson, [1]*lc*	Civil employ,	10 *Jan.* 28	17 *July* 32	10 *Jan.* 43	24 *Jan.* 45
O.	25	6	C. S. Salmon, †	Fur. P A 15 Apl. 59	10 *Jan.* 34	8 *Oct.* 39	.. ..	31 *Dec.* 47
	20	7	G. C. Hatch, *P*, [2]*m*	Judge Advo. G. Dept.	12 *Dec.* 38	11 *Nov.* 40		19 *Apl.* 51
	20	6	N. R. Sneyd, *PH*,	Regt., of Lucknow	11 *Jan.* 39	7 *Jan.* 41	.. ..	11 *July* 53
	18	4	J. L. Nation, *PH*,	Comdt. 9th Bengal Police Battn. Chota Nagpore Divn. ..	8 *Mar.* 41	12 *Aug.* 47	8 *Mar.* 56	28 *Sep.* 57
N.	18	..	T. H. Wilson, †	Fur. S.C. 26 Mar. 57	27 *June* 41	31 *Dec.* 47	27 *June* 56	17 *Nov.* 57
	12	4	G. J. D. Hay, *P*,	18th Regt. Irr. Cavy.	20 *Mar.* 47	4 *Nov.* 52	.. ..	21 *Nov.* 58
			LIEUTENANTS.					
	11	6	C. Shaw, *PH*,	.. ..	11 *Jan.* 48	11 *July* 53		
N.	8	5	G. H. Hale, *PH*,	Fur. S. C. 5 Nov. 57	20 *Jan.* 51	31 *Oct.* 53		
	7	7	F. H. Jenkins, †	4th Seikh Infantry,	20 *Dec.* 51	15 *Nov.* 53		
	7	1	E. E. B. Bond, *PH*,	Corps of Guides, ..	13 *June* 52	1 *Jan.* 54		
	7	..	E. Y. Walcott, *P*,	Commanding Arty. Rajah Jowahir Sing's Troops, ..	20 *June* 52	16 *Mar.* 56		
N.	5	7	Harry DeBrett, †	Fur. S. C. 22nd June 58, ..	10 *Dec.* 53	23 *Nov.* 56		
	4	1	A. W. Hearsey,	Shekhawattee Battn.,	9 *June* 55	23 *Nov.* 56		
N.	3	9	Robert A. Wauchope,	Fur. S. C. 2 March 1858, ..	4 *Oct.* 55	17 *Feb.* 58		
	3	6	E. C. Codrington,	4th Sikh Infy. ..	4 *Jan.* 56	28 *Sep.* 57		
	1	11	H. C. Garden,	.. ..	26 *July* 57	18 *May* 57		
	1	5	J. McNair,	.. ..	20 *Feb.* 58	21 *Nov.* 58		
			ENSIGNS.					
		9	J. M. Stewart,	.. ..	20 *Oct.* 58			
			*					
			*					
			*					
			*		*Appointed.*			
	..	..	*Adjutant,* C. Shaw,		13 *June* 55			
	..	..	*Intr.,* *					
	..	..	*Surgeon,* *					
	..	..	*Asst. Surg.,* *					

Raised in 1815.

58th Regiment of Native Infantry.

Disarmed, Rawul Pi ndee

"BHURTPORE"—"PUNNIAR."

Bisheshwur-ka-Pultun. Late 2nd Battalion 29th Regt. N.I.

FACINGS—*Buff.*

Fur. Reg.	Ser. Y	Ser. M	
N.	53	1	*Colonel* Henry Chambers Murray Cox. *Ens.* 24 May 1806; *Lieut.* 13 Aug. 1809; *Bt. Capt.* 24 May 1821; *Capt.* 1 May 1824; *Major* 9 Aug. 1836; *Lieut. Col.* 22 Oct. 1842; *Col.* 5 June 1853; *Major General* 28 Nov. 54.—Fur. S. C. 21 Dec. 58.
	46	11	*Lieut. Colonel* John Anderson Barstow. *Ens.* 30 July 1812; *Lieut.* 1 June 1817; *Bt. Capt.* 13 Aug. 1829; *Capt.* 31 March 1831; *Major* 1 Jan. 1845; *Lieut. Col.* 17 May 1851; *Bt. Col.* 28 Nov. 1854.—Commanding at Jhelum.
	~~19~~	~~6~~	~~*Major* A. Meyer.~~ *Ens.* 18 *Jan.* 1840; *Lieut.* 8 *Jan.* 1842; *Captain* 6 *Dec.* 1845; *Bt. Major* 22 Aug. 1857; *Major* 4 Sep. 1858.

Fur. Reg.	Y	M		REMARKS.	*Ensign*	*Lieut.*	CAPTAIN. *Brevet.*	CAPTAIN. *Regl.*
			CAPTAINS.					
	17	7	R. Duffin, *PH*,	.. ..	11 *Dec.* 41	3 *Feb.* 43	.. ..	10 *Apl.* 49
	17	6	A. K. Moffat, *PH*, (*a*)	Dept. Public Works Punjaub, ..	8 *Jan.* 42	3 *Mar.* 43	.. ..	16 *July* 49
	17	4	F. J. Davies, *P*, (*a*)	Lahore & Peshawur Road, ..	2 *Mar.* 42	4 *Feb.* 44	.. ..	19 *Oct.* 53
~~N.~~	~~17~~	~~1~~	~~C. W. D'Oyly, *PCH*,~~	Stud Department, ..	10 *June* 42	3 *Aug.* 44	.. ..	28 *Feb.* 55
	16	11	W. Elwyn, *PH*,	.. ..	23 *July* 42	24 *Jan.* 45	.. ..	23 *Nov.* 56
	15	5	T. Staples, *PH*, (*b*)	Civil employ, ..	27 *Jan.* 44	10 *Nov.* 47	.. ..	4 *Sep* 58
	14	7	F. J. Ellis, †	.. ..	10 *Dec.* 44	22 *July* 48	.. ..	26 Dec. 58
			LIEUTENANTS.					
	14	6	J. M. Mackenzie, *PH*,	.. ..	18 *Jan.* 45	10 *Aug.* 48		
	11	6	A. Tulloch, *PH—TC*, (*a*)	Dept. Public Works Oude, ..	11 *Jan.* 48	2 *Dec.* 49		
	11	5	A. Callander, *P*,	Fur. S. C. 6 May 56	20 *Feb.* 48	28 *Feb.* 55		
N.	11	1	C. L Richardson, *P*,	Fur. P.A. 18 Mar. 59	10 *June* 48	7 *Dec.* 55		
O.	10	4	J. Thompson, †	Fur. S. C. 9 Jan. 57	2 *Mar.* 49	23 *Nov* 56		
	4	5	Percy William Powlett, *PH*,	Civil employ, ..	4 *Feb* 55	23 *Nov.* 56		
	4	4	Geo. Augustus Way, *PH*,	3rd Punjaub Infy...	5 *Mar.* 55	14 *Mar.* 58		
	2	6	T. Dayrell, †	1st Regt. Hodson's Horse, ..	6 *Jan.* 57	30 *Apl.* 58		
	2	6	G. C. Gregory, †	.. ..	20 *Jan.* 57	30 *Apl.* 58		
	~~1~~	~~10~~	~~D. Pringle,~~	.. ..	4 *Sep.* 57	4 *Sep.* 58		
	~~1~~		~~T. T. Tucker,~~	.. ..	25 *June* 58	26 *Dec.* 58		
			ENSIGNS.					
			*					
			*					
			*					
			*					
			*		*Appointed.*			
	..	..	*Adjutant*, J. M. Mackenzie,	.. ..	27 *July* 58			
	..	..	*Intr.*, C. L. Richardson,	Fur. P. A. 18 March 59, .	30 *Dec.* 53			
	..	..	*Asst. Surg.*					

(*a*) Have furnished certificates of qualification in Surveying and Civil Engineering.
(*b*) Has passed an examination in Field Engineering.

Raised in 1815.

59th Regiment of Native Infantry.

Disarmed, Umritsur.

" SUBRAON."

Late 1st Battalion 30th Regt. N.I.

FACINGS—*Saxon-green.*

Fur. Reg.	SER. Y	SER. M	
	41	5	*Colonel* Charles Hamilton, C.B. *Ens.* 27 Jan. 1818; *Lieut.* 1 Aug. 1818; *Capt.* 9 Oct. 1826; *Major* 26 Nov. 1836; *Lt. Col.* 19 Jan. 1843; *Col.* 14 July 1853; *Maj. Genl.* 28 Nov. 1854.—Fur., P. A. 22 April 1853.
O.	35	6	*Lieut. Col.* Hugh Boyd. *Ens.* 17 Jan. 1824; *Lieut.* 27 March 1826; *Bt. Capt.* 17 Jan. 1839; *Capt.* 5 Nov. 1841; *Major* 20 Sept. 1849; *Lieut. Col.* 28 Nov. 1854. *Bt. Col.* 28 Nov. 1857.—Fur. S. C. 8 Feb. 59.
	33	5	*Major* G. W. Stokes. *Ens.* 4 Feb. 1826; *Lieut.* 2 July 1828; *Bt. Capt.* 4 Feb. 1841; *Capt.* 15 June 1845; *Bt. Major* 20 June 1854; *Major* 21 Aug. 1857.

☞ *Brevet.* [1] Major 11 June 50. Lt. Col. 28 Nov. 54.
[2] Major 6 Feb. 54.

Fur. Reg.	Y	M	CAPTAINS.	REMARKS.	*Ensign.*	*Lieut.*	CAPTAIN. *Brevet.*	CAPTAIN. *Regl.*
	24	1	H. F. Dunsford, C. B., *P[1]lc,*	20th Punjaub Infy.	13 *June* 35	3 *Oct.* 38	.. ..	10 *June* 50
	21	4	H. B. Lumsden,[2]*mP,* - -	Corps of Guides, ..	1 *Mar.* 38	16 *July* 42	1 *Mar.* 53	5 *Feb.* 54
	19	5	A. Blackwood, *P,* - - -	Comdt. Infy. Levy Mynpoory,	15 *Feb.* 40	23 *Dec.* 44	15 *Feb.* 55	5 *Apl.* 55
	18	11	R. G. Mayne, *PH,* - -	.. ..	10 *Aug.* 40	24 *Jan.* 45	.. ..	3 *Aug.* 55
	18	6	H. A. Dwyer, *P,* - - -	Civil employ,	25 *Dec.* 40	15 *June* 45	25 *Dec.* 55	23 *Nov.* 56
O.	17	1	R. D. Gibney, *P,* - - -	Fur. S.C. 16 Mar. 58	11 *June* 42	7 *July* 45	11 *June* 57	23 *July* 57
	14	6	D. K. Presgrave, *PCH,* -	.. ..	29 *Dec.* 44	10 *June* 50	.. ..	21 *Aug.* 57
			LIEUTENANTS.					
N.	14	6	W. H. Phillips,† - -	Fur. S.C. 28 June 59	1 *Jan.* 44	29 *Aug.* 51	1 Jan. 59	
	9	11	H. P. W. Wynch, *PCH,*	2nd Irregular Cavy.	28 *July* 49	10 *Nov.* 51		
	9	5	John Angelo, *P,* -	.. ..	7 *Feb.* 50	8 *May* 53		
	9	1	W. L. Randall,† - - - -		15 *June* 50	5 *Feb.* 54		
O.	8	3	M. G. Smith, *PH,*† - -	Fur. S.C. 25 June 58	10 *Apl.* 51	5 *Apl.* 55		
	8	1	W. S. Young,† - - - -		13 *June* 51	3 *Aug.* 55		
	6	10	A. Whiting,† - - - -		26 *Aug.* 52	23 *Nov.* 56		
	6	10	R. Smith,† - - - -	20th Punjaub Infy.	26 *Aug.* 52	23 *Nov.* 56		
N.	4	6	Geo. Carlyon H Armstrong, *PH,* - - -	Fur. S. C. 14 May 58	20 *Jan.* 55	23 *July* 57		
	4	1	Ed. Lacon Ommanney, *P,* -	Civil employ, ..	9 *June* 55	21 *Aug.* 57		
	2	..	E. Lightfoot, - - - -	.. ..	15 *July* 57	18 *May* 58		
			ENSIGNS.					
	1	6	J. B. Hay, - - - - -	9th Punjaub Infy.	20 *Jan.* 58			
			*					
			*					
			*					
			*					
	..	..	*Adjutant,**					
	..	..	*Intr.,**					
	..	..	*Surg.**		*Appointed.*			
	..	..	*Asst. Surg.**					

Raised in 1815.

60th Regiment of Native Infantry.

Disarmed, Umballah.

"BHURTPORE"—"CAUBUL 1842."

Late 2nd Battalion 30th Regt. N.I.
FACINGS—*Saxon-green.*

Fur. Reg.	Ser. Y	Ser. M	
	59	10	*Colonel* Suetonius Henry Tod. *Ens.* 14 Sept. 1799; *Lieut.* 28 Oct. 1799; *Capt.* 26 Feb. 1813; *Major* 11 July 1823; *Lieut. Col.* 12 Jan. 1825; *Bt. Col.* 1 Dec. 1829; *Col.* 5 April 1834; *Major Genl.* 28 June 1838; *Lieut. Genl.* 11 Nov. 51.—Europe, 19 Sep. 1823.
R O.	33	3	*Lt. Col.* W. R. Dunmore. *Ens.* 15 Apl. 26; *Lt.* 30 July 32; *Bt. Capt.* 15 Apl. 41; *Capt.* 3 Apl. 44; *Maj.* 27 July 51; *Bt. Lt. Col.* 28 Nov. 54; *Lt. Col.* 28 Nov. 56.—Fur. S. C. 30 Dec. 56.
	35	5	*Lt. Col.* R. Drought, C.B. *P Ens.* 13 Feb. 1824; *Lieut.* 9 July 1825; *Capt.* 2 Dec. 1836; *Bt. Maj.* 9 Nov. 46; *Bt. Lieut. Col.* 20 June 54; *Major* 25 Feb. 1855.; *Lt. Col.* 17 March 1859.—Lv. P. A. 15 October
N.	32	1	*Major* C. R. Browne, *P*, *Ens.* 14 June 27; *Lieut.* 12 July 33; *Bt. Capt.* 14 June 42; *Capt.* 21 Nov. 45; *Bt. Major.* 20 June 54; *Major.* 17 Mar. 59.—Civil employ.

☞ *Brevet.* [1] Maj. 20 June 1854. [2] Maj. 7 June 1849. Lt. Col. 28 Nov. 1854. [3] Major 19 Jan. 1858.

Fur. Reg.	Y	M	CAPTAINS.	REMARKS.	*Ensign.*	*Lieut.*	CAPTAIN. *Brevet.*	CAPTAIN. *Regl.*
	30	10	J. E. Verner,[1] *m*	Comdg. the Garrison of Attock.	12 *Sep.* 28	7 *Jan.* 36	12 *Sep.* 43	10 *Aug.* 49
	29	8	G. P. Whish, *PC*,[2] *lc* (a)	Brigade Staff,	19 *Nov.* 29	1 *Dec.* 36	19 *Nov.* 44	15 *Nov.* 49
	24	7	D. Stansbury,†	Offg. Pay Dept.,	12 *Dec.* 34	13 *Mar.* 37	12 *Dec.* 49	15 *Nov.* 53
R O.	18	7	J. C. Hay,†[3] *m*	Fur. S.C. 2 Mar. 58,	12 *Dec.* 40	5 *Feb.* 43	.. ..	25 *Feb.* 55
	18	5	W. C. Green,†	Lv. P. A. 15 Oct.,	4 *Feb.* 41	18 *Apl.* 43	4 *Feb.* 56	23 *Nov.* 56
	17	1	William Thurlow Baker, *P*	Extra Goorkha Regt.,	10 *June* 42	21 *Nov.* 45	.. ..	24 *Jan.* 57
O.	16	11	M. G. Brabazon,†	Fur. S.C. 18 Mar. 59	23 *July* 42	28 *Jan.* 48	23 *July* 57	17 *Mar.* 59
			LIEUTENANTS.					
Capt	15	4	R. H. Shebbeare, *P*,	15th Punjaub Infy.	29 *Feb.* 44	15 *Nov.* 49	1 *Mar.* 59	
O.	14	7	F. C. Innes, *PH*,	Fur. S.C. 18 Mar. 58	10 *Dec.* 44	1 *Mar.* 51		
	13	10	J. Keer, *P*,	Army Comt. Dept.	26 *July* 45	15 *Nov.* 53		
N.	11	7	P. S. Lumsden, *PH*,	Qr.Mr. Genl's. Dept.	10 *Dec.* 47	23 *May* 54		
	10	1	W. B. Shawe, *PH*,	Comdt. Goruckpore Levy.	8 *June* 49	15 *Jan.* 55		
	5	11	Richard Barton Hill,†	16th Punjaub Infy.	15 *Aug.* 53	23 *Nov.* 56		
N.	5	1	G. Anthy. Aufrere Baker,†	Fur. S. C. 30 Oct. 58.	8 *June* 54	24 *Jan.* 57		
	2	7	P. C. Dalmahoy,	Humeerpore Police,	13 *Dec.* 56	9 *Oct.* 57		
	2	7	Alan Murray,†	.. ..	20 *Dec.* 56	30 *Apl.* 58		
	1	..	R. M. Clifford,	.. ..	25 *June* 58	22 *Oct.* 58		
	1	..	C. H. Bergman,	.. ..	15 *July* 58	17 *Mar.* 59		
			ENSIGNS.					
Lt.		7	C. McNeile,	.. ..	11 *Dec.* 58			
			*					
			*					
			*					
			*		*Appointed.*			
	..	..	*Adjt.**					
	..	..	*Intr.**					
	..	..	*Surg.*					
	..	..	*Asst. Surg.*	.. ..				

(a) Received a certificate of high proficiency in the Oordoo language from the College of Fort William 17th Dec. 1850.

Raised in 1823.

61st Regiment of Native Infantry.

Mutinied, Jullundur.

Late 1st Battalion 31st Regt. N.I.

FACINGS—*Yellow.*

Fur. Reg.	Ser. Y	Ser. M	
	57	5	*Colonel* John Anderson. *Ens.* 6 Feb. 1802; *Lieut.* 28 March 1804; *Capt.* 1 Aug. 1818; *Major* 14 July 1825; *Lieut. Col.* 30 June 1830; *Col.* 7 July 42; *Major General* 20 June 1854; *Lieut. Genl.* 5 Dec. 1855.—Europe, 28 Feb. 42.
	47	7	*Lieut. Col.* Francis Jenkins. *Ens.* 2 Dec. 1811; *Lieut.* 11 May 1816; *Bt. Capt.* 2 Dec. 1826; *Capt.* 29 April 1830; *Bt. Major* 23 Nov. 1841; *Major* 22 Dec. 1845; *Lieut. Col.* 16 Oct. 1851; *Bt. Col.* 28 Nov. 1854.—Civil employ.
	31	1	*Maj.* J. C. Innes, *P*, *Ens.* 14 June 1828; *Lieut.* 26 Sep. 1833; *Bt. Capt.* 14 June 1843; *Capt.* 26 Dec. 1844; *Bt. Maj.* 20 June 1854; *Maj.* 3 July 1855.—Loyal Poorbeah Regt.,

☞ *Brevet.* [1] *Maj.* 28 *Nov.* 54. [2] Maj. 3 Apl. 46; Lt. Col. 7 June 49; Col. 28 *Nov.* 54.

Fur. Reg.	Y	M		Remarks.	*Ensign.*	*Lieut.*	Captain. *Brevet.*	Captain. *Regl.*
			CAPTAINS.					
	30	1	W. H. Ryves, *P*, [1] *m* - -	18th Irregular Cavy.	5 *June* 29	11 *Oct.* 38	28 *Mar.* 44	24 *Jan.* 45
	25	8	A. M. Becher, *c.* [2] C.B., - -	Qr. Mr. Genl. of the Army and H.A.D.C. to the Govr. Genl.	20 *Oct.* 33	16 *July* 39	.. ..	11 *Apl.* 45
	25	1	S. H. Becher, *PH*, - -	Adjt. Genl.'s Dept.	11 *June* 34	3 *Oct.* 40	.. ..	1 *Dec.* 46
	18	7	C. B. Basden, † - - -	.. ..	25 *Dec.* 40	16 *July* 42	.. ..	6 *July* 53
	18	1	M. R. Somerville, † - -	.. ..	12 *June* 41	25 *Jan.* 43	.. ..	3 *July* 55
	17	11	F. G. Stainforth, *PC*, -	.. ..	4 *Aug.* 41	26 *Dec.* 44	.. ..	29 *Dec.* 55
O.	17	6	E. H. C. Wintle, *PCH*, -	Fur. S.C. 2 Mar. 58	8 *Jan.* 42	24 *Jan.* 45	.. ..	23 *Nov.* 56
			LIEUTENANTS.					
	17	1	H. S. Obbard, *PC*, †(*a*) -	21st Punjaub Infy.,..	11 *June* 42	11 *Apl.* 45	11 *June* 57	
	16	11	T. A. Corbett, *PH*, -	Civil employ, ..	25 *July* 42	23 *Dec.* 45	25 *July* 57	
	14	1	A. Merewether, *PH*, -	.. ..	16 *June* 45	18 *May* 53		
	8	5	J. Gillespie, *PH*, - - -	..	20 *Jan.* 51	29 *Jan.* 54		
	6	10	H. Tyndall, *PH*, - - -	21st Punjaub Infy.	20 *Aug.* 52	12 *Apl.* 54		
	6	5	G. B. Stainforth, *P*, - -	4th Seikh Infy. ..	20 *Jan.* 53	3 *July* 55		
	6	1	R. J. Walker, † - - -	21 Punjaub Infy. ..	11 *June* 53	29 Dec. 55		
O.	5	7	William Owen, † - - -	Fur. S.C. 6 April 57,	14 *Dec.* 53	23 *Nov.* 56		
	3	7	R. Wheeler, *PH*, - - -	.. ..	8 *Dec.* 55	30 *Apl.* 58		
	2	3	W. Hamilton, † - - - -	21 Punjaub Infy., ..	20 *Apl.* 57	18 *May* 58		
	1	10	N. Lowis, - - - - -	.. ..	20 *Sep.* 57	17 *Jan.* 59		
			ENSIGNS.					
	..	10	A. D. Anderson, - - -	.. ..	4 *Sep.* 58			
	...	6	D. Adamson, - - -	.. ..	5 *Jan.* 59			
			*					
			*					
			*		*Appointed.*			
	..	..	*Adjutant,* *					
	..	..	*Intr.,* *					
	..	..	*Surg.,* *					
	..	..	*Asst. Surg.* *					

(*a*) Has passed an examination in the Punjaubee Language.

Raised in 1823. } **62nd Regiment of Native Infantry.** { Mutinied, Mooltan.

"ARRACAN."

Late 2nd Battalion 31st Regt. N.I.

FACINGS—*Yellow.*

Fur. Reg.	Ser. Y	Ser. M	
	53	1	*Colonel* George Richard Pemberton. *Ens.* 24 May 1806; *Lieut.* 22 May 1809; *Bt. Capt.* 24 May 1821; *Capt.* 1 May 1824; *Major* 25 June 1832; *Lieut. Col.* 13 Feb. 1839; *Col.* 19 March 49; *Major General* 28 Nov. 1854.—Furlough, 1 Feb. 50.
	39	9	*Colonel* Francis Rowcroft C.B. *Ens.* 7 Oct. 1819; *Lieut.* 14 Sept. 1821; *Capt.* 7 Aug. 1829; *Major* 26 May 1843; *Lieut. Col.* 14 Nov. 1849; *Bt. Col.* 28 Nov. 1854; *Col.* 15 May 1859.
O.	18	5	*Major* Fred. Johnston, *Ens.* 30 Jan. 1841; *Lieut.* 12 Aug. 1841; *Captain* 2 Feb. 1850; *Major* 18 Dec. 1857.—Fur. S. C. 12 May 1857. ☞ *Brevet* [1] Major 19 Jan. 58.

Fur. Reg.	Ser. Y	Ser. M	CAPTAINS.	REMARKS.	*Ensign.*	*Lieut.*	CAPTAIN. *Brevet.*	CAPTAIN. *Regl.*
	18	3	E. S. Denniss, *PH*, - -	.. ..	2 *Apl.* 41	16 *July* 42	.. ..	1 *June* 50
	18	1	H. D. Maunsell,† - - -	.. ..	11 *June* 41	22 *Mar.* 44	.. ..	3 *Oct.* 52
	17	7	C. F. G. Lamb, *P*, - -	Comdg. Recruit depot. Goruckpore,	11 *Dec.* 41	5 *July* 44	.. ..	11 *Feb.* 55
	17	1	J. E. Thomson, *P*, - -	ArmyCommt. Dept.	19 *June* 42	24 *Jan.* 45	.. ..	9 *Apl.* 56
O.	17	1	H. J. Hughes, *PH*, - -	Fur. S C 30 Apl. 59	11 *June* 42	17 *Dec.* 45	.. ..	23 *Nov.* 56
O.	15	10	F. J. Sidebottom, *PH*,-	Fur. S. C. 9 June 57	1 *Sep.* 43	15 *May* 48	.. ..	1 *June* 57
	15	7	T. H. Sibley, *PC*,[1]*m* -	Army Comt. Dept.	9 *Dec.* 43	2 *Feb.* 50	.. ..	18 *Dec.* 57
			LIEUTENANTS.					
	14	5	J. Leven, *P.*, - - -	Army Comt. Dept.	11 *Feb.* 45	1 *June* 50		
N.	12	1	J. B. Cox, *PH*, - - -	13th Punjaub Infy.	11 *June* 47	28 *May*, 51		
	12	..	H. B. Urmston, *P*, - -	Civil employ, ..	20 *July* 47	15 *Aug.* 51		
	9	6	T. G. Kennedy, *PH*, - -	Corps of Guides, ..	24 *Dec.* 49	3 *Oct.* 52		
	9	..	W. Cabell, *PH*,- - - -	.. ..	26 *June* 50	29 *May* 55		
	8	3	H. C. Cattley, *PH*, - -	Adjt. 4th Seikh Irr. Cavy. ..	20 *Mar.* 51	23 *Nov.* 56		
	6	1	J. P. Burton,† - - - -	3rd Punjaub Cavy.	11 *June* 53	23 *Nov.* 56		
N.	4	7	Patrick Robert Crolly,† -	Fur. S. C. 23 Dec. 58	9 *Dec.* 54	1 *June* 57		
	2	10	Frederick Hammond, - -	4th Punjaub Cavy.,	8 *Sep.* 56	8 *Aug.* 57		
	1	11	R. J. Foley, - - - -	.. ..	26 *July* 57	18 *May* 58		
R	~~1~~	~~4~~	~~F. H. Carleton,~~ - - -	.. ..	20 *Feb.* 58	19 *Sep.* 58		
			ENSIGNS.					
Z	..	8	R. C. Beavan, - - - -	.. ..	4 *Nov.* 58			
			*					
			*					
			*		*Appointed.*			
			*					
	..	..	*Adjt* W. Cabell, - - -	Officiating, ..	30 *May* 58			
	..	..	*Inter.*,*					
	..	..	*Surg.* J. P. Kelly, - - -	.. ...	5 *Feb.* 57			
	..	..	*Asst. Surg.*,*					

Raised in 1823. | **63rd Regiment of Native Infantry.** | Disarmed, Berhampore.

"Bhurtpore"—"Subraon."

Late 1st Battalion 32nd Regt. N.I.

Facings—*Yellow*.

Fur. Reg.	Ser. Y	Ser. M		Remarks.	Ensign.	Lieut.	Captain. Brevet.	Captain. Regl.
	51	3	*Colonel* Wm. John Gairdner, c. b. *Ens.* 9 April 1808; *Lt.* 16 Dec. 1814; *Bt. Capt.* 9 Apr 1823; *Capt.* 22 Sept. 1824; *Maj.* 16 June 1835; *Lt. Col.* 12 Jan. 1842; *Col.* 10 Sept. 1852 *Maj. Genl.* 28 Nov. 1854.—Fur. S.C. 7 Feb. 52.					
	40	11	*Lt. Col.* William George Lennox, *Ens.* 15 Aug. 1818; *Lieut.* 16 Aug. 1818; *Capt.* 23 April 1830; *Bt Major* 9 Nov. 1846; *Major* 11 Nov. 1847; *Lt. Col.* 14 July 1853; *Bt. Col.* 28 Nov. 1854.					
	31	8	*Major* Robert Troup,†. *Ens.* 24 Oct. 1827; *Lieut.* 5 April 1834; *Bt. Capt.* 24 Oct. 1842; *Capt.* 1 Oct. 48; *Bt. Maj.* 20 June 54; *Maj.* 31 Dec. 55.—Comdt. of the Landour Depôt.					
			Captains.					
	24	1	J. C. Brooke, *P*,	Meywar Bheel Corps	12 *June* 35	3 *Oct.* 40	12 *June* 50	15 *Nov.* 53
	18	4	H. L. Pester, *PH*,	.. ..	8 *Mar.* 40	24 *Jan.* 45	.. ..	12 *Feb.* 54
	17	..	J. G. Phillips,†	.. ..	23 *June* 42	9 *Oct.* 47	.. ..	19 *Jan.* 55
O.	15	..	George Sinclair, *PH*,	Fur. S. C. 1 Feb. 56	25 *June* 44	10 *Dec.* 47	.. ..	17 *Apl.* 55
	14	6	R. T. H. Barber, *PH*,	Offg. Intr. H. M. 67th Foot, ..	18 *Jan.* 45	30 *Apl.* 48	.. ..	31 *Dec.* 55
	13	11	W. J. P. Barlow, *PH*,	Lv. P. A. 10 Sep.,	22 *July* 45	1 *Oct.* 48	.. ..	23 *Nov.* 56
	13	6	W. H. Hawes, *P*,	Civil employ, ..	7 *Jan.* 46	2 *Dec.* 49	.. ..	15 *Jan.* 57
			Lieutenants.					
	13	6	B. W. Ryall, *PH*,	4th Punjaub Cavy,	14 *Jan.* 46	6 *Nov.* 50		
	12	1	T. E. Webster,†	.. ..	11 *June* 47	21 *Sep.* 51		
N.	12	1	C. H. Palliser, *PH*,	2nd Regt- Hodson's Horse, ..	11 *June* 47	15 *Nov.* 53		
O.	11	6	J. Reay,†	Fur. S.C. 17 July 57	11 *Jan.* 48	5 *Dec.* 53		
N.	9	7	Henri Campbell, *P*,	Fur. S.C. 16 June 58	11 *Dec.* 49	12 *Feb.* 54		
	9	1	R. D. Campbell, *PH*,	.. ..	15 *June* 50	19 *Jan.* 55		
O.	7	10	C. Richardes,	Fur. S.C. 22 Oct. 58	26 *Aug.* 51	31 *Dec.* 55		
	5	2	Hy. Wilson Gordon, *PH*,	3rd Punjaub Infy..	6 *May* 54	23 *Nov.* 56		
	3	6	William Snow,†	Sirmoor Rifle Regt.	20 *Jan.* 56	30 *Apl.* 58		
	2	6	F. F. J. Toke,†	.. ..	22 *Jan.* 57	30 *Apl.* 58		
	1	9	H. Rowland,	.. ..	29 *Sep.* 57	22 *Oct.* 58		
			Ensigns.					
	1	..	C. K. Mackinnon,†	.. ..	20 *July* 58			
	..	6	A. F. Lindsay,	.. ..	6 *Jan.* 59			
			*					
			*					
			*					
					Appointed.			
	..	..	*Adjutant* R. D. Campbell,	.. ..	13 *June* 59			
	..	..	*Inter.*, H. Campbell,	Fur S C 16 June 58	10 *Mar.* 55			
	..	..	*Surg.*,					
	..	..	*Asst. Surg.*,					

Raised in 1813.

64th Regiment of Native Infantry.

Disarmed, Peshawur.

"CAUBUL 1842."

Harriott-ke-Pultun. Late 2nd Battalion 32nd Regt. N.I.

FACINGS—*Yellow.*

Fur. Reg.	Ser. Y	Ser. M	
	52	3	*Colonel* Henry Francis Caley. *Ens.* 14 Apl. 1807; *Lieut.* 2 March 1814; *Bt. Capt.* 14 Apl. 1822; *Capt.* 1 May 1824; *Bt. Major* 10 Jan. 1837; *Major* 21 Jan. 1838; *Lieut. Col.* 16 Apl. 44; *Bt. Col.* 20 June 1854; *Col.* 7 Nov. 54; *Major Genl.* 18 March 1856.—Residing at Rawul Pindee.
O.	39	11	*Lt. Col.* Robert Garrett, *P.* *Ens.* 24 July 1819; *Lieut.* 29 Aug. 1821; *Bt. Capt.* 24 July 34; *Capt.* 1 Dec. 36; *Bt. Major* 9 Nov. 46; *Major* 31 July 49; *Bt. Lt. Col.* 20 June 54; *Lieut. Col.* 28 Nov. 1854; *Bt. Col.* 20 June 1857.—Fur. S. C. 7 Mar. 59.
O.	35	3	*Major* C. Prior, *PH.* *Ens.* 13 Apl. 1824; *Lt.* 13 May 1825; *Bt. Capt.* 13 Apl. 1839; *Capt.* 17 Jan. 1841; *Bt. Major* 11 Nov. 1851; *Major* 10 July 1857; *Bt. Lt. Col.* 25 Apl. 1858.—Fur. S. C. 29 Mar. 59.

☞ *Brevet.* [1] Maj. 20 June 54. [2] Maj. 2 Aug. 50. Lt. Col. 28 Nov. 54. Col. 28 Nov. 57. [3] Maj. 1 April 1859.

Fur. Reg.	Y	M		Remarks.	*Ensign.*	*Lieut.*	Captain. *Brevet.*	Captain. *Regl.*
			CAPTAINS.					
N.	~~33~~	..	~~C. H. Burt, *P,*~~ [1]*m*	Fur. S. C. 22 May 57	21 *July* 26	8 *Oct.* 27	21 *July* 41	24 *Jan.* 42
	22	3	W. E. Mulcaster, *PH,* [2]*c*	7th Irregular Cavy.	4 *Apl.* 37	29 *Aug.* 40	.. ..	26 *Oct.* 48
	20	4	H. E. Young, †	Goojranwallah Levy.	19 *Mar.* 39	17 *Jan.* 41	.. ..	15 *Nov.* 53
	19	7	T. Rattray, *PH,* [3]*m*	Inspector of Police Battn's. L. P. ..	9 *Dec.* 39	24 *Jan.* 42	.. ..	1 *Feb.* 54
	19	6	R. Nicholas, †	Lv. P. A. 15 Oct, ..	3 *Jan.* 40	24 *Apl.* 42	3 *Jan.* 55	23 *Nov.* 56
O.	18	9	A. L. Nicholson, †	Fur. P. A. 28 Apl. 59.	12 *Oct.* 40	11 *Dec.* 43	12 *Oct.* 55	18 *Mar.* 57
	18	4	R. M. Nott, *PH,*	.. ..	8 *Mar.* 41	24 *Jan.* 45	8 *Mar.* 56	10 *July* 57
			LIEUTENANTS.					
N.	17	11	D. A. Chase, *P, (a)* Capt.	Fur S. C. 16 Sep. 58	12 *Aug.* 41	29 *Mar.* 45	12 *Aug.* 56	
	17	7	J. S. Dunbar, *PC, (b)*	Offg. Army Comt. Dept. ..	11 *Dec.* 41	3 *June* 48	11 *Dec.* 56	
	17	..	H. B. A. Poulton, *PH,*	.. ..	10 *July* 42	26 *Oct.* 48	10 *July* 57	
N.	15	5	R. Davidson, *PC,*	Army Comt. Dept.	29 *Feb.* 44	15 *Oct.* 52	1 *Mar.* 59	
	14	6	C. H. Hall, *PH, (c)*	Civil employ, ..	29 *Dec.* 44	15 *Nov.* 53		
	11	6	R. D. Griffin, *PH,*	2nd Sikh Irr. Cavy.,	11 *Jan.* 48	1 *Feb.* 54		
	11	6	W. H. Wise, †	... ...	20 *Jan.* 48	23 *Nov.* 56		
	7	6	F. T. Bainbridge, †	... ..	20 *Jan.* 52	23 *Nov.* 56		
	7	1	A. McL. Stewart, *PH,*	6th Punjaub Infy. ..	20 *June* 52	18 *Mar.* 57		
	2	1	T. D. Madden,	.. ..	13 *June* 57	18 *May* 58		
	1	7	E. Kitson,	.. ..	12 *Dec.* 57	13 *Aug.* 58		
			ENSIGNS.					
Lt.	..	11	W. D. Macturk,	.. ..	26 *Aug.* 58			
			*					
			*					
			*					
			*		*Appointed.*			
	..	..	*Adjtt.,* H. B. A. Poulton,	Offg. Judge advocate Genl's. Dept. ..	6 *May* 57			
	..	..	*Interpreter,* J. S. Dunbar,	Offg. Army Commt. Dept. ..	30 *Dec.* 46			
	..	..	*Surg.,* G. C. Wallich, M.D.,	Fur. S. C. 3 Feb. 57	30 *Apl.* 57			
	..	..	*Asst. Surg.,* *					

(*a*) Has also passed an examination in the Burmese language.
(*b*) Received a certificate for high proficiency in the Oordoo language from the College of Fort William on the 18th Sept. 1849, and passed an examination in the Punjaubee language, 11th July 1853.
(*c*) Have furnished certificate of qualification as a Civil Engineer.

Raised in 1823. } **65th Regiment of Native Infantry, (Volunteers.)** { On Service in China.

(*Rifle Company.*)

Late 1st Battalion 33rd Regt. N.I.

Facings—*Yellow.*

Fur. Reg.	Ser. Y	Ser. M	
N.	39	11	*Colonel* Claud Douglas. *Ens.* 16 Aug. 1819; *Lieut.* 29 April 1823; *Capt.* 27 Aug. 1828; *Bt. Major* 23 Nov. 1841; *Major* 10 June 1842; *Lieut. Col.* 27 Oct. 1848; *Bt. Col.* 28 Nov. 1854; *Colonel* 1 May 1858.—Fur. S. C. 27 May 1858.
	39	10	*Lieut. Col.* George Burney, *PC.* *Ens.* 14 Sept. 1819; *Lieut.* 25 May 1821; *Capt.* 11 Nov. 1833; *Bt. Major* 23 Dec. 1842; *Major* 26 Feb. 46; *Lt. Col.* 6 Jan. 52; *Bt. Col.* 28 Nov. 54.
	23	..	*Major* F. M. Baker, *PH.* *Ens.* 6 July 1836; *Lieut.* 14 Apl. 1839; *Capt.* 11 Mar. 1847. *Major* 15 July 1857; Asst. to Chief Engineer, Punjaub.

☞ *Brevet.* [1] Maj. 20 July 58. [2] Major 24 Nov. 1856

Fur. Reg.	Y	M		Remarks.	Ensign.	Lieut.	Captain. Brevet.	Captain. Regl.
			Captains.					
	21	4	R. J. Meade, *PC*, (a)[1]*m*	Meade's Horse, ..	1 *Mar.* 38	17 *Mar.* 40	.. ..	6 *Nov.* 48
	20	7	H. L. Robertson, *P*,	.. ..	11 *Dec.* 38	3 *Oct.* 40	.. ..	13 *Dec.* 50
	20	5	T. Gordon, †	.. ...	24 *Jan.* 39	1 *Feb.* 41	.. ..	12 *Jan.* 53
O.	19	7	G. R. Weston, *PH*,	Fur. S. C. 19 Apl. 58	10 *Dec.* 39	21 *Feb.* 42	10 *Dec.* 54	1 *Oct.* 55
	19	6	C. T. E. Hinde, † *[2]*m*	Baghalcund Military Police, ..	3 *Jan.* 40	16 *July* 42	3 *Jan.* 55	23 *Nov.* 56
	18	10	F. J. Nelson, *PH*,	Brigade Staff, ..	21 *Aug.* 40	21 *June* 43	21 *Aug.* 55	14 *June* 57
O.	18	1	C. L. Montgomery, †	Fur. S. C. 15 Mar. 58	12 *June* 41	24 *Jan.* 45	12 *June* 56	15 *July* 57
			Lieutenants.					
O.	17	9	T. W. Hilton, †	Fur. S.C. 12 Feb. 58	27 *Sep.* 41	10 *June* 45	27 *Sep.* 56	
	16	7	R. M. S. Annesley, *P*,	Meywar Bheel Corps,	9 *Dec.* 42	11 *Mar.* 47	9 *Dec.* 57	
	16	1	T. J. Geldart, †	Dept. Public Works Pegu, Circle, ..	9 *June* 43	6 *Nov.* 48	9 *June* 58	
	14	5	W. Reveley, *PH*,	.. ..	11 *Feb.* 45	12 *Jan.* 53		
	13	1	A. Combe, †	.. ..	13 *June* 46	24 *July* 53		
	12	7	R. Y. Chambers, *PH*,	2nd Assam Light Infy. Battn. ..	11 *Dec.* 46	1 *Oct.* 55		
	11	5	R. S. Moseley, *P*,	.. ..	17 *Feb.* 48	1 *Apl.* 56		
N.	5	3	Wynyard Battye, *PCH*,	Fur. S. C. 21 Jan. 59	4 *Apl.* 54	23 *Nov.* 56		
	4	4	Robert Francis Firth, †	.. ..	17 *Mar.* 55	14 *June* 57		
N.	3	10	Joseph Park,	Fur.S.C. 19 June 57	4 *Sep.* 55	15 *July* 57		
	2	6	R. H. DeMontmorency, †	.. ..	4 *Jan.* 57	30 *Apl.* 58		
			Ensigns.					
	1	7	J. D. Macpherson,	.. ..	19 *Dec.* 57			
			*					
			*					
			*					
			*					
					Appointed.			
	..	..	*Adjutant*, W. Reveley,	.. ..	16 *Sep.* 57			
	..	..	*Intr.*, R. S. Moseley,	.. ..	24 *Feb.* 51			
	..	..	*Surgeon*, *					
	..	..	*Asst. Surg.* A. V. Best, M.D.	... ...	23 *Apl.* 58			

* Honorary rank of Lieut. Col. 5 Dec. 1856, for Service in Turkey.

(a) Passed the examinations in Surveying and Civil Engineering.

Raised in 1815.

66th or Goorka Light Infantry Regiment.

Seetapore.

"ALLIWAL"—"SUBRAON."

Embodied from the old Nusseree Battalion, 27th Feb. 1850.

FACINGS—*White.*

Fur. Reg.	Ser. Y	Ser. M	
O.	57	..	*Colonel* Frederick Young. *Ens.* 19 July 1802; *Lt.* 18 March 1805; *Capt.* 8 Jan. 1816; *Major* 21 Jan. 1826; *Lieut. Col.* 1 Nov. 1830; *Col.* 3 Oct. 1842; *Major General* 20 June 1854; *Lieut. Genl.* 18 Feb. 1856.—Furlough, P. A. 5 Jan. 55.
	39	10	*Lt. Col.* John Kennedy McCausland, C. B., *Ens.* 20 Sept. 1819; *Lt.* 5 Oct. 1821; *Bt. Capt.* 20 Sept. 1834; *Capt.* 1 July 1836; *Bt. Major* 9 Nov. 1846; *Major* 18 March 1847; *Bt. Lt. Col.* 7 June 1849; *Lieut. Colonel* 31 March 1853; *Bt. Col.* 28 Nov. 1854.—Brigadier Commanding at Sealkote.
			*Major**

Fur. Reg.	Y	M	CAPTAINS.	REMARKS.	*Ensign.*	*Lieut.*	CAPTAIN. *Brevet.*	CAPTAIN. *Regl.*
	26	1	W. S. Sherwill,†	Civil employ, ..	11 *June* 33	3 *Oct.* 40	.. ..	22 *Feb.* 47
O.	24	1	H. Strachey,†	Fur. S.C. 23 Feb. 59	12 *June* 35	7 *Nov.* 40	.. ..	19 *July* 48
N.	19	5	J. S. Phillpotts, *PCH*,	Fur. S.C. 30 Nov. 58	15 *Feb.* 40	25 *Nov.* 42	.. ..	28 *Oct.* 50
	18	3	C. C. G. Ross,†	Comdg. Recruit depôt, Petoragurh.	4 *Apl.* 41	16 *May* 44	.. ..	10 *May* 52
	17	1	A. L. Busk, *PC*,	Civil employ, ..	12 *June* 42	9 *Dec.* 44	.. ..	23 *Nov.* 56
	17	..	J. J. Hockley,†	.. ..	10 *July* 42	24 *Jan.* 45	.. ..	31 *May* 57
N.	16	10	J. A. Law, *PC*,	Fur. P.A. 28 Apl. 59	20 *Aug.* 42	5 *Aug.* 45	20 *Aug.* 57	8 *Nov.* 58
			LIEUTENANTS.					
	14	7	J. A. Tytler, *V.C.PH*,	.. ..	10 *Dec.* 44	19 *July* 48		
	14	4	E. B. Clay, *PH*, (*a*)	Camel Corps, ..	2 *Mar.* 45	24 *July* 50		
	14	1	J. Sykes, *P*,	Army Commt. Dept.	14 *June* 45	13 *Aug.* 50		
	10	4	R. S. Graves, *P*,	.. ..	2 *Mar.* 49	15 *Sep.* 54		
	9	7	A. U. F. Ruxton, *PH*, (*b*)	Punjaub Irr. Force	12 *Dec.* 49	23 *Feb.* 56		
	9	1	D. Macintyre,†	Sirmoor Rifle Regt.,	14 *June* 50	23 *Nov.* 56		
	3	7	E. T. FitzGerald, *P*,	Army Commt. Dept.	20 *Dec.* 55	12 *Feb.* 58		
	2	11	R. S. Hill,†	.. ..	4 *Aug.* 56	12 *Apl.* 58		
	2	7	G. D. A. Younghusband,†	.. ..	12 *Dec.* 56	30 *Apl.* 58		
	2	1	T. Pearson,	.. ..	13 *June* 57	18 *May* 58		
	1	7	St. G. M. Bishop,	.. ..	12 *Dec.* 57	8 *Nov.* 58		
			ENSIGNS.					
	1	7	P. Story,	.. ..	11 *Dec.* 57			
	..	11	G. Young,	.. ..	20 *Aug.* 58			
			*					
			*					
			*		*Appointed.*			
	..	..	*Adjutant*, J. A. Tytler,	.. ..	19 *Oct.* 53			
	..	..	*Intr.*, R. S. Graves,	.. ..	14 *Dec.* 58			
	..	..	*Surg.* H. Irwin, F.R.C.S.I.,	Lv. S. C. 15 Nov...	19 *Dec.* 54			
	..	..	*Asst. Surg.*, *					

(*a*) Has passed an examination in Field Engineering.

(*b*) Has passed an examination in Field Engineering and furnished the certificate of qualification in Civil Engineering.

Raised in 1823.

67th Regiment of Native Infantry, (Volunteers.)

Disarmed, and dispersed, Agra.

"PEGU."

(*Rifle Company.*)

Late 1st Battalion 34th Regt. N.I.

FACINGS—*Yellow.*

Fur. Reg.	Ser. Y	Ser. M	
D	55	6	~~Colonel John Graham~~. *Ens.* 1 Jan. 1804; *Lieut.* 1 Feb. 1807; *Bt. Capt.* 1 Jan. 1819; *Capt.* 13 May 1825; *Major* 29 July 1834; *Lieut. Col.* 11 July 1841; *Col.* 17 Mach 51; *Major General* 28 Nov. 54.—Fur., P.A., 16 Feb. 51.
D N.	51	10	~~Col. James Steel, C.B.~~ *Ens.* 4 Sept. 1807; *Lieut.* 16 March 1814; *Bt. Capt.* 4 Sept. 1822; *Capt.* 15 Dec 1824; *Bt. Major* 10 Jan. 1837; *Major* 15 Aug. 1842; *Lieut. Col.* 8 Mar. 1849; *Bt. Col.* 28 Nov. 1854; *Col.* 9 Oct. 1858.—Fur. S.C. 11 Mar. 59.
	29	8	*Major* R. N. Raikes, *Ens.* 19 Nov. 1829; *Lieut.* 28 June 1836; *Bt. Capt.* 19 Nov. 1844; *Captain* 20 Feb. 1852; *Bt. Major* 28 Nov. 1854; *Major* 28 Nov. 1857. *Brevet.* [1] Major 24 Mar. 58.

Fur. Reg.	Y	M	CAPTAINS.	REMARKS.	*Ensign.*	*Lieut.*	CAPTAIN. *Brevet.*	CAPTAIN. *Regl.*
O.	24	1	E. W. Hicks, *P*, - - -	Fur. S.C. 14 Nov. 56	12 *June* 35	5 *Aug.* 37	12 *June* 50	5 *Feb.* 53
O.	20	1	W. C. Clifton,† - - -	Fur. P. A. 5 Apl. 59	18 *June* 39	3 *Nov.* 43	.. ..	8 *Dec.* 53
D	~~17~~	~~1~~	~~G. F. D'Oyly~~, *P*, - - -	Civil employ, ..	10 *June* 42	1 *Aug.* 46	.. ..	17 *May* 54
	16	7	F C. Maisey, *PH*,[1]*m* - -	Judge Advocate General's Dept, ..	9 *Dec.* 42	8 *Sep.* 46	.. ..	10 *Nov.* 55
D	~~16~~	~~4~~	~~R. R. Harris, P~~, - - -	Cant. Joint Magte., Cawnpore, ..	20 *Feb.* 43	23 *Dec.* 46	.. ..	31 *Aug.* 56
	15	6	E. J. Spilsbury, *PH*, (*a*)-	Civil employ, ..	16 *Jan.* 44	28 *Feb.* 50	.. ..	23 *Nov.* 56
N.	13	5	W. B. Girdlestone, *PH*, -	Fur. S.C. 12 May 58	4 *Feb.* 46	9 *July* 52	.. ..	28 *Nov.* 57
			LIEUTENANTS.					
Capt.	9	7	E. Thompson, *P*, - -	Civil employ, ..	12 *Dec.* 49	21 *Mar.* 53		
	7	10	B. H. Smith,† -	Divl. Adjt. Mily. Police, Oudh, ..	20 *Aug.* 51	8 *Dec.* 53		
	6	11	J. T. Bushby, *PH*, -	Civil employ, ..	10 *Aug.* 52	17 *May* 54		
	6	7	S. A. T. Judge, *PH*, -	Adjt. district Police, Mundlah, ..	9 *Dec.* 52	10 *Nov.* 55		
	6	7	A. Brodie Melville, *PH*, (*b*)	Survey Dept., ..	10 *Dec.* 52	31 *Aug.* 56		
	5	10	H. McD. DeW. Douglas,†	Agra Levy, ..	29 *Aug.* 53	23 *Nov.* 56		
	5	6	H. L. A. Tottenham,† -	Fur. S.C. 17 June 59	20 *Dec.* 53	23 *Nov.* 56		
	5	1	Herbert Mills Repton, *PH*.	Alexander's Horse.	9 *June* 54	30 *May* 57		
	3	1	Charles Case,† - - -	Meade's Horse, ..	14 *June* 56	27 *June* 57		
	1	11	B. E. Reade, - - - -	.. ..	26 *July* 57	18 *May* 58		
	1	5	H. C. Marsh, - - - -	.. ..	20 *Feb.* 58	22 *Oct.* 58		
			ENSIGNS.					
Lt.	..	8	H. H. Oldham, - - - -	.. ..	4 *Nov.* 58			
			*					
			*					
			*					
			*					
					Appointed.			
	..	..	*Adjutant*,*					
	..	..	*Intr.**					
	..	..	*Surg.*,*					
	..	..	*Assistant Surg.* W. G. W. Clemenger, A. B. M. B.,	Offg. Civil, Meerut,	6 *Dec.* 56			

(*a*) Has passed an examination in the Burmese Language.
(*b*) Has passed an examination in Surveying at the Thomason College, Roorkee.

Raised in 1833.

68th Regiment of Native Infantry, (Volunteers.)

Mutinied, Bareilly.

(*Rifle Company.*)

"Subraon."—"Pegu."

Late 2nd Battalion 34th Regt. N.I.

Facings—*Yellow.*

Fur. Reg.	Ser. Y	Ser. M	
	58	8	*Colonel* Edmund Frederick Waters, c. b. *Ens.* 1 Nov. 1800; *Lieut.* 1 July 1803; *Capt.* 1 Sept. 1815; *Major* 11 July 1823; *Lieut. Col.* 13 May 1825; *Bt. Col.* 18 June 1831; *Col.* 16 Nov. 1835; *Maj. Genl.* 23 Nov. 41; *Lieut. Genl.* 11 Nov. 1851.—Europe, 21 Feb. 45.
	39	..	*Lieut. Col.* Colin Troup. *Ens.* 16 July 1820; *Lt.* 11 July 1823; *Bt. Capt.* 16 July 35 *Capt.* 8 Oct. 39; *Bt. Maj.* 19 June 46; *Maj.* 24 July 47; *Lt. Col.* 5 June 53; *Bt. Col.* 28 Nov. 54.—Brigadier Comdg. at Mooltan.
	24	6	*Lieut. Col.* B. Boyd,† *Ens.* 20 Jan. 1835, *Lieut.* 13 Nov. 1836, *Capt.* 20 May 1846, *Major* 20. April 1855; *Lieut. Col.* 15 May 1859.
	21	..	*Major* P. A. Roberton,† *Ens.* 7 July 1838; *Lieut.* 5 Sept. 1842; *Capt.* 1 Nov. 1849; *Major* 15 May 1859 —Comdg. district police Moradabad, ☞ *Brevet.* [1] Major 20 July 1858.

Fur. Reg.	Y	M	Captains.	Remarks.	Ensign.	Lieut.	Captain. Brevet.	Captain. Regl.
	~~18~~	~~9~~	~~R. C. Barclay,~~† [1]m - -	... ..	26 *Sep.* 40	5 *Sep.* 42	.. ..	21 *Nov.* 51
	18	7	G. Faithfull, *PH*, - - -	Civil employ,	12 *Dec.* 40	3 *Dec.* 43	.. ..	13 *Sep.* 53
	17	4	A. H. Paterson, *P*, - - -	.. ..	3 *Mar.* 42	14 *Apl.* 44	.. ..	20 *Apl.* 55
	17	2	J. I. Gibbs, *PH*, (*a*) - - -	Cant. Jt. Magte. and Supdt. of the Cant, Abkarry Mehal, Shahjehanpore, ..	24 *Apl.* 42	21 *Sep.* 44	.. ..	23 *Nov.* 56
	16	1	C. Warde *P*, - - - -	Offg. Cant. Jt. Magte. and Supdt. of the Abkarry Mehal, Agra, ..	10 *June* 43	14 *Aug.* 46	.. ..	8 *June* 57
O.	13	7	W. R. Gordon, *PH*, - -	Fur. S.C. 19 Apl. 58	12 *Dec.* 45	1 *Nov.* 49	.. ..	19 *Feb.* 59
	12	1	A. Francis, *PH*, - - -	.. ..	11 *June* 47	21 *Nov.* 51	.. ..	15 *May* 59
			Lieutenants.					
	~~11~~	~~5~~	~~A. W. Montagu,~~ *PH*, - -	Regt. of Ferozepore,	20 *Feb.* 48	13 *Sep.* 53		
	10	..	H H. Christian,† -	12th Punjaub Infy.,	27 *June* 49	16 *Dec.* 54		
	~~7~~	~~6~~	~~J. T. Stanton,~~† - -	.. ..	20 *Jan.* 52	23 *Nov.* 56		
	5	1	Brudenell Rogers,† -	.. ..	8 *June* 54	23 *Nov.* 56		
	~~4~~	~~1~~	~~W. G. Murray,~~ - -	Survey Dept. ..	8 *June* 55	1 *May* 57		
	2	9	C. M. MacGregor, † - -	1st Regt. Hodson's Horse. ..	20 *Oct.* 56	17 *Nov.* 57		
	2	3	A. Lindsay,† - - - -	.. ..	18 *Apl.* 57	18 *May* 58		
	1	10	J. E. Whitting, - - - -	.. ..	4 *Sep.* 57	5 *Oct.* 58		
	1	..	C. L. Woodruffe, - - -	.. ..	28 *June* 58	22 *Oct.* 58		
	1	..	J. Johnstone,† - - - -	Regt. of Ferozepore,	20 *July* 58	19 *Feb.* 59		
	..	7	H. V. Riddell, - - - -	.. ..	11 *Dec.* 58	15 *May* 59		
			Ensigns.					
	..	7	J. H. Baldwin, - - - -	.. ..	20 *Dec.* 58			
			*					
			*		*Appointed.*			
			*					
			*					
	..	..	*Adjutant*,*					
	..	..	*Interpreter*,*					
	..	..	*Surg.*, J. Bowhill, - -	.. ..	6 *Dec.* 56			
	..	..	*Asst. Surg.*, B. Simpson, m. d. and a. b., - - -	Fur. S. C. 21 Oct. 56	8 *Nov.* 55			

(*a*) Has furnished the Certificate of qualification in Civil Engineering.

Raised in 1825.

69th Regiment of Native Infantry.

Mutinied, Mooltan.

(*Rifle Company.*)

"PUNJAUB"—"CHILLIANWALLA"—"GOOJERAT."

FACINGS—*White.*

Fur. Reg.	SER. Y	SER. M	
	58	8	*Colonel* Richard Collyer Andree. *Ens.* 5 Nov. 1800; *Lieut.* 10 May 1802; *Capt.* 16 Dec. 1814; *Major* 1 May 1824; *Lieut. Col.* 27 Jan. 1826; *Col.* 20 June 1836; *Major Genl.* 23 Nov. 1841; *Lieut. Genl.* 11 Nov. 1851.—Europe, 11 Feb. 1838.
	35	6	*Lt. Col.* John William Hicks. *Ens.* 17 Jan. 1824; *Lieut.* 13 May 1825; *Capt.* 15 Feb. 1836; *Bt. Major* 9 Nov. 1846; *Major* 28 Feb. 50; *Bt. Lt. Col.* 20 June 1854; *Lt. Col.* 10 Nov. 1855. *Bt. Col.* 15 Feb. 1858. Lv. P, A. 1 Nov.
N.	24	11	*Major* E. Sissmore, *PH.* *Ens* 5 August 1834; *Lieut.* 22 Apl. 1840; *Capt.* 29 July 1848; • *Major* 11 July 1857.—Fur. S. C. 21 Dec. 58.

Fur. Reg.	Y	M	CAPTAINS.	REMARKS.	*Ensign.*	*Lieut.*	CAPTAIN. *Brevet.*	CAPTAIN. *Regl.*
	20	..	E. J. Simpson, *P*, - -	Army Commt. Dept.	24 *Jan.* 39	24 *Aug.* 40	.. ..	31 *July* 49
	20	..	John Nisbett, *PH*, - - -	.. ..	12 *June* 39	3 *Oct.* 40	.. ..	15 *Aug.* 50
	19	7	E. Tulloch, *PH*, - - -	.. ..	10 *Dec.* 39	2 *Feb.* 42	.. ..	17 *Nov.* 52
	18	7	J. Wedderburn,† - -	Lv. P. A. 15 Oct. ..	12 *Dec.* 40	12 *Sep.* 44	.. ..	28 *Nov.* 54
	17	6	G. A. Black, *P*, - - -	Joudpore Legion, ..	8 *Jan.* 42	24 *Jan.* 45	.. ..	23 *Nov.* 56
	17	..	J. E. Cracroft, *P*, - -	Civil employ, ..	10 *July* 42	11 *Sep.* 45	.. ..	10 *July* 57
N.	16	4	J. I. Willes, *P*, - - -	Army Commt. Dept.	22 *Feb.* 43	29 *May* 48	.. ..	11 *July* 57
			LIEUTENANTS.					
	15	17	J. T. Norgate, *PH*, - -	12th Punjaub Infy.	30 *Dec.* 43	29 *July* 48	30 *Dec.* 58	
	14	11	H. Hayley, *PH*, - -	Civil employ, ..	27 *July* 44	31 *July* 49		
	12	10	T. W. R. Boisragon, *P*, -	Nusseree Battn. ..	2 *Sep.* 46	15 *Aug.* 50		
N.	11	7	A. H. Millett, *P*, - -	Fur. S. C. 1 July 59,	11 *Dec.* 47	17 *Nov.* 52		
	13	1	C. G. Thorp, *PH*, - - -	.. ..	12 *June* 46	17 *July* 54		
	9	4	T. P. Harrison, *PH*, -	3rd Seikh Infy.	20 *Mar.* 50	28 *Jan.* 56		
	6	11	J. J. Boswell, *P*, (a) - -	.. ...	10 *Aug.* 52	23 *Nov.* 56		
	5	5	A. Haldane Eckford, *P*,	Civil employ, ..	20 *Feb.* 54	23 *Nov.* 56		
	3	7	R. H. Hudleston, *PCH*, -	Civil employ, ..	7 *Dec.* 55	1 *June* 57		
	2	1	F. S. Goad, - - -	.. ..	13 *June* 57	18 *May* 58		
	1	7	F. R. A. B. Constable, -	.. ..	19 *Dec.* 57	22 *Oct.* 58		
			ENSIGNS.					
	..	11	E. W. de Lousada, - -	.. ..	26 *Aug.* 58			
			*					
			*					
			*					
			*					
	..	..	*Adjutant*,*		*Appointed.*			
	..	..	*Intr.* *					
	..	..	*Surgeon*, T. R. Strover, -	Lv. S. C. 1 May prepy. to Fur. ..	10 *Apl.* 52			
	..	..	*Asst. Surg.*,*					

(*a*) Has attained a degree of proficiency in the Punjaubee language.

Raised in 1825.

70th Regiment of Native Infantry.

On Service in China.

"PUNJAUB"—"CHILLIANWALLA"—"GOOJERAT."
FACINGS—*Yellow*.

Fur. Reg.	Ser. Y	Ser. M	
	51	4	*Colonel* George Hicks, C. B. *Ens.* 1 March 1808; *Lieut.* 14 Sept. 1813; *Bt. Capt.* 1 March 1823; *Capt.* 9 Nov. 1824; *Major* 8 Jan. 1838; *Lieut. Col.* 13 March 1844; *Col.* 7 May 1854; *Major General* 18 Feb. 1856.—Furlough, S. C. 21 Mar. 1852.
	31	6	*Lieut. Col.* James Don Kennedy, *P. Ens.* 19 Jan. 1828; *Lieut.* 2 July 1833; *Capt.* 5 July 1837; *Major* 26 Dec. 1846; *Lieut. Col.* 10 Sep. 1852; *Bt. Col.* 28 Nov. 1854.
O.	35	5	*Major* P. Harris. *Ens.* 18 Feb. 24; *Lt.* 13 May 25; *Bt. Capt.* 18 Feb. 39; *Capt.* 8 Oct. 39; *Bt. Maj.* 30 Apl. 44; *Maj.* 20 July 57; *Bt. Lt. Col.* 20 June 54; *Bt. Col.* 8 June 1856.—Fur. S.C. 17 Mar. 57.

☞ *Brevet.* [1] Maj. 20 June 1854. [2] Maj. 9 Dec. 1853.

Fur. Reg.	Y	M	CAPTAINS.	REMARKS.	*Ensign.*	*Lieut.*	CAPTAIN. *Brevet.*	CAPTAIN. *Regl.*
	31	5	J. Hennessy,[1]*m* - - -	Comdg. Agra Police Battn., ...	3 *Feb.* 28	10 *Apl.* 36	3 *Feb.* 43	24 *Jan.* 45
	27	7	G. N. Greene,† - - -	.. ..	8 *Dec.* 31	1 *July* 36	8 *Dec.* 46	18 *Mar.* 47
	21	7	H. Hopkinson, *PCH*, (*a*) -	Civil employ, ..	12 *Dec.* 37	19 *Jan.* 40	12 *Dec.* 52	31 *Mar.* 53
	20	7	A. Fytche, *PCH*,[2]*m* - -	Civil employ, ..	11 *Dec.* 38	17 *Aug.* 40	.. ..	1 *Apl.* 53
O.	20	7	H. B. Impey, *P*, (*b*)- - -	Fur P. A. 6 Jan. 57,	12 *Dec.* 38	3 *Oct.* 40	12 *Dec.* 53	23 *Nov.* 56
	19	7	W. T. Garstin, *PH*,- - -	.. ..	11 *Dec.* 39	16 *July* 42	11 *Dec.* 54	20 *July* 57
	18	4	F. C. Wiggins,† - - -	.. ..	8 *Mar.* 41	18 *Mar.* 47	8 *Mar.* 56	11 *Jan.* 59
			LIEUTENANTS.					
	18	1	H. W. H. Coxe, *P*, - -	Civil employ, ..	21 *June* 41	8 *Apl.* 50	21 *June* 56	
	17	1	C. H. Byers, *PH*, - -	Political employ, ..	12 *June* 42	15 *May* 50	12 *June* 57	
	16	6	C. Murray, *PH*, - - -	Comdt. Sebundy Sappers & Miners, and Offg Ex. Offir. D. P. W.	28 *Dec.* 42	9 *Aug.* 51	28 *Dec.* 57	
	15	1	R. C. Whiting,† - - -	.. ..	8 *June* 44	31 *Mar* 53	8 *June* 59	
	10	7	W. M. Grierson, *P*, (*c*) -	.. ..	9 *Dec.* 48	15 *Nov.* 53		
	8	6	P. H. F. Harris, *PH*, - -	.. ..	20 *Dec.* 50	23 *Nov.* 56		
	7	6	F. J. Ripley, *PH* - -	.. ..	20 *Dec.* 51	23 *Nov.* 56		
O.	6	11	J. C. C. Daunt, *PH*, - -	Fur. S. C. 7 Jan. 59	20 *July* 52	20 *July* 57		
	5	3	Chas. Metcalfe Bushby,†	Hyderabad Contingent, ..	4 *Apl.* 54	30 *Apl.* 58		
	1	7	F. C. W. Drummond,- -	.. ...	20 *Dec.* 57	20 *Nov.* 58		
	..	7	C. G. Millett, - - - -	.. ..	11 *Dec.* 58	29 *Mar.* 59		
			ENSIGNS.					
			*					
			*					
			*		*Appointed.*			
			*					
			*					
	..	..	*Adjutant*, P. H. F. Harris,		22 *Oct.* 55			
	..	..	*Intr.*, W. M. Grierson, -	.. ..	4 *Apl.* 57			
	..	..	*Surg.*, H. B. Hinton, -	.. ..	4 *Apl.* 58			
	..	..	*Asst. Surg.*,	.. ..				

(*a*) Passed a successful examination in the Burmese language.

(*b*) Received certificates of high proficiency in the Hindee and Oordoo languages from the College of Fort William, 4th Feb. 1851. (*c*) Passed a successful examination in the Turkish language.

Raised in 1825.

71st Regiment of Native Infantry.

Mutinied, Lucknow.

"PUNJAUB."

FACINGS—*Black velvet.*

Fur. Reg.	Ser. Y	Ser. M	
	54	9	*Colonel* Alexander Dick. *Ens.* 5 Oct. 1804; *Lieut.* 5 Oct. 1804; *Capt.* 1 Jan. 1817; *Major* 22 April 1826; *Lieut. Col.* 4 May 1831; *Col.* 8 Feb. 1843; *Major Genl.* 20 June 1854; *Lt. Genl.* 4 July 1856.—Sirhind Circle.
N.	40	10	*Lt. Col.* David Birrell. *Ens.* 30 Aug. 1818; *Lieut.* 20 Oct. 1818; *Capt.* 26 April 1827; *Bt. Major* 23 Nov. 1811; *Major* 10 Nov. 1843; *Bt. Lieut. Col.* 3 April 1846; *Lieut. Col.* 1 March 1850; *Bt. Col.* 20 June 1854; *Major Genl.* 25 April 58.—Fur. S. C. 3 Aug. 1858.
N.	25	1	*Major* J. L. Walker, *PCH.* *Ens.* 13 June 1834; *Lieut.* 22 Mar. 1839; *Capt.* 1 May 1847; *Major* 31 May 1857.—Fur S. C. 3 Feb. 1857.

☞ Brevet [1] Major 24 Mar. 1858. [2] Major 20 July 1858. [3] Major 24 Mar. 1858.

Fur. Reg.	Y	M		Remarks.	Ensign.	Lieut.	Captain. Brevet.	Captain. Regl.
			Captains.					
N.	21	1	G. Strangways,† - - - -	Fur. S. C. 9 Mar. 58	16 *June* 38	3 *Oct.* 40	.. ..	21 *Aug.* 49
N.	20	..	H. Dinning,†[1]*m* - - -	Fur. S. C. 29 Apl. 58	10 *July* 39	16 *July* 42	.. ..	7 *Dec.* 49
N.	18	6	L R. Christopher, *P*, - -	Army Commt. Dept.	4 *Jan.* 41	1 *Nov.* 44	.. ..	28 *Dec.* 53
	17	4	J. Ross, *PCH*, - - -	Brigade Staff, ..	9 *Mar.* 42	24 *Jan.* 45	.. ..	30 *Dec.* 54
	16	7	J. I. Murray, *PH*, (a)[2]*m* -	Jat Horse, ..	10 *Dec.* 42	7 *Sep.* 45	.. ..	23 *Nov.* 56
	16	5	W. Briggs, *PH*, - - -	Offg. Army Commt. Dept.	17 *Feb.* 43	9 *July* 46	.. ...	31 *May* 57
	16	..	C. A. Barwell, *P.* [3]*m* - -	.. ..	20 *June* 43	1 *Apl.* 47	.. ..	30 *June* 57
			Lieutenants.					
	14	4	E. H. Langmore, *PH*, - -	Allahabad Levy. ..	1 *Mar.* 45	21 *Aug.* 49		
	14	1	J. Perkins, *P*, - - - -	Civil employ, ..	16 *June* 45	7 *Dec.* 49		
	13	7	F. C. Anderson, *P*, - - -	Reve. Survey Dept.	13 *Dec.* 45	18 *Mar.* 50		
	10	7	W. G. Davies, *P*, - - -	Civil employ, ..	9 *Dec.* 48	10 *July* 52		
	10	..	A. D. Vanrenen, *PH*, - -	Reve. Survey Dept.	7 *July* 49	28 *Dec.* 53		
	9	7	F. B. Foote, *PH*, - - -	Comdg. District Police, Hoshungabad,	11 *Dec.* 49	1 *Sep.* 54		
N.	7	6	R. M. Sewell,† - - - -	Fur. S. C. 12 May 58	20 *Dec.* 51	23 *Nov.* 56		
N.	5	3	F. Macdonald Birch, *PH*,	Fur. S. C. 3 May 58	4 *Apl.* 54	31 *May* 57		
	5	..	James Henry Worsley,	District Comdt. Mily. Police, Oude, ...	19 *July* 54	31 *May* 57		
	2	4	Wellesley Campbell, - -	Regt. of Lucknow,	4 *Mar.* 57	30 *Apl.* 58		
	2	1	F. L. S. Dyce, - - - -	Lv. S. C. 15 Nov...	13 *June* 57	18 *May* 58		
			Ensigns.					
R	~~1~~	~~7~~	~~A. P. Martin~~, - - - -	.. ...	12 *Dec.* 57			
			*					
			*					
			*					
			*					
	..	..	*Adjutant*,*		*Appointed.*			
	..	..	*Interpreter*,*					
	..	..	*Surg.**					
	..	..	*Asst. Surg.*,*					

(*a*) Has furnished the certificate of qualification in Surveying and Civil Engineering.

Raised in 1825.

72nd Regiment of Native Infantry.

Mutinied Neemuch.

(*Rifle Company.*)

"Punjaub"—"Mooltan"—"Goojerat."

Facings—*Yellow.*

Fur. Reg.	Ser. Y	Ser. M						
N.	46	11	*Colonel* Henry Lawrence. *Ens.* 30 July 1812; *Lieut.* 16 Dec. 1814; *Bt. Capt.* 1 Nov. 1826; *Capt.* 19 Jan. 1828; *Maj.* 3 Aug. 1837; *Lt. Col.* 3 Nov. 1843; *Col.* 15 April 1854; *Major Genl.* 5 Dec. 1855.—Fur. S. C. 8 Jan. 1856.					
	33	6	*Lieut. Col.* P. Abbott. *Ens.* 23 Dec. 1825; *Lieut.* 16 May 1827; *Capt.* 1 Dec. 1836; *Bt. Maj.* 9 Nov. 1846; *Maj.* 10 May 1853; *Bt. Lt. Col.* 20 June 1854; *Lieut. Col.* 28 Aug. 1857. *Bt. Col.* 20 June 1857; Leave P. A. 15 Oct.					
	22	7	*Major* T. F. Hobday, *P*, *Ens.* 17 Dec. 1836; *Lieut.* 3 Oct. 1840; *Capt.* 1 Feb. 1848; *Major* 28 Aug. 1857.—Army Commt. Dept.					
			Captains.	**Remarks.**	*Ensign.*	*Lieut.*	**Captain.** *Brevet.*	**Captain.** *Regl.*
	21	7	G. E. Ford,†	.. ..	21 *Dec.* 37	16 *July* 42	.. ..	17 *Mar.* 51
	19	1	G. E. Holmes, *PH*,	Brigade Staff, ..	12 *June* 40	1 *Feb.* 43	.. ..	10 *May* 53
	18	4	J. C. Curtis, *PH*,	6th Irregular Cavy.	17 *Mar.* 41	17 *Oct.* 43	.. ..	9 *Oct.* 54
	18	1	R. K. Gordon, *PH*,	.. ..	12 *June* 41	4 *Aug.* 44	12 *June* 56	23 *Nov.* 56
	16	11	C. Andrews,†	Camel Corps, ..	27 *Aug.* 42	11 *Apl.* 45	.. ..	1 *July* 57
	15	6	C. T. Hallett, *PCH*,	Comdg. Dist. Police,				
	14	6	A. T. Armstrong, *P*,	Allygurh, ..	30 *Dec.* 43	1 *Feb.* 48	.. ..	28 *Aug.* 57
				A. D. C. to C.-in-C., Bombay, ..	3 *Jan.* 45	20 *Jan.* 49	.. ..	24 *Aug.* 58
			Lieutenants.					
	14	6	H. P. Williams, *P*,	Pay Department, ..	18 *Jan.* 45	20 *Feb.* 51		
	13	4	W. C. MacDougall, *PH*,	Stud Dept.	20 *Feb.* 46	17 *Mar.* 51		
	~~12~~	~~1~~	~~F. T. Goldsworthy, *P*, (*a*)~~	Army Commissariat Dept. ..	11 *June* 47	9 *Oct.* 54		
	10	9	H. H. Lyster, *PH*,	Offg. Stud Dept. ..	20 *Sep.* 48	13 *Nov.* 54		
	8	6	C. F. Sharpe, *PC*,	District Comdt. Mily. Police, Oudh, ..	20 *Dec.* 50	23 *Nov.* 56		
~~N.~~	~~4~~	~~4~~	~~Wm. Brodnax Knight,~~	Fur. S.C. 3 Aug. 58	20 *Feb.* 55	1 *July* 57		
	6	1	E. S. Fox,†	Doing duty Recruit depot, Barrackpore,	11 *June* 53	23 *Nov.* 56		
	2	6	R. W. Henderson,	.. ..	20 *Jan.* 57	4 *July* 57		
	3	1	C. J. Griffiths,	Survey Dept. ..	13 *June* 56	30 *Apl.* 58		
	1	6	R. W. Sartorius,	.. ..	20 *Jan.* 58	18 *May* 58		
	..	10	Thomas Dawes,	.. ..	2 *Sep.* 58	1 *Mar.* 59		
	..	9	Chas. S. Noble.	.. ..	4 *Oct.* 58	6 *Mar.* 59		
			Ensigns.					
			*					
			*					
			*					
			*		*Appointed.*			
			*					
	..	..	*Adjt.**					
	..	..	*Interpreter,**					
	..	..	*Surg.* W. Shurlock,	Fur. S.C. 18 Mar. 58	30 *Oct.* 54			
	..	..	*Assist. Surg.,**					

(*a*) Has furnished certificates of qualification in Surveying and Civil Engineering.

Raised in 1825.

73rd Regiment of Native Infantry.

Jelpigoree, 2 Companies Mutinied at Dacca.

"MOODKEE"—"FEROZESHUHUR"—"PUNJAUB."

FACINGS—*Yellow.*

Fur. Reg.	Ser. Y	Ser. M	
	54	4	*Colonel* Samuel Swinhoe. *Ens.* 18 March 1805; *Lieut.* 27 March 1805; *Capt.* 1 Jan. 1818; *Major* 14 June 1825; *Lieut. Col.* 9 May 1830; *Col.* 23 June 42; *Maj. Genl.* 20 June 1854; *Lieut. Genl.* 15 Sep. 1855.—Europe, S. C., 10 Mar. 46.
	37	6	*Lieut. Colonel* George Moyle Sherer. *Ens.* 20 Dec. 1821; *Lieut.* 23 Aug. 1824; *Capt.* 8 July 1836; *Bt. Major* 9 Nov. 1846; *Major* 12 Aug. 1847; *Lieut. Col.* 11 July 1853; *Bt. Col.* 28 Nov. 1854.
R. N	32	6	~~*Major* James Sleeman~~, *P.* *Ens.* 7 Jan. 1827; *Lieut.* 21 May 1829; *Bt. Capt.* 7 Jan. 1842 *Capt.* 24 Jan. 1845; *Bt. Major* 20 June 1854; *Major* 18 July 1856.—Civil employ.

☞ *Brevet.* ¹ Maj. 20 June 54. ² Maj. 20 June 1854. ³ Maj. 19 Jan. 1858.

Fur. Reg.	Y	M		Remarks.	Ensign.	Lieut.	Captain. Brevet.	Captain. Regl.
			CAPTAINS.					
	31	6	W. Richardson, *P C*,[1] *m* -	Sylhet Lt. I. Battn.	19 *Jan.* 28	2 *Aug.* 39	19 *Jan.* 43	4 *Apl.* 45
N.	31	3	W. C. Erskine,[2] *m* - - -	Political employ, ..	16 *Apl.* 28	3 *Oct.* 40	16 *Apl.* 43	21 *Dec.* 45
	25	1	R. C. Lawrence, *PH*,[3] *m* -	Civil employ, ..	13 *June* 34	17 *Sep.* 41	13 *June* 49	7 *Apl.* 51
N.	18	10	J. Tickell, *P*, (*a*) - - -	Fur. S. C. 21 July 58	9 *Sep.* 40	13 *Jan.* 43	.. ..	19 *July* 53
O.	18	1	M. A. Garstin,† - - -	Fur. S. C. 21 Apl. 58	12 *June* 41	29 *May* 44	12 *June* 56	18 *July* 56
O.	17	1	S. Rogers,† - - - -	Fur. S. C. 21 Apl. 59.	19 *June* 42	24 *Jan.* 45	.. ..	23 *Nov.* 56
	16	6	S. B. Cookson, *PH*, - -	Brigade Staff, ..	28 *Dec.* 42	4 *Apl.* 45	28 *Dec.* 57	2 *June* 58
			LIEUTENANTS.					
	13	6	E. Dandridge, *PH*, (*a*) - -	Comdg. a Levy at Shahjehanpore, ..	14 *Jan.* 46	7 *Sep.* 52		
	13	9	F. R. N. Fortescue, *P*, - -	.. ..	20 *Sep.* 45	7 *Apl.* 51		
O.	11	10	C. D. S. Clarke, *PH*, - -	Fur. S. C. 2 Feb. 58	2 *Sep.* 47	21 *May* 53		
D	11	6	~~J. P. Jervois~~,† - - -	.. ..	20 *Dec.* 47	19 *July* 53		
O.	10	11	C. N. McMullin,† - -	Fur. S.C. 24 Apl. 58	7 *Aug.* 48	15 *Nov.* 53		
	7	3	C. K. M. Walter, *PH*, -	Civil employ. ..	20 *Mar.* 52	26 *Feb.* 56		
	6	1	P. C. Rynd, *PH*, - -	.. ..	11 *June* 53	23 *Nov.* 56		
	5	6	H. C. Plunkett Rice, *PCH*,	4th Punjaub Cavy.,	20 *Dec.* 53	23 *Nov.* 56		
	4	1	Thos. Myles Sandys, *PCH*,	.. ..	9 *June* 55	30 *Apl.* 58		
	2	2	L. Macdonald,† - - -	.. ..	8 *May* 57	18 *May* 58		
R	1	9	~~F. Cunliffe~~, - - - -	Fur. S. C. 8 May 58	20 *Oct.* 57	2 *June* 58		
			ENSIGNS.					
	1	5	G. W. Eaton, - - - -	.. ..	25 *Feb.* 58			
	..	6	H. G. Becher, - - - -	.. ..	6 *Jan.* 59			
			*					
			*		*Appointed.*			
			*					
	..	..	*Adjutant*, P. C. Rynd, ..	.. ..	9 *Aug.* 58			
	..	..	*Intr.* F. R. N. Fortescue, ..	.. ..	23 *June* 59			
	..	..	*Surg.*,*					
	..	..	*Asst. Surg.**					

(*a*) Have furnished the certificate of qualification in Surveying and Civil Engineering.

Raised in 1825.

74th Regiment of Native Infantry.

Mutinied Delhi.

Alexander-ka-Pultun.

FACINGS—*Yellow.*

Fur. Reg.	Ser. Y	Ser. M	
	59	9	*Colonel* John Truscott. *Ens.* 13 Oct. 1799; *Lieut.* 28 Oct. 1799; *Capt.* 4 March 1812 *Major* 6 Nov. 1818; *Lieut. Col.* 1 March 1824; *Col.* 4 March 1830; *Major Genl.* 2 June 1838; *Lieut. Genl.* 11 Nov. 1851; *General* 27 Jan. 1858.—Europe, 24 Jan. 31.
N	~~34~~	~~6~~	~~*Lieut. Col.* Robert Ramsay~~, *PC.* *Ens.* 8 Jan. 1825; *Lieut.* 9 Dec. 1825; *Bt. Capt.* 8 Jan. 1840; *Capt.* 17 Mar. 1841; *Bt. Maj.* 11 Nov. 1851; *Major* 14 July 1853; *Lt. Col.* 18 Nov. 1857.—Fur. S. C. 15 Dec. 1858.
	27	7	*Lt. Col.* H. E. S. Abbott, *P. Ens.* 8 Dec. 31; *Lt.* 23 May 36; *Capt.* 24 Jan. 45; *Maj.* 11 Nov. 54. *Lieut. Col.* 22 Aug. 1858.—Lv. P. A. 15 Oct.
	23	5	*Major* George Ryley.† *Ens.* 9 Feb. 36; *Lieut.* 1 Mar. 38; *Capt.* 16 Mar. 48; *Maj.* 22 Aug. 1858.—Doing duty Landour Depôt.

☞ *Brevet.* [1] Major 24 Mar. 1858.

Fur. Reg.	Y	M	CAPTAINS.	REMARKS.	*Ensign.*	*Lieut.*	CAPTAIN. *Brevet.*	CAPTAIN. *Regl.*
	22	..	J. P. P. T. Hawkey,† - -	.. ..	18 *July* 37	30 *Apl.* 38	.. ..	1 *Dec.* 48
	21	7	W. F. N. Wallace, *PH*, -	.. ..	11 *Dec.* 37	16 *July* 42	.. ..	1 *Feb.* 49
	18	1	A. G. Nedham, *P*, - - -	11th Irregular Cavy.	12 *June* 41	15 *Mar.* 44	12 *June* 56	23 *Nov.* 56
	16	4	G. S. Macbean, *P*, [1]*m* -	Army Commt. Dept.	22 *Feb.* 43	15 *Dec.* 47	.. ..	18 *June* 57
	15	10	H. Grant, *P*, - - - -	.. ..	24 *Aug.* 43	16 *Mar.* 48	.. ..	18 *Sep.* 57
	15	5	H. A. Taylor, *PCH*, - -	Army Commt. Dept.	3 *Feb.* 44	1 *Dec.* 48	.. ..	6 *Oct.* 57
N.	14	4	W. C. R. Mylne, *PC*, - -	Army Commt. Dept.	20 *Feb.* 45	2 *Aug.* 51	.. ..	22 *Aug.* 58
			LIEUTENANTS.					
N.	6	..	Arthur Parker Mew,† - -	11th Punjaub Infy.,	13 *July* 53	11 *May* 57		
	5	4	Herbert Sconce, *PCH*, (*a*) -	Offg. Civil employ,	20 *Feb.* 54	11 *May* 57		
	3	7	R. W. Elton,† - - - -	.. ..	8 *Dec.* 55	11 *May* 57		
	13	1	F. J. Gully, *PH*, - - -	Brigade Staff, ..	12 *June* 46	5 *Nov.* 51		
	8	~~6~~	~~A. H.~~ Carter,† - - -	.. ..	11 *Jan.* 51	22 *May* 54		
	5	10	R. Clifford,† - - - -	.. ..	30 *Aug.* 53	12 *July* 56		
	8	7	H. R. Osborn, *PH*, (*b*) -	7th Irr Cavalry, ..	9 *Dec.* 50	23 *Nov.* 56		
	4	2	F. J. Mackeson,† - - -	.. ..	11 *May.* 55	15 *Jan.* 57		
	3	1	W. D. Palmer. - - -	.. ..	14 *June* 56	18 *Sep.* 57		
	2	3	F. A. Bertie, - - - -	Lv. P. A. 1 Dec., .	26 *Mar.* 57	18 *May* 58		
	1	11	W. H. B. FitzGerald, - -	.. ..	15 *Aug.* 57	22 *Aug.* 58		
			ENSIGNS.					
	1	1	J. E. Kennedy, - - - -	.. ..	12 *June* 58			
	1	9	C. A. Dodd,† - - - -	.. ..	4 *Oct.* 57			
			*					
			*					
			*		*Appointed.*			
	..	..	*Adjutant*,*					
	..	..	*Interpreter*,*					
	..	..	*Surg.*,*					
	..	..	*Asst. Surg.*,*					

(*a*) Has passed a successful examination in the Assamese language.
(*b*) Has passed an examination in Field Engineering.

Raised 4th Oct. 1842. } **Regiment of Kelat-i-Ghilzie.** { Peshawur.

(*Native Infantry.*)

" KELAT-I-GHILZIE 1842"—" CANDAHAR"—" GHUZNEE"—" CAUBUL 1842."

The Flank Companies, " MAHARAJPORE."

Detachments at Abazaie and Michnee.

FACINGS—*White.*

RANK, NAMES AND CORPS.	*Army Rank.*	*Appointment.*	REMARKS.
Capt. H. B. Stevens, 41st N I., ..	25 *May* 52	20 *Mar.* 58	Commandant.
Lieut. G. C. Rowcroft, 41st N. I.,..	8 *Dec.* 52	24 *Mar.* 56	2nd in Command.
Lieut. W. Winson, 45th N. I., ..	10 *June* 53	24 *Mar.* 56	Adjutant.
*			Quarter Master.
Asst. Surgeon,*			

Strength—10 Companies, with 1 Sergeant Major—1 Quarter Master Sergeant—2 Native Doctors—10. Subadars—10 Jemadars—60 Havildars—60 Naicks—20 Drummers—1000 Sepoys.

SEIKH BATTALIONS.

Raised in 1846. } **Regiment of Ferozepore.** { Punjaub.

FACINGS—*Yellow.*

Detachment at Chunar.

Lt.Col. J. Brasyer, C.B.(*unattached,*)	20 *July* 58	8 *Feb.* 55	Commandant.
Lieut. A. W. Montagu, 68th N. I.,..	13 *Sep.* 53	8 *Feb.* 55	2nd in Command.
*			Adjutant.
*			Quarter Mr.
Lieut. P. H. M. Wynter, 32nd N.I.	18 *May* 58	2 *Mar.* 59	Doing duty.
Lieut. W. F. Mosley, 35th N. I. ..	18 *May* 58	2 *Mar.* 59	Ditto.
Lieut. J. Johnstone, 68th N. I., ..	19 *Feb.* 59	11 *May* 59	Ditto.
Asst. Surg. J. Brown, ..	24 *Jan.* 55	30 *Apl.* 57	Fur. S. C. 4th Dec 58.

Strength—10 Companies, with 1 Sergeant Major—1 Quarter Master Sergeant—2 Native Doctors—10 Subadars—10 Jemadars—50 Havildars—50 Naicks—20 Drummers—700 Sepoys.

Raised in 1846. } **Regiment of Loodianah.** { Benares, a portion Mutinied.

FACINGS—*Green.*

Major C. G. Walsh, 14th N.I., ..	20 *June* 54	12 *Feb.* 58	Commandant.
Lieut. R. W. Glasse, 14th N.I. ..	14 *Sep.* 53	1 *May* 58	2nd in Command.
*			Adjutant.
Asst. Surgeon, * ..			

Strength—The same as the Regiment of Ferozepore.

Raised in 1857.

SEIKH VOLUNTEERS,

Allahabad. (Camp Lohardaggah)

Rank, Names and Corps.	Army Rank.	Appointment.	Remarks.
*			Commandant.
*			2nd in Command.
*			Adjutant.
Asst. Surgeon*			

Strength—The same as the Regiment of Ferozepore.

Raised in 1857.

SEIKH BATTALION.

Rank, Names and Corps.	Army Rank.	Appointment.	Remarks.
*			Commandant.
*			2nd in Command.
*			Adjutant.

Strength—The same as the Regiment of Ferozepore.

Raised in 1835.

Shekhawattee Battalion.

Midnapore. (Camp Sumbulpore.)

" Alliwal."

Uniform—*Red.* Facings—*Blue.*

Rank, Names and Corps.	Army Rank.	Appointment.	Remarks.
Col. Henry Forster, c. b., ..	20 *June* 57	23 *Jan.* 35	Commandant.—Fur. S.C. 22 Sep. 58.
Capt. Wm. R. Forster, (*Unattached,*)	29 *July* 52	1 *Jan.* 37 6 *Oct.* 58	2nd in Command. Offg. Commandant.
Lieut. J. A. H. Moore, 23rd N.I. ..	10 *Oct.* 53	10 *Jan.* 56	Adjutant. Offg. 2nd in Command.
Lieut. A. W. Hearsey, 57th N.I. ..	23 *Nov.* 56	.. ..	Offg. Adjutant.
Asst. Surgeon H. R. Daniell, ..			

Strength—8 Companies, with 1 Subadar Major—1 Havildar Major—2 Native Doctors—8 Subadars—8 Jemadars—40 Havildars—40 Naicks—8 Drummers—8 Fifers and Buglers—800 Sepoys.

Raised by G. O. 27th Feb. 50.

Nusseree (Rifle) Battalion.

Meerut.

(New Corps.)

" Alliwal"—" Subraon."

Uniform—*Dark-green.* Facings—*Black.* Lace—*Black.*

Rank, Names and Corps.	Army Rank.	Appointment.	Remarks.
Major A. Bagot, 15th N. I., ..	24 *July* 54	1 *Sep.* 55	Commandant.
Lieut. T. W. R. Boisragon, 69th N.I.,	15 *Aug.* 50	18 *Apl.* 57	2nd in Command.
Lieut. G. Alexander, 35th L. I., ..	30 *Nov.* 54	6 *Aug.* 58	Adjutant.
Capt. R. A. Smith, 19th N. I., ..	.. ..	.. ..	On duty at the Juttog Depot.
Asst. Surg. A. Young, ..	20 *Oct.* 53	28 *Mar.* 59	

Strength—10 Companies, with 1 Sergeant Major—1 Quarter Master Sergeant—2 Native Doctors—1 Soobah—10 Subadars—10 Jemadars—60 Havildars—60 Naicks—20 Buglers—700 Sepoys

Raised 24th April 1815.

Sirmoor (Rifle) Regiment.

Deyrah Dhoon.

" Alliwal"—" Sobraon."

Uniform—*Dark-green.* Facings—*Scarlet.* Lace—*Black.*

Rank, Names and Corps.	Army Rank.	Appointment.	Remarks.
Lt. Col. Charles Reid, c.b., 10th N.I.	19 *Jan.* 58	24 *Feb.* 57	Commandant.
Lieut. J. F. L. Fisher, 19th N.I. ..	1 *Nov.* 50	18 *Mar.* 57	2nd in Command.
Lieut. D. Macintyre, 66th N. I, ..	23 *Nov.* 56	12 *Mar.* 59	Offg. Adjutant.
Lieut. W. Snow, 63rd N. I., ..	30 *Apl.* 58	24 *Apl.* 59	Doing duty.
Lieut. A. Battye, 19th N. I., ..	22 *Jan.* 58	9 *May* 59	Ditto.
Asst. Surgeon F. F. Allen, ..	20 *Nov.* 48	5 *Feb.* 58	

Strength—10 Companies, with 1 Sergeant Major—1 Quarter Master Sergeant—2 Native Doctors—1 Soobah—10 Subadars—10 Jemadars—60 Havildars—60 Naicks—20 Buglers—700 Sepoys,

Raised 24th April 1815. — Kemaoon.

Kemaoon Battalion.

Detachment at Attock.

UNIFORM—*Dark-green.* FACINGS—*Black.* LACE—*Black.*

Major R. A. Ramsay, 35th L. I. ..	19 *Jan.* 58	1 *Oct.* 47	Commandant.
Lieut. Baron F. Von Andlau, 28th N. I.	18 *June* 50	23 *Feb.* 58	2nd in Command.
Lieut. A. B. Temple, 49th N. I. ..	18 *July* 55	1 *Apl.* 58	Offg. Adjutant.
Surgeon G. Banister, ...	16 *June* 58	13 *May* 51	

Strength—10 Companies, with 1 Sergeant Major—1 Quarter Master Sergeant—3 Native Doctors—1 Soobah—10 Subadars—10 Jemadars—60 Havildars—60 Naicks—20 Buglers—700 Sepoys.

Raised 6th Aug. 1857. — Almorah.

Extra Goorkha Regiment.

Capt. W. T. Baker, 60th N. I., ..	24 *Jan.* 57	6 *Aug.* 58	Commandant.
Lieut. C. W. R. Chester, 19th N. I.	23 *Nov.* 56	6 *Aug.* 58	2nd in Command.
*			Adjutant.
Asst. Surg. O. Byrne, ..	23 *July* 58		

Strength.—The same as the Kemaoon Battalion.

Raised, 29th June 1795. — Disarmed Allipore.

Calcutta Native Militia.

(Civil.)

UNIFORM—*Red.* FACINGS—*Black.* LACE—*Gold.*

RANK, NAMES AND CORPS.	*Army Rank.*	*Appointment.*	REMARKS.
Major C. Herbert, 18th N.I. ..	2 *Jan.* 55	6 *May* 56	Commandant.
Lieut. F. Allen, 42nd L. I. ..	9 *Aug.* 54	3 *Oct.* 56	Adjt. (Offg. Army Commt Dept.)
Asst. Surgeon A. J. Payne, M. D. B.A.	20 *Dec.* 48	1 *Nov.* 56	

Strength.—10 Companies with 1 Sergeant Major—1 Quarter Master Sergeant—2 Native Doctors—10 Subadars—10 Jemadars—50 Havildars—50 Naicks—12 Buglers—1000 Sepoys

Raised, 29th June 1795. — Mutinied, Dorundah, Chota Nagpore.

Ramgurh Light Infantry Battalion.

(Civil.)

Irregular Cavalry attached. "PEGU."

UNIFORM—*Green.* FACINGS—*Black.* LACE—*Black.*

Col. W. P. Robbins, 15th N.I ..	28 *Nov.* 57	18 *July* 51	Commandant.
*			2nd in Comd. and Comdt. of Cavalry.
*			Adjutant.
Surg. C. F. Warneford, M. D., ..	8 *Aug.* 57	27 *Mar.* 54	

Strength—10 Companies of Infantry, 2 Ressallahs of Irregular Cavalry, and a detail of Artillery; viz. *Infantry,* 1 Sergeant Major—1 Quarter Master Sergeant—2 Native Doctors—10 Subadars—10 Jemadars—60 Havildars—60 Naicks—20 Buglers—1100 Sepoys.—2 *Ressallahs of Irregular Cavalry,* 1 Native Doctor—1 Ressaldar—2 Naib Ressaldars—2 Jemadars—2 Kote Duffadars—18 Duffadars—2 Nishanburdars—2 Trumpeters—170 Sowars.— *Artillery detail,*—1 Sergeant—1 Corporal—2 Tindals—16 Lascars—1 Chowdry—1 Sirdar—28 Drivers, with four 6-pounder brass Guns.

Raised, 24th April 1792.

Hill Rangers.

Bhaugulpore

Detachments at Monghyr, Titalyah, Purneah, and Buckalee.

UNIFORM—*Red.* FACINGS—*Dark-green.* LACE—*Silver.*

Major A. H. Duncan, 3rd En. Regt.	11 *Nov.* 51	17 *Mar.* 56	Commandant.
Lieut. G J Pasley, 6th En. Regt.	26 *Apl.* 54	10 *June* 58	Adjutant.
Asst. Surg. T. B. Farncombe, ..	20 *Feb.* 54	21 *Aug.* 55	

Strength—6 Companies, with 1 Sergeant Major—1 Quarter Master Sergeant—1 Native Doctor—6 Subadars—6 Jemadars—30 Havildars—30 Naicks—12 Buglers—540 Sepoys.

Raised, 16th May 1817.

1st Assam Light Infantry Battalion.

Debroogurh, Upper Assam.

Detachments at Saikwah, Jeypore, Jamoogooree, Seebsagur, Burpathar and Golaghaut.

UNIFORM—*Green.* FACINGS—*Black.* LACE—*Black.*

RANK, NAMES AND CORPS.	*Army Rank.*	*Appointment.*	REMARKS.
Col. S. F. Hannay, 43rd L. I., ..	20 *June* 57	25 *Mar.* 39	Commandant.
*			2nd in Command.
Lieut. C. P. Hunter, 5th En. Regt.	18 *April* 53	2 *July* 56	Adjutant.
Assist. Surgeon R. Moir, M. D., ..	20 *Dec.* 53	30 *Aug.* 54	Fur. S. C. 3 Dec. 58.
Surgeon T. Hastings, F. R. C. S, ..	... ..	.. ..	Leave to 16 August.

Strength—10 Companies, with 1 Sergeant Major—1 Quarter Master Sergeant—3 Native Doctors—10 Subadars—10 Jemadars—50 Havildars—50 Naicks—20 Buglers—900 Sepoys.

Raised, 13th April 1835.

2nd Assam Light Infantry Battalion.

Gowahatty, Assam.

Detachments at Gowalparah, Nowgong, Tezpore, Dewchonga, Assaloo, Mungledye, Koorreekhatta. and Kurreeaparah.

UNIFORM—*Green.* FACINGS—*Black.* LACE—*Black.*

Capt. R. Campbell, 47th N.I. ..	3 *Nov.* 52	20 *Mar.* 55	Commandant.
Capt. T. E. B. Lees, 43rd N. I. ..	18 *Sep.* 55	31 *Oct.* 58	Offg. 2nd in Command.
Lieut. R. Y. Chambers, 65th N.I..	1 *Oct.* 55	1 *May* 56	Adjutant.—(With his Regt.)
Lieut. W. A. Garden, 39th N. I.,	4 *June* 55	2 *June* 58	Offg. Adjutant.
Apothecary W. McKeon, ..	5 *Sep.* 49	24 *June* 52	Leave to 16 Aug.

Strength—10 Companies, with 1 Sergeant Major—1 Quarter Master Sergeant—3 Native Doctors—10 Subadars—10 Jemadars—60 Havildars—60 Naicks—20 Buglers—900 Sepoys.

Raised, 28th June 1822.

Mhairwarrah Battalion.

Bewar.

Detachment at Ajmere, &c. &c.

(*Civil.*)

UNIFORM—*Red.* FACINGS—*Dark-green.* LACE—*Silver.*

Capt. E. J Rickards, 5th En. Regt.	27 *Mar.* 53	20 *Nov.* 57	Commandant.—Offg. Civil employ.
Lieut. J. E. Caunter, 15th N. I. ..	15 *Nov.* 53	24 *Nov.* 58	2nd in Command.
Lieut. G. F. M. Phillips, 30th N. I.,	23 *Nov.* 56	11 *Jan.* 59	Adjutant.
Asst. Surgeon D. H. Small, ..	21 *Nov.* 46	19 *Nov.* 47	

Strength—8 Companies, with 1 Sergeant Major—1 Quarter Master Sergeant—2 Native Doctors—8 Subadars—16 Jemadars—40 Havildars—40 Naicks—16 Buglers or Drummers—640 Sepoys.

Mhair Regiment. { Ajmere.

Lieut. W. Carnell, 3rd En. Regt.,	15 *June* 49	4 *Dec.* 57	Commandant.
Lieut. H. Phillpotts, 15th N. I., ..	23 *July* 54	18 *Feb.* 58	2nd in Command—Offg. Potl. employ.
Lieut. J. G. Campbell, 15th N. I.,	22 *Mar.* 58	12 *Jan.* 59	Adjutant.
Dr. T. Murray, ...	..	8 *July* 58	

Strength—The same as the Mhairwarrah Battalion.

Raised, 19th Feb. 1824.

Sylhet Light Infantry Battalion. { Cherra Poonjee

Detachments at Sylhet, Cachar, Churgolah, Lungye, Joowye and Myrong.

Uniform—*Green.* Facings—*Black.* Lace—*Black.*

Major W. Richardson, 73rd N. I.,..	20 *June* 54	28 *Jan.* 58	Commandant.
Lieut. T. F. O. Scott, 41st N.I., ..	13 *Feb.* 50	3 *Mar.* 59	2nd in Command.
Lieut. D. S. Buist, 27th N. I., ..	23 *Nov.* 56	3 *Mar.* 59	Adjutant
Lieut. T. G. Ross, 21st N.I., ..	27 *Feb.* 56	19 *Sep.* 57	Doing duty.
Lieut. H. G. Waterfield, 34th N. I.,	19 *May* 58	21 *Apl.* 59	Doing duty.
Asst. Surgeon T. Dillon, ..	28 *June* 54	6 *Dec.* 56	

Strength—10 Companies, with 1 Sergeant Major—1 Quarter Master Sergeant—2 Native Doctors—10 Subadars—10 Jemadars—50 Havildars—50 Naicks—20 Buglers—800 Sepoys.—*Artillery detail attached,*—1 Tindal—8 Lascars, with two 6-pounder Guns.

Arracan Battalion. { Akyab.

Detachments at the Aeng Pass, Sandoway, Khyouk Phyoo, Koladyne, &c.
"Pegu."

Uniform—*Green.* Facings—*Black.* Lace—*Black.*

Rank, Names and Corps.	*Army Rank.*	*Appointment.*	Remarks.
Major H. M. Garstin, 36th N. I., ..	19 *Jan.* 58	23 *Feb.* 58	Commandant.
Capt. J. M. Evans, 6th En. Regt..	22 *Jan.* 59	2 *Nov.* 57	2nd in Command, at Kyook Phyoo.
Lieut. T. C. Hamilton, 35th N.I. ..	17 *Nov.* 52	13 *Oct.* 54	Adjutant.
Lieut. R. G. Rogers, 5th En. Regt.	28 *Aug.* 52	18 *Jan.* 56	Doing duty.
Asst. Surgeon F. J. Pettingal, ..	20 *Feb.* 56	17 *July* 56	Offg. Civil, Sandoway.
Lieut. P. C. Anderson, Arty., ..	9 *Dec.* 50	7 *May* 57	Comdt. of Artillery, (not joined.)

Strength—10 Companies, with 1 Sergeant Major—1 Quarter Master Sergeant—2 Native Docors—10 Subadars—10 Jemadars—60 Havildars—60 Naicks—20 Buglers—1000 Sepoys.

Raised, 11th July 1836.

Hurrianah Light Infantry Battalion. Mutinied. Hansi.

Uniform—*Green.* Facings—*Black.* Lace—*Black.*

*			Commandant.
*			2nd in Command.
*			Adjutant.
Asst. Surgeon, *			

Strength—9 Companies, with 1 Sergeant Major—1 Quarter Master Sergeant—2 Native Doctors—9 Subadars—9 Jemadars—48 Havildars—48 Naicks—18 Buglers—800 Sepoys.

Raised, 2nd July 1838.

Sebundy Sappers and Miners. { Darjeeling.

Uniform—*Green.* Facings—*Black.* Lace—*Black.*

Capt. C. Murray, 70th N. I.	28 *Dec.* 57	11 *July* 54	Commandant.

Strength— 2 Companies, with 2 Sergeants—2 Corporals—1 Native Doctor—2 Subadars—2 Jemadars—10 Havildars—10 Naicks—2 Buglers—180 Sepoys.

Raised, 5th April 1816. } **Resident's Escort—Katmandhoo.** { Nepaul.

Capt. C. H. Byers, 70th N. I. ..	12 *June* 57	20 *Mar.* 57	Commandant.

Strength—1 Native Doctor—1 Subadar—1 Jemadar—5 Havildars—5 Naicks—2 Buglers—80 Sepoys.

Raised in Upper Assam in 1840. } **Local Company of Artillery.** { Debroogurh, (Assam.)

Major J. S. Gibb, Artillery, ..	20 *July* 58	11 *May* 59	Commandant.

Srength—1 Sergeant—1 Subadar—1 Jemadar—7 Havildars —6 Naicks—2 Buglers—90 Privates.

Designation changed, 21st Feb. 1855. } **Nimaur Police Corps.** { Mundlaisir.

(Cavalry and Infantry.)
(*Civil.*)

Major R. H. Keatinge, Bo. Artillery (Political Assistant, Nimaur,) ..	20 *July* 58	20 *Feb.* 52	Commandant.—Furlough.

Strength—1 Jemadar—1 Kote Duffadar—3 Duffadars—67 Sowars—*Infantry*, 2 Jemadars—6 Duffadars—305 Peeadas.

Bheel Corps.

Raised, 24th Feb. 1840. } **Malwah Bheel Corps.** { Bhopawur.

(*Civil,*)
Detachment at Mundlaisir, &c. &c.
Uniform—*Dark Green.* Facings—*Scarlet.* Lace—*Black.*

Ranks, Names and Corps.	*Army Rank.*	*Appointment*	Remarks.
Lt. Col. G. C. Stockley, 3rd Bom. En. Regt., ..	11 *Nov.* 51	.. ..	Commandant.—Fur. S.C. 19 Apl. 58.
Lieut. W. F. Edwards, 45th N. I. ..	23 *Nov* 56	2 *Apl.* 59	Offg. 2nd in Command.
Asst. Surg. H. J. Gane, Bo. Estabt.	.. ..	24 *July* 58	

Strength—1 Native Doctor—1 Subadar Major—7 Subadars—8 Jemadars—32 Havildars—32 Naicks—16 Buglers—560 Privates—Two 3-pounder brass Guns.

Raised, 15th July 1840. } **Meywar Bheel Corps.** { Kherwarah.

(*Civil.*)
Detachment at Kotrah, &c.
Uniform—*Green.* Facings—*Black.* Lace—*Black.*

Captain J. C. Brooke, 63rd N.I. ..	12 *June* 50	27 *May* 48	Commandant.
Capt. R. M. S. Annesley, 65th N.I.	9 *Dec.* 57	23 *May* 49	2nd in Command.
Lieut. F.L. Mackeson, 19th Bo. N.I.	.. ..	3 *Dec.* 55	Adjutant.
Asst. Surg. J. Ewart, M. D., ..	20 *Dec.* 53	5 *Mar.* 57	

Strength—10 Companies, with 1 Sergeant Major—1 Quarter Master Sergeant—2 Thakoors—1 Sub-Assistant Surgeon—1 Native Doctor—10 Subadars—10 Jemadars—50 Havildars—50 Naicks—1 Bugle Major—10 Buglers—900 Sepoys.

Pegu Light Infantry Battalion.

At Myan Owng, Pegu. { Pegu.

Major W. F. Nuthall, 18th N. I...	9 *Dec.* 53	28 *Oct.* 53	Comdt.—Fur. S. C. 15 Nov. 1858
Capt. M. Wood, 9th M. N. I. ..	.. ..	7 *Dec.* 58	Offg. Commandant.
Lieut. H. Acton, 2nd M. N. I. ..	9 *May* 54	31 *Jan.* 54	2nd in Command. [Henzadah.
Lieut. G. W. Sanders, 9th M. N. I.	.. ..	1 *Dec.* 56	Adjutant.—(Offg. Assistant Commr.
Lieut. J. Duval, ..	.. ..	18 *Jan.* 58	Offg. Adjutant.
Lieut. S.C. Montgomerie, 3rd M.L.I.	.. ..	11 *Aug.* 58	Doing duty.
Lieut. T. Lowndes, 44th M. N. I.,	.. ..	25 *Sept.* 58	Doing duty.
Asst. Surg. C. Stewart, M. D., ..	26 *Feb.* 51	15 *Feb.* 54	

United Malwah Contingent.

{ Mutinied.

MEHIDPORE.

ARTILLERY, CAVALRY AND INFANTRY.

(*Civil.*)

RANK, NAMES AND CORPS.	*Army Rank.*	*When Appointed.*	REMARKS.
*			Commandant.
*			Comdt. of Arty.
*			Comdt. of Cavalry.
*			Comdt. of Infantry.
*			Adjutant of Cavalry.
Lieut. J. W. W. Osborne,.. ..	.. ..	20 *May* 57	Adjutant of Infantry.

Strength of Artillery—1 Sergeant Major—1 English Writer—1 Mootsuddy—1 Subadar—1 Jemadar—6 Havildars—5 Naicks—2 Buglers—60 Gunners—1 Tindal—12 Lascars—3 Sirdars—30 Drivers, with two 12-pounder iron Guns, and four 9-pounder brass and two 24-pounder brass Guns.

Strength of Cavalry—1 Woordee Major—1 English Writer—1 Persian Writer—1 Nagree Writer—8 Ressaldars—8 Jemadars—8 Kote Duffadars—64 Duffadars—8 Nishanburdars—8 Nuggarchees—5 Trumpeters—8 Farriers—640 Sowars.

Strength of Infantry, (Fusiliers)—1 Sergeant Major—1 Quarter Master Sergeant—1 English Writer—1 Mootsuddy—8 Subadars—8 Jemadars—1 Havildar Major—1 Drum Major—32 Havildars—32 Naicks—16 Drummers—640 Sepoys.

Bhopal Contingent.

{ Mutinied.

SEHORE.

ARTILLERY, CAVALRY AND INFANTRY.

(*Civil.*)

Col. J. Travers, 2nd Gredrs. ..	6 *Dec.* 56	12 *Feb.* 56	Commandant—Fur. S. C. 1st Sep. 1857.
Capt. F. L. Magniac, 5th M. L. C.,	.. ..	12 *Feb.* 56	2nd in Command.—Offg. Comdt.
*			Adjutant.
Assist. Surg. C. Thomson, M. D. Bombay Establishment, ...	.. ..	7 *Mar.* 56	
Apothecary A. Cumming, ..	.. ..	16 *May* 56	

Strength—1 Sergeant Major—1 Staff Sergeant of Artillery—1 Store Sergeant.

Artillery—1 Subadar—1 Jemadar—4 Havildars—4 Naicks—2 Buglers—60 Gunners.

Cavalry—(4 Troops)—4 Ressaldars—5 Jemadars—13 Duffadars—13 Naib Duffadars—4 Trumpeters—4 Farriers—212 Sowars.

Infantry—(8 Companies)—8 Subadars—8 Jemadars—40 Havildars—40 Naicks—16 Drummers—600 Sepoys.

Kotah Contingent.

{ Mutinied.

DEOLEE.

ARTILLERY, CAVALRY AND INFANTRY.

(Civil.)

RANK, NAMES AND CORPS.	Army Rank.	Appointment.	REMARKS.
*			Commandant.
Lt. W.H. Beynon, 21st Bombay N.I.	1 *Nov.* 51	31 *Dec.* 55	2nd in Command.
Lt. P. W. Bannerman, 10th B. N.I.	23 *May* 54	31 *Dec.* 55	Adjutant.
*			Doing duty.
Asst. Surgeon C. Mathias, ..	20 *Dec.* 46	25 *June* 49	In charge of the Ulwur Political [Agency.

Strength—1 Sergeant Major—1 QuarterMaster Sergeant—1 Drum Major—2 Native Doctors.

Artillery—1 Store Sergeant—1 Gun Sergeant—1 Jemadar—3 Havildars—3 Naicks—1 Bugler—28 Golundauzes—15 Sowars—1 Gun Lascar Tindal—6 Gun Lascars, with two 9-pounder brass Field Guns, and two 24-pounder Howitzers.

Cavalry—1 Woordee Major—4 Ressaldars—4 Naib Ressaldars—2 Nishanburdars—4 Kote Duffadars—12 Duffadars—12 Naib Duffadars—2 Trumpeters—2 Nuggarchees—240 Sowars.

Infantry—8 Subadars—8 Jemadars—40 Havildars—40 Naicks—15 Drummers—640 Sepoys

Joudpore Legion.

{ Mutinied.

ERINPOORAH.

ARTILLERY, CAVALRY AND INFANTRY.

(Civil.)

UNIFORM—*Green.* FACINGS—*Black.* LACE—*Black.*

RANK, NAMES AND CORPS.	Army Rank.	When Appointed.	REMARKS.
*			Commandant.
Capt. G. A. Black, 69th N. I. ..	23 *Nov.* 56	10 *Mar.* 59	2nd in Command.
Lieut. W. P. Conolly, 46th N. I. ..	1 *Nov.* 53	9 *Jan.* 57	Adjutant.
Asst. Surgeon W. Eddowes, ..	4 *Aug.* 56	15 *Apl.* 59	

The Joudpore Legion consists of *Artillery*—1 Gun Sergeant—1 Gun Corporal—1 Gun Tindal.—8 Gun Lascars—2 Drivers—20 Camel Sowars.

Cavalry—1 English Writer—1 Persian Writer—1 Mutsuddy—2 Dundeeahs—3 Ressaldars—1 Woordee Major—3 Naib Ressaldars—3 Kote Duffadars—18 Duffadars—3 Nishanburdars—2 Trumpeters—1 Nuggarchee—216 Sowars.

Infantry—1 Sergeant Major—1 Quarter Master Sergeant—1 Havildar Major—8 Subadars—8 Jemadars—32 Havildars—32 Naicks—4 Drummers—12 Buglers and Fifers—640 Sepoys—8 Lascars.—*Bheel Companies attached*, 3 Subadars—3 Jemadars—9 Havildars—9 Naicks—3 Buglers—195 Sepoys—3 Lascars.

4 Corps of Seikh Infantry.

*

1st Regiment of Infantry.

{ Trans Gogra.

" PUNJAUB."

UNIFORM—*Drab.* FACINGS—*Yellow.*

Has a Rifle Company.

RANK, NAMES AND CORPS.	Army Rank.	When Appointed.	REMARKS.
Lt. Col. G. Gordon, 50th N.I. ..	20 *July* 58	17 *Nov.* 51	Commandant.
*			2nd in Command.
*			Adjutant.
Lieut. C. D. P. Nott, 4th En. Regt,	10 *July* 57	4 *Dec.* 58	Doing duty, and Offg. Adjutant.
Lieut. A. England, 44th N. I., ..	9 *Nov.* 58	11 *May* 59	Doing duty.
Ensign W. H. Unwin, 56th N. I.,	20 *Dec.* 57	11 *May* 59	Doing duty.
Asst. Surg. C. A. Poole, ..	18 *Mar.* 56	20 *Mar.* 57	
ub-Asst. Surg. D. W. Renton, ..	.. ..	1 *Nov.* 51	Fur. P. A. 22 Jan. 57.

Strength of each Regiment of Seikh Infantry—10 Companies, 2 Native Doctors—1 Native Adjutant (Non-effective)—10 Subadars—10 Jemadars—60 Havildars—60 Naicks—20 Buglers—800 Sepoys.

2nd or Hill Regiment of Infantry. { Moradabad.

"PUNJAUB."

UNIFORM—*Drab*. FACINGS—*Black*.
Has a Rifle Company.

RANK, NAMES AND CORPS.	*Army Rank.*	*When Appointed.*	REMARKS.
Capt. G. W. Harding, 2nd Bo. N. I.	.. ..	26 *Dec.* 56	Commandant.—Fur. 4 Feb. 59.
Capt. J. P. W. Campbell, 47th N. I	23 *Nov.* 56	16 *Apl.* 57	2nd in Command.
		13 *Jan.* 59	Offg. Comdt. 2nd Punjaub Infy.
Lieut. R. D'O. C. Bracken, 52d N.I.	20 *May* 53	4 *July* 54	Adjutant.
		13 *Jan.* 59	Offg. Commandant.
Lieut. J. P. Sherriff, 35th L. I., ..	10 *July* 54	13 Jan. 59	Offg. 2nd in Command.
Lieut. A. Fitz Hugh, 21st N. I., ..	23 *Nov.* 56	13 *Jan.* 59	Offg. Adjutant.
Lieut. R. E. Boyle, 46th N. I., ..	14 *July* 57	13 *Jan.* 59	Doing duty,
Apothecary G. W. Harding, ..	25 *Oct.* 46	6 *Oct.* 47	

3rd Regiment of Infantry. { Goruckpore District.

UNIFORM—*Drab*. FACINGS—*Yellow*.
Has a Rifle Company.

RANK, NAMES AND CORPS.	*Army Rank.*	*When Appointed.*	REMARKS.
Capt. R. Renny, 47th N.I. ..	22 *Mar.* 50	21 *Sep.* 51	Commandant.
Lt. T. L. Roberts, H.M. 87th Foot,	.. ..	24 *Feb.* 59	2nd in Command.
Lieut. W. F. Leicester, 30th N. I...	15 *Nov.* 53	22 *Apl.* 52	Adjutant.—Fur. S. C. 31st Mar. 57.
Lieut. T. P. Harrison, 69th N. I...	28 *Jan.* 56	9 *Apl.* 58	Offg. Adjutant.
Asst. Surgeon F. Powell, M. B., ..	20 *Feb.* 56	7 *Nov.* 56	Fur. S. C. 15th June 1859.

4th Regiment of Infantry. { Abbottabad, (Hazarah.)

"PEGU."

UNIFORM—*Drab*. FACINGS—*Dark Green*.
Has a Rifle Company.

RANK, NAMES AND CORPS.	*Army Rank.*	*When Appointed.*	REMARKS.
Major O. E. Rothney, 45th N. I.	19 *Jan.* 58	8 *Dec.* 53	Commandant.
Lieut. G. A. Williams, 26th L.I. ..	1 *Apl.* 50	30 *Jan.* 57	2nd in Comd.—Fur. S. C. 7 May 58
Lieut. F. H. Jenkins, 57th N.I. ..	15 *Nov.* 53	3 *May* 58	Offg. 2nd in Command.
Lieut. G. B. Stainforth, 61st N. I.,	3 *July* 55	24 *Feb.* 59	Adjutant.
Lieut. E. C. Codrington, 57th N. I.,	28 *Sep.* 57	24 *Feb.* 59	Doing duty.
Surgeon H. B. Buckle, ..	16 *Sep.* 57	30 *Oct.* 56	

Corps of Guides. { On Field Service.

At Murdan, in Eusuf Zye.
Cavalry and Infantry.
UNIFORM—*Drab*. FACINGS—*Drab*.
Detachments "PUNJAUB"—"MOOLTAN"—"GOOJERAT."
Raised for general service on the 14th December 1846.

RANK, NAMES AND CORPS.	*Army Rank.*	*When Appointed.*	REMARKS.
Major H. B. Lumsden, 59th N.I...	6 *Feb.* 54	3 *Jan.* 56	Commandant.
Lieut. T. G. Kennedy, 62nd N. I.	3 *Oct.* 52	29 *Apl.* 59	2nd in Command.
Lieut. C. W. Hawes, 43rd N. I. ..	23 *Nov.* 56	17 *May* 56	Adjutant.—Offg. Comdt. of Cavy.
Lieut. E. E. B. Bond, 57th N. I...	1 *Jan.* 54	2 *July* 57	Offg. Adjutant.
Lieut. H. C. E. Ward, 5th N. I. ..	23 *Nov.* 56	23 *Sep.* 57	Doing duty.
Asst. Surgeon,*			

Strength of Cavalry—4 Ressaldars—4 Ressaidars—8 Jemadars—8 Kote Duffadars—48 Duffadars—316 Sowars—4 Trumpeters—8 Camel Sowars.

Strength of Infantry—8 Subadars—16 Jemadars—72 Havildars—72 Naicks—16 Buglers—640 Sepoys.

CAWNPORE INFANTRY LEVY.

{ Cawnpore,

RANK, NAMES AND CORPS.	*Army Rank.*	*When appointed.*	REMARKS.
Major H. C. Anderson, 54th N. I.,	20 *July* 58	19 *Feb.* 59	Commandant.
Lieut. G. Sullivan, H. M. 80th Foot,	31 *Oct.* 51	.. ..	2nd in Command.—Leave P. A. 15 Oct.
*			Adjutant.
Surgeon P. G. Lay, ..	13 *Feb.* 57	4 *Dec.* 58	

Strength—8 Subadars—8 Jemadars—40 Havildars—40 Naicks—16 Drummers—600 Sepoys.

ALLAHABAD INFANTRY LEVY.

RANK, NAMES AND CORPS.	*Army Rank.*	*When appointed.*	REMARKS.
Lieut. E. H. Langmore, 71st N. I.,	21 *Aug.* 49	.. ..	Commandant,
Lieut. S. Douglas, (Unattached,) ..	3 *Nov.* 51	.. ..	2nd in Command.
Lieut. R. G. Armstrong, 17th N. I.	16 *Jan.* 56	.. ..	Adjutant.
Surgeon S. H Batson, ..	31 *Dec.* 49	12 *Mar.* 59	

Strength—8 Subadars—8 Jemadars—40 Havildars—40 Naicks—16 Drummers—600 Sepoys.

MEERUT INFANTRY LEVY.

Raised, 26th Aug. 1858.

RANK, NAMES AND CORPS.	*Army Rank.*	*When appointed.*	REMARKS.
Capt. W. Hanmer, H. M. 87th Foot, ..	.. ..	26 *Aug.* 58	Commandant.
Capt. C. A. Reid, 20th N. I., ..	6 *Feb.* 58	3 *Dec.* 58	Offg 2nd in Command.
Lieut. C. F. Middleton, 40th N. I.	17 *June* 55	4 *Sep.* 58	Adjutant.—Fur, S. C. 28 Dec. 58.
*			Doing duty.

Strength—8 Subadars—8 Jemadars—40 Havildars—40 Naicks—16 Drummers—600 Sepoys.

AGRA INFANTRY LEVY.

{ Agra.

RANK, NAMES AND CORPS.	*Army Rank.*	*When appointed.*	REMARKS.
Capt. S. J. Becher, 11th N. I. ..	13 *May* 48	11 *Apl.* 59	Offg. Commandant.
Lieut. B. T. Stafford, 18th N. I., ..	12 *Aug.* 53	1 *June* 59	2nd in Command.
Lieut. H. McD. DeW. Douglas, 67th N. I., ..	23 *Nov.* 56	.. ..	Adjutant.

Strength—8 Subadars—8 Jemadars—40 Havildars—40 Naicks—16 Drummers—600 Sepoys.

ALLYGURH INFANTRY LEVY.

Capt. E. Hall, 52nd N. I., .. Commandant.
* .. 2nd in Command.
Lieut. F Gellie, 9th N I, .. Acting Adjutant.

Strength—1 Native Doctor—4 Subadars—4 Jemadars—20 Havildars—20 Naicks—8 Buglers and Drummers—320 Sepoys.

BAREILLY INFANTRY LEVY.

Captain P Drummond, 22nd N I, .. Commandant.
Captain H W Chapman, 28th N I, .. 2nd in Command.
Ensign H Holford, (unattached), .. Adjutant.
Ensign T. Hardy, (unattached), .. Doing duty.
Asst.-Surgeon* ..

Strength—1 Native Doctor—8 Subadars—8 Jemadars—40 Havildars—40 Naicks—16 Drummers—600 Sepoys.

MORADABAD INFANTRY LEVY. { Gondah (Oude).

Rank, Names and Corps.	Army Rank.	When appointed.	Remarks.
Captain G D D Cleveland, H M's 98th Regt.,	..		Commandant.
Lieut. W J Lance, H M 98th Regt.,	..		2nd in Command
Ensign P Gill, (unattached),	..		Adjutant.

Strength—1 Native Doctor—1 Native Dresser—8 Subadars—8 Jemadars—40 Havildars—40 Naicks—16 Drummers—600 Sepoys.

MYNPOORIE INFANTRY LEVY.

Captain A Blackwood, 59th N I,		
Captain J C Dickson, 33rd N I,	..	Commandant.
Ensign M Lyne, (unattached),	..	2nd in Command.
	..	Offg. Adjutant.

Strength—2 Native Doctors—8 Subadars—8 Jemadars—40 Havildars—40 Naicks—16 Drummers 600 Sepoys.

SEALKOTE INFANTRY LEVY.

Captain G Caulfield, 46th N I,	..	Commandant.
*	..	2nd in Command.
*	..	Adjutant.

Strength—1 Native Doctor—3 Subadars—3 Jemadars—15 Havildars—15 Naicks—300 Sepoys.

FUTTEHGURH INFANTRY LEVY. { Camp Raowah.

Captain S Sage, 30th N I,	..	Commandant.
Lieut. C C Dandridge, 49th N I,	..	2nd in Command.
Captain J S Bennett, 4th En. Regt.	..	Adjutant.
Asst.-Surgeon R K Buckell	..	

Strength—1 Native Doctor—8 Subadars—8 Jemadars—40 Havildars—40 Naicks—16 Drummers—600 Sepoys

BHOPAL LEVY.

	Army Rank.	When appointed.	Remarks.
*			Commandant.
Lieut. R. C. Cross, 17th N. I. ..	15 *Nov.* 53	18 *Jan.* 59	2nd in Command.
Lieut. E. Temple, 25th N. I. ..	17 *Dec.* 56	18 *Jan.* 59	Adjutant.

GOOJRANWALLAH LEVY.

Capt. H. E. Young, 64th N. I.,	..	Commandant.
*	..	2nd in Command.
*	..	Adjutant.

HODSON'S HORSE.

Lieut. Col. H. Daly, C. B. 1st Bo. Fusiliers,	..	Comdt. Fur. S. C. 29th Apl. 1859.
Major W. T. Hughes 48th N. I.,	..	Offg. Commandant.
Lieut. R. B. Anderson, 1st Bo. Fusiliers,	..	Brigade Major.

Raised, 26th Aug. 1858. }

1st Regiment of Hodson's Horse. { Fyzabad.

	Army Rank.	When appointed.	Remarks.
Capt. W. C. Grant, 2nd Drgn. Gds,	.. ..	13 *May* 59	Commandant.
Lieut. S. G. Warde, 11th N. I. ..	23 *Nov.* 56	30 *Mar.* 59	2nd in Command.
Lieut. T. Dayrell, 58th N. I., ..	30 *Apl.* 58	13 *May* 59	Adjutant.
Lieut. C. M. MacGregor, 68th N. I.	17 *Nov.* 57	.. ..	Doing duty.
Asst. Surg. G. H. Daly, M. D.,	4 *Nov.* 53	5 *Mar.* 59	

Raised 26th Aug. 1858.

2nd Regiment of Hodson's Horse. — Lucknow.

Rank, Names and Corps.	Army Rank.	When Appointed.	Remarks.
Lieut. C. H. Palliser, 63rd N. I.,	15 *Nov.* 53	13 *May* 59	Commandant.—Fur S. C. 21 Mar. 59.
Lieut. R. F. Godby, 35th N. I., ..	15 *Nov.* 53	23 *June* 59	Offg. Commandant.
*			2nd in Command.
Lt. *Hon* J. H. Fraser, 4th En. Regt.	23 *Nov.* 56	.. ..	Adjutant.
Lieut. A. P. Palmer, 5th En. Regt.,	30 *Apl.* 58	10 *June* 58	Doing duty.
Surgeon T. A. Wethered, M. D. ..	11 *Jan.* 52	19 *Nov.* 58	

Raised 26th Aug. 1858.

3rd Regiment of Hodson's Horse. — Camp Nawabgunge.

Rank, Names and Corps.	Army Rank.	When Appointed.	Remarks.
Lieut. C. H. Mecham, 27th M. N. I.	.. ..	13 *May* 59	Commandant.—Fur. S.C. 14 June 59.
Lieut. F. A. Lawford, 50th N. I.,..	28 *Oct.* 56	10 *Mar.* 59	2nd in Command
Lt. R. C. W. Mitford, 3rd En. Regt.	2 *May* 58	1 *Feb.* 59	Offg. Adjutant.

1st Regiment of Mahrattah Horse.

Rank, Names and Corps.	Army Rank.	When Appointed.	Remarks.
Major J. C. Phillips, 3rd En. Regt.	28 *Nov.* 56	15 *Oct.* 58	Commandant.
*			2nd in Command.
Lieut. E. D. H. Vibart, 54th N. I.	26 *Nov.* 56	26 *Aug.* 58	Adjutant.
Asst. Surg. F. H. O'Donel, M. D., ..	14 *Jan.* 54	13 *Jan.* 59	

2nd Regiment of Mahrattah Horse. — Morar (Gwalior.)

Rank, Names and Corps.	Army Rank.	When Appointed.	Remarks.
Capt. F. H. Smith, 34th N. I ..	2 *Apl.* 56	4 *Sep.* 58	Commandant.
Lieut. H. H. Gough, 1st E. L. C...	9 *Aug.* 55	26 *Aug* 58	2nd in Command.
Lieut. O. Barnes, 13th B. N. I. ..	.. ..	29 *Sep.* 58	Adjutant.
Asst. Surg. A. Eteson, ..	20 *May* 54	31 *Jan.* 59	

Raised 19th Oct. 1857.

Regiment of Alexander's Horse. — Cawnpore.

Rank, Names and Corps.	Army Rank.	When Appointed.	Remarks.
Capt. W. R. E. Alexander, 53rd N. I. ..	24 *Apl.* 55	19 *Oct* 57	Commandant.
Lieut. M. K. St. John, 49th N. I	18 *May* 56	9 *June* 58	2nd in Command.
Lieut. H. M. Repton, 67th N. I....	30 *May* 57	25 *Oct.* 57	Adjutant.
Lieut. H Chapman, 49th N. I. ..	23 *Nov.* 56	19 *Jan.* 58	Doing duty.
Lieut. R. Blair 32nd N. I., ..	16 *July* 57	19 *Feb.* 59	Ditto.
Asst. Surgeon, W. J. Haig, M. D.	27 *Jan.* 58	29 *Apl.* 59	
Dr. J. Sheetz, . G.M.C.B. ..	.. .	10 *Feb.* 58	

Alexanders' Horse—consists of 3—Ressaldars—3 Ressaidars—6 Naib Ressaldars—6 Jemadars—6 Kote Duffadars—60 Duffadars—6 Nishanburdars—6 Trumpeters and 420 Sowars.

ROHILCUND HORSE.

Major F. G. Crossman, 45th N. I., .. Commandant.
Lieut. M Hunter, 18th N. I., .. 2nd in Command.
Lieut. W. B. Barwell, 18th N. I., .. Adjutant.
Lieut. W. G. Alexander, 93rd Highlanders, .. Doing duty.
Asst. Surgeon J. C. Morice, ..

MOOLTANEE REGIMENT OF CAVALRY. { Peshawur.

Captain C Cureton, 38th N I, .. Commandant.
Lieut. H Dixon, 22nd M N I, .. 2nd in Command
Lieut. B Williams, 51st N I, .. Adjutant.
Lieut. B N Smith, 46th N I, .. Doing duty.
Asst.-Surgeon N B Baillie, ..

The Mooltanee Regiment of Cavalry—Consists of—5 Ressaldars –12 Jemadars—48 Duffadars—6 Nishanburdars—6 Nuggarchies and 600 Sowars.

FIRST SIKH REGIMENT OF CAVALRY.

Raised, 1st Aug. 1857. *Uniform.—Drab.* LACE.—*Silver.* { Roy Bareilly.

Major D. M. Probyn, C. B., 3rd E. L. C. .. Commandant.—Fur. S. C. 5th Apl. 58.
Capt. L. B. Jones, 56th N, I., .. Offg. Commandant.
Lieut. R. F. Godby. 35th N. I. .. 2nd in Command.—Offg. Comdt. 2nd Regt. Hodson's Horse.
Lieut. A. A. Dick. 52nd N. I. .. Adjutant.
Lieut. G. Stewart, 17th N. I. .. Doing duty.
Ensign C. E. Macaulay 23rd N. I. .. Doing duty.
Asst. Surgeon, J. H. Thornton, M. B, B. A. ..

SECOND SIKH REGIMENT OF CAVALRY,

Raised, 20th Oct. 1857. *Uniform—Khakee—Lace—*Silver—*Facings*—Blue. { Oude, (Field Service.)

Captain P R Hockin, 48th N I, .. Commandant.—Fur. S C 23rd Dec. 58.
Captain T Wright, 46th N I, .. Offg. Commandant.
Lieut. R D Griffin, 64th N. I,, .. 2nd in Command.
Lieut. F W Boileau, 16th N I, .. Adjutant.
Lieut. R D Osborne, 26th N I, .. Doing duty.
Asst.-Surgeon J Brake, ..

THIRD SIKH REGIMENT OF CAVALRY.

* .. Commandant.
* .. 2nd in Command.
Lieut. R. Gibson H. M. 87th Foot. .. Adjutant.

FOURTH SIKH REGIMENT OF CAVALRY. { Delhi.

Lieut. J. Watson, 28th Bo. N. I. .. Comdt.—On furlough.
Lieut. W. Fane 11th M. N. I. .. Offg. Commandant.
Lieut. R. C. Low, 4th En. L. C. .. 2nd in Command.
Lieut. H. C. Cattley, 62nd N. I. .. Adjutant.
Lieut. G. Farquhar Smith 3rd E. L. C. .. Doing duty.

BEHAR IRREGULAR CAVALRY. { Patna.

Captain H C Adlam, 42nd N I, .. Commandant.
* .. 2nd in command.
* .. Adjutant.

BEATSON'S HORSE, 2 REGIMENTS.

*	..	Commandant.
Captain H. E. Wood, H. M. 17th Lancers.	..	Brigade Major.

FIRST REGIMENT. {*

Captain E. G. Wood, 6th M. L. C,	..	Commandant.
*	..	2nd in Command.
Lieut. J. B. Tudor, 5th En. Regt.,	..	Adjutant.

SECOND REGIMENT. {Jaulnah.

*	..	Commandant.
Lieut. H. Fraser, 3rd M. L. C.,	..	2nd in Command.
*	..	Adjutant.
Lieut.-H M Stanley Clarke,	..	Actg. Brigade Major & Adjutant.
Asst-Surgeon T Beaumont,	..	

This Regiment—Consists of—3 Ressaldars—3 Ressaidars—6 Naib Ressaldars—6 Jemadars—1 Woordie Major—48 Duffadars—6 Trumpeters—6 Camel Gunners and 420 Sowars.

MEADE'S HORSE. {Gwalior

Major R J Meade, 65th N I,	..	Commandant.
Captain H A Cockburn, 53rd N I,	..	2nd in Command.
Lieut. W M Gibbon, 44th N I,	..	Adjutant.
Lieut. H M B Burlton, 5th En. Regt.	..	Doing duty.
Lieut. C Case, 67th N I,	..	Doing duty.
Surgeon W F B Dalzel, M. D.,	..	

Meade's Horse—Consists of—3 Ressaldars—3 Ressaidars—1 Woordee Major—6 Naib Ressaldars—6 Jemadars—6 Kote Duffadars—48 Duffadars—6 Nishanburdars—6 Trumpeters and 420 Sowars.

Raised, 4th Nov. 1857.

THE BENARES HORSE. {Ghazeepore.

Captain J B Y Matheson, 52nd N I,	..	Commandant.
Capt. W F Stewart, 45th N I,	..	2nd in Command.
Lieut. E H C Simpson, 39th N I,	..	Adjutant.—Fur. S. C. 4 Sept. 58
Ensign H A Pakenham, (unattached)	..	Offg. Adjutant.
Asst-Surgeon J B S Brown,	..	On Furlough.
Asst.-Surgeon J J Clarke,	..	

The Benares Horse—Consists of—3 Ressaldars—3 Ressaidars—6 Naib Ressaldars—6 Jemadars—6 Kote Duffadars—48 Duffadars—6 Nishanburdars—6 Trumpeters and 420 Sowars.

Raised, 30th June 1858.

THE JAT HORSE YEOMANRY REGIMENT. {Goruckpore.

Major J J Murray, 71st N I,	..	Commandant.
Lieut. R Chalmers 45th N I,	..	2nd in Command.
Ensign A C Hennessy, 1st Batt. 24th Foot,	..	Adjutant.
Captain H C Cuppage, 15th N I,	..	Doing duty, Dostpore.

The Jat Horse Yeomanry Regiment—Consists of—6 Ressaldars—6 Jemadars—36 Duffadars—6 Trumpeters—6 Camels and 420 Sowars.

THE GWALIOR CAMEL CORPS. { Camp Jadoonathpore.

Captain H J Templer, 5th En. Regt. .. Commandant.
* .. 2nd in Command.
Lieut. E B Clay, 66th N I, .. Pay. Master.
Lieut. E. Page, (Local) .. Adjt. and Qr. Master.
Lieut. C E Buckley, H. M. 3rd Battn. Rifle, Brigd., .. Detachment at Shergotty.
Bt. Major A J Nixon, H M 2nd Bn. Rif. Brig. .. Doing duty.
Captain C. Andrews, 72nd N. I., .. Ditto.
Major H R L Newdigate, H M 3rd Bn. Rif. Brig. .. Ditto.
Lieut. G L Austin, ditto ditto .. Ditto.
Lieut. E James, ditto ditto .. Ditto.
Asst.-Surgeon W H Pollard, H M's 22nd Foot, ..

Strength—Europeans—1 Assistant Apothecary—10 Sergeants—10 Corporals — 4 Buglers—176 Privates.

Natives—3 Naib Officers—5 Havildars—24 Naicks—130 Sepoys—347 Sowars and 332 Camels.

Jhansie Divisional Battalion.

JHANSIE.

Major W Davis, 31st N I, .. Commanding division.
Lieut. A G Remington, 12th N I, .. 2nd in Command.—Fur S. C., 30 July 58
Capt. J S D Tulloch, 17th N. I., .. Offg. 2nd in Command.
Lieut. A Ollivant, 9th N I, .. Adjutant of Division.

JALOUN.

Captain G Swiney, 6th En. Regt. .. Commandant.
* .. 2nd in Command.
Mr. T. F. Catania, .. Adjutant.

CHUNDEYREE.

Lieut. A. S. Thain, 13th N I, .. Commandant.
* .. 2nd in Command.
Lieut. F R Turner, 33rd N I, .. Adjutant.

HUMEERPOOR.

Lieut. J L Sawers, 37th N I, .. Commandant.
* .. 2nd in Command.
Lieut. P C Dalmahoy, 60th N I, .. Adjutant.

Jubbulpore Divisional Battalion.

JUBBULPORE.

Captain G G Moxon, 52nd N I, .. Commanding the Battalion.
Captain G A Harrison, 33rd M N I, .. 2nd in Command.
Lieut. H M Bromley, 52nd N I, .. Adjutant of the Division.—Fur. S.C. 10 June [59.
Lieut. S. S. Sutherland, 42nd N. I., .. Offg. Adjutant.

SAUGOR.

Lieut. F A Dickins, 31st N I, .. Commandant.
* .. 2nd in Command.
Lieut. S S Sutherland, 42nd N I, .. Adjutant. (Offg. Adjt. Jubbulpore Police.)
Mr. G. H. Volkers, .. Offg. Adjutant.

SEONEE.

Lieut. G F Pearson, 33rd M N I, .. Commandant.
* .. 2nd in Command.
* .. Adjutant.

BAITOOL.

Lieut. E R H Twyford, 22nd M N I,	.. Commandant.
*	.. 2nd in Command.
Cornet H Gibson, (*Local*)	.. Adjutant.

MUNDLAH.

Lieut. R Cadell, 20th N I,	.. Comdt. Offg. Comdt. Cawnpore Police.
*	.. 2nd in Command.
Lieut. S A T Judge, 67th N I,	.. Adjutant.

HOSHUNGABAD.

Lieut. F B Foote, 71st N I,	.. Commandant.
*	.. 2nd in Command.
Cornet Durnford,	.. Adjutant.

NURSINGPOOR.

Lieut. F N Miles, 53rd N I,	.. Commandant.
*	.. 2nd in Command.
*	.. Adjutant.

DUMOH.

Lieut. C S B Walton, 28th M. N. I.	.. Commandant.
*	.. 2nd in Command.
Mr. E Berrill,	.. Adjutant.

Rohilcund Divisional Battalion.

BAREILLY.

Captain J W Carter, 54th N I,	... Commanding the Division.
Captain E Bowles, 60th Rifles,	... 2nd in Command.
Lieut. G L K Hewett, 41st N I,	... Adjutant of the Division.

MORADABAD.

Major P A Roberton, 68th N I,	.. Commandant,
*	.. 2nd in Command.
Mr W Swetenham,	.. Offg. Adjutant.

BIJNOUR.

Captain R Barter, H M 7th Fus.	.. Commandant,
*	.. 2nd in Command.
Mr. T. J. Ryves,	.. Offg. Adjutant.

BUDAON.

Lieut. A F Corbett, 43rd N I,	.. Commandant.
*	.. 2nd in Command.
Lieut. R. J. Young,	.. Adjutant.

SHAHJEHANPOOR.

Captain L P Faddy, 29th N I, .. Commandant.
* .. 2nd in Command.
Lieut. G L Smith, 29th N I, .. Adjutant.

Strength—Head Quarters District—2 Troops of Horse and 8 Companies of Infantry—*Each other District*—1 Troop of Horse and 4 Companies of Infantry.
Each Troop of Horse—Consists of—1 Ressaldar—1 Naib Ressaldar—1 Jemadar—5 Duffadars—5 Naib Duffadars—1 Moonshee—1 Trumpeter—1 Nalbund—2 Camel Sowars, and 98 Troopers
Each Company of Infantry—Consists of—1 Subadar—1 Jemadar—1 Pay Havildar—5 Havildars—5 Naicks—2 Buglers and 100 Privates.

Agra Divisional Battalion.

AGRA.

Major J Hennessy, 70th N I, .. Commanding the Division.
Lieut. H T Oldfield, 9th N I, .. 2nd in Command.
Lieut. H N Noble, 44th N I, .. Adjutant of the Division.
Strength—The same as the Meerut Divisional Battalion.

MUTTRA.

Capt. W S Pierson, 54th N I, .. Commandant.
* .. 2nd in Command.
Lieut. R B Graham, 13th N I, .. Adjutant.
Strength—Mounted Police—5 Duffadars—1 Naib Duffadar—1 Drill Instructor—190 Troopers—195 Horses —*Foot Police*—2 Subadars—4 Jemadars—17 Havildars—21 Naicks—2Drummers—314 Nujeebs.

MYNPOORIE.

Capt. J J Eckford, 5th En Regt., .. Commandant.—Leave S. C. to 10th Sept.
* .. 2nd in Command.
* .. Adjutant.

ETAWAH.

Lieut. L Forbes, 2nd N I, (Grs) .. Commandant.
* .. 2nd in Command.
Lieut. G F J Graham, 4th En Regt., .. Adjutant.

ETAH.

Captain W J Hicks, 22nd N I, ... Commandant.
* .. 2nd in Command.
Lieutenant L J H Grey, 16th N I, (Grs.) .. Adjutant.

FUTTEHGURH.

Captain J P Caulfield, 4th En. Regt., ... Commandant.—Lv. S. C. 1st Nov.
* .. 2nd in Command.
Lieut. G R Hennessy, 34th N I, .. Adjutant.

Meerut Divisional Battalion.

MEERUT.

Captain E Tyrwhitt, 51st N I, .. Commanding the Division.
Lieut. E. P. Gurdon, 33rd N I, .. 2nd in Command.
Lieut. G W H Hoggan, 4th N I, .. Adjutant of the Division.
Asst. Surgeon J M Cunningham, .. Offg. Civil Surgeon.

Strength—Head-quarters District—3 Troops of Horse and 8 Companies of Infantry—*Each other District*—1 Troop of Horse and 4 Companies of Infantry.
Each—Troop of Horse Consists of 1 Ressaldar—1 Naib Ressaldar—1 Jemadar—5 Duffadars—5 Naib Duffadars—1 Pay Sowar—1 Trumpeter—1 Nalbund—2 Camel Sowars—98 Troopers.
Each Company of Infantry—1 Subadar—1 Jemadar—1 Pay Havildar—5 Havildars—5 Naicks—2 Buglers—100 Privates.

BOOLUNDSHUHUR.

Capt. W H S Earle, 20th N I, .. Commandant.
* .. 2nd in Command.
Lieut E C Corbyn, 46th N I, .. Adjutant.
Asst. Surgeon W Wood, M D, ..
Strength—Mounted Police—1 Jemadar—4 Duffadars—4 Naib Duffadars—100 Sowars—and 111 Horses.
Foot Police—4 Subadars—4 Jemadars—21 Havildars—20 Naicks—8 Buglers—and 400 Najeebs.

ALLYGURH.

Capt. C T Hallett, 72nd N I, .. Commandant.
* .. 2nd in Command.
Lieut R M Skinner, 56th N I, .. Adjutant.
Surgeon R Paton, ..
Strength—Mounted Police—3 Native Officers—8 Non-commissioned Officers—and 97 Troopers.
Foot Police—6 Native Officers—44 Non-commissioned Officers—and 353 Privates.

SAHARANPORE.

Capt. J. S. Rawlins, 44th N. I. .. Commandant.
* .. 2nd in Command.
Mr. J. W. Williams, .. Offg. Adjutant.
Surgeon W Hutchinson, ..
Strength—Mounted Police—1 Commissioned—and 2 Non-commissioned Officers—and 88 Sowars.
Foot Police—6 Commissioned—and 32 Non-commissioned Officers—and 388 Privates.

DEHRA DOON.

Capt. *The Hon* W M Fraser, 44th N I, .. Commandant.
* .. 2nd in Command.
Lieut. H Macdonald, 19th N I, .. Adjutant.
Asst Surgeon D F Faller, ..

MOZUFFURNUGGUR.

Capt. R W Chambers, 11th N I, .. Commandant.—Lv. prepy. to Fur.
* .. 2nd in Command.
Lieut A S Heathcote, 60th Rifles, .. Adjutant.—Offg. Commandant.
Mr. H. Leeson, .. Offg. Adjutant.
Asst Surgeon J Cunningham, M D, .. Offg. Civil Surgeon Meerut.
Strength—Mounted Police—1 Jemadar—4 Duffadars—4 Naib Duffadars—and 98 Troopers.
Foot Police—1 Sergeant Major—4 Subadars—4 Jemadars—22 Havildars—16 Naicks—1 Bugler—45 Recruits—and 349 Privates.

Benares Divisional Battalion.

BENARES.

Captain J Cockerell, 2nd E L C, .. Commanding the Division.
Lieut. P P L Stafford, .. 2nd in Command.
Lieut. W H Garton, 50th N I, .. Adjutant of the Division.

MIRZAPORE.

Lieut. F A C Knyvett, 24th N I, .. Commandant.
* .. 2nd in Command.
Lieut. A B E Thomas, 4th En. Regt., .. Adjutant.
Assist.-Surgeon G R Pemberton, ..

JOUNPOOR.

Captain G A St. P Fooks, 50th N I, .. Commandant.
* .. 2nd in Command.
Lieut. J W O'Dowda, 50th N I, .. Adjutant.

GHAZEEPOOR.

Lieut. B G VanderGucht, 2nd N I, (Grs.,) .. Commandant.
* .. 2nd in Command.
Lieut. W G Keppell, 6th En. Regt., .. Adjutant.

AZIMGURH.

Captain H D Manning, 19th N I, .. Commandant.
* .. 2nd in Command.
Lieut. R O H Forbes, 3rd En. Regt., .. Adjutant.

Strength—Head Quarters District—Consists of—3 Troops of Horse and 8 Companies of Infantry. —*Each other District*—Consists of—1 Troop of Horse and 4 Companies of Infantry.

Strength of Each Troop—1 Ressaldar—1 Naib Ressaldar—1 Jemadar—5 Duffadars—5 Naib Duffadars—1 Monshee—1 Trumpeter—1 Nalbund—2 Camel Sowars and 98 Troopers.

Strength of Each Company—1 Subadar—1 Jemadar—1 Pay Havildar—5 Havildars—5 Naicks—2 Buglers and 100 Privates.

Allahabad Divisional Battalion.

ALLAHABAD.

Lieut. T Dennehy, 2nd N I, (Grs.,) .. Commanding the Division.
Captain F C Chapman, (Local,) .. 2nd in Command.
Lieut. W D Shaw, 2nd N I, (Grs.,) .. Adjutant of the Division.—Lv. S. C, 15 Oct.

SURAON.

Captain W. Irwin, 49th N I, .. Commandant.
* .. 2nd in Command.
* .. Adjutant.

FUTTEHPORE.

Lieut. E J Wild, 40th N I, ... Commandant.
* .. 2nd in Command.
Mr. A. Bates, .. Adjutant.

CAWNPORE.

Lieut. M Thomson, 53rd N I, .. Commandant.—Fur. S. C., 25th May 58.
Lieut. R. Cadell 20th N. I, .. Offg. Commandant.
Lieut. W A Franks, 12th N I, .. Adjutant.

BANDA.

Lieut. W F Metge, H M 8th Foot, .. Commandant.—On Leave.
Captain W H Binny, 9th N I, .. Officiating Commandant.
Mr. W. Braybrooke, .. Adjutant.

Strength—Head Quarters District—3 Troops of Horse and 8 Companies of Infantry—*Each other District*—Consists of—1 Troop of Horse and 4 Companies of Infantry.

Each Troop—Consists of—1 Ressaldar—1 Naib Ressaldar—1 Jemadar—5 Duffadars—5 Naib Duffadars—1 Moonshee—1 Trumpeter—1 Nalbund—2 Camel sowars and 98 Troopers.

Each Company—Consists of—1 Subadar—1 Jemadar—1 Pay Havildar—5 Havildars—5 Naicks—2 Buglers and 100 Privates.

REGIMENT OF LUCKNOW.

Raised, 8th Dec. 1857 — Cawnpore.

Colonel H Palmer, 48th N I, .. Commandant.
Captain W C L Ryves, 12th N I, .. 2nd in Command.
Lieut. W Campbell, 71st N I, .. Offg. Quarter Master.
Lieut. *The Hon.* H H Hare, 17th N I, .. Offg. Adjutant.
Captain J MacDougall, 19th N I, .. Doing duty.
Capt. G V Balderston, 23rd N I, .. Ditto.
Captain N. R. Sneyd, 57th N. I., .. Ditto.
Lieut. J. Upperton, 46th N. I., .. Ditto.
Surgeon F M Clifford, ..
Asst. Surgeon R. Banbury, ..

Strength—8 Companies—1 Sergeant Major—1 Quarter-Master Sergeant—2 Native Doctors—1 Subadar Major—9 Subadars—10 Jemadars—50 Havildars—50 Naicks—20 Drummers and —800 Sepoys.

LOYAL POORBEEAH REGIMENT.

Phillour.

Major J C Innes, 61st N I, .. Commandant.
Captain J Marquis 4th En. Regt., .. 2nd in Command.
Lieut. M Ramsay, 36th N. I, .. Adjutant.
Lieut. H H Birch, .. Doing duty.
Surgeon J H Jones, ..

Strength—2 Native Doctors—1 Subadar Major—7 Subadars—8 Jemadars—48 Havildars—48 Naicks—16 Drummers—640 Sepoys.

FURRUCKABAD INFANTRY POLICE CORPS. { Furruckabad.

Captain J P Caulfield, 4th En. Regt. .. Commandant. Leave S. C. 1 November.
Lieut G R Hennessy, 34th N I, .. Offg. Commandant.
* .. Adjutant.
Strength.—Foot—1 Native Doctor—1 Subadar—4 Jemadars—16 Havildars—13 Naicks—3 Buglers —386 Nujeebs.
Horse—1 Ressaldar—1 Jemadar—4 Duffadars—4 Naib Duffadars—99 Troopers and —109 Horse.

GHAZEEPORE POLICE BATTALION. { Ghazeepore.

Lieut. B G Vander Gucht 2nd (Grendrs.) .. Commandant.
Lieut. W G Keppell 6th En. Regt. .. Adjutant.
Strength—1 Sergeant Major—4 Subadars—4 Jemadars—20 Havildars—20 Naicks—400 Sepoys

---

SEIKH POLICE CORPS. { Goruckpoor. (Camp Bulliah).

Captain J R McMullin, 50th N I, .. Commandant.
* .. 2nd in Command.
Lieut. A Pullan, 36th N I, .. Adjutant
Lieut. A Bruce. 28th N I, .. Doing duty.—On Command to Rusarah.
Lieut. J Bartleman, 23rd N I, .. Ditto—On Command to Gurnniah.
Lieut. A Goldney, 50th N I, .. Ditto—On Command to Burragoun.
Strength—10 Subadars—10 Jemadars—50 Havildars—50 Naicks—10 Drummers—1,000 Sepoys.

Bengal Military Police.

MAJOR T RATTRAY, 64TH N. I,
Inspector of Military Police Battalions.—Lower Povinces.

Raised at Lahore 1856. } 1ST BATTALION (SEIKHS.) { Head-Quarters Dehree

Uniform—Drab—*Facings*—Blue—*Lace*—Silver.

		Appointed,		
*			..	Commandant.
Lieut. C G Baker,	..	15 April 1856	..	2nd in command, Comdt. of cavalry, and Offg. commandant.
Lieut. W Campbell,	..	15 April 1856	..	Adjutant—Offg. 2nd in command and Comdt. of Cavalry.
Lieut. A N M Macgregor,	..	10 Nov. 1857	..	
Lieut. J H Thompson,	..	7 Sept 1858	..	
Asst.-Surgeon J M Coates, M D.,		4 July 1857	..	

Strength—10 Companies of Infantry and—1 Troop of Irregular Cavalry, *viz;*—2 Native Doctors 10 Subadars—10 Jemadars—60 Havildars—60 Naicks—1 Bugle Major—9 Buglers—1000 Privates—*Cavalry*—1 Ressaldar,—2 Jemadars—4 Duffadars—4 Naib Duffadars—1 Trumpeter —99 Troopers—1 Tindal—5 Classies—2 Moonshees—1 Driver—5 Dhooly Bearers—1 Sweeper —21 Bheesties and—22 Cooks.

BAGHALCUND MILITARY POLICE. { Myheer.

UNIFORM—*Zucve.* LACE.———

Lieut. Col. C T E Hinde, 65th N I., .. Commandant.
Lieut. H V Mathias, 50th N I., .. 2nd in Command.
Lieut. B Cracroft, 50th N I., .. Adjutant.
Lieut. W F Ireland, 25th N I., .. Doing duty.
Mr. Kirke, .. Ditto.

Strength—Cavalry—3 Ressaldars—3 Naib Ressaldars—15 Duffadars—15 Naib Duffadars—6 Trumpeters—3 Moochees—300 Troopers.

Infantry—9 Subadars—9 Jemadars—9 Pay Havildars—45 Havildars—45 Naicks—18 Buglers—900 Sepoys.

Regiments of Irregular Cavalry.

1st Irregular Cavalry.

{ Jullundur.

"BHURTPORE"—*Detachment*, "CANDAHAR 1842."

UNIFORM—*Yellow*. LACE—*Silver*.

RANK, NAMES AND CORPS.	*Army Rank.*	*Appointment.*	REMARKS.
Major C. T. Chamberlain, 28th N.I.	2 *May* 52	19 *Nov.* 49	Commandant.
Lieut. G. C. Thomson, 51st N.I. ..	7 *Sept.* 54	8 *Feb.* 59	2nd in Command.
Lt. T.R.D. Bingham, H. M. 70 Foot,	.. ..	8 *Feb.* 59	Offg. Adjutant.
Asst. Surg. J. D. Crawford, A.B., M.D.,	11 *Aug.* 46	5 *Oct.* 50	

Strength of each Regiment of Irregular Cavalry—6 Ressallahs, with 2 Native Doctors—3 Ressaldars—3 Ressaidars—6 Naib Ressaldars—6 Jemadars—6 Kote Duffadars—48 Duffadars—6 Nishanburdars—3 Trumpeters—3 Nuggarchies—420 Sowars.

2nd Irregular Cavalry.

{ Goordaspore.

"ARRACAN"—"SUBRAON"—"PUNJAUB."

UNIFORM—*Green*. LACE—*Silver*.

RANK, NAMES AND CORPS.	*Army Rank.*	*Appointment.*	REMARKS.
Major G. Jackson, 3rd E. L.C. ..	20 *June* 54	24 *Feb.* 48	Commandant.—Lv. P. A. 15th Oct.
Major C. Cureton, 38th L.I. ..	20 *July* 58	4 *May* 52	2nd in Command, Offg. Comdt. Mooltanee Cavalry.
Lieut. H. P. W. Wynch, 59th N. I.	10 *Nov.* 51	30 *Aug.* 56	Adjutant, Offg. 2nd in Command.
Asst. Surg. S. C. Townsend, ..	1 *June.* 52	17 *Feb.* 59	

3rd Irregular Cavalry.

{ Mutinied, Saugor.

"CAUBUL 1842"—"FEROZESHUHUR"—"PUNJAUB"—"CHILLIANWALLA"—"GOOJEERAT."

UNIFORM—*Red*. LACE—*Gold*.

RANK, NAMES AND CORPS.	*Army Rank.*	*Appointment.*	REMARKS.
*			Commandant.
Lieut. A. Cory, 16th N. I. (Grs.) ..	13 *Dec.* 54	15 *Jan.* 59	2nd in Command.
Lieut. B. N. Smith, 46th N. I. ..	10 *Feb.* 55	21 *Jan.* 59	Adjutant.—Fur. P. A. 10 May 59.
Lieut. J. R. Pearson, 27th N. I. ..	30 *Apl.* 58	27 *Jan.* 59	Doing duty.
Asst. Surgeon,			

4th Irregular Cavalry.

{ Seetapore.

"AFFGHANISTAN"—"GHUZNEE"—"MAHARAJPORE"—2 *Ressallahs* "KELAT."—*Detachment*
"MOODKEE"—*Detachment*, "FEROZESHUHUR"—"ALLIWAL."

UNIFORM—*Yellow*. LACE—*Silver*.

RANK, NAMES AND CORPS.	*Army Rank.*	*Appointment.*	REMARKS.
Major A. Martin, 33rd N.I. ..	28 *Nov.* 54	23 *Nov.* 50	Commandant.—Fur. S. C. 16 Mar. 1858.
Major G. W. M. Hall, 26th L.I. ..	19 *Jan.* 58	23 *Nov.* 50	2nd in Command.—Offg. Comdt.
Capt. W. J. Ward, 51st N. I. ..	25 *July* 57	21 *Oct.* 58	Offg. 2nd in Command.
Lieut. *Sir* A.K. Lake, 2nd En. Fus.	.. ..	.. ..	Adjutant.
Asst. Surgeon, S. G. Bousfield, ..	10 *Nov.* 48	9 May 59	

5th Irregular Cavalry. { Mutinied, Bhagulpore.

UNIFORM—*Red.* LACE—*Gold.*

RANK, NAMES AND CORPS.	*Army Rank.*	*Appointment.*	REMARKS.
*			Commandant.
*			2nd in Command.
*			Adjutant.
Asst. Surgeon,*			

6th Irregular Cavalry. { Mooltan.

Armed with Musketoons.

UNIFORM—*Red.* LACE—*Gold.*

Capt. J. C. Curtis, 72nd N.I. ..	17 *Mar.* 56	26 *Feb.* 53	Commandant.
Capt. G. C. Hankin, 28th N. I. ..	8 *Dec.* 58	26 *Feb.* 53	2nd in Command.
Lieut. A. G. Owen, 1st En. B. F...	23 *Nov.* 56	23 *Feb.* 58	Adjutant.
Asst. Surgeon,*			

Raised, 28th April 1841.

7th Irregular Cavalry. { Peshawur.

"PUNJAUB"—"MOOLTAN."

Detachments at Fort Mackeson and Fort Abazaie.

UNIFORM—*Red.* LACE—*Gold.*

Col. W. E. Mulcaster, 64th N. I. ..	28 *Nov.* 57	14 *Jan.* 52	Commandant.
Lieut. H. R. Osborn, 74th N. I. ..	23 *Nov.* 56	22 *Apl.* 58	2nd in Command.
Lieut. H. D. E. W. Chester, 36th N.I.	23 *Nov.* 56	22 *Apl.* 58	Adjutant.
Asst. Surg. J. Picthall, ..	14 *Dec.* 53	17 *Feb.* 59	

Raised, 29th Jan. 1858.

8th Irregular Cavalry. { Seetapore.

UNIFORM—*Blue.* Facings White—LACE—*Gold.*

Major J.F. Richardson, C.B., 49th N.I.	20 *July* 58	10 *Oct.* 54	Commandant.
		18 *Aug.* 57	Comdg. Bengal Yeomanry Cavalry.
Captain A. H. Campbell, 9th N. I.	.. ..	.. ..	Officiating Commandant.
Capt. A. M. Mackenzie, 56th N. I.	9 *Dec.* 57	10 *Oct.* 54	2nd in Comd.—Fur S. C. 1 Oct. 58.
Lieut. T. G. Blackburne, 20th N. I.	10 *May* 57	31 *May* 58	Officiating Adjutant.
Asst. Surgeon J. A. Currie, M.A. M.D.,	4 *Dec.* 53	17 *Dec.* 56	

Raised, 3rd Feb. 1844.

9th Irregular Cavalry. { Bunno.

Detachments at Loodianah and Umballah.

"GHUZNEE"—"CANDAHAR"—"GHUZNEE"—"CABUL"—*Detachment,* "JELLALABAD"—*Detachment,* "SCINDE"—*Detachment,* "PUNNIAR"—*Detachment,* "MAHRAJPORE." "MOODKEE"—"FEROZESHUHUR"—"SUBRAON"—"PUNJAUB"—"CHILLIANWALLA"—"GOOJERAT."

UNIFORM—*Red.* LACE—*Gold.*

Col. J. M. B. F. Tytler, C.B. 37th N.I	19 *Jan.* 58	28 *Apl.* 54	Commandant.—Fur. S.C. 5 Apl. 58.
Capt. H. L. Campbell, 52nd N. I. ..	13 *July* 57	29 *July* 56	2nd in Command. Offg. Commdt.
Lieut. F. J. N. Mackenzie, 52nd N.I.	27 *June* 57	11 *Sep.* 58	Offg. Adjutant.
Asst. Surg. D. McDonald, M. D., ..	20 *May* 46	16 *Dec.* 54	

Raised in 1838.

10th Irregular Cavalry.

Disarmed Nowshera

Detachment at Abazaie.

This Corps was originally raised as a portion of the late Bundelkund Legion in October 1838, *and subsequently incorporated with the Bengal Army, from the* 18*th of March* 1844.

Designation changed { 5*th Octr.* 1846. 18*th Sept.* 1847.

UNIFORM—*Blue.* FACINGS—*Scarlet.* LACE—*Gold.*

RANK, NAMES AND CORPS.	*Army Rank.*	*Appointment.*	REMARKS.
*			Commandant.
Capt. C. P. St. J. Law, 11th N. I.	10 *July* 54	27 *Mar.* 49	2nd in Command.—Fur. S.C. 22 Oct. [58.
Lieut. G. H. Griffiths, 6th En. Regt.	1 *Feb.* 52	25 *Jan.* 55	Adjutant.
Asst. Surgeon *			

N. B.—This Regt. has received four standards, as allowed to Regular Cavalry.

Raised, 2nd Jan. 1846.

11th Irregular Cavalry.

Disarmed, Berhampore.

"PUNJAUB"—"MOOLTAN"—"GOOJERAT."

UNIFORM—*Scarlet.* LACE—*Gold.*

*			Commandant.
Capt. A. G. Nedham, 74th N. I. ..	12 *June* 56	12 *June* 55	2nd in Command.
Lieut. Q. D. Parsons, 6th En. Regt.	20 *Feb.* 56	1 *May* 57	Adjutant.
Surgeon H. Cape, ..	7 *Aug.* 57	24 *Jan.* 54	

Raised 2nd Jan. 1846.

12th Irregular Cavalry.

Mutinied, Meerut.

"PUNJAUB"—"GOOJERAT."

UNIFORM—*Green.* LACE—*Silver.*

Capt. T. Watson, 33rd N. I. ..	12 *Dec.* 50	6 *Oct.* 58	Commandant.
Lieut. E. H. Woodcock, 55th N.I...	14 *Nov.* 54	8 *Feb.* 59	2nd in Command.
		14 *June* 59	Offg. Comdt. Mily. Police, Oude.
Lieut. J. H. Tyler, 20th N. I. ..	23 *Nov.* 56	29 *Oct.* 58	Offg. Adjutant.
Asst. Surg.*			

Raised 2nd Jan. 1846.

13th Irregular Cavalry.

Mutinied, Sultanpore, (Benares.)

"PUNJAUB"—"GOOJERAT."

UNIFORM—*Blue.* FACINGS—*Scarlet.*—LACE—*Gold..*

*			Commandant.
*			2nd in Command.
*			Adjutant.
Asst. Surg.*			

Raised 2nd Jan. 1846. | Mutinied, Jhansie, and Nowgong.

14th Irregular Cavalry.

UNIFORM—*Yellow*. LACE—*Gold*.

"PUNJAUB."

Detachment "MOOLTAN"—*Detachment* "GOOJERAT."

RANK, NAMES AND CORPS.	*Army Rank.*	*Appointment.*	REMARKS.
Captain H. Skinner, (*Unattached*,)	16 *Jan.* 52	27 *Jan.* 52	Commandant.—Fur. S. C. 3 Jan. 57
Maj. C. J. Robarts, 43rd L.I. ..	8 *Mar.* 55	24 *Jan.* 46	2nd in Command.
*			Adjutant.
Asst. Surg. *			

Raised 14th Jan. 1846. | Mutinied, Oude, (Sultanpore.)

15th Irregular Cavalry.

"PUNJAUB."

UNIFORM—*Red*. LACE—*Gold*.

RANK, NAMES AND CORPS.	*Army Rank.*	*Appointment.*	REMARKS.
*			Commandant.
*			2nd in Command.
*			Adjutant.
Asst. Surgeon*			

Raised 14th Jan. 1846. | Rawul, Pindee.

16th Irregular Cavalry.

Head-quarters and Detachment "PUNJAUB."

UNIFORM—*Red*. LACE—*Gold*.

RANK, NAMES AND CORPS.	*Army Rank.*	*Appointment.*	REMARKS.
Major W. W. Davidson, 32nd N.I.	20 *June* 54	24 *Jan.* 46	Commandant. [58.
Lieut W. A. Battine, 53rd N.I. ..	9 *Mar.* 55	21 *Oct.* 58	2nd in Command.—Fur. S.C. 15 Jan.
Lieut. T. R. Davidson, 49th N. I...	23 *Nov.* 56	21 *Oct.* 58	Adjutant.
Asst. Surgeon A. L. S. Campbell,..	11 *July* 46	13 *Nov.* 55	

Raised 24th Jan. 1846 | Rawul Pindee.

17th Irregular Cavalry.

Left Wing "PUNJAUB."

UNIFORM—*Scarlet*. LACE—*Gold*.

RANK, NAMES AND CORPS.	*Army Rank.*	*Appointment.*	REMARKS.
Major J. Liptrott, 2nd En. B. F. ..	28 *Nov.* 54	24 *Jan.* 46	Commandant.—Lv. S. C. 1 Nov.
Capt. R. J. F. Hickey, 1st En.B. F.	7 *June* 57	10 *Apl.* 58	2nd in Command.—(Offg. Comdt.)
Lieut. B. C. Urquhart, 39th N. I...	26 *Aug.* 55	29 *Dec.* 58	Adjutant.
Asst. Surgeon R. Parker, M. D., ..			

Raised 24th Jan. 1846. | Peshawur.

18th Irregular Cavalry.

UNIFORM—*Blue*. FACINGS—*Scarlet*. LACE—*Gold*.

RANK, NAMES AND CORPS.	*Army Rank.*	*Appointment.*	REMARKS.
Major W. H. Ryves, 61st N.I. ..	28 *Nov.* 54	24 *Jan.* 46	Commandant.
Capt. G. J. D. Hay, 57th N. I. ..	21 *Nov.* 58	27 *Oct.* 58	2nd in Command.
Lieut. J.S. Hand, H. M. 82nd Foot,	18 *Aug.* 54	27 *Oct.* 58	Adjutant.
Asst. Surgeon G. V. Currie, ..	14 *Jan.* 54	19 *Nov.* 56	

Punjaub Irregular Force.

Raised by G. O. G. G., 18th May 1849. Remodelled by G. O. G. G., 15th Feb. 1851.

Rank, Names and Corps.	Army Rank.	Appointment.	Remarks.
Brigr. Genl. N. B. Chamberlain, C. B., 16th N.I., ..	28 *Nov.* 54	15 *Dec.* 57	Commandant.
Capt. S. Black, 37th N. I., ...	20 *Mar.* 57	16 *Jan.* 57	Staff Officer to the Force.
Capt. J. R. Sladen, Artillery, ..	11 *June* 57	8 *July* 51	Comdg. 1st Horse Lt. Field Battery, Dera Ishmael Khan, 19th Jan. 1857.—Fur. S. C. 7 May, 1858.
*			Offg. Comdt. No. 1 Lt. Field Battery.
Lt. W. B. Cumberland, Arty., ..	4 *July* 57	27 *June* 56	Doing duty with ditto.
Capt. G. Maister, Artillery, ..	11 *June* 57	3 *Apl.* 56	Comdt. No. 2 Horse Light Field Battery, Kohat, 22nd Jan. 57.
Lt. E. H. Ryan, Arty., ..	27 *Apl.* 58	5 *Nov.* 58	Doing duty with ditto.
Capt. R. Mecham, Artillery, ..	12 *Aug.* 57	3 *Apl.* 56	Comdt. No. 3 Horse Light Field Battery, Bunno, 7th Feb. 57.—Fur. S. C. 11 May 1858.
Capt. T. E. Hughes, Arty. ..	27 *Aug.* 58	2 *Dec.* 56	Offg. Comdt. Ditto.
*			Comdg. No. 4 or Garrison Company of Arty. and Commy. of Ordnance. —Dera Ishmael Khan.—
Conductor T. Newbold, ..	.. ..	20 *Apl.* 54	

The 1st, 2nd, and 3rd Horse Light Field Batteries, each consist of 1 Rough Rider and Farrier Sergeant—1 Asst. Saddler Sergeant—1 Subadar—2 Jemadars—8 Havildars—8 Naicks—2 Buglers—122 Privates—1 Tindal—6 Store Lascars—1 Tent Lascar—1 Native Farrier—2 Bheestees—1 Sweeper—1 Native Doctor—1 Dresser.

The 4th or Garrison Arty. Co. consists of 1 Subadar—2 Jemadars—8 Havildars—8 Naicks—2 Buglers—130 Privates—1 Tent Lascar—1 Native Doctor.

CAVALRY.

FIRST REGIMENT.

{ Trans Gogra.

Uniform—*Blue.* Lace—*Silver.*

Rank, Names and Corps.	Army Rank.	Appointment.	Remarks.
Major W. T. Hughes, 48th N. I. ..	24 *Mar.* 58	22 *Apl.* 52	Comdt. — Offg. Comdt Hodson's [Horse.
Capt. H. L. Millett, 28th N.I. ..	27 *June* 57	20 *Apl.* 58	2nd in Command.
Lieut. C. S. Maclean, 10th N. I., ..	23 *Nov.* 56	20 *Apl.* 58	Adjutant.—Fur. S. C. 13 Mar. 58.
Lieut. W. C. Anderson, 22nd N. I...	17 *Nov.* 57	20 *Apl.* 58	Offg. Adjutant.
Asst. Surgeon C. M. Smith, M.D., ..	20 *Dec.* 54	6 *May* 58	Fur. S. C. 11 Feb. 59.

SECOND REGIMENT.

{ Kohat.

Uniform—*Red.* Lace—*Gold.*

Rank, Names and Corps.	Army Rank.	Appointment.	Remarks.
Major S. J. Browne, 46th N.I. ..	20 *July* 58	8 *Jan.* 51	Commandant.—Fur. S. C. 3 Jan. 59.
Lieut. F. J. Craigie, 21st N.I. ..	13 *Apl.* 55	5 *July* 58	2nd in Command.
Lieut. T. C. Graham, 4th E. L. C...	23 *Nov.* 56	3 *May* 58	Adjutant.—Fur. S. C. 6 Sep. 58.
Asst. Surgeon T. Maxwell, M. D., ..	26 *Jan.* 46	18 *May* 49	Fur. P. A. 28 Apl. 59.
A. M. Garden, ..	11 *Jan.* 55	29 *Apl.* 59	

THIRD REGIMENT.

{ Dera Ghazee Khan.

Uniform—*Blue.* Lace—*Silver.*

Rank, Names and Corps.	Army Rank.	Appointment.	Remarks.
Capt. J. S. Gell, 10th Bombay N. I.	.. ..	27 *Mar.* 56	Commandant.
Lieut. W. Fane, *PH*, 11th M. N. I.	21 *June* 45	9 *Apl.* 57	2nd in Command.—Offg. Commdt. 4 Sikh Irr Cavy.
Lieut. D. Mainwaring, 1st Bo. F., ..	.. ..	30 *Apl.* 58	Offg. 2nd in Command.
Lieut. G. B. Crispin, 4th Bombay N.I.	.. ..	3 *Oct.* 56	Adjutant.
Lieut. J. P. Burton, 62nd N. I. ..	23 *Nov.* 56	3 *May* 58	Doing duty.
Asst. Surgeon W. Delpratt, ..	20 *Nov.* 47	10 *Feb.* 54	Fur. P. A. 10 May 59.

FOURTH REGIMENT. { Asnee.

UNIFORM—*Green*. LACE—*Gold*.

Rank, Names and Corps.	Army Rank.	Appointment.	Remarks.
Capt. C. J. Godby, 36th N. I., ..	10 *July* 52	29 *Apl.* 59	Commandant.
Lieut. B. W. Ryall, 63rd N. I. ..	6 *Nov.* 50	24 *Feb.* 59	2nd in Command.
Lieut. H. C. P. Rice, 73rd N I, ..	23 *Nov.* 56	.. ..	Offg. Adjutant.
Lieut. F. Hammond, 62nd N. I., ..	8 *Aug.* 57	31 May 59	Doing duty.
Asst. Surg. N. D. S. Wallich, ..	20 *Dec.* 48	9 *June* 54	Fur. P. A. 14 June 59.

FIFTH REGIMENT. { Dera Ishmael Khan.

UNIFORM—*Green*. LACE—*Gold*.

Rank, Names and Corps.	Army Rank.	Appointment.	Remarks.
Capt. W. H. Paget, 54th N. I. ..	8 *June* 57	26 *June* 58	Commandant.—Fur. S. C, 7 June 59
Lieut. C. E. Goddard H. M 87th Foot,	30 Dec. 53	13 *Jan.* 59	2nd in Command.
Lieut. W. C. B. Ryan, 45th N. I...	21 *Aug.* 54	3 *May* 58	Adjutant.
Lieut. A. Butler, H. M. 87th Foot,	.. ..	13 *Jan.* 59	Doing duty.
Asst. Surgeon R. Rouse, ..	20 *Dec.* 54	22 *Jan.* 58	

The 1st, 2nd, 3rd, 4th, and 5th Regiments of Punjaub Irregular Cavalry, each consist of 6 Ressallahs—with 1 Woordee Major—1 Nakeeb—1 Persian Writer—2 Native Doctors—3 Ressaldars—3 Ressaidars—6 Naib Ressaldars—6 Jemadars—6 Kote Duffadars—48 Duffadars—6 Nishanburdars—6 Trumpeters—6 Bheestees—500 Sowars.

Punjaub Irregular Force.

INFANTRY.

FIRST REGIMENT. { Dera Ghazee Khan.

(*Rifles.*)

Coke ka Pultun.

UNIFORM—*Green*. LACE—*Black*. FACINGS—*Green*.

Rank, Names and Corps.	Army Rank.	Appointment.	Remarks.
Col. J. Coke, C. B., 10th N. I. ..	20 *July* 58	18 *May* 49	Commandant.—Fur. S. C. 3Jan. 59.
Maj. F. W. Lambert, 56th N. I., ..	20 *July* 58	5 *July* 58	2nd in Command.
Lieut. J. P. Davidson, 4th N. I., ..	23 *Nov.* 56	6 *Oct.* 57	Adjutant.
Lieut. H. W. Pitcher, 13th N. I. ..	18 *May.* 58	15 *Mar.* 59	Doing duty.
Assist. Surg. J. R. Jackson, M. D., ..	4 *Jan.* 55	23 *Nov.* 55	In charge of the Civil Medical duties Moradabad.

SECOND REGIMENT. { Bunno.

Johnson ka Pultun,

UNIFORM—*Drab*. FACINGS—*Black*.

Rank, Names and Corps.	Army Rank.	Appointment.	Remarks.
Lt. Col. G. W. G. Green, C. B. 2nd En. B. F., ..	24 *Mar.* 58	8 *Aug.* 53	Commandant.—Fur. S. C. 22 Oct. 58
Capt. J. P. W. Campbell, 47th N. I.	23 *Nov.* 56	13 *Jan.* 59	Offg. Commandant.
Lieut. W. P. Fisher, 4th En. Regt.	14 *Oct.* 55	13 *Apl.* 58	2nd in Command.
Lieut. F. J. Keen, 35th L. I., ..	4 *June* 57	15 *Mar.* 59	Adjutant.
Asst. Surgeon W. F. Clark, ..	4 *June* 54	27 *Dec.* 55	Fur. S. C. 27 Apl. 58.
G. Farrell, F. R. C. S., ..	4 *Aug.* 56	19 *Apl.* 59	

THIRD REGIMENT. { Kohat.

Moorcroft ka Pultun.

UNIFORM—*Drab* FACINGS—*Drab* LACE—*Green*.

Rank, Names and Corps.	Army Rank.	Appointment.	Remarks.
Capt. B. Henderson, 48th N. I. ..	5 *June* 53	28 *Mar.* 51	Commandant.—Civil employ.
Lieut. A. U. F. Ruxton, 66th N. I...	23 *Feb.* 56	2 *Mar.* 57	2nd in Command.—Offg. Comdt.
Lieut. G. A. Way, 58th N. I. ..	14 *Mar.* 58	3 *May* 58	Offg. Adjutant.
Lieut. H. W. Gordon, 63rd N. I., ..	23 *Nov.* 56	3 *May* 58	Doing duty.
Apothecary J. R. Deane, ...	20 *May* 46	8 *Oct.* 52	

FOURTH REGIMENT.

{ Bunno.

(*Rifles.*)

Denniss ka Pultun.

UNIFORM—*Drab.* FACINGS—*French Grey.*

Major A. T. Wilde, 19th M. N. I. ..	19 *Jan.* 58	21 *Feb.* 53	Comdt.—Fur. S. C. 14 May 1858.
Capt. W. Graydon, 16th N. I. (Grs.)	12 *June* 54	24 *Feb.* 59	Offg. Commandant.
Capt. G. A. Graham, 28th N. I. ..	10 *June* 57	18 *May* 58	2nd in Command.
Lieut. J. W. McQueen, 27th N. I...	4 *June* 57	3 *May* 58	Adjutant.
Asst. Surg. J. Fairweather, M. D., ..	4 *Aug.* 55	11 *July* 56	

FIFTH REGIMENT.

{ Trans Gogra.

Gastrell ka Pultun.

UNIFORM—*Drab.* FACINGS—*Green.*

Major J. L. Vaughan, 21st N.I. ..	6 *June* 56	22 *Oct.* 52	Commandant.
Lieut. J. B. Lind, 24th N.I. ..	26 *Feb.* 50	7 *Apl.* 57	2nd in Command.
Lieut. C. E. Stewart, H. M. 27th Foot,	1 *May* 55	13 *Apl.* 58	Adjutant.
Lieut. S. J. Browne, 55th N. I. ..	23 *Nov.* 56	9 *Apl.* 58	Doing duty.
Asst. Surgeon*			

Transferred to Bengal, 1st Oct. 1849.

SIXTH REGIMENT.

{ Kohat.

At Kohat.

" Ready-aye-Ready."

UNIFORM—*Drab.* FACINGS—*Red.*

Lieut. C. P. Keyes, 30th Madras N.I.	30 *Nov.* 48	30 *May* 54	Comdt.—Fur. S. C. 31st July 57.
Lieut. Thomas Quin, 22d N. I. ..	17 *Oct.* 54	1 *Dec.* 55	2nd in Command.—Lv. p. to Fur.
Lieut. B. S. B. Parlby, 6th En. Regt.,	7 *May* 54	3 *May* 58	Offg. 2nd in Command.
Lieut. G. N. Saunders, 24th N. I.,..	19 *Oct.* 56	5 *July* 58	Adjutant.
Lieut. A. M. Stewart, 64th N. I., ..	18 *Mar.* 57	5 *July* 58	Doing duty.

SEVENTH REGIMENT.

{ Phillour.

Capt. J. F. Stafford, 4th N. I., ..	11 *Aug.* 57	4 *Dec.* 57	Commandant.
Lieut. J. C. P. Baillie, 35th N. I., ..	23 *Nov.* 56	19 *May* 59	2nd in Command.
*			Adjutant.
Lieut. H. A Lewes, 20th N. I., ..	10 *May* 57	16 *Feb.* 59	Doing duty.
Asst. Surg. D. Hood, ..	4 *Aug.* 55	6 *July* 58	

EIGHTH REGIMENT.

{ Nowshera.

Capt. C. H. Brownlow, 4th En. Regt.,	3 *Nov.* 58	4 *Dec.* 57	Commandant.
Lieut. G. A. McNair, H.M. 70th Foot,	30 *June* 48	4 *Dec.* 57	2nd in Command.
*			Adjutant.
Lieut. E. Chapman, 14th N. I., ..	21 *May* 57	29 *Apl.* 59	Doing duty.
Asst. Surgeon W. H. Corbett, M.D , ..	.. ..	13 *Jan.* 59	Ditto.

NINTH REGIMENT.

{ Fyzabad.

Lieut. J. Williamson, 49th N. I., ..	13 *Apl.* 48	4 *Dec.* 57	Commandant.—Offg. Comdt. 18th. [Punjaub Infantry
Capt. J. B. Thelwall, H. M. 24th Foot,	21 *Dec.* 49	8 *June* 58	Offg. Commandant.
Capt. T. C. Darnell, 51st N. I., ..	23 *Nov.* 56	23 *Mar.* 58	2nd in Command.—Lv. S. C. 15 [Nov.
Lieut O. Menzies, 35th L I , ..	27 *June* 57	15 *July* 58	Adjutant.
Lieut. H. Collett, 53rd N. I., ..	27 *June* 57	9 *Apl.* 58	Doing duty.
Lieut. H. B. Sanderson, 22nd N. I.,	8 *June* 57	11 *May* '59	Ditto.
Ensign J. B. Hay, 59th N. I., ..	20 *Jan.* 58	1 *Feb.* 59	Ditto.

TENTH REGIMENT.

Dera Ishmael Khan.

Capt. P. F. Gardiner, 29th N. I., ..	27 *Sep.* 55	4 *Dec.* 57	Commandant.
Capt. G. H Gordon, 39th N. I., ..	11 *June* 57	4 *Dec.* 57	2nd in Command.
Lieut. T. C. S. Speedy, ..	.. ..	13 *Jan.* 59	Adjutant.
Lieut. R. Gunning, 14th N. I., ..	23 *Mar.* 58	13 *Jan.* 59	Doing duty.
Asst. Surgeon C. K. Webb, ..	1 *July* 46	19 *Apl.* 59	

ELEVENTH REGIMENT.

Lahore.

Capt. W. J. F. Stafford, 36th N. I.,..	15 *Feb.* 53	24 *Feb.* 59	Commandant.
Lieut. M. J. White, 26th L. I. ..	7 *June* 47	13 *Jan.* 59	2nd in Command.
Lieut. A. P. Mew, 74th N. I., ..	11 *May* 57	4 *Dec.* 57	Adjutant.—Fur. S.C. 22d June 58.
Lieut. C. T. Battye, 33rd N. I. ..	21 *July* 57	11 *May* 59	Offg. Adjutant,
Lieut. L. Wavell, 45th N. I., ..	25 *Aug.* 57	24 *Feb.* 59	Doing duty.
Surgeon H. W. Tytler, ..	14 *July* 56	31 *May* 59	

TWELFTH REGIMENT.

Jullundur.

Major W. F. Ring, H. M. 87th Foot,..	.. ..	13 *Jan.* 59	Commandant.
Capt. J. T. Norgate, 69th N. I. ..	30 *Dec.* 58	24 *Feb.* 59	2nd in Command.
Lieut H. H. Christian, 68th N. I ,..	16 *Dec* 54	25 *May* 58	Offg. Adjutant.
Lieut. J. Liston, 10th N. I., ..	17 *Oct.* 56	4 *Mar.* 58	Doing duty.
Asst. Surgeon J. C. Annesley, ..	30 *Dec.* 54	.. ..	

THIRTEENTH REGIMENT.

Delhi.

Capt. C. Dysart, 3rd M. En. Regt.,..	.. ..	24 *Feb.* 59	Commandant.
Lieut. J. B. Cox, 62nd N. I., ..	28 *May* 51	4 *Dec.* 57	2nd in Command.—Fur. P. A. 28 [Apl. 59
Lieut. H. S. Ruxton, 56th N. I., ..	8 *Oct.* 56	4 *Dec.* 57	Adjutant.
Lieut. T. H. Scott, 26th N. I., ..	30 *Apl.* 58	4 *Dec.* 57	Doing duty.
Lieut, S. W. Wyndham, 12th N,I. ..	22 *Oct.* 58	5 *Apl.* 59	Ditto.
Lieut. G. S Goad, 49th N, I, ..	30 *Apl.* 58	8 *Apl.* 59	Ditto.
Asst. Surgeon C. O. Daniell, M. D.,..	.. ..	13 *Jan.* 59	

FOURTEENTH REGIMENT.

Peshawur

UNIFORM—*Facings—Black.*

*			Commandant.
Capt. G. W. Fraser 27th N. I. ..	23 *Sept.* 57	9 *Nov.* 57	2nd in Command.
Lieut. J. Trevenen, 24th N. I., ..	29 *Aug.* 54	19 *Sep* 57	Adjutant.
Lieut. A. Shaw, 24th N. I. ..	30 *Apl.* 58	20 *Feb.* 58	Doing duty.
Asst. Surgeon J. L. Stewart M. D.,	4 *Aug.* 55	29 *Jan.* 59	

FIFTEENTH REGIMENT.

Lucknow.

Capt. R. H. Shebbeare, 60th N.I.,	1 *Mar.* 59	.. ..	Offg. Commandant.
Capt. W. D. Hoste, 55th N. I., ..	4 *Apl.* 58	1 *Apl.* 58	Offg. 2nd in Command.
Lieut J. T. Harris 2nd En. B. F...	13 *Nov.* 54	13 *Jan.* 59	Adjutant.
*			Doing duty.

SIXTEENTH REGIMENT.

Peshawur.

Capt. G. N. Cave, 21st N. I., ..	27 *Feb.* 56	4 *Dec.* 57	Commandant.
Lieut. E. H. Scott, 55th N. I., ..	10 *May* 56	4 *Dec.* 57	2nd in Command.
Lieut. F. Lance, 55th N. I., ..	14 *Sep.* 57	4 *Dec.* 57	Adjutant.—(On Leave.)
Lt.W.P.Browne,H.M. 7th Royal Fus.	.. ..	19 *May* 59	Offg. Adjutant.
Lieut. R. B. Hill, 60th N. I.,	23 *Nov.* 56	14 *Jan.* 59	Doing duty.

SEVENTEENTH REGIMENT.

Bareilly.

Major R. Larkins, 49th N. I., ..	20 *July* 58	4 *Dec.* 57	Commandant.
Lieut. J. W. Hoggan, 45th N. I.,..	15 *May* 52	4 *Dec.* 57	2nd in Command.
Lieut. A. W. Cripps, 26th L. I., ..	23 *Nov.* 56	4 *Dec.* 57	Adjutant.
Lieut. R. Dougal, 53rd N. I., ..	10 *Oct.* 56	8 *Dec.* 57	Doing duty.

EIGHTEENTH REGIMENT.

Peshawur.

Lieut. J. Williamson, 49th N. I., ..	13 *Apl.* 48	23 *Mar.* 58	Offg. Commandant.
Capt. H. King 39th N. I., ..	10 *Dec.* 57	13 *Jan.* 59	2nd in Command.
Lieut. T. Gardiner H. M. 98th Foot.,	.. ..	24 *Feb.* 59	Adjutant.
Lt. G. E. J. Maidman, 24th N. I., ..	29 *Nov.* 56	16 *Sep.* 58	Doing duty.
Asst. Surgeon A. H. Hilson, M. D.,..	23 *Jan.* 57	16 *Sep.* 58	

NINETEENTH REGIMENT.

{ Roy Bareilly.

Capt. J. Doran, 24th N. I., ..	1 *Jan.* 55	4 *Dec.* 57	Commandant.
Capt. C. Irvine, 51st N. I., ..	9 *Dec.* 57	4 *Dec.* 57	2nd in Command.
Lieut. J. R. Currie, 4th N. I., ..	15 *Sep.* 49	22 *June* 58	Adjutant.
Lieut. H. C. Fagan 36th N. I., ..	5 *Sep.* 57	4 *Dec.* 58	Doing duty.

TWENTIETH REGIMENT.

{ Ferozepore.

Lt. Col. H. F. Dunsford, C.B. 59th N.I.,	28 *Nov.* 54	.. ..	Offg. Commandant.
*			2nd in Command.
Lieut. H. C. T. Jarrett, 26th N. I. ..	27 *Aug.* 57	19 *May* 59	Offg. Adjutant.
Lieut. R. Smith, 59th N. I., ..	23 *Nov.* 56	17 *June* 58	Doing duty.
Ensign H. A. Plowden, 51st N. I. ..	12 *Dec.* 57	30 *Apl.* 59	Ditto.
Asst. Surgeon L. F. Dickson, M. D.,	4 *Aug.* 57	14 *Feb.* 59	

TWENTY-FIRST REGIMENT.

{ Jullundur.

Capt. T. Tulloh, 33rd N. I., ..	30 *Dec.* 52	4 *Dec* 57	Commandant.
Capt. H. S. Obbard, 61st N. I., ..	11 *June* 57	4 *Dec.* 57	2nd in Command.
Lieut H. Tyndall, 61st N. I., ..	12 *Apl.* 54	4 *Dec.* 57	Adjutant.
Lieut. R. J. Walker, 61st N. I. ..	29 *Dec.* 55	24 *Feb.* 59.	Doing duty.
Lieut. W. Hamilton, 61st N. I. ..	18 *May* 58	30 *May* 59.	Ditto.
Surgeon J. Macintire, ..	8 *Apl.* 52	31 *May* 59.	

TWENTY-SECOND REGIMENT.

{ Jullallabad, (Rohilcund.)

Capt. G. McAndrew, 47th N. I., ..	8 *Mar.* 56	4 *Dec.* 57	Commandant.—Civil employ.
*			2nd in Command.
*			Adjutant.
*			Doing duty.

TWENTY-THIRD REGIMENT.

{ Delhi.

Capt. G. C. Bloomfield, 45th N. I., ..	10 *June* 53	.. ..	Commandant.
Lieut. H. N. Hodgson, 9th N I. ...	5 *Jan.* 50	16 *Sep.* 58	2nd in Command.
Lieut. G. F. Graham, 5th En. Regt. ..	1 *Sep.* 55	15 *Mar.* 59	Adjutant.
Capt. J. E. L. Willows, 10th N. I., ..	23 *June* 57	16 *Feb.* 59	Doing duty.
Lieut. H. Goschen, 3rd En. Regt. ..	30 *Apl.* 58	24 *Feb.* 59	Ditto.

TWENTY FOURTH REGIMENT.

Major J. St. J. Hovenden Engrs., ..	28 *Aug.* 58	20 *Nov.* 58	Commandant.
*			2nd in Command.
Ensign. T. P. Stevens, (unattached) ..	.. ..	13 *Jan.* 59	Adjutant.
Lieut. J. F. Trevanion, 21st N. I. ..	6 *Nov.* 58	.. ..	Doing duty.
Lieut. J. Stevenson, 33rd N. I. ..	23 *Nov.* 56	26 *Jan.* 59	Ditto.

TWENTY FIFTH REGIMENT.

*			Commandant.
Major H. F. M. Boisragon, 1st En. B.F.	19 *Jan.* 58	22 *May* 58	2nd in Command.—Offg. Comdt.
Capt. H. Close, 27th B. N. I., ..	.. ..	5 *July* 58	Offg. 2nd in Command.
Lieut. H. L. C. Bernard, 4th En. Regt.	10 *Sep.* 55	13 *Jan.* 59	Adjutant.
Lieut H. M. Pratt, 51st N. I ..	30 *Apl.* 58	13 *Jan.* 59	Doing duty.

The 1st, 2nd, 3rd, 4th, 5th, 6th, 7th, 8th, 9th, 10th, 11th, 12th, 13th, 14th, 15th, 16th, 17th, 18th, 19th, 20th, 21st 22nd 23rd, 24th and 25th Regts. of Punjaub Irregular Infy., consisting of 10 Companies each, with—2 Native Doctors—10 Subadars—10 Jemadars—60 Havildars—60 Naicks—20 Bugglers—800 Sepoys.

MUNEEPOOR REGIMENT.

{ Jamulpore.

Rank, Names and Corps.	*Army Rank.*	*When Appointed.*	Remarkes.
*			Commandant.
*			2nd in Command.
*			Adjutant.

KAMROOP REGIMENT.

{ Furreedpore.

Capt. H. R. Drew, 6th En. Regt ..	22 *Dec.* 55	30 *Nov.* 57	Commandant.
*			2nd in Command.
Lieut. R. Travers, 6th En. Regt. ..	9 *Jan.* 55	30 *Nov.* 57	Adjutant.
Assist. Surgeon C. Brettingham, ..	4 *Aug.* 55	30 *Nov.* 57	

Hyderabad Contingent.

THE CONTINGENT CONSISTS OF FOUR FIELD BATTERIES OF ARTILLERY, FOUR REGIMENTS OF CAVALRY, AND SIX REGIMENTS OF INFANTRY.

RANK, NAMES AND CORPS.	*Army Rank.*	*When Appointed.*	REMARKS.
Brigadier W. Hill, 1st M. Fusiliers,	9 *Dec.* 53	30 *Jan.* 56	Commandant.
Captain H. Hoseason, 24th M. N. I.	.. ..	13 *Aug.* 58	Brigade Major.
ARTILLERY.			
1st Company, Hingolee.			
Lieut. S. H. E. Chamier, M. Arty.	.. ..	15 *Apl.* 59	Commandant.
2nd Company, Ellichpore.			
Lieut. N. G. Campbell, Mad. Arty.	2 *Aug.* 48	15 *Jan.* 55	Comdt.—Lv. S. C. to 31 Dec.
Lieut. C. H. Strutt, Bombay Arty.	.. ..	13 *Dec.* 58	Offg. Commandant.
3rd Company, Bolarum.			
Lieut. H. Biden, Madras Arty., ..	12 *June* 46	28 *Feb.* 56	Commandant. Furlough.
Lieut. R. A. Baker, M. Arty. ..	.. ..	21 *Apl.* 59	Offg. Commandant.
4th Company, Aurungabad.			
Lieut. R. C. Henchy, M. Arty., ..	.. ..	13 *Sep.* 58	Commandant.
CAVALRY.			
1st Regiment, Mominabad.			
Capt. W. Murray, 46th M. N. I., ..	.. ..	13 *Aug.* 58	Commandant.
Capt. A. Grant, 3rd Madras Cavy.,	26 *Feb.* 46	15 *Jan.* 59	2nd in Command.
Lieut. W. Tweedie, 4th En. Regt...	30 *Apl.* 58	26 *Mar.* 59	Adjutant.
Surg. D. Macpherson, M.D., Madras Establishment, ..	11 *Dec.* 52	11 *Apl.* 55	Fur. S. C. for 12 months, G. O. 12 Oct. 54.
Asst. Surg. A. Sanderson, M. B. M.A., Madras Estabt., ..	.. ..	29 *Nov.* 58	
2nd Cavalry, Bolarum.			
Captain A. W. Macintire, Madras Arty., ..	9 *June* 46	27 *Jan.* 54	Commandant.
Capt. H. M. Clogstoun, 19th M. N. I.	29 *Aug.* 52	7 *Aug.* 56	2nd in Command.
Lieut. G. R. Westmacott, 23rd N. I.,	15 *Nov.* 53	15 *Jan.* 59	Adjutant.
Surg. W. H. Bradley Bombay Estabt.	20 *Nov.* 49	27 *Oct.* 54	
3rd Cavalry, Aurungabad.			
Lt. C. Nightingale, 18th M. N. I.,	24 *Jan.* 45	13 *Sep.* 58	Commandant.—Fur. S. C. 3 Mar. 57
Lieut. E. W. Dun, 42nd M. N. I.,	.. ..	15 *Jan.* 59	2nd in Command.
*			Adjutant.
Surgeon W. Mackenzie, A. M. M. D., Madras Establishment, ..	15 *Feb.* 51	20 *Mar.* 55	In charge of 4th Compy. Arty.
Assist. Surgeon T. L. Bell, M. D., Madras Establishment, ..	8 *Jan.* 42	27 *Jan.* 54	
4th Cavalry, Hingolee and Ellichpore.			
Capt. H. D. Abbott, 31st M. N. I...	9 *Feb.* 51	13 *Sep.* 58	Commandant.
Lieut. H. C. Dowker, 22 M. N. I...	.. ..	4 *Mar.* 59	2nd in Command.
Lieut. R. C. Stewart, 8th M. L. C.,	.. ..	2 *Aug.* 58	Adjutant.
Surg. J. H. Orr, Madras Estabt., ..	17 *July* 53	20 *Mar.* 55	Fur. S. C. 20 Nov. 58.
Asst. Surgeon G. A. Burn, A. M. M D., Madras Estabt., ..	.. ..	29 *Nov.* 58	

Infantry.

1st Regiment, Wurungul.

Capt. C. S. Fagan, 40th M. N.I.,	26 *Feb.* 49	18 *Nov.* 58	Commandant.
Lieut. A. C. Lilly, 2nd M. E. Regt.,	... ..	15 *Jan.* 59	Offg. 2nd in Command.
Lieut. H. A. Justice, 38th M.N.I..	.. ...	18 *Nov.* 58	Adjutant.
Asst. Surg.*			

2nd Regiment, Aurungabad.

Capt. J. B. Speid, 34th M. N.I., ..	.. ..	13 *Aug.* 58	Commandant.
Lieut. T. T. Turton, 47th M. N. I..	.. ..	18 *Nov.* 58	2nd in Comd.—Fur. S. C. 23 Mar. 59.
Lieut. —— Pedler, ——, ..	.. ..	31 *Mar.* 59	Offg. 2nd in Command.
Lieut. A. C. Lilly, 2nd M. E. R., ..	.. ...	21 *Apl.* 58	Adjtt.—Offg. 2nd in Comd. 1st Infy.
Lieut. F. J. Innes, 27th B. N. I. ..	.. ..	15 *Jan.* 59	Offg. Adjutant.
Asst. Surg. C.T. Eves Madras Estabt.	.. ..	15 *Jan.* 59	

3rd Regiment, Hingolee.

Capt. J. C. P. Prescott, 10th M. N. I.	1 *June* 54	4 *Mar.* 59	Commandant.
Lieut. H.I. E. Teed, ..	.. ..	15 *Jan.* 59	2nd in Command.
Lieut. C. J. Smith, 27th M. N. I. ..	.. ..	15 *Jan.* 59	Adjutant.—Lv. P. A. 7th Sep.
Asst. Surg. J. G. Reed, M. Estabt...	.. ..	8 *May* 57	

4th Regiment, Lingoosoor.

Captain A. Wyndham, 2nd Madras N. I., ..	31 *Mar.* 46	27 *Jan.* 54	Commandant.
Capt. G. Adey, 31st M. N. I., .. {	.. ..	27 *Aug.* 56	2nd in Command.
	.. ..	27 *May* 59	Offg. Commandant 6th Infantry.
Lieut. C. Jameson, 25th B. N. I., ..	.. ..	27 *May* 59	Offg. 2nd in Command.
Lieut. T. H. Way, 35th M. N. I.,	.. ..	31 *Mar.* 59	Offg. Adjutant.
Assist. Surg. B. Williamson, M. B., Madras Establishment, ..	.. ..	19 *Mar.* 57	

5th Regiment, Ellichpore.

Capt. J. Woodcock, 1st M. Fus. ..	.. ..	15 *Jan.* 59	Commandant.
Lieut. R. K. Macquoid, 13th M. N. I.,	.. ..	15 *Jan.* 59	2nd in Command
Lieut. H. Watson, 33rd M. N. I...	.. ..	18 *Nov.* 58	Adjutant.

6th Regiment, Bolarum.

Captain S. P. Scott, 22nd M. N. I.,	7 *Jan.* 49	27 *Jan.* 54	Commandant.—Fur. S.C. 27 May 59.
Capt. G. Adey, 31st M. N. I., ..	.. ..	27 *May* 57	Offg. Cammandant.
Lieut. J. W. Sinclair, 51st M. N.I.,	.. ..	28 *Feb.* 56	2nd in Command.
Lieut. C. Jameson, 25th Bom. N.I. {	.. ..	31 *May* 58	Adjutant.
	.. ..	27 *May* 59	Offg. 2nd in Command 4th Infy.
Lieut. C. M. Bushby, 70th N. I. ..	.. ..	27 *May* 59	Offg. Adjutant.
Assist. Surgeon A. Boggs, ..	.. ..	6 *Jul.* 59	

Nagpore Irregular Force.

Consisting of 1 *Horse Field Battery,* 1 *Cavalry, and* 3 *Infantry Regiments. Raised by G. O. G. G.* 11*th September* 1854.

Brigdr. M. Carthew, 34th M. N. I.,	.. ..	20 *May* 58	Commandant.
Captain J. C. Day, 17th Madras N. I. ..	.. ..	26 *May* 57	Brigade Major.

HORSE FIELD BATTERY.—*Seetabuldee.*

RANK, NAMES AND CORPS.	*Army Rank.*	*When Appointed.*	REMARKS.
Lieut. E. M. Playfair, Madras Arty.	11 *May* 54	29 *Sep.* 54	Commandant.

The Establishment of the Battery consists of 1 Subadar—2 Jemadars—8 Havildars—8 Naicks—2 Buglers—122 Privates—1 Farrier—1 Tindal—1 Tent Lascar—6 Store Lascars—2 Bheesties—1 Sweeper—66 Syces—133 Grasscutters—3 Bullock Drivers—1 Mistry Smith—2 Filemen—2 Firemen—2 Hammermen—1 Mistry Carpenter—2 Workmen—1 Moochee. *Staff:* 1 Rough Rider and Farrier Sergeant—1 Assistant Farrier and Saddler—1 Pay Havildar and 1 Drill Naick, *non-effective. Hospital Establishment:* 1 Native Doctor—1 Dresser or Shop Cooly—1 Sweeper. *BazarEstablishment:* 1 Mutsuddy—1 Weighman.

REGIMENT OF IRREGULAR CAVALRY.—*Seetabuldee.*

Capt. H. J. C. Shakespear, 25th Bl. N. I.	26 *Dec.* 46	29 *Sept.* 54	Comdt. of the Force and Comdt. of Cavy.
Capt. E. G. Wood, 6th Madras L. C.	8 *Mar.* 56	6 *Nov.* 54	2nd in Command.—(on Leave.)
Lieut. J. Nuttall, 17th M. N. I. ..	1 *May* 53	21 *July* 58	Adjutant.—Offg. 2nd in Command.
Lieut. Walford, 7th M. L. C. ..	.. ..	1 *Feb.* 59	Offg. Adjutant.
Asst. Surg. W. R. Grylls, M. D. ..	.. ..	21 *Feb.* 59	

The Establishment of the Cavalry, consists of 3 Ressaldars—3 Ressaidars—6 Naib Ressaidars—6 Jemadars—6 Kote Duffadars—48 Duffadars—6 Nishanburdars—6 Trumpeters and Nuggarchies—480 Sowars—6 Bheesties. *Staff:* 1 Woordee Major—1 Nukeeb—2 Native Doctors—1 Trumpet Major and 6 Pay Duffadars, *non-effective*—1 Persian Writer—2 Lascars in cantonment, or 6 Lascars when marching—1 Chowdry—1 Mutsuddy—3 Flag or Weighmen. *Hospital Establishment:* 1 Shop Cooly.

1ST REGIMENT OF INFANTRY.—*Seetabuldee.*

Captain L. H. H. Holland, 37th Madras N. I., ..	15 *Apl.* 54	20 *July* 58	Commandant.—Fur. S. C. 5 Oct. 1857.
Lieut. C. L. Pereira, 3rd M. E. Regt., ..	.. ..	30 *May* 56	Adjutant.—Offg. Commandant.
Lieut. J. Warmer, 32nd M. N. I.	.. ..	31 Jun. 59	Offg. Adjutant.
George Law, ..	23 *Dec.* 53	20 *Mar.* 55	Apothecary.

2ND REGIMENT OF INFANTRY.—*Chandah.*
2 *Companies at Chindwarrah.*

Major W. G. Arrow, 28th Bombay N. I., ..	14 *Feb.* 57	20 *July* 58	Commandant.
Lieut. T. E. L. Higginson, 40th M. N. I.	14 *July* 50	12 *May* 55	Adjutant.—(On Leave to Bombay.)
Lieut. T. Wakefield, ..	.. ..	21 *May* 59	Offg. Adjutant.
Asst. Apothecary G. Macqueen, -	.. ..	31 *Jan.* 56	

3RD REGIMENT OF INFANTRY.—*Raypore.*
2 *Companies at Belaspore.*

Captain the *Baron* Fred. August Von Meyern, 53rd Bengal N. I.,	15 *Nov.* 52	29 *Sept.* 54	Comdt.—Fur. P. A. 13 May 59.
Lieut. H. M. Nepean, 37th M. N. I.	8 *Sep.* 53	22 *Apl.* 56	Adjutant.—Offg. Commandant.
Lieut. A. Cockburn, 52nd N. I. ..	10 *May* 57	25 *Apl.* 59	Comdg. the Detachment at Belaspore.
Asst. Surg. C. E. W. Bensley, M. D.,	4 *Aug.* 56	7 *Nov.* 56	In charge of the Civil Station and Govt. Dispensary, Raepore.
Asst. Apothecary H. Watson, ..	.. ..	27 *Oct.* 56	

The Establishment of each Regiment of Infantry, of 8 Companies each, consists of 8 Subadars—8 Jemadars—48 Havildars—48 Naicks—16 Drummers—800 Sepoys—8 Lascars—8 Bheesties—8 Sweepers. *Regimental Staff:* 1 Sergeant Major—1 Quarter Master Sergeant—2 Native Doctors—1 Drum Major—1 Fife Major—8 Pay Havildars,—8 Color Havildars—1 Drill Havildar and 1 Drill Naick, *non-effective*—1 Moonshee—1 Pundit—1 Moulvie—1 Tindal—1 Chowdry—1 Mutsuddy—3 Flag or Weighmen—2 Bildars. *Hospital Establishment:* 2 Cooks—2 Bheesties—1 Head Sweeper—1 Goorgah—1 Shop Cooly.

Gwalior Contingent.

1st REGIMENT OF INFANTRY. { *

Gwalior.

Capt. H. T. Macpherson, H. M. 78th Foot, ...	.. ..	4 *Sept.* 58	Commandant.
Lieut. W. W. Clark, 36th N. I., ..	3 *July* 56	27 *Oct.* 58	Offg. 2nd in Command.
Lieut E. H. Hood, 30th N I., ..	17 *Nov.* 57	27 *Oct.* 58	Offg. Adjutant.
Asst. Surgeon J. H. Loch, M. D., ..	20 *Dec.* 54	13 *Jan.* 59	

Strength of each Regiment of Infantry—1 Sergeant Major—1 Quarter Master Sergeant—2 Native Doctors—1 Drum Major—1 Fife Major—1 Drill Havildar—1 Drill Naick—8 Subadars—8 Jemadars—40 Havildars—40 Naicks—16 Drummers—600 Sepoys.

2nd REGIMENT OF INFANTRY. { *

Gwalior.

Rank Names and Corps.	*Army Rank.*	*Appointment.*	Remarks.
Capt. T. Wheler 1st En. B. F., ..	5 *Mar.* 56	8 *Feb.* 59	Commandant.
Lieut. E. O'B. Horsford, 46th N.I...	23 *Nov.* 56	3 *Mar.* 59	2nd in Command and Offg. Adjutant.
*			Adjutant.
Asst. Surgeon G. B. Hadow, ..	20 *Jan.* 55	13 *Jan.* 59	

OUDE MILITARY POLICE.

Uniform, { Cavalry.—*French Grey.* Infantry.—*Zouave.* }

	When appointed.	
Major H. Bruce, ..	24 *July* 58	Chief of Military Police.
Capt. J. B. Hearsey, Oude Local service, ..	11 *Feb.* 56	Fur. S. C. 22 Sep. 58.
Capt. A. P. W. Orr, ditto. ..	11 *Feb.* 56	Comdt. 3rd Regt. of Infy. Lucknow. —Lv. S. C. 15 Oct.
Lieut. O. L. Smith, 48th N. I., ..	14 *May* 58	Doing duty.
Lieut. T. C. Ffrench, H. M. 53rd Foot, ..	do	Ditto.
Lieut. P. Roddy, (*unattached*), ..	do	Ditto.

The Cavalry of the Oude Military Police consists of 9 Ressaldars—18 Jemadars—36 Duffadars—36 Naib Duffadars and 900 Sowars—45 Carriage Camels.

The 1st, 2nd and 3rd Regiments of Infantry of the Military Police each consist of 10 Companies, with 1 Sergt. Major—1 Native Doctor—10 Subadars—10 Jemadars—50 Havildars—50 Naicks—10 Buglers—800 Sepoys—1 Tindal—5 Lascars and 10 Bheestees—50 Carriage Camels.

MEDICAL DEPARTMENT.

Rank and Names.	Appt. to present Rank.	Remarks.
Senior Surg. John Forsyth, ..	12 *Nov.* 57	Director General.
Senior Surg. J. Row, ..	26 *Jan.* 58	Inspector General, L. P.—Fur. S. C. 21st Dec. 58.
Surg. C. McKinnon, M. D., ..	3 *Sep.* 58	Inspector General, N. W. P.
Senior Surg. G. G. Brown, M.D. ..	7 *June* 59	Offg. Inspector General L. P.
Asst. Surgeon N. Chevers, M. D.,	26 *Jan.* 58	Secretary to the Director General.

MEDICAL STAFF AT THE PRESIDENCY.

Rank and Names.	Date of Appointment.	Remarks.
Surgeon Allan Webb, M. D., ..	5 *April* 55	Surgeon Native Hospital.
	2 *June* 54	Presidency Surgeon.
Surgeon T. W. Wilson, ..	19 *May* 54	Presidency Surgeon.
	14 *April* 55	Professor of Midwifery, Medical College, and Ex-officio Obstetric Physician Medical College Hospital.
Surgeon A. C. Macrae, ..	11 *Feb.* 53	Presidency Surgeon.
	16 *Feb.* 53	Marine Surgeon.
Surgeon T. Cantor, M. D., ..	17 *Dec.* 55	Superintendent of the European and Native Insane Asylums at Bhowanipore and Dullunda.
Surg. J. Macpherson, M. D., ..	27 *Dec.* 55	Supdt. General of vaccination. Presidency Surgeon.
Surgeon T. Thomson, M. D., ..	17 *April* 55	Supdt. of the H. C. Botanical Garden, Calcutta. and Professor of Botany in the Medical College,
Surg. F. J Mouat, M. D. & F. R. C. S.	18 *Dec.* 55	Inspector Genl. of Jails, Ex-Officio Visitor of Lunatic Asylum.
Surgeon J. P. Brougham, M. D.	21 *May* 59	Surgeon Presidency General Hospital.
	28 *June* 59	Presidency Surgeon.
Surgeon Alexander Grant, ..	5 *Jan.* 57	Apothecary to the East India Company.
Surg. Ed. Goodeve, M. B., ..	24 *Sep.* 56	Professor of Medicine in the Medical College, and Ex-officio 1st Physician of the College Hospital.
Surgeon W. C. B. Eatwell, M. D.,	31 *Mar.* 57	Principal of the Medical College, and Professor of Materia Medica and Clinical Medicine. Physician Medical College, Hospital.
Surgeon Richard O'Shaughnessy, F. R. C. S., ...	10 *Mar.* 45	Professor of Surgery in the Medical College.
	15 *Mar.* 35	Ex-Officio 1st Surgeon, College Hospital.—Fur S. C. 1 Mar 59.
Surgeon C. Archer M. D., ...	21 *Jan.* 57	Supdt. of the Eye Infirmary Medical College.
Surgeon W. Crozier, ..	28 *July* 57	Professor of Anatomy, Physiology, Comparative Anatomy and Zoology, Medical College.
Asst. Surg. Herbert Baillie, ..	11 *Mar.* 57	Civil 24-Pergunnahs.
Asst. Surgeon N. Chevers, M. D.,	26 *Jan.* 58	Secy. to the Director Genl. Medical Department.
Asst. Surg. A. J. Payne, M. D., B.A.,	31 *Oct.* 56	2nd Assistant Presidency General Hospital.
Asst. Surgeon J. Fayrer, M. D., ..	12 *May* 59	Offg. Professor of Surgery, Medical College, and Ex-officio first Surgeon of the College Hospital.
Asst. Surgeon J. B. Scriven, ..	31 *Oct.* 56	1st Assistant Presidency General Hospital.
Asst. Surgeon S. B. Partridge, ..	2 *Feb.* 59	Professor of Descriptive and Surgical Anatomy Medical College, Ex-Officio Second Surgeon & Professor of Clinical Surgery, College Hospital.-
Asst. Surg. F. N. Macnamara, M. D., ...	26 *Oct.* 53	Professor of Chemistry Medical College.
	5 *Nov.* 53	Chemical Examiner.
Asst Surg. S. C. G. Chuckerbutty,	23 *June* 55	Assist. Physician to the Medical College Hospital.

SUPERINTENDING SURGEONS.

Rank and Names.		Date of Appointment as Suptg. Surgeon.	Date when posted to the Division.	Where Posted.
Senior Surgeons.				
John Greig, ..	..	24 *Feb.* 56	6 *Dec.* 56	Saugor Circle.—Fur. S. C. 1 Apl. 59
William Thomson,	..	21 *Mar.* 56	17 *May* 56	Dacca Circle.
George G. Brown, M. D.,	..	10 *Apl.* 57	26 *Aug.* 58	Barrackpore Circle.—Offg. Inspector Genl. of Hospitals L. P.
J. B. Dickson,	..	30 *July* 58	26 *Aug.* 58	Cawnpore Circle.
A. Wilson,	..	30 *July* 58	26 *Aug.* 58	Peshawur Circle.
W. S. Dicken,	..	30 *July* 58	26 *Aug.* 58	Trans-Ravee Circle, (Sealkote.)
W. A. Green,	..	30 *July* 58	26 *Aug.* 58	Lahore Circle.
J. Murray, M. D.,	..	30 *July* 58	26 *Aug.* 58	Agra Circle.
J. Wilkie, M. D.,	..	3 *Sep.* 58	22 *Sep.* 58	Meerut Circle.
Henry A. Bruce, M. D.,	..	21 *May* 59	11 *Jun.* 59	Sirhind Circle (Umballah.)
James Anderson, M. D.,	..	21 *May* 59	*Ditto,*	Presidency Circle.
Alexander Gibbon,	..	21 *May* 59		
J. Balfour,	..	14 *June* 59	.. ..	Offg. Saugor Circle.
F. Anderson, M. D.,	..	14 *June* 59	.. ..	Offg. Barrackpore Circle.
*				
*				

GARRISON SURGEONS.

Rank and Names.		Date of Appointment.	Station.
Surgeons.			
Hubbersty Maddison Tweddell,	..	24 *July* 46	Chunar.
T. S. Lacy,	..	4 *Sep.* 56	Agra.
E. Campbell,	..	5 *Jan.* 57	Fort William.—Fur. S.C. 11 Feb.59
R. B. Kinsey, F. R. C. S.,	..	14 *Feb.* 59	Offg. Fort William.

GARRISON ASSISTANT SURGEONS.

H. Stewart,	..	29 *Dec.* 56	Delhi.—Offg. Civil Budaon.
Thomas Anderson, M. D.,	..	19 *Apl.* 58	Fort William.—Fur. S. C. 5 Apl. 59.
T. E. Charles, M. D.,	..	27 *Aug.* 58	Allahabad.
A. G. Duff, M. D.,	..	19 *Apl.* 59	Offg. Fort William.

MEDICAL STORE KEEPERS.

Surgeon R. W. Faithful,	..	7 *Nov.* 56	Umballah.
Surgeon H. R. Bond,	..	19 *Sep.* 57	Sealkote.
Asst. Surgeon, D. Scott, M. D.,	..	20 *Sep.* 58	Allahabad.

SURGEONS—140.

Fur. Reg.	SER Y	SER M	NAMES.	Assistant Surgeon.	Surgeon.	Date of Appointment to Regiment or Staff.	REMARKS,
			SENIOR SURGEONS.				
N.	43	9	John Row,¶ ..	5 *Oct.* 15	23 *June* 26	26 *Jan.* 58	Inspector General of Hospitals, L. P. including Pegu.—Fur. S. C. 21 Dec. 58.
	39	6	John Forsyth, ...	10 *Jan.* 20	18 *Nov.* 30	12 *Nov.* 57	Director General of the Medical Department.
N.	36	2	*John Greig,¶.. ..	24 *Apl.* 23	21 *Mar.* 37	6 *Dec.* 56	Saugor Circle. —Fur. S. C. 1 Apl. 59.
	35	2	*William Thomson, ..	9 *May* 24	2 *Apl.* 38	17 *May* 56	Dacca Circle.
	34	3	*George G. Brown, M.D.,	20 *Mar.* 25	29 *Jan.* 39	26 *Aug.* 58 7 *June* 59	Barrackpore Circle. Offg. Inspector Genl. of Hospitals, L. P. including Pegu.*
	34	1	Hubbersty M Tweddell¶	3 *June* 25	16 *Apl.* 39	24 *July* 46	Garrison Surgeon, Chunar.
	33	3	Ezra Thomas Downes,¶	30 *Mar.* 26	1 *Jan.* 41	18 *Jan.* 43	Civil employ, Bombay.
	33	..	John Ransford, ..	16 *July* 26	12 *Jan.* 43	16 *Jan.* 55	2nd Battalion Foot Artillery.
	32	5	James Barber,¶ ..	3 *Feb.* 27	18 *Apl.* 43	11 *Dec.* 50	4th Battalion Artillery.
	32	4	*Andrew Wilson, ..	10 *Mar.* 27	25 *Sep.* 43	26 *Aug.* 58	Peshawur Circle.
	32	2	Archd. Campbell, M. D.,	8 *May* 27	16 *Jan.* 44	12 *Feb.* 40	Civil employ.
	31	3	*John Burnie Dickson,	26 *Mar.* 28	1 *Jan.* 45	26 *Aug.* 58	Cawnpore, Circle.
			SURGEONS.				
	30	1	*William S. Dicken, ..	17 *June* 29	6 *Mar.* 46	26 *Aug.* 58	Trans Ravee Circle (Sealkote.)
	29	9	Malcolm McNeill Rind,†	10 *Oct.* 29	6 *Apl.* 46	11 *Sep.* 57	..
	29	5	Henry John Thornton,	5 *Feb.* 30	4 *July* 46	.. ..	Medical Store-Keeper Gualior.
	29	3	Cam. McKinnon, M. D.†	30 *Mar.* 30	2 *Aug.* 46	3 *Sep.* 58	Inspector General of Hospitals N. W. P. including Punjaub.
N.	29	3	John McClelland, ..	7 *Apl.* 30	30 *Nov.* 46	.. ..	Fur. S. C. 17th Sep. 58.

* Superintending Surgeons.
¶ Non-Subscribers to the Medical Retiring Fund.
† Restored from 8th December 1852.

SURGEONS—*Continued.*

Fur. Reg.	SER. Y	SER. M	NAMES.	*Assistant Surgeon.*	*Surgeon.*	*Date of Appointment to Regiment or Staff.*	REMARKS.
	29	1	*William Abbott Green,	6 *June* 30	10 *Feb.* 47	26 *Aug.* 58	Lahore Circle.
	28	11	*Henry A. Bruce, M. D.,†	17 *Aug.* 30	5 *June* 47	11 *June* 59	Sirhind Circle (Umballah.)
	26	11	*John Murray, M. D.,†	6 *Aug.* 32	17 *Apl.* 48	26 *Aug.* 58	Agra Circle.
	26	4	*John Wilkie, M. D., ..	26 *Feb.* 33	17 *Apl.* 48	22 *Sep.* 58	Meerut Circle.
	26	3	*James Anderson, M.D.,¶	18 *Apl.* 33	17 *Apl.* 48	11 *June* 59	Presidency Circle.
	25	11	*Sir* Wm. B. O'Shaughnessy, *Kt.* M. D., F.R.C.S.,	8 *Aug.* 33	5 *Dec.* 48	8 *Nov.* 53	Supdt. of Electric Telegraphs.
	24	5	Geo. Paton, A.M. M. D.,†	24 *Jan.* 35	10 *Aug.* 49	13 *Mar.* 54	Post Master General N. W. P.
	24	[illegible]	Harman Read Bond,†..	24 *Feb.* 35	11 *Sep.* 49	19 *Sep.* 57	Medical Store Keeper, Sealkote.
D	~~24~~	~~4~~	~~Allan Webb,~~ M. D., ..	20 *Mar.* 35	10 *Oct.* 49	5 *Apl.* 55	Civil employ, Native Hospital.
	24	..	William Brydon, C.B...	9 *July* 35	14 *Nov.* 49	5 *Mar.* 59	In Charge of the Depot Hospital Dinapore.
N.	23	4	John Wood,†	8 *Mar.* 36	31 *Dec.* 49	11 *Dec.* 54	38th N.I.—Fur. S.C. 15 Dec. 58.
	23	2	Stanlake Henry Batson,†	22 *Apl.* 36	31 *Dec.* 49	12 *Mar.* 59	Allahabad Infy. Levy.
	23	1	*Alexander Gibbon, ..	15 *June* 36	19 *Jan.* 50		[Field force.
	23	..	John C. Brown, C.B.,†..	5 *July* 36	3 *Feb.* 50	.. ..	Offg. Supdg. Surgeon Lucknow
	22	7	John Balfour,† ..	18 *Dec.* 36	15 *May* 50	15 *July* 53	Civil, Delhi. [Circle.
						14 *June* 59	Offg. Supdg. Surgeon Saugor
	22	6	Francis Anderson, M.D.,†	15 *Jan.* 37	13 *Aug.* 50	30 *June* 58	4th European Lt. Cavy.
	22	4	Thos. W. Wilson, M.D.,†	14 *Mar.* 37	22 *Dec* 50	14 *Apl.* 55	Civil employ.
						19 *May* 54	Presidency Surg.
N.	22	4	George Rae,† ..	14 *Mar.* 37	1 *Jan.* 51	.. ..	Fur. S. C. 31st July 56.
	22	4	Richard C. Guise,† ..	14 *Mar.* 37	11 *Feb.* 51	5 *Jan.* 57	46th Native Infy.
	21	11	George S. Cardew, M.D.,†	8 *Aug.* 37	3 *Mar.* 51	6 *Mar,* 57	Artillery Division, Ferozepore.
	21	7	James A. Dunbar, M.D.,†	12 *Dec.* 37	31 *Mar.* 51	3 *Dec.* 58	5th European Regt.
D	~~21~~	~~5~~	~~Richard Wm Faithfull~~,†	10 *Feb.* 38	31 *Mar.* 51	7 *Nov.* 56	Medl. Store-keeper Umballah.
N.	21	1	Geo. Chas. Wallich, M.D.,	27 *May* 38	10 *Dec.* 51	30 *Apl.* 57	64th N. I.—Fur. S. C. 3 Feb. 1857.
	21	1	Thos. Allman Wethered, M. D.,†	27 *May* 38	11 *Jan.* 52	.. ..	2nd Regt. Hodson's Horse.
	21	1	Thos. Rogers Strover,†	27 *May* 38	31 *Jan.* 52	10 *Apl.* 52	69th Native Infantry.
	21	1	James Alex. Guise,† ..	30 *May* 38	20 *Feb.* 52	2 *Oct.* 58	Civil, Moorshedabad.
						30 *Nov.* 58	Register of Deeds and Marriage Registrar, Moorshedabad.
O.	21	..	Wm. Shillito, F.R.C.S.,†	7 *July* 38	31 *Mar.* 52	.. ..	Leave S. C. to the Cape of G. H. for 2 years, G. O. 15 Dec. 1857.
	21	..	John Macintire,† ..	20 *July* 38	8 *Apl.* 52	31 *May* 59	21st Punjaub Infantry.
	20	10	William Jameson, ..	30 *Aug.* 38	10 *Apl.* 52	6 *Mar.* 43	Civil employ, Seharunpore Gardens.
N.	20	10	Chas. Gould Andrews,†	15 *Sep.* 38	30 *Aug.* 52	22 *Sep.* 56	30th N. I.—Fur. S.C. 19th Nov. 1858.
R	~~20~~	~~8~~	~~C. M. Henderson,~~ M. D.,†	1 *Nov.* 38	6 *Dec.* 52	27 *Apl.* 59	3rd European Regiment.
	20	6	Henry Irwin, F.R.C.S.I.	13 *Jan.* 39	17 *Dec.* 52	19 *Dec.* 54	66th Native Infantry.
	20	6	Hy. Benjamin Hinton,†	14 *Jan.* 39	31 *Dec.* 52	4 *Apl.* 58	70th Native Infantry.
	20	5	Alexr. C. Macrae, M. D.†	24 *Jan.* 39	16 *Jan.* 53	16 *Feb.* 53	Marine and Presidency Surgeon.
	20	5	Duncan McRae,† ..	24 *Jan.* 39	27 *Jan.* 53	3 *Dec.* 58	5th European Light Cavalry.
	20	5	Robert Bancroft Kinsey, F. R. C. S.,† ..	17 *Feb.* 39	15 *Mar.* 53	14 *Feb.* 59	[William. Offg. Garrison Surgeon, Fort
	20	4	Edward Hare,† ..	24 *Feb.* 39	15 *Mar.* 53	19 *Feb.* 57	2nd European Bengal Fusiliers.
O.	20	4	William Martin,† ..	9 *Mar.* 39	8 *May* 53	.. ..	Fur. S. C. 21st Jan. 57.
O.	20	..	W. H. B. Ross,† ..	13 *July* 39	12 *June* 53	.. ..	Fur. S. C. 6th Mar. 57.
	19	11	George Harper,† ..	25 *July* 39	25 *Aug.* 53	17 *Feb.* 59	2nd Brigade of Horse Artillery.
N.	19	10	Geo. Smyth Mann,† ..	22 *Aug.* 39	7 *Sep.* 53	.. ..	Fur. S. C. 20 Nov. 58.
	19	10	Theodore Cantor, M. D.,	12 *Sep.* 39	9 *Sep.* 53	17 *Dec.* 55	Supdt. of the European and Native Insane Asylums at Bhowanipore and Dullunda.

¶ Non-Subscribers to the Medical Retiring Fund.
* Superintending Surgeons.

SURGEONS—*Continued.*

Fur. Reg.	Ser. Y	Ser. M	NAMES.	*Assistant Surgeon.*	*Surgeon.*	*Date of Appointment to Regiment or Staff.*	REMARKS.
	19	9	T. C. Hutchinson,† ..	16 *Oct.* 39	7 *Oct.* 53	9 *July* 56	43rd Native Infy.
N.	19	9	William Shurlock,† ..	16 *Oct.* 39	11 *Oct.* 53	30 *Oct.* 54	72nd Native Infantry.—Fur. S. C. 18 Mar. 58.
N.	19	8	Edward Campbell,† ..	14 *Nov.* 39	15 *Nov.* 53	5 *Jan.* 57	Garrison Surgeon, Fort William. —Fur. S. C. 11 Feb. 59.
	19	7	J. Macpherson, M. D.,†	4 *Dec.* 39	1 *Dec.* 53	18 *Dec.* 55	Civil employ.
	19	7	~~A. W. Crozier, F.R.C.S.~~†	19 *Dec.* 39	1 *Dec.* 53	.. ..	Lv. p. to Fur.
	19	6	Thos. Thomson, M.D.,†	21 *Dec.* 39	1 *Dec.* 53	17 *Apl.* 55	Profr. of Botany, Medical College Supdt. H. C. Botanical Garden.
	19	6	Juxon Henry Jones,†	3 *Jan.* 40	1 *Dec.* 53	.. ..	Loyal Poorbeeah Regiment.
	19	6	James Hy. Butler, F. R. C. S. *PCH*, ..	3 *Jan.* 40	1 *Dec.* 53	30 *June* 58	3rd European Light Cavalry.
	19	6	Frederic J. Mouat, M. D., F. R. C. S., ..	3 *Jan.* 40	1 *Dec.* 53	18 *Dec* 55	Civil employ.
	19	6	Alfred Howorth Cheek,†	3 *Jan.* 40	1 *Dec.* 53	4 *July* 55	Civil, Benares.
	19	5	Anthony Beale, ..	8 *Feb.* 40	1 *Dec.* 53	24 *Feb.* 59	Surg. to the Governor General.
	19	4	J. P. Brougham, M. D.,†	8 *Mar.* 40	31 *Dec.* 53	21 *May* 59 28 *June* 59	Surgeon, Presy. General Hospital. Presidency Surgeon.
	19	4	John Naismith, M. D.,†	12 *Mar.* 40	20 *Jan.* 54	14 *Dec.* 54	17th Native Infantry.
N.	19	2	Warrick Walter Wells, F. R. C. S., ..	10 *May* 40	1 *Mar.* 54	12 *April* 54	48th Native Infantry.—Fur. S. C. 23 Feb. 58.
	19	1	John Bowhill,† ..	4 *June* 40	31 *Mar.* 54	6 *Dec.* 56	68th Native Infantry.
	19	..	Thos. Saumarez Lacy,†	1 *July* 40	27 *Apl.* 54	4 *Sep.* 56	Garrison Surgeon, Agra.
O.	18	8	Joseph Jowett, ..	20 *Oct.* 40	8 *Aug.* 54	.. ..	Fur. S. C. 8 Feb. 59.
	18	8	~~Alexander Grant~~,† ..	11 *Nov.* 40	3 *Sep.* 54	5 *Jan.* 57	Apothecary to the East Inda Company.
	18	7	C. Bonnor Chalmers,†	4 *Dec.* 40	28 *Sep.* 54	6 *Dec.* 56	44th N. I.
N.	18	6	J. Campbell, C.B. M.D.,†	22 *Dec.* 40	3 *Oct.* 54	.. ..	Fur. S. C. 9 Mar. 58.
O.	18	6	William Keates, *PH*, ..	25 *Dec.* 40	27 *Dec.* 54	.. ..	Fur. S. C. 18 Mar. 59.
	18	6	Richard Whittall,† ..	25 *Dec.* 40	31 *Dec.* 54	14 *Feb.* 59	5th Battn. of of Foot Arty.
N	18	6	Herbert Diaper,† ..	25 *Dec.* 40	1 *Feb.* 55	.. ..	Fur. S. C. 27th May 59.
N.	18	6	H. William Rumley,†	25 *Dec.* 40	1 *Feb.* 55	.. ..	Fur. S.C. 12 Apl. 59.
	18	6	J. Hilliard, M. D., F. R. C. S. L.† ..	8 *Jan.* 41	10 *Mar.* 55	19 *Feb.* 58	25th Native Infy.
	18	5	~~Archibald White, M.D.~~,†	30 *Jan.* 41	10 *Apl.* 55	.. ..	Allahabad Depôt Hospital.
	18	5	John Sutherland,† ..	4 *Feb.* 41	16 *Apl.* 55	9 *Feb.* 58 9 *July* 58	Civil Surgeon of Patna. Register of Deeds and Marriage Registrar, Patna.
	18	4	George Edward Morton, M. D., *PH*, ..	27 *Feb.* 41	19 *Apl.* 55	3 *Dec.* 58	6th European Regiment.
	18	4	Edward Goodeve, M. B.,†	8 *Mar.* 41	17 *May* 55	5 *June* 50	Civil employ, Medical College.
O.	18	4	Ed. Brouncker Thring,†	24 *Apl.* 41	6 *July* 55	8 *Dec.* 55	31st Native Infantry.—Fur. S. C. 1 Feb. 59.
	18	1	Wm. C. Beaty Eatwell, M.D.,† ..	11 *June* 41	1 *Aug.* 55	31 *Mar.* 57	Civil employ, Medical College.
	17	11	Chas. L Cox, A. B.,† ..	27 *July* 41	22 *Sep.* 55	3 *July* 58	2d European Light Cavalry.
N.	17	7	~~Rd. O'Shaughnessy, F.~~ R. C. S., ..	4 *Dec.* 41	9 *Oct.* 55	10 *Mar.* 45	Civil employ, Medical College.
N.	17	6	Daniel James O'Callaghan,† ..	8 *Jan.* 42	6 *Dec.* 55	18 *Oct.* 56	11th N.I.—Fur. S.C. 28 Sep. 58.
	17	6	Richard Henry Oakley,†	8 *Jan.* 42	31 *Dec.* 55	9 *July* 56	18th N. I.
	17	6	Charles Harland,† ..	8 *Jan.* 42	31 *Jan.* 56	7 *June* 56	36th N.I.
	17	5	Charles Archer, M. D.,	10 *Feb.* 42	24 *Feb.* 56	21 *Jan.* 57	Supdt. of the Eye Infirmary Medical College.

SURGEONS—*Continued.*

Fur: Reg.	Ser. Y	Ser. M	Names.	*Assistant Surgeon.*	*Surgeon.*	*Date of Appointment to Regiment or Staff.*	Remarks.
O	17	5	J. Rees Withecombe, M. D.,† ..	15 *Feb.* 42	21 *Mar.* 56	5 *Jan.* 57	4th N.I.—Fur. S.C. 16 Dec. 56.
	17	4	Henry Wm. Tytler,† ..	23 *Feb.* 42	14 *July* 56	31 *May.* 59	11th Punjaub Infantry.
	17	4	Samuel A. Homan,† ..	3 *Mar.* 42	18 *July* 56	17 *Mar.* 59	3rd Battn. Foot Artillery.
O.	17	3	Jas. Harrison, M. D., *P*,	5 *Apl.* 42	6 *Sep.* 56	.. ..	Fur. S. C. 25 Apl. 59.
	17	3	John H. Littler, M. D.,†	17 *Apl.* 42	28 *Sep.* 56	.. ..	Leave P. A. 3rd Oct.
	17	1	John Price Kelly,† ..	18 *June* 42	11 *Jan.* 57	5 *Feb.* 57	62nd N. I.
N.	16	11	George Saunders.† ..	28 *July* 42	20 *Jan.* 57	.. ..	Fur. S. C. 1 Apl. 59.
	16	10	Peter Goodall Lay,† ..	9 *Sep.* 42	13 *Feb.* 57	4 *Dec.* 58	Cawnpore Levy.
	16	10	Thos. Hastings, F. R. C. S.,	9 *Sep.* 42	21 *Mar.* 57	.. ..	1st Assam Light Infy. Battn.
	16	10	William Crozier,† ..	18 *Sep.* 42	10 *Apl.* 57	28 *July* 57	Civil employ, Medl. College.
	16	10	Hugh Martin Macpherson,† ..	18 *Sep.* 42	2 *May* 57	7 *Aug.* 57	Arty. Divn. Dum-Dum, Cossipore Gun Foundry, and Ex. Ameers of Scinde.
N.	16	5	William Craddock, *PCH*,	30 *Jan.* 43	22 *May* 57	.. ..	Fur. S. C. 3 May 58.
	16	5	John Barton Harrison, M. D.,† ..	1 *Feb.* 43	31 *May* 57	8 *Oct.* 58	1st En. B. F.
	16	3	F. Morrison Clifford,†	4 *Apl.* 43	6 *June* 57	4 *Dec.* 58	Regiment of Lucknow.
O.	16	2	A. Sprenger, M. D.† ..	12 *May* 43	15 *June* 57	.. ..	Fur. S. C. 2nd Sep. 56.
	16	1	J. Rose, ..	25 *May* 43	27 *June* 57	4 *Aug.* 45	Civil, Penang.
	16	1	J. F. Beatson, M. D., A. B.,†	16 *June* 43	27 *June* 57	3 *July* 58	1st European L. Cavalry.
	15	11	C. Hathaway, M. D.,† ..	10 *Aug.* 43	27 *June* 57	4 *Mar.* 53	Inspector of Prisons Punjaub.
	15	10	H. N. Elton,† ..	9 *Sep.* 43	27 *June* 57	4 *Apl.* 58	32nd N. I.
	15	6	H. Cape,† ..	30 *Dec.* 43	9 *July* 57	24 *Jan.* 54	11th Irr. Cavalry.
	15	6	Char. Fras. Warneford, M. D.,†	30 *Dec.* 43	11 *July* 57	27 *Mar.* 54	Ramghur Battn.
O.	15	6	John William Fletcher, F. R. C. S.,† ..	1 *Jan.* 44	12 *July* 57	.. ..	Fur. S, C. 9th Jan. 57.
N.	15	6	Chas. R. Francis, M. B. *P. C. H.*, ..	16 *Jan.* 44	4 *Aug.* 57	.. ..	Fur. S. C. 6th March 57.
	15	6	James Stuart Morrieson, M. D.,† ..	27 *Jan.* 44	7 *Aug.* 57	16 *Jan.* 55	21st N. I.
	15	4	Alex. Simpson, M. D.,† ..	28 *Feb.* 44	8 *Aug.* 57	13 *Sep.* 58 4 *Oct.* 58	Civil, Dacca. Register of Deeds and Marriage Registrar at Dacca.
	15	4	Henry Bruges Buckle,†	18 *Mar.* 44	16 *Sep.* 57	30 *Oct.* 56	4th Seikh Infantry.
	15	..	James Allan, F. R. C. S.,†	3 *July* 44	10 *Mar.* 58	21 *Feb.* 57	34th N. I.
	14	8	George Ranken Playfair, M. D.,† ..	3 *Nov.* 44	28 *Mar.* 58	26 *Aug.* 58	Civil, Agra.
	14	7	W. Fullarton Mactier, M. D., ..	3 *Dec.* 44	29 *Mar* 58	26 *Aug.* 58	1st Brigade of Horse Arty.
N.	14	6	James Lee, M. D.,† ..	10 *Jan* 45	16 *Apl.* 58	.. ..	Fur. S. C. 25 Feb. 59.
	14	6	Geo. Banister,† ..	12 *Jan.* 45	16 *June* 58	13 *May* 51	Kemaoon Battn. and Civil Deyrah.
	14	6	Francis Douglas, M. D.†	18 *Jan.* 45	16 *June* 58	20 *May* 58	Offg. Civil, Lucknow,
	14	5	Robert J. Atkinson,† ..	24 *Jan.* 45	2 *Sep.* 58	28 *Nov.* 57	Offg. Civil Midnapore.
N.	14	5	Francis Turnbull, M.D.,†	11 *Feb.* 45	30 *Sep.* 58	26 *Apl.* 57	Sappers and Miners.
	14	4	J. N. Tresidder,† ..	1 *Mar.* 45	30 *Oct.* 58	6 *Jan.* 54	Civil, Cawnpore.
	14	4	St.Geo. W. Tucker. M.D.†	14 *Mar.* 45	22 *Dec.* 58	17 *Mar.* 57	Civil, Jhansie,
	14	4	Chas. Manners Smith,†	19 *Mar.* 45	21 *Feb.* 59	12 *Apl.* 53	Civil, Lahore.
N.	14	3	R. W. Macaulay, M. D.,†	20 *Mar.* 45	24 *Feb.* 59	.. ..	Fur. S. C. 26 Jan. 58.
	14	3	J. P. Walker, M. D. P. H.	5 *Apl.* 45	1 *Apl.* 59	1 *Mar.* 58	
	14	2	R. S O. Thring, M. D.,†,	20 *Apl.* 45	21 *Apl.* 59		
	14	2	John Squire,† ..	30 *Apl.* 45	24 *Apl.* 59	....	4th Compy. 5th Battn. Arty.
O.	14	1	J. T. Glover, M. D.,† ..	14 *June* 45	26 *Apl.* 59	.. ..	Fur. S. C. 13 Mar. 58.
	13	11	J. T. C. Ross, F. R. C. S.,†	26 *July* 45	5 *June* 59	23 *Dec.* 57	In Joint Medical charge at Simla.

ASSISTANT SURGEONS

Fur Reg.	Ser. Y	Ser. M	Names.	Date of Commission.	Date of Nomination to Corps or Staff Appt.	Remarks.
	42	9	*George Nicholas Cheek,¶ ..	30 *Sep.* 16	12 *Sep.* 39	Civil, West Burdwan (Bancoorah.)
	13	9	Andrew Fleming, M. D.,† ..	29 *Sep.* 45	26 *July* 53	Civil Surgeon and Regtr. of Deeds Sarun.
	13	6	David Scott, M. D.,† ..	20 *Dec.* 45	20 *Sep.* 58	Medical Store Keeper, Allahabad.
N.	13	5	Thomas Maxwell, M. D.,† ..	26 *Jan.* 46	18 *May* 49	2nd Regiment Punjaub Cavalry.
	13	5	Charles Palmer, M. D., ..	20 *Feb.* 46	25 *Aug.* 56 6 *July* 57	Civil, Howrah. Register of Deeds, Howrah.
	13	5	*(a)* James King Walter,† ..	20 *Feb.* 46	6 *Aug.* 57	Civil, employ.
	13	3	Herbert Baillie,† ..	20 *Apl.* 46	11 *Mar.* 57 2 *May* 57	Civil 24-Pergunnahs. Register of Deeds, 24-Pergunnahs.
D	~~1[illegible]~~	~~8~~	~~Major Ainger, F. R.~~ C. S.,† ..	15 *May* 46	28 *Sep.* 58 4 *Oct.* 58	Offg. Civil, Hooghly. Register of Deeds and Marriage Registrar, Hooghly.
	13	1	Donald McDonald, M. D.,† ..	20 *May* 46	16 *Dec.* 54	9th Irregular Cavalry.
N.	13	1	Henry Mills Cannon, M. B.,†	1 *June* 46	.. ..	Fur. S. C. 29 Apl. 59.
	13	1	Wm. Geo. Ward Clemenger, A. B., M. B.,† ..	18 *June* 46	6 *Dec.* 56	67th Native Infantry.
	13	..	Charles Knight Webb,† ..	1 *July* 46	19 *Apl.* 59	10th Punjaub Infantry.
	13	..	Arthur L. Stuart Campbell,†	11 *July* 46	13 *Nov.* 55	16th Irregular Cavalry.
	12	11	George Edward Givins,† ..	25 *July* 46	10 *June* 47	17th Irregular Cavalry.
	12	11	Henry A. Oldfield, M. D.,† ..	25 *July* 46	5 *Jan* 50 11 *June* 58	Residency, Nepaul. Honorary Assistant to the Resident at Nepaul.
	12	11	John D. Crawford, A.B., M.B.,	11 *Aug.* 46	5 *Oct.* 50	1st Irregular Cavalry.
	12	11	Alex. Russeli Atkinson, M.D.,†	11 *Aug.* 46	16 *Nov.* 53	39th Native Infantry.
N.	12	8	James B. Samuel Brown,† ..	20 *Oct.* 46	.. ...	Benares Horse—Fur. S. C. 30 Dec. 57.
	12	8	John William Mountjoy,† ..	20 *Oct* 46	13 *July* 48 26 *April* 56	Civil, Akyab. In Medical charge of the Arracan Battn.
	12	7	David Henry Small,† ..	21 *Nov.* 46	19 *Nov.* 47	Mhairwarrah Battalion.
	12	6	Charles Mathias,† ..	20 *Dec.* 46	... ...	In charge of the Ulwur Political Agency.
O.	12	6	Geo. Hutchinson Ray, M. D.,†	3 *Jan.* 47	.. ..	Furlough S. C. 30 December 56.
N.	12	5	E. Courtenay Thorp, M. D.,†	20 *Jan.* 47	11 *Mar.* 57 15 *Apl.* 57	Civil, Hooghly. Regiter of Deeds and Marriage Registrar, Hooghly.—Fur. S.C. 14Sep. 58.
	12	5	Robert Cockburn,† ..	20 *Jan.* 47		
N.	12	4	John White, M. D.,† ..	9 *Mar.* 47	1 *Jan.* 59	21st Native Infantry.—Fur. P. A. 30 Mar. 59.
	12	1	James Irving, M. D.,† ..	27 *May* 47	19 *May* 58	Civil, Surgeon Allahabad.
N.	12	1	John Williams,† ..	19 *June* 47	.. ..	Fur. P. A. 15 Apl. 59.
	12	..	Thomas Atchison,† ..	26 *June* 47	7 *May* 59	In charge of the Garrison duties, Kangra.
	11	11	Haldane Stewart,† ..	22 *July* 47	29 *Dec.* 56	Garrison asst. Surg. Delhi.
O.	11	9	Hen. Anderson Ebden, M. D.,†	7 *Oct.* 47	.. ..	Leave S. C. to the Cape of Good Hope for 2 years G. O. 18 May 58.
N.	11	8	Thomas Farquhar, M D.,† ..	20 *Oct.* 47	18 *Mar.* 58	Superintendent of the central jail, Allahabad.
	11	8	Alex. Laing Bogle, M. D.,† ..	20 *Oct.* 47		
N.	11	7	William Delpratt,† ..	20 *Nov.* 47	10 *Feb.* 54	3rd Punjaub Cavy.
	11	7	Robert Kemp Buckell,† ..	20 *Nov.* 47	2 *April* 55	44th Native Infantry.
	11	6	John Charles Collins,† ..	22 *Dec.* 47	8 *Aug.* 55	Civil, Darjeeling.
N.	11	5	George R. Pemberton, M. D.,†	20 *Jan.* 57	3 *Jan.* 54	Civil, Mirzapore.—Fur. P. A. 27 May. 59.

Given up promotion.

¶ Non-Subscribers to the Medical Retiring Fund.

(a) Permitted to wear the Ribbon and Medal presented to him by the Spanish Government.

ASSISTANT SURGEONS—*Continued.*

Fur. Reg.	Ser. Y	Ser. M	NAMES.	*Date of Commission.*	*Date of Nomination to Corps or Staff Appt.*	REMARKS.
	11	2	John Campbell Bow, M. D.,†	20 *Apl.* 48	8 *Apl.* 59	Offg Supdt. of the Allahabad central Prison.
O.	11	..	Cavendish Johnson,† ..	21 *June* 48	.. ..	Fur. P. A. 8 Apl. 59.
	11	..	Francis Pearson,† ..	2 *July* 48	9 *Dec.* 54	Supdt. of Vaccination Rohilcund Districts.
	11	..	William White,† ..	4 *July* 48	26 *Aug.* 57	Civil, Rajshahye.
					19 *Oct.* 57	Register of Deeds and Marriage Regr., Rajshahye.
	10	11	Norman Chevers, M. D., ..	1 *Aug.* 48	26 *Jan.* 58	Secy. to the Director Genl. Medical Department.
	10	10	Aylmer St A. Wilson, M. D.,†	20 *Aug.* 48	28 *Dec.* 58	In charge of the Petoragurh recruit [Depot.
	10	8	Sydney George Bousfield,†	10 *Nov.* 48	9 *May* 59	4th Irregular Cavalry.
	10	7	Frederick Freeman Allen,† ..	20 *Nov.* 48	5 *Feb.* 58	Sirmoor Battalion.
	10	6	A. J. Payne, A.B., M. D., *PH*,	20 *Dec.* 48	31 *Oct.* 56	2nd Assistant Presidency General Hospital.
					1 *Nov.* 56	In charge of the Calcutta N. Militia.
N	10	6	Nathaniel D. Scott Wallich,†	20 *Dec.* 48	9 *June* 54	4th Regt. Punjaub Cavalry.
	10	6	Robert Parker, M. D.,† ..	1 *Jan.* 49	.. ..	17th Irregular cavalry.
	10	3	Adolphus John Gee,†	11 *Apl.* 49		
	10	2	John McDonogh Stokes,† ..	5 *May.* 49	9 *May* 59	21st N. I.
	10	..	William Peskett, M. D.,† ..	26 *June* 49	23 *Mar.* 58	Superintendent of vaccination in the Hills.
	9	9	Frederick Corbyn, M. D.,† ..	20 *Sep.* 49	10 *June* 58	Civil Surgeon at Bareilly.
O.	9	8	Charles Lowdell,† ..	20 *Oct.* 49	.. ..	Fur. S. C. 10 Dec. 58.
	9	7	Stewart Clark,† ..	24 *Nov.* 49	9 *Sep.* 52	Civil, Allygurh.
	9	5	John Hooper,† ..	16 *Feb.* 50	6 *Dec.* 56	16th Native Infantry (Grs.)
O.	9	3	David Young, M. D.,† ..	20 *Mar.* 50	.. ..	Fur. S. C. 15 Apl, 59.
	9	..	Joseph Fayrer, M.D., F.R.G.S. F.R.S.E. and F.R.C.S E. *PCH*,	29 *June* 50	20 *Mar.* 56	Civil Surgeon, Lucknow.
					12 *May* 59	Offg. Civil employ.
O.	8	11	John Watkins,† ..	11 *Aug.* 50	.. ..	Fur. S. C. 5 Feb. 58.
	8	10	William Henry Adley,† ..	2 *Sep.* 50	15 *Apl.* 59	In charge of a Regiment of Irregular Cavalry, Meerut.
	8	7	Henry F. Williams, M.D.,† ..	20 *Nov.* 50	11 *Mar.* 57	Civil, East Burdwan.
					25 *June* 57	Register of Deeds and Marriage Regtr., Burdwan.
	8	7	Edward John Vivian,† ..	20 *Nov.* 50	25 *July* 56	In Medical charge of the horse Artillery at Peshawur.
	8	7	Jas. A. C. Hutchinson, M. D.,†	20 *Nov.* 50	10 *Dec.* 56	Civil, Seharunpore.
	8	6	John B. Scriven,† ..	11 *Jan.* 51	31 *Oct.* 56	1st Assistant Presidency General Hospital.
N.	8	5	Joseph Walter R. Amesbury,†	20 *Jan.* 51	.. ..	Fur. S. C. 15 June 58.
	8	4	Charles Stewart, M.D.,† ..	26 *Feb.* 51	15 *Feb.* 54	Pegu Light Infantry Battalion.
	8	..	Edward McKellar,† ..	9 *July* 51	19 *June* 59	Civil, Meerut.
	7	11	James Bedford Allen,† ..	25 *July* 51	15 *Nov.* 54	Civil, Behar.
					11 *Dec.* 55	Register of Deeds and Marriage Registrar, Behar.
	7	11	Annesley C. C. DeRenzy, B. A.,†(*a*) ..	29 *July* 51	9 *Apl.* 59	Under Sup dg. Surgeon, Umballah
	7	8	Alexander Christison, M.D.,†	20 *Oct.* 51	8 *June* 58	Superintendent of Vaccination in the Agra Division and Assist. Lecturer in the Medical School at Agra.
	7	8	James M. Cunningham, M.D.†	20 *Nov.* 51	1 *Dec.* 58	In charge of Nynee Tâl.
	7	7	Jos. Christian Corbyn, M.D.,†	24 *Nov.* 51	2 *Apl.* 59	Offg. Political employ.
	7	6	Geo. Moncrieff Govan, M.D..	20 *Dec.* 51	17 *May* 59	Haupper Stud.

(*a*) Has passed an examination in the Burmese language.

ASSISTANT SURGEONS—*Continued.*

Fur. Reg	Ser. Y	Ser. M	Names.	Date of Commission	Date of Nomination to Corps or Staff Appt.	Remarks.
	7	2	Richard Henry Perkins, ..	20 *Apl.* 52	23 *Aug.* 55	Civil, Hidgellee and Assistant Salt Agent.
	7	1	Stephen Chapman Townsend,†	1 *June* 52	17 *Feb.* 59	2nd Irregular Cavy.
	7	..	Wm. Burns Beatson, M. D.,†	30 *June* 52	25 *Apl.* 54	Civil, Chittagong.
	6	10	Chas. Thos. Paske,† ..	26 *Aug.* 52	13 *Mar.* 58	Civil, Juanpore.
	6	9	W. F. Blyth Dalzell, M. D.,†	20 *Sep.* 52	26 *June* 58	In charge of Meade's Horse.
	6	9	Samuel B. Partridge, F. R. C.S. E., *PCH*, ..	12 *Oct.* 52	2 *Feb.* 59	Civil employ, Medical College.
	6	5	Richd. Chalmers Knight, M.D.,†	4 *Feb.* 53	9 *Nov.* 58	Civil, Bijnore.
	6	3	William B. Butt,† ..	20 *Mar.* 53	14 *June* 56	Station of Loodianah.
	6	2	Thomas James Duthoit, M.B.,†	20 *Apl.* 53	13 *Sep.* 55	25th N. I.
	6	2	John James Clarke,† ..	14 *May* 53	.. ..	Offg. Benares Horse.
N.	6	2	George Olans Baillie, M.D.,† ..	14 *May* 53	.. ..	Fur. S. C. 1 May 56.
	6	1	John Edward Tuson,† ..	17 *June* 53	1 *Apl.* 58	In charge of the civil station of Murree.
	6	1	Francis N. Macnamara, M.D.,†	18 *June* 53	26 *Oct.* 53	Professor of Chemistry, Medl. College.
	5	11	John Francis Tierney,† ..	26 *July* 53	27 *Jan.* 59	5th European Regiment.
	5	11	Edward Tayler,† ..	1 *Aug.* 53	28 *Mar.* 59	31st Native Infantry.
	5	9	Henry William Spry,† ..	4 *Oct.* 53	5 *Mar.* 57	Civil, Ajmere.
N.	5	8	Alfred James Dale, M.B.,† ..	20 *Oct.* 53	13 *Sep.* 55	49th Native Infy.—Eur. S. C. 9 Feb. 1857.
	5	8	Arthur Young,† ..	20 *Oct.* 53	28 *Mar.* 59	Nusseree Battalion.
O.	5	8	Benjamin Simpson, M. D. and A.B. *PH*, ..	20 Oct. 53	8 *Nov.* 55	68th Native Infantry.—Fur. S. C. 21 Oct. 56.
	5	8	George Hickie Daly, M.D.,†	4 *Nov.* 53	5 *Mar.* 59	1st Regt. Hodson's Horse.
N.	5	7	Peter O'Brien,† ..	20 *Nov.* 53	.. ..	Fur. S. C. 21 June 58.
	5	7	George Barnard,† ..	25 *Nov.* 53	.. ...	Leave P. A. 15 Oct,
	5	7	Robt. Faure Hutchinson, M.D.†	3 *Dec.* 53	27 *Nov.* 57	Civil, Shahabad (Off. civil, Sarum.)
	5	7	J. Allan Currie, M. A., M. D.†	4 *Dec.* 53	17 *Dec.* 56	8th Irregular Cavalry.
	5	7	John Picthall,† ..	14 *Dec.* 53	17 *Feb.* 59	7th Irregular Cavalry.
	5	7	Alfred Godley Crewe,† ..	14 *Dec.* 53	2 *Dec.* 54	Civil, Nursingpoor.
N.	5	7	Nathaniel James Grant,† ..	18 *Dec.* 53	25 *Nov.* 57	Civil, Tipperah.
					15 *Feb.* 58	Register of Deeds and marriage Registrar, Tipperah.—Fur. S.C. 8 Dec. 58.
N.	5	6	Marcus Wm. Mott,† ..	20 *Dec.* 53	.. ..	Fur. S. C. 27 May 56.
	5	6	Joseph Ewart, M. D.,† ..	20 *Dec.* 53	5 *Mar.* 57	Meywar Bheel Corps.
N.	5	6	Robert Moir, M. D.,† ..	20 *Dec.* 53	30 *Aug.* 54	1st Assam Light Infy. Battn.
	5	6	Theodore Duka, M.D.,† ..	4 *Jan.* 54	6 *Dec.* 55	Civil, Moonghyr.
					29 *Mar.* 56	Register of Deeds, Monghyr.
	5	6	George Vernon Currie,† ..	14 *Jan.* 54	19 *Nov.* 56	18th Irregular Cavalry.
	5	6	Lachlan H. John Maclean,†	14 *Jan.* 54	13 *Dec.* 56	Govindgurh Garrison.
					17 *Apll.* 59	In charge of 2d compy. 2d Battn. Arty.
	5	6	Francis Hugh O'Donel, M.D.,†	14 *Jan.* 54	13 *Jan.* 59	1st Regt. Mahrattah Horse.
	5	5	John J. Trevor Lawrence,† ..	20 *Jan.* 54	19 *Nov.* 55	4th Native Infantry.
N.	5	5	Henry Martineau Greenhow,†	20 *Jan.* 54	.. ..	Fur. S. C. 8 Apl. 58.
	5	5	Henry William Graham,† ..	14 *Feb.* 54	29 *Dec.* 58	Offg. Civil Tipperah.
	5	5	Martin Brydon Lamb, M.D.†	14 *Feb.* 54	1 *Apl.* 56	45th N. I.
	5	4	John Elliot, M. D.,† ..	20 *Feb.* 54	20 *Apl.* 57	Civil, Jessore.
					19 *May* 57	Register of Deeds and Marriage Registrar Jessore.
	5	4	Thomas Beard Farncombe,†	20 *Feb.* 54	21 *Aug.* 55	Bhaugulpore, Hill Rangers.
					15 *Nov.* 55	In charge of the Civil duties Bhagulpore.
	5	3	Frederick John Earle,† ..	20 *Mar.* 54	9 *Dec.* 56	Civil, Purneah.
					17 *Jan.* 57	Register of Deeds and Marriage Registrar, Purneah. [59.
N.	5	3	Theobald Ringer, M. D.,† ..	17 *Apl.* 54	19 *Mar.* 58	Lahore Light Horse.—Fur. S.C. 12 July
		2	Samuel Delpratt,† ..	6 *May* 54	17 *Mar.* 56	Civil, Hazareebaugh.
	5	2	Philip Warren Sutherland, †	6 *May* 54		
N.	5	1	Thomas Anderson, M. D.,† ..	20 *May* 54	19 *Apl.* 58	Garrison Asst. Surgeon, Fort William.

ASSISTANT SURGEONS—*Continued.*

Fur Reg.	Ser. Y	Ser. M	Names.	Date of Commission	Date of Nomination to Corps or Staff Appt.	Remarks.
	5	1	Alfred Eteson,† ..	20 *May* 54	31 *Jan.* 59	2nd Regt Mahrattah Horse.
	5	1	Hugh Davies Jones,† ..	20 *May* 54	25 *Feb.* 59	Governo'r General's Body Guard.
N.	5	1	William Falconer Clark,† ..	4 *June* 54	27 *Dec.* 55	2nd Infy., Punjaub Irr. Force.—Fur. S. C. 27 Apl. 1858.
	5	1	John Jas. Halls, B.A., F.R.C.S.,†	10 *June* 54	20 *Aug.* 57 19 *Oct.* 57	Civil, Nuddea. Register of deeds and Marriage Registrar, Nuddea.
	5	..	Albert Rich. Waghorn,† ..	22 *June* 54	2 *June* 56	In Medical charge of the Station of Hissar.
	5	..	Fredk Farmer Dukes,† ..	24 *June* 54	13 *Apl.* 59	Depot hospital, Raneegunge.
	5	..	Thomas Dillon, M. D.,† ..	28 *June* 54	6 *Dec.* 56	Sylhet Light Infantry Battalion.
	4	11	Wm. Watson, M. B.,† ..	1 *Aug.* 54	10 *May* 58	Civil Surgeon, Mynpoorie.
	4	11	Alex. John Cowie,† ..	4 *Aug.* 54	.. ..	With the details & Civ. Station, Prome.
	4	10	Chas. Cooper W. Wilson,† ..	26 *Aug.* 54	18 *Mar.* 56	In Medical charge of the Canal and Thomason College Estbts. Roorkee.
	4	10	Patrick Francis Bellew,† ..	6 *Sep.* 54	3 *Mar.* 56 15 *Feb.* 56	Civil, Mymensing. Register of deeds and Marriage Registrar, Mymensing.
N.	4	10	Henry Wm. Robinson, B.A., †	7 *Sep.* 54	.. ..	Fur. S. C. 13 Mar. 57.
	4	10	William John Palmer,† ..	7 *Sep.* 54	20 *Aug.* 57 6 *Nov.* 57	First Asst and Opium Examiner at the Benares Opium Agency. In charge of the Civ. Statn. Ghazeepore
	4	10	Alex. Pakington Tomkyns,†	20 *Sep.* 54	7 *June* 56	26th Native Infy.
	4	9	Robert Pringle, M.D.,† ..	4 *Oct.* 55	22 *Mar.* 59	Civil, Cuttack.
N.	4	8	Augustin FitzGerald, B. A.,†	3 *Nov.* 54	.. ..	Fur. S. C. 20 Feb. 58.
	4	8	Nottige Chas. Macnamara,†	4 *Nov.* 54	5 *Apl.* 58 22 *May* 58	Civil, Tirhoot. Register of Deeds and Marriage Registrar, Tirhoot.
	4	6	James Henry Loch, M. D.,†	20 *Dec.* 54	13 *Jan.* 59	1st Regt. Gwalior Infantry.
	4	6	Robert Rouse,†	20 *Dec.* 54	22 *Jan.* 58	5th Punjaub Cavalry.
N.	4	6	~~Clement Madeley Smith~~, M.D.†	20 *Dec.* 54	6 *May* 58	1st Punjaub Cavalry.—Fur. S. C. 11 Feb. 59.
	4	6	John Chas. Annesley,† ..	30 *Dec.* 54	.. ..	12th Punjaub Infy.
	4	6	J. Rawlinson Jackson, M.D.,†	4 *Jan.* 55	23 *Nov.* 55	1st Punjaub Infantry.
	4	6	A. Macdonald Garden,† ..	11 *Jan.* 55	29 *Apl.* 59	2nd Punjaub Cavy.
	4	6	S. Cornwallis Amesbury,†	14 *Jan.* 55	23 *Feb.* 57 1 *Apl.* 57	Civil, Dinagepore. Register of Deeds and Marriage Registrar, Dinagepore.
	4	5	Gilbert Bethune Hadow,† ..	20 *Jan.* 55	13 *Jan.* 59	2nd Regt. Gwalior Infantry.
	4	5	Geo. Nicholas Cheek, Jr.†	20 *Jan.* 55	20 *May* 59	In Joint medical charge at Simla.
	4	5	Soorjoo Coomar Goodeve Chuckerbutty, M. D.,† ..	24 *Jan.* 55	23 *June* 55	Assist. Physician to the Medical College Hospital.
	4	5	John Brake,†	24 *Jan.* 55	.. ..	2nd Sikh Irr. Cavy.
	4	5	Alfd. Adams Mantell, M. D.,†	24 *Jan.* 55	6 *Oct.* 55	Civil, Balasore.
	4	5	John Bowmer Collison,† ..	24 *Jan.* 55	8 *Nov.* 58	In charge of the Civil station of Duriabad.
	4	5	John Bishop King, M. D.,† ..	24 *Jan.* 55	11 *Nov.* 56	Under the disposal of the Govr. of Prince of Wales' Island, Singapore & Malacca.
	4	5	Arthur Morgan,† ..	24 *Jan* 55	12 *July* 59	Civil, Bancoorah.
N.	4	5	John Brown, ..	24 *Jan.* 55	30 *Apl.* 57	Regiment of Ferozepore.—Fur. S. C. 4 Dec. 58.
	4	4	Augustus Keppel Reed† ..	28 *Feb.* 55	12 *Nov.* 57	Offg. Garrison Asst. Surgeon, Attock.
	4	4	Geo. Kenneth Poole,† ..	14 *Mar.* 55	23 *Feb.* 56 24 *Nov.* 56	Civil. Rungpore. Register of Deeds and Marriage Registrar of Rungpore.
	4	3	Alexander Garden, M. D.,† ..	28 *Mar.* 55	2 *Apl.* 57	Civil, Goruckpore.
	4	3	John Dick Wylie, M. D.†	4 *Apl.* 55	.. ..	
	3	11	Wm. Walker, A. M., M. D.,†	4 *Aug.* 55	15 *Mar.* 58	Supdt. of the Central Jail, Agra.
	3	11	Charles Brettingham,† ..	do	30 *Nov.* 57	In charge of the Kamroop Regt.

Assistant Surgeons—*Continued.*

Fur. Reg.	Ser. Y	Ser. M	Names.	Date of Commission.	Date of Nomination to Corps or Staff Appt.	Remarks.
N.	3	11	George Alder Watson,† ..	4 *Aug.* 55	.. ..	Fur. S. C. 6 Sep. 58.
	3	11	Bernard Kendall,† ..	do	22 *Mar.* 59	Civil, Pooree.
	3	11	John Lindsay Stewart, M.D.,†	do	29 *Jan.* 59	14th Punjaub Infantry.
	3	11	Theobald Mathew, M. B.† ..	do	4 *Nov.* 57	H. M. 81st Foot.
	3	11	James Fairweather, M. D.,†	do	11 *July* 56	4th Infy. Punjaub Irr. Force.
	3	11	David Hood, M. D.,† ..	do	4 *Oct.* 58	Civil, Boolundshuhur.
	3	11	Charles Julian Jackson,† ..	do	19 *July* 58	Civil, Azimgurh.
	3	11	Robert Bird, M. D.,† ..	do	29 *Sept.* 58	3rd Troop, 1st Brigade of Horse Arty.
N.	3	11	Archbd. Alex. Duncan, M.B.†	do	.. ..	Fur. S. C. 26 Feb. 58.
	3	11	John Martin Coates,,† ..	do	24 *Mar.* 59	Civil, Chumparun.
	3	11	Henry Thom, M. D.,† ..	do	.. ..	In charge of the Civil Station of Sul- [tanpore, (Oude.)
N.	3	11	Francis Synge Sillifant,† ..	do	.. ..	Fur. S. C. 9 Mar. 58.
	3	11	Daniel McAuley, M. D.,† ..	do	4 *Aug.* 55	Left Wing 1st En. B. Fus.
	3	11	Charles Plank,† ..	do		
N.	3	11	Frederick Carter,† ..	do	.. ..	Fur. S. C. 6 May 59.
	3	11	William Henry Hayes,† ..	do	5 *June* 58	Civil Asst. Surg. & Asst. to the Commr of Chota Nagpore at Chyebassa.
	3	8	Henry Walter Bellew,† ..	14 *Nov.* 55		
	3	8	David Boyes Smith, M. D.,†	28 *Nov.* 55		
	3	6	Edward John Gayer,† ..	2 *Jan.* 56	24 *June* 58	Civil, Backergunge.
	3	6	J. H. Thornton, B.A., B.M.† ..	9 *Jan.* 56	25 *Feb.* 59	1st Sikh Irr. Cavy.
	3	5	Jas. Frederick Stuart, M.D.†	20 *Feb.* 1855	20 *Aug.* 57	Field Hospital, Allahabad.
	3	5	Edmund Darby, M.D.,† ..	do		
N.	3	5	Frank Powell, M. B.,† ..	do	7 *Nov.* 56	3rd Seikh Infy.
N.	3	5	Edward Livesey Dixon,† ..	do	6 *May* 59	Civil Fyzabad, (Oude)—Fur. S. C. 13 [May 59.
	3	5	John Ince, M. D.† ..	do	26 *Nov.* 56	1st Company 3rd Battn. Arty.
	3	5	Frederick James Pettingal,†	do	17 *July* 56	Arracan Battn.
	3	5	John Jones, M. D.† ..	do	1 *Jan.* 59	In charge of Mussoorie Depôt.
	3	5	James Browne B. A.,† ..	do	.. ..	Umballah.
	3	5	Robert S. Bateson,† ..	do	5 *Feb.* 57	Doing duty 3rd En. Regt.
	3	5	Thomas P. Wright,,† ..	do	.. ..	3rd Compy. 5th Battn. Arty.
	3	5	Alex. Morison Dallas,† ..	do	.. ..	Noorpoor.
	3	5	C. Kilkelly, A.B., M.B. F R.C.S.†	do	6 *June* 57	Detachment H. M. 64th Foot.
	3	4	Charles Andrew Poole,† ..	18 *Mar.*	20 *Mar.* 57	4th Seikh Infantry
	3	3	Neil Benjamin Baillie,† ..	8 *April*	23 *Apl.* 58	Mooltanee Regt. of Cavalry.
	3	2	John Wilson,† ..	7 *May*		
	3	..	Sarkies Michael Shircore, † ..	2 *July*	11 *Mar.* 57	In charge of the Civil Medical duties, [Cachar.
	3	..	J. Fownes Norton Wise, M.D.	16 *July*	31 *Jan.* 59	3rd Troop 3rd Brigade of Horse Arty.
	2	11	William Eddowes, ..	4 *Aug.*	15 *Apl.* 59	Joudpore Legion.
	2	11	J. Lumsdaine Bryden, M.D.,†	do	21 *Apl.* 59	In charge of Buxar and Kurruntadhee [Studs.
N.	2	11	Robert Foyer, ..	do	.. ..	Furlough S. C., 3rd Aug. 58.
	2	11	Thomas T. Sherlock, B. A.,†	do	19 *Feb.* 59	Civil, Futtehpoore.
	2	11	W. Henry Kirton, ..	do	30 *May* 59	Offg. Civil Mirzapore.
	2	11	Robert Westcott,† ..	do	.. ..	Peshawur Circle.
	2	11	George Farrell, F.R.C.S.† ..	do	19 *Apl.* 59	2nd Punjaub Infantry.
	2	11	C. E. Wimond Bensley, M.D.†	*do*	.. ..	3rd Infy. Nagpore Irr. Force.
N.	2	11	T. Fitzpatrick, A. B. M. B. ..	do	.. ..	Fur. S. C. 19th Jan. 57.
	2	11	William Roche Rice, M. D.,†	do	14 *Jan.* 59	Civil, Saugor.
	2	10	Hickman Rose Daniell,† ..	21 *Sep.*		
N.	2	10	J. Arthur Sewell, M. D.,† ..	24 *Sep.*	.. ..	Fur. S. C. 5 Apl. 59.
	2	9	Alex. Groves Duff, M. D.† ..	1 *Oct.*	19 *Apl.* 59	Offg. Garrison Asst. Surgeon, Fort [William.
	2	9	John Charles Morice,† ..	8 *Oct.*	14 *Aug.* 58	Rohilkund Horse.
	2	9	T. Edmondstone Charles M.D †	22 *Oct.*	27 *Aug.* 58	Garrison Asst. Surgeon, Allahabad.
	2	7	R. Theophilus Abbott, M.D.,†	10 do	6 *June* 57	H. M. 84th Foot.
	2	6	Henry Caley,† ..	29 *Jan.* 1857	.. ..	In charge of the Civil Medical duties, [Goruckpore.
	2	6	Alexander Vans Best, M. D.,†	do	23 *Apl.* 58	65th Native Infantry.
	2	6	James Henry White,† ..	do	.. ..	Bareilly.
	2	6	James Champion Penny, M.D.†	do	.. ..	3rd Troop, 2nd Brigade of Horse Arty.
	2	6	Archd. Hamilton Hilson, M.D.†	do	16 *Sep.* 58	18th Punjaub Infantry.
	2	6	James Charles Dickinson, ..	do	31 *Jan.* 59	2nd En. L. Cavalry.
	2	6	William C. Smith, M. D.,† ..	do		
	2	6	Charles Edwin Raddock,† ..	do		
	2	6	John Sheil, B. A. and M. B.,†	do	30 *Jan.* 59	Recruit Depôt Barrackpore.
	1	11	William S. Playfair, M. D.,†	4 *Aug.*	15 *July* 59	In charge of the Meenah Regt.
	1	11	Hugh Clark, M. D.,† ..	do	31 *Jan.* 59	5th En. L. Cavalry.

ASSISTANT SURGEONS—*Continued.*

Fur. Reg.	R. Y	R. M	NAMES.	Date of Commission.		Date of Nomination to Corps or Staff Appt.		REMARKS.
	1	11	G. Sackville Sutherland, M.D.†	4 *Aug.*	57	27 *Apl.*	59	1st Troop 1st Brigade of Horse Arty.
	1	11	William E. Caird,† ..	do		31 *Jan.*	59	1st En. L. Cavalry.
	1	11	Richard Banbury,† ..	do		13 *Mar.*	59	Regiment of Lucknow.
	1	11	James Bremner, M. D. †	do		23 *Apl.*	58	47th Native Infantry.
	1	11	Emmanuel Bonavia, M. D.†	do		..	..	Mily. Police, Oudh.
	1	11	Adam Taylor,† ..	do		..	..	21st Punjaub Infantry.
	1	11	Lindsay Fred. Dickson, M.D.,†	do		14 *Feb.*	59	20th Punjaub Infantry.
	1	11	Denis B. Daly, M. D.,† ..	do		..	..	Upper Provinces.
	1	7	John McL. Pemberton, M. D.†	9 *Dec.*				
	1	6	J. A. P. Colles, M. D., F.R.C.S.†	27 *Jan.*	58	25 *Feb.*	59	3rd Troop 1st Brigade of Horse Arty.
	1	6	William James Haig, M. D.†	do		29 *Apl.*	59	Alexander's Horse.
	1	6	Alex. Dugald Campbell, M.D.†	do				2nd Company 3rd Battn. Arty.
	1	6	Sydney Charles Courtney, MD.†	do		31 *Jan.*	59	3rd En. L. Cavalry.
	1	6	Charles Prentis,† ..	do		..	..	7th Punjaub Infantry.
	1	6	R. C. Chundra,† ..	do				Towana Horse.
	1	6	Robert Lidderdale, M. D.† ..	do		13 *May*	59	Goruckpore Recruit Depot.
	1	6	J. E. T. Aitchison, M. D.† ..	do		..	..	Lahore Circle.
	1	6	Leonard Horner Lees, M. D.†	do		..	..	Arty. Hospital, Mean Meer.
	1	6	Thomas Stick Veale,† ..	do				
	1	6	Bamlet Walker Switzer, M. D.†	do		..	..	Depôt Hospital, Allahabad.
	1	6	Cyrus O. Daniell, M. D.,† ..	do		13 *Jan.*	59	13th Punjaub Infantry.
	1	2	Daniel Wright, M. D. A. M.† ..	28 *May*				
	1	2	Henry Charles Cutcliffe,† ..	do		..	..	2nd En. L. Cavalry.
	1	..	Thomas E. B. Brown, M. D.†	23 *July*	58	..	..	Presidency General Hospital.
	1	..	Henry Potter, M. D.	do		..	...	1st Compy. 6th Bn. Arty.
	1	..	Albert Marc Verchere,	do		...	..	Lucknow Field Force.
	1	..	Charles Hatchell,† ..	do		...	..	3rd En. Regiment.
	1	..	Oscar Byrne,† ..	do		..	...	Extra Goorkha Regiment.
	1	..	John Charles Whishaw, ...	do		..	..	Dinapore Circle.
	1	..	F. W. A. De Fabeck,† ..	do		..	...	Depôt Hospital, Dinapore.
	1	..	John Berry White,† ..	do				
	1	..	Robert Brown, ..	do		...	...	In charge of Recruits, Campbellpore.
	1	..	A. F. Richmond, ..	do		...	...	Bareilly.
	1	..	P. M. Crosbie, B. A. M. B., ...	do		..	...	3rd En. Regiment.
	1	..	John J. McDermott, M. D.†...	do		..	..	Lucknow Field Force.
	1	..	W. P. Harris, M. D.† ...	do		...	..	Cawnpore Field Hospital.
	1	1	M. Scanlan, ..	11 *Aug.*	58	..	..	Umballa.
..		5	William Edward Allen, ...	10 *Feb.*	59			
..		5	Alex Carroll Maingay, M. D.	do				
..		5	Riners Mantell, M. B.	do				
..		5	William John Thomson, ..	do				
..		5	Edwin Clement Bensley, ..	do				
..		5	James Fawcus M. D. ..	do				Presidency Genl. Hospital.
..		5	George Bremner, M. D. ..	do				
..		5	Thomas William Sheppard,..	do				
..		5	John Ellis, M. B. ..	do				
..		5	Edric Selons, ..	do				
..		5	Charles Peter Costello, ..	do				
..		5	James John Durrant, ..	do				
..		5	Ferdinand Odevaine, ..	do				
..		5	Robert Rhind, ..	do				
..		5	George Grant, M. B. ..	do				
..		5	William Nichol M. D. ..	do				
..		5	George Cochet Chesnaye, ...	do				
..		5	John Duncan, M. D. ..	do				
..		5	Edward Ord Tandy, ..	do				
..		5	James Robert Purefoy M. D.	do				
..		5	Francis Parsons, ..	do				
..		5	Henry Seymour Smith, M.B...	do				
..		5	Frederick Geo. Constant, M. D.	do				
..		5	James Hunt Condon, ...	do				
..		5	William Roe Hooper, ..	do				
..		5	Mark Henry Lackersteen, ..	do				
..	..		W. H. James, M.D., F.R.C.S.I.,					

APOTHECARIES.

Ser. Y	Ser. M	Names.	Date of Appt. in the Service.	Date of present Rank	Remarks.
43	1	Daniel Hodgkinson, ..	12 *June* 16	21 *Oct.* 24	Medical Depôt, Umballah.
37	10	Henry Watson, ..	31 *Aug.* 21	23 *Jan.* 34	Under Civil Surgeon, Agra.
34	8	George Edward Pool, (4) ..	21 *Oct.* 24	8 *Oct.* 38	Simla Jail and Dispensary.
33	9	James George Scott, ..	5 *Oct.* 25	25 *Mar.* 40	Honorable Company's Dispensary, Calcutta.
32	8	John Bensley, ..	30 *Oct.* 26	23 *Mar.* 42	Honorable Company's Dispensary, Calcutta.
32	8	James Parnell, ..	30 *Oct.* 26	15 *Apl.* 42	H. M. 94th Foot.
25	5	John Taylor, ..	23 *Jan.* 34	15 *Apl.* 42	H. M. 88th Foot.
25	5	John Harris Peter, (8) ..	23 *Jan.* 34	1 *Aug.* 42	Furlough, S.C., 13 Jan. 53.
32	8	Thomas Nulty, ..	30 *Oct.* 26	2 *Dec.* 42	7th Dragoon Guards.
32	8	George Oliver, (9) ..	30 *Oct.* 26	19 *Sep.* 43	In Medical charge of the "Lawrence Asylum," Kussowlie.
38	8	Frederick Hottinger, (10) ..	28 *Oct.* 20	26 *June* 44	1st Brigade Horse Artillery,
32	3	Charles Marshall, ..	14 *Apl.* 27	15 *Nov.* 44	
30	...	Daniel Wedgberry, (12) ..	18 *July* 29	31 *Jan.* 45	H. M. 97th Foot.
29	8	Charles Hayes, (19) ..	7 *Nov.* 29	12 *Feb.* 45	Field Hospital Lucknow, Lv. s. c., [30th Nov.
37	6	George William Harding, (24)	14 *Jan.* 22	25 *Oct.* 46	2nd Seikh Infantry.
34	6	Samuel Slater, (14) ..	30 *Dec.* 24	20 *Nov.* 46	Presy. Genl. Hospital.
35	7	James Gibson, (15) ..	3 *Dec.* 23	22 *Oct* 47	Garrison of Agra.
25	4	John McClatchey, (11) ..	10 *Mar.* 34	18 *June* 48	Medical Depôt, Sealkote.
24	10	Fredk. Jas. L'Estrange, (16)	4 *Sep.* 34	27 *July* 48	Presy. Genl. Hospital.
24	10	Thomas Murphy, ..	4 *Sep.* 34	13 *Aug.* 49	Depôt Hospital, Landour.
24	10	William McKeon, ..	4 *Sep.* 34	5 *Sep.* 49	Leave S. C. 4 Sep.
24	10	Alexander Glegg, ..	4 *Sep.* 34	5 *Oct.* 49	Her Majesty's 27th Foot.
24	10	Charles Hurley, ..	4 *Sep.* 34	1 *Nov.* 49	European Invalid Battn., Chunar.
22	2	William Marshall, (24) ..	3 *May* 37	8 *Mar.* 50	Medical Depôt. Allahabad.
19	7	John Prince, (18) ..	17 *Dec.* 39	11 *Apl.* 51	H. M. 75th Foot.
19	2	James B. Goff, (18) ..	13 *May* 40	30 *Nov.* 51	Her Majesty's 81st Foot.
19	2	Thomas Murray, L.M.D., †(27)	13 *May* 40	9 *July* 52	Mhair Regiment.
23	4	Charles Baker, (22) ..	23 *Feb.* 36	9 *July* 52	42nd Royal Highlanders.
21	2	John Richd. Higgins, (19) ..	18 *May* 38	9 *July* 52	On Leave.
19	10	James McCormick, ..	23 *Aug.* 39	30 *Nov.* 51	Depot Hospital, Berhampore.
19	2	Henry C. Connolly, (26) ..	13 *May* 40	4 *Oct.* 52	Her Majesty's 87th Fusiliers.
21	9	Christopher Corbett, ...	9 *Oct.* 37	27 *July* 53	2nd European Bengal Fusiliers.
18	6	John McKimm, ..	1 *Jan.* 41	24 *Nov.* 53	2nd Brigade of H. Arty.
18	2	William Henry Kelly, (18) ..	1 *May* 41	24 *Nov.* 53	Her Majesty's 53rd Foot.
17	7	William Wilson, (18) ..	4 *Dec.* 41	24 *Nov.* 53	51st Native Infantry.
19	11	Robert Fred. Thompson, (17)	6 *Aug.* 39	24 *Nov.* 53	In charge of the Civil Station of Maldah.
17	6	John Richard Deane, ..	4 *Jan.* 42	24 *Nov.* 53	In Medical charge of the dispensary and Jail Hospital, Bunno.
17	5	John Mervin, ..	15 *Feb.* 42	24 *Nov.* 53	Her Majesty's 8th Foot.
17	5	William John Hannigan, ..	15 *Feb.* 42	24 *Nov.* 53	3rd European Regiment.
18	..	William Rawson Hart, (18)	12 *Sep.* 40	27 *June* 55	H. M. 6th Dragoon Guards.
17	5	James Winn, (20) ..	15 *Feb.* 42	3 *Nov.* 55	4th European Regiment.
17	1	James Saint, (20) ..	7 *June* 42	7 *Dec.* 55	Anarkully Dispensary, Lahore.
17	..	George James Cooper, (28) ..	18 *July* 42	12 *Dec.* 55	Her Majesty's 70th Foot.
17	..	John Hefferan, (18) ..	18 *July* 42	2 *July* 56	1st European Light Cavalry.
17	..	Charles Earle, ..	18 *July* 42	7 *July* 56	H. M. 9th Lancers.
19	10	Joseph Hurst, ..	23 *Aug.* 39	11 *Nov.* 56	Depot Hospital, Allahabad.
19	4	James Sylvester, (18) ..	17 *Dec.* 39	10 *Feb.* 57	Hospital of H. M. 60th Rifles.

APOTHECARIES.—(Continued.)

Ser. Y	Ser. M	Names		Date of Appt. in the Service.	Date of present Rank.	Remarks.
17	..	John Law,	..	18 *July* 42	27 *June* 57	4th Battn. Arty.
17	..	George Law,	..	18 *July* 42	31 *July* 57	In charge of 1st Regt. of Infantry, Nagpore, Irr. Force.
17	..	John Reilly,	..	18 *July* 42	23 *Oct.* 57	2nd Battn. Arty.
16	5	John Hogan,	..	24 *Jan.* 43	20 *Nov.* 57	H. M. 79th Highlanders.
19	2	John A. Fleming, (18)	..	13 *May* 40	29 *Jan.* 58	2nd Brigade Horse Artillery.
16	5	Garrett Hogan,	..	24 *Jan.* 43	29 *Jan.* 58	H. M. 52nd Foot.
16	5	William Moore Martin,	..	18 *July* 42	25 *May* 58	H. M. 98th Foot.
16	5	Robert Wm. Beale,	..	24 *Jan.* 43	30 *June* 58	Her Majesty's 9th Lancers.
20	7	Joseph Vyall,	..	30 *Nov.* 38	25 *Sep.* 58	Her Majesty's 7th Hussars.
16	5	William Buckley,	..	24 *Jan.* 43	26 *Sep.* 58	2nd Brigade of Horse Arty.
16	2	W. Cox,	..	13 *May* 43	18 *Nov.* 58	3rd Battalion Rifle Brigade.

SENIOR STEWARDS.

Ser. Y	Ser. M	Names.		Date of Appt. in the Service.	Date of present Rank.	Remarks.
42	8	Robert Morrow,	..	9 *Nov.* 16	4 *Nov.* 56	3rd Brigade Horse Artillery.
38	8	William Bond, (20)	..	21 *Nov.* 20	4 *Nov.* 56	1st European Bengal Fusiliers.
34	8	John William Franks, (21)		17 *Nov.* 24	4 *Nov.* 56	Garrison Hospital, Chunar.
		STEWARDS.				
29	8	James Bowser,	..	7 *Nov.* 29	31 *Jan.* 45	Medical College, Presidency.
23	11	Alexander Gibson, (13)	..	28 *July* 35	30 *Jan.* 46	Head Quarters 1st Brigade H. Arty.
23	11	Charles Bath,	..	28 *July* 35	18 *May* 46	H. M. 60th Foot.
21	8	Henry William Tibbetts,	..	3 *Nov.* 37	25 *Oct.* 46	Her Majesty's 52nd Light Infy.
22	2	Peter McDonald, (19)	..	3 *May* 37	18 *June* 48	1st Company 3rd Battalion Arty.
19	11	William Bonner,	..	6 *Aug.* 39	31 *Mar.* 49	Field Hospital, Allahabad.
19	10	Francis Joseph Murphy,	..	23 *Aug.* 39	13 *Aug.* 49	Her Majesty's 61st Foot.
19	2	John Considine, (19)	..	13 *May* 40	14 *Dec.* 49	Artillery Divn. Hospital, Meerut.
19	2	William Mayes, (18)	..	13 *May* 40	14 *Dec.* 49	Her Majesty's 98th Foot.
18	10	John Wm. Wilkinson,	..	12 *Sep.* 40	9 *July* 52	7th Dragoon Guards.
18	6	Edgar Grove Roderick, (18)		1 *Jan.* 41	9 *July* 52	H. M. 23rd Fusiliers.
18	2	George Hart, (18)	..	20 *Apl.* 41	9 *July* 52	Her Majesty's 6th Dragoon Guards.
17	5	Francis Hamilton,	..	15 *Feb* 42	24 *Nov.* 53	3rd European Regiment.
17	..	William Hefferan,	..	18 *July* 42	24 *Nov.* 53	Head Quarters 6th Battn. Arty.
17	5	Thomas Joseph Lisbey,	..	15 *Feb.* 42	27 *June* 55	Her Majesty's 53rd Foot.
19	2	James Alex. Barthelemy,	..	13 *May* 40	11 *Nov.* 56	4th Battalion Artillery.
17	1	Thomas Prince, (21)	..	7 *June* 42	10 *Feb.* 57	2nd Battalion Artillery.
15	7	Francis J. Grose,	..	15 *Dec.* 43	7 *Mar.* 57	H. M. 42nd Highlanders.
15	7	John Tresham,	..	15 *Dec.* 43	15 *June* 57	1st Troop 2nd Brigade Arty.
15	2	Robert Duncan Logg,	..	27 *Apl.* 44	27 *June* 57	Lahore Circle.
15	7	Joseph A. Cooper,	..	15 *Dec.* 43	31 *July* 57	Landour Depôt.
15	2	James E. Harrison,	..	27 *April* 44	18 *Sep.* 57	Simla Dispensary.
15	2	James Joseph O'Brien,	..	27 *April* 44	23 *Oct.* 57	5th European Regiment.
14	6	Robert Davis,	..	20 *Dec.* 44	20 *Nov.* 57	H. M. 20 Foot.
16	5	Thomas Sharpe,	..	24 *Jan.* 43	29 *Jan.* 58	Her Majesty's 81st Foot.
14	6	John Richmond,	..	20 *Dec.* 44	29 *Jan.* 58	Sasseram Depot, Hospital.
14	6	James Johnston,	..	20 *Dec.* 44	15 *Apl.* 58	H. M. 87th Foot.
14	2	William O. Rollo,	..	20 *Apl.* 45	4 *May* 58	H. M. 20th Foot.—Lv. s. c. 1st Nov.
6	..	Thomas Green,	..	18 *July* 53	25 *May* 58	H. M. 81st Foot.
5	7	Thomas Briscoe,	..	24 *Nov.* 53	30 *June* 58	Delhi.
5	7	Henry D. Cooper,	..	24 *Nov.* 53	12 *July* 58	Murree Depot.
16	5	Frederick Volkers,	..	24 *Jan.* 43	3 *Aug.* 58	Ditto.
5	7	Edward Vyall,	..	24 *Nov.* 53	23 *Aug.* 58	H. M. 9th Lancers.
5	7	William C. Giddons,	..	24 *Nov.* 53	25 *Sep.* 58	1st European B. F.
5	7	Thomas Cullen,	..	24 *Nov.* 53	26 *Sep.* 58	Field Hospital Allahabad.
5	7	Thomas Davis,	..	24 *Nov.* 53	18 *Nov* 58	4th Battalion Artillery.

ASSISTANT APOTHECARIES.

Ser. Y	Ser. M	Names.	Date of Appt. in the Service.	Date of present Rank.	Remarks.
16	5	Charles W. Stoney, ..	24 *Jan.* 43	25 *June* 51	H. M. 82nd Foot.
14	6	William Henry Must, ..	20 *Dec.* 44	17 *Aug.* 52	Depot Hospital, Allahabad.
14	3	Edmund Tanney, ..	27 *Mar.* 45	4 *Oct.* 52	Arty. Division, Jullunder.
14	1	Samuel Turvey, ..	21 *May* 45	15 *Dec.* 52	Arty. Division Meerut.
5	7	James Fenn, ..	.. ..	24 *Nov.* 53	2nd Brigade Horse Arty.
5	7	Lewis Augustus Sakes, ..	.. ..	24 *Nov.* 53	Field Hospital, Allahabad.
5	7	William Farrell, ..	.. ..	24 *Nov.* 53	
5	7	John Edwin Tanks, ..	.. ..	24 *Nov.* 53	
5	7	Fred. H. A. Leach, ..	.. ..	24 *Nov.* 53	Under Civil Surgeon, Lucknow.
5	7	William Price, ..	.. ..	24 *Nov.* 53	Medical Depôt, Umballa.
5	7	Charles Levlin Fox, ..	.. ..	24 *Nov.* 53	1st En. Bengal Fusiliers.
5	7	John Hemming, ..	.. ..	24 *Nov.* 53	3rd Battn. Rifle Brigade.
5	7	James Green, ..	.. ..	24 *Nov.* 53	Her M's. 35th Foot.
5	7	Richard Edward Wrafter, ..	.. ..	24 *Nov.* 53	Arty. Division, Meerut.
5	7	James Hughes, ..	.. ..	24 *Nov.* 53	Arty. Division Hospital, Govindghur.
5	7	Michael John Carny, ..	.. ..	24 *Nov.* 53	Landour Convalescent Depôt.
5	7	George McEvoy, ..	.. ..	24 *Nov.* 53	Her Majesty's 75th Foot.
5	7	William Sinclair, ..	.. ..	24 *Nov.* 53	2nd Battn. Arty.
5	7	R. W. Harrison, ..	.. ..	24 *Nov.* 53	Under Civil Asst. Surgeon, Mooltan.
5	7	Robert Freeland, ..	.. ..	24 *Nov.* 53	H. M. 8th Foot.
5	7	Richard James Quinnell, ..	.. ..	24 *Nov.* 53	Landour Depôt.
5	7	James Connor, ..	.. ..	24 *Nov.* 53	
5	7	Wm. Arnold Kidd, ..	.. ..	24 *Nov.* 53	H. M. 97th Foot.
5	7	John Rehill, ..	.. ..	24 *Nov.* 53	Left Wing 6th Battn. Artillery.
5	5	Edwin Pearsall, ..	.. ..	27 *Jan.* 54	H. M. 9th Lancers.
5	5	James Ellis, ..	.. ..	14 *Feb.* 54	European Hospital, Jullundur.
5	3	Samuel Wade, ..	.. ..	20 *Mar.* 54	Artillery Division, Sealkote.
5	2	Richard McCurley, ..	.. ..	28 *Apl.* 54	H. M. 81st Foot.
5	..	John Hart, ..	.. ..	24 *May* 54	2nd Company 5th Battn. Arty.
4	4	Alex. Hogan, ..	.. ..	16 *Mar.* 55	
4	5	Henry Andrews, ..	.. ..	1 *Feb.* 55	Engineer Brigade.
4	4	James Donaghue, ..	.. ..	16 *Mar.* 55	Darjeeling Convalescent Depôt.
4	3	Edward Gabriel Collins, ..	.. ..	28 *Mar.* 55	Offg. Garrison Dispensary, Fort William.
4	3	James Cameron, ..	.. ..	17 *April* 55	H. M. 84th Foot.
3	9	Elisha Grassby, ..	.. ..	28 *Sep.* 55	Sappers and Miners.
3	8	James Farnon, ..	.. ..	3 *Nov.* 55	Arty. Hospital Lahore.
3	7	Henry Lamb, ..	.. ..	7 *Dec.* 55	2nd En. B. F.
3	4	John Slane, ..	.. ..	12 *Mar.* 56	Depôt Hospital Benares.
3	..	John Sleigh, ..	.. ..	24 *Aug.* 56	H. M.'s 82nd Foot.
2	10	James Judd, ..	.. ..	21 *Sep.* 56	Arty. Division, Meerut.
3	7	Richard Clarke, ..	.. ..	8 *Dec.* 55	Det. 2nd Battn. Rifle Brigade.
2	8	Alex. Geo. Price, ..	.. ..	11 *Nov.* 56	H. M. 79th Highlanders.
2	8	Joseph James Barnes, ..	.. ..	13 *Nov.* 56	H. M. 24th Foot.
2	8	John Bailey, ..	.. ..	20 *Nov.* 56	H. M. 13th Light Infy.
2	4	James Charles Ellis, ..	.. ..	7 *Mar.* 57	
17	5	Geo. Ward Roofe, ..	15 *Feb.* 42	31 *July* 46	Dett. of Invalids.
2	2	William Byrnes, ..	.. ..	10 *May* 57	
2	1	John Birch, ..	.. ..	9 *June* 57	H. M. 90th Foot.
2	1	John Routcliff, ..	.. ..	15 *June* 57	
2	1	John W. K. Patterson, ..	.. ..	27 *June* 57	
2	1	Thomas Browne, ..	.. ..	27 *June* 57	
2	1	Fdward Charles Tiernan, ..	.. ..	27 *June* 57	

ASSISTANT APOTHECARIES.—*Continued.*

Ser. Y	Ser. M	Name.	Date of Appt. in the Service.	Date of present Rank.	Remarks.
2	1	Henry Stella Settle,	.. .. ..	27 *June* 57	4th Company 4th Battn. Arty.
2	..	A. Daniel Cooper.	.. .. ..	19 *July* 57	H. M. 19th Foot.
1	10	D. T. Mills,	.. .. ..	18 *Sep.* 57	Depôt Hospital, Dinapore.
2	..	William Byron,	.. .. ..	31 *July* 57	H. M. 46th Foot.
1	9	William James Gill,	.. .. ..	23 *Oct.* 57	Detachment of recruits, Peshawur
1	8	Fredk. William Hall,	.. .. ..	20 *Nov.* 57	4th. En. L. C.
1	4	Thomas Fernandez,	.. .. ..	1 *Jan.* 58	Left wing H. M. 7th Royal Fusiliers.
1	6	Samuel Wilson,	.. .. ..	22 *Jan.* 58	
1	6	R. Goulbourne,	.. .. ..	29 *Jan.* 58	
1	6	John Reilly,	.. .. ..	29 *Jan.* 58	H. M. 79th Highlanders.
1	3	H. R. Jackson,	.. .. ..	8 *Apl.* 58	
1	3	W. B. Grassby,	.. .. ..	15 *Apl.* 58	
1	2	D. G. McCulloch,	.. .. ..	4 *May* 58	
1	2	J. H. Lockwood,	.. .. ..	25 *May* 58	
1	1	J. Stephens,	.. .. ..	8 *June* 58	Depot Hospital, Mooltan.
1	..	J. A. Kidd,	.. .. ..	30 *June* 58	
1	..	J. D. Berkeley,	.. .. ..	12 *July* 58	
..	11	H. F. McDonald,	.. .. ..	3 *Aug.* 58	
..	11	D. J. Tresham,	.. .. ..	11 *Aug.* 58	H. M. 6th Foot.
..	11	J. Cullen,	.. .. ..	17 *Aug.* 58	
..	11	R. G. Philpott,	.. .. ..	23 *Aug.* 58	
..	10	R. Barker,	.. .. ..	23 *Sep.* 58	
..	10	R. Pereira,	.. .. ..	25 *Sep.* 58	
..	10	J. F. Mills,	.. .. ..	26 *Sep.* 58	
..	8	J. P. Lamb,	.. .. ..	18 *Nov.* 58	
..	8	C. Briscoe,	.. .. ..	24 *Nov.* 58	
..	7	J. M. Courtney,	.. .. ..	15 *Dec.* 58	

VETERINARY SURGEONS.

Fur. Reg.	Names.	Date of Rank.	Date of Appointment.	Remarks.
N.	Robert Burgess Parry, ..	10 *Apl.* 27	19 *May* 54	Fur. S.C. 13 Mar. 58.
	James Harris, ...	3 *Jan.* 28	29 *Mar.* 51	3rd European Light Cavalry.
	Isaac Bicknell, ...	10 *May* 28	19 *Jan.* 56	1st Brigade Horse Artillery.
	Henry Charles Hulse, ..	23 *Aug.* 28	10 *Nov.* 52	Govr. Genl.'s Body Guard.
	William McDermott,† ..	11 *Feb.* 39	27 *June* 44	5th En. Light Cavalry.
	John Robert Hoey,† ..	1 *Apl.* 40	11 *Feb.* 56	3rd Brigade Horse Artillery.
	Archibald Campbell Williams,†	5 *Oct.* 43	31 *Jan.* 59	Artillery Division, Peshawur.
	John Siddall,†	17 *July* 44	24 *Dec.* 52	Stud Department.
	William Johnson,†	19 *June* 46	5 *Nov.* 47	2nd European Light Cavalry.
	Archibald Turnbull,† ..	13 *Mar.* 47	13 *Aug.* 58	Cavalry Recruit Depôt. Hazareebaugh.—Lv. S. C. 2nd Nov.
	Thomas Pengree Page,† ..	21 *Nov.* 49	29 *Mar.* 53	1st European Light Cavy.
	John Samuel Woods,† ..	31 *May* 50	30 *Mar.* 59	Seharunpore Stud.
	John Whitmore Garrad,† ..	14 *Feb.* 54	20 *May* 58	Haupper Stud.
N.	Thomas Hickman,† ..	18 *Mar.* 54	20 *Mar.* 59	Artillery Division, Peshawur.
	George Kettlewell,† ..	5 *Dec.* 54	18 *Mar.* 57	1st Troop 1st Brig. Horse Arty —Fur. S. C. 17 July 58.
	Mathew Joseph Marshall, ..	22 *Dec.* 54	15 *Apl.* 56	2nd Brigade of Horse Arty.
	Chambre Corker,† ..	17 *May* 55	.. ..	Lahore Light Horse.
N	Robert Walter Murray, ..	30 *May* 57	.. ..	Fur S. C. 16 Feb. 59.
	Henry Dawson, ..	6 *Nov.* 57	.. ..	Allahabad.
	John George Bushman, ..	7 *Jan.* 58	9 *Dec.* 58	3rd Brigade of Horse Artillery.
	Robert Moorhead, ..	12 *Apl.* 58	.. ..	In charge of Arty. Horses, Rawul Pindee.
	Henry Bath, ..	12 *Apl.* 58	. ..	Remount Depôt at Allahabad,
	Samuel Thomas Goddard, ..	4 *Jan.* 59		
	James Quallett, ..	21 *June* 59		
	John Field, ..	15 *July* 59		

RIDING MASTERS.

Names.	Date of Rank.	Corps to which Posted.
Thomas Ray, *(Lieut. Vet. Estabt.)* ..	12 *Dec.* 40	
Thomas Bradshaw, *(Lieut. Vet. Estabt.)*	23 *Oct.* 46	4th European Light Cavalry.
William Keily, *(Lieut. Vet. Estabt)* ..	18 *Feb.* 48	1st European Light Cavalry.
Charles Loder, *(Lieut. Vet. Estabt.)* ..	5 *Mar.* 49	2nd European Light Cavalry.
S. Budd., *(Unattached Capt. 14th Sep. 57.)*	1 *June* 50	1st Brigade Horse Artillery.
James Boucher, ...	28 *Mar.* 52	3rd European Light Cavalry.
David Walsh, ...	8 *Dec.* 52	
Richard Crux, ...	30 *Mar.* 53	2nd Brigade H. A.
John Brennan, ...	17 *Sep.* 53	
William Langdale, ..	23 *Oct.* 56	Cavalry Depôt. Hazareebaugh.
Valentine Blake Cullen, ..	16 *Jan.* 57	5th European Light Cavalry.
Jeremiah O'Brien, *(Unattached Ensign,)*	20 *Apl.* 58	3rd Brigade of Horse Artillery.

INVALID ESTABLISHMENT.—Remodelled by G. G. O. 23 *June* 1857.

Head-Quarters, Chunar.

Two Companies of Artillery and two Companies of Infantry—Europeans.

Facings—*Blue*. Lace—*Gold*.

N. B. The Names in Italics are those of Officers who have been transferred to the Invalid Pension List.

Fur. Reg.	Cadet.	Lieut. Colonels.	From what Regiment.	2nd Lieut. Cornet, or Ensign.	Lieut.	Captain.	Major.	Lieut. Colonel.	Period of Service before transfer. Y	M.	When Invalided.	Period of Service.		Remarks.
	1807	John Angelo, ..	8th Lt. Cavy.	30 *Apl.* 08	1 *Sep.* 18	1 *May* 24	30 *Oct.* 48	19 *June* 46	45	1	27 *May* 53	51	2	Deyrah.
	1808	George Blake, ..	Artillery, ..	27 *Mar.* 09	23 *Aug.* 13	16 *July* 23	25 *Apl.* 38	15 *Jan.* 44	38	8	1 *Dec.* 47	50	8	Commanding at Chunar.
	1807	S. Lewis Thornton,	13th Regt.N.I.	9 *Oct.* 08	16 *Jan.* 12	13 *May* 25	28 *June* 38	9 *Mar.* 49	41	4	1 *Mar.* 50	50	8	Meerut.
	1821	C. D. Blair, C. B., *P.*,	8th Lt. Cavy.	17 *May* 22	1 *May* 24	23 *Dec.* 31	4 *Nov.* 39	20 *Apl.* 49	30	5	28 *Oct.* 52	37	1	Umballah.
	1808	L. H. Smith, ..	5th Lt. Cavy.	24 *Apl.* 09	1 *Sept.* 18	24 *Apl.* 24 1 *May* 24	28 *June* 38 12 *Apl.* 49	11 *Nov.* 51 4 *Nov.* 54	44	8	1 *April* 54	49	11	
		Majors,												
	1805	Francis Rutledge, ..	38th N. I.,	.. ..	.. ..	.. ..	1 *Dec.* 30		..	..	31 *Dec.* 30	53	6	Calcutta.
	1815	Edmund Swetenham,	Engineers,	1 *Sep.* 18	18 *May* 21	28 *Sep.* 27	20 *May* 39		22	0	30 *Sep.* 40	40	9	Hills North of Deyrah.
	1819	Frederick Angelo, ..	7th Cavalry,	10 *Jan.* 20	14 *Aug.* 22	6 *Aug.* 31	26 *July* 41		21	8	28 *Sep.* 41	39	5	Presidency.
	~~1817~~	~~Ralph Thorpe,~~ ..	14th Regt.N.I.	.. ..	21 *Oct.* 18	23 *May* 28	23 *Nov.* 41		..	..	10 *June* 42	41	6	Presidency.
	1820	Wm. Mills Tritton,	26th Regt.N.I.	4 *July* 21	1 *Nov.* 23	30 *Jan.* 30	22 *Nov.* 43		22	5	14 *Dec.* 43	38	..	Mussoorie.
O.	1816	Henry Patch, ..	73rd Regt.N.I.	.. ..	1 *Aug.* 18	6 *Aug.* 34	29 *May* 44		..	..	4 *Apl.* 45	..	..	Fur. S. C. 26 Feb. 56.
	1818	James Stevens, ..	6th Regt.N.I.	20 *May* 19	28 *June* 21	18 *July* 31	9 *Nov.* 46		..	..	31 *Dec.* 50	38	1	
	1823	H. Christian Talbot,	61st Regt.N.I.	17 *Jan.* 24	13 *May* 25	11 *Oct.* 38	11 *Apl.* 51		27	7	1 *Aug.* 51	35	5	
O.	1822	Charles Boulton, ..	47th Regt.N.I.	23 *May* 23	13 *May* 25	15 *Apl.* 38	11 *Nov.* 51 13 *Dec.* 53		31	..	31 *Jan.* 54	36	5	Fur. S. C. 24 Feb. 59.
	~~1828~~	~~James Grant,~~ ..	22nd Regt.N.I	16 *Apl.* 28	20 *June* 36	*Brevet* 16 *Apl.* 43 3 *June* 45	*Brevet* 20 *June* 54 15 *May* 55		27	8	1 *Dec.* 55	31	2	
	1824	J. H. Blanshard, ..	63rd Regt.N.I.	11 *May* 24	13 *May* 25	*Brevet* 11 *May* 39 14 *Oct.* 41	*Brevet* 11 *Nov.* 51 19 *Jan.* 55		31	8	31 *Dec.* 55	35	2	
	1824	*M. E. Loftie P.*, ..	30th N. I.,	21 *Oct.* 24	12 *May* 27	*Brevet* 21 *Oct.* 39 1 *Dec.* 39	*Brevet* 19 *June* 46 11 *May* 57	*Brevet* 20 *June* 54	33	8	9 *June* 58	34	9	Meerut.
	1836	W. K. Haslewood, ..	1st Europeans,	27 *June* 36	10 *Aug.* 38	1 *Apl.* 49	20 *Sep.* 58		13	6	23 *Jan.* 50	23	..	

INVALID ESTABLISHMENT.—(*Continued.*)

Fur. Reg.	Cadet.	Captains.	From what Regiment.	2nd Lieut. Cornet, or Ensign.	Lieut.	Captain.	Period of Service before transfer.		When Invalided.	Period of Service.		Remarks.
	1823	Richard Francis Macvitie, ..	49th Regt. N.I.	1 *May* 24	13 *May* 25	26 *Apl.* 33	20	10	14 *Mar.* 45	35	2	Calcutta.
N.	1820	Robert Henry Miles, ..	1st Regt. N.I.	5 *May* 21	11 *Sep.* 23	20 *June* 33	28	8	1 *Feb.* 50	38	1	Lv. S.C. to 19 Aug.
	1823	John Dixon Nash, ..	33rd Regt. N.I.	.. ..	7 *Jan.* 25	30 *May* 34	..	..	11 *Dec.* 37	35	6	Chandernagore.
	1822	Charles Jorden, ..	1st Europeans.	1 *July* 23	27 *May* 24	16 *Dec.* 35	21	0	23 *July* 44	35	11	Offg. Barrack Master. Meerut.
	1823	Lewis William Gibson, ..	27th Regt. N.I..	13 *Feb.* 24	22 *Sep.* 25	15 *Feb.* 36	21	11	6 *Feb.* 46	35	4	Meerut.
	1825	Thomas Hutton, ..	37th Regt. N.I.	28 *Sep.* 25	12 *Sep.* 27	27 *Oct.* 38	16	2	24 *Dec.* 41	33	8	Meerut.
	1823	William James Rind, ..	71st Regt. N.I.	27 *Jan.* 24	14 *July* 25	17 *Jan.* 39	25	10	7 *Dec.* 49	35	5	Ditto.
O.	1824	Henry Charles Gilmore, ..	59th Regt. N.I.	19 *Jan.* 25	3 *Apl.* 26	9 *Jan.* 40	18	5	7 *July* 43	34	5	Leave S. C. for 2 years G. O. 21 August 1857.
	1828	Collin Mc. F. Collins, ..	25th Regt. N.I.	8 *Jan.* 29	7 *Aug.* 34	7 *Nov.* 40	12	3	5 *May* 41	30	5	Mussoorie.
	1825	Jos. R. B. Andrews, ..	52nd Regt. N.I.	1 *Jan.* 26	18 *Feb.* 28	1 *Jan.* 41	20	9	2 *Oct.* 46	33	6	Simla.
	1825	William Hutton Tweedale, ..	8th Cavalry, ..	5 *Feb.* 26	5 *Oct.* 36	5 *Feb.* 41	23	6	1 *Sep.* 49	33	4	Hills North of Deyrah,
	1825	John Dunkin Macnaghten, *P*	5th Cavalry, ..	13 *June* 26	14 *Dec.* 35	13 *Jan.* 41	19	8	6 *Mar.* 46	33	..	Presidency Division.
	1826	Frederick Samler, ..	10th Regt. N.I.	8 *May* 27	10 *Jan.* 33	8 *May* 42	18	4	10 *Sep.* 45	32	2	Darjeeling.
	1826	Samuel Smith, ..	9th Cavalry, ..	13 *Oct.* 27	28 *Apl.* 32	13 *Oct.* 42	19	0	16 *Oct.* 46	31	9	Residing at Nynee Tâl.
	1827	Thomas Septimus Jervis, ..	71st Regt. N.I.	4 *Nov.* 27	31 *Jan.* 35	4 *Nov.* 42	19	5	1 *May* 47	31	7	Hills North of Dehra.
	1828	James Masson, ..	57th Regt. N.I.	4 *Dec.* 28	8 *July* 36	4 *Dec.* 43	19	0	31 *Dec.* 47	30	6	Darjeeling.

INVALID ESTABLISHMENT.—*(Continued.)*

Fur. Reg.	Cadet.	Captains.	From what Regiment	2nd Lieut. Cornet, or Ensign.	Lieut.	Captain.	Period of Service before transfer.		When Invalided.	Period of Service.		Remarks.
	1824	Edward Pelham Master, ..	Artillery, ..	16 *Dec.* 24	24 *May* 29	*bt. m.* 7 *June* 49. 20 *Feb.* 44.	26	6	1 *July* 51	34	6	Cawnpore Divn.—Bt. Capt. 16 Dec. 39.
O.	~~1828~~	~~Edward Magnay,~~ ..	1st Europeans,	31 *Mar.* 29	15 *Nov.* 36	31 *Aug.* 44	19	1	1 *Apl.* 49	29	3	Fur., P. A. 21 Jan. 59.
	....	John Cross, ..	From Warrant	Officers' list.	.. ..	17 *Apl.* 45	...	..	17 *Apl.* 45	..	..	Penang.
	1836	Charles Henry Deane Spread,	72nd Regt. N.I.	1 *July* 36	7 *Feb.* 38	6 *June* 45	11	7	1 *Feb.* 48	22	..	Mussoorie, or Deyrah Dhoon.
	1835	Gerald Aug. Fk. Hervey, *P C*	3rd N.I.	12 *Dec.* 34	19 *Apl.* 39	12 *Oct.* 45	..	..	7 *Jan.* 53	23	6	Offg. Barrack Master at Umballah.
	1831	Philip G. Cornish,† ..	10th N.I. ..	8 *Dec.* 31	8 *Sep.* 40	8 *Dec.* 46	12	0	1 *Oct.* 52	18	9	Darjeeling.
	1836	Frederick J. Thompson,† ..	2nd Europeans,	6 *Feb.* 36	16 *July* 49	21 *July* 48	16	1	1 *Mar.* 52	23	5	Sirhind Division.
	1833	Alexander Carre Boswell,† ..	19th Regt. N.I.	1 *Mar.* 34	14 *Apl.* 37	1 *Mar.* 49	16	8	1 *Nov.* 50	25	4	Sirhind Circle.
	1838	P. J. Comyn, *P H,* ..	68th Regt. N. I.	9 *Mar.* 38	26 *Aug.* 42	10 *Mar.* 49	15	4	13 *Sep.* 53	21	4	Meerut Circle.
	1837	R. Wm. H. Fanshawe, ..	1st Eur. Bl. Fus.	12 *June* 37	3 *Oct.* 40	21 *Dec.* 45	16	7	1 *Oct.* 53	22	..	Allygurh.
	1840	James Murray,† ..	9th Regt. N. I.	31 *July* 40	22 *Dec.* 43	24 *Dec.* 53	15	1	7 *Sep.* 55	18	11	Landour Depôt.
O.	1834	E. W. Bristow,† ..	1st Regt. N. I.	12 *Dec.* 34	6 *July* 37	*Brevet* 12 *Dec.* 49 1 *Feb.* 50	21	1	4 *Jan.* 56	24	7	Leave S. C. to the Cape of Good Hope for 2 years G. O., 22 July 58.
N.	1843	P. R. Innes,(*a*) ..	1st Eur. Bl. Fus.	30 *Dec.* 43	6 *Feb.* 46	10 *May* 54	12	1	1 *Feb.* 56	15	6	Army clothing Agent, 1st Division, Allahabad.
	1839	W. W. Aubert, *P H,* ..	34th N.I. ..	28 *July* 39	13 *Oct.* 41	29 *June* 53	18	3	11 *Dec.* 57	19	10	Pay Master and Supdt. of Native Pensioners Barrackpore Circle.
	1835	W. O. Harris,† ..	32nd N. I. ...	11 *Dec.* 35	28 *Oct.* 39	3 *Apl.* 50	22	..	20 *Nov.* 57	23	8	
O.	1828	B. Cary,†(*b*) ..	6th N. I. ..	4 *Dec.* 28	12 *Dec.* 37	*Brevet* 4 *Dec.* 43 17 *Nov.* 50.	29	1	29 *Jan.* 58	30	7	Fur. S. C. 14 July 57.
	1840	*R. W. Pilkington, P, H,* ..	20th N. I., ..	17 *Sep.* 40	14 *Mar.* 43	28 *Nov.* 54	17	4	5 *Feb.* 58	18	10	Fur. S. C. 5 Feb. 58.
	1840	*M. J. Vibart,*† ..	Artillery, ..	11 *June* 40	20 *Jan.* 42	7 *July* 53	17	9	26 *Mar.* 58	19	1	
	1841	N. M. Strover, *PH,* ..	3rd En. Regt. ..	27 *Feb.* 41	19 *Nov.* 42	17 *Dec.* 55	17	17	1 *May* 58	18	4	Presidency.
	1843	*J. R. R. Coombs, P, C, H,* ..	42nd L. I., ..	25 *Feb.* 43	21 *Dec.* 45	18 *Sep.* 57	15	6	24 *Aug.* 58	16	5	

(*a*) Has furnished certificates of qualification in Surveying and Civil Engineering.
(*b*) Brevet Major, 20th June 1854.

INVALID ESTABLISHMENT.—(Continued.)

Fur. Reg.	Cadet.	Lieutenants.	From what Regiment.	2nd Lieut. Cornet, or Ensign.	Lieut.	Period of Service before transfer.		When Invalided.	Period of Service.		Remarks.
	1818	Solomon Earle, ..	43rd N. I. ..	.. ..	8 *June* 20	..	..	11 *Apl.* 28	40	6	Presidency.
N.	1825	Osborne Campbell, ..	43rd N. I. ..	.. ..	24 *Jan.* 29	..	..	10 *Sep.* 38	33	6	Fur. S. C. 18 Feb. 59.
	1827	George Pengree, ..	39th N. I. ..	.. ..	1 *Oct.* 32	..	..	13 *Nov.* 37	31	6	Simla.
	1828	Thomas Harvey Hunter, ..	26th Regt. N. I.	7 *Feb.* 29	7 *May* 35	12	8	3 *Nov.* 41	30	4	Mussoorie.
	1827	Craufurd Crossman,	7th Regt. N. I.	12 *June* 28	8 *Oct.* 39 c12 *June* 43	17	5	5 *Dec.* 45	31	..	Post Master, Barrackpore.
	1835	John Samuel Bristow, ..	71st Regt. N. I.	17 *Jan.* 36	18 *Aug.* 40	8	9	1 *Nov.* 44	23	5	Presidency.
	1838	William Hampton, ..	14th Regt. N. I.	21 *Aug.* 39	12 *Jan.* 42	8	8	1 *May* 48	19	10	Presidency Division.
	1836	Fredk. James Alexander, ..	8th Cavalry, ..	26 *July* 37	10 *July* 44	11	6	17 *Feb.* 49	21	11	Hills, Meerut Circle.
	1839	John Frederick Pogson, P. (a)	47th Regt. N. I.	6 *July* 39	16 *July* 42	12	0	31 *July* 51	19	11	
	1844	*Hon.* C. J. D. Arbuthnott, ..	10th Regt. L. C.	29 *Jan.* 44	20 *Apl.* 49	9	..	1 *Sep.* 53	14	6	2nd in Command of the 4th Bengal Police, Battn
	1845	Fredk H. Kennedy,† ..	• 8th Regt. N. I,	12 *Jan.* 45	21 *June* 50	7	..	1 *Feb.* 52	14	5	Sirhind Division (Umballah).
	1844	Harry Bowles, ..	61st Regt. N. I.	29 *Feb.* 44	11 *April* 51	..	..	24 *Oct.* 51	14	6	Offg Barrack Master at Nynee Tal and Moradabad
O.		John Moore, (Unattached,)	ScindeRifleCorps	.. ..	13 *Feb.* 52	..	..	1 *Dec.* 55	..	..	Fur. S. C. 13 Mar. 56.
	1845	*E. J. Goodridge,* ..	Artillery, ..	14 *June* 45	20 *June* 49	12	11	25 *May* 58	14	1	Fur. S. C. 8 May 1858.
		Surgeons.		*Asst. Surg.*	*Surgeon.*						
	1798	William Woolley, ..	.. ..	24 *Aug.* 11	1 *June* 13	..	..	.. ..	60	6	Serampore.
	1820	William Edward Carte, A.B.	.. ..	7 *Oct.* 33	15 *Nov.* 42	..	..	.. ..	38	6	Simla.
	1830	Thomas Smith, M.D.,† ..	.. ..	16 *Mar.* 48	15 *Mar.* 53	21	6	15 *Mar.* 53	27	10	Meerut.

(a) Has furnished the certificate of qualification in Surveying.

EUROPEAN INVALID VETERAN COMPANY.—CHUNAR.

VETERAN ESTABLISHMENT.

Name		Date	Year	Remarks
Captains.				
John Cross,	..	17 *Apl.*	45	Penang.
Thomas Spencer,	..	1 *Nov.*	56	Assist. Comy., Ordnance Department.
William Raynor,	..	11 *May*	57	Depy. Comy., Ordnance Department.
George Forrest,	..	11 *May*	57	Assist. Comy., Ordnance, Dept.
Henry Michell,	..	20 *Sep.*	58	Assist. Comy. Ordnance Department.
Lieutenants.				
George McDowell,	..	31 *July*	50	Peshawur.
Thomas Ray,	..	28 *June*	51	
Joseph Hamilton,	..	2 *Sep.*	51	Fur. S. C. 15th Sep. 57.
Isham Baggs,	..	2 *Feb.*	52	Depy. Comy., Army Comt. Department.
William Keily,	..	31 *May*	52	Riding Master 1st En. Light Cavalry.
John Fairweather,	..	30 *May*	53	Agra.
Joseph Green,	..	16 *Jan.*	54	Assist. Comy., Ordnance Dept.
T. Bradshaw,	..	16 *May*	54	Riding Master 4th En. Light Cavalry.
Charles Loder,	..	7 *Apl.*	56	Riding Master 2nd En. Light Cavalry.
William May,	..	3 *Feb.*	57	Deputy Comy. Army Commt. Dept.
Sylvester Fox,	..	31 *Aug.*	57	Asst. Comy. Ordnance Dept.
John Stotesbury,	..	14 *Sep.*	57	Depy. Asst. Comy. Ordnance Dept.
William Kelly,	..	12 *July*	58	Asst. Comy. Ordnance Dept.
William Parry,	..	12 *July*	58	Asst. Comy. Ordnance Dept.
I. J. Corcoran,	..	20 *Sep.*	58	Deputy Asst. Comy. Ordnance Dept.
James Lamb,	..	20 *Sep.*	58	Asst. Comy. Ordnance Dept.
C. Sheridan,	..	18 *Oct.*	58	Deputy Asst. Comy. Ordnance Dept.
J. Buckley,	..	18 *Oct.*	58	Deputy Asst. Comy. Ordnance Dept.
J. Burnell,	..	3 *Jan.*	59	Junior Commy. Army Commt. Dept.
M. McGrath,	..	3 *Jan.*	59	Deputy Asst. Commy. Ordnance Dept.
D. Gair,	..	18 *May*	59	Deputy Asst. Commy. D. P. Works.
Conductors.				
Isaac Lemon,	..	10 *Mar.*	54	Attached to the Office of the Adjt. Genl. of the Army.
Edward Skiddy,	..	11 *Mar.*	59	Ditto, ditto.

PENSION ESTABLISHMENT.

Names.	Former Rank.	Date of Rank.	When Pensioned.	Remarks.
Mr. Thomas Saunders Knox,	Capt. of Cavalry,..	11 *Mar.* 05	1 *May* 09	Europe.
Mr. John Henry Warner, ..	Capt. of Infantry,	12 *May* 11	1 *Sep.* 15	Presidency.
Mr. Francis Palmer, ..	Capt. of Cavalry,..	9 *Apl.* 23	28 *Dec.* 27	Presidency.
Mr. Geo. Brydges P. Field,.	Capt. of Infantry,	1 *Jan.* 18	15 *Apl.* 28	Presidency.
Mr. John Tauzia Savary, ..	Capt. of Infantry,	10 *May* 28	26 *Mar.* 30	Cawnpore.
Mr. James Gresham, ..	Lieut. of Infantry,	11 *July* 23	25 *Feb.* 25	
Mr. Francis Warwick, ..	Lieut. of Infantry,	11 *July* 23	2 *Feb.* 27	PostMaster, Moradabad.
Mr. William Bartlett, ..	Lieut. of Infantry,	8 *May* 29	30 *Apl.* 30	Presidency.
Mr. Robert Crofton, ..	Lieut. of Infantry,	1 *May* 24	15 *Apl.* 31	Presidency.
Mr. John Russell, ..	Lieut. of Infantry,	31 *July* 23	13 *May* 31	Cawnpore.
Mr. James Warner Scott, ..	Lieut. of Artillery,	14 *Jan.* 21	28 *Jan.* 33	
Mr. James Vansittart Law,..	Lieut. of Infantry,	23 *Sep.* 26	30 *Aug.* 33	Cawnpore.
Mr. Arthur Pitt Begbie, ..	Bt. Capt. of Arty.,	18 *Dec.* 38	11 *Mar.* 39	Meerut.
Mr. Arthur Campbell Wale,	Lieut. of Infantry,	11 *Oct.* 47	31 *Dec.* 47	Europe.
Mr. George Durant, ..	Ensign of Infantry,	13 *June* 26	31 *Oct.* 33	Europe.
Mr. John Keighley, ..	3rd Seikh Infy. unattached Ensign,	26 *Feb.* 47	17 *Dec.* 52	Presidency.

WARRANT OFFICERS.

On the Pension Establishment.

Rank and Names		Date of Rank.	When Invalided.	Remarks.
Conductors.				
John Tresham,	..	22 *Nov.* 23	26 *Sep.* 36	Presidency.
Edward Townsend,	..	20 *May* 25	9 *Dec.* 40	Fur. P. A. 21 Dec. 55.
John McGowan,	..	18 *Sep.* 30	20 *Nov.* 46	Cawnpore.
William Hunt,	..	28 *July* 33	30 *Dec.* 39	Meerut.
William Cox,	..	25 *Sep.* 33	26 *Mar.* 47	Presidency.
Luke Keelan,	..	1 *Jan.* 34	3 *Feb.* 43	Benares.
George Patton,	..	17 *June* 38	13 *Sep.* 44	Benares.
Thomas Johnson,	..	8 *Nov.* 40	25 *Nov.* 48	Umballah.
Francis Volkers,	..	19 *Jan.* 42	20 *Feb.* 46	Benares.
Martin Lahey,	..	3 *Feb.* 43	8 *May* 46	Presidency.
John Todd,	..	5 *Dec.* 43	9 *May* 51	Meerut.
Robert Grassby,	..	18 *Feb.* 45	19 *Mar.* 52	Within the Presy. of Bengal.
Charles Ryall,	..	17 *Apl.* 45	2 *May* 51	Fur S. C. 22 Sep. 58.
W. Parsons,	..	15 *Aug.* 45	27 *Nov.* 52	Presidency.
Bartholomew Rattigan,	..	19 *Oct.* 52	29 *Dec.* 52	Lahore.
J. Hume,	..	30 *Sep.* 48	4 *Mar.* 53	Presidency.
W. H. Blackburne,	..	25 *Nov.* 48	7 *Apl.* 54	Landour.
E. McGuire,	..	28 *June* 49	7 *Jan.* 53	Cawnpore.
Charles Jones,	..	21 *Feb.* 51	28 *Nov.* 53	Europe.
Edward Kinsley,	..	13 *Oct.* 51	15 *Nov.* 53	Cawnpore.
Robert Hampton,	..	12 *Jan.* 53	22 *Apl.* 55	Europe.
Thomas Wear,	..	27 *Nov.* 52	23 *Dec.* 53	Presidency.
Thomas Mills,	..	6 *Sep.* 48	8 *Mar.* 55	Presidency.
Daniel O'Brien,	..	8 *Apl.* 54	28 *Sep.* 55	
William Murphy,	..	6 *May* 50	20 *May* 56	India.
William Vials,	..	18 *Aug.* 53	26 *Sep.* 56	Calcutta.
John Crawford,	..	21 *June* 54	29 *Nov.* 55	India.
Sub-Conductors.				
William Workman,	..	26 *Nov.* 30	27 *Dec.* 33	Presidency.
Ormond Stonehewer,	..	4 *Oct.* 51	8 *Apl.* 52	Presidency.
John Still,	..	21 *April* 54	5 *Feb* 56	
William Andrews,	..	27 *Mar.* 56	2 *July* 58	India.
Riding Master.				
Urial Jordan,	..	25 *May* 27	1 *Nov.* 44	Residence unknown.
Apothecaries.				
Valentine William Hurley,	..	7 *Sep.* 16	8 *May* 29	Benares.
James Davoren,	..	26 *Dec.* 18	15 *Apl.* 42	Presidency.
James Purkis,	..	21 *Oct.* 24	11 *Nov.* 39	Cawnpore.
Charles Lamborn,	..	25 *Nov.* 24	25 *Mar.* 40	Presidency.
John Wilson,	..	23 *Jan.* 34	31 *Oct.* 45	Presidency.
W. G. Carrison,	..	11 *Nov.* 39	14 *Mar.* 51	Calcutta.
James Jarves,	..	15 *Nov.* 44	11 *Apl.* 51	Calcutta.
Anthony Defegrady,	..	15 *Jan.* 29	6 *Dec.* 52	Presidency.
John Robinson,	..	15 *Nov.* 44	28 *Dec.* 49	Meerut.
William Watson,	..	27 *Mar.* 49	18 *Sep.* 57	India.
Edward George,	..	5 *Aug.* 39	22 *Oct.* 57	India.
John Beale,	..	26 *May* 17	20 *Nov.* 57	India.
James Watson,	..	28 *Sep.* 40	29 *Jan.* 58	India.
William Overitt,	..	31 *Oct.* 45	29 *Jan.* 58	India.
John Ogden,	..	18 *Apl.* 53	25 *May* 58	India.
Charles Simons,	..	13 *Oct.* 36	18 *Nov.* 58	India.
James Hefferan,	..	17 *Aug.* 43	24 *Feb.* 59	India.
M. R. Crawford, M. R. C. S.	..	27 *Oct.* 43	24 *Feb.* 59	India.
George Hurst,	..	5 *Oct.* 50	26 *May* 59	India.
Assistant Apothecary.				
John O'Connor,	..	9 *Dec.* 24	27 *Dec.* 33	Europe.
Hospital Stewards.				
William Kidd,	..	17 *Feb.* 21	25 *July* 33	Benares.
John Lewis DeSouza,	..	15 *Dec.* 21	29 *Sep.* 41	Benares.
John Roberts,	..	21 *Oct.* 24	24 *May* 44	Meerut.
Gabriel Dalby,	..	30 *Oct.* 29	4 *Sep.* 46	Benares.
Francis Valley,	..	23 *Jan.* 34	12 *May* 41	Presidency.
Robert Cummins,	..	10 *July* 39	14 *Apl.* 52	Cawnpore.
Abraham Beatson,	..	12 *Feb.* 41	8 *Sep.* 49	Umballah.
John Gorman,	..	15 *Nov.* 44	23 *Apl.* 47	Presidency.
John Hennessy,	..	17 *Dec.* 24	15 *Mar.* 59	India.

LIST OF MILITARY AND MEDICAL OFFICERS ON CIVIL OR POLITICAL EMPLOY.

Corps.	Rank and Names.	Date of Appointment.	Designation.
	MILITARY.		
Artillery, ..	Col. *Sir* R. C. Shakespear, *Kt.*, ..	30 *Apl.* 59	Agent to the Governor Genl. for Central India.
Artillery, ..	Major H. E. L. Thuillier,	13 *Apl.* 49	Deputy and Reve. Surveyor General, and Supdt. of the Mathematical Instrument Maker's Dept.
		6 *Dec.* 50	And a Commissioner for the Improvement of the Town of Calcutta.
Artillery, ..	Major C. Douglas, ...	25 *Apl.* 59	Offg. Professor of Natural Philosophy and Astronomy in the Presy. College.
Artillery, ..	Capt. D. C. Vanrenen, ..	3 *Oct.* 46	Revenue Surveyor, 1st Division, Nagpore—Fur. S. C. 29 Mar. 59.
Artillery, ..	Major C. V. Bowie, ..	26 *June* 54	Supdt. Mysore Princes, Ex-Ameers of Scinde, and Sikh Sirdars.—Fur. S. C. 15 Mar. 59.
Artillery, ..	Captain H. M. Boddam,	22 *June* 58	Assist. General Supdt. for the Suppression of Thuggee and Dacoitee in the Moorshedabad Circle and Assist. to the Commr. for the Suppression of Dacoitee in Bengal.
Artillery, ..	Capt. A. R. Fuller, ..	27 *Mar.* 55	Inspector in the Dept. of Public Instruction in the N.W.P.—Fur. P. A. 10 May 59.
Artillery, ..	Capt. R. Murray, ..	29 *Oct.* 57	Depy. Supdt. of Electric Telegraphs in India and in charge of the Lines in the Punjaub and Scinde. —Fur. S, C, 13 Jan. 59.
Artillery, ..	Capt. J. H. Grant, ..	8 *June* 56	Assist. Revenue Surveyor, Nagpore Survey.
Artillery, ..	Capt. E. L. Earle, ..	30 *June* 56	Professor of Surveying in the Thomason Civil Engineering College, Roorkee.
Artillery, ..	Capt. E. H. Willoughby,	9 *Feb.* 58	Revenue Surveyor, No. 2, Bengal Estab., G. T. Survey, Nagpore..—Fur. S. C. 30th Apl. 58.
Artillery, ..	Capt. G. C. Depree, ..	20 *Oct.* 54	Asst. Surveyor Topographical Survey.
		13 *Sep.* 56	Ex. Officio Asst. Commissioner of Chota Nagpore. —Fur. S. C. 5th Jan, 59.
Artillery, ..	Lieut. P. Thompson, ..	6 *Oct.* 58	Asst. Reve. Surveyor Sind Saugor Doab.
Engineers, .	Lt. Col. *Sir* R. Napier, K. C. B., ..	1 *May* 54	Chief Engr. in the Punjaub and in charge of Civil Engr.'s Dept. in the Punjaub.
		30 *June* 57	Offg. Chief Engineer, L. P.—(On Field Service.)
Engineers, .	Lt. Col. A.S. Waugh, ..	16 *Dec.* 53	Surveyor Genl. of India, and Supt. of the Great Trigonometrical Survey, Deyrah Dhoon.
Engineers, .	Lt.Col. E.L.Ommanney,	14 *Apl.* 57	Offg. Chief Engr. Punjaub and in charge of the Civil Engr.'s Dept. Punjaub. [S. C. 31 Dec.
Engineers, .	Major R. Strachey, ..	13 *Sep.* 58	Consulting Engineer, Railway Department.—Lv.
Engineers, .	Major J. R. Becher, ..	28 *Apl.* 54	Deputy Commr., 1st class, Punjaub (Hazarah.) On duty at Cashmere.
Engineers, .	Lt. Col. H. Yule, ..	5 *Jan.* 59	Secy. to the Govt. of India Dept. P. W.
Engineers, .	Captain R. Maclagan, ..	13 *Oct.* 57	Principal of the Thomason College of Civil Engineering at Roorkee.
Engineers, .	Major E. J. Lake, ..	4 *Oct.* 57	Commissioner, Trans Sutlej States.
Engineers, .	Capt. C. J. Hodgson, ..	6 *Apl.* 58	Deputy Consulting Engr., Railway Department, Bengal (Offg. Consulting Engineer.)
Engineers, .	Capt. G. Sim, ..	5 *July* 58	Deputy Consulting Engineer, Railway Dept.
Engineers, .	Capt. A. Fraser, ..	9 *Mar.* 59	Under Secy. to the Govt. of India D. P. Works.
Engineers, .	Captain R. Young, ..	2 *July* 59	Deputy Commr. Hosheyarpore.
Engineers, .	Maj. WW.H. Greathed,	14 *June* 59	Consulting Engr. Railway Dept N. W. P.
Engineers, .	Capt. W. Henderson, ..	10 *Apl.* 51	Asst. Civil Engineer, Punjaub.
Engineers, ,	Major J. G. Medley, ..	21 *Sep.* 58	Deputy consulting Engineer, Railway Dept.,
Engineers, .	Capt. E. Davidson, ..	6 *Dec.* 58	Deputy consulting Engineer, Railway Dept.,
Engineers, .	Capt. E.C. S. Williams,	15 *Sep.* 56	Princpl. of the Civil Engrg. College, Presidency,
		13 *Jan.* 57	Member of the Board of Examiners.—Fur. S. C. 17 Jan. 59.

Officers on Civil or Political Employ—*Continued.*

Corps.	*Rank and Names.*	*Date of Appointment.*	Designation.
	Military.		
Engineers,..	Capt. H. W. Gulliver, ..	28 *Mar.* 54	Asst. Civil Engineer, Punjaub. [Roorkee.
Engineers, ..	Maj. G. T. Chesney ..	31 *Mar.* 56	Asst. to the Principal of the Thomason College,
		21 *Jan,* 59	Offg. Principal of the Civil Engineering College, Calcutta. [mere series, Dehra Dhoon.
Engineers, .	Capt.T.G.Montgomerie,	24 *Mar.* 54	First Asst. Great Trigonometrical Survey, Cash-
Engineers,..	Capt. D. G. Robinson,	25 *Oct.* 47	In charge of Topographical Survey, No. 1, Bengal Estabmt., G. T. Survey, Dehra Dhoon.
Engineers, .	Lieut. J. P. Basevi, ..	1 *Jan.* 58	First Assistant Great Trigonometrical Survey, Indus series, Dehra Ishmael Khan.
Engineers,	Lieut. A. M. Brandreth,	5 *May* 59	Offg. Asst. Principal of the Thomason Civil Engineering College, Roorkee.
Engineers,	Lieu t. HT. Gordon,..	16 *June* 59	Professor of Constructive design in the Civil Engineering College, Calcutta.
1st E. L. C.,	Lt. Col. H. Drummond,	7 *Mar.* 56	Continuing a further exploration of the Iron beds along the face of the Kumaon Hills.
2nd E. L. C.	Col. G. St. P. Lawrence,	11 *Sep.* 57	Agent to the Governor General for the states of Rajpootanah.—Fur. S. C. 25 Apl. 59.
2nd E.L. C.,	Major R. G. Taylor, ..	15 *May* 58	Deputy Commisioner 1st Class, Punjaub.
		24 *Mar.* 59	Offg. Commr. of Leia Division.
3rd En. L. C.	Capt. W. Wyld, ..	20 *Jan.* 59	Captain of Police Umballa.
		1 *Feb.* 59	Offg. Asst. Military Secy. Lt. Governor, Punjab.
3rd En. L.C.	Capt. G. Delane, ..	22 *Mar.* 59	Offg. Supdt. Mysore Princes, Ex. Ameers of Scinde and Sikh Sirdars.
5th En. L.C.	Capt. A. P. C. Elliot, ..	23 *Feb.* 49	Asst. to the Genl. Supdt. of the operations for the suppression of Thuggee, Indore.—Fur. S. C. 8 Oct. 57.
5th E. L. C.,	Capt. W. F. Stephens,	10 *July* 57	Director of Public Instruction, Mysore.
1st En.B.F.,	{ Lieut. Col. H. B. Edwardes, C. B., }	19 *Oct.* 53	Commissioner and Supdt. of Peshawur—Furlough.
1st En.B.F.,	Capt. G. M. Battye, ..	24 *Feb.* 58	Asst. Commr. 1st class, Punjaub.—Fur. S. C. 20 Nov. 58. [bhoom.)
1st En. B.F.	Lieut. R. C. Birch, ..	26 *Aug.* 57	Senior Asst, Commr. of Chota Nagpore, (Sing-
2nd En.B.F.	Capt. R. N. Tronson,..	2 *Dec.* 51	A Captain of Police, Mooltan Division.
2nd En.B.F.	Capt, G. Gaynor, ..	19 *Dec.* 56	Town Magistrate at Dalhousie (Pegu.)—Fur. S. C. 23 Dec. 57. [Western Malwa.
2nd En.B.F.	Capt. B. Hawes, ..	22 *June* 59	Offg. Political Asst. in Nimar and Political Agent,
2nd En.B.F.	Capt. C. Baldwin, ..	12 *Mar.* 57	Asst. to the Commissioner of the Saugor and Nerbudda Territories.—Fur. P. A. 27 May 59
2ndEn.B.F.	Lieut. W. C. Hamilton,	11 *Oct.* 56	Asst. Commr. Saugor and Nerbudda Territories.
		4 *Dec.* 56	Offg. Depy. Commr. of Seonee.
3rd En. R.	Major H. M. Nation, ..	5 *Feb.* 50	Comdt. of the Behar Station Guards & Asst. Supdt. for the Suppression of Thuggee, Patna Circle, —Fur. P. A. 17 March 59.
3rd En. R.	Capt. E. T. Dalton, ..	1 *May* 58	Commissioner of Chotah Nagpore. [May 59.
3rd En. R.	Capt. B. T. Reid, ..	15 *May* 58	Depy. Commr. 2nd class, Punjaub Fur. S. C. 27th
3rd En. R.	Capt. T. H. Chamberlain,	11 *Apl.* 51	Asst. to the Supdt for the Suppression of Thuggee (Etawah.)—Invested with powers of Jt. Magte. in the Agra, Allahabad and Benares Divisions.
3rd En. R.	Capt. E. D. R. Ross,..	3 *Feb.* 57	Offg. Asst. to the Genl. Supdt. of operations for the suppression of Thuggee and Dacoitee atEtawah.
		25 *Mar.* 57	Vested with the powers of jt. magte. in the Ghazeepore, Azimghur, Juanpore, Benares, Mirzapore, Allahabad, Banda, Futtehpore, Humeerpore, Jaloun, Cawnpore, Etawah, Furruckabad, Mynpoorie, Etah, Agra, Allyghur, Muttra, Meerut, Delhi and Paneeput Districts.
4th En. R.	Capt. H. J. Hawes, ..	21 *June* 58	Deputy Commissioner, 3rd class, Punjaub, (Dera Ishmael Khan.)—Fur. S. C. 7th May 1858.
4th En. R.	Lieut. J. P. Martin, ..	20 *May* 57	Junior Asst. to the Commissioner of Assam, (Kamroop.)—Fur. S. C. 12 Mar. 1858.
4th En. R.	Capt. A. H. Ternan, ..	17 *Jan.* 59	Deputy Commissioner, Jaloun.—Lv. p. to Fur.
4th En. R.	Capt. H. Rose, ..	8 *Apl.* 52	Asst. Civil Engineer, Punjaub.
5th En. R.	Capt. H. C. Johnstone,	27 *May* 53	Revenue Surveyor, Derajat.
5th En. R.	Capt. W. McNeile,	15 *June* 59	Deputy Commr., 2d class, Punjaub.
5th En. R.	Lieut J. E. B. Parsons,	15 *May* 58	Asst. Commissioner 2nd class, Punjaub.

Officers on Civil or Political Employ—*Continued.*

Corps.	*Rank and Names.*	*Date of Appointment.*	Designation.
	Military.		
5th En. R.,	Lieut. E. C. Impey, ..	25 *Sep.* 58	Political Agent at Ulwur.
5th En. R.,	Capt. E. J. Rickards, ..	6 *Feb.* 58	Offg. Deputy Commissioner, Ajmere.
5th En. R,	Capt. S. F. Graham, ..	11 *Nov.* 58	Deputy Commissioner, 2nd class, Punjaub (Kohat.)
		9 *Feb.* 59	Offg. Deputy Commissioner, Peshawur.
6th En. R.,	Lt. Col. A. P. Phayre,	31 *Dec.* 52	Comr., Province of Pegu.
6th En. R.,	Captain R. T. Leigh, ..	9 *June* 58	Junior Assist. to the Commr. of Arracan.
6th En. R.,	Capt. G. H. Thompson, -	14 *Jan.* 59	Revenue Surveyor, of the Hazareebaugh Division.
6th En. R.,	Lieut. J. C. Horne, ..	15 *June* 59	Asst. Commr. 2d class in the Punjaub, (Umballah.)
6th En. R.	Captain W. R. Eliott, ..	15 *May* 58	Depy. Commr., 3rd class, Punjaub, (Thaneysur.)
2nd Gredrs.,	Capt. J. J. Hamilton, ..	12 *Aug.* 53	Asst. Commissioner, 1st class, Nizam's Territories.
4th N. I.,..	Captain O. J. McL. Farrington, ...	24 *Feb.* 58	Deputy Commr., 1st class, Punjaub, (Jullundur.) —Fur. S. C. 3rd Jan. 59.
4th N. I.,..	Lt. N. W. Elphinstone,	15 *June* 59	Deputy Commr. 3rd class Punjaub.—Lv. p. to Fur.
9th N. I.,..	Major G. Verner, ..	6 *Dec.* 58	Commissioner of Arracan.
10th N. I.,.	Lieut. Col. G. Ramsay,	1 *Apl.* 53	Resident, Nepal.
10th N. I.,..	Capt. C. P Hildebrand,	4 *Dec.* 56	Assistant Commissioner, Theyat Mew.
10th N. I.,..	Lieut. H. A. Browne,	28 *Jan.* 59	Settlement Officer in Pegu.
11th N. I.,.	Capt. B. P. Lloyd, ..	4 *Dec.* 57	Deputy Commr. of Ajmere, and Mhairwarra.—
11th N. I.,.	Capt. C. C. Robertson,	6 *Oct.* 54	Personal Asst. to the Commr., of Nagpore.
12th N. I...	Capt. R. R. Adams, ..	10 *Jan.* 59	Deputy Commr. 3rd class Punjaub.
12th N. I...	Capt. H. Stokes, ..	10 *May* 55	Asst. Commr. Punjaub.—Fur. S.C. 10 Apl. 56.
13th N. I.,.	Major W. McCulloch,..	7 *Mar.* 45	Political Agent, Munneepore.
13th N. I.,.	Capt. A. R. E. Hutchinson,	30 *Apl.* 59	Political Agent at Bhopal.
13th N. I.,.	Lt. W. B. Thomson, ..	17 *Jan.* 59	Deputy Commr. 2nd class, (Seonee.)
14th N. I.,.	Captain C. L. Showers,	4 *Feb.* 48	Asst. to the Govr. Genl.'s Agent, Rajpootana.
		13 *Mar.* 57	Offg. Political Agent in Meywar.
14th N. I.,..	Capt. F. A. V. Thurburn,	11 *Feb.* 56	Special Asst. to the Deputy Commr. of Lucknow, for Fyzabad.
		10 *May* 59	Offg. Depy. Commr. of Mohumdee, (Oudh.)
14th N. I.,.	Lieut. R. G. Sandeman,	6 *May* 59	Asst. Commr. 3rd Class Punjaub. [16 May 59.
15th N. I.,.	Major J. W. Carnegie,	17 *June* 59	Deputy Commr. 1st class Lucknow—Fur. S. C.
15th N. I.,.	Lieut. H. Phillpotts, ...	15 *Nov.* 57	Offg. Asst. Agent Govr. Genl., Rajpootanah.
15th N. I.,.	Lieut. C. T. O. Mayne,	18 *Oct.* 58	Asst. Commr. Jubbulpore Division.
16th (Grs.,)	Lieut. W. W. Boddam,	9 *Oct.* 58	Lieut. of Police, Jhujjur.
16th N. I. .	Lieut. G. G. Young, ..	12 *June* 58	Asst. Commr. 3rd Class, Rawul Pindee.
17th N. I.,	Lt. Col. G. W. Hamilton,	1 *May* 54	Comr., Mooltan Division.
17th N. I.,.	Capt. J. Fendall, ..	24 *Feb* 58	Asst. Commr. 1st class, Punjaub. (Hosheyarpore.)
		18 *Apl.* 59	Offg. Deputy Commr. of Jhujjur.
17th N. I.,.	Capt. J. A. Steel, ..	12 *Aug.* 58	Asst. Commr. 1st class, Oudh.
18th N. I.,.	Capt. H. S. Bivar, ..	4 *June* 58	1st class Princl. Asst. to the Commr. of Assam.
18th N. I...	Capt. A. K. Comber, ..	12 *July* 59	1st class Principal Asst. to the Commr. of Assam. (Nowgong.)
18th N. I.,.	Lieut. J. Macdonald, ..	4 *Sept.* 52	Offg. Revenue Surveyor, Sindh.
18th N. I.,.	Lt. J. W. H. Johnstone,.	6 *May* 58	Asst. Commr. 3rd class, Punjaub.
19th N. I.,.	Captain J. W. Bristow,	15 *May* 58	Deputy Commissioner, 3rd class, Punjaub, Khan Ghurh.
19th N. I.,.	Lieut. I. F. Mac Andrew,	23 *Nov.* 58	Asst. Commr. 2nd class, Oudh.
20th N. I.,.	Major J. K. Spence, ..	14 *Aug.* 54	Deputy Commissioner, 1st class, Nagpore.
20th N. I.,	Capt. E. M. Ryan, ..	15 *July* 59	Deputy Commr. 3rd class, in the Tenasserim and Martaban Provinces. [Lv. prepy. to Fur.
20th N. I.,.	Capt. H. Mackenzie, ..	10 *Jan.* 59	Deputy Commr., 2nd class, Punjaub, (Goojerat.)—
21st N. I.,.	Captain E. A. Rowlatt,	28 *Aug.* 58	Principal Assistant, 1st class, to the Commissioner of Assam at Kamroop.
21st N. I.,..	Lieut. E. G. Clark, ..	13 *Apl.* 57	Assist. Commr. 2nd class, Oude.
22nd N. I.,.	Capt. F. W. Ripley, ..	27 *Feb.* 58	1st Class Princl. Asst. to the Commr. of Arracan,
		2 *Dec.* 57	at Ramree.
22nd N. I.,	Lieut. R. Stewart, ..	17 *Dec.* 58	Superintendent of Cachar.

Officers on Civil or Political Employ—*Continued.*

Corps.	*Rank and Names.*	*Date of Appointment.*	Designation.
	Military.		
23rd N. I.,	Major R. R. W. Ellis, .	30 *Sep.* 43	Political Agent in Bundelcund, and in charge of the Thuggee Dept. at Gwalior.—Fur. S.C. 15 Apl. 59.
23rd N. I.,	Capt. J. S. Davies, ..	27 *Nov.* 49	1st class Asst., Govr. Genl.'s Agent, S. W. Frontier, Singbhoom.
		1 *Sep.* 54	Senr. Asst. Commissioner Chota Nagpore.
23rd N. I.,	Major A. L. McMullin,	5 *June* 59	Offg. Deputy Opium Agent in Malwa.
23rd N. I.,	Lieut. G. S. Dysart, ..	10 *June* 59	Depy. Bheel Agent and Political Asst. to the Agent to the Govr. Genl, for Central India at Maunpore.
23rd N. I., .	Lieut. W. G. Waterfield,	9 *June.* 58	Asst. Comr. 3rd class, Punjaub.
23rd N. I.,	L. W. R. M. Holroyd,	26 *July* 58	Inspector of Schools in the Delhi Territory.
24th N. I.,	Capt. E. P. Lloyd, ..	17 *Feb.* 59	Offg. Junior Asst. to the Commr. of Assam, (Kamroop.)
24th N. I.,	Lieut. H. F. Newmarch	8 *Apl.* 59	Asst. Commr. Saugor, & Nerbudda Territories.
25th N. I.,	Lt. Col. J. Clarke, ..	15 *Apl.* 58	Commissioner of Oude.—Fur. S. C. 5th Jan. 59.
26th L. I.,	Captain J. M. Cripps, ..	15 *May* 58	Deputy Commr., 3rd class, Punjaub, (Peshawur.) Leave to 15th Oct.
28th N. I.,	Capt. W. Paske, ..	15 *May* 58	Assistant Commr., 1st class Punjaub, (Kangra.)
29th N. I.,	Lt. Col. G. W. Williams,	19 *Dec.* 55	Extra Ass. to the Genl. Supdt. of Operations for the Suppression of Thuggee and Dacoitee at Agra.
		11 *May* 58	Superdt. of Cantonment Police, N. W. P.
		29 *Jan.* 59	Ex.-Officio Mily. Secy. to the Govt. of the N.W.P.
29th N. I., .	Capt. L. P. Faddy, ..	3 *Dec.* 58	Asst. to the Commr. of Military Police Battn., Shahjehanpore.
29th N. I.,	Captain W. Agnew, ..	25 *June* 59	Deputy Commissioner of Assam.
29th N. I.,	Lieut. J. B. Smyly, ..	15 *May* 58	Asst. Commr. 1st class Punjaub.—Furlough S. C. 31st May 59.
30th N. I.,	Lieut. T. Pierce, ..	23 *Oct.* 58	2nd Asst. to the Commr. of Ajmere.
		2 *Apl.* 59	Offg. 1st Asst. Commr. of Ajmere.
30th N. I.,	Lieut. H. S. V. Fisher,	9 *Nov.* 58	Asst. Commr. 3rd class, Oudh.
30th N. I.,	Lieut. J. C. Wood, ..	28 *Feb.* 56	Depy. Commr. 1st class in the Saugor and Nurbudda Territories, (Hoshungabad.)
		14 *Apl.* 51	Vested with the powers of a Jt. Magt.
		28 *Apl.* 52	In charge of Seonee District.
		6 *May* 56	Marriage Registrar, Hoshungabad.
30th N. I.,	Lt. B. W. D. Morton,	4 *June* 58	2nd class Principal Assist. to the Commr. of Assam.—Fur. S. C. 12 May 58.
31st N. I.,	Major S. R. Tickell, ..	14 *Feb.* 55	Depy. Commr. of the Tenasserim and Martaban Provinces at Amherst.
31st N. I., .	Lieut. F. A. Dickins, ...	24 *Mar.* 58	An Assistant in the Saugor and Nerbudda Territories.
33rd. N. I.	Capt. W. S. Row, ...	21 *Aug.* 55	Asst. Rev. Surveyor Burdwan, 2nd or Southern Division.—Fur. S. C. 17th Jan. 59.
34th N. I., .	Lieut. F. E. A. Chamier,	17 *June* 59	Asst. Commr. 1st class, Oude.
35th N. I.,	Maj. P. A. P. Bouverie,	30 *Apl.* 59	Political Agent at Bhurtpore,
36th N. I.,	Capt. C. Holroyd,	20 *May* 57	1st class Principal Assistant to the Commissioner of Assam.
37th N. I., .	Capt. J. Reid, ..	18 *Mar.* 59	Deputy Commissioner, 1st class, Oude.—Fur. S. C. 5th Nov. 58.
37th N. I. .	Capt. P. Maxwell, ..	2 *Jan.* 57	Assistant Commr., 1st class Punjaub, (Simla.)
37th N. I.	Lieut. S. S. Boulderson,	24 *Mar.* 58	Assist. Commissioner, 1st class, Punjaub.
37th N. I., .	Lieut. C. R. Shaw, ...	18 *Mar.* 59	Asst. Commr. 2nd class, Oude.
38th N. I., .	Capt. J. B. Dennys, ...	4 *Dec.* 57	Supdt. of Neemuch.
39th N. I.,	Lt. Col. F. E. Voyle, ..	24 *Mar.* 58	Deputy Commissioner 1st class, Mooltan.
39th N. I.,	Capt. R. H. D. Tulloh, .	15 *Apl.* 59	Asst. Commr. 1st class, Oude.
39th N. I.,	Capt. J. L. Sherwill, ..	3 *Jan.* 59	Offg. Revenue Surveyor of the 2nd or south Division.
39th N. I.,	Capt. C. F. Smith, ..	9 *Oct.* 58	Capt. of Police, Dera Ishmael Khan.
39th N. I.,	Lieut. F. M. H. Forbes,	16 *Dec.* 57	Offg. Inspector of Schools, Punjaub.
39th N. I.,	Lieut. J. Chalmers, ..	2 *May* 59	Asst. Commr. Rawul-Pindee.
39th N. I.,	Lieut. T. F. Forster, ..	14 *Dec.* 55	Asst. Commr. in the Punjaub.
40th N. I.,	Capt. J. P. Briggs, ..	14 *Feb.* 55	Deputy Comr. of the Tenasserim and Martaban Provinces at Tavoy.—Fur. S. C. 17th Nov. 58.

Officers on Civil or Political Employ—*Continued.*

Corps.	*Rank and Names.*	*Date of Appointment.*	Designation.
	Military.		
42nd N. I.,	Col. *Sir* A. Bogle, *Kt*	31 *Dec.* 53	Commissioner Tenasserim and Martaban Provinces.—Fur. S. C. 20 Mar. 57.
42nd N. I.,	Lieut. W. N. Lees, L. L. D., ..	5 *Mar.* 53 24 *Jan.* 54	Member and Secretary Board of Examiners.
		18 *April* 54	Offg. Persian Translator Govt. of India.
		20 *Sep.* 56	Principal Calcutta Madrissa, Ex-officio Visitor and Director Hooghly Madrissa, and Examiner of Candidates for the situation of Law Officers.
42nd N. I.,	Lieut. W. G. B. Tyler,	1 *Jan.* 58	Assistant to the Commissioner of the Saugor and Nerbudda Territories.
43rd N. I.,	Major E. K. Elliot, ..	14 *Aug.* 54	Deputy Commr. 1st class, Nagpore.
44th N. I.,	Capt. H. R. James, ..	28 *Apl.* 54	Depy. Commr., 1st class, Punjaub, (Peshawur.)
		24 *Mar.* 59	Offg. Commr. of Peshawur.
44th N. I.,	Capt. A. P. S. Moncrieff,	2 *Nov.* 57	Junior Assistant to the Commissioner of Chot Nagpore,—Fur. P. A. 21 Apl. 59.
44th N. I.,	Lieut. F. K. Hawkins, .	5 *May* 58	Asst. Commr. 3rd class, Oude.—Lv. p. to Fur.
45th N. I.,	Major W. H. Oakes,..	9 *Sep.* 56	Depy. Comr. Chota Nagpore, (Lohardugga.)
46th N. I.,	Capt. G. N. Oakes, ..	9 *Sep.* 56	Principal Asst. Commr. Chota Nagpore, (Maunbhoom.)
46th N. I.,	Capt. T. W. Mercer, ..	24 *Mar.* 58	Asst. Commissioner, 1stclass, Jullundur(Punjaub.)
		1 *Mar.* 59	Offg. Depy. Commr. Jullundur.
47th N. I.,	Capt. G. McAndrew, ..	9 *Sep.* 53	Assistant Commissioner, Punjaub Goojranwalla.
		8 *Jan.* 58	Extra Assistant Genl. Supdt. of operations for the suppression of Thuggee and Dacoity, Punjaub.
47th N. I.,	Lieut. C. V. Jenkins, ..	6 *May* 59	Asst. Commr. 3rd class, Punjaub, (Jhelum.)
48th N. I.,	Captain B. Henderson,	31 *Dec.* 55	Depy. Commr., Kohat.—Fur. S. C. 28 May 58.
49th N. I.,	Lt. Col. C. Davidson,..	13 *Mar.* 57	Resident at the Court of His Highness the Nazam.
49th N. I.,	Capt. F. R. Pollock, ..	15 *June* 59	Deputy Commr. 1st class, Punjaub, Dera Ghazee Khan.
50th N. I.	Lieut. A. A. Munro, ..	15 *June* 59	Assistant Commissioner 1st class, Punjaub.
		9 *Feb.* 59	Offg. Deputy Commissioner of Kohat.
51st N. I.,	Lt. Col. S. A. Abbott,..	29 *Apl.* 58	Commissioner, Oudh.
52nd N. I.,	Major R. Morrieson, ..	30 *Apl.* 59	Political Agent at Harowtee.
52nd N. I.,	Capt. G. G. Moxon, ..	6 *Nov.* 57	Personal Asst. to the Commr. of Saugor.
		6 *July* 58	Divisional Commandant, Jubbulpore.
52nd N. I.,	Capt. H. F. Waddington,	11 *Oct.* 56	Deputy Comr. 2nd class in charge of the Mundlah District.
53rd N. I.,	Major H. Ramsay, ..	10 *Feb.* 56	Commissioner of Kumaon.
53rd N. I.,	Lieut. E. H. Paske, ..	13 *July* 58	Personal Asst. to the Financial Commr. of the Punjaub.
54th N. I.,	Capt. J. C. Haughton,	19 *July* 59	Supdt. of the settlement at Port Blair, in the Andaman Island.
55th N. I.,	Capt. H. P. Babbage,	16 *Dec.* 57	Asst. Commr. Punjaub.
55th N. I.,	Lieut. R. J. D. Ferris,..	31 *Mar.* 54	Asst. Commr., Punjaub, (Dera Ishmael Khan.)
55th N. I.,	Lieut. W. Nembhard,..	14 *May* 58	Depy. Commr. 1st class Jubbulpore.

OFFICERS ON CIVIL OR POLITICAL EMPLOY—*Continued.*

Corps.	*Rank and Names.*	*Date of Appointment.*	Designation.
	MILITARY.		
56th N. I.,	Capt. H. D. Battye,	8 *Dec.* 55	Asst. Commr. in the Punjaub.
57th N. I.,	Lt. Col. T. Simpson, ..	9 *Feb.* 41	Principal Assistant to the Comr. S. W. Frontier (Hazareebaugh.)
		1 *Sep.* 54	Principal Asst. Commr. Chota Nagpore, Hazareebaugh.
58th N. I.,	Capt. T. Staples, ..	9 *Oct.* 58	Captain of Police, Goorgaon.
58th N. I.,	Lt. P. W. Powlett, ..	18 *Nov.* 58	Asst. Commr. 3rd class, Punjaub.
59th N. I.,	Capt. H. A. Dwyer, ...	12 *June* 58	Asst. Commr. 2nd class, Jhujjur district, Delhi.
59th N. I.,	Lt. E. L. Ommanney,	9 *May* 59	Asst. Commr. 3rd Class, Lahore (Punjaub.)
60th N. I.,	Major C. R. Browne,..	30 *Dec.* 57	Commr. of the Leia Divn.—Fur. S.C. 26 Mar. 59.
61st N. I.,	Col. F. Jenkins, ..	28 *Jan.* 34	Agent to the Governor Genl. N. E. Frontier and Commr. for the Divn. of Assam in Kamroop.
61st N. I.,	Capt. T. A. Corbett, ..	9 *July* 58	Asst. Commr. Jhansie.
62nd N. I.,	Lieut. H. B. Urmston,.	9 *May* 59	Assist. Commissioner 1st class, Sealkote.
63rd N. I.,	Capt. W. H. Hawes, ..	30 *Nov.* 58	Deputy Commr 3rd class Oudh.
64th N. I.,	Lieut. C. H. Hall, ..	29 *Apl.* 56	Asst. Commr. Ferozepore (Punjaub.)
		27 *May* 59	Offg. Deputy Commissioner, Peshawur.
66th N. I.,	Captain W. S. Sherwill,	22 *Nov.* 56	Professor of Surveying in the Civil Engineering College, Presidency.
66th N. I.,	Capt. A. L. Busk, ..	6 *Apl.* 59	Depy. Commr. 1st class, Punjaub, (Thanessur.)
		9 *May* 59	Offg. Deputy Commr. 1st class Umballah.
67th N. I.,	Capt. G. F. D'Oyly, ..	4 *Dec.* 56	Assist. Commr., Tounghoo.
		22 *Oct.* 58	Offg. Deputy Commr. of Prome.
67th N. I.,	Capt. E. J. Spilsbury,..	1 *Mar.* 58	Depy. Commr. of Henzada.
67th N. I.,	Lieut. E. Thompson,..	18 *Mar.* 59	Deputy Commr. 3rd Class, Oude.
67th N. I.,	Lieut. J. T. Bushby, ..	12 *July* 58	Extra Asst. Commr. in the Hyderabad, assigned districts.
68th N. I.,	Capt. G. Faithfull, ..	31 *Dec.* 57	Princl. Asst. to the Comr. of Arracan, Akyab.
69th N. I.,	Capt. J. E. Cracroft, ..	21 *June* 58	Depy. Commr. 2nd class, Punjaub.
69th N. I.,	Lieut. H. Hayley, ...	9 *Oct.* 58	Captain of Police, Delhi Division.
69th N. I.,	Lieut, A, H. Eckford,...	11 *Oct.* 58	Asst, Commr, 3rd class, Oude.
69th N. I.,	Lt. R. H. Hudleston,..	12 *June* 58	Asst. Commr. 3rd class, Dera Ishmael Khan, (Punjaub.)
70th N. I.,	Capt. H. Hopkinson, ..	18 *Aug.* 58	Commr. of the Tenasserim and Martaban Provinces.
70th N. I.,	Major A. Fytche, ..	31 *Dec.* 52	Depy. Commr., Bassein.
70th N. I.,	Capt. H. W. H. Coxe,	6 *Apl.* 59	Deputy Commr., 2nd class, Punjaub.
70th N.I.,	Capt C. H. Byers, ..	20 *Mar.* 57	Asst. Resident, Nepal.
71st N. I.,	Lieut. J. Perkins, ..	22 *Dec.* 58	Asst. Commr. 1st class, Oude.
71st N. I.,	Lieut. F. C. Anderson,	19 *Nov.* 57	Revenue Surveyor Sindh Saugor Doab. [Fur.
71st N. I.,	Lieut. W. G. Davies, ..	25 *Apl.* 56	Asst. Settlement Officer (Googairah.)—Lv. p. to
71st N. I.,	Lieut. A. D. Vanrenen,	26 *Nov.* 58	Revenue Surveyor, Jhansie.—At Agra.
72nd N, I.,	Lieut. C. J. Griffiths,..	25 *Feb.* 59	Asst. Revenue Surveyor in the Derajat, Punjaub.
73rd N. I.,	Major J. Sleeman, ..	26 *June* 45	Jt. Magt. in the Saugor and Nerbudda Territories.
		26 *Mar.* 49	General Superintendent of the Operations for the Suppression of Thuggee and Dacoitee, Jubbulpore.—Fur. S. C. 19 Feb. 59.
73rd N. I.,	Major W. C. Erskine,..	31 *Mar.* 54	Agent to the Lieut. Governor in the Saugur and Nerbudda Territories.—Fur. S. C. 16 Dec. 58.
73rd N. I.,	Major. C. Lawrence, ..	5 *Jan.* 53	Captain of Police, Lahore Division.
73rd N. I.,	Lieut. K. M. Walter, ..	18 *Feb.* 58	Asst. Agent Governor General, Rajpootanah.
74th N. I.,	Lieut. H. Sconce, ..	12 *July* 59	2nd class, Principal Asst. to the Commr. of Assam in charge of North Cachar.

MEDICAL OFFICERS ON CIVIL OR POLITICAL EMPLOY.

Rank and Names.	*Date of Appointment.*	DESIGNATION.
SURGEONS.		
E. T. Downes, ..	6 *Mar.* 51	Assay Mr., Bombay Mint.
A. Campbell, M. D., ..	5 *Mar.* 51	Superintendent of Darjeeling, and in charge of the Political relations with Sikhim.
	29 *June* 57	Commr. under Section VII. Act XIV. of 1857.
J. Murray, M. D., ..	7 *Mar.* 54	Member of the Local Committee of Public Instruction at Agra.
Sir W B. O'Shaughnessy, Kt. M. D. F. R. C. S. ..	8 *Nov.* 53	Superintendent of Electric Telegraphs.
G. Paton, A M., M. D., ..	13 *Mar.* 54	Post Master General, N. W. P.
J. A. Guise, ..	30 *Nov.* 58	Register of Deeds and marriage Registrar, Moorshedabad.
W. Jameson, ..	6 *Mar.* 43	Supdt. Govt. Botanical Gardens, N. W. Provinces.
F. J. Mouat, M. D. F. R. C. S., ..	18 *Dec.* 55	Inspector Genl. of Jails and Ex. Officio Visitor of Lunatic Asylum.
J. Sutherland, ..	9 *July* 58	Register of deeds and Marriage Registrar, Patna.
C. Hathaway, M. D., ..	4 *Mar.* 53	Inspector of Prisons, Punjaub.
A. Simpson, M. D. ..	4 *Oct.* 58	Register of Deeds and Marriage Registrar, Dacca.
ASSISTANT SURGEONS.		
Andrew Fleming, M. D., ..	26 *July* 53	Register of Deeds, Sarun.
Charles Palmer, M. D., ..	6 *July* 57	Register of Deeds, Howrah.
J. K. Walter, ..	6 *Aug.* 57	Principal Asst. to the Opium Agent of Behar.
H. Baillie, ..	2 *May* 57	Register of deeds, 24-Pergunnahs.
M. Ainger, F. R. C. S., ...	4 *Oct.* 58	Register of Deeds & Marriage Registrar, Hooghly.
E C. Thorp, M. D., ..	15 *Apl.* 57	Regtr. of deeds and Marriage Registrar, Hooghly. —Furlough, S. C. 14 Sep. 58.
T. Farquhar, M. D., ...	18 *Mar.* 58	Supt. of the Central Jail, Allahabad.—Fur. S.C. 7 March 59.
J. C. Bow, M. D., ...	8 *Apl.* 59	Offg. Supdt. of the Allahabad Central Prison.
W. White, ..	19 *Oct.* 57	Register of Deeds and Marriage Registrar, Rajshahye.
A. J. Payne, M. D. B. A., ..	31 *Oct.* 56	2nd Assistant Presidency General Hospital.
H. F. Williams, M. D., ..	25 *June* 57	Register of Deeds and Marriage Regtr., Burdwan.
J. B. Scriven, ..	31 *Oct.* 56	1st Asst. Presidency General Hospital.
James Bedford Allen, ..	11 *Dec.* 55	Register of Deeds and Marriage Registrar, Behar.
A. Christison, M. D., ..	8 *June* 58	Supdt. of Vaccination in the Agra Divn. and Assist. Lecturer in the Medical School at Agra.
J. C. Corbyn, M. D., ..	2 *Apl.* 59	Offg. Supdt. of the Meerut Central Prison.
R. H. Perkins, ..	23 *Aug.* 55	Civil Hidgellee and Asst. Salt Agent.
W. B. Beatson, M. D., ..	2 *Feb.* 53	Register of Deeds, Chittagong.
N. J. Grant, ...	15 *Feb.* 58	Regtr. of Deeds and marriage Regtr., Tipperah. —Fur. S. C. 8 Dec. 58.
T. Duka, ..	29 *Mar.* 56	Register of Deeds, Monghyr.
John Elliot, M. D., ..	19 *May* 57	Register of deeds and Marriage Registrar, Jessore.
F. J. Earle, ..	17 *Jan.* 57	Regtr. of Deeds and Marriage Registrar, Purneah.
J. J. Halls, B. A. F. R. C. S., ..	19 *Oct.*. 57	Regtr. of Deeds and Marriage Registrar, Nuddea.
P. F. Bellew, ..	15 *Feb.* 56	Register of Deeds and Marriage Registrar, Mymensing.
W. J. Palmer, ..	20 *Aug.* 57	First Asst. and Opium Examiner at the Benares Opium Agency.
N. C. Macnamara, ..	22 *May* 58	Regtr. of Deeds and Marriage Registrar, Tirhoot.
S. C. Amesbury, ..	1 *Apl.* 57	Regtr. of deeds and Marriage Regtr., Dinagepore.
W. Walker, A. M., M. D., ..	15 *Mar.* 58	Supdt. of the Central Jail, Agra.

LIST OF ECCLESIASTICAL SERVANTS IN THE TWO DIVISIONS OF THE BENGAL PRESIDENCY.

METROPOLITICAL SEE OF CALCUTTA.

The Right Reverend George Edward Lynch Cotton, D. D., Bishop of Calcutta, consecrated 13th May 1859.

The Venerable John Henry Pratt, M. A., Archdeacon of Calcutta, appointed 1st Dec. 1849.

The Reverend T. H. Burn, Domestic Chaplain to the Lord Bishop of Calcutta, appointed 15th Nov. 1858.

Wm. H. Abbott, Esq., Registrar of the Archdeaconry and Secretary to the Lord Bishop and Metropolitan—

THE REVEREND CHAPLAINS.

Names and Degrees.	*Colleges and Universities,*	*Commencement of Service in India.*	*Dates of becoming full Chaplains.*	*Stations or Appointments, &c.*
*Henry S. Fisher, A.M.,	Catherine Hall, Cambridge,	9 *Aug.* 24	.. ..	Darjeeling.
*Henry Hutton, B. A.,	Queen's College, Cambridge,	9 *Oct.* 31	.. ..	Old Church, Calcutta.
*Wm Sturrock, B. A.,	Trinity College, Dublin, ..	23 *May* 33	.. ..	Berhampore.
*Arthur B. Spry, B. A.,	Trinity College, Oxford, ..	20 *Oct.* 38	1 *Mar.* 45	Allahabad.—Fur. S.C. 14 Dec. 58.
*John H. Pratt. M. A.	Caius College, Cambridge, ..	16 *Jan.* 39	16 *Mar.* 45	Archdeacon.
*Charles Garbett, A.B.,	Brasenose College, Oxford, ..	1 *Oct.* 39	15 *Dec.* 48	Umballa.
*J.J. Carshore, D. D.,	Trinity College, Dublin, ..	9 *Sep.* 40	8 *Oct.* 49	Jhelum and Murree.
*Richd. Panting, A.M.,	Christ Church, Oxford, ..	8 *June* 41	17 *Dec.* 50	Sealkote.
*Robert M. Price, B.A.,	Queen's College, Cambridge,	18 *July* 41	17 *Dec.* 50	Jullundur.
*Anthony Garstin, ..	Bishop's College, Calcutta,	8 *Nov.* 41	1 *Feb.* 51	Dacca.
*Horatio Moule, M.A.,	Queen's College, Oxford, ..	17 *Feb.* 42	1 *Jan.* 52	St. Paul's Cathedral.
*Thomas Wood, M.A.,	St. John's College, Cambridge, ..	11 *May* 42	1 *Aug.* 53	Fort William and Military Hospital.
Jas. Falconer Sharpe, B. A., ...	Sidney Sux. College, Cambridge, ..	20 *June* 42	3 *Apl.* 54	Mussoorie.
*James Coley, M. A.,	Christ Church, Oxford, ..	23 *Mar.* 43	30 *Mar.* 55	St. John's Church, Calcutta
*H.H. Harington, M. A.	Magdalen Hall, Oxford, ..	8 *Dec.* 43	25 *Mar.* 56	Cuttack.
*W. T. Humphrey, ..	Church Missionary Institution, Islington, ..	21 *Dec.* 43	11 *May* 57	Barrackpore.
*Robert James Bland, A. B., ..	Jesus College Cambridge, ..	18 *Feb.* 44	15 *July* 57	Gowhatty.
*Francis Hinde, A. B.,	Lincoln College, Oxford, ..	15 *Oct.* 44	24 *Feb.* 58	Nynee Tâl.
*Julian Robinson, M. A., ..	Jesus College, Cambridge, -	21 *Dec.* 44	3 *Apl.* 58	Chunar.
H. B. Burney, M. A., -	Oriel College, Oxford, - -	28 *Jan.* 46	11 *Aug.* 58	St. Paul's Cathedral, Calcutta.
Chas. Wm. Cahusac, A. B., ..	St. John's College, Cambridge, ..	8 *Dec.* 45	25 *Oct.* 58	Simla.
*Fitz-Henry W. Ellis, M.A., ..	Trinity College, Cambridge,	4 *Feb.* 46	1 *Jan.* 59	Juanpore and Azimgurh.
*Chas. D. Hamilton, M.A., ..	St. Mary Hall, Oxford, ..	2 *June* 46	23 *Feb.* 59	Mhow and Indore.
*T. A. C. Firminger, M. A., ..	Pembroke College, Cambridge. ...	4 *Oct.* 46	4 *May* 59	Howrah, Lv. to 23 Sep.
*John B. D'Aguilar, B. A., ..	St. John's College, Cambridge ..	28 *Oct.* 46	4 *May* 59	Roorkee.
A. W. Wallis, A. B.,	Magdalen Hall, Oxford. ..	6 *Apl.* 47	4 *May* 59	Thyet Myoo.
*Leopold Poynder, M. A., ...	Trinity College, Cambridge.	8 *Jan.* 48	4 *May* 59	Delhi—Fur. S. C., 10 Sep. 58.
*Ed. Godfrey, M. A.,	Clare College, Cambridge, ..	17 *Oct.* 48	7 *May* 59	Fur. S. C. 26 Feb. 1858.

* Surrogates for granting Marriage Licences.

THE REVEREND ASSISTANT CHAPLAINS.

Names and Degrees.	*Colleges and Universities.*	*Commencement of Service.*	*Stations or Appointments, &c.*
*Henry Smith, D. D., - -	Trinity College, Dublin, - -	17 *Oct.* 48	Hazareebaugh.
*Francis Charles Viret, B. A.,	Trinity College, Cambridge, -	8 *Dec.* 48	Landour.
*Henry Tuson, - - - -	St. Bee's College, - - - -	23 *Jan.* 49	Ferozepore.
*Charles Sloggett, A. B., -	Christ College, Cambridge, -	7 *Mar.* 49	Anarkullee.
*Fredk. O. Mayne, M. A., -	Trinity College, Cambridge, -	11 *Oct.* 49	Fur. S. C. 28 Feb. 59.
*Thomas Wm. Shaw, M. A.,	Exeter College, Oxford, - -	13 *Oct.* 49	Fur. S. C. 8 Feb. 58.
*Thomas C. Smyth, M. A.,	Catherine Hall, Cambridge, -	26 *Nov.* 49	Singapore.
*William J. Jay, M. A., -	Catherine Hall, Cambridge -	14 *Jan.* 51	Allahabad.
*John E. W. Rotton, M. A.,	Emmanual College, Cambridge,	18 *Jan.* 51	Meerut.
*John Cave-Browne, M. A.,	Wadham College, Oxford, - -	18 *Nov.* 51	Subathoo.
C. S. P. Parish, - - - -	St. Edmund Hall, Oxford, - -	29 *Sept.* 52	Moulmein.
*F. Farrer, B. A. - - -	St. John's College, Oxford, -	13 *Dec.* 52	Kussowlie.
*John Sharkey, A. B., -	Trinity College, Dublin, - -	16 *Mar.* 53	Peshawur.
*M. R. Burge, - - - -	Exeter College, Oxford, - -	8 *June* 53	Lv. to 31 Dec.
*James Pasker Harris, - -	Brasenose College, Oxford, -	9 *Jan.* 54	Dugshaie.
*H. W. Crofton, - - -	Trinity College, Dublin, - -	2 *Nov.* 54	Rangoon.
*W. W. Phelps, A. M. - -	Queen's College, Oxford. - -	4 *Dec.* 54	Lucknow.
*S. H. Beamish, - - -	Clare Hall, Cambridge, . -	30 *Aug.* 55	Jhansie.
*J. F. A. Gavin, - - -	Trinity College, Dublin - -	16 *Aug.* 55	Saugor.—Fur. S.C. 30 Dec. 58.
*J. Richards, M. A. - -	Christ College, Cambridge, - -	16 *Aug.* 55	St. John's Church Calcutta.
*Henry Murray, A. M., -	St. John's College, Cambridge,	1 *Dec.* 55	Mean Meer.
George Lovely, - - -	Trinity College, Dublin, - -	9 *Dec.* 55	Old Church.
*R. A. H. Norman, - -	.. .. ..	19 *Mar.* 56	Dum-Dum.
W. Hazledine - - - -	St. Aidan's College, Birkinhead	18 *Mar.* 56	Fur. S. C. 27 June 57.
Alex. D. Nicolson, M. A., -	St. Peters' College, Cambridge,	29 *May* 56	Ghazeepore.
H. P. Woodington, - -	St. Aidan's College, Birkinhead,	2 *Dec.* 56	Delhi.
*M. D. C. Walters, M. A., -	University College, Durham, -	2 *Dec.* 56	St. James' Church, Calcutta.
*J. K. Stuart, M.A. - - -	Queen's College Cambridge, ..	15 *Sep.* 56	Rawul Pindee.
H. D. James, M. A., - -	Magdalen College, Oxford - -	9 *Jan.* 57	Mooltan.
*Charles Ed. Hadow, B.A.,	Trinity College, Oxford, - -	2 *Feb.* 57	Chinsurah.
*James Mackay, B. D., - -	Trinity College Hartford Connecticut, U. S. - - - -	19 *Mar.* 57	Penang.
Thomas Moore, B. A., - -	St. Johns' College, Cambridge,	31 *Aug.* 57	Benares.
John Wm. Young, M.A., -	St. Johns' College, Cambridge,	9 *Sep.* 57	Tounghoo (Pegu.)
John Richard Baldwin, -	St. Bee's Cumberland, - -	31 *Oct.* 57	Lucknow.—Fur. S. C. 9 Dec. 58.
M. S. Laing, . - - -	St. Bee's Cumberland, - -	14 *Jan.* 58	Futtehgurh.
*W. G. Cowie, B. A. -	Trinity College, Cambridge, -	29 *Jan.* 58	Bareilly.
C. J. Waterhouse, M. A., -	St. John's College, Cambridge,	27 *Jan.* 58	Lucknow.
*F. F. Mazuchelli, D. D., -	St. Mary's College, Baltimore,	27 *Jan.* 58	Kidderpore.
*W. Simpson, M. A., -	Trinity College, Dublin, - -	13 *Feb.* 58	St. George's Church, Agra.
G. D. Symonds, B. A., -	Trinity College, Dublin, ..	26 *Nov.* 58	Fyzabad.
*E. W. Tarleton, M. A., -	Trinity College, Dublin, - -	2 *Jan.* 59	Gwalior.
C. A. L. Whyte, M. A., -	.. .. ..	18 *Feb.* 59	Cawnpore.
F. W. Kingsford, B. A., -	Clare Hall, Cambridge, ..	8 *Apl.* 59	Allahabad.
E Templeman, B. A., -	Pembroke College, Oxford, ..	.. ..	Shahjehanpere.
T. H. Burn, B. A., - - -	Trinity College, Cambridge ..	.. ..	Domestic Chaplain to the Bishop.
W. C. Bromehead, -			
W. Spencer, -			
W. D. Cowley, -			
T. Y. Mitchinson, -			
C. C. Anstey, -			

* Surrogates for granting Marriage Licences.

CHURCH OF SCOTLAND—CHAPLAINS.

Names and Degrees.	Appointments.	Commencement of Service.	Dates of Promotion.	Stations.
The Revd. James C. Herdman, M. A., Chaplain, - - - -	SeniorChaplain, St. Andrew's, - -	22 *Nov.* 49	.. ..	Calcutta.
The Revd. Robert Henderson,-	Junior Chaplain,St. Andrews, - -	1 *Nov.* 51	.. ..	Calcutta.

DISPOSITION OF THE BENGAL ARMY.

GARRISON OF FORT WILLIAM.

GOVERNOR.

The Right Hon'ble Charles John Viscount CANNING

Brigadier M. Smith, H. M. 81st Foot, .. *Commanding in Fort William and the Troops in Calcutta.*
Major S. J. Blane, H. M. 52nd Foot, ... *Brigade Major, Queen's Troops.*
Capt. R. J. Evans, H. M. 27th Foot, ... *Depy. Asst. Qr. Mr. General.*
Capt. M. R. Nightingale, 2nd En. B. Fusiliers, .. *Fort Adjt. and Supt. Gent. Cadets.*
Surgeon Edward Campbell, ... *Garrison Surg.*—Fur. S. C. 11 Feb. 59.
Surgeon R. B. Kinsey, F. R. C. S., ... Offg. Garrison Surgeon.
Assistant Surgeon Thomas Anderson, M. D.,.. .. *Garrison Asst. Surgeon.*—Fur. S. C. 5 Apl, 59.
Assistant Surgeon A. G. Duff, M. D., ... Offg. Garrison Asst. Surgeon

Troops—H. M. 99th Regt.—5 Companies H. M. 3rd Regt. (Buffs.)—Detachments of Native Infantry.

ALLIPORE.

Troops—Calcutta Native Militia.

BALLYGUNGE.

Governor General's Body Guard.

Presidency Division.

BARRACKPORE.

Major Genl. *Sir* J. B. Hearsey, K.C.B., 3rd En. L.C. *Comdg. the Division.*
Lieut. J. Hearsey, 38th N. I., ... *Aide-de-Camp.*
Major A. H. Ross, 42nd L. I., ... *Asst. Adjt. Genl.*
Brigadier J. Christie, 1st En. L. C. .. .. .. *Commanding the Station.*
Captain S. Richards, 55th N. I., ... *Brigade Major.*
Major G. C. Hatch, 57th N. I., ... *Deputy Judge Advocate General.*
Major G. M. Hill, 17th Native Infantry, ... *Pay Master.*
Captain W. W. Aubert, Invalid Establishment, .. *Pay Master and Supdt. of Native Pensioners.*
Senior Surgeon G. G. Brown, M. D., ... *Superintending Surgeon. Offg- Inspector Genl. of Hospitals L. P.*
Surgeon F. Anderson, M. D., ... Offg. Superintending Surgeon.

Troops—H. M. 67th Foot—European Infantry Recruit depôt—2nd, 32nd, 34th and 43rd Native Infantry.

DUM-DUM.

Colonel C. S. Reid, Artillery, ... *Commanding.*
Capt. A. W. Pixley, Artillery, ... *Station Staff and Arty. Divn. Staff.*

Troops—3rd Company, 9th Battn. of Royal Arty. with T. Battery—The Head-Quarters and 1st, 2nd, 3rd and 5th Companies of the 9th Battn. Native Foot Artillery, 5 Companies H. M.'s 3rd Regt. (Buffs)—Depôts of H. M.'s Troops—Detachment of Naval Brigade.

DISPOSITION OF THE BENGAL ARMY—*Continued.*

CHINSURAH.

Major M. Walker, H. M. 3rd Buffs—Comdt. Recruit Depot.

TROOPS—Depôt of H. M. Troops.

BERHAMPORE.

TROOPS—5th European Regiment—63rd N. I. 11th Irregular Cavalry,

MIDNAPORE.

TROOPS—Shekawattee Battalion.

CHITTAGONG.

TROOPS—*

Arracan.

KHYOUK PHYOO.

TROOPS——Detachment Arracan Battalion.

AKYAB.

TROOPS—Arracan Battalion.

AENG PASS—KOLADYNE SANDOWAY.

TROOPS—Detachment Arracan Battalion.

Eastern Frontier.

JELPIGOREE.

TROOPS—73rd Native Infantry—Detachment 11th Irregular Cavalry.

DACCA.

TROOPS—3 Companies H. M.'s 19th Foot.—Two Companies 73rd N. I.

CHERRA POONJEE.

TROOPS—Sylhet Light Infantry Battalion, with two 6-pounders attached.

SYLHET—CHURGOLAH—LUNGYE—JOOWYE AND MYRONG.

TROOPS—Detachment Sylhet Light Infantry Battalion.

CACHAR.

TROOPS—Detachment Sylhet Light Infantry Battalion—Kookee Levy.

DEBROOGURH.

TROOPS—1st Assam Light Infantry Battalion—A Company of Assam Local Artillery.

SAIKWAH—JEYPORE—JAMOOGOOREE—SEEBSAGUR—BURPATHAR—GOLAGHAUT.

TROOPS—Detachment 1st Assam Light Infantry Battalion.

GOWAHATTY.

TROOPS—2nd Assam Light Infantry Battalion.

GOWALPARAH—NOWGONG—TEZPORE—DECHONGA—MUNGLEYDE—ASSALOO—KHOOREEKHATA AND KURREEAPARAH.

TROOPS—Detachment 2nd Assam Light Infantry Battalion.

RANEEGUNGE.

TROOPS—Detachment 63rd Native Infantry.

Dinapore Division.

HEAD-QUARTERS BENARES.

Major Genl. G. Campbell, Artillery, ...	*Comdg. the Division.*
Capt. A. H. Bogle, Artillery, ...	*Aide-de-camp.*
Major W. Lydiard, 11th N. I., ...	*Asst. Adjutant General.*
Brigadier P. Gordon, 11th N. I., ...	*Commanding the Station.*
Lieut. E. K. O. Gilbert, 27th N. I., ...	*Brigade Major.*
Capt. A. Turner, 4th En. Regt., ...	*Depy. Judge Advocate Genl. (with his Regt.)*
Capt. H. B. A. Poulton, 64th N. I., ...	*Offg. Deputy Judge Advocate General.*
Capt. C. L. Brown, 46th N. I., ...	*Supdt. and Pay Master of Native Pensioners.*
Capt. C. Nedham, H. M. 34th Foot, ...	*Offg. Depy. Asst. Quarter Master Genl.*
*	*Superintending Surgeon.*

TROOPS—4th Company, 5th Battalion Foot Artillery, with No. 11 Horse Light Field Battery—Her Majesty's 19th and 35th Foot—40th Native Infantry.

Disposition of the Bengal Army—*Continued.*

BHAUGULPORE.

Troops—Hill Rangers.

MONGHYR—TITALYAH—BUCKALEE—PURNEA.

Troops—Detachment Hill Rangers.

DARJEELING.

Capt. G. R. Hopkins, H. M. 53rd Foot, ... *Commanding the Depôt.*
Lieut. G. A. Ferris, H. M. 29th Foot, ... *Station Staff.*

Troops—Convalescent Depôt, consisting of Detachments of Her Majesty's and the Honorable Company's Troops—Sebundy Sappers and Miners.

DORUNDAH.

Troops—Ramgurh Light Infantry Battalion, with four 6-pounder Brass Guns—two Ressallahs of Irregular Cavalry attached.

CHYEBASSA—PURULIA—SUMBHULPORE—KHURRUCKDEAH—BANCOORAH.

Troops—Detachment Ramgurh Light Infantry Battalion.

NEPAUL.

Troops—Resident's Escort.

HAZAREEBAUGH.

Troops—6th European Regiment.

SOORIE.

Troops—Military Police Corps.

SASSERAM AND PALAMOW.

Troops—H. M. 29th Regiment.

ROHNEE

Troops—5th Irregular Cavalry.

SECROLE. (BENARES.)

Major R. J. Edgell, 53rd N. I., ... *Deputy Pay Master.*
* *Superintending Surgeon.*

Troops—1st Battalion H. M. 6th Foot—a wing of 2nd Battalion H. M. 60th Rifles (a wing at Arrah.)—25th an d 37th N. I.—Regiment of Loodianah.

SULTANPORE, BENARES.

Troops—13th Irregular Cavalry,—50th Native Infantry,

GHAZEEPORE.

Troops—H. M. 37th Foot,—65th Native Infantry.

JUANPORE.

Troops—Detachment Regiment of Loodianah.

GORUCKPORE.

Troops—5th Company 12th Battalion Royal Artillery, with Q. Light Field Battery—Jat Horse,—1st Battalion H. M. 13th Light Infantry, H. M. 73rd Foot.—3rd Sikh Infantry.

CHUNAR.

Lieutenant Colonel G. Blake, Invalids,.. .. .. *Commanding.*
Lieut. G. Weld, 14th N. I., ... *Fort Adjutant and Ex.-officio Supt. of Sudder [Bazar.*
* *Adjt. and Qr. Mr. European Invalid Batt.*
Surgeon H. M. Tweddell, ... *Garrison Surgeon.*

Troops—Two Companies of European Artillery Invalids—Two Companies European Infantry Invalids—European Veteran Company—Detachment Native Infantry.

MIRZAPORE.

Troops—*

AZIMGURH.

Troops—A detail of Native Foot Artillery—17th Native Infantry,

Saugor District.

SAUGOR.

Brigadier F. Wheler, 1st E. L. C., ... *Commanding.*
Lieut. F. J. Gully, 74th N. I., ... *Brigade Major.*
* .. .. *Asst. Adjutant General.*
Captain C. P. Trower, 23rd N. I., ... *Offg. Deputy Judge Advocate General.*
Senior Surgeon John Greig, ... *Superintending Surgeon.*—Fur. S. C. I Apl. 1859.
Surgeon J Balfour, ... *Officiating Superintending Surgeon*

Troops—42nd and 52nd Native Infantry—3rd Irregular Cavalry.

Cawnpore Division.

CAWNPORE.

Major General Sir J. E. W. Inglis, K. C. B., H. M.'s Service. .. *Comdg. the Division.*
Lieut. C. W. Fletcher, 48th N. I., .. *Aide-de-Camp.*
Major T. F. Wilson, C. B., 13th N. I., .. *Depy. Assistant Adjt. General.*—Fur. S. C. 21 Feb. 59.
Capt. G. S. Young, H. M. 80th Foot, .. *Offg. Depy. Asst. Adjutant General.*
Capt. C. F. Browne, H. M. 35th Foot., .. *Depy. Judge Advocate Genl.*
* *Commanding the Station,*
Major A. B. Johnson, 5th En. Regt., ... *Brigade Major.*—Fur. S. C. 30 Dec. 58.
Lieut. C. A. McDougall, 4th En. Regt. .. *Offg. Brigade Major.*
Major H. S. Grimes, 46th N. I. .. *Offg. Deputy Pay Master.*
* *Depy. Asst. Qr. Mr. Genl.*
Surgeon J. B. Dickson, ... *Supdg. Surgeon.*

Troops—2nd Company, 3rd Battalion Artillery with No. 12 Horse Field Battery,—3rd Company, 5th Battalion Artillery—6th Company 9th Battalion Native Foot Artillery—H. M.'s 80th Foot.

FUTTEHGURH DISTRICT.

Troops—7th Company, 14th Battalion Royal Artillery,—H. M. 8th Foot.

MYNPOORIE AND ETAWAH.

Troops—*

NOWGONG.

Troops—*

OORAIE.

Troops.—*

JHANSI.

Troops—*

BANDAH.

Troops—H. M. 48th Foot, and 97th Foot.

CALPEE.

Troops—31st Native Infantry.

ALLAHABAD.

Brgdr. M. G. Dennis, H. M., 60th Foot, .. *Commanding.*
Captain J. Hudson, H. M. 15th Foot, .. *Brigade Major.*
Capt. F. C. Tombs, 18th N. I., .. *Pay Master and Supdt. of Native Pensioners* (Field Pay Master.)
Capt. D. Stansbury, 60th N. I., .. Offg. Supdt. of Native Pensioner.
* *Garrison Surgeon.*

Troops—The 3rd Company, 14th Battalion Royal Artillery,—2nd Troop, 2nd Brigade Bengal Horse Artillery—1st European Light Cavalry,—1st Battalion 5th Fusiliers—77th Foot—4th Bengal European Regiment.

Oude District.

OUDE, (LUCKNOW.)

Brigadier T. Chute, H. M. 70th Foot, ... *Commanding.*
Capt. E. J. N. Burton, H. M. 37th Foot, .. *Offg. Brigade Major.*
Major H. D' O. Torrens, H. M. 23rd Fusiliers, .. *Offg. Deputy Judge Advocate General.*
Major H. R. Garden, 2nd N. I. (Grs.) .. *Asst. Qr. Mr. General.*—Fur. S.C. 19 Jan. 58.
Capt. M. J. Slater, 5th En. Regt., ... *Pay Mr. and Supt. of Native Pensioners.—(with his Regiment.)*
Captain G.G. Anderson, 15th N. I., ... *Officiating.*

Troops—5th and 6th Companies, 13th Battalion Royal Artillery,—1st Troop 1st Brigade Bengal Horse Artillery,—3rd Company 1st Battalion Artillery, with No. 17 Horse Field Battery,—1st Company 6th Battalion of Artillery,—23rd Company Royal Engineers,—2nd Dragoon Guards,—4th European Light Cavalry,—2nd Regiment of Hodson's Horse—1st Battalion 23rd Fusiliers,—88th Foot,—2nd Battalion Rifle Brigade—15th Punjaub Infantry. (Pioneers.)

FYZABAD.

Troops—5th Company 3rd Battalion, Royal Artillery, with J. Light Field Battery,—4th Company Royal Engineers,—1st Regt. of Hodson's Horse,—H. M. 34th Foot,—Left Wing 54th Foot,—9 Punjab Infantry.

SEETAPORE.

Troops—E Troop Royal Horse Artillery,—4th Company, 4th Battalion Bengal Artillery 4th and 8th Irregular Cavalry,—1st Battalion 60th Rifles,—90th Light Infantry,—66th (Goorkha) Light Infantry.

TRANS GOGRA.

Brigadier A. H. Horsford, c. b., 3rd Battalion Rifle Brigade, ... *Commanding.*
Major M. Dillon, 2nd Battalion Rifle Brigade, .. *Brigade Major.*

Troops—3rd Troop 1st Brigade of Horse Artillery,—1st Punjab Cavalry,—5th Punjab Infantry,—1st Sikh Infantry.

ROY BAREILLY.

Troops—4th Company 14th Battalion Royal Artillery with No. 3, Horse Battery,—H. M. 38th Foot,—19th Punjab Infantry,—1st Sikh Irregular Cavalry.

PHILLIBHEET.

Troops—5th Troop 1st Brigade of Horse Artillery.

THE NEPAUL FRONTIER.

Troops—Her Majesty's 53rd Foot.

SULTANPORE.

Troops—Head Quarters and Wing of H. M. 54th Foot.

Meerut Division.

MEERUT.

Major General J. F. Bradford, c.b., 2nd E. L. C., *Comdg. the Division.*
Capt. W. J. Bradford, M. Artillery, ... *Aide-de-Camp.*
Brigadier A. Abbott, c. b., Artillery, ... { *Comdt. of Artillery.—And Commanding the Station.*—Fur. S. C. 27th May 1858.
Brigadier R. Horsford, Artillery .. .. *Offg. Comdt. of Arty. and Comdg. the Station.*
Lt. Col. E. B. Johnson, c. b., Artillery, ... *Asst. Adjt. Genl. Arty.*
Captain H. Lewis, Artillery, ... *Principal Commissary of Ordnance.*—Fur.
Colonel C. Hogge, c. b., Artillery, ... *Director Artillery Depôt of Instruction.*
Captain R. G. Simeon, 4th E. L. C., ... *Deputy Asst. Adjutant General.*
Capt. C. C. Johnson, 33rd N. I., ... *Depy. Asst. Qr. Mr. Genl.*
Lt. Col. G. P. Whish, 60th N.I., ... *Brigade Major.*
Capt. R. Blackall, H. M. 75th Foot, ... *Offg. Deputy Judge Advocate General.*
Lt. Col. H. J. Stannus, 5th En. Light Cavalry, .. *Deputy Pay Master.* [*Hauper.*
Captain O. Hamilton, 2nd E. L. C., ... *Pay Master and Supt. of Native Pensioners*
Surgeon J. Wilkie, m. d., ... *Superintending Surgeon.*

Troops—F. Troop, Royal Horse Artillery—The Head Quarters of the Regiment of Bengal Artillery,—The Head-Quarters and 2nd Troop 1st Brigade Horse Artillery,—2nd European Light Cavalry,—Her Majesty's 75th Foot,—12th Irregular Cavalry,—Nusseeree (Rifle) Battalion.

BOOLUNDSHUHUR.

TROOPS—*

ROORKEE.

TROOPS—The Head Quarters of the Corps of Sappers and Miners, with the 1st, 2nd, 3rd, 4th 7th, 8th, 9th, 10th, 11th and 12th Companies.

DELHI.

Brigadier H. Troup, 6th En. Regiment, ... *Commanding.*
Major H. Nicoll, 50th N. I., ... *Brigade Major.*—Fur. S. C. 29th Apl. 59.
Captain J. Woods. H. M., 81st Foot, ... *Offg Brigade Major.*
Asst. Surgeon, H. Stewart, ... *Garrison Asst. Surgeon,* (Offg. Civil, Budaon.)

TROOPS—Head Quarters and 4th Company 1st Battalion with No. 9 Horse Field Battery,—The Head-Quarters 1st Battalion of Foot Artillery,—1st Company 4th Battn. Arty.—H. M. 61st Foot,—2nd En. B. F.—13th Punjaub Infy.—a wing of 23rd Punjaub Infantry,—2nd Sikh Cavy. 4th Irregular Cavalry.

ALLYGURH.

TROOPS—*

DEYRAH.

TROOPS—Sirmoor Battalion.

LANDOUR.

Major R. Troup, 63rd N. I., ... *Commanding.*
Lieut. D. M. Murray, H. M. 64th Foot, ... *Station Staff.*

TROOPS—Convalescent Depôt, consisting of Detachments of Her Majesty's Troops.

Agra and Muttra.

AGRA.

Brigadier St. G. D. Showers, C. B. 2nd En. B. F., *Commanding.*
Capt. R. Patton, 3rd En. Regiment, .. *Brigade Major.*
Surgeon J. Murray, M. D., .. *Supdg. Surgeon.*
Surgeon T. S. Lacy, ... *Garrison Surgeon.*

TROOPS—2nd Company, 6th Battalion Foot Artillery, with No. 8 Horse Field Battery,—The Head Quarters of 5th Battalion Foot Artillery,—H. M. 64th Foot—3rd Battalion Rifle Brigade.

MUTTRA.

TROOPS—3rd Troop, 3rd Brigade Bengal Horse Artillery,—H. M. 6th Dragoon guards (Carabineers.)

Rohilcund.

BAREILLY.

* .. .. *Commanding.*
* .. .. *Brigade Major.*

TROOPS—The Head-Quarters and 2nd Company, 8th Battalion of Foot Artillery,—1st Company, 5th Battalions Artillery,—3rd Company 3rd Battalion of Foot Artillery, with No. 14 Horse Battery.—H. M. 42nd Highlanders.

MORADABAD.

TROOPS—2nd Company, 4th Battalion of Artillery.—2nd Sikh Infantry.

SHAHJEHANPORE.

TROOPS—1st Company, 1st Battalion of Foot Arty. with No. 7 Horse Battery.—4th Company 6th Battalion of Foot Artillery.—H. M. 82nd Foot.

ALMORAH.

TROOPS—Kemaon Battalion.

LOHOOGHAUT.

TROOPS—Detachment 66th Native Infantry.

NYNEE TAL.

Major J. Drysdale. 42nd Highlanders, ... *Comdg. Convalescent Depot.*
Ensign F. G. Coleridge, 42nd Highlanders, ... *Station Staff.*

Gwalior Division.

GWALIOR.

Brigr. General *Sir* R. Napier, K. C. B., Engrs., .. *Commanding.*
* .. *Brigade Major.*
Major E. G. Daniell, H. M. 8th Foot, .. *Offg. Deputy Judge Advocate General.*
Surgeon* .. *Superintending Surgeon.*
Surgeon H. J. Thornton, .. *Medical Store-Keeper.*

TROOPS—2nd Company, 5th Battalion Bengal Artillery, with No. 21 Horse Battery,—1st and 2nd Regts. of Infantry, Gwalior Contingent, 3rd European Regiment.

AUGUR.

TROOPS—*

SEEPREE.

TROOPS—*

LULLUTPORE.

TROOPS—*

SIRDARPORE.

TROOPS—Malwah Bheel Corps.

MUNDLAISIR.

TROOPS—Nimar Police Corps—Detachment Malwah Bheel Corps.

MEHIDPORE.

TROOPS—United Malwah Contingent, consisting of Artillery, Cavalry and Infantry.

SEHORE.

TROOPS—Bhopal Contingent, consisting of Artillery, Cavalry and Infantry.

DEOLEE.

TROOPS—Kotah Contingent, consisting of Artillery, Cavalry and Infantry.

BEWAR.

TROOPS—Mhairwarrah Battalion.

AJMERE.

TROOPS—Detachment Mhairwarrah Battalion.

ERINPOORAH.

TROOPS—Joudpore Legion, consisting of Artillery, Cavalry and Infantry,

KHERWARAH.

TROOPS—Meywar Bheel Corps.

KOTAH.

TROOPS—Detachment Meywar Bheel Corps.

Sirhind Division.

UMBALLAH.

Major Genl. *Sir* Robert Garrett, K. C. B., H. M. Service, ... *Commanding the Division.*
Major A. R. Garrett, H. M.'s 46th Foot, ... *Aide-de-Camp.*
Major D. S. Dodgson, 30th N. I., ... *Depy. Assist. Adjt. General.*
Major D. C. Shute, 19th N. I. .. .. *Offg. Asst. Qr. Mr. Genl.*
* *Comdg. the Station.*
Major C. St. G. Brownlow, 15th N. I., ... *Brigade Major,*—Leave S. C. 1 Nov.
Lieut. C. M. Pym, H. M. 75th Foot, ... *Offg. Brigade Major.*
Major F. C. Maisey, 67th N. I., ... *Depy. Judge Advocate General.*
Capt. C. F. M. Mundy, 34th N. I., ... *Depy. Pay Master.*
Surgeon H.A. Brace, M. D., ... *Superintending Surgeon.*

TROOPS—Head-quarters and 1st Company, 7th Battalion Artillery, with a 6-pounder Battery, attached.—Head-Quarters and 2nd Troop 3rd Brigade of Horse Artillery,—Her Majesty's 7th Hussars.

HANSI.

TROOPS—Hurrianah Lt. Infy. Battalion.

SIRSA.

TROOPS—Detachment Hurrianah Light Infantry Battalion—Detachment 4th Irr. Cavy.

HISSAR.

TROOPS—Detachment Hurrianah Lt. Infy. Batt.—Detachment 4th Irr. Cavy.

LOODIANAH.

TROOPS—Detachment 3rd N. I.—Detachment 9th Irr. Cavy.

DUGSHAIE.

TROOPS.—1st European Bengal Fusiliers, Detachment H. M. 27th Foot.

KUSSOWLIE.

Lieut. M. W. Hyslop, H. M. 93rd Highlanders Station Staff,
* Comdg. Convalescent Depot.

TROOPS—Detachment Her Majesty's 27th Foot.

SUBATHOO.

TROOPS—93rd Highlanders.

JULLUNDUR.

Brigadier E. C. W. M. Milman, H. M. 37th Foot, *Commanding.*
Captain G. E. Holmes, 72nd N. I., ... *Brigade Major.*
Major T. G. St. George, 17th N. I., ... *Deputy Pay Master.*

TROOPS—Half of 1st Troop, 3rd Brigade Horse Artillery,—The Head Quarters and 4th Company 3rd Battalion Foot Artillery,—with No. 24 Horse Battery,—H. M's. 87th Foot,—33rd 36th and 61st Native Infantry,—1st Irregular Cavalry.

PHILLOUR.

TROOPS—Half of 2nd Company 2nd Battalion of Foot Artillery.

HOSHEYARPORE.

TROOPS—9th Irregular Cavalry—33rd Native Infantry.

Lahore Division.

Includes all the Military Stations, between the "Sutledge," "Beas" and "Jhelum."

MEEAN MEER—LAHORE.

Major Genl. C. A. Windham, C. B., H. M. Service, *Comdg. the Division.*
Captain R. Swire, H. M. Service, ... *Aide-de-Camp.*
Brigadier W. G. Brown, H. M. 24th Foot, ... *Commanding the Station.*
Major W. Lamb, 51st N. I., ... *Asst. Adj. Genl.*
Capt. C. E. Mills, 28th N. I., ... *Brigade Major.*
Lieut. F. B. Norman, 14th N. I.,.. .. .. .. *Deputy Asst. Quarter Mr. General.*
Capt. J. N. Young, 3rd En. Regt., ... *Deputy Judge Advocate General.*
Lieut. H. P. Williams, 72nd N. I., ... *Depy. Pay Master.*
Surgeon W. A. Green, ... *Superintending Surgeon.*

TROOPS—The Head-quarters and 1st Troop, 2nd Brigade Horse Artillery. (Meean Meer)—The Head-quarters and 3rd Company, 4th Battalion Foot Artillery, (Meean Meer)—4th Company 7th Battalion of Foot Artillery,—3rd Bengal European Light Cavalry—Her Majesty's 7th Fusiliers,—(Meean Meer) 16th Grenadiers (Meean Meer)—26th (Meean Meer),—and 49th Native Infantry, (Meean Meer.)

DISPOSITION OF THE BENGAL ARMY—*Continued.*

JHUNG.

TROOPS—Detachment 26th Native Infantry,

GOOJERAT.

TROOPS—Detachments 16th, 35th, and 64th Regiments of Native Infantry.

UMRITSIR.

TROOPS—2nd Company 1st Battalion Native Foot Artillery, with No. 16 Horse Light Field Battery, Wing 1st Bombay Fusiliers—35th and 59th Native Infantry.

GOVINDGURH.

TROOPS—*

FEROZEPORE.

Brigr. J. Mackenzie, 5th En. L. C. .. .. .. *Commanding.*
Major W. Birch, 6th European Regiment, ... *Brigade Major.*
TROOPS—The Head-Quarters and 1st Co. 2nd Battalion Foot Artillery, with No. 10 Horse Light Field Battery—½ of 2nd Company 2nd Battn. Foot Artillery—Her Majesty's 24th Foot—45th and 57th Native Infantry.

GOORDASPORE.

TROOPS—Detachment 59th Native—2nd Irregular Cavalry.

GOOJRANWALLAH.

TROOPS—Detachment 35th Native Infantry.

MOOLTAN.

Brigadier C. Troup, 68th N. I. .. .. *Commanding.*
Capt. W. Gordon, 49th N. I., ... *Brigade Major.*
* .. *Depy. Asst. Qr. Mr. Genl.*
TROOPS—V. Battery attached to 1st Company 6th Battn. Royal Arty.; Wing 1st Bombay Fusiliers—6th Irregular Cavalry.

SEALKOTE.

Brigadier I. K. McCausland,, C. B., 66th N. I., .. *Commanding.*
Captain J. Ross, 71st N. I., ... *Brigade Major.*
Surgeon W. S. Dicken, ... *Superintending Surgeon.*
TROOPS—Half of 1st Troop, 3rd Brigade Bengal Horse Artillery—Her Majesty's 7th Dragoon Guards—Her Majesty's 52nd Foot—39th and 46th Native Infantry.

SHAHPORE.

TROOPS—Detachments 35th and 46th Regiment of Native Infantry

NOORPORE.

TROOPS—½ of 1st Company 7th Battalion Native Foot Arty.—Head Quarter and Right Wing of 4th Native Infantry.

KANGRA.

TROOPS—½ of 1st Company 7th Battalion Native Foot Artillery—Left Wing of 4th Native Infy.

Peshawur Division,

Includes all the Military Stations beyond the "Jhelum."

PESHAWUR.

Maj. Genl. *Sir* S. J. Cotton, K.C.B., H. M. Service, *Comdg. the Divn.*
Lieut. L. S. Cotton, H. M. 22nd Foot, .. *Aide-de-Camp.*
Captain T. Wright, 46th N. I., ... *Asst. Adjt. Genl.*
Brigadier T. J. Galloway, H. M.'s 70th Foot, .. *Commanding the Station.*
Capt. A. H. Bamfield, 56th N. I., ... *Brigade Major.—Fur. S. C. 18 June 58.*
Capt. H. E. Iremonger, 21st N.I., ... *Officiating Brigade Major.*
Capt. L. B. Jones, 56th N. I., ... *Deputy Judge Advocate General.*
Capt. P. S. Lumsden, 60th N. I., ... *Deputy Asst. Qr. Master Genl.—Fur. P. A. 28 Apl. 1859.*
Capt. F. N. Edmonstone, 3rd E. L. C., ... *Depy. Pay Master (at Rawul Pindee.)*
Senior Surgeon A. Wilson, ... *Supdg. Surgeon.*
TROOPS—3rd Troop 2nd Brigade Horse Arty.—C. Battery attached to 6th Company 7th Battalion Royal Arty.—The Head-Quarters and 3rd Company 6th Battalion Foot Artillery, with No. 19 Horse Light Field Battery—3rd and 4th Companies 2nd Battn. Foot Artillery—Her Majesty's 81st Foot—Her Majesty's 94th Foot,—5th En. Lt. Cavy—21st, 24th, 27th, 51st, and 64th Regts. Native Infantry—7th and 18th Regts. of Irr. Cavalry.—Kelat-Ghilzie Regiment.

DISPOSITION OF THE BENGAL ARMY—*Continued.*

MURDAN.

TROOPS—Corps of Guides.

FORT MACKESON.

TROOPS—Detachment 64th Native Infantry—Detachment 7th Irr. Cavalry.

FORT BARRAH.

TROOPS—Detachment 64th Native Infantry—Detachment 7th Irregular Cavy.

ABAZAIE.

TROOPS—Detachment 10th Irregular Cavalry—Detachment Kelat-i-Ghilzie Regiment.

ATTOCK.

Major J. E. Verner, 60th N. I., ... *Commandant of the Garrison.*
Capt. T. M. Cameron, 55th N. I., ... *Fort Adjutant*—(On leave.)
Capt. M. Batt. H. M. 98th Foot,.. .. .. .. *Offg. Fort Adjutant.*

TROOPS—Detachment Kemaoon Battalion.

SHUBKUDDUR.

TROOPS—Detachment 5th Light Cavalry.

MICHNEE.

TROOPS—Detachment Kelat-i-Ghilzie Regiment.

NOWSHERA.

TROOPS—Her Majesty's 27th Foot.—55th Native Infantry—10th Irregular Cavalry, Mountain Train Battery.

Sind Sagur District.

RAWUL PINDEE.

Brigadier A. H. Ferryman, C. B. H. M. 89th Foot, *Commanding.*
Capt. S. B. Cookson, 73rd N. I., ... *Brigade Major.*
Capt. F. N. Edmonstone, 3rd E. L. C., ... *Deputy Pay Master.*

TROOPS—4th Troop 2nd Brigade Horse Artillery—Her Majesty's 70th Foot — 58th Native Infantry, —16th and 17th Irregular Cavalry.

MURREE.

TROOPS—Convalescent Depôt.

JHELUM.

Col. J. A. Barstow, 58th N. I., ... *Commanding.*
Lieut. W. Elwyn, Adjutant, 58th N. I... .. .. *Station Staff.*

TROOPS—14th Native Infantry.

ABBOTTABAD (HAZARAH.)

TROOPS—4th Regiment of Seikh Infantry.

Punjaub Irregular Force.

KOHAT.

TROOPS—2nd Punjaub Horse Field Battery, 2nd Punjaub Cavalry—3rd and 6th Regiments of Punjaub Infantry.

BUNNO.

TROOPS—3rd Punjaub Horse Field Battery—3rd Regiment of Punjaub Cavalry—1st and 4th Regiments of Punjaub Infantry.

ASNEE.

TROOPS.—4th Regt. of Punjaub Cavalry.

DERA GHAZEE KHAN.

TROOPS—2nd Punjaub Infantry.

DERA ISHMAEL KHAN.

TROOPS—1st Punjaub Horse Field Battery—The Garrison Company of Artillery—5th Regt. of Punjaub Cavalry.

MYAN-OUNG, IN ARRACAN.

TROOPS—Pegu Light Infantry Battalion

GRADATION LIST

OF THE

GENERAL AND FIELD OFFICERS

AND

SENIOR CAPTAINS

OF THE

BENGAL, MADRAS AND BOMBAY PRESIDENCIES.

Names.	Presidency.	Date.
GENERALS.—25.		
1854.		
Sir Hopetoun Stratford Scott, K.C.B., ..	Madras Infy.	20 June
Sir Jas. Lillyman Caldwell, G.C.B.,	Madras Engrs	,,
Sir David Leighton, K.C.B., ..	Bombay Infy.	,,
James Welsh, ..	Madras ,,	,,
Sir James Russell, K.C.B.,	,, Cav.	,,
Richard Podmore, ..	Madras Infy.	,,
Sir Robt. Houstoun, K.C.B.,	Bengal Cav.	,,
George Rees Kemp, ..	Bombay Infy.	,,
John Alex. Paul Macgregor,	Bengal	,,
Sir Wm. Richards, K.C.B.,	,, ,,	,,
Jerry Francis Dyson,	Bombay ,,	,,
Alexander Fair, C.B., ..	Madras Infy.	,,
William Gilbert, ..	Bombay ,,	,,
1855.		
James A'hmuty, ..	Bengal Arty.	15 Sep.
1856.		
Mossom Boyd, ..	Bengal Infy.	9 April
1857.		
Henry Geo. Andrew Taylor, C.B.,	Madras Infy.	23 Sep.
Brook Brydges Parlby, C.B., ..	,, ,,	13 Oct.
Sir Robert Henry Cunliffe, Bart. and C.B., ..	Bengal ,,	13 ,,
GENERALS.—25. (*Continued.*)		
1858.		
John Truscott,	Bengal Infy.	27 Jan.
Edward Melian Gullifer Showers, ..	Madras Arty.	4 Mar.
Patrick Cameron, ..	Madras Cavy.	24 Oct.
1859.		
John Carfrae, ..	Madras Infy.	5 Mar.
George Jackson, ..	,, ,,	13 ,,
LIEUTENANT GENERALS.—50.		
1851.		
George Swiney, ..	Bengal Arty.	11 Nov.
Sir George Pollock, G.C.B.,	,, ,,	,,
Samuel Goodfellow, ..	Bombay Engrs.	,,
Alexander Lindsay, C.B.,..	Bengal Arty.	,,
James Stuart Fraser, ..	Madras Infy.	,,
Peter Delamotte, C.B., ..	Bombay Cavy.	,,
Edward Frederick, C.B.,..	,, Infy.	,,
George Benjamin Brooks,	,, ,,	,,
Peter Lodwick,	,, ,,	,,
James Morse,	,, ,,	,,
Suetonius Henry Tod, ..	Bengal Infy.	,,
John Briggs, ..	Madras ,,	,,
Harry Thomson, ..	Bengal Cavy.	,,
James Kennedy, C.B., .	,, ,,	,,
Charles Wm. Hamilton, ..	,, Infy.	,,
Edmund Frederick Waters, C.B., ..	,, ,,	,,
Richard Collyer Andree,	,, ,,	,,
Sir Mark Cubbon, K.C.B.,	Madras ,,	,,
Thomas Shubrick, ..	Bengal Cav.	,,
Thomas King, ..	Madras ,,	,,
William Cullen, ..	Madras Arty.	,,
David Barr, ..	Bombay Infy.	,,
William Vincent, ..	Bengal ,,	,,
Thomas Marrett, ..	Madras ,,	,,
Thomas Henry Paul, ..	Bengal ,,	,,

Names.	Presidency.	Date.
LIEUT. GENERALS.— *(Continued.)*		
1851.		
Francis Farquharson,	Bombay Infy.	11 Nov.
1855.		
John Henry, ..	Madras Infy.	3 Aug.
Samuel Swinhoe, .	Bengal ,,	15 Sep.
John Anderson, ..	,, ,,	5 Dec.
1856.		
Frederick Young, ..	Bengal Infy.	18 Feb.
Thos. Monteath Douglas, C.B., ..	,, ,,	18 Mar.
William R. C. Costley, ..	,, ,,	2 April
Charles Herbert, C.B., ..	Madras ,,	9 ,,
Sir George Petre Wymer, K. C. B., ...	Bengal ,,	8 June
Alexander Dick, ..	,, ,,	4 July
William Pattle, C.B., ..	,, Cavy.	18 ,,
Thomas Fiddes, ..	Bengal Infy.	15 Sep.
James Perry, ..	Madras Infy.	6 Dec.
1857.		
Hugh Ross, ..	Madras Infy.	29 May
James Ketchen, ..	Madras Arty.	13 Oct.
Abraham Roberts, C.B.,..	Bengal Infy.	13 ,,
1858.		
John Morgan, C.B. ..	Madras Infy.	27 Jan.
Charles Arthur Grenado Wallington, ..	Bengal ,,	4 Mar.
Thomas Oliver, ..	,, ,,	4 May
†*Sir* Jas. Outram, *Bart*, G. C. B., ..	Bombay ,,	16 July
Duncan Gordon Scott, ..	Bengal ,,	23 July.
Henry Hall, C.B., ..	,, ,,	24 Oct.
1859.		
Julius George Griffith, ..	Bombay Arty.	4 Feb.
Samuel Shaw, ..	Bengal Arty.	5 Mar
Frederick Larkins Doveton,	Madras Cavy.	13 ,,
MAJOR GENERALS.— 145.		
1854.		
Charles Butler James, ..	Bombay Infy.	20 June
Matthew Coombs Paul, ..	Bengal Infy.	,,
Sir John Cheape, K.C.B.,	,, Engrs.	,,
John Low, C.B., ..	Madras Infy.	,,
Joseph Harris, ..	Bengal ,,	,,
John Tulloch, C.B., ..	,, ,,	,,
Richard Powney, ..	,, Arty.	,,
Geo. Edward Gowan, C.B.,	Bengal Arty.	,,
Patrick Montgomerie, C.B.,	Madras ,,	,,
James Stuart, C.B., ..	Bengal Infy.	,,

Names.	Presidency.	Date.
MAJOR GENERALS.— *(Continued.)*		
1854.		
William Henry Hewitt, ..	Bengal. Infy.	20 June.
John Home, ..	,, ,,	,,
Geo. Wm. Aylmer Lloyd, C.B., ..	,, ,,	,,
Alex. Tulloch, C.B., ..	Madras ,,	,,
Archibald Brown Dyce, ..	,, ,,	,,
John Wheeler Cleveland,..	,, ,,	,,
Robert Blackall, ..	Bengal Infy.	,,
David Capon, C.B., ..	Bombay ,,	,,
William Donald Robertson,	,, ,,	,,
Duncan Sim, ..	Madras Engrs.	,,
George Sandys, ..	,, Cavy.	28 Nov.
James Eckford, C.B., ..	Bengal Infy.	,,
Mathew Soppitt, ..	Bombay ,,	,,
Andrew Hervey, C.B., ..	Bengal Infy.	,,
Sir Scudamore Winde Steel, K.C.B., ..	Madras ,,	,,
Frederick Schuler, ..	Bombay Arty.	,,
George Moore, ..	,, Infy.	,,
Maurice Tweedie, ..	Madras ,,	,,
Charles Montabin Carmichael, C.B., ..	Bengal Cavy.	,,
Henry Lechmere Worrall,	,, ,,	,,
Sir John Bennet Hearsey, K.C.B., ..	,, ,,	,,
George Richard Pemberton, ..	,, Infy.	,,
Donald Macleod, ..	Madras Cavy.	,,
Stephen Davis Riley, ..	Bengal Infy.	,,
Christopher Godby, C.B.,..	,, ,,	,,
David Cunninghame, ..	Bombay Cavy.	,,
Charles Dennis Dun, ..	Madras Infy.	,,
James Parsons, C.B., ..	Bengal ,,	,,
George Warren, ..	,, ,,	,,
†Henry Fisher Salter, C.B.	,, Cavy.	,,
Thomas Mathew Taylor,..	,, Cavy.	,,
Howard Dowker, ..	Madras Infy.	,,
Henry Sargent, ..	,, ,,	,,
George James Wilson, ..	Bombay Infy.	,,
~~Lewis Wentworth Watson,~~	~~Madras ,,~~	,, D
Joseph Garnault, ..	,, ,,	,,
Robert Hawkes, ..	Bengal Cavy.	,,
Archibald Fullerton Richmond, C.B., ..	Bengal Infy.	,,
James Bell, ..	Madras Infy.	,,
George Conran, ..	,, Arty.	,,
†*Sir* Patrick Grant, K. C.B.* ..	Bengal Infy.	,,
Christopher Dixon Wilkinson, C.B., ..	,, ,,	,,
William Taylor, ..	Madras Infy.	,,
Westrop Watkins, ..	,, ,,	,,
John Laurie, ..	,, ,,	,,
James Edwin Williams, ..	Madras Infy.	,,
Francis Turnley Farrell, ..	Bombay ,,	,,
William Henry Marshall,..	Bengal ,,	,,
Robert Alexander, ..	Madras ,,	,,
John Day Stokes, ..	,,	,,
F. Spencer Hawkins, C.B.,	Bengal ,,	,,

† Unattached Supernumerary Lieutenant Colonels Regimentally.
* Lieut. General in the East Indies 25th January 1856.

Names.	Presidency.	Date.
MAJOR GENERALS.— *(Continued.)*		
1854.		
John Kynaston Luard, C.B.,	Madras Infy.	28 Nov.
John Graham,	Bengal	,,
Edward Garstin,	,, Engrs.	,,
Adolphus Derville,	Madras Infy.	,,
Richard Home,	Bengal ,,	,,
Sir Robert John Hussey Vivian, K.C.B.,	Madras ,,	,,
Thomas Littleton Green,	,, ,,	,,
Alexander Carnegy, C.B.,	Bengal ,,	,,
George Tomkyns,	,, ,,	,,
Sir Henry Gee Roberts, K.C.B.,	Bombay ,,	,,
William Cavaye,	,, ,,	,,
David Forbes,	,, ,,	,,
Francis Straton,	Madras Cavy.	,,
Chas. Richard Wm. Lane, C.B.,	Bengal Infy.	,,
Wm. John Gairdner, C.B.,	,, ,,	,,
George Brooke, C.B.,	,, Arty.	,,
John Yaldwyn,	Madras Infy.	,,
Benja. Robertson Hitchins,	,, ,,	,,
Watkin Lewis Griffies Williams,	Madras ,,	,,
Eyre Evans Bruce,	,, ,,	,,
†Henry Coningham,	,, Cavy.	,,
William Justice,	,, Infy.	,,
Thomas Dickinson,	Bengal ,,	,,
Hy. Chambers Murray Cox,	,, ,,	,,
John Hoggan, C.B.,	,, ,,	,,
George Huyshe, C.B.,	,, ,,	,,
Frederick Blundell, C.B.,	Madras Arty.	,,
John Campbell, C.B.,	,, Infy.	,,
Thomas Bowes Forster,	,, ,,	,,
Fras. Frankland Whinyates,	,, Arty.	,,
James Adam Howden,	,, Infy.	,,
Augustus Clarke,	,, ,,	,,
Charles Hamilton, C.B.,	Bengal ,,	,,
Eaward Armstrong,	Madras	,,
Maurice Stack, C.B.,	Bombay Cavy.	,,
William Wyllie, C.B.,	,,	,,
Walter John Browne, C.B.	,,	,,
1855.		
†Philip Francis Story, C.B.,	Bengal Cavy.	13 Apl.
Alex. Woodburn, C.B.,	Bombay Infy.	1 May.
George Grantham,	Madras ,,	3 Aug.
Henry Cracklow,	Bombay ,,	22 ,,
William Prescott,	Madras ,,	15 Sep.
Henry Lawrence,	Bengal ,,	5 Dec.
1856.		
Richard Budd,	Madras Infy.	10 Feb.
George Hicks, C.B.,	Bengal	18 ,,
Henry Francis Caley,	,,	18 Mar.
Hope Dick,	,,	2 Apl.
Joseph Nash, C.B.,	,,	9 ,,
†James Alexander, C.B.,	,, Arty.	18 May.
†John Theophilus Lane, C.B.	,, ,,	8 June.
George Hutton,	Madras Infy.	4 July.
Robert Stewart,	Bengal Infy	15 Sept.

Names.	Presidency.	Date.
MAJOR GENERALS.— *(Continued.)*		
1856.		
Edward Pettingal,	Bengal, Infy.	4 Nov.
Henry Hancock,	Bombay ,,	28 ,,
1857.		
Edward Huthwaite, C.B.,	Bengal Arty.	14 Mar.
†Isaac Campbell Coffin,	Madras Infy.	29 May
†*Sir* G. Cornish Whitlock, K.C.B.,	,, ,,	27 June
Frederick George Lister,	Bengal ,,	22 Aug.
Sir Archdale Wilson, *Bart* K.C.B.,	Bengal Arty.	14 Sep.
David Downing,	,, Infy.	15 Sep.
†Tho. Macknight Cameron	Madras ,,	3 Oct.
Wlam Nugent Tho. Smee,	Bombay ,,	13 ,,
Thomas Chase Parr,	,, ,,	13 ,,
Fredk. Hervey Sandys,	Bengal ,,	15 ,,
†Henry Prior,	Madras ,,	2 Dec.
†Nicholas Johnson,	,, ,,	3 ,,
1858.		
John Moule,	Bengal Infy	27 Jan.
Louis Saunders Bird,	,, ,,	4 Mar.
†David Birrell,	,, ,,	12 April
†Thomas Polwhele,	,, ,,	5 May
†Richard James Holwell Birch, C.B.,	,, ,,	4 ,,
†George Campbell,	,, Arty.	4 July
†Peter Innes,	,, Infy.	13 ,,
†Alex. William Lawrence,	Madras Cavy.	20 ,,
†John Fowler Bradford, C.B.,	Bengal Cavy.	23 ,,
†Harry Meggs Graves,	,, Infy.	27 Aug.
†Charles Grant, C.B.	,, Arty.	14 Oct.
†Archibald Spiers Logan,	Madras Infy.	24 ,,
Æneas Sherriff,	,, Arty.	14 Nov.
Edward Messiter,	Madras Infy.	23 ,,
1859.		
Stuart Corbett, C.B.,	Bengal Infy.	4 Feb.
†Henry Macan,	Bombay ,,	5 Mar.
†William Sage,	Bengal ,,	13 Mar.
COLONELS.		
1854.		
*Peter Hammond,	Madras Arty.	28 Nov.
Augustus Abbott, C.B.,	Bengal ,,	,,
*Eames Amsink,	Madras ,,	,,
Sir Justin Sheil, K.C.B., and K.L.S.,	Bengal Infy.	,,
*Charles Wahab,	Madras ,,	,,
*Richard Horsford,	Bengal Arty	,,
James Manson,	,, Infy.	,,
George Twemlow,	,, Arty.	,,
*Thomas Assheton Duke,	Madras Infy.	,,
Nathaniel Jones,	Bengal	,,
James Clarke Charnock Gray,	Bengal ,,	,,
*Thomas David Carpenter,	Madras Infy.	,,
*James Davidson,	Madras ,,	,,
*Thomas Alexander Augustus Munsey,	,, Cavy.	,,

† Unattached supernumerary Lieutenant Colonels regimentally.
* Brevet.

Names.	Presidency.	Date.
COLONELS.—*(Continued.)*		
1854.		
*Charles Edward Faber,	Madras Engrs.	28 Nov.
*Robert Thorpe,	Madras Infy.	,,
*James Scott,	Bombay ,,	,,
*Charlton Holl,	Madras ,,	,,
*Charles Hewetson,	,, ,,	,,
*Morden Carthew,	,, ,,	,,
*James Edward Gordon Morris,	Bombay Infy.	,,
*Walter Scott,	,, Engrs.	,,
Claud Douglas,	Bengal Infy,	,,
*Joseph Hale,	Bombay Infy.	,,
*Henry Goodwyn,	Bengal Engrs.	,,
*William George White,	Madras Infy.	,,
*James FitzGerald,	Madras ,,	,,
~~James Steel, C.B.,~~ D	Bengal ,,	,,
*Clement Clemons,	,, ,,	,,
Charles Haldane,	,, ,,	,,
*Alexander Henry Edmonstone Boileau,	Bengal Engrs.	,,
*George Connolly Ponsonby,	Bengal Cavy.	,,
*~~Clements Blood,~~ R	Bombay Arty.	,,
Frederick Brooke Corfield,	Bengal Infy	,,
*Edward Green, C.B.,	Bombay ,,	,,
*George Farquharson,	Bengal ,,	,,
*William Robert Corfield,	,, ,,	,,
*John Sackville Leeson,	Bombay Arty.	,,
*Robert St. John,	Bombay Infy.	,,
*John Christie,	Bengal Cavy.	,,
**Sir* Robert Napier, K.C.B.,	,, Engrs.	,,
*Arthur Mitford Becher, C.B.,	,, Infy.	,,
*John Fordyce,	,, Arty.	,,
*Thomas Fergusson Flemyng.	,, Infy.	,,
*Francis Wheler,	,, Cavy.	,,
*John Studholme Hodgson,	,, Infy.	,,
*John Kennedy McCausland, C.B.	,, ,,	,,
*John Hobson,	Bombay ,,	,,
*James Mackenzie,	Bengal Cavy.	,,
*Robert William Honner, C.B.,	Bombay Infy.	,,
*George St. Patrick Lawrence,	Bengal Cavy.	,,
Sir Richmond Campbell Shakespear, *Kt.*	,, Arty.	,,
*James Sommers Down,	Bombay Infy.	,,
*William Marcus Coghlan,	,, Arty.	,,
*William Cotton,	Madras Infy.	,,
*Willoughby Trevelyan,	Bombay Cavy.	,,
Francis Rowcroft, C.B.	Bengal Infy.	,,
*John Macourtie Shortt,	Bombay ,,	,,
*M. Francklin Willoughby, C.B.,	,, Arty.	,,
*James Matthie,	Bengal Infy.	,,
*Charles Alfred Browne,	Madras Infy.	,,
*Arthur Thomas Cotton,	Madras Engrs.	,,
*George Macan,	Bombay Infy.	,,
*Hugh Troup,	Bengal ,,	,,
*George Inglis Jameson,	Bombay ,,	,,
*James Sinclair,	,, Arty.	,,
*William Maule Ramsay,	Bengal Infy.	,,

Names.	Presidency.	Date.
COLONELS.—*(Continued.)*		
1854.		
*Humphrey Lyons,	Bombay ,,	28 Nov.
*George Willoughby Osborne,	Madras. ,,	,,
**Sir* Archibald Bogle, *Kt*,	Bengl Infy.	,,
*Richard Albert Bayly,	Bomby ,,	,,
*David Simpson,	Bengal ,,	,,
*John Anderson Barstow,	,, ,,	,,
*Edward Altham Cumberlege,	,, ,,	,,
*John Macdonald,	,, ,,	,,
*Andrew Rowland,	Bombay Arty.	,,
*George Burn,	Madras Infy.	,,
**Sir* Charles S. Stuart, K.C.B.,	Bombay ,,	,,
*John Millar,	Madras ,,	,,
*East Apthorp, K.S.F.C.B.,	,, ,,	,,
*Alexander Peter LeMesurier,	Bombay ,,	,,
*Thomas Henry Shuldham,	Bengal ,,	,,
*John Butler,	,, ,,	,,
*George Logan,	Madras ,,	,,
*Thomas Sewell,	Bengal ,,	,,
*William Barclay Goodfellow,	Bombay Engrs.	,,
*Francis Jenkins,	Bengal Infy.	,,
*Albert Pinson,	Madras Infy.	
*John Francis Bird,	,, ,,	,,
*George Monro Carmichael Smyth,	Bengal Cavy.	,,
*David Davidson,	Bombay Infy.	,,
*George Burney,	Bengal Infy.	,,
*Thomas Anderson,	Madras Cavy.	,,
*Haughton James,	Bombay Infy.	,,
*William Lang,	,, ,,	,,
*Josiah Webbe Goldsworthy	Madras ,,	,,
*Edmund Wintle,	Bengal ,,	,,
*James Don Kennedy,	,, ,,	,,
*Robt. Turnbull Sandeman,	,, ,,	,,
*Peter Melvill Melvill,	Bombay ,,	,,
*Chas. Harington Græme,	Madras Cavy.	,,
*Bulstrode Whitelocke Cumberlege,	,, ,,	,,
*William Swatman,	Bengal Infy.	,,
*St. G. Danl. Showers, C.B.,	,, ,,	,,
*Wm. Couperus McLeod,	Madras ,,	,,
*Colin Troup,	Bengal ,,	,,
*George Alexander Baillie,	Madras ,,	,,
*George Moyle Sherer,	Bengal ,,	,,
*William George Lennox,	,, ,,	,,
*John Welchman, C.B.,	,, ,,	,,
*Fras. Archibald Reid, C.B.,	Madras ,,	,,
*Daniel Hall Stevenson,	,, ,,	,,
*Arthur Wheatley,	Bengal Cavy.	,,
*David Babington,	Madras Infy.	,,
*William Robert Andrew Freeman,	Madras ,,	,,
*Wm. Ferguson Beatson,	Bengal ,,	,,
*Bulstrode Bygrave,	,, ,,	,,
*Geo. LeGrand Jacob, C.B.	Bombay ,,	,,
*Richmond Houghton,	Bengal ,,	,,
*Richard Hall,	Madras ,,	,,
*William Hill,	,, ,,	,,

* Brevet.

Names.	Presidency.	Date.
COLONELS.—(Contd.)		
1854.		
*Charles Samuel Reid, ..	Bengal Arty.	28 Nov.
*J. Edmonstoune Landers,	Bengal Infy.	,,
*Howland Roberts, ..	Madras ,,	,,
*Arthur McCally, ..	,, ,,	,,
*Edward John Dickey, ..	Bengal ,,	,,
*Alfred Shepheard, ..	Bombay ,,	,,
*Henry Templer, ..	Bengal ,,	,,
*G. Cumberland Hughes,..	Madras ,,	,,
1855.		
*Henry Pelham Burn, ..	Bengal Infy.	1 May
*E. Rowland Mainwaring,	,, ,,	7 ,,
*Astley George Francis John Younghusband, ..	,, ,,	3 Aug.
*John Craigie Halkett, C.B.,	,, ,,	15 Sep.
*William Riddell, ..	,, ,,	5 Dec.
1856.		
*Thomas Townsend Pears, C. B.,	Madras Engrs.	10 Feb.
*R. Cornwallis Moore, C.B.	,, Arty.	18 ,,
*Auchmuty Tucker, C. B.,	Bengal Cavy.	2 April
*George Balfour, C. B., ..	Madras Arty.	9 ,,
*Henry Clayton, ..	Bengal Cavy.	18 May
*Philip Harris, ..	,, Infy.	8 June
*F. C. Wells, ..	Bombay ,,	18 July
*Robert Henderson, C.B.,	Madras Engrs.	4 Nov.
*James Travers, ..	Bengal Infy.	6 Dec.
1857.		
William Erskine Baker, ..	Bengal Engrs.	10 Mar.
*John Lewis Taylor, ..	,, Infy.	14 ,,
W. Beveridge Thomson,	,, ,,	29 May
*Charles James Green, ..	Madras Engs.	20 June
*Henry Blois Turner, ..	Bombay ,,	,,
*John Grant, ..	,, Arty.	,,
*Francis Burton Boileau,	Bengal Arty.	,,
*Patrick Gordon, ..	,, Infy.	,,
*Henry Forster, C. B., ..	Shekhawattee Battalion.	,,
~~*Thomas Bernard Chalon.~~	Madras Infy.	,,
*John Liptrap, ..	Bengal ,,	,,
*Arthur Cleghorn Wight,	Madras ,,	,,
*Charles Pooley, ..	,, ,,	,,

Names.	Presidency.	Date.
COLONELS.—(Contd.)		
1857.		
*Robert Garrett, ..	Bengal Infy.	20 June
*Simon Fraser Hannay, ..	,, ,,	,,
*Alexander McLeod, ..	Madras Cavy.	,,
*John Blaxland, ..	,, Infy.	,,
*Hubert Marshall, ..	,, ,,	,,
*Hamlyn Lavicount Harris, ..	,, ,,	,,
*John Liddell, C.B. ..	Bombay ,,	,,
*Edward Darvall, ..	Bengal ,,	,,
*Peter Abbott, ..	,, ,,	,,
*Donald Mackay Scobie,..	Bombay ,,	,,
*G. H. Swinley, ..	Bengal Arty.	27 ,,
*Henry Palmer, ..	Bengal Infy.	29 July
*David Pott, ..	,, ,,	22 Aug.
*Archibald Lorne Campbell,	,, Cavy.	15 Sep.
*Thomas Lowth Harington, ..	,, ,,	12 Oct.
*Douglas Seaton, ..	Bengal Infy.	15 ,,
*Robert Codrington, ..	Madras Infy.	16 ,,
*James Victor Hughes, ..	Madras Infy.	28 ,,
*Charles Lucas, ..	Bombay Arty.	13 Nov.
*N. B. Chamberlain, C. B,	Bengal Infy.	27 ,,
*John William Croggan,..	Madras Arty.	28 ,,
*J. Abbott, ..	Bengal Arty.	,,
*John Glasfurd, ..	,, Engrs.	,,
*H. C. Gossling, ..	,, Infy.	,,
*Peter Thomas Cherry, ..	Madras Cavy.	,,
*T. J. Fischer, ..	Madras Infy	,,
*J. C. G. Stuart, ..	,, ,,	,,
*W. M. Gabbett, ..	Madras Arty.	,,
*T. Tapp, C. B., ..	Bombay Infy.	,,
*H. Stiles, ..	,, ,,	,,
*J. W. H. Jamieson, ..	Bengal Infy.	,,
*P. K. Skinner, ..	Bombay ,,	,,
*W. P. Robbins, ..	Bengal ,,	,,
*C. Hogge, C.B., ..	,, Arty.	,,
*Hugh Boyd, ..	,, Infy.	,,
*N. P. MacDougall, ..	Bombay ,,	,,
*W. E. Mulcaster, ..	Bengal ,,	,,
*Orfeur Cavenagh, ..	,, ,,	,,
*H. Jacob, ..	Bombay ,,	,,
*J. S. Paton, ..	Bengal ,,	,,
*J. C. Heath, ..	Bombay ,,	,,
*R. Farquhar, C. B., ..	,, ,,	,,
*H. J. Pelly, ..	,, ,,	1 Dec.
*George Nott, ..	Madras ,,	8 ,,
1858.		
*John Byng, C B. ..	Madras Cavy.	15 Jan.
*J. M. B. F. Tytler, C B.	Bengal Infy.	19 ,,
Richard Rodney Ricketts,	Madras ,,	27 ,,
*John William Hicks, ..	Bengal ,,	15 Feb.
*R. R. Younghusband, .	Bombay ,,	2 Mar.
*William Pitt Macdonald,	Madras ,,	4 ,,
*Vincent Eyre, C.B., ..	Bengal Arty.	24 ,,
*Frank Turner, C. B., ..	,, ,,	,,

* Brevet.

Names.	Presidency.	Date.
COLONELS.—*(Contd.)*		
1858.		
*J. D. McPherson, C. B.,	Bengal Infy.	5 Apl.
*Andrew Munro McCally,	Madras Infy.	23 April
*John Swanson, ..	Bombay ,,	25 ,,
*Alfred Borradaile, ..	Madras Cavy.	25 ,,
*John Reid Brown, ..	,, ,,	1 May
*R. Shubrick, ..	Madras Infy.	18 June
*G. B. Arbuthnot, ..	Madras Cavy.	4 July
*William Reece, ..	,, Infy.	13 ,,
*Robert Nicholas Faunce,	,, Infy.	20 ,,
*H. M. Durand, C. B. ..	Bengal Engrs.	,,
*J. Coke, C. B. ..	,, Infy.	,,
*Henry Tombs, C. B., ..	,, Arty.	,,
*Benjamin Crispin, ..	Bombay Infy.	,,
*Arthur C. Spottiswoode,	Bengal ,,	23 ,,
*Joseph Graham, ..	,, ,,	27 Aug.
*James Templeton Brett,	Madras Cavy.	14 Oct.
*C. Simson Maling, ..	Bengal Infy.	24 ,,
*James Walker Bayley, ..	Madras ,,	14 Nov.
*J. H. B. Congdon, ..	,, ,,	23 ,,
1859.		
*T. G. E. G. Kenny, ..	Madras Infy.	4 Feb.
*John Skardon Ramsay, ..	Bombay ,,	5 Mar.
*Edwin Henry Atkinson, ..	Madras ,,	13 ,,
LIEUT. COLONELS.		
1851.		
H. W. Trevelyan, C. B., ..	Bombay Arty.	28 Apl.
W. H. Miller, ..	Madras Arty.	15 May
T. K. Whistler, ..	,, ,,	2 July
1854.		
F. Gaitskell, C. B., ..	Bengal Arty.	17 May
*Henry Bower, ..	Madras Infy.	20 June
*Coghill Glendower Ottley,	,, ,,	,,
John Hill, ..	,, ,,	,,
*Francis Dudgeon, ..	,, ,,	,,
*Nathaniel John Gordon,	,, ,,	,,
*Charles Moray Macleane,	Madras ,,	,,
*Henry Drummond, ..	Bengal Cavy.	,,
William Binfield Wemyss,	,, Cavy.	,,
Richard Drought, C.B., ..	,, Infy.	,,
*J. M. Madden, ..	Madras ,,	28 Nov.
*E. H. Hart, ..	Bombay ,,	,,
*T. Moore, ..	Bengal Cavy.	,,
LIEUT. COLONELS.—*(Continued.)*		
1854.		
*C. Campbell, ..	Bengal Infy	28 Nov.
R. A. Master, C. B., ..	,, Cavy.	,,
*G. Cautley, ..	,, Cavy.	,,
R. R. Kinleside, ..	,, Arty.	,,
A. Huyshe, ..	,, ,,	,,
*J. Clarke, ..	Bengal Infy.	,,
*G. P. Whish, ..	,, ,,	,,
*M. E. Sherwill, ..	,, Infy.	,,
*J. Abercrombie, ..	,, Arty.	,,
A. Cunningham, ..	,, Engrs.	,,
*R. W. D. Leith, ..	Bombay Infy.	,,
William St. Leger Mitchell,	Bengal ,,	,,
*G. Malcolm, C. B., ..	Bombay ,,	,,
Thomas Maughan, ..	,, ,,	,,
E. L. Russell, ..	,, ,,	,,
*H. B. Edwardes, C.B., ..	Bengal ,,	,,
*H. J. Stannus, ..	Bengal Cavy.	,,
*H. F. Dunsford, C. B., ..	,, Infy.	,,
*C. Cheape, ..	,, ,,	,,
W. C. Campbell, ..	,, ,,	,,
*S. A. Abbott, ..	,, ,,	,,
J. C. Hannyngton, ..	,, ,,	,,
*C. J. Owen, C. B., ..	Bombay Cavy.	,,
*J. R. Keily, ..	Bombay ,,	,,
W. R. Dunmore, ..	Bengal Infy.	,,
*R. Shortrede, ..	Bombay ,,	,,
1855.		
F. Burgoyne, ..	Madras Arty,	11 Feb.
*W. W. Dunlop, ..	Madras Infy.	13 Apl.
*C. Macleod, ..	,, ,,	1 May
J. H. G. Crawford, ..	Bombay Engrs.	10 ,,
A. S. Waugh, ..	Bengal ,,	3 Aug.
G. W. Y. Simpson, ..	Madras Arty.	14 Aug.
C. W. Tremenhere, ..	Bombay Engrs.	13 Sep.
W. J. B. Knyvett, ..	Bengal Infy.	15 ,,
*C. F. Liardet, ..	Madras ,,	5 Dec.
1856.		
*W. H. Budd, ..	Madras Infy.	10 Feb.
*N. D. Barton, ..	Bengal ,,	18 Mar.
*C. Birdwood, ..	Bombay Infy.	9 April
E. L. Ommanney, ..	Bengal Engrs	15 ,,
A. Hall, ..	Bengal Cavy	5 May
*J. Whistler, ..	Madras	18 ,,
H. J. Margary, ..	Bombay Engrs.	24 ,,
*John Holmes, ..	,, Infy.	6 June
*Richard Crewe, ..	Madras ,,	,,

* Brevet.

Names.	Presidency.	Date.
LIEUT. COLONELS.— *(Continued.)*		
1855.		
G. Briggs,	Madras Arty.	7 June
J. Brind, C. B.,	Bengal Arty.	26 ,,
G. Pope,	Bombay Infy.	18 July
*G. C. Stockley,	,, ,,	6 Dec.
1857.		
H. Forster,	Bombay Arty.	12 Jan.
J. Laughton,	Bengal Engrs.	10 Mar.
H. Vetch,	,, Infy.	29 May
Arthur Sanders,	,, ,,	,,
C. Davidson,	,, ,,	31 ,,
G. W. Bishop,	,, ,,	,,
*H. S. Waters,	Madras Cavy	27 June
J. Powell,	Bengal Infy.	,,
G. Ramsay,	,, ,,	,,
F. C. Burnett,	,, Arty.	,,
E. G. J. Champneys,	,, ,,	1 July
R. Y. B. Bush,	,, ,,	15 ,,
J. G. A. Rice,	,, ,,	29 ,,
J. H. Hampton,	,, ,,	22 ,,
W. A. Cooke,	,, ,,	3 Sep.
A. Broome,	,, Arty.	14 ,,
*H. Pritchard,	Madras ,,	15 ,,
H. Rigby,	Bengal Engrs.	20 ,,
*S. H. Partridge,	Bombay ,,	23 ,,
R. E. Knatchbull,	Bengal Arty.	28 ,,
T. H. Sale,	,, Engrs.	1 Oct.
E. Lawford,	Madras	2 ,,
*K. Young, C. B.,	Bengal Infy.	12 ,,
*A. R. J. Swinton,	,, ,,	15 ,,
J. Maitland,	Madras Arty.	4 Nov.
R. Ramsay,	Bengal Infy.	18 ,,
*A. G. Young,	Madras ,,	1 Dec.
H. W. Matthews,	Bengal Infy.	3 ,,
1858.		
A. Prescott,	Bombay Cavy.	1 Jan.
*H. A. Olpherts,	Bengal Arty.	15 ,,
*E. Kaye,	Bengal Arty.	19 ,,
*C. Reid, C. B.,	,, Infy.	,,
*R. B. Smit C. B.,	,, Engrs.	,,
*W. F. Curtis,	Bombay Cavy.	,,
*R. S. Ewart,	Bengal Infy.	,,
E. W. S. Scott,	,, ,,	,,
*E. S. Blake, C. B.,	Bombay Arty.	,,
*H. J. Barr,	,, Infy.	,,
N. C. Macleod,	Bengal Engrs.	,,
*E. B. Johnson, C. B.,	,, Arty.	,,
W. D. Graham,	Bombay Engrs.	1 Mar.
*H. B. Blogg,	Madras Cavy.	4 ,,
*C. Apthorp,	Bengal Infy.	24 ,,
J. D. Stewart,	Bombay ,,	,,
*W. A. Orr, C. B.,	Madras Arty.	,,
*T. Simpson,	Bengal Infy.	,,
*G. J. Montgomery,	,, ,,	,,
*G H Robertson, C. B.,	Bombay ,,	,,
*H. H. Maxwell,	Bengal Arty.	,,
G. Kirby,	,, ,,	,,
T. J. W. Hungerford,	,, ,,	,,
*M. Galwey, C. B.,	Madras Infy.	,,
*J. H. Smyth,	Bengal Arty.	,,
*G. Bourchier, C, B.,	,, ,,	,,
LIEUT. COLONELS.— *(Continued.)*		
1858.		
*W. Olpherts C. B.,	Bengal Arty.	24 Mar.
*G. W. G. Green, C. B.,	,, Infy.	,,
*F. F Remmington, C. B.,	,, Arty.	,,
*J. Metcalfe,	,, Infy.	,,
*C. H. Blunt, C. B.,	,, Arty.	,,
*C. Prior,	,, Infy.	25 Apl.
D. Wilkie,	,, ,,	26 ,,
*W. W. Apperley,	,, Cavy.	1 May
*W. Cantis,	Madras Infy.	4 ,,
*Wm. Edwyn Evans,	Bombay ,,	14 ,,
G. W. Hamilton,	Bengal ,,	19 ,,
J. W. Auld,	Bombay Infy.	,,
F. Gottreux,	Madras ,,	21 ,,
G. DeSaumarez,	,, ,,	29 June
*C. Cooper,	,, ,,	4 July
J. M. Glasse,	Bombay Arty.	,,
*J. Dew, C. J. Moir,	Bengal Infy.	20 ,,
*G. Gordon,	,, ,,	,,
*G. S. Cotter,	Madras Arty.	,,
*R. Hamilton,	Madras Infy.	,,
*A. J. M. Boileau,	,, Engrs.	,,
H. A. Carleton, C. B.,	Bengal Arty.	,,
*J. Forbes, C. B.	Bombay Cavy.	,,
*A. T. Wilde, C. B.	Madras Infy.	,,
*H. Daly, C. B.,	Bombay ,,	,,
*D. M. Stewart,	Bengal ,,	,,
*A. Taylor, C. B.	Bengal Engrs.	,,
*J. Brasyer,† C. B.,	,, Infy.	,,
R. Macdonell,	Bengal Cavy.	23 ,,
*J. J. Losh,	Madras Infy.	,,
F. Russell,	,, ,,	24 ,,
W. Barr,	Bengal Arty.	18 Aug.
H. E. S. Abbott,	,, Infy.	22 ,,
*H. S. Watkin,	Bombay Infy.	27 ,,
T. Martin,	Bengal ,,	,,
J. Butler,	,, ,,	,,
*T. McGoun,	Madras ,,	14 Oct.
*E. A. Guerin,	Bombay ,,	24 ,,
E Brice,	Madras Arty.	5 Nov.
R. C. Wormald,	Bombay ,,	10 ,,
G. Rowlandson,	Madras ,,	13 ,,
*F. W. Burroughs,	Bengal Infy.	14 ,,
W. H. Delamain,	,, Arty.	,,
*G. Timins,	,, Infy.	23 ,,
C. Ireland,	Madras	,,
*G. B. Munbee,	Bombay Engrs.	,,
G. R. Grimes,	,, Infy.	28 ,,
H. Vincent,	,, ,,	2 Dec.
J. B. Woosnam,	,, Arty.	6 ,,
David Reid,	Bengal Arty.	23 ,,
1859.		
G. Halpin,	Madras Infy.	14 Jan.
A. P. Phayre,	Bengal Infy.	22 ,,
*H. A. Shuckburgh,	,, ,,	4 Feb.
J. H. Bell,	Madras Engrs.	27 ,,
*H. D. Sheppard,	,, Infy.	5 Mar.
*J. W. Coates,	,, ,,	13 ,,
B. Boyd,	Bengal ,,	15 May
F. E. Voyle,	,, ,,	4 June
Official rank.		
W. Augustin J. Mayhew,	Bengal Infy.	
G. W. Williams,	,, ,,	
H. Yule,	,, Engrs.	

† Unattached.

MAJORS.

Names.	Presidency.	Date.
1851.		
J. F. Porter, ..	Madras Cavy.	11 Nov.
T. T. Christie, ..	Bombay Infy.	,,
H. Green, ..	Madras ,,	,,
D. R. J. Brett, ...	,, ,,	,,
C. Briggs, ..	,, ,,	,,
A. F. Macpherson, ..	Bengal ,,	,,
J. M. Drake, ..	,, ,,	,,
A. H. Duncan, ..	,, ,,	,,
W. K. Babington, ..	Madras ,,	,,
G. A. Tulloch, ..	,, ,,	,,
R. R. W. Ellis, ..	Bengal ,,	,,
L. P. D. Eld, ..	,, ,,	,,
J. R. Arrow, ..	Madras ,,	,,
C. Pattenson, ..	Bengal ,,	,,
E. Marriot, ..	,, ,,	,,
R. G. Taylor, ..	,, ,,	16 Dec.
1852.		
C. T. Chamberlain, ..	Bengal Infy.	2 May.
A W. C. Plowden, ..	,, Cavy.	22 Oct.
1853.		
C. V. Cox, ..	Bengal Arty.	4 Mar.
P. Cristie, ..	,, ,,	4 ,,
H. W. Blake, ..	Madras ,,	16 Nov.
W. A. J. Mayhew, -	Bengal Infy.	9 Dec.
G. Allan, -	Madras ,,	,,
W. F. Nuthall, -	Bengal ,,	,,
A. Fytche, -	,, ,,	,,

MAJORS.—*(Continued.)*

Names.	Presidency.	Date.
1854.		
H. B. Lumsden, -	Bengal Infy.	6 Feb.
R. Strachey, -	,, Engrs.	16 ,,
C. F. North, -	Bombay ,,	,,
G. F. Salmon, -	Madras Infy.	24 Mar.
R. Cotton, -	,, ,,	13 April
R. W. O'Grady, -	Madras Infy.	4 May
W. R. Strange, -	,, Cavy.	23 ,,
G. G. McDonell, -	Madras ,,	20 June
C. Mackenzie, -	,, ,,	,,
R. Taylor, -	,, Cavy.	,,
F. E. Lys, -	,, Infy.	,,
G. R. Edwards, -	,, Cavy.	,,
H. A Thompson, -	,, Infy.	,,
J. Stewart, -	,, ,,	,,
H. Nott, -	,, ,,	,,
W. H. Welch, -	,, ,,	,,
T. P. Walsh, -	,, ,,	,,
G. B. B. Groube, -	,, Cavy.	,,
A. B. Kerr, -	,, Infy.	,,
J. E. Hughes, -	,, ,,	,,
J. W. G. Kenny, -	,, ,,	,,
J. Campbell, -	,, ,,	,,
D. Hodson, -	,, ,,	,,
G. Carr, -	,, ,,	,,
G. W. Stokes, -	Bengal ,,	,,
W. Lamb, -	,, ,,	,,
E. F. Smith, -	,, ,,	,,
C. G. G. Munro, -	Bombay ,,	,,
W. B. Salmon, -	,, ,,	,,
H. Mackenzie, -	Bengal ,,	,,
W. Lydiard, -	,, ,,	,,
G. B. Reddie, -	,, ,,	,,
G. W. Williams, -	,, ,,	,,
A. Thomas, -	Bombay ,,	,,
J. K. Spence, -	Bengal ,,	,,
F. Westbrooke, -	Bombay ,,	,,
G. M. Hill, -	Bengal Infy.	,,
W. J. Birdwood, -	Madras Engrs.	,,
J. C. Scott, -	Bengal Infy.	,,
T. F. B. Beatson, -	,, Cavy.	,,
H. S. Grimes, -	,, Infy.	,,
~~G. H. Burt,~~ -	,, ,,	,,
J. Bontein, -	,, ,,	,,
F. Maitland, -	,, ,,	,,

Names.	Presidency.	Date.	Names.	Presidency.	Date.
MAJORS.—*(Continued.)*			**MAJORS.**—*(Continued.)*		
1854.			1854.		
J. Barrett,	Bengal Infy.	20 June	W. G. Woods,	Madras Cavy.	20 June
R. J. Kempt,	Madras ,,	,,	J. W. Farran,	,, Infy.	,,
L. MacQueen,	Madras Cavy.	,,	R. Gordon,	,, ,,	,,
T. Stock,	Bombay Infy.	,,	R. Travers,	Bombay Infy.	,,
J. E. Mawdsley,	Madras Arty.	,,	J. H. Tapp,	Madras ,,	,,
E. Andrews,	Bombay Infy.	,,	W. Bissett,	Madras ,,	,,
J. Sleeman,	Bengal ,,	,,	W. C. Erskine,	Bengal ,,	,,
A. Russell,	Madras ,,	,,	C. R. Whitelock,	Bombay Infy.	,,
F. S. Paterson,	Bengal ,,	,,	R. S. Simpson,	Bengal ,,	,,
G. T. Haly,	Madras ,,	,,	J. C. Innes,	Bengal Infy.	,,
H. J. Nicholls,	,, ,,	,,	W. B. Legard,	,, ,,	,,
S. C. Macpherson,	,, ,,	,,	S. Gompertz,	Madras ,,	,,
E. P. Lynch,	Bombay Infy.	,,	W. W. Davidson,	Bengal ,,	,,
C. R. Hogg,	,, ,,	,,	G. Jackson,	,, Cavy.	,,
S. W. Hennah,	Madras Cavy.	,,	W. F. Cormack,	Bombay Infy.	,,
R ~~G. Haines,~~	,, Infy.	,,	W. J. Wilson,	Madras Infy.	,,
R. Morrieson,	Bengal ,,	,,	J. E. Verner,	Bengal Infy.	,,
R ~~T. R. Stewart,~~	Bombay Infy.	,,	R. J. Hawthorne,	,, Cavy.	,,
A. M. Haselwood,	,, ,,	,,	P. A. P. Bouverie,	Bengal Infy.	11 July
E. Baynes,	,, ,,	,,	A. Bagot,	,, ,,	24 ,,
C. J. Cooke,	Madras Arty.	,,	A. G. Goodwyn,	,, Engrs.	2 Aug.
W. H. Godfray,	Bombay Infy.	,,	J. R. Becher,	Bengal ,,	,,
R ~~H. T. Hillyard,~~	Madras ,,	,,	J. H. Maxwell,	,, ,,	,,
D. Gausson,	Bengal ,,	,,	W. Kendall,	Bombay ,,	,,
C. R. Browne,	Bengal ,,	,,	E. J. Lake,	Bengal Engrs.	22 Aug.
W. Baker,	Bengal Cavy.	,,	G. Newbolt,	Bengal Infy.	28 Nov.
R. S. Dobbs,	Madras Infy.	,,	W. T. Money,	Madras ,,	,,
J. Campbell,	,, ,,	,,	R. T. Snow,	,, ,,	,,
W. Borthwick,	,, ,,	,,	J. Kitson,	,, ,,	,,
R. Troup,	Bengal ,,	,,	J. T. Daniell,	Bengal ,,	,,
A. Strange,	Madras Cavy.	,,	J Liptrott,	,, ,,	,,
R ~~F. C. Hawkins,~~	,, Infy.	,,	E K Elliot,	,, ,,	,,
H. Boye,	Bombay ,,	,,	E Pereira,	Madras ,,	,,
G. M. Gumm,	Madras Arty.	,,	T S Horsbrugh,	Bengal ,,	,,
B. W. Black,	,, ,,	,,	H. Milne,	,, ,,	,,
W. K. Worster,	,, ,,	,,	G Harvey,	Madras ,,	,,
H. H. Bell,	,, ,,	,,	W H Ryves,	Bengal ,,	,,
W. J. Church,	Madras Infy.	,,	S F Macmullen,	,, Cavy	,,
C. G. Walsh,	Bengal ,,	,,	R Thatcher,	,, Infy	,,
R. Wallace,	Bombay ,,	,,	W L Boulderson,	Madras ,,	,,
H. C. Jones,	,, ,,	,,	B R Powell,	Bombay ,,	,,
R. J. Shaw,	Bombay ,,	,,	H R Phillott,	Madras ,,	,,
C. Burton,	Madras ,,	,,	F J Carruthers,	,, Cavy	,,
W. Richardson,	Bengal ,,	,,	C D Mylne,	Bombay Infy	,,
M. Nation,	,, ,,	,,	J Smith,	Bengal ,,	,,
C. J. Elphinstone,	Madras ,,	,,	S R Tickell,	,, ,,	,,
H. J. Brockman,	,, ,,	,,	J Babington,	Madras Arty	,,
J. Hennessy.	Bengal ,,	,,	J L Barrow,	,, ,,	,,
H. W. Preedy,	Bombay ,,	,,	J A Gunthorpe,	Madras Arty	,,
K. Jopp,	,, ,,	,,	M F Gordon,	Bombay Engrs	,,
H. W. Evans,	Bombay Infy.	,,	A J Kelso,	Madras Cavy	,,
J. Jackson,	Madras ,,	,,	R N Raikes,	Bengal Infy	,,
F. J. Harriott,	Bengal Cavy.	,,	A Martin,	,, ,,	,,
W. P. Hampton,	,, Infy.	,,	A M Molyneux,	Madras Infy	,,

Names.	Presidency.	Date.
MAJORS.—*(Continued.)*		
1854.		
W H Horsley,	Madras Engrs	28 Nov
G P Eaton,	,, Arty	,,
J D Mein,	,, ,,	,,
E Armstrong	,, Infy	,,
A H Ross,	Bengal ,,	,,
C Mauger,	Bombay ,,	,,
A Crawford,	,, ,,	,,
G Sturruck,	Madras ,,	,,
W H Wapshare,	,, ,,	,,
W K Wollen,	Bengal ,,	,,
J G Gaitskell,	,, ,,	,,
P T Snow,	Madras ,,	,,
W Middleton,	,, ,,	,,
S D Young	,, ,,	,,
C Hasell,	Bengal ,,	,,
J McGrigor,	Bombay ,,	,,
W H Freese,	Madras ,,	,,
A S Findlay,	,, ,,	,,
C E M Walker,	Madras ,,	,,
J Morrieson,	Bengal ,,	,,
S S Coffin,	Madras ,,	,,
E E Miller,	,, Cavy	,,
J Stewart,	,, Infy	,,
C Gill,	Madras Infy.	,,
E Harvey,	Bengal Cavy	,,
F Vardon,	Madras Infy	,,
P W Luard,	Bengal ,,	,,
H L Bird,	Bengal Infy	,,
T G St George,	,, ,,	,,
F. A. C. Kane,	Bombay Infy.	12 Dec.
1855.		
C. Herbert,	Bengal Infy	2 Jan.
G. Fitzmaurice,	Madras ,,	9 ,,
C. J. Robarts,	Bengal ,,	8 Mar.
P G Cazalet,	Madras Infy	1 May
W. H. C. Lye,	Bombay ,,	,,
R Kinkead,	Madras Arty	7 ,,
J G Balmain,	Madras Arty	3 Aug.
G Selby,	Madras Arty	15 Sep.
S. J. Hire,	Bengal Infy	2 Dec.
Alex. R. Manson,	Bombay Infy	10 ,,
1856.		
C V Bowie,	Bengal Arty	22 Jan
H T M Berdmore,	Madras ,,	10 Feb
W F Hutton,	, Infy	18 Mar
J Fowler,	,, Cavy	2 April
G Verner,	Bengal Infy	18 May
G T S Carruthers,	Madras ,,	6 June
E W Boudier,	,, ,,	,,
J E Mayne,	,, Cavy	,,
J G Stephen,	Bengal Infy.	,,
J L Vaughan,	,, ,,	,,
F J Goldsmid,	Madras ,,	,,
R B Brett,	Bombay Arty	,,
E Wray,	,, ,,	,,
R Richardson,	Bengal Cavy	,,
R O Gardner,	Madras Infy	8 ,,
A R West,	,, ,,	4 July
W A A Thomson,	Bengal Cavy	13 ,,
MAJORS.—*(Continued.)*		
1856.		
A Robertson,	Madras Infy	18 July
H W Tulloch,	,, ,,	15 Sep.
A. C. Silver,	,, ,,	20 ,,
A. C. Honner,	Bombay ,,	15 Oct.
J G Halliday,	Madras ,,	4 Nov.
C T E Hinde,	Bengal Infy	24 ,,
W H R Green,	Bombay ,,	,,
W. L. Merewether,	,, ,,	,,
J C Phillips,	Bengal ,,	28 ,,
J. P. Coode,	Madras ,,	30 ,,
1857.		
W. G. Arrow,	Bombay Infy	14 Feb.
A E Saunders,	,, ,,	14 Mar.
J. T. Shakespear,	Bengal ,,	1 May
T P Sparks,	Madras ,,	29 ,,
S B Faddy,	Bengal, ,,	31 ,,
J L Walker,	,, ,,	,,
R Phayre,	Bombay ,,	16 June
E C Marston,	,, ,,	,,
J F Stevens,	Madras ,,	27 ,,
C V Jenkins,	Bengal Cavy	1 July
E Sissmore,	,, Infy	11 ,,
F M Baker,	,, ,,	15 ,,
W C Gott,	,, ,,	,,
H Ramsay,	,, ,,	,,
E D Watson,	,, ,,	21 ,,
A Meyer,	,, ,,	22 Aug.
T F Hobday,	,, ,,	28 ,,
W McCulloch,	,, ,,	4 Sep.
G G Denniss,	,, ,,	14 ,,
S O E Ludlow,	Madras ,,	23 ,,
A. J. de H. Harris,	Madras Infy.	25 ,,
T Thompson,	,, ,,	15 Oct.
W H Oakes,	,, ,,	7 Nov.
T L Jameson,	Bombay ,,	1 Dec.
A. Wyndham,	Madras ,,	2 ,,
E C Beale,	Bombay ,,	3 ,,
L. S. Hough,	,, ,,	4 ,,
F. Johnston,	Bengal ,,	18 ,,
1858.		
J. M. Taylor,	Bombay Cavy.	1 Jan.
W. Ballingall,	,, Infy	16 ,,
C R W Hervey,	,, ,,	19 ,,
E K Money,	Bengal Arty	,,
A Boyd,	,, Infy	,,
J C Graves,	Bombay Cavy	,,
R. C. Lawrence,	Bengal Infy	,,
H. Nicoll,	,, ,,	,,
S. Greville,	,, ,,	,,
D C Shute,	,, ,,	,,
A B Kemball, C. B.,	Bombay Arty.	,,
R. L. Taylor,	,, Infy	,,
W. D. Harris,	Bengal ,,	,,
R A Ramsay,	,, ,,	,,
H R Grindlay,	,, Cavy	,,
O E Rothney,	,, Infy.	,,
J Worgan,	Bombay Arty.	,,
J Wray,	,, Infy.	,,
J Young,	Bengal Arty.	,,
W S Hatch,	Bombay ,,	,,
H L Gibbard,	,, ,,	,,

Names.	Presidency.	Date.	Names.	Presidency.	Date.
MAJORS.—*(Continued.)* 1858.			MAJORS.—*(Continued.)* 1858.		
E P Arthur,	Bombay Cavy	19 Jan.	W F Eden,	Madras Infy	20 July
B K Finnimore,	,, Arty	,,	A. W. Macintire, C.B.	,, Arty.	,,
J. C. Hay,	Bengal Infy	,,	G. E. Ashburner,	Bengal Infy.	,,
E. Brown,	,, ,,	,,	R. Larkins,	,, ,,	,,
G. W. M. Hall,	,, ,,	,,	J. W. F. Sandwith,	Bombay ,,	,,
H M Garstin,	,, ,,	,,	R. J. Meade,	Bengal ,,	,,
H F. M. Boisragon,	,, ,,	,,	C. Douglas,	,, Arty.	,,
M S Green,	Bombay ,,	,,	J. W. Carter,	,, Infy.	,,
D. Kemp,	Bengal ,,	,,	J. Hood,	,, ,,	,,
C H Barchard, C. B.	,, ,,	,,	W. W. Anderson,	Bombay Cavy.	,,
T. E. Kennion,	,, Arty	,,	J. F. Richardson, C. B.,	Bengal Infy.	,,
A. Light,	,, ,,	,,	J. Gordon,	,, ,,	,,
J. T. Walker,	Bombay Engrs.	,,	A. Hume,	,, ,,	,,
T. H. Sibley,	Bengal Infy.	,,	R. C. Barclay,	,, ,,	,,
G S Montgomery,	Bombay Infy	27 ,,	C. S. Weston,	,, ,,	,,
A. H. A. Hervey,	Madras ,,	15 Feb.	J. H. Brooks,	,, Cavy.	,,
H Drury,	Madras ,,	4 Mar.	G. Moir, C. B.,	,, Arty.	,,
W. Maxwell.	Bengal Arty.	24 Mar.	J. G. Lightfoot, C.B.,	Bombay ,,	,,
E H Simpson,	Bombay Cavy	,,	J. C. Coley,	,, Infy,	,,
J W Carnegie,	Bengal Infy	,,	F. O Salusbury,	Bengal ,,	,,
D S Dodgson,	,, ,,	,,	E. Campbell,	Bombay ,,	,,
L Barrow, C. B.,	Madras Cavy	,,	H. H. A. Wood,	,, ,,	,,
T F Wilson, C. B.,	Bengal Infy	,,	T. Raikes,	Madras ,,	,,
H Dinning,	,, ,,	,,	W. P. Pelly,	Bombay ,,	,,
F. W. Baugh,	,, ,,	,,	E. J. Lawder,	Madras ,,	,,
F. G. Crossman,	,, ,,	,,	A. G. Austen,	Bengal Arty.	,,
M F Kemble,	,, ,,	,,	G. W. Boileau,	,, Infy.	,,
H. D. Abbott, C. B.,	Madras ,,	,,	F. W. Pinkney,	Madras ,,	,,
G. C. Hatch,	Bengal ,,	,,	S. J. Browne,	Bengal ,,	,,
H. M. Wilson,	,, ,,	,,	W. Scott,	Bombay ,,	,,
H L Evans,	Bombay ,,	,,	W. D. Morgan,	Bengal ,,	,,
H Hammond,	Bengal Arty	,,	W. A. Mackinnon, C. B.	,, Arty	,,
J J Lawrie,	Bombay Infy	,,	R. L. Thompson,	,, Infy.	,,
J D Woolcombe, C. B.,	,, Arty	,,	A. L. McMullin,	,, ,,	,,
R C Germon,	Bengal Infy	,,	J. H. Balmain,	,, Cavy.	,,
E L Grant,	Madras ,,	,,	H Forbes,	,, ,,	,,
H. D. Taylor,	,, ,,	,,	J. I. Murray,	Bengal Infy.	,,
C. St. G, Brownlow,	Bengal ,,	,,	J. B. Spurgin,	Madras ,,	,,
J G C Fraser.	Madras ,,	,,	R. H. Keatinge	Bombay Arty.	,,
J W Sanders,	Bengal ,,	,,	H C. Anderson,	Bengal Infy.	,,
H Bruce, C. B.,	Bombay ,,	,,	C. Cureton,	,, ,,	,,
T T Boileau,	Bengal Cavy	,,	F. A. E. Loch,	Bombay Cavy.	,,
R J Edgell,	,, Infy	,,	C Cookworthy,	Bengal Arty.	,,
F. C. Maisey,	,, ,,	,,	F.W. Lambert,	,, Infy.	,,
E Oakes,	,, ,,	,,	C. J. S. Gough,	,, Cavy.	,,
W A Crommelin, C. B.,	,, Engrs	,,	A. B. Little,	Bomby Infy.	,,
Henry Lane,	,, Cavy	,,	E. A. H. Bacon,	,, ,,	,,
T A Carey.	,, Infy	,,	H. Drummond,	Bengal Engrs.	,,
R P Anderson,	,, ,,	,,	W. A. Dick,	Bombay Cavy.	,,
H LeG Bruce,	,, Arty	,,	A. B. Johnson,	Bengal, Infy.	,,
A D Dickens,	,, Infy	,,	A. Pearson,	,, Artv.	,,
W T Hughes,	,, ,,	,,	A. Bunny,	,, ,,	,,
G S Macbean,	,, ,,	,,	G. A. Renny,	,, ,,	,,
C A Barwell,	,, ,,	,,	G. Hutchinson,	,, Engrs.	,,
D M Probyn, C. B.,	,, Cavy	,,	O. Wilkinson,	,, Cavy.	,,
J C Anderson,	Madras Engrs	,,	J. Keating,	Madras Infy.	23 ,,
T James,	Bengal Infy.	,,	H. Stanley,	Bombay ,,	21 Aug.
J. Temple,	Madras ,,	13 April	G Ryley,	Bengal ,,	22 ,,
J. W. Schneider,	Bombay ,,	25 ,,	H. Richards,	Bombay Infy.	27 ,,
W. S. Ferris,	Bengal ,,	,,	R. Cadell,	Madras Arty.	28 ,,
C. J. Richards,	,, ,,	1 May	E. W. E. Walker,	Bengal Arty.	,,
C. H. Case,	Madras ,,	4 ,,	H. P. Bishop,	,, ,,	,,
R. C. Tytler,	Bengal ,,	16 ,,	J. S. Frith,	,, ,,	,,
D. Hamilton,	Madras ,,	29 June	W. W. H. Greathed,	,, Engrs.	,,
Hon. H. Arbuthnot,	,, Cavy.	4 July	W. T. Brown,	,, Arty.	,,
T. Clerk,	,, Infy.	13 ,,	J. S. Gibb,	,, ,,	,,

Names.	Presidency.	Date.
MAJORS.—(*Continued.*)		
1858.		
W. Wilson, ..	Bengal Arty.	28 Aug.
R. Pittman, ..	Bombay ,,	,,
F. R. Maunsell, ..	Bengal Eng rs.	,,
G. E. Watson, ..	,, ,,	,,
J. F. Tennant, ..	,, ,,	,,
J. G. Medley, ..	,, ,,	,,
J. A. Ballard, C. B. ..	Bombay ,,	,,
J. J. Mc L. Innes, ..	Bengal ,,	,,
G. T. Chesney, ..	,, ,,	,,
W. E. Warrand, ..	,, ,,	,,
H. A. Brownlow, ..	,, ,,	,,
P. Stewart, ..	,, ,,	,,
J. St. J. Hovenden, ..	,, ,,	,,
H. J. Willoughby, ..	Bombay Infy	14 Oct.
A. Wyndham, ..	Madras ,,	24 ,,
R. A. Doria, ..	,, ,,	1 Nov.
G. A. Fisher, ..	Bengal ,,	14 Nov.
T. J. Gardiner, ..	,, ,,	23 ,,
J. S Gell, ..	Bombay ,,	2 Dec.
H. R. Garden, ..	Bengal ,,	26 ,,
1859.		
W Birch, ..	Bengal Infy.	22 Jan.
C. A. Orr, ..	Madras Engrs.	4 Feb.
R. H. Sale, ..	Bengal Infy.	5 Mar.
R. Warburton, ..	,, Arty	13 ,,
T Rattray, ..	Bengal Infy	1 Apl.
P. A. Roberton, ..	,, ,,	15 May
T. Pownall, ..	,, ,,	4 June
Official rank.		
F. D. Atkinson, -	Bengal Infy	
H. E. L. Thuillier, -	,, Arty	
H W Norman, -	,, Infy	
CAPTAINS.		
1846.		
J Pottinger, -	Bombay Arty.	9 June
W G Robertson, -	2 Madras N I	4 Aug.
A R Thornhill, -	25 ,, Cavy	26 ,,
R S Dobbie, -	39 ,, N I	7 Sep
T D T Dyer, -	26 ,, ,,	5 Oct
R Woolley, -	28 ,, ,,	16 ,,
J Wilson, -	66 Madras N I	10 Nov.
S H Becher, -	71 Bengal N I	1 Dec.
G N Greene, -	0 ,, ,,	8 ,,
T H Campbell, -	Madras Arty	,,
G P Sealy, -	Bombay ,,	,,

Names.	Presidency.	Date.
CAPTAINS.—(*Continued.*)		
1846.		
E B Marsack, -	13 Madras N I	15 Dec.
G W Peyton, -	25 ,, ,,	18 ,,
H J C Shakespear, -	25 Bengal N I	26 ,,
C F Fenwick, -	30 ,, ,,	,,
1847.		
H J Piercy, -	49 Bengal N I	22 Jan.
S Richards, -	55 ,, ,,	15 Feb
A K Gore, -	29 Madras N I	22 ,,
W S Sherwill, -	66 Bengal N I	,,
W Dent, -	22 Madras N I	23 ,,
E H S Bowdich, -	26 Bombay N I	25 Mar.
F H Scott, -	8 Mad Cavy	3 April
J H M Babington, -	48 Madras N I	2 May
C Harris, -	27 Bengal N I	3 ,,
W T Nicolls, -	24 ,, ,,	1 June
F T Wroughton, -	8 Bengal N I	2 ,,
W S Snow, -	20 Madras N I	14 June
J G Forbes, -	23 Bombay L I	,,
J S D Tulloch, -	17 Bengal N I	,,
J Ouchterlony, -	Madras Engrs	,,
T A Cowper, -	22 Bombay N I	27 ,,
H B Sweet, -	39 Madras N I	11 July
F D Atkinson,* -	2 En Ben Fus	12 ,,
G W Russell, -	2 Madras Cavy	18 ,,
E Yates, -	28 ,, N I	20 ,,
W D Grant, -	50 Madras N I	1 Aug
C S Whitehill, -	3 Bo En Regt	7 ,,
D Boyd, -	11 Bombay N I	19 ,,
R Chester, -	7 Madras N I	24 ,,
J Chambers, -	21 Bengal N I	27 ,,
J C McCaskill, -	51 ,, ,,	27 Sep
H B Herbert, -	7 ,, ,,	22 Oct
J Cameron, -	1 ,, Cavy	7 Nov
J A Campbell, -	7 ,, ,,	16 ,,
C H Winfield, -	3 M En Regt	27 ,,
H T Vincent, -	7 Bombay N I	6 Dec
S Pott, -	,, Engrs	14 ,,
H E L Thuillier,* -	,, Arty	,,
J D Scott, -	Madras Arty	,,
H C Wade, -	,, ,,	,,
P L Hart, -	Bom Engrs	,,
T M Cameron, -	55 ,, ,,	30 ,,
C S Salmon, -	57 ,, ,,	31 ,,
M C Spottiswoode, -	24 Madras N I	,,

* Official Majors.

LIST

OF

RETIRED OFFICERS

OF THE

BENGAL, MADRAS AND BOMBAY PRESIDENCIES,

ABOVE THE RANK OF CAPTAIN.

LIEUTENANT GENERAL.

28th November 1854.
William Monteith, Madras engineers

MAJOR GENERALS.

28th November 1854.
Sir Charles Hopkinson, CB., Madras artillery
Hanbury Raynsford, Madras light cavalry
Brice Wakeford Lee, Madras native infantry
Henry Smith, Bombay light cavalry
George Augustus Litchfield, Bombay lt. cavalry
William Miles, Bombay native infantry
Andrew Campbell, Bombay artillery
Thomas Dickinson, Bombay engineers
Stanley Bullock, Madras light cavalry
25th January 1856.
Wm. Edward Allured Elliott, Madras infantry
John Ludlow, Bengal infantry
25th March 1856.
Benjamin Trarell Phillips, Bengal cavalry
24th June 1856.
Henry Tod Tucker, C. B., Bengal infantry
19th August 1856.
George Alcock, Madras artillery
17th October 1856.
George Borlase, Tremenheere Bengal engineers
5th Dec. 1856.
Edward Fitzgerald Day, Bengal artillery
17th Feb. 1857.
William Brett, Bombay artillery
13th March 1857.
John Forbes Musgrove, Madras infantry
29th May 1857.
John Theophilus Boileau, Bengal engineers
2nd February 1858.
Peter James Begbie, Madras, Artillery
Charles Forbes Jackson, Bombay Cavalry
21st May 1858.
Thomas Failerton, Bombay infantry.
James Kilner, Bombay Engineers
23rd July 1858.
John Brownrigg Bellasis, Bombay Infantry.
James Allardyce, Madras Infantry.
George Bruce Michell, Bengal Infantry.
17 September 1858.
William Biddle, Madras Infantry.

MAJOR GENERALS.—*Continued.*

19th November 1858.
William Edmund Litchfield, Madras L. Cavy.
18th January 1859.
Stephen Glynne Wheeler, Bengal Infantry.
George Tylee, Bengal Infantry.
Archibald Neil Maclean, Bombay Infantry.
George Hutt, C. B., Bombay Artillery.
18th March 1859.
Philip Anstruther, C. B. Madras Artillery,
Richard Blood, Bombay Infantry,
George Hall McGregor, C. B. Bengal Artillery,
Edward Haldane, Madras Infantry,
George Munro Arthur, Madras Infantry,
22nd April 1859.
Augustus Samuel Hawkins, Bombay Infantry.

COLONELS.

28th November 1854.
Robert John Hudleston, Madras light cavalry
Hugh Griffiths, Bengal native infantry
Sir Anthony Weldon, *Bart.*, Madras artillery
William Collyer, Bengal native infantry
George Cadell, Madras native infantry
James William Blackney, Bengal native infantry
James Ferguson, Bengal native infantry
William Moxon, Bengal native infantry
Pownall Phipps, Bengal native infantry
Thomas Fiott De Havilland, Madras engineers
Hamilton Tennent, Bombay native infantry
Cornelius Bowyer, C.B., Bengal native infantry
Charles Ferrior, Madras native infantry
James J. Preston, Bombay European regiment
Charles William Elwood, Bombay native infy.
William Morison, Bombay native infantry
Philip Case Gilman, Bengal native infantry
Robert Short, Madras native infantry
George Tweedie, Bombay native infantry
Richard Bayer Otto, Madras light cavalry
John Elliot, Bengal native infantry
Thomas Taylor, Bengal native infantry
Wm. Geo. Augustus Fielding, Bengal light cavy
John Duncan, Bengal native infantry
John Mallandaine, Madras native infantry

COLONELS.—*Continued.*

Charles Fitzgerald, C.B., Bengal light cavalry
Frederick Browne, Madras European regiment
Robert Smith, C.B., Bengal engineers
John Rodber, Bengal artillery
William Henry Sykes, Bombay native infantry
Philip William Pedler, Bombay native infantry
George Hawes, Bengal native infantry
Richard Thomas, Bombay light cavalry
Broadfield Sissmore, Bengal native infantry
Thomas Theophilus Paske, Madras artillery
John Josiah Meredith, Madras light cavalry
Evan Jervis, Bombay light cavalry
William Glendower White, Bombay artillery
Edward Cadogan, Madras native infantry
Henry Geo. Jourdon, Madras native infantry
Stephen Townsend, Madras native infantry
James Barclay, Bombay native infantry
William White Moore, Bengal native infantry
Hugh Morrieson, Bengal native infantry
Hugh Kyd, Madras European regiment
Robert Seymour, Bengal native infantry
Philip Brewer, Bengal native infantry
James Dalgairns, Madras native infantry
Christopher Lethbridge, Madras native infantry
John Watkins, Madras light cavalry
John Colvin, C.B., Bengal engineers
Robert Sutherland, Bombay native infantry
Hugh Caldwell, Bengal native infantry
Nathaniel Alves, Madras native infantry
Archibald Inglis, Madras native infantry
James Morison, Madras light cavalry
Charles George Alves, Madras native infantry
Charles Graham, C.B., Bengal artillery
Edward John Honywood, Bengal light cavalry
James Watkins, Bengal native infantry
William James Bradford, Madras native infy.
James Little, Bombay European regiment
George Everest, Bengal artillery
Thomas Chadwick, Bengal artillery
Jonathan Trelawny, Bengal native infantry
Henry Brown Smith, Madras light cavalry
James Nicholas Abdy, Madras artillery
Archibald Crawford, Madras artillery
William Low, Madras native infantry
Vincent Mathias, Madras native infantry
Thomas Wardlaw, Bengal native infantry
Sir Claude Martin Wade, C.B., Bl. native infy.
Angus Macpherson, Madras native infantry
William Borthwick, Madras native infantry
John Freke Palmer, Madras native infantry
Hugh Mitchell, Madras native infantry
Philip Downing Ottey, Bombay native infantry
Edward Biddulph, C.B., Bengal artillery
Thomas Marshall, Bombay native infantry
Frederick Bond, Madras artillery
William Martin, Bengal native infantry
William Nicol Burns, Madras native infantry
James Shaw Wyllie, Madras native infantry
James Kerr, Madras European regiment
John Morgan Ley, Madras artillery
William Burlton, C.B., Bengal light cavalry
Francis Farrant, Bombay light cavalry
John James Underwood, Madras engineers
Robert Low, Bengal native infantry
George Young, Bengal native infantry
George Fryer, Madras native infantry
John Lloyd, C.B., Bombay artillery
John Thomas Leslie, C.B., Bombay artillery
Charles William Grant, Bombay engineers
John Wilson, Madras native infantry

COLONELS.—*Continued.*

John Armstone Thompson, C.B., Bl. En. regt.
Thomas Lumsden, C.B., Bengal artillery
Henry Clapton Barnard, Bengal native infantry
William Geddes, C.B., Bengal artillery
Alexander Lawe, Madras engineers
Charles Griffiths, Bengal native infantry
Bruce Seton, Bombay native infantry
John Willis Watson, Bombay artillery
Marcus Claudius Decluzeau, Bombay artillery
Thomas Atherton Howard, Madras native infy.
John Wynch, Madras artillery
John Cowslade, Bengal European regiment
Michael Maxwell Shaw, Bombay nativy infy.
Henry Spencer, Bombay native infantry
Robert Tierney Wallace, Madras native infantry
Jas. Gray Wm. Curtis, C.B., Bengal native infy.
Charles Marshall, Bengal native infantry
James Ferdinand Douglas, Bengal native infantry
Joseph Walker Jasper Ouseley, Bl. native infy.
Onslow Baker, Bengal artillery
Crawfurd Hagart, Bombay European regiment
James Houstoun Mackinlay, Bengal native infy.
George Augustus Underwood, Madras engineers
David Ewart, Bengal artillery
James Dickson, Madras native infantry
John Dillon Browne, Bombay native infantry
Godfrey Thomas Greene, Bengal engineers
Archibald Geddes Hyslop, Madras artillery
Charles Thoresby, Bengal native infantry
Robert Lindsay Anstruther, Bengal light cavy.
Sir Proby Thomas Cautley, K.C.B., Bl. artillery
Thomas Edmund Sampson, Bengal native infy.
Charles Griffin, Bengal native infantry
Edward Fitzgerald Day, Bengal artillery
George Joseph Mant, Bombay native infantry
Cifton Benbow, Bombay native infantry
Skeffington Poole, Bombay light cavalry
Colin Campbell, Bengal native infantry
Chas. Henry Delamain, C.B., Bombay lt. cavy.
Hugh Inglis, Madras light cavalry
Rawson John Crozier, Bombay native infantry
Hector Mackenzie, Madras native infantry
Geo. Craven Armstrong, Bengal native infantry
Hugh Augustus Boscawen, Bl. native infantry
Gustavus Couper Rochfort, Madras native infy
William S. Pillans, Bengal artillery

11th May 1855.

Robert Campbell, Bengal infantry
William Anderson, C. B., Bengal artillery
S. Hennell, Bombay infantry
A. Knyvett, Bengal infantry
S. J. Grove, Bengal infantry

10th Aug. 1855.

Partick Hay, Bengal infantry

26th Oct. 1855.

Hon'ble Harry Burrard Dalzell, Bengal arty.

30th November 1855.

Edward Anstruther Farquharson. Bombay arty.

25th Jan. 1856.

Charles James Lewes, Bengal infantry
William Scott Adams, Bombay infantry

25th March 1856.

George Wright, Madras infantry

29th April 1856.

John Jackson, C.B., Bombay infantry
Thomas Wilson Oldfield, Bengal infantry
Edward Down, Madras cavalry

24th June 1856

John Cooper, Bombay infantry
Anthony Blake Rathborne, Bombay infantry

COLONELS.—*Continued.*

19th September 1856.

William Carleston Ormsby, Bengal infantry

5th December 1856.

James Chicheley Plowden, Bengal infantry
Edward Griffiths Austin, Bengal artillery
Honry Foquett, Bengal infantry
Nathaniel Hill Fishe, Madras artillery
Francis Kyan Duncan, Bengal artillery
John Ramsay, Bombay infantry
James Roger Western, Bengal engineers
Samuel Smith Trevor, Madras artillery
William Charles Hicks, Bengal infantry
George Stephens Brown, Bombay infantry

19th Dec. 1856.

John James Hamilton, Bengal infantry

17th Feb. 1857.

John Carne Boulderson Madras infantry

13th March 1857.

John Lang, Bengal infantry

17th April 1857.

James Benwell, Madras infantry
William Russell, Madras infantry
James Holland, Bombay infantry

29th May 1857.

Edward DuPré Townshend, Bengal infantry
James Smith DuVernet, Madras infantry

7th August 1857.

Jeseph Corfield, Bengal infantry
David Carstairs, Bombay infantry
Hugh Hughes Lloyd, Bengal infantry

23rd October 1857.

John Thomas Smith, Madras engineers
John Charles Haslock, Bengal infantry
James Stephen Davies, Bengal infantry
Charles Yates, Madras infantry
John Rawdon Oldfeild, Bengal engineers

4th December 1857.

Alexander Corse Scott, Bengal infantry
Charles Seton Guthrie, Bengal engineers

2nd February 1858.

John Hill, Bombay Engineers

26th March 1858.

Robert Waller, Bengal, Artillery

21st May 1858.

James Pope, Bombay Infantry
James Kilner, Bombay Engineers
Augustus DeButts, Madras Engineers

23rd July 1858.

Thomas Plumbe, Bengal Infantry,

17th September 1858.

Robert Edward T. Richardson, Bengal Infy.
Samuel Landon, Bombay Infantry.

19th November 1858.

James Hunter Campbell, Bengal Artillery

18th January 1859.

James Ramsay, Bengal Infantry
Thomas William Hicks, C. B., Bombay Artillery
G. F. C. Fitzgerald, Bengal Artillery
Stuart Bayley, Madras Infantry

18th March 1859.

Thomas John Nuthall, Bengal Infantry
Adam Cuppage, Madras Infantry
Zachary Mudge Mallock, Bengal Artillery
George Girdwood Channer, Bengal Artillery
Joseph Alexander Weller, Bengal Engineers

22nd April 1859.

Frederick C. Cotton, Madras Infantry.
Tudor Lavie, Madras Artillery.
John Wilson Auld, Bombay Infantry.

LIEUTENANT COLONELS.

28th November 1854.

Robert Hamilton Fotheringham, Madras engrs.
James Simpson, Madras light cavalry
John Dalziel, Madras native infantry
Henry Coyle, Madras native infantry
Thomas Hall, Bengal native infantry
Patrick Dunbar, Bengal light cavalry
Robert Close, Madras light cavalry
Sir William Lloyd, Bengal native infantry
Henry Sinnock, Bengal native infantry
Edward Osborn, Madras native infantry
Benjamin Baker, Madras native infantry
William Godley, Madras native infantry
Alexander Maclaren, Madras native infantry
Peter Barclay, Madras native infantry
William Curphey, Bengal artillery
Hugh L. Playfair, Bengal artillery
Robert Thew, Bombay artillery
John Jeffery O'Donoghue, Madras native infy.
George Arden, Bombay native infantry
Augustus Grafton, Bombay native infantry
James Harrison, Madras artillery
Thomas Wm. Wigan, Madras native infantry
Thomas Henry John Hockley, Madras artillery
James Tennent, Madras native infantry
John Russell Ardagh, Madras native infantry
William Ledlie, Bengal native infantry
Henry Capel Sandys, Bengal native infantry
Samuel Parlby, Bengal artillery
Thomas Watson, Madras native infantry
Alex. Brodie Campbell, Bombay native infantry
William Price, Bengal native infantry
James Palmer Woodward, Madras native infy.
John Campbell, Bengal native infantry
Charles Christie, Bengal native infantry
John Hancock, Bombay native infantry
Peter Grant, Bengal native infantry
George Kingsley Babington, Madras native infy.
Charles Savage, Bengal native infantry
Robert Pouget, Bombay engineers
John Thornton Lowis, Bengal native infantry
Wm. Wilkins De Winton, Bombay light cavy.
David Pringle, M.A., Bengal native infantry
Charles Sinnock, Madras native infantry
Harry Salmon, Madras native infantry
Walter Hamilton, Madras cavalry
Peter Teulon, Bengal native infantry
George Thornton, Bengal light cavalry
Thomas Lane Groundwater, Bombay artillery
George Anderson Vetch, Bengal native infantry
Robert William Gillum, Bombay native infantry
John Race Godfrey, Madras native infantry
Alexander Horsburgh, Bengal native infantry
James Fagan, Bengal native infantry
John Clarke, Bombay native infantry
Edward Ford Hamilton, Bombay native infantry
James C. Hyde, Bengal artillery
Thomas Reynolds, Bengal native infantry
George Scott, Madras native infantry
Thomas Roe, Bombay native infantry
Fras. Macartney Iredell, Bombay native infy.
Edward Jeffreys, Bengal native infantry
John Harding Bonnette, Madras native infantry
Francis Chancellor Rybot, Bombay light cavy.
Morgan Charles Chase, Madras light cavalry

LIEUTENANT COLONELS.—*Continued.*

William Turner, Bengal native infantry
John Jopp, Bombay engineers
William Stewart, Madras European regiment
Robert Arding Thomas, Bengal native infy.
Charles Adolphus Munro, Bengal native infy.
Stephen Robson, Bombay European regiment
Samuel Maltby, Bengal native infantry
John Clunes, Bombay native infantry
William Warde, Bengal light cavalry
Edward Mason, Bombay native infantry
John Davies, Bengal native infantry
Edward Thurlow Hibgame, Madras native infy.
William Shaw, Madras native infantry
John Purton, C.B., Madras engineers
William Aldous, Bengal native infantry
William Sterling, Bombay native infantry
Charles Fitzgerald, Bengal native infantry
George Home Johnstone, native infantry
Peter Johnston, Bengal native infantry
George Joseph Bidmead Johnston, Bl. n. infy.
William Hough, Bengal native infantry
James Richard Colnett, Bengal native infantry
John Brandon, Bengal native infantry
Benjamin Ashe, Bengal native infantry
George Freer Holland, Bengal native infantry
Robert Butler, Madras native infantry
Hugh Robertson Murray, Bengal native infantry
Charles Rogers, Bengal native infantry
Alexander Mackintosh, Madras native infantry
William Macleod, Madras native infantry
James Malton, Madras native infantry
Thomas Timbrell, C. B., Bengal artillery
George Washington Gibson, Bombay artillery
John Lawrie, Bombay artillery
William Stokoe, Madras native infantry
Francis Hunter, Madras cavalry
John Forbes, Bombay native infantry
George Frederick Penley, Bombay native infy.
James Allen, Bengal light cavalry
James Bedford, Bengal European regiment
George Barker, Bengal native infantry
George Chapman, Bengal native infantry
John Thomas Croft, Bengal native infantry
James William Douglas, Bengal native infantry
Alexander Davidson, Bengal European regt.
John Hailes, Bengal native infantry
Henry Barkley Henderson, Bengal nativeinfy.
Humphrey Hay, Bengal light cavalry
Frederick Samuel Sotheby, C.B. Bengal arty.
William Frederick Steer, Bengal native infy.
William Simonds, Bengal native infantry
John Henry Simmonds, Bengal native infy.
Thomas Wilkinson, Bengal light cavalry
George Henry Woodrooffe, Bengal artillery
Thomas Biddle, Madras artillery
John Monson Boyes, Madras native infantry
John Chisholm, Madras artillery
John Howison, Madras native infantry
Duncan Montgomerie, Madras light cavalry
Richard Graves Polwhele, Madras artillery
Richard Sonner Seton, Madras artillery
Francis Hugh Massey Wheeler, M. E. regt.
George Brooks Aitchison, Bombay native infy.
John Farquharson, Bombay native infantry
Thomas Best Jervis, Bombay engineers
John Worthy, Bombay native infantry

LIEUTENANT COLONELS.—*Continued.*

James Oliphant, Madras engineers
James Glencairn Burns, Bengal native infy.
George Thomson, C.B., Bengal engineers
Charles Wyndham Hodges, Bengal light cavy.
William Hyslop, Madras light cavalry
Matthew George White, Bengal native infy.
Charles Richardes, Bombay native infantry
James Edward Butcher, Madras native infy.
James Brady Barnett, Madras native infantry
William Veysie, Bengal light cavalry
Robert Nutter Campbell, Madras native infy.
Henry Moore, C.B., Bengal native infantry
Charles Daviniere, Madras native infantry
Richard Ord, Bombay native infantry
James Arden Crommelin, Bengal engineers
Charles Thynne Thomas, Bengal native infy.
Frederick John Simpson, Bengal native infy.
James Croudace Bengal native infantry
James Fraser, C.B., Bengal light cavalry
William Forbes, Bengal native infantry
William Minto, Bengal native infantry
William Payne, Bengal native infantry
David Thompson, Bengal native infantry
George Fredk. FrBank Vincent, Bl. native infy.
James Briggs, Madras native infantry
Andrew Fraser, Madras native infantry
James Mellor, Madras native infantry
James Wyllie, Madras native infantry
Frederick Broadwood White, Madras native infy.
Robert Sarrell Yolland, Madras artillery
Richard May Mignan Cooke, Bombay native infy
John Fawcett, Bombay European regiment
William Langford, Madras native infantry
Richard Gardner, Bengal native infantry
Julius Brockman Backhouse, C.B., Bengal arty
James Macadam, Bengal native infantry
Charles Fludgate, Madras native infantry
Nicholas Geoghegan, Madras native infantry
Bruce Boswell, Bengal native infantry
Charles Butler, Madras European regiment
Philip Bedingfield, Madras native infantry
George Fisher, C.B., Bombay native infantry
Stephen Jas. Stevens, C.B., Bombay native infy
Fraas. Nathaniel Burton Tucker, Bo. native infy
John James McMurdo, Madras native infantry
Richard Radford Hughes, Bl. native infantry
Richard Cautley, Bengal light cavalry
Henry Joseph Guyon, Bengal native infantry
James Horsburgh McDonald, Bengal artillery
George Smith, Bombay native infantry
Henry Doveton, Bengal native infantry
Henry Rutherford, Bengal artillery
George Yeadell, Bombay native infantry
Oswald Bell, Madras native infantry
John Assey Fairhead, Bengal European infantry
Clements Gillespie Macan, Bengal native infy.
Thomas Rose Wynter, Bombay European regt
George Johnstone, Bengal native infantry
Andrew Macdougall, Bengal native infantry
Æneas John Mackay, Bengal native infantry
Pringle O'Hanlon, Bengal light cavalry
Charles Corfield, Bengal native infantry
William Hoggan, Bengal native infantry
William Hunter, Bengal native infantry
George Thornton, Bombay European regiment
John Horatio Clarkson, Bengal native infantry

LIEUTENANT COLONELS.—*Continued.*

Andrew Charlton, Bengal native infantry
Frederick Charles Elwall, Bengal native infantry
George Farmer, Bengal native infantry
Henry Hudleston, Bengal native infantry
Alfred Lewis, Bengal native infantry
William Macgeorge, Bengal native infantry
William Mitchell, Bengal native infantry
Charles James Oldfield, Bengal native infantry
Joseph Liverton Revell, Bengal European regt
James Roxburgh, Bengal native infantry
William Saurin, Bengal native infantry
Earquharson Tweedale, Bengal light cavalry
Edward John Watson, Bengal native infantry
Robert Dennis White, Bengal native infantry
Alexander Adam, Madras native infantry
Mark Blaxland, Madras native infantry
Frederick Joseph Clerk, Madras native infantay
Francis Anthony Clark, Madras native infantry
John Henry Cramer, Madras native infantry
Thomas Ditmas, Madras artillery
Francis Eades, Madras native infantry
Francis Forbes, Madras light cavalry
Robert Garstin, Madras light cavalry
George Henry Harper, Madras native infantry
John Hutchings, Madras native infantry
Samuel Richard Hicks, Madras native infantry
Authony Harrison, Madras native infantry
Henry Hall, Madras native infantry
John Lewis, Madras native infantry
Charles Francis Le Hardy, Madras native infy.
Henry Morland, Madras native infantry
Henry Power, Madras native infantry
Emanuel Roberts, Madras native infantry
Michael John Rowlandson, Madras native infy.
Alexander Shirrefs, Madras native infantry
Richard Wheeler Sparrow, Madras native infy.
Edward Servante, Madras native infantry
Franeis Charles Scott, Madras native infantry
David Scotland, Madras native infantry
Arthur Trotter, Madras native infantry
Frederic William Todd, Madras native infantry
Thomas Exton Cotgrave, Bombay artillery
Thomas Donnelly, Bombay native infantry
Alex. McDonald Elder, Bombay European regt.
Henry Heaton Hobson, Bombay European regt.
Charles Hunter, Bombay native infantry
Robert Marsh Hughes, Bombay native infantry
Charles Brooke Morton, Bombay native infy.
Edward Stanton, Bombay artillery
Henry Stamford, Bombay artillery
Robert Long Skawe, Bombay native infantry
Edward Walter, Bombay light cavalry
Arnold Rawson Wilson, Bombay native infantry
John Bower, Madras native infantry
William John Manning, Madras European regt.
Daniel Heffernan Considine, Madras native infy.
William Innes, Bengal native infantry
Harvey Terrick Combe, Bengal European regt.
William Henry Graham, Bengal engineers
Conway Stafford, Madras native infantry
Jas. Alex. Duncan Fergusson, Bengal light cavy.
John Dowdeswell Shakespear, Bengal artillery
Mungo William Gilmore, Bengal native infantry
Hugh Johnson, Bengal native infantry
Robert Wyllie, Bengal native infantry
Robert Warden Fraser, Bengal native infantry

LIEUTENANT COLONELS.—*Continued.*

George Arthur Brownlow, Bengal light cavalry
Richard Chitty, Bengal native infantry
Colpoys Dickson, Bengal native infantry
Augustine Fitzgerald, Bengal artillery
Maxwell Hyslop, Bengal native infantry
Samuel Athill Lyons, Bengal native infantry
Henry Lyell, Bengal native infantry
William Joseph Martin, Bengal native infantry
Frederick Calder Minchin, Bengal native infy
Hippesley Marsh, Bengal light cavalry
Charles Norgate, Bengal native infantry
Nathaniel Sneyd Nesbitt, Bengal native infantry
Thomas Smith Price, Bengal native infantry
Edward Thomas Tierney, Bengal native infantry
James Dickson Wilson, Bengal native infantry
Joshua Wilcox, Bengal native infantry
Edward Watt, Bengal light cavalry
James Grissell, Bengal native infantry
John Robertson Younger, Bengal native infy
Charles Brown Constable, Bengal native infantry
Edward Buckle, Madras engineers
William Tudor Boddam, Madras light cavalry
William Cross, Madras native infantry
James Forbes, Madras European regiment
William Edward Gibb, Madras native infantry
George Jackson, Madras native infantry
William Kirkman Loyd, Madras artillery
Montague Watts, Madras artillery
Simon Fraser Mackenzie, Madras light cavalry
John Witherston Richards, Madras native infy.
Ponsonby Shaw, Madras native infantry
Henry Aston, Bombay native infantry
Edward Paterson Del Hoste, Bomby native infy.
Thomas Jackson, Bombay native infantry
William Purves, Bombay native infantry
George Nelson Prior, Bombay native infantry
Nathaniel Henry Thornbury, Bombay native infy.
Elgate Whichelo, Bombay native infantry
Charles Alexander Stewart, Bombay native infy.
Samuel Parr, Bombay native infantry
George Wilson, Bombay native infantry
Samuel Watson Fenning, Bengal artillery
Charles Pratt Kennedy, Bengal artillery
William Harvey Marcer, Madras native infantry
William Green Johnstone, Madras native infy.
George Singleton, Madras native infantry
William Walter Davidson, Bengal native infy.
Francis Henry Sansom, Madras European regt.
George Wm. Grant Bristow, Bengal native infy.
Christopher George Fagan, Bengal light cavalry
Robert Mathison, Bengal European infantry
Joseph Towgood, Bengal native infantry
William Campbell Onslow, Madras infantry
George Poyntz Ricketts, Bengal cavalry
William Elsey, Madras infantry.
Henry Colbeck Madras infantry
Thomas David Colyear, Bengal cavalry
Robert Henry Seale, Bengal infantry
Edward Clutterbuck, Madras infantry
John Macdonald, Bengal Infantry

11th May 1855.

William Ward, Madras artillery
A. J. Begbie, Madras artillery
H. W. Burt, Bengal infantry
George Cecil, Bengal infantry
J. C. Salkeld, Bengal infantry

LIEUTENANT COLONELS.—*Continued.*

G. F. Whitelocke, Bengal infantry
Thomas Brodie, Bengal infantry
John Samuel Knox, Bengal infantry
T. Elliot Colebrooke, Bengal infantry
James Roger Western, Bengal engrs.

15th June 1855.

John Kingston Phibbs, Bengal infantry
John Anderson, Bombay infantry
Edward Samuel Capel, Bengal infantry
Josh. Atwell Small Coxwell, Madras infantry
Robarts William Elton, Bengal infantry

10th Aug. 1855.

David Nisbett, Bengal infantry
James Hunter, Bengal infantry
George Augustus Hayward Falconar, Mds infy
Joseph Estridge, Bombay engineers

21st September 1855.

Thomas Dickson, Bombay infantry.
John Hunt, Bengal infantry
Charles Young Bazett, Bengal cavalry

26th Oct. 1855.

William Charles Hicks, Bengal infantry
John Richard Abbott, Bengal infantry
Francis George John Lascelles, Madras lt. cavy.
Samuel Smith Trevor, Madras artillery
John Ramsay Bombay infantry

30th November 1855.

George Stephens Brown, Bombay infantry
William George Hebbert, Bombay engineers
Peter Eyles Lingen Rickards, Madras infantry
Josiah Smith, Madras infantry
Charles Hagart, Bengal infantry

25th January 1856.

Thomas Gamble Fraser, Bombay infantry
Edward Sunderland, Bengal artillery
William Piers Meares, Bengal infantry
Frederick Alfred Close, Bengal infantry
Henry Robert Cornwallis King, Madras cavalry

26th February 1856.

Arthur Salmon, Madras infantry
Thomas Robert Morse, Bombay infantry
Augustus Hart Dyke, Bengal infantry

25th March 1856.

Pringle Shortreed, Bengal infantry
Sir Hy. Creswicke Rawlinson, K.C.B., Bom.infy.

29th April 1856.

George Gordon, Madras infantry
Edward Skipper, Bombay infantry
John Grimes, Madras infantry
John William Bennett, Bengal infantry

27th May 1856.

William Humphrey Lomer, Bengal infantry
Thomas James, Bengal infantry

22nd July 1856.

Henry Fitz Simons, Bengal infantry

19th August 1856.

John Fulton, Bengal infantry
John Graham, Bengal infantry
George Edward Herbert, Bengal cavalry

17th October 1856.

John Harding Mayow, Bengal infantry
Charles Robert Hobart, Madras infantry
John Sims Freshfield, Madras light cavalry

5th December 1856.

William Carlisle Stather, Bombay infantry
Herbert William Wood, Madras infantry
William Vernon Mitford, Bengal cavalry
Charles Elliott Goad, Bengal infantry

LIEUTENANT COLONELS.—*Continued.*

Charles Andrew Kitson, Bengal cavalry
Patrick Ogilvie, Madras infantry
George Hickson Fagan, Bengal engineers
David Edward Brewster, Bengal infantry
Thomas Francis Blois, Bengal infantry

16th January 1857.

John Hamilton Kennedy, Madras infantry
George Scott, Bengal Cavalry

17th Feb. 1857.

Henry Daniel Maitland, Bengal infantry
Arundel Barker, Madras infanfry
Richard Horsmonden Baldwin, Bengal artillery

13th March 1857.

John Howard Wakefield, Bengal infantry
William Charles Birch, Bengal infantry
William Jervis, Bengal infantry
Charles Thorold Hill, Madras infantry
Henry Edgar Duff Jones, Bombay infantry
Henry Augustus Morrieson, Bengal infantry
John Guise, Bengal infantry

17th April 1857.

Lowther Thomas Forrest, Bengal infantry

29th May 1857.

James Gordon, Bengal Light cavalry

19th June 1857.

Arnold Christian Pears, Madras artillery

7th August 1857.

Alexander Cumming Dewar, Bengal infantry
William Anthony Halsted, Madras infantry
James Tobin Bush, Bengal infantry

23rd October 1857.

Ed. Vere Peregrine Holloway, Madras infantry
George Forster, Madras infantry
Thomas Henry Sissmore, Bengal artillery
Augustus Price, Bombay infantry
Frederick Carleton Marsden, Bengal infantry.

4th December 1857.

William Freeth, Bengal infantry

2nd February 1858.

Frederick Minchin, Madras infantry.
Frederick Knyvett, Madras infantry.
Robert Mackenzie, Madras infantry.
Henry Rolland, Bombay infantry.
Thomas Smythe, Madras Engineers.

26th March 1858.

Edward Baker, Madras infantry·

21st May 1858.

George Paulet Cameron, Madras infantry
George Pott, Bengal infantry.
Richard Cooper, Madras infantry.

23rd July 1858.

William John Morris, Bombay Infantry.
John Davies Leckie, Bombay Infantry.
Ralph Smyth, Bengal Artillery.
William L. Walker, Madras Cavalry.
Charles Swinton, Bengal Infantry.
John Mann, Madras Infantry.

17th September 1858.

Charles William Hodson, Madras Infantry.

19th November 1858.

John Macdougall, Madras Infantry
Thomas Eyre, Bombay Light Cavalry
Matthews Beachcroft Madras Infantry
Adam Augustus Drummond, Bombay Infantry.

18th January 1859.

John Alexander Church, Madras Infantry
Henry Lawford, Madras Artillery

LIEUTENANT COLONELS.—*Continued.*
18th March 1859.
Edward P. Bryant, Bengal Infantry
John B. Ramsay, Bombay Infantry
Frederick S. Gabb, Madras Infantry
22nd April 1859.
William Charles Western, Madras infantry
William Henry Larkins, Bengal infantry

MAJORS.
28th November 1854.
Charles Stuart, Madras infantry
Fletcher N. Balmain, Madras cavalry
Richard Armstrong, Bengal infantry
Thomas Frobisher, Bengal infantry
Robert Bateman Wilkins, Bengal infantry
Charles Pearce, Bengal infantry
Gilbert Watson, Bengal infantry
James Craigie, Bengal infantry
James John Hammond, Madras infantry
Henry James Bland, Bengal infantry
George Maxwell, Madras infantry
Robert McMullin, Bengal infantry
John Robson Woornum, Bengal infantry
Nathaniel Lawrence Austen, Madras infantry
Thomas Charles Seymour Hyde, Madras infy.
John Rodway Stock, Bengal infantry
Robert Frew, Madras infantry
William Napper Pace, Madras infantry
George Willock, Madras light cavalry
Hugh Cossart Baker, Bengal artillery
Thomas Webster, Bengal infantry
Robert Gordon, Madras infantry
Henry Thomas Van Heythuysen, Madras infy.
Thomas Eales Soady, Bengal infantry
John Macartney, Madras infantry
Thomas Bennett Penwarne Festing, Bengal infy.
John Edward Watson, Bengal infantry
Richard Blechynden Brittridge, Bengal infantry
William Barnett, Bengal infantry
John Pyne, Bengal infantry
Charles Joshua Crane, Bengal infantry
Henry Philip Hughes, Bengal artillery
George William Jones Hickmam, Bengal infy.
Francis Turnley Boyd, Bengal infantry
Thomas Des Voeux, Bengal infantry
George Hutton Rawlinson, Bengal artillery
Michael Hughes, Bengal infantry
John Woolmore Michell, Bengal infantry
Henry Pelham, Bombay infantry
Lewis Burroughs, Bengal artillery
John Townsend Somerville, Bengal infantry
Charles Turner, Madras infantry
Giles Emly, Bengal artillery
Thomas Slator Rooke, Madras infantry
Edward Raphael Watts, Bengal artillery
Henry Lloyd, Bengal infantry
Alfred Ford Johnson, Bombay infantry
Henry Hawker Arnaud, Bengal infantry
James Henry Murray Martin, Bombay artillery
Ralph Gore Roberts, Bengal artillery
Charles Henry Cobbe, Bengal infantry
William James Symons, Bengal artillery
John Hamilton Hall, Bombay infantry
George Miller, Bengal infantry
John Peter Wade, Bengal infantry
Richard Hippesley Bingham, Madras infantry
Richard Pretyman, Madras infantry
Francis Carleton Reeves, Bengal infantry
George Preston Vallancey, Madras infantry
Alexander Ker Agnew, Bengal infantry

MAJORS.—*Continued.*
Robert Percival Pennefather, Bengal light cavy.
Patrick Alexander Reynolds, Madras infantry
Fredk. Skene Courtandy Chalmers, Madras infy.
George Alexander Barbor, Bengal light cavalry
Charles O'Hara, Bengal light cavalry
Frederick R. Moore, Bengal infantry
Samuel Talman, Madras infantry
Frederick Wilson Hardwick, Bengal infantry
Francis Winter, Bengal infantry
John Symes Gifford, Bengal infantry
Owen Reynolds, Madras infantry
Lord Henry Gordon, Bengal infantry
Patrick Oliphant, Madras infantry
Hugh Walker, Madras infantry
Robert Guthrie McGregor, Bengal artillery
Robert Steuart, Bengal infantry
William Henry Robson Boland, Bengal infantry
Gerard Edward Van Heythuysen, Bengal infy.
James Whitmore, Bombay infantry
Henry Cheere, Bengal infantry
Benjamin Heyne, Madras infantry
John Connor Power, Madras infantry
George Salter, Bengal infantry
Francis Gresley, Bengal infantry
Charles Graham, Bengal infantry
Charles Henry Thomas, Bengal infantry
John Thomas Ashton, Madras artillery
William Osborne Pellowe, Madras infantry
Charles Lowth, Bengal light cavalry
John Peere Farquharson, Bengal infantry
Henry Wilson, Bengal infantry
Andrew Fisher, Bengal infantry
William John Cade, Bengal infantry
William Lloyd Lewis Scott, Bengal light cavy
Frederick Christopher Holl, Bombay infantry
Thomas Henry Gatehouse Besant, Bengal infy
John Stubbs, Bengal infantry
John Alex. Armstrong Eckford, Bombay infy.
William Gibb, Bengal infantry
George Turner, Bengal infantry
Thomas Digby Roberts, Madras infantry
Thomas Wallace, Bengal infantry
James Wemyss, Bengal infantry
John Edmund Glynn, Madras infantry
Augustus Howell Shepherd, Bengal infantry
Gilbert Hamilton, Bengal infantry
Sir Alexander Mackenzie, Bart., Bengal infantry
Joseph Tucker Geils, Bengal infantry
Nathaniel Vicary, Bengal infantry
John Macdonald, Bengal infantry
William Martin, Bengal infantry
William Somerville Mitchell, Mardas infantry
Charles Giberne, Bombay infantry
Thomas Bradbridge Studdy, Bengal light cavy.
Charles Wright, Bengal infantry
Philip Sinckler Chinn, Bengal infantry
Stewart Murray Fullarton, Bengal infantry
William Kennedy, Bengal infantry
Philip Annesley Secundus Powys, Madras infy.
Henry Octavius Marshall, Madras infantry
Lorenzo Moore, Madras cavalry
Peter Penny, Madras infantry
John Arthur James, Bengal infantry
John Wilton, Madras infantry
Charles Robert Gwatkin, Bengal infantry
Patrick John Chiene, Bengal infantry
Henry Hirst Say, Bengal infantry
Claude Clifton Lucas, Bombay infantry

MAJORS.—*Continued.*

George Hutchins Bellasis, Bombay infantry
Richard Samuel Tickell, Bengal infantry
William Blackwood, Bengal infantry
George Rowcroft Budd, Bengal light cavalry
James Whitefoord, Bengal artillery
John Power Beresford, Madras artillery
Edward Samuel Græme Showers, Madras artillery
Charles Manners Gascoyne, Bengal light cavy.
Francis Cissen Brooke, Bengal infantry
Thomas Derisley Martin, Bengal infantry
Frederic Ditmas, Madras engineers
Mathew Richard Onslow, Bengal light cavalry
John Joseph Poett, Bengal infantry
Samuel John Saunders, Bengal infantry
John Turton, Bengal infantry
Charles Lloyd Edwards, Bengal infantry
Thomas Askwith Jenkins, Madras infantry
William Taylor, Madras infantry
Henry Puget White, Madras infantry
John Godfrey, Bengal infantry
George Ranken, Bengal infantry
Valpy Francis Thomas Turner, Bengal infantry
William Augustus St. Clair, Bombay artillery
Samuel Cross Starkey, Bengal infantry
David Davidson, Bombay infantry
Arthur Francis Rowan, Bombay infantry
Frederick Rainsford, Bengal infantry
Robert Molesworth Gurnell, Bengal infantry
Arthur Quin Hopper, Bengal infantry
Charles William Maude, Bombay infantry
George Hay Smith Yates, Madras infantry
Charles Hamilton Wake, Bengal infantry
John Innes, Bengal artillery
Thomas Gaisford, Bombay artillery
Henry Virtue Stephen, Bengal infantry
Henry George Mainwaring, Bengal infantry
Henry Pix Hill, Madras infantry
James Douglas Moffatt, Bengal cavalry
Henry Lavie, Bombay infantry
John Larkins Cheese Richardson, Bengal arty.
Edward Walter Agar, Bombay infantry
Henry Rudd, Bombay infantry
Frederick Bayley Wardroper, Bombay En. infy.
James Irving, Bengal cavalry
John Norris Warrington, Madras infantry
Roger Montagu North, Madras light cavalry
Edward Innes Robinson, Bengal cavalry
Albert Vaillant, Bombay infantry
Thomas Renny Tailyour, Bengal engineers
George Wingate, Bombay engineers
Robert Shaw, Bengal infantry
John Henry Bean, Madras infantry
George Paris Salmon, Bengal artillery
Charles Foveaux Kirby, Madras infantry
William Borlase Stevens, Madras artillery
John Hutchinson Fergusson, Bengal infantry
Jas. Hastings Lindsay MetcalfeToone, Bl. cavy.
Henry Jacob Woodward, Bombay infantry
Henry Cracroft, Bombay infantry
Samuel Boileau Goad, Bengal cavalry

MAJORS.—*Continued.*

Frederick Augustus Charleton, Bengal infy.
James Skinner, Bengal cavalry
11th May 1855.
William Cumberland, Bengal infantry
J. S. Phillips, Bengal artillery
D. E. Brewster, Bengal infantry
10 Aug. 1855.
Henry Marcell Conran, Bengal artillery
26th Oct. 1855.
Hugh John Houstoun, Bengal infantry
30th November 1855.
Chas. Andrew Kitson, Bengal lt. cavalry
25th January 1856.
William Jones, Bengal engineers
26th Feb. 1856.
Ralph Reid Scutt, Madras infantry
Patrick Ogilvie, Madras infantry
Charles Alex. Blagrave Madras infantry
25th March 1856.
James Duncan, Bengal infantry
24th June 1856.
Robert Wilberforce Bird, Bengal infantry
27th May 1856.
Erskine Thomas Erskine, Bengal infantry
19th September 1856.
Alfred Cooper Hutchinson, Bengal artillery
17th Feb. 1857,
George Robert Remington, Bombay infantry
13th March 1857.
Thomas William Cooke, Madras infantry
Alfred Henry Corfield, Bengal infantry
17th April 1857.
Claude Frederick Irby, Madras infantry
Richard Boulton, Bengal cavalry
John Peter Mouat Biggs, Madras infantry
19th June 1857.
Mark Sykes Ottley, Madras cavalry
4th December 1857.
James Dennis DeVitre, Bombay infantry
William Swainson Stuart Bombay engineers
2nd February 1858.
James Mungavin, Bombay Veterans
26th March 1858.
Samuel Robertson Wallace, Bengal infantry
David Blair, Madras infantry
21st May 1858.
Alexander Wood, Madras Infantry
Thomas Newbury, Madras Cavy
Whalley Master, Bengal Cavalry
23rd July 1858.
Joseph Chilcott, Bengal Infantry.
Frederick Fanning, Bombay Infantry.
17th September 1858.
David Lester Richardson, Bengal Infantry.
John William Goad, Madras artillery
Robert L. J. Ogilvie, Madras Infantry.
19th November 1858.
D'Oyley Richard Bristow, Bengal Artillery
18th March 1859.
Roderick Robertson, Bengal Infantry.

BENGAL MILITARY ORPHAN SOCIETY.

GOVERNOR.

His Excellency General the Right Honorable LORD CLYDE, G. C. B., Commander-in-Chief.

DEPUTY GOVERNOR.

Colonel C. S. REID, Artillery.

MANAGERS.

	Division or Station.
Capt. W. N. LEES, L. L. D., 42nd Light Infantry, ...	Presidency Station.
Surgeon A. C. MACRAE, M. D., ...	Ditto ditto.
Major M. J. TURNBULL, 7th Light Cavalry, ...	Ditto ditto.
The Revd. H. B. BURNEY, M A., ...	Ditto ditto.
Captain M. R. NIGHTINGALE, 2nd En. B. F., ...	Dinapore Division.
Surgeon J. ANDERSON, M. D., ...	Benares ditto.
*	Cawnpore ditto.
Capt. H. K. BURNE, 2nd N. I. (Grs.,)	Meerut ditto.
Dr. F. N. MACNAMARA, ...	Sirhind ditto.
The Revd. G. LOVELY, ...	Punjaub ditto.
Major C. HERBERT, 18th N. I., ...	Wuzeerabad ditto.
*	Peshawur ditto.

Lieut. Col. J. C. HANNYINGTON, Honorary Manager,
C. J. GRAY, ESQUIRE, Secretary, Kidderpore.
The Rev. E. K. MADDOCK, M. A., Home Agent, No. 27, Cannon Street, London.
J. B. SCRIVEN, Esq., Surgeon Upper Orphan School.
ALLAN WEBB, Esq., M. D., Surgeon Lower Orphan School.
Mrs. Harris, Lady Superintendent, Upper Orphan School.
Mrs. A. CROLL, Head Mistress, Lower Orphan School.

BENGAL MILITARY FUND.

DIRECTORS.

Major G. NEWBOLT, *President.*

Lt. Col. R. RAMSAY, 74th N. I...
Col. C. S. REID, Artillery. ..
J. ANDERSON, Esq., M. D. ..
Captain M. R. NIGHTINGALE, 2nd En. B. F.
Lieut. W. N. LEES, L. L. D., 42nd L. Infy.

Major J. C. HANNYNGTON, ... *(Honorary Director.)*
E. G. DUNBAR, Esq., ... *Secretary.*
Lt. Col. H. B. HENDERSON, ... *Home Agent.*

Office of the Home Agent, No. 27, Cannon Street, London.

War Services of Officers of the Bengal Army.

REGIMENT OF ARTILLERY.

General A'hmuty served during Lord Lake's campaign, present at the battles of Delhi and Deig, Siege of Bhurtpore, India medal.

Lieut. Genl. Swiney was present at the battle of Deig; commanded the Artillery in the three first assaults on Bhurtpore, wounded, medal; commanded the Artillery at the siege and capture of Emaum Ghur 1810, for which services he received the thanks of the Vice President in Council and the Commander-in-Chief.

Lieut. Genl. *Sir* G. Pollock, G. C. B., was present at the following actions: Deig 1804, Bhurtpore, Gwalior 1805, Rewah 1806, Nepal 1815-16, Burmah 1824-25-26, India medal, commanded the force employed in Affghanistan 1842 for the relief of Jellalabad and re-occupation of Cabul, medal and G. C. B.

Lieut. Genl. Lindsay, C. B., served with the Subsidiary Force in Gohud and Gwalior under Colonel Bowie in 1805 and 1806, and was present at the siege of Gohud in 1806. Was present at the sieges of Kommonah and Gunnowrie in 1807; served throughout both campaigns of the Nepal war, with the Dinapore division of the army in 1814-15 and 1816, and was severely wounded in the attack of the *fort* and *stockade* of Hurriarpore in 1816; served with the force under Major General Marshall in 1817, and was present at the siege of Hattrass, and with the left division of the grand army during the Pindaree war in 1817-18; was present at the sieges and capture of Dhamoonee and Mundela; served during the Burmese war with the S. E. division of the army under Brigadier Genl. Morrison; was present at the attack on and capture of Arracan in 1825, medal.

Lieut. Genl. Shaw served in Java from 1813 to 1817; accompanied the expedition to Palambang 1813, and the expedition to Balli under Genl. *Sir* M. Nightingale in 1815.

Maj. Genl. Gowan, C.B., was present at the capture of the Cape of Good Hope 1806; served n Java 1813-14-15; present at the siege and bombardment of Hattrass 1817; Pindaree campaign under Lord Hastings 1817-18; served with Col. Vanrenen's Detachment at Tonk; commanded the Artillery with Col. Ludlow's Field Force, on particular service in Malwa and Meywar 1818-19-20; and under Brigadier Lumley in operations against the Bheel Tribes, towards the Mhye River in 1824; commanded the Artillery in the Gwalior campaign 1843-44; present at Maharajpore, bronze star; also commanded the Artillery in the campaign of the Sutledge 1845-46; present in the affair of Budiwal and battle of Sobraon, medal; nominated C. B. in 1844, and A.D.C. to the Queen 1846.

Maj. Genl. Brooke, C. B., served in Bundelkund during 1809-10; also throughout the Nepal war under *Sir* D. Ochterlony 1814-15, including attacks upon Nallaghur, the heights of Ramgurh and Fort Malown; present at the siege of Hattrass 1817; served throughout the Mahrattah campaign 1817-18 under Lord Hastings; present at the siege and capture of Bhurtpore, (blown up) 1826, medal; army of the Sutledge 1845-46, including the battles of Moodkee, Ferozeshuhur and Sobraon; in the two former of which actions he commanded the whole of the Artillery, medal, 2 clasps and C.B.; army of the Punjaub 1848-49, as a Brigadier commanding the Horse Artillery, present at Ramnuggur, also in the actions of Chillianwalla and Goojerat, medal and 2 clasps.

Maj. Genl. Huthwaite, C. B., served in the Nepal war in 1815-16; taking of Dwarka and other forts in Oude in the hot season of 1817; Mahratta war 1817-18; in Cachar during the Burmese war 1823-4; siege and capture of Bhurtpore 1825-26, India medal; commanded 3rd Brigade Horse Artillery at Ferozeshuhur (C. B.) and at Sobraon, 1845-46 (medal and clasp;) Brigadier, Commanding Foot Artillery with army of Punjaub 1848-49; present at the passage of the Chenab and action of Chillianwalla and Goojerat, medal and 2 clasps; and commanded the Artillery with the force under *Sir* W. R. Gilbert in pursuit of the Seikhs across the Jhelum in 1849.

Col. Twemlow served with the army of Observation Nepaul frontier 1813-14; Nepaul campaign 1815-16; (medal) Pindaree and Mahratta campaigns; sieges of Chandah and Asseerghur 1817-18; from 1821 to 1853 served in the Nizam's army, and on three several occasions received the high approbation of the Governor General in Council viz. for the capture of the Forts of Jamood, Baroda and Byrooghur, and an Autograph letter of thanks, from the Governor General.

Major Genl. *Sir* A. Wilson *Bt.* K. C. B. was present at the siege and capture of Bhurtpore in 1826, medal, and commanded the Artillery with Brigadier Wheeler's force in the Jullundur Dooab, 1848-49, medal.

Col. Abbott, C. B., was present at the siege and capture of Bhurtpore in 1825-26, medal; served in Affghanistan during 1839-40-41-42; present at the capture of Ghuznee; defence of Jellalabad under *Sir* R. Sale (wounded); re-occupation of Caubul under *Sir* G. Pollock, medals for Ghuznee, Jellallabad and Caubul, and C. B.

Major Genl. Grant, C.B. (Supy. unattached,) served in Bundelkund in 1821; also in Oude in 1822; and throughout the Ava campaign during the years 1824-25-26, medal; present at the capture of Ghuznee 1839, medal; battle of Maharajpore 1843, bronze star; Sobraon 1846, (wounded) medal and Bt. Lieut. Col.; army of the Punjaub 1848-49, including actions of Ramnuggur, Sadoolapore, Chillianwalla and Goojerat, medal, 2 clasps and C. B.

Lt. Col. (Bt. Col.) Horsford was present at the siege and capture of Bhurtpore 1825-26, medal; Sutledge campaign 1845-46; present at the battles of Moodkee, Ferozeshuhur and Sobraon, medal, 2 clasps and Bt. Major; army of the Punjaub 1848-49, including actions of Sadoolapore, Chillianwalla and Goojerat, medal, 2 clasps and Bt. Lt. Col.

Major Genl. Alexander, C.B. (Supy. unattached,) present at the siege and capture of Bhurtpore 1825-26, medal; capture of Biana and Weir 1825-26; commanded the Artillery with the force under Major Genl. Pollock, C. B.,; at the forcing of the Khyber Pass, 5th April 1842; action of Tazeen and capture of Caubul, 15th Sept. 1842, medal and Bt. Major; present at the battle of Maharajpore 1843, bronze star and Bt. Lt. Col.; affair of Budiwal 21st Jan. 1846; battles of Alliwal and Sobraon 1846, medal, clasp and C. B.

Major Genl. Lane, C. B. (Supy. unattached,) served throughout the Caubul campaign 1841-42; present at the forcing of the Khyber Pass, and other engagements leading to the re-occupation of Caubul, medal, and Bt. Major; present at the battle of Maharajpore, bronze star and Bt. Lt. Col.; Sutledge campaign 1845-46, including

ARTILLERY.—*Continued.*

the battles of Alliwal and Sobraon, medal, clasp and C. B.; army of the Punjaub 1848-49, including actions of Ramnuggur Chillianwalla and Goojerat, medal and 2 clasps.

Lt. Col. (Bt. Col.) Fordyce served in the campaign on the Sutledge 1845-46, including the battles of Ferozeshuhur and Sobraon, medal and 1 clasp; army of the Punjaub 1848-49, including actions of Chillianwalla and Goojerat, medal, 2 clasps and Bt. Lt. Col.

Major Genl. Campbell (Supy. unattached,) served in Ava in 1824-25-26, medal; Gwalior campaign 1845-46; present at the battle of Punniar, bronze star and Bt. Major; Sutledge campaign 1845-46, including the battles of Ferozeshuhur and Sobraon, medal, clasp and Bt. Lt. Col.

Lt. Col. (Bt. Col.) Swinley served with the force in Cachar in 1824-25 under Major Genl. Shuldham; present at the battles of Moodkee, Ferozeshuhur and Sobraon 1845-46; commanded a troop of Horse Artillery in these actions, medal, 2 clasps and Bt. Major; present with Brigadier Genl. Wheeler's force in the Punjaub 1848-49, medal.

Lt. Col. (Bt. Col.) Abbott was present at the siege and capture of Bhurtpore 1826, medal; Affghanistan 1839.

Lt. Col. (Bt. Col.) Boileau was present at the siege and capture of Bhurtpore 1825-26, medal; capture of Biona and Weir 1825-26; served throughout the Sutledge campaign; present at the affair of Budiwal and battle of Alliwal 1845-46 medal and Bt. Major.

Lt. Col. (Bt. Col.) Reid served with the Burmah Expedition 1852-53; present at the taking of Martaban, and at the operations in the vicinity and capture of Rangoon, April 1852; commanded the Artillery with Sir John Cheape's Force during the operations against the rebel Chief Mya Toon from the 17th Feb. to 19th Mar. 1853, severely wounded at the attack and capture of the stockade near Donabew, right arm amputated, medal and Bt. Lt. Col.

Lt. Col. Kinleside served with the army of the Punjaub 1848-49, including the actions of Sadoolapore and Goojerat, medal, 2 clasps and Bt. Major.

Lt. Col. Burnett served with Brigadier Genl. Wheeler's force in the Punjaub 1848-49, medal.

Lt. Col. Huyshe served in the Gwalior campaign 1843-44, bronze star; army of the Punjaub 1848-49, including the actions of Sadoolapore, Chillianwalla and Goojerat, medal, 2 clasps and Bt. Major.

Lt. Col. (Bt. Col.) *Sir* R. C. Shakespear served in Affghanistan in 1839 and 1842, medal; army of the Punjaub 1848-49, including the actions of Chillianwalla and Goojerat, (wounded) medal, 2 clasps and Bt. Lt. Col.

Lt. Col. (Bt. Col.) V. Eyre, C. B., served in Affghanistan 1841-42; commanded Horse Artillery in two successful actions under Brigadier Shelton (severely wounded); taken prisoner on retreat from Caubul, commanded Field force for relief of Arrah, and defeated the mutineers and rebels under Kooer Sing on 2nd and 12th August 1857, (Lt. Col. and C. B..) defeated and destroyed a force of Oude rebels at Khoordun-puttee 11th September, commanded heavy gun battery in the actions of Mungurwar and Alumbagh and first relief of Lucknow under Major Genl. *Sir* H. Havelock, K. C. B. was Brigadier of artillery and cavalry under *Sir* Jas. Outram, G. C. B. at Lucknow and Alumbaugh, and commanded artillery division at latter during the final operations against Lucknow under His Excellency *Sir* C. Campbell G. C. B. March 1858.

Lt. Col. Barr was present at the forcing of the Khyber Pass in July 1839, and advance on Caubul with Lt. Col. Wade and Shahzada Timour during the same year; campaign on the Sutledge 1845-46, including the affair of Budiwal, and battles of Alliwal and Sobraon, medal and clasp.

Lt. Col. Bt. Col. Hogge C. B., served with the army of the Punjaub in 48-49; present at the passage of the Chenab and actions of Chillianwalla and Goojerat, medal, 2 clasps and Bt. Major.

Lt. Col. (Bt. Col.) Turner C. B., served in Affghanistan in 1838-39-40-41-42; and in the several engagements during the period, including Candahar, Ghuznee and Caubul, medal.

Lt. Col. Carleton served under Brig. Genl. *Sir* Colin Campbell, K. C. B., in the operations against the Momunds and Hill tribes west of Peshawur in October, November and December 1851: was present at the siege and capture of Lucknow in March 1858. Bt. Lieut. Col. and C. B., also medal and clasp: commanded the Artillery in the action at Nawabgunge in June 1858, under *Sir* Hope Grant, K. C. B.

Capt. (Bt. Lt. Col.) Abercrombie served in Affghanistan 42; present in the several engagements leading to the re-occupation of Caubul, medal; Sutledge campaign 1845-46, including the battles of Ferozeshuhur and Sobraon, medal and clasp; army of the Punjaub 1848-49, as Assistant Adjutant General of Artillery, including the actions of Ramnuggur, Chillianwalla and Goojerat, medal, 2 clasps and Bt. Major.

Capt. (Bt. Major) Warburton served in Affghanistan in 1839-40-41-42; present at the assault and capture of Ghuznee, medal; delivered over in Dec. 1841, as a hostage to Nawab Mahomed Zuman Khan, by whom he was transferred in July 1842, into the charge of Mahomed Akbar; with the army of Gwalior at the battle of Maharajpore, bronze star.

Capt. (Bt. Lt. Col.) J. H. Smyth served at the action of Punniar, bronze star.

Capt. (Bt. Major.) Money served in Affghanistan in 1842; present at the re-occupation of Caubul, medal, Burmah, 1852-53, medal.

Capt. (Bt. Major) Douglas served in Affghanistan in 1842; present at the re-occupation of Caubul, medal.

Capt. (Bt. Lt. Col.) Kaye served in Affghanistan in 1838-39-40; present at the affair near Fowladee; also in the campaign on the Sutledge 1845-46, including the battles of Moodkee, Ferozeshuhur and Sobraon, medal and 2 clasps, and with the army of the Punjaub, passage of the Chenab and actions of Chillianwalla and Goojerat; and accompanied the Field Force under *Sir* W. Gilbert, G. C. B., beyond the Jhelum, medal, 2 clasps and Bt. Major.

Capt. Brougham served in Affghanistan in 1841-42, medal; present at the battle of Sobraon 1846, medal; and capture of Kangrah 1846.

Capt. DeTeissier served in the campaign on the Sutledge 1845-46; present at the battle of Sobraon, medal; army of the Punjaub 1848-49, including the actions of Chillianwalla and Goojerat, medal and 2 clasps.

Capt. (Bt. Major) Cox was present at the battle of Punniar 1843, bronze star; Moodkee, (slightly wounded) Ferozeshuhur and Sobraon 1845-46, medal and 2 clasps; served in the army of the Punjaub 1848-49, including the passage of the Chenab and actions of Chillianwalla and Goojerat, medal, 2 clasps and Bt. Major.

Capt. (Bt. Lt. Col.) Bourchier C. B., was present at the battle of Punniar 1843, bronze star.

Capt. (Bt. Major) Moir C. B. was present at the battle of Maharajpore 1843, bronze star; throughout the campaign on the Sutledge 1845-46, including the battles of Moodkee, Ferozeshuhur and Sobraon, medal and 3 clasps; present at the siege and surrender of Mooltan 1848-49, and battle of Goojerat, medal and 2 clasps.

Capt. (Bt. Major) Christie was present at the battles of Maharajpore 1843, bronze star, Sobraon 1846, medal; siege and surrender of Mooltan 1848-49, and action of Goojerat, medal 2 clasps and Brevet Major.

Capt. (Bt. Lt. Col.) W. Olpherts C. B. V. C., present at the action of Punniar bronze star and served with the force under Sir Charles Napier against the Hill Tribes in Scinde.

Capt. (Bt. Lt. Col.) H. A. Olpherts served in the army of the Punjaub 1848-49, as A. D. C. to Brigadier Genl. Tennant, and was present in the actions of Ramnuggur, Chillianwalla and Goojerat, medal 2 clasps and Brevet Major.

Capt. Swinhoe served in Scinde in 1845, in the campaign against the Belochee Hill Tribes; present at the siege and surrender of Mooltan and battle of Goojerat, 1848-49, medal and 2 clasps.

Capt. Voyle served in the Sutledge campaign 1845-46, including the affair of Budiwal and battles of Alliwal and Sobraon, medal and clasp; with the Expedition to Burmah; present at the taking of Martaban, and operations in the vicinity and capture of Rangoon, April 1852, medal.

Capt. Wintle was present at the battle of Maharajpore 1843, bronze star, and served during the Sutledge campaign, including the action of Sobraon, medal.

Capt. (Bt. Col.) Tombs, C.B.V.C. was present at the battles of Punniar, bronze star, Moodkee and Ferozeshuhur; affair of Budiwal, and battle of Alliwal, as A.D.C. to *Sir* Harry Smith, medal and 2 clasps; army of the

ARTILLERY.—*Continued.*

Punjaub 1845-46 as Deputy Assistant Quarter Master General of the Artillery, including the actions of Ramnuggur, passage of the Chenab, Chillianwalla and Goojerat, medal and 2 clasps.

Capt. (Bt. Major) Austen was present at the battles of Ferozeshuhur, Alliwal and Sobraon, medal and 2 clasps.

Capt. Paton was present in the actions of Moodkee and Ferozeshuhur 1845, (wounded), medal and clasp; served with the expedition to Kangrah 1846, under Brigadier Wheeler, C. B., and A.D.C. with Brigadier Genl. Wheeler's force in 1848-49, medal.

Capt. Woodcock was present at the battle of Soobraon 1846, medal.

Capt. C. W. Timbrell was present in the actions of Ferozeshuhur and Sobraon 1845-46, medal and clasp.

Capt. (Bt. Major) Mackinnon C.B. was present in the actions of Moodkee, Ferozeshuhur and Sobraon 1845-46, medal and 2 clasps; with Brigadier Wheeler's force in the Punjaub 1848-49, medal.

Capt. Fooks served at the action of Sobraon, medal; with the army of the Punjaub; present at the siege and surrender of Mooltan 1848-49; battle of Goojerat, & subsequent pursuit of the Seikhs & Affghans, medal & 2 clasps.

Capt. (Bt.Major) Bowie was present in the actions of Moodkee, Ferozeshuhur and Sobraon, 1845-46, (wounded) medal and 2 clasps; taken prisoner by Raja Shere Singh and released at the conclusion of the Punjaub campaign.

Capt. (Bt.Lt. Col.) Remmington C. B. served at Maharajpore in 1843, bronze star, Sutledge Campaign, including the actions of Ferozeshuhur and Sobraon, medal and clasp; Punjaub (Lahore Garrison,) 1848-49, medal.

Captain Courtenay was present at the battle of Sobraon 1846, medal; army of the Punjaub 1848-49, including the actions of Ramnuggur, Chillianwalla and Goojerat, medal and 2 clasps.

Capt. Alexander served with the expedition into Beloochee Hills under *Sir* C. Napier in 1845, Mooltan and Punjaub in 1848-49, including first and second operations against the Fort of Mooltan and the affair of Dhurmsala, on the 12th Sep. 1848, Soorujkhoond on the 7th Nov. 1848, & storming of the Suburbs 27th Dec. 1848, medal & clasp.

Capt. Macleod was present at the battles of Ferozeshuhur and Sobraon 1846, medal and clasp.

Capt. Francis served at the action of Sobraon, medal, and with the army of the Punjaub; present at the siege and surrender of Mooltan and battle of Goojerat, medal and 2 clasps.

Capt. Atlay was present in the actions of Moodkee, Ferozeshuhur (wounded) and Sobraon, medal and 2 clasps; expedition to Kangrah 1846, with Brigadier Genl. Wheeler's force 1848-49, medal.

Capt. (Bt. Major) H. LeG. Bruce was present at the battle of Maharajpore, bronze star: affair of Budiwal; actions of Alliwal and Sobraon, medal and clasp; army of the Punjaub 1848-49, including the actions of Sadoolapore, Chillianwalla and Goojerat, medal and 2 clasps.

Capt. McNeil served in Gwalior campaign of 1843-44, and present at the battle of Maharajpore; served in Sutledge campaign of 1845-46, and present at actions of Ferozeshuhur, and Sobraon; served with Brigadier H. Wheeler's Field Force, and present at Capitulation of Kotkangra in May 1846; served on Dehrajat frontier, 1850-51-52; served with the Turkish Contingent, in the Crimean campaign, of 1855-56; served in the Oude campaign of 1857-58; was present at siege and capture of Lucknow.

Capt. (Bt. Lt. Col.) Johnson C.B. was present at the battles of Ferozeshuhur and Sobraon 1845-46, medal and clasp; army of the Punjaub 1848-49, including the actions of Ramnuggur, Chillianwalla and Goojerat, medal and clasp.

Capt. (Bt. Lt. Col.) Maxwell was present at the battle of Maharajpore 1843, bronze star; served as Depy. Asst. Quarter Master Genl. of the Artillery in the army of the Sutledge; present at Moodkee, Ferozeshuhur and Sobraon, medal and 2 clasps.

Capt. Kennion was present at the battles of Moodkee, Ferozeshuhur and Sobraon 1845-46, medal & 2 clasps.

Capt.(Bt.Lt. Col) Blunt C.B. was present at the battles of Ferozeshuhur and Sobraon 1845-46, medal and clasp.

Capt. (Bt. Major) Cookworthy served at the battle of Sobraon, medal, and throughout the Punjaub campaign 1848-49; including the actions of Sadoolapore, Chillianwalla and Goojerat, medal and 2 clasps.

Capt. Russell was present at the battles of Ferozeshuhur and Sobraon 1845-46, medal and clasp.

Capt. Maister present at Maharajpore, bronze star, Punjaub campaign, battles of Chillianwalla and Goojerat, surrender of Seikh army and occupation of Peshawur, medal and 2 clasps. Served with the force under Brigadier Bradshaw in the Eusofyze country in 1849-50; under Sir C. Napier forcing the Kohat Pass 1850, the affairs against the Momunds and Ootman Khails in the Eusofyze country in 1852 and under Brigadier General Chamberlain against the Belooch Bozdars in 1857.

Capt. Sladen was present at the battle of Maharajpore 1843, bronze star; Upper Scinde 1845, with the force under *Sir* C. Napier, G. C. B., against the Belochee Hill Tribes; served with Major Fordyce's Troop of Horse Artillery at the battle of Goojerat, medal and clasp; served with the expedition under Brigadier Chamberlain to the Meeranzaie valley and upper Koorum in 1856; also present at the operations in the Bozdar Hills in 1857.

Capt. Dundas was present at the affair of Budiwal and battle of Alliwal, medal; served in the army of the Punjaub 1848-49, and was present in the actions of Ramnuggur, Chillianwalla (wounded) and Goojerat, medal and 2 clasps.

Capt. Mecham was present at the siege and surrender of Mooltan 1848-49, and action of Goojerat, medal and 2 clasps.

Capt. (Bt. Major) Pearson served in the army of the Punjaub 1848-49, medal, and was present in the actions of Ramnuggur, Sadoolapore, Chillianwalla and Goojerat; also served throughout the Sutledge campaign 1845-46, Moodkee, Ferozeshuhur and Sobraon, medal and 2 clasps.

Capt. Holland was present at the battles of Maharajpore 1843, medal; Ferozeshuhur and Sobraon, medal and clasp; expedition to Kangrah 1846; army of the Punjaub 1848-49, including the actions of Chillianwalla and Goojerat, medal and 2 clasps.

Capt. Angelo served during the Sutledge campaign and was present at the battle of Sobraon, medal and clasp; army of the Punjaub 1848-49, and was present in the actions of Sadoolapore, Chillianwalla and Goojerat, medal and 2 clasps.

Capt. Newall was present at the battle of Sobraon, medal; during the Punjaub campaign, including siege and surrender of Mooltan 1848-49, and action of Goojerat, medal and 2 clasps.

Capt. Watson served in the army of the Punjaub 1848-49, including the actions of Sadoolapore, (wounded) Chillianwalla and Goojerat, medal and 2 clasps.

Capt. Bt. Maj. Bunny was present at the battle of Sobraon 1846, medal; action before Mooltan (wounded) on the 12th Sept. 1848, in the affair of Soorujkhoond, 7th November 1848, and battle of Goojerat, medal and 2 clasps.

Capt. Gowan served with the army of the Punjaub 1848-49; present at the actions of Chillianwalla and Goojerat, medal and 2 clasps.

Capt. Gray served with the army of the Punjaub 1848-49; present at the actions of Chillianwalla and Goojerat, medal and clasp.

Capt. Tulloh served in the Sutledge campaign 1845-46, including the battle of Ferozeshuhur; affair of Budiwal and battle of Alliwal, medal and clasp; expedition to Kangrah 1846 under Brigadier Wheeler, C. B., and A.D.C.; army of the Punjaub 1848-49, including the actions of Ramnuggur, Chillianwalla and Goojerat, medal and 2 clasps.

Capt. G. R. Brown served with the army of the Punjaub 1848-49; present at the actions of Sadoolapore, Chillianwalla and Goojerat, medal and 2 clasps.

Capt. Harrison present at the battle of Sobraon 1846, medal.

Capt. Cox was present at the battle of Sobraon 1846, medal; army of the Punjaub 1848-49, including the actions of Chillianwalla and Goojerat, medal and 2 clasps.

ARTILLERY.—*Continued.*

Capt. Bt. Major Renny served with the army of the Sutledge; present at the battle of Sobraon, medal.

Capt. Griffith served during the Sutledge campaign; present at the action of Sobraon, medal, and with the expedition to Khote Kangrah.

Capt. Bt. Major Walker served with the expedition to Khote Kangrah 1846, and throughout the campaign in the Punjaub including the actions of Sadoolapore, Chillianwalla and Goojerat, medal and 2 clasps.

Capt. Mylne served with the army of the Punjaub 1848-49, including the actions of Sadoolapore, Chillianwalla and Goojerat, medal and 2 clasps.

Capt. Cookes served with the army of the Punjaub 1848-49, and was present at the actions of Ramnuggur, Sadoolapore, Chillianwalla and Goojerat, medal and 2 clasps.

Capt. Heath served with the army of the Punjaub 1848-49, including the actions of Sadoolapore, Chillianwalla and Goojerat, medal and 2 clasps.

Capt. Raper was present at the siege and surrender of Mooltan 1848-49, & battle of Goojerat, medal & 2 clasps.

Capt. Bt. Major Bishop was present at the siege and surrender of Mooltan 1848-49, and battle of Goojerat, medal and 2 clasps.

Capt. DeBude served with the army of the Punjaub 1848-49; was present at the siege and surrender of Mooltan and the battle of Goojerat, medal and 2 clasps.

Capt. Machell served with the expedition to Kangrah in 1846, under Brigadier Wheeler, C. B.; army of the Punjaub 1848-49, and was present at the battles of Chillianwalla and Goojerat, medal and 2 clasps.

Capt. Currie was present at the battle of Sobraon 1846, medal.

Capt. Hunter served with the army of the Punjaub 1848-49, including the siege and surrender of Mooltan, (wounded) battle of Goojerat, and subsequent pursuit of the Seikhs and Affghans, medal and 2 clasps.

Capt. Darling served with the army of the Punjaub 1848-49, including the actions of Sadoolapore, Chillianwalla and Goojerat, medal and 2 clasps.

Capt. Bt. Major Frith served with Brigadier Wheeler's force in the Punjaub 1848-49, medal.

Capt. Parish served in the Sutledge campaign 1846-47, expedition against Kangra 1847, Punjaub campaign 1848-49, medal.

Capt. Baillie served with the expedition to Kangrah 1846, under Brigadier Wheeler, C. B., medal.

Capt. Fulton served with the expedition to Khote Kangrah 1846, and in the Punjaub with the force under Brigadier Wheeler 1848-49, medal.

Capt. Salt served with the army of the Punjaub 1848-49, present at the actions of Sadoolapore, Chillianwalla and Goojerat, medal and 2 clasps.

Capt. Murray served with the army of the Punjaub 1848-49, medal.

Capt. Ross served throughout the Punjaub campaign, including the battles of Chillianwalla and Goojerat, medal and 2 clasps.

Capts. Dickson, Delane and Simeon served with the army of the Punjaub 1848-49, present at the battles of Chillianwalla and Goojerat, medals and clasps.

Capt. Pixley served with the army of the Punjaub 1848-49, including the action of Ramnuggur, medal; served with the force under Brigadier Sir C. Campbell, K. C. B., employed against the Hill Tribes of Ootman Khail and the subsequent operations in the Ranazye Valley, near Peshawur in May 1852.

Capt. Presant served in the Punjaub with the force under Brigadier Wheeler 1848-49, medal.

Capt. Denniss served in the Punjaub with the force under Brigadier Wheeler 1848-49, medal.

Capt. F. C. Simons served during the Punjaub campaign, present at the siege and surrender and operations in the vicinity of Mooltan and action of Goojerat, medal and 2 clasps.

Capt. (Bt. Major) W. T. Brown served throughout the campaign in the Punjaub, including the passage of the Chenab, medal and clasp

Capt. Thomson served in the Punjaub with the force under Brigadier Wheeler 1848-49, medal.

Capt. Sankey served with the army of the Punjaub 1848-49, present at the siege and surrender of Mooltan, (severely wounded,) medal and two clasps.

Capt. Worthington was present at the siege and surrender of Mooltan 1848-49, and action of Goojerat, medal.

Capt. Dobbin and Lieut. Percivall served with the Burmese expedition, present at the operations in the vicinity and capture of Rangoon, April 1852, and attack of the Burmese stockades, 19th March 1853, medals.

Lieuts. Anderson and Cadell, served with the Burmah Expedition, present at the operations in the vicinity and capture of Rangoon, April 1852, medals.

Lieut. FitzGerald served with the force under Brigadier Genl. Chamberlain against the Bozdar Beloochees in March 1857, present at the siege and capture of Delhi 1857.

Lieut. Manderson served with the Burmah expedition: present at the operations in the vicinity and capture of Rangoon April 1852: and with the force employed under Major Fytche in the Bassein District in 1853, medal.

Lieut. C.V. Arbuckle served with the Burmese expedition in 1852; served in the Crimean campaign in 1855 on the staff of Lieut. Genl. Cannon as Aide-de-Camp, and on the staff of Field Marshall His Highness Omer Pasha, as Brigade Major, was attached to the 4th Division under Genl. Sir Colin Campbell, G. C. B., was present at the siege and bombardment of Sevastopol, medal and clasp.

Lieut. Roberts served at the siege and capture of Delhi 57-58; (horse shot under him) present at the actions of Boolundshuhur and Agra, at the battle of Cawnpore and was present at the relief and capture of Lucknow, victoria cross.

Lieut. Cumberland served with the expedition under Brigadier Chamberlain to the Meeranzaie valley and upper Koorum in 1856, also present at the operations in the Bozdar Hills in 1857.

Lieut. J. Alexander served in the defence of the Lucknow Residency from June 30th 1857 to Nov. 22nd 1857 (gun shot wound through left arm and right breast) also with Major Genl. Sir J. Outram's force at the Alumbagh, from 22nd November 1857 to 6th March 1858; present at the siege and capture of Lucknow.

Unattached Lieut. Douglas served during the campaign on the Sutledge, present at the battle of Sobraon, medal, and throughout the war in the Punjaub, medal.

Unattached Captain Budd *(Riding Master)* served in Affghanistan 1842, and in the several engagements leading to the re-capture of Caubul, medal: present at the battle of Maharajpore, bronze star, with the army of the Sutledge, at the affair of Budiwal, on the 21st January 1846, and battles of Alliwal and Sobraon, medal and 1 clasp, also throughout the Punjaub campaign 1848-49, (wounded) medal, 2 clasps and unattached Ensigncy.

CORPS OF ENGINEERS.

Major General *Sir* J. Cheape, K. C. B., served in the Mahrattah war 1817-18; Burmese war 1824-26; was Chief Engineer at Mooltan and Goojerat, medal and K. C. B.; commanded the force employed in the capture of the Burmese stockades, 19th March 1853, medal, and Hony. A. D. C. to Her Majesty.

Major General Garstin, Nepaul war 1815-16; Mahrattah war 1817-18, medal.

ENGINEERS.—*Continued.*

Col. Goodwyn was present at the siege and capture of Bhurtpore in 1825-26, India medal, and in the late Punjaub campaign, medal.

Col. A. H. E. Boileau served throughout the siege of Bhurtpore, and commanded two companies of Sappers and Miners during the storming of that fortress, medal.

Col. Baker present at Sobraon, medal and Bt. Major.

Lt. Col. (Bt. Col.) *Sir* R. Napier, K. C. B., was Brigade Major in the Sutledge campaign and actions of 1845-46, (severely wounded) medal & Bt. Major; was acting Chief Engr. during part of the siege of Mooltan, (severely wounded,) also present, at Goojerat, medal & Bt. Lt. Col.; accompanied *Sir* Walter Gilbert's column in pursuit of the Seikh army in 1849.

Lt. Col. (Bt. Col.) Glasfurd served in the Punjaub campaign, passage of the Chenab, Chillianwalla & Goojerat, medal & Bt. Maj.

Lieut. Col. (Bt. Col.) Durand, C. B., headed the explosion party and fired the train at Ghuznee: present at the battles of Maharajpore, Chillianwalla and Goojerat, bronze star, 2 medals and Bt. Major.

Lt. Col. Laughton served in Persia 1834-36, in action with the Russian Troops: Affghanistan 1839.

Lt. Col. A. Cunningham served in the Gwalior campaign, at Punniar, bronze star; Punjaub campaign; present at Chillianwalla and Goojerat, medal and Bt. Major.

Capt. (Bt. Lt. Col.) MacLeod served with the Army of the Indus; present at the capture of Ghuznee, medal.

Capt. Pott was present at Maharajpore, bronze star.

Capt. C. B. Young was present at Maharajpore, bronze star, and served in the Punjaub campaign, present at Chillianwalla and Goojerat, medal, served in Burmah 1852-53, capture of Prome, medal.

Capt. (Bt. Lt. Col.) Smith, C. B., served in the Sutledge campaign, presentat the action of Sobraon, medal: Punjaub campaign, present at Sadoolapore, Chillianwalla and Goojerat, medal.

Capt. Turnbull served in the Sutledge campaign, medal.

Capt. (Bt. Major) Goodwyn served in Affghanistan 1842, medal; in the Sutledge campaign, medal; present at Ferozeshuhur and in the Punjaub campaign, Chillianwalla and Goojerat, medal.

Capt. (Bt. Major) Becher served in Affghanistan in 1842, was at the forcing of the Khyber Pass by *Sir* G. Pollock, medal: served in the Sutledge campaign, present at Sobraon and severely wounded, medal

Capt. (Offl. Lt. Col.) Yule served in the Sutledge campaign, medal, and in the Punjaub campaign, Chillianwalla, medal.

Capt. Morton served in the Punjaub campaign, present at Chillianwalla and Goojerat, medal; accompanied *Sir* W. Gilbert's column in pursuit of the Seikh army in 1849.

Capts. Beadle, C. W. Hutchinson and Dyas served in the Sutledge campaign, medals.

Capt. (Bt. Major) Maxwell was with the Bundelkund Field Force in 1842, and affairs with insurgents near Jytepore in that year; present at Punniar, bronze star; served in Scinde 1845, in the Hill campaign, under *Sir* C. Napier; present at Mooltan throughout the siege operations and surrender (clasp;) present at Goojerat, 1849, (Punjaub, medal and clasp.)

Capt. Campbell was present at Maharajpore, bronze star, Burmah 1852-53, capture of Pegu, and 1st and 2nd defence of Pegu, medal.

Capt. (Bt. Major) Lake served with the army of the Sutledge, at the actions of Moodkee (wounded) and Alliwal, medal and clasp, during the campaign in the Punjaub, commanded the troops of H. H. the Nawab of Bhawulpor throughout the siege and operations in the vicinity of Mooltan (wounded); present at the battle of Goojerat and subsequent pursuit of the Seikhs and Affghans by the force under Genl. Gilbert, medal, clasp and Local Major.

Capts. Atkinson and Short were present at the action of Maharajpore, bronze stars.

Capt. (Bt. Major) Crommelin, C. B., served in the Sutledge campaign, medal; and in the Punjaub campaign, present at Sadoolapore, Chillianwalla and Goojerat, medal.

Capt. Nicolls was present at Maharajpore, bronze star; served in the Sutledge campaign, (severely wounded,) medal.

Capt. Robinson served in the Sutledge campaign of 1845-46, present at Sobraon, medal, also in the Punjaub campaign, Chillianwalla and Goojerat, medal.

Capt. (Bt. Lt. Col.) A. Taylor served in the Sutledge campaign, present at Sobraon, medal: also in the Punjaub war, present at Mooltan (wounded) and Goojerat, medal and clasp.

Capt. Sim served in the Sutledge campaign of 1845-46, present at Sobraon, medal.

Capt. (Bt. Major) Drummond served in the Sutledge campaign of 1845-46, medal, employed at the capture of Kote Kangra in 1846 and Burmah war of 1852, medal.

Capts. Bt. Majors Greathed and Maunsell and Capts. Glover, Hyde, Oliphant, Pollard, Steward, and Garnett, served at the siege of Mooltan, and were present at Goojerat, medals. Lieuts Pollard and Garnett, wounded.

Capt. A. Fraser served in the Sutledge campaign of 1845-46, medal; also in the Punjaub campaign, of 1848-49 at the siege of Mooltan and battle of Goojerat medal and two clasps; also in the Burmah campaign of 1852-53, accompanied the Martaban Column under Brigadier General Steel, C. B., to Tonghoo, medal.

Capt. R. Young served at the siege of Mooltan, medal.

Capt. C. D. Newmarch served in Burmah 1853, medal.

Capt. Gulliver served at the siege of Mooltan, (severely wounded.)

Capts. Williams (slightly wounded) and Craster served with the Burmah Expedition, present at the operations in the vicinity and capture of Rangoon, April 1852, medals. Capt. Craster was subsequently engaged at the taking of Bassein.

Capt. W. S. Trevor served with the Burmah Expedition, present at the operations in the vicinity and capture of Rangoon, April 1852, (severely wounded) and attack on the Burmese stockades, 19th March 1853, (slightly wounded,) medal.

CAVALRY.

COLONELS.

Genl. Sir R. Houstoun, K.C.B., 4th En. L. C., served during the Maharattah war, present at the battles of Delhi and Laswarrie 1803, India medal.

Lieut. Genl. Thomson, 1st En. L. C., served during the campaign under Lord Lake, present at the battle of Laswarrie 1830, Ufzulghur and assault of Bhurtpore 1805, India medal.

Lieut. Genl. Kennedy, C. B., 5th En. L. C., served with the force under General Sir James Craig 1800; in Bundelkund 1804, with Col. Adams' division of the army of the Dekkan 1816-17-18; present in every action and led a dismounted Squadron at the storm of the Fort of Choundah, commanded the 5th L. Cavalry at the battle of Kotah in 1821, India medals.

Lieut. Genl. Shubrick, 2nd En. L. C., served in Oude and Rohilcund 1802; Lord Lake's campaigns 1804-5; present at the battles of Coel, Allyghur, Delhi, Agra, Laswarrie, Shumlee and Futtehghur 1803; capture of Deig 1804; Ufzulghur; assault of Bhurtpore 1805; Bundelkund 1810-11; siege and capture of Kulinger 1813, and Mahrattah and Pindaree wars 1817-18, India medal.

Lieut. General Pattle, C. B., 3rd En. L. C., served in Oude and Rohilkund 1802, throughout Lord Lake's campaign 1804-5, present at Sarsnee, Bidjyghur 1802, Coel, Allyghur, Delhi, Agra, Laswarrie, Shumlee and Futtehghur 1803. capture of Deig 1804, India medal; assault of Bhurtpore 1805, campaign in Bundelkund under Genl. Sir Thomas Brown 1810-11, siege and capture of Kulinger 1812, with the right wing of Lord Hastings' army during the Pindaree war 1817-18-19; and commanded the Cavalry of Sir Charles Napier's force, at the actions of Meeanee and Hyderabad, medals, C. B. and A.D.C. to the Queen.

Maj. Genl. Carmichael, C. B., 5th En. L. C., served at the siege of Kulinger 1812, Rewah campaign 1813, Alwah 1814, siege and capture of Hatrass 1816-17: Mahrattah war 1817-18-19, against Bheels as Major of Brigade to Brigr. J. R. Lumley in 1823-24, commanded a Light Detachment against Jowra Mairpoor in 1837 and took military possession of that country, under the orders of Col. A. Spiers, Political Agent, marched in Command of the 4th Irregular Horse as Volunteers to join the army of the Indus and Affghanistan and served the campaign 1838-39, present at the siege and capture of Ghuznee, C. B. Dooranee order, and medal.

Maj. Genl. *Sir* Hearsey, K.C.B., 3rd En. L. C, served in Bundelkund in 1809-10, Rewah 1812-13, Pindaree campaign 1817-18: battle of Seetabuldee, (dangerously wounded:) siege and capture of Bhurtpore, 1826 (wounded,) India medal and clasp, and commanded one of the Cavalry divisions army of the Punjaub, present at the action of Goojerat, medal and C. B.

Maj. Genl Taylor, 1st En. L. C., served with the expedition employed in the capture of Java, and in the Pindaree campaigns of 1816-17-18.

LIEUTENANT COLONELS.

Major General Hawkes, (Supy. unattached,) served during the Maharattah war 17-18, employed with the dismounted Cav. at the storm of Choundah 1818, medal.

Maj. Genl. Salter, C.B., (Supy. unattached,) served with the army of the Indus: present at the assault and capture of Ghuznee, medal, and the operations in the Kohistan, at the action of Punniar, bronze star and during the Punjaub campaign, including the siege of Mooltan, medal, and C. B.

Maj. Gen. Story, C.B. Supy. unattached, served throughout the Scinde campaign in 1843: present at the battles of Meeanee and Hydrabad, medal, C. B., and Bt. Lt. Col.

Maj. Genl. Bradford, C. B., (Supy. unattached,) served in Affghanistan 1842; in the several engagement leading to the re-occupation of Caubul, medal: present at the battle of Maharajpore 1843, bronze star: battle of Alliwal 1846, medal and Bt. Lt. Col., army of the Punjaub, including the passage of the Chenab, actions of Chillianwalla and Goojerat 1848-49, medal and C. B.

Lieut. Col., Bt. Col. Wheatley, 4th En. L. C., was present at the battle of Punniar, bronze star; commanded the Regiment with the army of the Punjaub, during the latter part of the action at Ramnuggur, (slightly wounded,) and at the battles of Sadoolapore, Chillianwalla and Goojerat, medal and Bt. Major.

Lieut. Col., Bt. Col. Mackenzie, 5th En. L. C., was present at the siege and capture of Bhurtpore 1826, medal; served with the army of the Sutledge, and during the Punjaub campaign, including the actions of Chillianwalla and Goojerat, medal and Bt. Lt. Col.; served in Scinde 1844, commanded at the attack of the Hill Tribes near Mobarakpore for which he received special thanks of *Sir* C. Napier, C. B.

Lieut. Col., Bt. Col. Clayton, 3rd En. L. C., was present at the siege and capture of Bhurtpore 1826, medal; also at Maharajpore 1843, as Dy. Qr. Mr. Genl. of the Cavalry Division, bronze star.

Lieut. Col. Wemyss, 4th En. L. C., served throughout the campaign in Scinde in 1843: present at the battles of Meeanee and Hyderabad, medal.

Lieut. Col., Bt. Col. Wheler, 1st En. L. C., accompanied the army of the Indus, and was present at the assault and capture of Ghuznee, medal, pursuit of Dost Mahomed Khan 1839, and 3rd class Dooranee order; also served with the army of the Punjaub throughout the operations in the vicinity and siege and capture of Mooltan, medal and Bt. Lt. Col.: commanded the Cavalry in the attacking column at the battle of Soorujkhoond, 7 Nov. 1848.

Lieut. Col. Master, C. B., 2nd En L. C., served at the siege and capture of Bhurtpore 1825-26, medal, and with the army of the Punjaub, at the operations (including the action of Soorujkhoond) in the vicinity and siege and surrender of Mooltan 1848-49, battle of Goojerat and subsequent pursuit of the Seikhs and Affghans by the force under Genl. Gilbert, medal, clasp and Bt. Major.

Lieut. Col. Bt. Col. Campbell, 3rd En. L. C., served at the action of Maharajpore, bronze star: during the campaign on the Sutledge, present at the battles of Alliwal, and as A.D.C. to Sir Robert Dick, at Sobraon, (horse killed under him,) medal, clasp and Bt. Major.

Lieut. Col., Bt. Col. Smyth, 1st En. L. C., was present at the siege and capture of Bhurtpore 1826, medal, Affghanistan 1838-39: present at the capture of Ghuznee, medal; Sutledge campaign 1845-46, including the affair of Budiwal: and actions of Alliwal and Sobraon, medal and clasp.

Lieut. Col. Hall, 5th En. L. C., served throughout the campaign in the Punjaub 1848-49, including the skirmish at Ramnuggur, and actions of Sadoolapore, Chillianwalla and Goojerat, medal.

Lt. Col. Macdonell, (4th En. L. C.) served in Affghanistan with the force under Genl. Pollock, medal, and at the action of Maharajpore, bronze star.

1st REGIMENT EUROPEAN LIGHT CAVALRY.

RIGHT WING.

Major Jenkins served with the force in Affghanistan under Genl. Pollock 1842, medal: battle of Maharajpore 1843, bronze star: Alliwal 1846, medal: army of the Punjaub 1848-49, medal.

Capt. Brooks served at the battles of Maharajpore 1843, bronze star: Alliwal 1846, medal: and with the army of the Punjaub, including the passage of the Chenab, actions of Chillianwalla and Goojerat, 1848-49, medal.

served with the Sarun field force in 1857-58; present at the battle of Sonepore 26th December 1857, in military charge of Gorucknath Regiment of Ghoorkas at the battle of Phoolpore 20th February 1858, in military charge Ramdull Regiment of Ghoorkhas and at the battles of Amorah on the 5th March and 17th April 1858, in military charge Buruk Regiment of Ghoorkas, medal.

Capt. Nicholetts was present at the battle of Alliwal 1846, medal. served with the Rohilkund field force as Interpreter to H. M. 6th Carabineers and as Major of Brigade to the field force at the capture of Bareilly, medal.

Capt. Bt. Major Forbes was present at the battles of Moodkee, (horse killed under him) Ferozeshuhur. and Sobraon, medal and 2 clasps: army of the Punjaub, including the passage of the Chenab, actions of Chillianwalla and Goojerat, 1848-49, medal; was a member of the Lucknow Garrison 1857, (slightly wounded) served afterwards with the Punjab Cavalry and again wounded; served as Major of Brigade 2nd Cavalry Brigade at the final advance and capture of Lucknow 1858, medal clasp and Bt. Major.

Capt *Sir* J. Hill *Bart* and Lieut. Stapleton, served in the defence of the fort of Neemuch 1857, Lieut. Stapleton (horse shot under him) and subsequently with the Rajpootanah field force with the 2nd Bombay Cavalry present at the capture of Kotah, *Sir J.* Hill was present as Major of Brigade of the Rajpootanah field force at the action of Gwalior 1858, under *Sir* Hugh Rose, medals.

Lieut. Martin served with the Malwah Field force with H. M. 14th Dragoons, present at the capture of Dhar 1st Nov. 57, and actions at Mundesore on the 21. 22 and 23rd Nov. 1857 (severely wounded) medal.

Lieut. Luard served with the Bengal Artillery in defence of the Fort of Neemuch 1857, with H. M. 14th Dragoons; with the Central India Field force at the capture of Chundeyree, action of the Betwa, capture of the town and fort of Jhansie, action at Koonch and capture of Culpee 1858, medal.

Lieuts. Dent and Chapman served with the Malwah field force in 1857 at the capture of Dhar and Battles at Mundesore in Nov. 1857, and with H. M. 14th Dragoons, with Central India field force at the capture of Chundeyree, action of the Betwa, capture of the town and fort of Jhansie, action at Coonch and capture of Culpee 1858, medal,

Lieut. Birch served with the Volunteer Cavy. with the Oude field force, under *Sir* J. Outram in 1857, severely wounded at the 1st relief of Lucknow medal.

Captain Brownlow served during the Punjaub campaign, including the passage of the Chenab, actions of Chillianwalla and Goojerat, 1848-49, medal.

Lieut. W. Keily served at the siege and capture of Bhurtpore 1825-26, medal; with the force in Affghanistan under Genl. Pollock; present at the forcing of the Khyber Pass, and in all subsequent operations leading to the occupation of Caubul, including those in the Mazeena Valley, medal; battle of Maharajpore, bronze star, and during the campaign on the Sutledge, including the actions of Ferozeshuhur and Sobraon, medal and clasp.

LEFT WING.

Major Bt. Lieut. Col. Drummond was present at the siege and capture of Bhurtpore 1826, medal, served against the Coles 1832; in Affghanistan 1838-39; siege and capture of Ghuznee, medal; was delivered over in Dec. 1841 as a hostage to the Newab Zeman Khan.

Capt. Bt. Col. Christie served at the siege and capture of Bhurtpore 1826, medal; commanded the 1st Regt. of Cavalry Shah Shoojah's force, during the campaign in Affghanistan, 1839-40-42; present at the storm and capture of Ghuznee, medal and 3rd class Dooranee order, and capture of Pushoot, with the Candahar force under Major General Nott; engaged in the different operations leading to the re-occupation of Caubul and taking of Istaliff, medal; battle of Punniar, bronze star; with the army of the Sutledge: present at the actions of Moodkee, Ferozeshuhur and Sobraon, medal, 2 clasps and Bt. Major; and throughout the Punjaub campaign, including the passage of the Chenab, battles of Chillianwalla and Goojerat, and subsequent pursuit of the Seikhs and Affghans by the force under Genl. Gilbert medal and Bt. Lt. Col.

Capt. Bt. Major Plowden served in Affghanistan 1838-39; capture of Ghuznee, medal; Sutledge campaign 1845-46; present at the affair of Budiwal; actions of Alliwal and Sobraon, (horse disabled) medal and clasps;

Cap. Bt. Major Richardson served in the Sutledge campaign 1845-46, including the affair of Budiwal, actions of Alliwal and Sobraon, for which he has received a medal and clasp.

Capt. Craigie served with the 5th Light Cavalry in the Punjaub campaign 1848-49; present at the battle of Goojerat, medal.

2ND REGIMENT EUROPEAN LIGHT CAVALRY.

RIGHT WING.

Major Bt. Col. Ponsonby served at the siege of Bhurtpore, India medal: during the campaign in Affghanistan, (severely wounded:) present at the assault and capture of Ghuznee, medal, and the operations leading to the re-occupation of Caubul by the force under Genl. Pollock, medal: battle of Sadoolapore; with the army of the Punjaub at the actions of Chillianwalla and Goojerat, medal and Bt. Lt. Col., 3rd class Dooranee Order.

Capt. Bt. Col. Lawrence served with the army of the Indus 1839-40-41, present at the capture of Ghuznee, medal, pursuit of Dost Mahomed Khan 1839, and forcing of the Khoord Caubul Pass by the force under Sir Robert Sale, Oct. 1841, 3rd class Dooranee order; taken prisoner on the 23d Dec. 1841, and released on the 29th of the same month; in the retreat from Caubul surrendered as a hostage to Akbar Khan, released 21st Sept. 1842, fell into the hands of Sirdar Chutter Singh after the night attack made by the Seikh army on the Peshawur Agency, Oct. 1848, retreated to Kohat, then made prisoner by Sirdar Sultan Mahomed Khan, liberated 7th March, 1849, on the submission of the Sirdar to Major Genl. Gilbert, medal and Bt. Lieut. Col.

CAVALRY.—*Continued.*

Capt Bt. Major Taylor, and Captain Warner, served at the action of Punniar, bronze stars, and with the army of the Punjaub: throughout the operations in the vicinity and siege and surrender of Mooltan, medals. Major Taylor, Local Major—and Capt. Vibart were present at the battle of Soorujkhoond 7th Nov. 1848.

Capt. Bt. Major Taylor served in the Sutledge campaign; received 3 sabre wounds, medal; also with the Punjaub. campaign, medal.

Capt. Cotton was present at the engagement of Maharajpore, bronze star.

Lieut. Wells served under Brigadier Genls. Chamberlain and Nicholson in the Punjaub moveable Column, present at the action of Nimmoo Ghat, marched with Genl. Nicholson to Delhi and served at its siege and capture. served under Brigadier Showers in the Delhi, Goorgaon and Jhujjur districts, also with Brigadier *Sir* T. Seatons' Column in the Dooab, present at the actions of Gungeree and Putia'ee.

Lieut. Irvine served with the force under Brigadier Lord Mark Kerr at the relief of Azimghur, April 1858.

Lieuts. Loch and Brodhurst served with the Queen's Bays in Sir J. Outrams' Division at the siege and capture of Lucknow March 1858, and during the subsequent operations in Oude.

Lieut. Montgomerie served with the guide Cavalry at the siege and capture of Delhi, including the Battle of Nuzufghur and with Brigadier Showers' Column in the Delhi, Gorgaon and Jhujjur districts, served with the 1st Siekh Cavalry with the force under Genl. *Sir* J. Outram at the Alumbagh from 16th of January to 2nd March 1858. during the siege and capture of Lucknow from 2nd to 21st March 1858, and with Genl. Grant's Column in the subsequent operations in Oude, was present at the affair of Simre.

LEFT WING.

Major Hawthorne, Capt. and Bt. Major Boileau and Capt. Turnbull served in Sindh in 45-46; and with the force employed under General Wheeler, in the Punjaub 1848-49, medals.

Capt. Hamilton served under *Sir* C. Napier against the Hill Tribes in Scinde in 1848, also in the Punjaub campaign in 1848-49, medal.

Capt. Alexander served with H. M. 7th Hussars at the siege and capture of Lucknow, March 1858, and during the subsequent operations in Oude.

Capt. A. C. Warner formed one of the Garrison of Lucknow from the 30th of June till the 22nd Nov. 1857, was brought to the favorable notice of the Governor Genl. in Council in the despatch of Major Genl. *Sir* J. Inglis K. C. B. dated 25th Septr. 1857. and thanked by the Governor Genl. in Council in General Order No. 1543 dated 8th Decr. 1857, was present with the force under His Excellency the Commander-in-Chief which drove the Gwalior rebels from Cawnpore at the action of Khodagunge, and re-occupation of Futtyghur, served as Aide-de-Camp to Brigr- Genl. Walpole C. B. during the siege nnd Capture of Lucknow in March 1858 and at the action and re-occupation of Bareilly in May 1858 mentioned in despatches on both occasions.

Capt. Melvill served in the "Kumaon Militia" during the year 1857, commanded the Cavalry in an attack made from Nainee Tal upon a portion of the Rohilcund Rebels on the 18th of September 1857, served with the Oude Police Cavalry from May till September 1858, was in command of a Police force (Cavalry and Infantry,) at "Mahon" near Lucknow when an attack was made on that Post by the enemy on the evening of the 7th of August 1858, commanded the Cavalry in an attack made by a Police force, upon the Fort and position of "Birwa" on the 26th August 1858.

Lieut. Trench was present at the siege and capture of Delhi, served with Hodson's Horse with Brigadier Shower's column in the Delhi, Goorgaon and Jhujjur districts, with Brigr. Sir T. Seaton's column in the Doab including the engagements of Gungerea, Putialee and Mynpoorie, also at the siege and capture of Lucknow, March 1858.

3RD REGIMENT EUROPEAN LIGHT CAVALRY.

RIGHT WING.

Major (Bt. Lt. Col.) Apperley served at the siege and capture of Bhurtpore, medal.

Capt. Bt. Major Jackson served in Bundelkund in 1842, and in the Punjaub, with the force under Brigr. Genl. *Sir* H. M. Wheeler, K.C.B., in 1848-49, medal.—Served under *Sir* C. Campbell, K. C. B., during the operations on the Peshawur Frontier 1851-52, when in command of the Outpost of "Mutta," repulsed the attack made thereon by the combined Momund Tribes, 8th December, 1851, wounded twice in an attack on a body of the 26th Light Infantry Mutineers in 1857.

Capts. Wyld (horse shot under him at Sobraon, and Macleod served at the action of Maharajpore, bronze stars, and during the Sutledge campaign, present at the battles of Moodkee, Ferozeshuhur and Sobraon) medals and clasps.

Capt. Howard was present at the battles of Moodkee, Ferozeshuhur and Sobraon 1845-46, medal and 2 clasps.

LEFT WING.

Major Bt. Lieut. Col. Barton, and Capt. (Bt. Major) Macmullen, Capts. Farquharson, Theobald, and Lane served with the army of the Punjaub, medals.

Capt. Bt. Major Grindlay served with the army of the Punjaub, at the battles of Chillianwalla, (severely wounded,) and Goojerat, medal.

Capt. Delane served throughout the Punjaub campaign 1848-49, present at the passage of the Chenab and battles of Chillianwalla and Goojerat, medal.

Lieut. T. Ray Riding Master served with the Governor General's Body Guard throughout the war in Burmah in 1824; also throughout the Scinde campaign in 1843 present at the battles of Meeanee and Hyderabad, medal.

4TH REGIMENT EUROPEAN LIGHT CAVALRY.

RIGHT WING.

Major Bt. Col. Tucker, C. B., (2nd Lieut. 1st Bn. 60th Rifles, 1825, Lt. H. M. 41st Foot, 17th March 1826,) served with the 9th Regt. L. C. throughout the campaign in Scinde in 43: present at the battle of Meeanee, (severely wounded in five places) medal, C. B., and Bt. Major.

Capt. Snow served throughout the campaign in Scinde in 1843: present at the battles of Meanee and Hyderabad, (horse shot under him,) medal; served during the campaign of the Sutlej 1857, wounded 30th September (severely wounded 16th October.)

Capt. Bt. Major Thomson served throughout the Scinde campaign in 1843, on the Staff of Sir Chas. Napier, G. C. B., as A. D. C. present at the battles of Meeanee and Hydrabad, medal.

Capt. (Bt. Major) J. H. Balmain served during the Sutlej campaign in 1846, employed against the Jhuts in the Googaira district during the months of October and November 1857, served with the Column under Brigadier Franks, C.B. in Oude 1858; present at the siege and capture of Lucknow by Sir Colin Campbell in March 1858, at the battle and taking of Bareilly May 1858, served with Soraon field force under Brigadier Berkeley, C. B. present at the capture of Forts Deghain, Turoul, and Blyspoor in 1858.

Capt. G. Bushby, served during the campaign of the Sutledge with the force, employed against the Jhuts in the Googaira district during the months of October and November 1857, siege and cpture of Lucknow March 1858.

Riding Master Bradshaw served throughout the campaign in Scinde in 1843; present at the battles of eeanee and Hydrabad medal.

LEFT WING.

Capt. Simeon served in Affghanistan with the force under Genl. Pollock, medal, and at the action of Maharajpore, bronze star.

Capt. Dumbleton was present at the engagement of Maharajpore, bronze star.

Capt. W. C. Alexander served in Affghanistan, medal, and during the campaign on the Sutledge: present at the battle of Sobraon, medal.

Capt. W. Alexander Shaw served in Affghanistan, 1842, medal.

Capt. Bt. Major Wilkinson served during the Punjaub campaign present at the skirmish at Ramnuggur, medal.

Lieut. H. G. Jenkins, late Commanding 2nd Squadron "Bengal, Yeomanry Cavalry" forming part of Sarun Field Force "served with the Regiment" at the Battle of Amorah on the 5th March 1858, (charger shot under him) at Pilza on the 17th April, and again at Amorah, on the 25th April, and at Nuggur on the 29th April 1858.

5TH REGIMENT EUROPEAN LIGHT CAVALRY.

RIGHT WING.

Major Bt. Col. Harington served with the 3rd Regt. Lt. Cavalry against the Coles 1832, during the Affghanistan campaign of 1842, at the forcing of the Khyber Pass, and the battle of Mamoo Khail, medal, present at the battle of Punniar, bronze star, served throughout the Sutledge campaign, including the actions of Moodkee (wounded) and Sobraon, served with the army of the Punjaub in the affair of Ramnuggur, and battles of Sadoolapore, Chillianwalla and Goojerat, 2 medals, clasp and Bt. Major.

Capt. Bt. Lt. Col. Stannus served in the campaign of 1842 in Affghanistan, at the forcing of the Khyber Pass, and the battle of Mamoo Khail, medal; commanded a detachment of the Regiment on Escort with His Excellency the Commander-in-Chief at the battle of Maharajpore, bronze star, throughout the campaign on the Sutledge, present at the actions of Moodkee, Ferozeshuhur, Alliwal and Sobraon, medal and 3 clasps, with the army of the Punjaub, at the action of Ramnuggur, and commanded the 3rd troop of the Regiment on Escort with the Commander-in-Chief at the battles of Chillianwalla and Goojerat, (severely wounded,) medal.

Capt. Elliot served at the battle of Punniar, bronze star, and with the army of the Punjaub, present at the action of Ramnuggur, and the battle of Chillianwalla (severely wounded,) medal.

Capt. Stephens commanded a detachment of the Regiment on Escort duty with the Commander-in-Chief at Moodkee, medal.

Capt. Bt. Maj. Lane served during the Sutledge campaign, present at the battles of Moodkee, Ferozeshuhur, Alliwal and Sobraon, (charger shot,) medal and 3 clasps, with the army of the Punjaub, at the action of Ramnuggur, and the battles of Sadoolapore, Chillianwalla and Goojerat, medal.

Capt. Jenkins served at the battle of Alliwal, medal, and with the army of the Punjaub, present at the action of Ramnuggur, and the battles of Sadoolapore, Chillianwalla (charger shot,) and Goojerat, medal.

Riding Master Cullen served with the army of the Indus and was present at the assault and capture of Ghuznee, 1838-39-40 medal, with the army of Gwalior and was present at the battle of Maharajpore 1843, star; with the army of the Sutledge was present at the action at Budiwal, battle of Alliwal and general engagement at Sobraon, 1846, medal and clasp; with the army of the Punjaub was present at the actions of Ramnuggur and Sadoolapore, battles of Chillianwallah and Goojerat 1848-49 medal and 2 clasps.

CAVALRY.—*Continued.*

LEFT WING.

Major (Bt. Lt. Col.) Moore commanded a detachment of Troops at Punwarri in Bundelkund in 1842, against a body of insurgents, (wounded through the left knee by a matchlock ball:) also served with the army of the Punjaub 1848-49, at the skirmish near Ramnuggur, actions of Sadoolapore, Chillianwalla and Goojerat, medal and Bt. Major.

Capt. (Bt. Lt. Col.) Cautley served at the battle of Ferozeshuhur, medal, and throughout the Punjaub campaign, including the skirmish near Ramnuggur and actions of Sadoolapore, Chillianwalla and Goojerat, medal and Bt. Major.

Major Gough served throughout the Punjab campaign of 1848-49, present at the actions of Ramnuggur, Sadoolapore, Chillianwalla and Goojerat, medal and two clasps, served at the siege and capture of Delhi from the 17th July with the guide Corps; commanded the guide Cavalry in the affairs at Rhotuk 17th and 18th August under Major Hodson, engaged in the Cavalry affair in rear of Camp on the 11th September, served with the column under Brigr. Showers in the Delhi and Jhujjur Districts, engaged at the action of Narnole under Brigr. Gerrard, served with Hodson's Horse at the actions of Gungeeree, Putteealee and Mynpoorie under Sir J. Seaton, at the action of Shumshabad, near Futtehghur, (wounded) under Brigr. Hon. A. Hope, served in command of a squadron of Hodson's Horse with the column under Sir Hope Grant in Oude in February; engaged at the action of Meahgunj present throughout the siege and capture of Lucknow, medal two clasps and Brevet Majority.

Capt. Best served in the Punjab campaign medal, at the siege of Delhi 57, and the battle of Boolundshuhur, severely wounded.

Capt. Drummond served at the battles of Punniar, bronze star, Ferozeshuhur, medal, and throughout the Punjaub campaign, present at the skirmish near Ramnuggur, and actions of Sadoolapore, Chillianwalla and Goojerat, medal.

Capt. Ward served at the battle of Ferozeshuhur, medal, and throughout the campaign in the Punjaub, including the skirmish near Ramnuggur, and actions of Sadoolapore, Chillianwalla and Goojerat, medal.

Lieut. Shepherd employed against the Jhuts in the Googaira district, during the Months of October and November 1857, served with the column under Brigadier Franks, c. b. in Oude 1858, present at the siege and capture of Lucknow by *Sir* Colin Campbell in March 1858; at the battle and taking of Bareilly May 1858, served with Soraon field force under Brigadier Barkeley, c. b. present at the capture of Forts, Deghain, Turoul, Bhyspoor, 1858.

INFANTRY.

COLONELS.

Genl. Macgregor, (54th N. I.) served in Mysore, at the siege and capture of Seringapatam 1799: Northern Circars 1800, medal: campaign under Lord Lake, Delhi, Deig, (two horses shot under him) Kutchowra, Agra 1808, and Bhurtpore 1805, India medal.

Genl. *Sir* Wm. Richards, k. c. b., (26th N. I.) was present with the Volunteer Battn. at the siege of Seringapatam, and throughout the operations in Mysore 1799, medal, also against the Rajah of Palanewur, returned to Bengal and was employed with his Regt. at the taking of the Fort of Budoon, in April 1802, at Jeitpore 20th July 1804, served throughout the operations in Bundelkund, in command of the Native Brigade of Newab Mahomed Jeewun Khan. In 1807 was present at the storming of Kemonah, and taking of Gunowur. Nepal war 1814-15-16, medal; present at the assault of Kalinjer; commanded the force at Peacock Hill, and the affair in the Punjore Valley, medal; marched with his Regt. from Moradabad to Bareilly in 24 hours, and quelled the insurrection here in 1816. In March 1821, commanded a force in the Lurka Cole country. In 1821 till 1824 commanded the Fortress of Asseerghur, and commanded the 1st Brigade of Genl. Morison's force in Arracan 1825, and was present throughout the operations in that country, c. b.

General Boyd, 53rd N. I., served during Lord Lake's campaign, including the battle of Delhi and taking of Agra, India medal.

General *Sir* R. H. Cunliffe, *Bt.*, c. b., 4th N. I., served during the campaign in the Doab 1804 at Kullinger 1812, Nepal war 1814-15, Hattrass 1817, Pindaree war 1818, and Bhurtpore 1825-26, India medal.,

General Truscott, 74th N. I., served at the battle of Delhi, India medals.

Lieut. Genl. Tod, 60th N. I., served at the siege and capture of Bhurtpore, India medal.

Lieut. Genl. Hamilton 40th N. I., served under Brigadier Genl. Harcourt at the capture of Cuttack and siege of the Forts of Barra Battee and Khoordah: Nepal war 1814-15: present at the taking of the Forts of Ramghur, Tarraghur and Chumbulsoorjghur, and commanded a column in the attack on the heights of Malown, India medal: Pindaree campaign 1817-18: employed at the surrender of the fort of Tarraghur, and capture of Jumshaid Khan's guns on the Sambhur Lake: commanded in various engagements with the insurgent Bheels 1822-23-24.

Lieut. Genl. Waters, c. b., 68th N. I., served at the assault and capture of Allygurh: battle of Dehlee, and throughout the campaign under Lord Lake 1803-04-05: Nepal war 1815, Assam 1824, India medal and clasp.

Lieut. Genl. Andree, 69th N. I., was present at the engagements of Allygurh, Coel, Chundrus, (wounded) Teekolabad and Deig, India medal.

INFANTRY.—*Continued.*

Lieut. Genl. Kemm, 25th N. I., served during the Nepal war, India medal.

Lieut. Genl. Vincent, 6th En. Regt., served at the capture of Java, medal, and during the campaign in Ava, medal.

Lieut. Genl. Paul, 20th N. I., served at the capture of Java 1810, (wounded,) medal.

Lieut. Genl. Anderson, 61st N. I., was present at the storm of Kaomonah, 1807, and served during the Nepaul war, India medal.

Lieut. Genl. Young, 66th N. I., served with the Bengal Volunteers at the taking of Balasore and operations on the coast 1803-04: with the army under Lord Lake 1805: present at the assault of Bhurtpore, Nepal war 1814-15-16, including the actions of Nalapanee, Nahun and Jeetuk, Rajpootanah 1817-18, India medal, and commanded a detachment employed in the capture of the Ghurra of Kooryah 1824.

Lieut. Genl. Costley, 9th N. I., served at Chundrus, and at the storming of a Fortified Village near Allyghur; was present at the battle and siege and capture of Deig in 1804; engaged in pursuit of Holkar from Muttra under Lord Lake; served also during the Nepaul war, medal.

Lieut. Genl. Dick, 71st N. I., served against the mud fort of Jurhapoora, and throughout the campaign under Lord Lake 1805, with the expedition against Java 1811: present at the storm and capture of Fort Cornelis, medal and clasp.

Lieut. Genl. Fiddes, 42nd L. I., served at Indore 1805-6; Java 1811, medal; Burmah 1824-25, India medal.

Lieut. General Roberts, C. B., 1st En. B. F. served under Lord Lake in the Punjaub in 1805, when the army crossed the Sutledge in pursuit of Holkar and Ameer Khan in 1806; served in Bundlekund in 1807; at the siege of Komona and Gunnowree, in the Doab, under Genl. Dickens. In the Nepaul war 1814-15; at the Storm of Knullunga; commanded the 1st Batt. 13th N. I., in action at Peacock Hill, near the Fort of Jytuk, and was afterwards engaged at Birlake Tebee, medal; being on staff employ joined and marched with his Regt. to Bareilly, where it was sent to quell the insurrection in April 1816. Served in Affghanistan 1838 to 1841; commanded the 4th Brig. of the army of the Indus: present at the storm and capture of Ghuznee succeeding *Sir* R. Sale in the command of the Fortress; caused the capture of Hyder Khan, the Governor of the Fortress and son of Dost Mahommed Khan, for which he received the thanks of the Commander-in-Chief, medal and C. B.; afterwards commanded the Shah's Troops, 2nd class Doranee order. In 1842 commanded the 4th Brig. of the army of Reserve.

Lieut. Genl. Wallington, 18th N. I., served at the siege and capture of Bhurtpore, India medal.

Maj. Genl. Oliver, 37th N. I., served during the Nepal war 1815, India medal.

Maj. Genl. Scott, 30th N. I., served in Bundelkund 1810-11, and during the Nepal war 1814-15, (severely wounded,) India medal.

Lieut. Genl. Hall, C. B., 21st N. I., served at the siege and capture of Bhurtpore, India medal.

Maj. Genl. Paul, 29th N. I., served at the capture of the Cape of Good Hope in 1805-6, also at the capture of the Isle of France in 1810-11: served during the Goorka campaigns of 1814-15-16, including the affairs of Jeetghur and Brootwal, in the Mahratta campaign of 1817-18: present at the capture of Mundlah: served with the Volunteer Battalion, ordered to Ceylon in 1818-19, and with the 1st Grenadier Battn. at Arracan in 1825-26, India medal.

Lieut. Genl. *Sir* G. P. Wymer, K. C. B., 38th N. I., served during the Nepal war 1814-15, India medal, and in Affghanistan 1839-40-41-42: present throughout the operations of the Candahar force under the command of Genl. Nott, medal, C. B., and A. D. C. to the Queen.

Lieut. Genl. Monteath Douglas, C. B., 35th N. I., has received three gun shot wounds, two sabre cuts and one spear wound: served in Bundelkund 1809-10: Nepal war 1814: present at the assault of the Timlee Pass, and the attack on Kulinger: also the capture of Jountgurh, Chumnagurh and Sreenuggur 1815, Bikaneer 1813: Mhairwarrah 1820: siege of Bhurtpore, 1826, India medal and clasp: commanded the Corps throughout the campaign in Affghanistan, from 1838 to 1842: storm and capture of Ghuznee, medal, 3rd class Dooranee order and C. B.: forcing the Khoord Caubul and Jugdulluck Passes: defence of Jellalabad, terminating with the general action and defeat of Akbar Khan, 7th April 1842: medal and A. D. C. to the Queen, present with the force under Genl. Pollock in all the operations leading to the re-occupation of Caubul, including those in the Mazeena Valley, medal.

Maj. Genl. Tulloch, C. B., 51st N. I., served at the Cape of Good Hope 1806, Bhowaree 1809, Bundelkund 1810, Java 1811, medal and clasp, Mahrattah war 1816-17, including the battle of Nagpore, and subsequent storm of that city, India medal; Arracan 1825; with the force under Genl. Pollock in Affghanistan 1842: present at the forcing of the Khyber Pass, and the different engagements leading to the re-occupation of Caubul, assault and capture of Istaliff, medal and C. B.

Maj. Genl. Stuart, C. B., 34th N. I., served during the Nepal war 1814; present at the assault of Kalunga, India medal; battle of Maharajpore, bronze star; and throughout the Sutledge campaign, including the action of Moodkee, medal and C. B.

Maj. Genl. Hewitt, 27th N. I., served with the expedition to Java 1811, medal, and during the Burmese war 1824-25-26. India medal,

Major Genl. J. Home, 57th N. I., served at the siege and capture of Bhurtpore 1825-26, India medal.

Maj. Genl. Lloyd, C. B., 28th N. I., served in China 1808, Java 1811, medal, Pindaree war 1817, Assam, India medal, and China 1840-42, medal and C. B.

Major Genl. Blackall, 2nd En. B. F. served at Hattrass Pindaree war 1817-18; Cole campaign 1832-33.

Major Genl. Eckford, C. B., 56th N. I., served with Sir Home Popham's expedition: present at the bombardment of Boulogne and Havre de Grace, and subsequent destruction of the French flotilla (as Midshipman of H. M.'s Frigate *Greyhound:*) at the capture of Chamur and neighbouring parts in Bundelkund 1806-07: taking of Java 1811: battle of Cornelis: and assault of Djokjucurta 1812, medal: siege and capture of Bhurtpore, India medal: in Affghanistan, with the force under Genl. Pollock: during the campaign on the Sutledge, and in command of a Brigade with the army of the Punjaub at the passage of the Chenab and action of Sadoolapore, medal and C. B.

Major General Hervey, C. B., 52nd N. I, served during the Nepal campaign 1814-15, India medal, Jubbulpore 1817, Mahrattah campaign 1817-18, siege and capture of Mundella 1818, commanded 1st Infy. Brigade during the siege and operations in the vicinity of Mooltan, commanded the force at the storming of the Dhurmsalah on the 12th Sept. 48, the whole of the reserves on the 7th November 48, or battle of Sooruj-khoond, and the right reserve on the storming and capture of the City of Mooltan, commanded the 1st Infy. Brigade in the actions at Goojerat on the 21st February 1849, medal, 2 clasps and C. B.

Maj. Genl. Pemberton 62nd N. I., served with the expedition to Java 1811: present at the storm and capture of Cornelis, medal.

Maj. Genl. Riley 47th N. I., served during the Nepal war 1814-15, wounded, India medal; Pindaree campaign 1817-18, and at the battle of Maharajpore, bronze star.

Maj. Genl. Richmond 24th N. I. was at the siege of Kalinger in 1811; in the Nepal war 1814-15; at the assault on Kalunga, at Nalagurh, wounded, and Nahun; at the siege and capture of Bhurtpore 1826, India medal and clasp; commanded the Regt. in the Affghan campaign of 1842, including the engagement in the Mazeena valley; that of Tazeen (where he commanded the rear guard) and the advance on Caubul, medal and C. B.

INFANTRY.—*Continued.*

Maj. Genl. Godby, C. B., 55th N. I., served during the Nepal war 1815-16, Cuttack 1817-18-19: siege and capture of Bhurtpore, (severely wounded,) India medal: campaign on the Sutledge, including the battle of Alliwal, medal and C.B.: and in command of a Brigade, with the army of the Punjaub at the action of Chillianwalla, medal: A. D. C. to the Queen.

Major Genl. Wilkinson, C. B., 6th En. Regt. served during the campaign on the Sutledge: and commanded a Brigade at the action of Sobraon, medal and C. B.

Maj. Genl. Marshall 32nd N. I., served at the siege and capture of Bhurtpore, India medal.

Maj. Genl. Graham 67th N. I., was appointed an Ensign by *Sir* David Baird, in the Battalion of Company's recruits which served with the army under his command, and was present at the capture of the Cape of Good Hope in 1805.

Maj. Genl. Carnegy, C. B. 15th N. I., served at Kemaoon 1815: Hattrass 1817; Mahratta campaign 1817-18; siege and capture of Bhurtpore 1826, India medal: during the campaign on the Sutledge, medal; and commanded the 5th Brigade of the army of the Punjaub at the action of Goojerat, medal and C. B.

Major General Tomkyns, 19th N. I., served during the Mahrattah war in 1817-18.

Maj. Genl. Lane, C.B., 5th En. Regt. served at the storming of the Palace of Dehlee 1809; throughout the Nepal campaign 1814-15; Mahrattah war 1817-18, including the siege and capture of Hattrass, Dhumonee and Ghurry Mundlah; siege and capture of Asseergurh 1819; against the Bheels 1823; Burmese war 1825-26, India medal; and with the force in Affghanistan under Genl. Nott; commanded at the defence of Candahar 10th March 1842, and present at the different operations leading to the re-occupation of Caubul by the Candahar Division, medal and C. B.

Maj. Genl. Gairdner, C. B., 63rd N. I., served in the campaign against the Bhuttees 1810-11: Oude 1812: storm of Nyabusty: throughout the Rewah campaign 1813-14: successfully led the storm of the fort of Etar, (wounded:) served in the 2nd campaign against Nepal under General Nicholls: present at the suppression of the rebellion at Bareilly 1816: served throughout the last Mahratta and Pindaree wars 1816-17-18, and in Ava 1824-25-26: in the three general actions before Rangoon: the escalade and storm of numerous stockades, and general engagements before Donabew and Prome medal: commanded the 14th Regt. in the battle of Maharajpore, bronze star and C. B. and in the campaign on the Sutledge, including the action of Ferozeshuhur, medal.

Maj. Genl. Parsons, C.B., 50th N. I., served at the capture of the Isle of France 1810-11, Nepa campaign 1815-16, India medal, Pindaree war 1817-18, Rajpootanah 1820, with the army of the Indus 1839: present at the assault and capture of Ghuznee, (wounded) medal, Bt.Lt. Col. and 2nd class Dooranee order: battle of Punniar, bronze star: throughout the campaign on the Sutledge, including the actions of Moodkee, Ferozeshuhur and Sobraon, medal, 2 clasps and C. B.

Maj. Genl. T. Dickinson 10th N. I., served in the first Burmese war, commanded the Mug Levy, with the division under Brigadier General Morrison; served during the campaign on the Sutledge, medal; and during the Burmese war 1853, including the operations in the vicinity of Pegu, medal.

Maj. Genl. Cox 58th N. I., accompanied the 5th Volunteer Battn. during the expedition to Java 1811: present at the assault and capture of Fort Cornelis, medal; served at the siege and taking of Hattrass, Mahrattah campaign 1817, and in Oude 1822.

Maj. Genl. Hoggan, C. B., 45th N. I., served at the Nepal war 1815, medal: suppression of the in surrection at Bareilly 1816: Mahrattah campaign 1817-18: with the force under Genl. Pollock in Affghanistan: present at the forcing of the Khyber Pass, and the operations in the Mazeena Valley, medal: commanded a Brigade attached to the army of the Punjaub, and engaged at Ramnuggur, Sadoolapore, Chillianwalla and Goojerat, medal and C. B.

Maj. Genl. Hamilton, C. B., 59th N. I., was present at the action of Maharajpore, bronze star and C.B.: served throughout the campaign on the Sutledge, including the battle of Moodkee and Ferozeshuhur, medal and 1 clasp, and with the expedition against Kote Kangra.

Major General Huyshe, C. B., 3rd En. Regt. served in the Burmese campaign 1825, commanded the 26th Regt. Light Infantry throughout the operations in Affghanistan, under Major Genl. *Sir* George Pollock; present at the forcing of the Khyber Pass, actions at Mamoo Khail, (severely wounded), Jugdulluck and Tazeen, and the capture. of Istaliff, medal, Bt. Lt. Col. and C. B.

Maj. Genl. Warren 13th N. I. served at the siege of Bhurtpore, in 1826; commanded one of the Companies selected for the escalade at the Jungeena Gate; (severely wounded) India medal; served with the army of the Indus in Affghanistan in 1839, present at the assault and capture of Ghuznee, again severely wounded, medal, 3rd class Dooranee order, and Bt. Lt. Col.; Commanded the Bengal Brigade in the expeditionary force to Burmah under Maj. Genl. Godwin, C. B., present at the operations in the vicinity of Rangoon in April 1852, medal.

Maj. Genl. Lawrence 72nd N. I., served on board the *Astell* East India man in command of two guns on her Quarter Deck in a severe action fought in the Mosambique channel on the 3 July 1810, between three India men and two French frigates and a Corvette, served in the operations against and at the attack of the Fortress of Malown in the Nepaul war of 1814-15, served with the Reserve of the Grand Army during the Mahrattah Campaign of 1817-18-19, also against the Coles in 1835, and in command of a Brigade of all arms employed against the same Tribes in 1836-37, India medal.

Maj. Genl. Hicks, C. B., 70th N. I., commanded a Brigade throughout the Sutledge campaign, including the actions of Moodkee, Ferozeshuhur, Budiwal and Alliwal, medal, 2 clasps and C. B.

Major Genl. Caley 64th N. I., served during the Nepaul war 1814-15, medal; siege of Hattrass 1817: against the Mahrattahs 1817-1818: Saugor, Mundla and Asseergurh 1819; Bheel campaign 1824.

Major Genl. Stewart 41st N. I., served in Bundelkund 1809-10-11, Beekaneer, 1813 and Nepaul war 1814-15.

Major Genl. Dick 4th En. Regt. served in Rewah 1813, Mahrattah and Pindaree war 1817-18, including the reduction of Dhamony, and storm and capture of Ghurrah Mundlah: commanded the 56th Regt. N. I. at the battle of Maharajpore bronze star, and Bt. Lt. Col.

Major Genl. Pettingal 12th N. I., served at the taking of the Cape of Good Hope 1805; taking of the Mauritius 1810; assault of Kullunga in Oct. 1813, Nepaul War 1813-14, medal; Mahratta Campaign 1817-18, and Burmah war in 1824-25, medal.

Major Genl. Downing 39th N. I., served with the force employed under Brigr. Wheeler in the Punjaub, 1848-49, medal.

Major Genl. Sandys 36th N. I., served in the Nepal war of 1815-16, against insurgents in the Khoordah Districts in 1817-18, in 1824 as Deputy Assistant Qr. Mr. Genl. with Force under Brigr. Knox in Capture of Petty Forts in the Jeypore Territory 1827; Civil and Political Departments up to 1856.

Maj. Genl. Hawkins 2nd N. I., grs. served during the Mahrattah war 1817-18: in Oude 1819-20: siege and capture of Bhurtpore 1826, India medal: throughout the China war 1840-41-42-43: present at the first capture of Chusan, storming of Canton heights, and action of 30th May 1841, taking of Amoy, assault of heights at Chinhae, Ningpo, storm of Sigoun heights, Chupoo, Woosung, and Shanhaee, assault and capture of Chinkeangfoo, and advance to, and investment of Nankin, Bt. Lt. Col., medal and C. B.

Maj. Genl. Moule 33rd N. I., served during the Nepal campaign: 1815-16, and at the siege and capture of Bhurtpore 1826, medal and clasp.

INFANTRY.—Continued.

Maj. Genl. Bird 23rd N. I., served at the capture of the Island of Mauritius 1810: with the column under the command of Sir David Ochterlony during the Nepaul campaign 1816, and the force under Brigadier Nation in Oude 1816-17 India medal; Pindaree war 1817-18-19, Bundelkund 1821; Hurrianah 1824-25; against the Coles 1832-33, and throughout the campaign on the Sutledge including the battles of Moodkee Ferozeshuhur, Budiwal and Alliwal, medal, 2 clasps and Bt. Lieut. Col.

Major Genl. Corbett, C. B., 16th N. I., grs. served during the campaign in the Punjaub, and commanded the 25th Regt. at the actions of Sadoolapore, Chillianwalla and Goojerat, medal and C. B.

Major Genl. Sage 22ndN. I., served in Rewah 1812: Nepal war including the capture of Narragurreh, Burruya and the assault of the heights above Mukwanpore, medal: with the army of the Indus in Affghanistan; present at the storm and capture of Ghuznee, medal.

Col. Sheil, K.C. B. and K. L. S., 17th N. I., served at the siege and capture of Bhurtpore, India medal.

Col. Manson 44th N. I., served with the 2nd Volunteer Battalion at the capture of Mauritius in 1810 and in both campaigns against the Nepaulese. India medal.

Col. Jones 49th N. I., served in Burmah 1825-26.

Col. Gray 48th N. I., served during the Nepal war, at the siege and capture of Bhurtpore, India medal, and at Gureah Kote.

Maj. Genl. Nash, C. B., 46th N. I., served throughout the Nepal compaign 1814-15; present at the siege and surrender of Malown, medal; during the Mahratta war, including the storm and capture of the enemy's guns and camp 16 Dec. and City of Nagpore 24 Dec. 1817; siege and surrender of Asseerghur 1819; Lamba 1823; and throughout the campaign in Affghanistan 1839-40-41-42, including the assault and capture of Ghuznee 1839, medal; comded. the 43rd Lt.I. at the repulse of the enemy at Candahar, (slightly wounded 29 May 1842,) and storm and capture of Istaliff, medal; commanded the 43rd N.I. at the battle of Maharajpore, bronze star and Lt. Col., campaign on the Sutledge; present at the action of Sobraon, medal and C. B.; commanded the 72nd N. I. at the second siege and capture of Mooltan, led the right centre column at the storming of the suburbs of Mooltan, (wounded) medal.

Col. Steel, C. B., 67th N. I., served against the Garrows 1810, (wounded ;) served in the Light Infantry Volunteer Battalion in Java 1811; in the 2nd Bttn. 21st N. I. in Oude in 1817; in the 1st Lt. Infy. Bttn. in Arracan 1824-25; siege and storm of Bhurtpore 1826, India medal; commanded the 2nd Fusiliers with the army of the Punjaub during the campaign of 1848-49, including the affair at Ramnuggur 22nd Nov.; passage of the Chenab, and in the actions of Chillianwalla and Goojerat, also the subsequent pursuit of the Seikhs and Affghans by the force under *Sir* W. Gilbert, medal and C. B.

Col. Haldane 44th N. I,. served at the siege and capture of Bhurtpore 1826, India medal.

Colonel F. B. Corfield 5th Eu. Regt. served during the campaign in the Punjaub, including the actions of Chillianwalla and Goojerat, medal, clasp and Bt. Lieut. Colonel.

LIEUTENANT COLONELS.

Major Genl. Polwhele (Supy.) unattached. served in the Nepaul campaign 1816, India medal: with the expedition to Ceylon 1818: Burmese war 1824-25: present at the attack and capture of Mahatee and Arracan: throughout the Affghanistan campaign in 1839-40-41-42, and served as Asst. Adjutant General throughout the whole of the operations of the Candahar force under Genl. Nott, medal and Bt. Maj.: commanded the 42nd Regt. during the Sutledge campaign: present at the actions of Moodkee, Ferozeshuhur and Sobraon, (wounded) medal, 2 clasps and Bt. Lt. Col.

Maj. Genl. Birrell (Supy) unattached, served during the Burmese war 1825-26, medal, and with the army of the Indus in Affghanistan 1839-40: present at the assault and capture of Ghuznee, medal, and the operations in the Wuzeera Valley, 3rd class Dooranee Order: Ferozeshuhur (horse killed under him) and Sobraon, at Sobraon, he commanded a Brigade, medal, clasp and Bt. Lt. Col.

Lt. Col. Bt. Col. Matthie 21st N. I., served at the siege and capture of Bhurtpore, India medal; served also with the expedition to Burmah in 1852-53.

Lt. Col. Bt. Colonel Farquharson 46th N. I., served with the army of the Punjaub 1848-49: commanded the 8th Regt. throughout the operations in the vicinity, (including the storming of the Dhurmsalah 12th Sept. and action of Soorujkhoond 7th Nov.) and siege and surrender of Mooltan, and battle of Goojerat, (dangerously wounded) medal, clasp and Bt. Lt. Col.

Lt. Col. Bt. Col. Troup 6th Eu. Regt.. served against the Hill Tribes under Sir Colin Campbell, 1851-52.

Lt. Col. Bt. Col. Ramsay 35th L. I., served in the Burmese war 1824-25, and at Arracan.

Lt. Col. Bt. Col *Sir* A. Bogle 42nd L. I., served in the first Burmese war; present at the taking of the Fort of Rungpore in Assam and of the stockades of Duffa and Beessa, in the Now Dheeing in 1825, medal. At the defeat of the Dewanghiri (Bootan) Rajah and capture of his stockade at Sooban Kottah 1836. Served in the second Burmese war; present at the taking of Martaban and Rangoon, April 1852, severely wounded, medal. At the re-capture of Beeling stockade, April 1853.

Lt. Col. Bt. Col. Simpson 54th N. I., served in Command of a Force against the rebels in Hills North of Jullundur, 1848-49; present at the storming of the heights of "Umb" and subsequent occupation of Fort of "Oonah," medal.

Lt. Col. Bt. Col. Barstow 58th N. I., served during the Nepaul war 1814-15-16, and at the siege and capture of Bhurtpore, India medal, and in Affghanistan 1839, wounded.

Lt. Col. Bt. Col. W. R. Corfield 22nd N. I., was present at the siege and storm of Bhurtpore, India medal, employed in the Cole country in 1836-37: served with the army of the Indus from 1838-39-40: present at the storm and capture of Kelat 1839: battle of Maharajpore, bronze star: commanded, the 30th Regt. throughout the Punjaub campaign including the actions of Sadoolapore, Chillianwalla and Goojerat, and subsequent pursuit of the Seikhs and Affghans to Peshawur under General Gilbert, medal and Bt. Lt. Col.

Lt. Col. Bt. Col. Cumberlege 40th N. I., served during the Sutledge campaign, and was present at the battle of Sobraon, medal, and during the Punjaub campagin, medal.

Lt. Genl. Grant, C. B., (Supy.) unattached, served at Maharajpore, bronze star and Bt. Major: throughout the campaign on the Sutledge, including the battles of Moodkee (twice severely wounded) and Sobraon, medal and clasp, Bt. Lt. Col. C. B.: also with the army of the Punjaub: present at the passage of the Chenab, actions of Chilianwalla and Goojerat, medal and clasps.

Lt. Col. Bt. Colonel Shuldham 15th N. I., served with the expedition to China 1842-43, medal.

Lt. Col. Bt. Col. Butler, 11th N. I, served in the Punjaub 1848-49, with the force under Brigadier Wheeler, and were present at the assault of the heights of Dullah medals.

Lt. Col. Bt. Col. Sewell 25th N. I., served at the siege and capture of Bhurtpore, India medal.

Lt. Col. Bt. Colonel Jenkins 61st N. I., served during the Nepaul campaign, India medal.

INFANTRY.—*Continued.*

Lt. Col. Bt. Col. Burney 65th N. I., served in Sylhet 1824: throughout the operations in Affghanistan with the force under Genl. Nott, medal and Bt. Major, and with the army of the Sutledge, Sobraon, medal.

Lt. Col. Bt. Colonel Wintle 24th N. I., served with the force under Brigadier Wheeler in the Punjaub 1848-49, medal.

Lt. Col. Bt. Col. Kennedy 70th N. I., was present at the action of Maharajore, bronze star and served during the campaign on the Sutledge, medal.

Lt. Col. Bt. Colonel Sandeman 33rd N. I., commanded the Regiment throughout the Sutledge campaign 1845-46, at the battles of Ferozeshuhur and Sobraon, medal, clasp and Bt. Major.

Lt. Col. Bt. Col. McCausland C. B., 66th N. I., served with the army of Punjaub at Ramnuggur, passage of the Chenab, battles of Chillianwalla & Goojerat, (severely wounded,) medal, clasp, and Bt. Lieut. Col.

Lieut. Col. (Bt Col.) St. G. D. Showers C. B. 2nd En. B. F., commanded the 1st Infantry Brigade at the Battle of Badleeka Seraie. and during the operations before Delhi severely wounded in two places whilst commanding a column in a successful attack made on the enemy's Position on 12th August 1857, commanded the moveable column in the District of Delhi after the capture of the city C. B.

Lt. Col. Bt. Col. Troup 68th N. I., served against the Bheels 1827: throughout the operations in Affghanistan 39-40-41-42: storm and capture of Ghuznee, medal: taken prisoner during the retreat from Caubul, Jan. 42: commanded the 48th Regt. at the battle of Alliwal, medal and Bt. Major.

Lt. Col. Bt. Col. Lennox 63rd N. I., served throughout the operations in Affghanistan with the force under Genl. Nott 1839-40-41-42, medal: at Maharajpore, bronze star: during the campaign on the Sutledge, including the battle of Sobraon medal.

Lt. Col. Bt. Col. Welchman C. B. 1st En. B. F. served in Burmah in 1852-53; present at the relief of the garrison of Pegu 14th Dec. 1852 and operations in its vicinity, accompanied the Martaban column under the command of Maj. Genl. Sir W. S. Steel, K. C. B., to Thong Gheeu and Tonghoo, medal; Commanded the Regiment in the action fought at Badleeka Seraie on the 8th June 1857, and on the 23rd June in the Subzee Mundee, severely wounded.

Lt. Col. Bt. Col. Bygrave 31st N. I., served on the Sylhet frontier and in Arracan, during the Burmese war; joined the army of the Indus as Field Pay Master in Nov. 1838, and was employed in Affghanistan until the termination of the campaign in 1842; present at the storm and capture of Ghuznee, medal and 3rd class Dooranee order; taken prisoner by Mahomed Akbar Khan, during the retreat from Caubul; released 27th Sep. 1842.

Lt. Col. Bt. Col. W. F. Beatson 4th En. Regt. (Lieut.-General Turkish Army) was a Major General in the British Army in Turkey; served in Spain and was wounded in 1836, served in Bundelkund, Scinde and Deccan from 1838 to 1851, Turkey and the Crimea 1854-55, has received the Cross of San Fernando for services in Spain, the Sultan's Gold Medal for the Danube Campaign, the Crimean Medal with clasps for Balaclava, Inkerman and Sevastopol.

Lt. Col. Bt. Col. Houghton 16th N. I., (grs.) served at the siege and capture of Bhurtpore 1826, India medal: throughout the campaign, on the Sutledge, A. D. C. to Major Genl. Gilbert at the actions of Moodkee and Ferozeshuhur, Asst. Adjutant Genl. of the 2nd or General Gilbert's division at Sobraon, medal, 2 clasps and Bt. Major.

Lt. Col. Bt. Col. Landers 9th N. I., commanded the Bhopal Contingent in on engagement with a party of insurgents, 1846.

Lt. Col. Bt. Col. Templer 6th En. Regt. served in the Nepaul war, India medal.

Lt. Col. Bt. Col. Graham 29th N. I., served in Rajpootanah 1820-21, and against the Coles 1832-33.

Lt. Col. Mitchell 56th N. I. served against the insurgents at Punjaubee in Bundelkund in 1842, and throughout the Punwar campaign, including the passage of the Chenab and battle of Goojerat, medal.

Lt. Col. Bt. Col. Garrett 64th N. I., served against the Bheels 1857.

Lt. Col. Bt. Col. Halkett, C. B. 20th N. I., served with the 2nd Lt. Infy. Battalion during the Burmese war in 1825-26; present at the assault and capture of Arracan, India medal; throughout the campaign in Affghanistan 1839 to 1842, including the assault and capture of Ghuznee, medal, and 3rd class Dooranee order; defence of Kelat-i-Ghilzie, medal, C. B. and Bt. Major; and the operations of the Candahar force leading to the re-occupation of Caubul, medal; present at the action of Maharajpore, bronze star.

Lt. Col. Bt. Colonel Boyd 59th N I., served in Arracan 1824-25, and at the siege of Bhurtpore 1826, India medal.

Major Genl. Birch, C. B., Supy. unattached, served at Maharajpore. bronze star and Bt. Major; throughout the Sutledge campaign, including the actions of Moodkee, Ferozeshuhur and Sobraon, medal, 2 clasps and Bt. Lt. Col.; employed with the army of the Punjaub; present at the actions of Chillianwalla and Goojerat, medal, clasp and C. B.

Major Genl. Graves, Supy. unattached, served in Cachar 1823-1824, (wounded:) Affghan campaign of 1839: present at the storm and capture of Ghuznee (severely wounded in two places) medal: also at the battle of Maharajpore, (severely wounded) bronze star and Bt. Major; commanded the 16th Grenadiers at the battle of Sobraon, medal and Lt Col.

Lt. Col. Bt. Col. Maling 18th N. I., served in Arracan in 1825-26, and during the Sutlej campaign; present to the battle of Sobraon medal.

Lt. Col. Bt. Col. Riddell 3rd En. Regt. served with 60th N. I. at the siege of Bhurtpore, India medal. Also during the campaign in Affghanistan 1842. medal and Bt. Major; commanded 3rd En. Regt. during the mutinies of 1857, 58, in the actions near Agra against the insurgent Neemuch Brigade 5th July, and against the Indore and Mhow mutineers 10th October 1857; commanded Mynpooree moveable column throughout the operations near and at Sherghur Ghat 16th May and the Agra column towards Dholpore, cooperating with the Central India Field Force under Sir H. Rose G. C. B. against Gwalior in June 1858.

Lt. Col. Bt. Col. Liptrap 45th N. I., served in the Burmese war, medal, including the attack and capture of Mahatee and Arracan: also during the campaign in Affghanistan 1839-40.

Lt. Col. Bt. Col. Hicks 69th N. I., served during the Burmese war 1825-26.

Lt. Col. Bt. Col. Taylor, 26th L. I., was present at the siege and capture of Bhurtpore, 1825-26, India medal; served throughout the whole of the operations in Affghanistan with the force under Major Genl. Pollock, medal; and during the campaign on the Sutledge, including the actions of Moodkee, Ferozeshuhur and Sobraon, medal, 2 clasps and Bt. Major.

Lt. Col. J. C. Hannyngton 34th N. I., served against the Coles 1832-33.

Lt. Col. Bt. Col. Spottiswoode 37th N. I., served at the siege and capture of Bhurtpore, India medal, and during the campaign in Affghanistan 1838-39.

Lt. Col. Dunmore 60th N. I., served in the Cole country 1836-37: present at the battle of Maharajpore, bronze star during the Punjaub campaign: present at the actions of Sadoolapore, Chillianwalla (wounded) and Goojerat, and subsequent pursuit of the Seikhs and Affghans to Peshawur under General Gilbert, medal.

Lt. Col. Bt. Col. Jamieson, 52nd N. I., (commanded the Regt. throughout the campaign of 1848-49,) served at the 1st and 2nd siege operations, and surrender of Mooltan, (including the repulse of the enemy's night attack on the British Camp at Mathe Ghol 17th August 1848, action of Soorujkhoond 7th November 1848, attack on the Suburbs of Mooltan, 27th December 1848, and battle of Goojerat; (wounded,) medal and clasp; Lt. Col. Bt. Major.

INFANTRY.—*Continued.*

Lt. Col. Campbell 30th N. I., served in the Caubul campaign 1842: present at the actions at the mouth of the Khyber Pass, in Jan. 1842, medal: with the army of the Punjaub 1848-49, as Maj. of Brigd. to the 3rd Infy. Brigade: at the battles of Sadoolapore (wounded) and Chillianwalla, (severely wounded) medal.

Lt. Col. Knyvett 38th N. I., served during the Bheel campaign under Col. Doveton.

Lt. Col. Bt. Col. Flemyng 36th N. I., served at the siege of Bhurtpore, India medal; commanded the Regt. during the campaign on the Sutledge, including the action of Alliwal, medal and Bt. Major; also with the army of the Punjaub, at the affair of Ramnuggur and actions of Sadoolapore and Chillianwalla, medal and Bt. Lt. Col.

Lieut. Col. Rice, 4th En. Regt. served with the Force under Major General *Sir* G. Pollock, during the Affghan campaign 1842; and also during the campaign on the Sutledge.

Lt. Col. Cooke 2nd N. I., (grs.) served throughout the campaign in Affghanistan with the force under Genl. Nott, 1840-41-42, medals: the former was also employed during the Cole war, 1832.

Lt. Col. Bt. Colonel Palmer 48th N. I., served against the Bheels 1827-28: during the operations in Affghanistan 1839-40-41, severely wounded in the Bholan Pass: present at the storm and capture of Ghuznee, medal: throughout the campaign on the Sutledge, including the battles of Moodkee, Ferozeshuhur, (horse killed) (in which engagements he commanded the Regt.) and Alliwal, (wounded) medal, 2 clasps and Bt. Major: employed at the taking of Kote Kangra, and with the force under Brigdr. Genl. Wheeler, in the Punjaub, 1848-49, medal.

Lt. Col. Bt. Col. Darvall 57th N. I., served in the Burmese war, medal.

Lt. Col. Ramsay 74th N. I., served at the siege and capture of Bhurtpore, India medal, and in Burmah 1852-53, medal.

Lt. Col. Bt. Col. Hodgson 12th N. I., served in the campaign of the Sutledge 1845-46, including the battle of Sobraon, (wounded), medal and clasp: served in the campaign of the Punjaub 1848-49, and engaged in the various affairs against the insurgents under Ram Sing, medal and Bt. Lt. Col. In 1853 commanded a force employed against the Hill Tribes, west of the Derajât.

Lt. Col. Bt. Col. Pott 47th N. I., served against the insurgents at Dek Kanal.

Maj. Genl. Innes (Supy.) unattached, served in Cachar 1824-25; at the battle of Maharajpore, bronze star and Bt. Major, and during the campaign on the Sutledge; present at the action of Ferozeshuhur, medal and Bt. Lt. Col.

Lt. Col. Hamilton 17th N. I., served during te Cole Campaign 1832-33.

Lt. Col. Hampton 50th N. I., served against the Coles 1832-33, also in the Punjaub, medal.

Lt. Col. Vetch 54th N. I., served with the 2nd Grenadier Battn. during the Burmese war of 1825-26, medal: against the Cossyahs in 1829-30: captured a Standard in the attack on the Dewangiri Rajah at Soobung Kottah in 1836.

Lt. Col. Bt Col, Thomson C. B., 3rd En. Regt. served during the campaign on the Sutledge; present at the action of Ferozeshuhur, medal and Bt. Major, also throughout the Indian mutinies of 1857-58; present during the siege of Delhi and capture of that City, 14th September 1857, C. B.

Lt. Col. Butler, 55th N. I. conducted two Military expeditions to the Augami Naga Hills, in 1845-46 and 1846-47.

Lt. Col. Martin 20th N. I. served during the Campaign in the Punjaub, including the actions of Chillianwallah and Goojerat, medal and clasp.

Lt. Col. Bt. Col. Robbins 15th N. I. served as Orderly Officer to Major Genl. Gilbert at the battles of Chillianwallah and Goojerat and subsequently as A. D. C. to the General in pursuit of the Seikhs and Affghans, medal and 2 clasps.

Lt. Col. Bt. Col. Mainwaring 16th N. I. (Grs.) served throughout the whole of the Affghan campaign in 1839-40-41-42: including the assault and capture of Ghuznee: in the subsequent year was engaged at the night attack at Baboo Kooshgoh and the destruction of Khoodawah; was one of the Garrison of Jellalabad and in the general action and defeat of Akbar Khan. and subsequent operations leading to the re-occupation of Caubul: attached to the left wing of the army of Gwalior and was present on the Staff at the battle of Punniar: present with the army on the Sutledge, including the battle of Sobraon: engaged with the army of the Punjaub, at the actions of Ramnuggur, Sadoolapore, Chillianwalla and Goojerat, 5 medals and a bronze star.

Lieut. Col. Matthews, 43rd L. I. served in Affghanistan, 1839-40-41-42, throughout the whole of the operations of the Candahar force and the taking of Istaliff, (wounded in the Jugdulluck Pass,) medal, battle of Maharajpore, bronze star, and the campaign on the Sutledge, including the action of Sobroan, medal.

Lieut. Col. Boyd, 68th N. I. served during the Sutledge campaign, including the battle of Sobroan, Medal, also served during the war in Burmah, 1852-53, medal.

Lieut. Col. Voyle, 39th N. I. served against the Bheels in 1837.

1st EUROPEAN BENGAL FUSILIERS.

Major Bt. Col. Seaton served in the campaign on the Sutledge including the battles of Ferozeshuhur and Sobraon, in the latter action he commanded the Regt. and his Horse was shot under him, medal, clasp and Bt. Major; served, in Burmah in 1852-53; present at the relief of the garrison of Pegu, 14th December 1853; and throughout the operations in the vicinity; accompanied the Martaban column under the command of General Steel, medal

Major Dennis served throughout the sutledge campaign in 1845-46, present at the actions of Ferozeshuhur and Sobraon under the command of Lord Hardinge G. C. B. and Sir Hugh Gough, G. C. B., (severely wounded in the latter engagement) medal and clasp, Burmah 1852-53-54; present at the recapture of Pegu, under the command of General Godwin C. B. 21st Nov. 1852, in command of 9th Company, part of the storming party against the stockade, medal; present with his Regiment at the battle of Badleeka Seraie under the command of Sir Henry Burnard K. C. B. on the 8th of June 1857, and in the operations against the city of Delhi; succeeded to the command of the Regiment on Col. Welchman being severely wounded on the 23rd June 1857, in the Subjee Mundee, when he was struck down by a Coup-de-Soleil; commanded the force at Duriabab, when 5 guns were captured from the Mutineers at Sahadutgunge on the 30th October 1858, by the Rajah Capurtullah contingent and one hundred and fifty men of the 1st En. B. F, the whole under the command of Capt. T. Wheler of the latter corps.

Capt. Bt. Lt. Col. Edwardes, C. B., served as A. D. C. to His Excellency the C. in C. during the campaign on the Sutledge, including the actions of Moodkee (severely wounded) and Sobraon, medal and clasp; commanded an Irregular force raised by himself on the Indus, with which, in conjunction with the troops of the Nawab of Bhawulpore, he twice defeated the army of Dewan Moolraj at Kineyree on the 18th June, and Suddoosam 1st July 1848, taking 10 guns, medal, C. B., and Local Major, and throughout the siege and operations in the vicinity of Mooltan, medal and clasps.

Capt. Bt. Major Greville served throughout the campaign on the Sutledge; present at the actions of Ferozeshuhur and Sobraon, medal and clasp. was present on the 8th June 57, at the battle of Badleeka Serie, severely wounded, commanded the Left Wing of the Regiment on the 12th Aug. 57, in an attack made on the Koodsee Baugh and Ludlow Castle, when his men captured two of the enemies guns, severely wounded. present at the siege and capture of Delhi and commanded the Right Wing which formed part of the storming party after his commander the gallant Major G. O. Jacob, fell mortally wounded in the breach, dangerously wounded.

Capt. (Bt. Major) Hume served in the campaign on the sutledge, including the actions of Ferozeshuhur and Sobraon 1845-46 in the latter engagement twice wounded once dangerously through the right lung, Medal and clasp; commanded the regiment in the Trans Goomtee operations under general Sir J. Outram G. C. B, and subsequently at the storm and capture of Lucknow, under the personal command of the Right Honorable Lord Clyde, Commander-in-chief, medal and clasp and Bt. Major, also commanded the Regiment with the Lucknow field force under Genl. Sir J. H. Grant K. C. B. likewise commanded the column at Durriabad, Oude, for nearly two months, during which period it was several times engaged with the rebels, when five Guns were captured from the enemy, besides completely routing the same.

Capt. Bt. Major Salusbury served at the battle of Ferozeshuhur (severely wounded) medal; Burmah 1852-53; present at the recapture of Pegu 21st Nov., relief of the garrison 14th December and the operations in its vicinity, medal, present with his Regiment at the storm and capture of Lucknow.

Capt. Palmer served throughout the campaign on the Sutledge; present at the actions of Ferozeshuhur and Sobraon, (slightly wounded) medal and clasp; Burmah 1852-53; present at the relief of the garrison of Pegu, 14th December 1853, accompanied the Martaban column under the command of General Steel, medal.

Capt. Bt. Major Brown served throughout the Sutledge campaign; present at the battles of Ferozeshuhur and Sobraon, medal and clasp, Burmah 1852-53; present at the recapture of Pegu 21st November, relief of its garrison and operations in the vicinity in December 1852, medal, present with his Regiment at the battle of Badleeka Seraie, 8th June 1857, also with four Companies of his Regiment in an attack made on the Erdgah on the 17th June under the command of Col. Tombs, C. B., Horse Artillery, in which one of the enemies Guns was captured, wounded in five places, one dangerously.

Capt. Lambert served at the battle of Sobraon, medal; Burmah 1852-53; present at the relief of the garrison of Pegu 14th December and the operations in its vicinity, accompanied the Martaban column, present at the storm and re-capture of Belin in April 1853, medal.

Capt. Wheler served during the campaign on the Sutledge; present at the actions of Budiwal, Alliwal and Sobraon, medal and clasp; with the Burmah Field force, present at the re-capture and relief of Pegu in Nov. and Dec. 1852, and served with the Martaban Column under Genl. Steel K. C. B; with Lord Clydes. army at the capture of Lucknow in March 1858, and commanded the force that defeated the Nusseerabad Brigade at Sahadutgunge on the 30th Oct 1858, medals and clasps.

Capt. St. George served in the Sutledge campaign, includin. the battles of Moodkee, Ferozeshuhur, and Sobraon, medal and 3 clasps; served in Burmah in 1852-53, medal, present with his Regiment at the storm and capture of the City of Lucknow, dangerously wounded.

Capt. Bt Maj. Boisragonserved in the Burmesewar 1852-53'; present at the relief of the garrison of Pegu, 14th Dec. 1852, medal, present with the Kemaoon Battalion at the storm andcapture of Delhi, 14thSeptember 1857, severely wounded.

Capt. R. J. F. Hickey and 1st Lieut. Battye served in the Burmese war; present at the storming and re-capture of Pegu 21st November 1852 and relief of the Pegu garrison 14th December 1852, medals.

Capt. Parsons served in Burmah campaign during 1852-53 and 54; was present at the storm and re-capture of Pegu 21st Nov. 1852; also at the relief of the garrison of Pegu 14th Dec. 1852; and throughout the operations in the vicinity, medal, present with H. M. 64th Regiment in defending the Cantonments and Town of Cawnpore under the command of Genl. C. A. Windham, C. B., dangerously wounded.

1st Lt. Birch served in Burmah 1852-53; present at the relief of the garrison of Pegu 14th December 1852, and throughout the operations in the vicinity; accompanied the Martaban column under General Steel, medal.

1st Lt. Davison served in Burmah 1852-53; present at the relief of the garrison of Pegu 14th December 1852, and throughout the operations in the vicinity; accompanied the Martaban column and present at the storm and re-capture of Belin in April 1853, medal.

1st Lt. Maxwell served in Burmah 1852-53; present at the storm and re-capture of Pegu 21st November 1852, medal; also served as Depy. Assistant Quarter Master General to the Martaban Column under Genl. *Sir* Steel, K. C. B., on its advance to Tonghoo, also present as adjutant of his Regiment in the operations Trans Goomtee, under Sir J. Outram G. C. B. terminating in the final assault and Capture of Lucknow under the personal command of the Right Honorable Lord Clyde, Commander-in-Chief, medal and clasp and subsequent operations in Oude, acting as staff officer to the column at Duriabad, accompanying the same into action with the rebels on different occasions, when the rebels were totally defeated and their guns captured.

1st Lieut. Wemyss was present with his Regiment at the battle of Badleeka Seraie, 8th June 1857, and in some of the subsequent operations before Delhi, present at the siege and capture of that City, 14th September 1857, slightly wounded.

1st Lt. Morland served in Burmah 1852-53; present at the storm and re-capture of Pegu 21st November 1842; also at the relief of the garrison 14th December 1852; and throughout the operations in the vicinity, medal, present with Sir Henry Havelock's force at the relief of Lucknow also at the storm and capture of that City under the personal command of his Excellency Sir Colin Campbell, G. C. B.

1st Lt. Ingram served in Burmah 1852-53; present at the relief of the garrison 14th December 1852 and operations in the vicinity; accompanied the Martaban column under General Steel, medal.

1st Lt. McFarlane served in Burmah1852-53; present at the storm and recapture of Pegu, 21st Nov. 18,ep medal; present with his Regiment on the 8th June 1857 at the battle of Badleeka Seraie, in many of t52f subsequent engagements with the enemy before Delhi, present at the siege and capture of that City 14th Seho 1857, in all the operations under the command of Brigadiers Gerrard and Seaton, en route to Futtyghur, present at the storm and capture of Lucknow.

1st Lieut. Magniac served in Burmah 1852-53; present at the relief of the garrison of Pegu 14th December 1852, medal, with Genl. Wyndham throughout the attack by the Gwalior Rebels on Cawnpore 26th, 27th and 28th Nov 1857, with his Regiment at the capture of Lucknow in March 1858, and subsequent operations in Oude, medal and clasp.

1st Lieut. Daniell served in Burmah in 1852-53 present at the relief of the Garrison of Pegu, 14th Dec. 1852 and throughout the operations in the vicinity, accompanied the Martaban column under Genl. steel, medal; present under Sir Henry Burnard at the Battle of Budleeka Seraie on the 8th June 1857, in the affair under the Walls of Delhi on the 14th July 1857, under the Command of Brigadier General Chamberlain C. B. severely wounded; served at the siege and capture of Lucknow in March 1858, under the personal command of Lord Clyde, and in the subsequent operations in Oude, under Sir Hope Grant, K. C. B. medal and 2 clasps

1st Lieut. Lambert served in Burmah in 1852-53; accompanied the Martaban column under the command of General Steel, medal, present with his Regiment at the battle of Badleeka Seraie on the 8th June 1857, in some of the subsequent engagements under the walls of Delhi, and at Nazufgurh on the 24th July 1857, under the command of General Nicholson, present at the storm and capture of Delhi on 14th September 1857, slightly wounded.

1st Lieut. M. Hall served in Burmah during the Campaign in 1853 (medal) as assistant field engineer with General Sir H. Havelock's force, present at the actions of Mungulewar, Alumbaugh, assault of Lucknow and relief of the residency 25th September, during the siege of Lucknow from that date till the 23rd Nov. 1857, at the storming of the Herukannah 16th Nov., with the force at the Alumbaugh, under Sir J. Outram G. C. B., till the 8th June 1858, with his Regiment at the capture of Lucknow in March 1858, and subsequent operations in Oude, medal and clasps.

1st Lieut. Money served in Burmah during the campaign of 1853-54, brought down a detachment of the Regiment to Delhi 1st July 1857, was present in all the subsequent engagements under the walls of Delhi and at the storm and capture from 14th to 20th Sept. 1857; was detachment staff officer to Colonel Gerrard's column, present at Narnoul (horse shot under him) and as Adjutant to the Regiment in all the operations under Brigadier Sir Thomas Seaton K. C. B. including the actions of Gungeree, Puttealee and Mynpoorie, was present with the Regiment at Alumbaugh and the Trans Goomtee operations under Sir Jas. Outram, G. C. B. at the storm and capture of Lucknow and with Sir J. Hope Grants' column at the affair of Bharrie.

1st Lieut. Butler present with his Regiment from the 10th of June 1857, in all the engagements under the walls of Delhi, including the affair under Brigadier General Nicholson on the 24th July 1857, present at the storm and capture of Delhi 14th Sept. 1857, slightly wounded; present with the columns under Brigadiers John Grant Gerrard, and Sir Thomas Seaton K. C. B. including the actions of Gungeeree 14th Dec. 1857, Puttialee 17th Dec. 1857, and Mynpoorie 27th Dec. 1857, en route to Futtyghur, present at the storm and capture of Lucknow under Lord Clyde, Swam the River Goomtee under a heavy fire and inspected the Enemys entrenchments "Victoria Cross" and served in the subsequent operations in Oude under Sir Hope Grant, K. C. B., medal and 2 clasps.

1st Lieut. Newton Wallace present with the Regiment at the battle of Badleeka Seraie 8th June 1857, in all the subsequent operations under the walls of Delhi including the affair in the rear of camp 19th of June 1857, and under Genl. Nicholson at Nazufghur on the 24th of July 1857, present at the storm and capture of Delhi 14th Sept. 1857, served in the Columns under the Command of Brigadiers John Grant Gerrard and Sir Thomas Seaton K. C. B., present at the actions of Narnoul 16th Nov. 1857, Gungerree 14th Dec. 1857, Puttiallee 17th Dec. 1857, and Mynpoorie 27th Dec. 1857, En route to Futtyghur; present with Lord Clydes' Army at the siege and capture of Lucknow in March 1858, and subsequent operations in Oude under Sir Hope Grant K. C. B. medal and 2 clasps.

1st Lieut. Owen present at the battle of Badleeka Seraie, in all the subsequent engagements under the walls of Delhi, including the affair of Nazufghur, present at the storm and capture of Delhi 14th September 1857, dangerously wounded.

1st Lieut. Nelson Ellis present with his Regiment under the command of Sir Henry Burnard at the action of Badleeka Seraie 8th June 1857 (severely wounded.) present in some of the subsequent engagements under the walls of Delhi, present with the column under the command of Brigadier John Grant Gerrard at the action of Narnoul 16th Nov. 1857, also with the column under the command of Sir Thomas Seaton K. C. B. at the actions of Gungeeree 14th December 1857, Puttiallee 17th Decr. 1857 Mynpoorie 27th Dec. 1857, present with Lord Clyde's army at the storm and capture of Lucknow March 1858 "wounded" and in the subsequent operations in Oude under Sir Hope Grant K. C. B. medal and 2 clasps.

1st Lieut. Chapman served throughout the siege of Delhi; present at the battle of Badleeka Seraie; was present with the columns under Col. Gerrard and Sir Thoms Seaton K. C. B., served with Lord Clyde's army at the siege and capture of Lucknow and the subsequent operations in Oude.

1st Lieut. Jervis present with H. M. 82nd Regiment in the defence of the Town and cantonments of Cawnpore under the command of General C. Ash. Windham, C. B., present with his Regiment at the storm and capture of Lucknow.

1st Lieut. W. H. Warner was present with his Regiment at the battle of Badleeka Seraie, under the personal Command of Sir Henry Burnard in all the subsequent operations under the Walls of Delhi, including the affair under Genl. Nicholson at Nuzufghur 24th July 1857, up to the assualt and capture of that City on the 14th of September 1857, served wih his Regt. in the columns under the command of Brgadiers John Grant Gerrard and Sir Thomas Seaton K. C. B., present at the action of Narnoul 16th Nov. 1857. Gungeeree 14th Dec. 1857, Puttiallee 17th Dec. 1857, and Mynpoorie 27th Dec. 1857; present with the Army under the Right Hon'ble Lord Clyde at the storm and capture of Lucknow in March 1858, and all the subsequent operations in Oude under Sir Hope Grant, K. C. B., medal and 2 clasps.

1st Lieut. Partridge served with the Central India field force under Major General Sir. Hugh Rose, G. C. B., 1857-58; was present with the 2nd Brigade in all the engagements in the Saugor district, present at the siege and capture of Jhansi, Battles of Baitwa and Koonch, actions at and in front of Calpee; present with his Regiment in some of the subsequent operations in Oude.

2ND REGIMENT EUROPEAN BENGAL FUSILIERS.

Major Liptrott served with the force under Genl. Pollock, throughout the operations in Affghanistan 1842, medal; served also during the campaign on the Sutledge; present at the battle of Alliwal (horse shot under him,) medal.

Major Bt. Lt. Col. Sherwill served throughout the campaign in the Punjaub; present at the affair of Ramnuggur; passage of the Chenab, battles of Chillianwalla, Goojerat, and subsequent pursuit of the Seikhs and Affghans, and occupation of Peshawur by Genl. Gilbert s force, medal, clasp and Bt. Major.

Capt. Bt. Majors Mackenzie, and Harris, Captain Tronson Lieutenants Clark, Hamilton, (charger killed under him at Goojerat,) Toogood, Becher, Blair, Trotter and Matheson served with the army of the Punjaub 1848-49; present at Ramnuggur and at the passage of the Chenab; actions of Chillianwalla and Goojerat, (in which latter engagement Lieuts. Toogood and Matheson were wounded,) and subsequent pursuit of the Seikhs and Affghans by the force under Genl. Gilbert, medals and clasps;

Capt. Bt. Lt. Colonel Green, C. B., served against the Hill Tribes in Scinde under Sir Charles Napier; and during the Punjaub campaign, present at the Battle of Goojerat, and advance on Peshawur by the force under General Gilbert medal; commanded the 2nd Punjab Infantry in the assault on, and capture of the Bozdar strong hold on the Derajat Frontier in March 1857 as well as in other affairs on the same Frontier between 1853 and 1857; also during the campaign in Hindustan in 1857-58; present at the siege, assault, (wounded) and capture of Delhi, including the Battle of Nujufghur, (Brevet Major) accompanied the moveable column under Colonel Greathed after the fall of Delhi; present at the battles of Bolundshur and Agra, the relief of the Lucknow Garrison, and the Battles of Cawnpore, and Khodagunge (near Futtyghur). Brevet Lieut. Colonel, the siege and capture of the City of Lucknow and the re-occupation of Bareilly, besides many other minor affairs. Medal and clasps and C. B.

Lieut. Toogood also served in the Crimea with the Turkish contingent during the occupation of Kertch by that Force.

Capt. Bt. Major Atkinson, and Captain Hawes served against the Hill Tribes in Scinde under *Sir* Charles Napier.

Capt. Bt. Major Boyd (wounded at Goojerat) Capts. Gaynor, Farrington. Campbell, and Baldwin served in the campaign against the Hill Tribes in Scinde under *Sir* Chas. Napier, also with the army of the Punjaub 1848-49; present at the passage of the Chenab; actions of Chillianwalla and Goojerat, and subsequent pursuit of the Seikhs and Affghans by the force under Genl. Gilbert, medals and clasps; commanded the Regt., at the battle of Badleeka Seraie, 8th June 1857 and during all the operations before Delhi, storm and capture of the City, 14th September 1857, Brevet Major.

Capt. Bleaymire served against the Hill Tribes in Scinde under Sir Charles Napier: with the army of the Punjaub 1848-49; present at Ramnuggur and at the passage of the Chenab; action of Chillianwalla, (severely wounded) and advance on Peshawur by the force under Genl. Gilbert, medal and clasp.

Capt. Harris was present with his regiment during the operations before Delhi storm and capture of the City on 14th September 1857, served in the moveable column in the district of Delhi under the command of Brigadier Showers, C. B.

Capt. Nightingale served during the campaign in the Punjaub; present at Ramnuggur and the passage of the Chenab, and battle of Chillianwalla, (very severely wounded) medal.

Capt. Paterson served throughout the Punjaub campaign of 1848-49; present at the affair before Ramnuggur, passage of the Chenab and battles of Chillianwalla and Goojerat, medal and clasps; served in Burma, 1853; present at the operations against the Rebel Chief Mong Goung Gie, medal and clasp.

Lieut. Bt. Capt. Elderton (wounded at Goojerat) and Lieut. McDowell served during the Punjaub campaign, including the affair of Ramnuggur, passage of the Chenab, and actions of Chillianwalla and Goojerat, medals and clasps. Lieut. Elderton also accompanied the army under Sir W. R. Gilbert in pursuit of the Seikhs and Affghans; was severely wounded at the assault of Delhi and was present during the whole of the siege. Lieut. Elderton was present with his Regiment, during the operations before Delhi, siege and capture of the City on 14th September 1857 (severely wounded).

Lieut. C. Clark served throughout the Punjab campaign of 1848-49; present at Ramnuggur, passage of the Chenab, Battles of Chillianwalla and Goojerat, and subsequent pursuit of the Seikhs and Affghans by the force under General Gilbert, medal and clasps; served in Burmah 1853; medal present with H. M's. 88th. Connaught Rangers in the defence of the town and cantonments of Cawnpoor under the command of General C. A. Windham C. B. 1857, very dangerously wounded.

Lieut. Becher commanded detachment 8th Irregular Cavalry, on the occasion of the repulse of the rebels from Huldwanie on 18th September 1857.

Lieut. Blair present with his regiment during all the operations before Delhi, including battle of Badleeka Seraie, 8th June 1857, dangerously wounded through the body.

Lieut. the Hon'ble F. B. Best served with Her Majesty's 64th Regiment under General Wyndham, during the siege of Cawnpore, also under Lord Clyde Commander-in-Chief, at the expulsion of the rebels from Cawnpore and the "Kalee Nuddee," on the road to Furrackabad.

Lieut. J. T. Harris present with his regiment during the operations before Delhi including battle of Badleeka Seraie, 8th June 1857, wounded through the thigh.

Lieut. Willes present with his regiment during the whole of the operations before Delhi, including battle of Badleeka Seraie, 8th June 1857, final storming and capture of the City on 14th September 1857, served in the moveable column under Brigadier Showers C. B. in the District of Delhi.

Lieut. K. J. W. Coghill served as Adjutant with the 2nd Bengal Fusiliers, during the operations before Delhi, including the battle of Badleeka Seraie 8th June 1857, and subsequent operations during the siege, present at the storming and capture of the City of Delhi on 14th September 1857, served in the moveable column under Brigadier Showers, C. B. in the Delhi district.

Lieut. Bishop served with H. M. 64th regiment under General Wyndham, during the siege of Cawnpore also, under Lord Clyde, Commander-in-Chief, at the expulsion of the rebels from Cawnpore, and the "Kalee Nuddee" on the road to Furrackabad 1857.

Lieut. Cadell served as Quarter Master with the 2nd Bengal Fusiliers, during the whole of the operations before Delhi, battle of Badleeka Serai, 8th June 1857, final assault and capture of the City, 14th Sept. 1857, and subsequent operations with the moveable column under Brigadier Showers, C. B. in the District of Delhi.

Lieut. Sir A. K. Lake present with his regiment during all the operations before Delhi, battle of Badleeka Serai 8th Juna 1857, final assault and capture of the City 14th Sept. 1857, subsequent operations with the moveable column under Brigadier Showers, C. B. in the District of Delhi.

Lieut. Hunter present with his regiment, during all the operations before Delhi, battle of Badleeka Serai, 8th June 1857, final assault and capture of the City on 14th September 1857, operations with the moveable column under Brigadier Showers, C. B. in the Distrct of Delhi.

Lieut. Mitchell presentwith his regiment, during all the operations before Delhi, storming, and capture of the City 14th Sept. 1857, operations with the moveable column in the District of Delhi.

Lieut. McNair present with his regiment, during all the operations before Delhi, final assault and capture of the City 14th Sept. 1857, subsequent operations in the District of Delhi with the meveable column under command of Brigadier Showers, C. B.

Lieut. Cantor present during the operations before Delhi, assault and capture of the City 14th Sept. 1857, served with the moveable column under command of Brigadier Showers, C. B. in the District of Delhi.

Lieut. Spalding served with H. M. 53rd Regiment against the rebels in Oudh, 1858

3RD EUROPEAN REGIMENT.

Major Duncan served throughout the campaign in Affghanistan from 1839 to 1842, including the operations in the vicinity of Candahar, advance on Caubul, and taking of Istaliff, medal; present also at the battle of Maharajpore, bronze star.

Major Phillips served throughout the operations in Affghanistan with the force under General Pollock (wounded in the Khyber Pass). medal.

Captain Dalton served throughout the Indian mutinies of 1857-58 on the S. W. Frontier.

Captain Patton served throughout the indian mutinies of 1857-58; present at the action near Agra against the Indore and Mhow mutineers on 10th October; also at Futtipore Sikree with the column under Col. H. Cotton, C. B., 28th October 1857.

INFANTRY.—*Continued.*

Captain Thomas served with the army of Gwalior, bronze star; also with the army of the Punjaub; present at the affair of Ramnugger, passage of Chenab, actions of Chillianwalla and Goojerat. and subsequent pursuit of the Seikhs and Affghans by the force under Genl. Gilbert, medal and clasps.

Captain Stevenson served with the column under Brigr. Showers, C. B., in the action at Dowsa on the 14th January 1859, against a body of rebels headed by Tantia Topee.

Captain Young accompanied the force under General Pollock into Affghanistan; present at the forcing of the Khyber Pass, and in different engagements leading to the reoccupation of Caubul, medal.

Captain Bacon served during the mutinies of 1857; present at the actions near Agra against the Neemuch insurgents 5th July; and against the Indore and Mhow mutineers 10th October, also in the engagement near Allyghur 24th August 1857.

Captain Reid served with H. M. 10th foot at the siege and surrender of Mooltan, and battle of Guzerat, medal and clasp.

Captain Chamberlain served during the campaign of the Sutledge.

Captain Forsyth served throughout the Punjaub campaign 1848-49. medal; also during the Indian mutinies of 1857: present at the action near Agra against the Neemuch insurgents 5th July and the battle of Agra 10th October 1857; served also with the column under Brigr. Showers, C. B., in the action at Dowsa 14th January 1859 against Tantia Topee.

Captain Ross served throughout the Sutledge campagin; present at the actions of Moodkee Ferozeshuhur and Sobraon, medal and clasps; also throughout the Punjaub campagin. medal; and throughout the mutinies of 1857-58. present at the battle of Agra 10th October 1857, and with the Agra column towards Gwalior in June 1858.

Captain Pond served throughout the Sutledge campaign including the action of Alliwal, medal; also throughout the Indian mutinies of 1857-58: present at the actions near Agra against the Neemuch mutineers 5th July (wounded) and against the Indore and Mhow insurgents 10th October; also with the force under Col. Cotton, C. B., at Futtipore Sikree, 28th October 1857, throughout the operations at Shreghur ghat on 16th May 1858 and with the Agra column towards Gwalior in June 1858-

Captain Fellowes served during the campaign on the Sutledge also during the Indian mutiny 1857, including the action near Agra on 5th July against the rebel Neemuch brigade, (wounded).

Lieut. Carnell served throughout the Punjaub campaign; present at the passage of the Chenab and battle of Goojerat, medal and clasp; also throughout the Indian mutinies 1857-58.

Lieut. Anderson served through the campaign in the Punjab, including the passage of the Chenab and the actions of Chillianwalla and Goojerat, medal and clasps; also throughout the Indian mutinies of 1857-58. present with the Meerut light Horse in several minor engagements and with the 3rd. E. R. at the battle of Agra 10th October 1857; also with Col. Cotton's column at Futtipore Sikree, and the Agra column towards Gwalior in June 1858, accompanied Brigr. Showers' column and present at the action of Dowsa 14th January 1859, against Tantia Topee.

Lieut. Prinsep served during the Indian mutinies of 1857-58, present at the battle of Agra 10th Octr. 1857.

Lieut. Stephenson served during the Indian mutinies including the action near Agra against the Neemuch rebels 5th July 1857.

Lieut. White served during the Sutlej campaign, present at the battle of Sobraon, medal and clasp; also throughout the Indian mutinies of 1857-58, including the actions near Agra 5th July and near Allyghur 24th Augt. 1857, the operations at Shereghur Ghat 16th May; also with the Agra column towards Gwalior in June 1858, present with column under Brigr. Showers C. B. in the action at Dowsa Jany 1859, against Tantia Topee.

Lieut. Blake served throughout the Indian mutinies, present in the actions near Agra against the Neemuch mutineers 5th July and the Indore and Mhow Rebels 10th. Octr. the affair at Maun Sing's garden near Allyghur 24th Augt. 1857 (mentioned in the despatch) and with Col. Riddell's column at Shereghur Ghat in May and towards Gwalior in June 1858.

Lieut. Templer was present with 23rd. N. I. in the force employed against the Afreedees in the Kohat Pass. February 1850.

Lieut. Forbes served during the Indian mutinies including the Battle of Agra 10th October, in the affair at Futtipore Sikree 28th October 1857, also with the Agra column towards Gwalior in June 1858.

Lieut. Maddock served during the Indian mutinies with H. M. 13th. L. I. present at the relief of Azimghur 6th April 1858.

Lieut. Orchard served during the mutinies 1857, present in the actions near Agra against the insurgent Neemuch Brigade 5th July and the Indore and Mhow mutineers 10th October 1857-

Lieut. Macpherson served throughout the Indian mutinies present at the actions near Agra against the Neemuch mutineers 5th July, and against the Indore and Mhow Rebels 10th October. Commanded a detachment of the Regt. under Brig. Sir T- Seaton K. C. B., at Gungeeree 14th December and Puttialee 18th Dec. 1857; also throughout the Operations at Shereghur Ghat in May and with the Agra column towards Gwalior June 1858.

Lieut. Stevenson present with the force under Brigr. Showers C. B. in the action at Dowsa 14th. January 1859 against Tantia Topee.

Lieut, Thomson served throughout the mutinies in India, including the Battle of Agra 10th October 1857 the operations at Shereghur Ghat in May 1858 - and with the Agra column towards Gwalior in June 1858-

Lieut. Saunders served throughout the Indian Mutinies 1857-58. including the action near Agra against the Neemuch Rebels 5th. July 1857. the operations at Shereghur Ghaut in May and the column from Agra towards Gwalior in June 1858.

Lieut. Wimberley served throughout the mutinies; present at the actions near Agra against the Neemuch mutineers 5th July and against the Indore and Mhow insurgents 10th October, in the engagement at Maun Sing's Garden near Allyghur 24th August; the affair at Futtipore Sikree with the force under Col. Cotton C. B., 28th October 1857 (slightly wounded) present also with the Mynpoore moveable column in the operation at Shereghur Ghaut (acting Adjutant) in May and with the Agra column towards Gwalior in June 1858.

Lieut. Mitford served throughout the Indian mutinies present at the actions near Agra of the 5th July and 10th. October 1857 and the affair at Futtipore Sikree with Col. Cotton's force 28th October, served also in several engagements with Hodson's Horse in Oude 1858.

Lieut. Holdsworth served throughout the mutinies including the action near Agra against the Neemuch mutineers and at the Battle of Agra 10th October; severely wounded by an explosion in an attack on the village of Chulhaslee 16th August; also with the column under Col Cotton. C. B., at Futtipore Sikree October, 1857 and with the Agra column towards Gwalor in June 1858.

Lieut. Birkett served through the mutiny in India, present in actions near Agra of the 5th July and 10th October, the engagement near Allyghur at Maun Sing's Garden in August and the affair at Futtipore Sikree under Col. Cotton C. B., also accompanied the Agra column towards Gwalior, June 1858.

Lieut. Goschen served throughout the Indian mutinies, present in the actions near Agra against the Neemuch mutineers, 5th July and the Indore and Mhow rebels, 10th October, also with the force under Brigr. Sir T. Seaton, K. C. B., at Gungeeree and Puttialee in December 1857, and with the Agra column towards Gwalior in June 1858.

Ensign Money served during the Indian mutinies of 1857-58, present with 79th Highlanders at the defence of Cawnpore under Genl. Windham and defeat of the Gwalior Rebels at that place, also at the subsequent operations including the affair at Suraj Ghat, the passage of the Kalee Nuddee and entry into Futtyghur, served with 1st E. B. F. during the operations ending in the assault and capture of Lucknow 21st March 1858, including the attack on the Kaisar Bagh palace; also with 3rd. E. R. (as Orderly Officer to Brigr. Showers, C.B.,) in the action at Dowsa against Tantia Topee, 14th January 1859.

Ens. Gerard served with the 13th L. I. during the Indian mutinies, present at the relief of Azimghur, with the force under Lord Mark Kerr 6th Apl. the action at Amorah, 1st Oct. and the attack on Jugdeespore, 26th October 1858.

4th EUROPEAN REGIMENT.

RIGHT WING.

Major Bt. Col. Burn served throughout the campaign in Affghanistan 1840-41-42, including the siege of Jellalabad and defeat of Akbar Khan, 7th April 1842, medal and Bt. Major; also at the re-occupation of Caubul, medal; served as Depy. Adjt. Genl. with the Force sent across the Jhelum in pursuit of Shere Singh and the Affghans, medal.

Capt. Brownlow was severely wounded in an engagement with the Momunds near Michnee, 1854.

Lieut. McDougall, was severely wounded in an engagement with the Hill Tribes, near Michnee in Au ust 1854

LEFT WING.

Capts. Marquis, and Merrick Lts. Cuyler, Higgins and Bruce severed in the Punjaub 1848-49, with the force under Brigadier Wheeler, and were present at the assault of the heights of Dullah, medals.

Capts. Caulfeild, Stuart, and Reynolds, served with the force under Brigadier Wheeler, employed in 1848-49, medals.

Capt. Ternan served at the action of Alliwal, medal, with the force under Brigadier Genl. Wheeler employed in the Punjaub 1848-49; present at the taking of the heights at Dullah, medal.

Lieut. Fisher served with the 23rd Punjab Infantry in the assault on and capture of the Bozdar stronghold, on the Derajat Frontier in March 1857, also during the campaign in Hindustan in 1857-58, present at the siege, assault and capture of Delhi, including the battle of Nuzufghur; accompanied the moveable column under Col. Greathed after the fall of Delhi; present at the battles of Boolundshuhur and Agra, the relief of the Lucknow garrison, the battles of Cawnpore and Khodagunge (near Futtyghur) the siege and capture of the City of Lucknow and the re-occupation of Bareilly, besides many other minor affairs, medal and clasps.

Lieutenant Tweedie was present at the emeute which attended the disarming and dispersion of tha Native Troops at Benares on the 4th of June 1857. (Severely wounded). Volunteering his Services, was attached to H. M. 78th Highlanders, and joined the Head-quarters of that Regiment in time to take part with Havelocks Column in the action at Bithoor, and in the several engagements leading to and ending in the first relief and subsequent defence of the Residency of Lucknow; served with General Outram's Force in the occupation of the entrenched position at Allumbagh, including the repulse of the numerous attacks, and in the operations ending in the final capture of Lucknow, was present with the Force under Lord Clyde, in the advance through Rohilcund, and re-capture of Bareilly.

5th EUROPEAN REGIMENT.

RIGHT WING.

Captains Slater, and Fenwick served in Affghanistan with Genl. Pollock's force in 1842, and were present in the different engagements leading to the re-occupation of Caubul, medals.

Captain Bt. Major A. B. Johnson served with the Force under *Sir* John Cheape at the attack on the Burmese Stockades, 19th March 1853, medal.

LEFT WING.

Capt. Bt. Major Gordon Capts. Rickards and Graham served with the force under Major Genl. Sir G. Pollock, during the Affghan campaign 1842, and also during the campaign on the Sutledge.

Capt. Cunningham served with the force under Major Genl. Pollock 1842, in the Affghan campaign, and during the Punjaub campaign; present at the action of Sadoolapore, medal.

Captains Nuttall, Hicks, Eckford, and Templer served during the Sutledge campaign.

6TH EUROPEAN REGIMENT.

RIGHT WING.

Captain Leigh served with 27th Regt. during the Sutledge campaign, medal.

Capt. Need, served with the 14th Irregular Cavalry during the Punjaub Campaign, medal.

Lieut. R. S. Robertson served with Col. Eyre's force in the Shahabad District in August 1857, present at the capture of Jugdespore, present at the siege and capture of Lucknow with Sir E. Lugard's force in the Shahabad district in 1858.

LEFT WING.

Major Bt. Lt. Col. Mayhew served as Asst. Adjt. Genl. Burmah Expedition; present at the taking of Martaban and operations in the vicinity and capture of Rangoon, Apl. and at Pegu, Dec. 1852, medal and Bt. Maj. Capts. Eliott, and Grindall and Lt. Hamilton served with the force under Genl. Whish, at the siege and surrender of Mooltan, and action of Goojerat, medals and clasps. Capt. Wroughton served in the Punjaub campaign 1849; present throughout the operations in the vicinity (including the attack on the Dhurmsalah, wounded) and siege and surrender of Mooltan and battle of Goojerat, medal and clasp.

Captains Wilson, Drew, and Oakes, Lts. Grant, and Griffiths served with the army of the Punjaub; throughout the operations in the vicinity, (including the attack on the Dhurmsalah and action of Sooruj-khoond) and the siege and surrender of Mooltan, and battle of Goojerat, Lieut. Turnbull was wounded in the attack on the Dhurmsalah and Lieut. Griffiths severely so at Goojerat. in which engagement also Capts. Wilson and Turner's horses were wounded, medals and clasps.

Capt. Bt. Major J. G. Stephen served in the Crimea with the Turkish Contingent from October 1855 to the close of the war, order of the Medjidie and Brevet Major.

2ND REGIMENT NATIVE INFANTRY (GRENADIERS).

Capt. Bt. Col. Travers served throughout the campaign in Affghanistan, 1840-41-42, during the latter part of which period he was attached to the 1st Regt. I. C. (wounded at Babawullee,) medal: and Brevet Major, commanded the Nusseree Battalion in the action of Sobraon, medal: commanded the Cavalry Bhopal Contingent in the attack on a party of Bhopal insurgents at Kallea Kearee, 6th Oct. 1846.

Capts. Boswell and Mills served with the force under Genl. Nott, during the campaign in Affghanistan, 1842. medals: were present at the action of Maharajpore, bronze stars and also employed throughout the campaign on the Sutledge, including the actions of Moodkee and Ferozeshuhur, medals and clasps; the former was also attached to the expedition against Kote Kangra.

Capt. Hamilton served at the action of Maharajpore, bronze star, also engaged against a body of insurgents at Gowrie in the Nizam's territory, 6th May 1849.

Capt. Burne served throughout the campaign on the Sutledge, including the actions of Moodkee and Ferozeshuhur, medal and clasp, and at the capture of Kote Kangra, also with the Burmah Force, present at the operations in the vicinity of Pegu.

Capt. James, and Bt. Maj. Garden served throughout the campaign on the Sutledge, including the actions of Moodkee and Ferozeshuhur, medals and clasps, and with the expedition against Kote Kangra. Major Garden was also present with the army of the Punjaub, at the battles of Shadoolapore, Chillianwalla and Goojerat, medal and clasp, and with the force under Brigr. Genl. Sir J. Cheape at the capture of the Burmese stockades, 19th March 1853.

Lieuts. Couper and Vander Gucht served with the expedition under Brigr. Wheeler, against Kote Kangra in 1846.

4TH REGIMENT OF NATIVE INFANTRY.

Maj. Pattenson, Capts. Fraser, D'Aguilar, Cumine and Stafford, Lieuts. Stothert, Currie, Packe and Elphinstone served with the force employed under Brigadier Wheeler in the Punjaub 1848-49, medals. Captains Farrington and Fraser Lieuts. Elphinstone, Orchard and Mitchell served against the rebels during the rebellion of 1857, medals.

Capt. Aikman served during the Sutledge campaign, present at the battle of Sobraon, medal; and with the force employed under Brigadier Genl. Wheeler in the Punjab 1848-49. medal, also at the siege of Delhi in 1857, and other engagements during the rebellion, medal, clasp and Victoria Cross.

Lieut. Packe served during the siege of Delhi in 1857, severely wounded. medal and clasp.

Lieut. Davidson volunteered and was permitted by Brigadier Sydney Cotton, Commanding the Force to do duty with the 1st Seikh Local Infantry in the affair near Michnee in 1854; also served with Col. Craigie's force against the Bussee Khail tribes in March 1855. served with the 1st Punjaub Rifles throughout the siege of Delhi, present at the action of Nuzufghur, the assault and final capture of the City also with the 1st Punjaub Rifles throughout the Rohilkund campaign, when the regiment formed part of Brigadier General Jone's column, medal and clasp.

9TH REGIMENT OF NATIVE INFANTRY.

10TH REGIMENT OF NATIVE INFANTRY.

Major Bt. Col. Coke, C. B. actions of Chillianwalla (horse shot under him,) and Goojerat; pursuit of the Seikh and Affghans under Genl. Gilbert, medal and clasp; with the force under Lt. Col. Bradshaw in the Eusofzie country in 1849,1850; also in the affairs in the Eusofzie country and Ranazie Valley in 1852; commanded 1st Punjaub Infantry at the attack on the Afreedees in the pass leading to Kohat under Brigadier Campbell. Wounded in a skirmish near the Kohat Pass, Nov. 1853. Dersummund May 1855, Summana Mountain September 1855, and Bozdar Hills March 1857. (wounded) commanded moveable column at Delhi from 4th July to 12th August when wounded at the capture of the guns at Ludlow castle, commanded a Brigade in Rohilkund, 1858.

Capt. Bt. Lt. Col. Reid C. B. served the Sirmoor Battalion throughout the campaign on the Sutledge, including the actions of Alliwal and Sobraon, in which latter engagement he brought the corps out of action on the death of Capt. Fisher, medal and clasp, and in Burmah 1852-53. medal; served with his Regiment the Sirmoon Battalion, throughout the siege of Delhi, commanded the main picquet at Hindoo Roas' House, from the 8th June till the 14th September 1857, during which period he sustained and defeated 26 separate attacks upon his position and two were made on that of the enemy viz. 17th June (when Kissengunge was taken and enemy's Batteries destroyed,) commanded the 4th column of attack on the morning of the 14th September severely wounded, Lt. Col. and C. B.

Capt. Bt. Major Thompson, Capts. Irwin, Willows, Martineau, Trenchard and Hildebrand, and Lieut. Browne, served in Burmah, 1852-53, medals.

Lieut. Bt. Capt. Houchen served during the campaign on the sutledge; present at the battle of Sobraon, medal.

Lieut. Armstrong was present as a volunteer with H. M. 49th at the attack on the Redan 18th June 1855, Crimea medal and clasp with 2nd Battalion Rifle Brigade, with Major General Wyndham before Cawnpore. 26th, 27th, 28th and 29th Nov. 1857, severely wounded, right leg amputated.

11TH REGIMENT OF NATIVE INFANTRY.

Major Bt. Col. Gordon served throughout the Sutledge campaign, including the actions of Moodkee, Froozeshuhur and Sobraon, medal, 2 clasps and Bt. Major.

Capt. Robertson was employed in the Commissariat Department during the Sutledge campaign, medal.

Capt. Law served throughout the Hill campaign in Scinde 1844-45, under Sir Charles Napier.

Captains Bird, Dennys Owen, Chambers, and Sage, and Lieut. Moller served during the campaign on the Sutledge, medals: they were also present at the capture of Kote Kangra 1846.

Capt. Lloyd was present at the action of Maharajpore, bronze star; also served during the Sutledge campaign, and with the expedition to Kote Kangra medal.

Lieut. Champion-Moller served with his Regiment throughout the Sutlej Campaign 1845-46 under Genl. Lord Gough G. C. B., medal; was present at the siege of Kote Kangra under Genl. Wheeler K. C. B.. present at the action of Badleeka Seraie on the 18th June 1857, and the subsequent advance on Delhi also at the affairs of the 12th (Horse wounded) 23rd and 30th June and 18th July and capture of Delhi.

Lieut. Graham served in Burmah 1852-53; present at the operations against Myah Toon near Donabew, March 1853, medal.

12TH REGIMENT OF NATIVE INFANTRY.

Major Ferris served in Burmah 1852-53, medal.

Major Ferris, and Capts. Wroughton, Hall, Scot, and Jackson served throughout the Sutledge campaign and were present at the action of Ferozeshuhur, medals.

Capt. Wroughton served in Burmah 1852-53, (horse shot under him) medal.

Capt. Adams served with the army of Gwalior: present at the action of Punniar, bronze star.

Capt. Stokes served throughout the Sutledge campaign, medal.

13TH REGIMENT OF NATIVE INFANTRY.

Capt. Bt. Maj. Germon and Capts. Waterman, Smyth, Hutchinson, and Bean, and Lieut. Aitken served throughout the Punjaub campaign; present at the passage of the Chenab and battle of Goojerat, medals and clasps.

INFANTRY.—*Continued.*

Capt. Gastrell served during the Punjaub campaign; present at the passage of the Chenab, and battles of Chillianwalla and Goojerat, medal and clasp.

Capt. Bt. Major Wilson C. B., served against the insurgents at Chirgong and Penwara in Bundelkund 1841-42, and with the army of the Punjaub, at the passage of the Chenab and action of Goojerat, medal.

14TH REGIMENT OF NATIVE INFANTRY.

Capt. Bt. Maj. Walsh served at Ferozeshuhur, (wounded) medal.

Capt. Showers served with the army of the Punjaub: present at the action of Goojerat, medal.

Capt. Bt. Col. Paton served at Maharajpore, bronze star: during the Sutledge campaign, including the actions of Ferozeshuhur and Sobraon, medal and clasp: employed at the capture of Khote Kangra, 1846, and with the Force under Brigr. Genl. Wheeler in the Punjaub in 1848; during the Punjaub campaign, present at the actions of Ramnuggur, passage of the Chenab, Sadoolapore and Chillianwalla, (severely wounded) medal and clasp; with the force employed against the Affreedees in the Kohat Pass, Feb. 1850.

Capts. Fullerton, Wood, (severely wounded at Ferozeshuhur), Thurburn and Perkins were present at Maharajpore, bronze stars; and served throughout the Sutledge campaign, including the action of Ferozeshuhur, medals. Capt. Thurburn commanded the Infy. Bhopal Contingent in the attack on a party of Bhopal insurgents at Kallia Kerie, 6 Oct. 1846.

Capt. Ryder and Lieut. Weld served at Ferozeshuhur(the latter being severely wounded,) medals.

Lieut. R. G. Sandeman served with Brigadier Showers' column in Delhi and Jujjur districts, was with the 1st Seikh Cavalry at Seih and capture of Lucknow, also at the affair at Moora Bagh wounded, served with columns under General Sir. Hope Grant and Brigadier Eveligh in Oude.

Lieut. Durand served in the campaign of 1857-58 against the mutineers including the actions at Cawnpore, 6th Dec. 57 Seriaghat, Kydgunj and Shumsabad, siege and fall of Lucknow and assault on the Martiniere, Bank's Bungalow, and Bigum's kotee, attack on the post of Rooya, action at Allyghur and attack and capture of Bareilly.

15TH REGIMENT OF NATIVE INFANTRY.

Captains. Loveday and Anderson, Captain Anderson twice severely wounded and horse shot under him at Chillianwalla) Capts. Brownlow and Cuppage, Lieut. Prichard served throughout the campaign in the Punjaub including the passage of the Chenab and the actions of Chillianwalla and Goojerat, medals.

Capt. Bt. Lt. Col. Montgomery served at the battle of Ferozeshuhur, medal.

Lieuts. Caunter and Magniac were engaged at the battle of Goojerat, medals.

Capt. Bt. Maj. Bagot served as A. D. C. to the Comr. in Chief Maharajpore, bronze star; and throughout the Sutledge campaign, including the actions of Moodkee, Ferozeshuhur and Sobraon, medal and 2 clasps: with the army of the Punjaub: present at the passage of the Chenab and battles of Chillianwalla and Goojerat, medal and clasp.

Capt. Macpherson served with the Expedition to Burmah. Present at the taking of Rangoon, Apl. 1852. medal.

Capt. Ellice (wounded at Chillianwalla-served at the passage of the Chenab and action of Chillianwalla, medals.

16TH REGIMENT OF NATIVE INFY. (GRS.)

Capt. Bt. Col. Chamberlain C. B. served throughout the Affghan campaign of 1839-40-41-42, during which he was attached to Christie's Corps of Irr. Cavalry: wounded on six different occasions, 2 medals: Ghuznee 1839, Candahar, Ghuznee and Caubul 1842: present with the Govr. Genl.'s Body-guard at the battle of Maharajpore bronze star; employed with the army of the Punjaub at the actions of Chillianwalla and Goojerat, medal and clasp.

Capt. Graydon served in the Affghan campaign of 1841-42: present at Maharajpore, (wounded); served also in the Sutledge campaign, 2 medals, 2 clasps and bronze star. Candahar, Ghuznee, Caubul 1842. Maharajpore and Moodkee, Ferozeshuhur and Sobraon.

Capt. Unwin served with Major Genl. Nott's force from Candahar to Caubul 1842: at Maharajpore and throughout the Sutledge campaign, 2 medals, 2 clasps and bronze star. Ghuznee, Caubul 1842. Maharajpore and Moodkee, Ferozeshuhur and Sobraon. Served with 29th Regt. N. I. against the rebels in Jullundur 1848-49, medal.

Capt. Mainwaring was present at the battle of Maharajpore, and served in the Sutledge campaign: medal, clasp and bronze star, Maharajpore and Moodkee, Ferozeshuhur and Sobraon.

Capains Dansey and O'Bryen served throughout the Sutledge campaign: Lieut. O'Bryen slightly wounded: they have each a medal and 2 clasps, Moodkee, Ferozeshuhur and Sobraon.

Lieut. Arthur Cory served on special duty with the Goorkha Army, under H. H. Jung Behadaur, during the campaign north of the Gogra including the capture of Goruckpore 6th Januray 1858, present during the subsequent operations in Oude and at the final siege and capture of Lucknow ,served with the 3rd Irregular Cavalry under General Whitlock in operations in Central India (medal and one clasp.)

Lieut. F. W. Boileau was engaged with the force under Genl. Van Cortlandt in the suppression of the mutiny in 1857 (medal) dangerously wounded.

17TH REGIMENT OF NATIVE INFANTRY.

Major Bt. Lt. Col. Burroughs was present a Budiwal 21st January 1846. Served as A. D. C. to Maj. Genl. *Sir* J. H. Littler, G. C. B., in the Sutledge campaign, and as Asst. Adjutant General of division in the campaign in the Punjaub; present at Ramnuggur 22nd Nov. 1848. and with the force under Bridgr Genl. Wheeler at the capture of the Heights of Dullah, 16th January 1849, medal.

Lieut. J. N. B. Hewett served with the 3rd Infantry Brigade before Delhi, present as officiating adjutant to the 4th Regt. Sikh Infantry during the repulse of the enemy's sortie on the 23rd June 1857, and in all the subsequent engagements before the walls of Delhie.

18TH REGIMENT OF NATIVE INFANTRY.

Major Nuthall surprized and captured the Narijan stockade in the Yooma Mountains with a party of the Arracan Battalion, January 6, 1853, (wounded) medal and Bt. Major; has received the thanks of the Governor General in Council for services with the Pegu Light Infantry on the several following occasions, in expelling the marauding bands under the chiefs Ngakcike and Nashean in the Rangoon district in 1853; under Ngapo in the Pegu district in 1853-54, and under Gouhggye in the Tharawaddy district in 1854.

Capt. Tombs served with the army of the Punjaub, present at the siege and surrender of Mooltan, and battle of Goojerat, medal and clasp.

Capt. Bt. Major Herbert assumed command of Attock 1st Sept. 1848, and defended it against the rebel force under Sirdar Chuttur Sing from 10th Nov. to 2nd Jan. 1849, medal, and Local Major in the Punjaub.

Capt. Bivar served at the taking of the Fort of Konomah in the Augami Naga Hills on the 10thDec. 1850.

Capts. Gowan, Nightingale, and Comber, and Lieut. Macdonald served in the Punjaub, 1848-49, medals.

19TH REGIMENT OF NATIVE INFANTRY.

Major Shute served throughout the Field Force before Delhi in 1857, as Depy. Asst. Qr. Mr. Genl. in the action of Badleeka Seraie, medal and Bt. Major.

20TH REGIMENT OF NATIVE INFANTRY.

Capt. Bt. Major Barchard and Capts. Earle, and Mackenzie and Lieutenant Reid, served during the campaign in the Punjaub, including the actions of Chillianwalla and Goojerat, medals and clasps.

Capt. Bt. Major Spence served during the campaign in Affghanistan 1839-40, medal.

Lieut. Shuldham served with the army of the Punjaub, at the battle of Goojerat, medal.

21ST REGIMENT OF NATIVE INFANTRY.

Major Milne served with the army of the Indus, on its march to Caubul, being attached to Shah Shoojah's force as Commissariat Officer; present at the assault and capture of Ghuznee, medal; and throughout the campaign in Affghanistan 1839-40-41-42, including the defence of Kelat-i-Ghilzie, medal; and the operations of the force under Genl. Nott, leading to the re-occupation of Caubul, medal.

Capt. Bt. Maj. Vaughan served as Aide-de-Camp to Major Genl. Sir John Littler, at the battle of Maharajpore, bronze star; served in the Crimea from October 1855, till the end of the war as Asst. Quarter Master General and as Depy. Quarter Master General of the Turkish Contingent.

22ND REGIMENT OF NATIVE INFANTRY.

Major Bt. Col. McPherson C. B., served as Brigade Major during the Punjaub campaign: present at the actions of Chillianwalla and Goojerat, medal and Bt. Major.

Capts. Drummond, Hicks, Smith, Morgan, and Fowle, Lieuts, Bacon, and Stewart served throughout the Punjaub campaign 1848-49, medals.

Capt. Bt. Major Hire served as A.D.C. to H.E. the Commander-in-Chief during the campaign in the Punjaub: present at the actions of Chillianwalla and Goojerat, medal.

Lieut. Duffin served throughout the Campaign on the sutledge: present at the action of Moodkee and Ferozeshuhur, medal and clasp.

23rd REGIMENT OF NATIVE INFANTRY.

Major Bt. Lt. Col. Cooper was present at the siege of Bhurtpore 1825-26, medal; and served with the force employed against the Affreedees in the Kohat Pass, Feb. 1851.

Capts. Trower and Bradford, Lieutenants Balderston, and Moore were present with the Regt. with the force employed against the Affreedees in the Kohat Pass, February 1850.

Lt. Fraser served at the action of Goojerat, medal and with the force employed against the Affreedees n the Kohat Pass, Feb. 1850.

24th REGIMENT OF NATIVE INFANTRY.

Major Shakespear and Capt. Doran served with the army of the Sutledge, and were present at the actions of Moodkee and Ferozeshuhur, medals and clasps.

Capts. Waddilove, Smith, Grubb, (slightly wounded at Ferozeshuhur) Earle and Irvine, served throughout the campaign on the Sutledge, including the actions of Moodkee, Ferozeshuhur, Budiwal and Alliwal, medals and clasps.

Capt. Lloyd served throughout the campaign on the Sutledge, including the battles of Moodkee, Ferozeshuhur, Budiwal and Alliwal, and against the insurgents in the Jullundur Dooab in 1848-49, medals and clasps.

Lieut. Lind commanded a detachment of the 5th Punjab Rifles in the expedition to Koorum with General Chamberlain, C, B., in 1856, served as 2nd in command, of the 5th P. R. at the action at Hoti Murdan, May 57, commanded "Lind's Mooltani Horse, in the action at Jhelum. 7th July 57, (slightly wounded, Horse killed and second Horse wounded,) proceeded to Delhi with General Nicholson's column, present at the battle of Nuzufghur August 1857 and the right attack on the 14th September 57, (charger wounded). at Narnool 18th Nov. (charger bayonetted) with General Penny C. B., column at Kukraoli, April 58 (slightly wounded and Horse cut down) with His Excellency the C. in C. in the operations before and capture of Bareillyin May 58 with Brigadier Coke C. B., column in the operations before Shahjehanpoor ending in the capture of Mohundi in the end of May 1858.

25th REGIMENT OF NATIVE INFANTRY.

Major Bt. Lt. Col. Clarke, Capt. Bt. Major Anderson, Captains Eagar, and Taylor served during the campaign in the Punjaub, and were present at the actions of Sadoolapore, Chillianwalla and Goojerat, medals. Capt. Clarke, Bt. Major.

Capt. Shakespear present at the siege and capture of the Fort and Town of Baloorgee in the Deccan in September 1841, and Adjutant of the 2nd Nizams' Cavalry, during the operations of the field force in that district; commanded the detachment of 3rd Nizams' Cavalry employed in the Golconda Zemindaree, February, March and April 1848; commanded the 3rd Nizams' Cavalry and the Detachment that captured the insurgent Seikhs at Homdah near Hingolee, January 1851; commanded the 5th Nizam's Cavalry and led the 30 dismounted troopers of that Regimeut who carried by assault the stokaded village of Eshwuntpoora or Devulgaon near Aurungabad 22rd September 1853, severely wounded; commanded the field force composed of Nagpore Irregular Troops employed in the Eastern frontier of the Raepore District and western frontier of the Sumbulpore District in January, Febuary and March 1858, forced the Singora Pass and Niswighat, defended by a body of the Sumbulpore rebels, 19th January 1858; commanded the field force composed of Nagpore Irregular Troops employed in the Chanda Zemindarees east of the Wynegunga and Prechestur rivers, May and June 1858.

Capt. Bt. Maj. R. P. Anderson served during the campaign in the Punjaub and was present at the actions of Sadoolapore, Chillianwallah and Goojerat, medal and two clasps; commanded a dangerous outpost throughout the entire siege of Lucknow, i. e. from the 30th June till the 22nd November 1857: was present at Cawnpore on its re-occupation by the rebles, and was Commissariat Officer with the Highland Brigade (under General Hope Grant) in the pursuit of the Gwalior rebles and capture of their guns at Seraighaut. Major Anderson went out as a guide to an assaulting party (under Col. Napier) in an attack on some guns in a garden at Lucknow, in which Sortie he was knocked down and slightly wounded in the head and face, he was also struck in the foot by a piece of a shell during the siege of Lucknow.

Lieut. Ireland commanded the Skirmishers of the Loodianah and Ferozepore Regiments of Sieks at the attack on Fort Tiroul in Oude on the 21st March 1858; commanded the Cavalry of the centre column of attack at the storming of the heights of Punwaree on the 29th Decr. 58, at which operation all the enemy's guns were taken and their leaders killed.

26th REGIMENT OF NATIVE INFANTRY.

Capt. Blagrave served with the army of the Sutledge, at the battle of Sobraon, medal.

Capt. Bt. Maj. Baugh, Capts. Cripps, and Mackenzie (severely wounded at Sobraon and Hall; served throughout the campaign in Affghanistan with the army under Genl. Pollock, medals; and also that on the Sutledge, including the actions of Moodkee, Ferozeshuhur and Sobraon, medals and clasps.

Capts. Emerson, Mocatta, and Baillie, Lts. White and Hind served throughout the campaign on the Sutledge, including the actions of Moodkee, Ferozeshuhur and Sobraon, medals and clasps.

Lieut. Whish served as a Volunteer at the siege of Mooltan, medal and clasp.

27TH REGIMENT OF NATIVE INFANTRY.

Maj. Simpson served with the army of the Indus in Affghanistan; present at the assault and capture of Ghuznie, medal; with the army of the Punjaub, medal, and with the Burmah Expedition; present at the capture of Rangoon, April 1852, medal.

Capt. Harris served in Affghanistan during the operations of 1841-42, medal.

Capts. Forbes and Seager served with the force under Genl. Pollock: present at the forcing of the Khyber Pass, medals: also during the campaign on the Sutledge, medals.

Capts. Langmore, Fraser, and Boileau and Hyndman served during the Sutledge campaign, medals.

28TH REGIMENT OF NATIVE INFANTRY.

Capt. Bt. Major Chamberlain served throughout the whole of the perations in Affghanistan 1839-40-41-42: present at the assault and capture of Ghuznee medal: with the force under Genl. Nott at Candahar, medal: and also with the army of the Punjaub at the actions of Chillianwalla and Goojerat, (wounded in a skirmish with a body of Seikh horsemen) medal.

Capt. Wright. served with the Army of the Punjaub at the battles of Chillianwallah and Goojerat, was present at the affair of Ramnuggur and passage of the Chenab and in the subsequent pursuit of the Seikhs and Affghans, by the force under Genl. Gilbert, medal and clasp.

Captain Gibbs served with the Army of the Punjaub 1848-49; present at the siege and surrender of Mooltan and the action of Goojerat, medal and clasp.

Lieut. Walters, present with the 1st Bn. B. F. at the battle of Badleeka Seraie on the 8th June 1857 also in some of the subsequent engagements, under the walls of Delhi.

Lieut. Bruce, was present with Brigr. General Franks' Division, at the engagement of Sultanpore, 23rd Feb. 1858 and at the siege and fall of Lucknow.

29TH REGIMENT OF NATIVE INFANTRY.

Capt. Bt. Major Reddie served with the army of the Indus: present at the assault and capture of Ghuznee, medals: and during the campaign in the Punjaub 1848-49, medal.

Capt. H. M. Davidson served against the rebles north of Jullundur 1848-49, present at the storming of the heights of Umb, and occupation of the Fort of Oonah, (medal) with the force under Sir Colin Campbell, K. C. B. in Eusofzaie and Ranezaie against the hill Tribes 1852-53, defence of Nainee Tal including the affair of Hulduonee, 17th September 1857.

Capts. Faddy, Gardiner, and Thomson, Lieut. Bt. Capt. Lamb, and Lieut. Smyly served against the rebels north of Jullundur, 1848-49: present at the storming of the heights of "Umb," and occupation of the Fort of "Oonah," medals. Capt. Faddy was severely wounded in an engagement with the insurgents under Ram Singh in the Jullundur Dooab.

Lieut. Millar served against the rebels north of Jullundur 1848 and 1849, present at the storming of the heights of Umb, and occupation of the Fort of Oonah medal, with the force under Sir Colin Campbell, K. C. B. in Eussofzaie and against the Momunds including the affair of Pung Pass 1851-52.

Lieut. Orman served with the force under Sir Colin Cambell K. C. B. in Eusofzaie and Ranezaie and against the Momunds and other Hill Tribes in 1851-52-53, defence of Nynee Tal, including the affair of Hulduonee 17th September 1857.

30TH REGIMENT OF NATIVE INFANTRY.

Major Bt. Lt. Col. Ewart and **Capt. Bt. Maj.** Morrieson served with the force in Affghanistan under Genl. Pollock: present at the engagement of the 19th, 23rd and 24th Jan. 42, and the forcing of the Khyber Pass, medals: during the campaign on the Sutledge, including the action of Alliwal medals, and with the army of the Punjaub, at the passaga of the Chenab, battles of Chillianwalla (both wounded) and Goojerat, and subsequent pursuit of the Seikhs and Affghans, medals.

Captain Fenwick served throughout the Caubul campaign of 1842: was present at the engagements of the 19th, 23rd and 24th January 1842, at the mouth of the Khyber Pass: present at the forcing of the Pass on the 5th April, medal: throughout the campaign on the Sutledge, including the action of Alliwal, medal: was also engaged with the army of the Punjaub, at the passage of the Chenab and battle of Chillianwalla, (very severely wounded) medal, served as Interpreter to the 2nd Battlion Rifle Brigade during the operations, leading to and the capture of Lucknow, medal

Capt. Bt. Major Dodgson served with the force under General Pollock: was present at the engagements of the 19th, 23rd and 24th January 1842, at the mouth of the Khyber Pass, and at the forcing of the Pass on the 5th April, medal: served throughout the campaign on the Sutledge, including the actions of Budiwal and Alliwal, medal.

Capt. Bishop served with the force under Genl. Pollock: present at the forcing of the Khyber Pass, medal: during the campaign on the Sutledge: also with the army of the Punjaub: present at the battles of Chillianwalla and Goojerat, medal.

Capts. Sage, and Swinhoe, and Lieut. Pierce served in the Sutledge campaign, including the action of Alliwal, medals, and with the army of the Punjaub: present at the passage of the Chenab: battles of Chillianwalla (Capt. Swinhoe and Lieut. Pierce wounded, the former severely) and Goojerat, and subsequent pursuit of the Seikhs and Affghans, with the force under Genl. Gilbert. medals.

Capt. Vincent served throughout the Sutledge campaign including the action of Alliwal, medals, also served at the taking of the Fort Komonah in the Augami Naga Hills, on the 10th Decr. 1850.

Lieuts. Wood and Leicester served in the Punjaub campaign, including the passage of the Chenaband battle of Chillianwalla, (both very severely wounded) medals.

31ST REGIMENT OF NATIVE INFANTRY.

Maj. Hampton served against the Coles, 36-37, in Affghanistan & at the capture of Kelat in 39: action of Maharajpore, bronze star: with the army of the Punjaub 48-49: present at the battles of Sadoolapore Chillianwalla and Goojerat, and in the subsequent pursuit of the Seikh army and occupation of Peshawur, medal and clasps: and with the force employed against the Affreedees in 1850. Capt. Bt. Major Legard was employed in the Cole country: also served with the army of the Indus: present at the capture of Kelat: engaged with the army of the Punjaub at the actions of Sadoolapore, Chillianwalla and Goojerat, and subsequent pursuit of the Seikhs and Affghans to Peshawur under General Gilbert, medal, served against the insurgent Sonthals in 1855; served with the regiment in the Saugor district during the rebellion of 1857-58.

Capt. Bt. Major Newbolt served with the army of the Indus in Affghanistan 1838-39-40: present at the storm and capture of Ghuznee, medal: during the campaign on the Sutledge and throughout the Punjaub campaign, including the passage of the Chenab, actions of Chillianwalla and Goojerat, and subsequent pursuit of the Seikhs and Affghans to Peshawur under General Gilbert, medal. Capt. Bt. Major Tickell served in the Cole country 1832-33-35-36-37. Capt. Roberts served in the Cole country 1836-37: Affghanistan 1839: present at the storm and capture of Kelat, and at the battle of Maharajpore, bronze star.

Capts. Smalpage and Davis were present at the battle of Maharajpore, bronze stars: served with the army of the Punjaub, including the passage of the Chenaub: present in the actions of Sadoolapore, Chillianwalla and Goojerat, and subsequent pursuit of the Seikhs and Affghans to Peshawur under Genl. Gilbert, medals and clasps: present with the expedition against the Affreedees in the Kohat Pass.

Capt. Bt. Major Legard, Capts. Roberts and Finch, Lieuts. Ellis, Dickins, Fellowes and Campbell, (wounded) served with the Regiment in the Saugor District during the rebellion of 1857-58.

Capt Finch served throughout the Gwalior campaign and present at the battle of Maharajpore 1843, bronze-star, in the second Punjab campaign and was present at Ramnuggur, passage of the Chenab, in the actions of Sadoolapore, Chillianwallah and Goojerat (medal and two clasps) and subsequent pursuit of the Seikhs and Affghans to Peshawur and occupation of Attock and Peshawur 1848-49; was also present with the force empoyed against the Affreedees in the Kohat Pass, under the late Genl. Sir J. Napier in 1850; employed against the insurgent Sonthals in 1855-56, present with his regiment during the whole of the mutiny of 1857-58, during the months of July, August and September 1857. Commanded and kept together a Detachment of 500 Native Troops with 2 guns, took the Fort, Treasure, and ammunition from a mutinous detachment of the 42nd Regt. N. L. I. at Dumoh, captured the town of Kamkheres (wounded) took the town and Fort of Hindooreah and 2 Guns, defeated the whole of the Shahghur Rajah's force on two different occasions when they attacked the Town of Dumoh, present at Tendukera storming the heights of Jalimpore, under Brigadier Wheler, occupation of Shahghur and several other skirmishes in Bundelkund, and Commanded at the taking of the town and heights of Bophail, the Fort and town of Patna and at the fight and re-occupation of the Fort Gurrakota and town of Hindunuggur.

Capt. Price, Lieut. Bt. Capt. Norman, Lieuts. Ellis, and Dickins, served with the army of the Punjaub, at the actions of Sadoolapore, Chillianwalla and Goojerat, medals and clasps: pursuit of the Seikhs and Affghans to Peshawur. Lt. Norman served against the Affreedees, Momunds, Gotman Kail, and other Hill tribes in 1850-51-52-53-54. Capt. Smalpage, Lts. Price, Norman, Dickins, Baker, Fellowes, Sitwell and Campbell served against the insurgent Sonthals in 1855.

32ND REGIMENT OF NATIVE INFANTRY.

Major Bt. Lt. Col. Swinton served in Arracan 1824: at the siege and capture of Bhurtpore 1826, India medal: China expedition 1842, medal.

Capt. Bt. Major Davidson served throughout the China expedition 1842, medal: as Comdt. of the 16th I. C. accompanied Brigdr. Genl. Wheeler's force: employed in the Punjaub 1848-49: present at the storm and capture of the Fort of Shahpore, and assault of the heights of Noorpore and Dullah, severely wounded in the latter engagement, medal. With the expedition under Col. Mackeson in 1852.53, commanded the left column of attack against the Hosunzais on the Black Mountain; was present in the affair with the Momunds near Michnee, 1854. On all these occasions Major Davidson volunteered his services.

Capt. James was engaged at Sobraon, (wounded) medal: also served with the army of the Punjaub: present at Ramnuggur, Sadoolapore, Chillianwalla and Goojerat, medal and clasps.

Capt. (Bt. Col.) Cavenagh seved with the 4th Irr. Cavy. at the battle of Maharajpore, (severely wounded, left leg amputated, horse shot under him,) bronze star: during the campaign on the Sutledge, (severely wounded at the action of Buddiwal,) medal.

Lieut. Gleig served during the Punjaub campaign: present at the passage of the Chenab and action of Chillianwalla., medal.

Lieut. Rannie served throughout the campaign in the Punjaub, including the passage of the Chenab and battles of Chillianwalla and Goojerat, medal and clasp.

Lt. Hill served during the Punjaub campaign 1848-49, with the force under Genl. Whish at the siege and surrender of Mooltan, medal.

33RD REGIMENT OF NATIVE INFANTRY.

Major Martin served in the Cole campaign 1832: Affghan campaign of 1842: present with the Regt. in every engagement from the Khyber Pass to Caubul, medal; Sutledge campaign 1845-46, including the battle of Sobraon, medal; and with the 4th Irr. Cavy. at the surrender of Kote Kangra.

Capt. Watson served with the Regiment throughout the Affghan campaign of 1842; present in every engagement from the Khyber to Caubul, medal.

Capt. Tulloh served throughout the Affghan campaign of 1842, with the Regt. in every engagement, medal: Sutledge campaign of 1845-46, including the battles of Ferozeshuhur (horse shot under him,) and Sobraon, (wounded), medal and clasp.

Capts. Shum and Twysden served throughout the Affghan campaign of 1842: both present at the forcing of the Khyber Pass and operations in the Mazeena valley, the latter also at the engagements in the advance on Caubul, medals: throughout the Sutledge campaign 1845-46, including the battles of Ferozeshuhur & Sobraon, medals and clasps.

Capts. RowDickson, and Stubbs served during the Sutledge campaign 1845-46, including the battles of Ferozeshuhur and Sobraon, medals and clasps.

Lieut. (Bt. Capt.) Johnson served during the Sutledge campaign: present at the action of Sobraon, medal.

34TH REGIMENT OF NATIVE INFANTRY.

Major Bt. Lt. Col. Timins served during the Cole Campaign 1832-33.
Captain Dewaal was present at the taking of Kote Kangra.
Capt. Smith served with the force under Brigdr General Wheeler in the Punjaub 1848-49, medal.
Capt. Baugh served throughout the campaign on the Sutledge, and was present at the actions of Moodkee, Ferozeshuhur and Sobraon, medal and 2 clasps.
Lieut. Bt. Capt. Bunbury served during the Sutledge campaign present at the battle of Ferozeshuhur, medal, and at the taking of Kote Kangra.

35TH REGIMENT OF NATIVE INFANTRY.

Major Bt. Col. Younghusband was present at the siege and capture of Bhurtpore, India medal: served in Affghanistan 1840-41-42: battle of Bameean, 3rd class Dooranee order: forcing the Khoord Cabul Pass, (severely wounded) and defence of Jellalabad, medal and Bt. Major.

Capt. Bt. Major Ramsay served in Affghanistan: present at the taking of Ghuznee, medal.

Capt. Bt. Major Bouverie, Capts. Trench, Metcalf, and Wiggins accompanied the force under Genl. Pollock: present at the forcing of the Khyber Pass, and in the different engagements leading to the re-occupation of Caubul, medals. Major Bouverie also served at Maharajpore, bronze star and throughout the Sutledge campaign, including the actions of Moodkee (in the latter part of which he commanded the Governor General's Body Guard and brought it off the field; Horse shot under him) Ferozeshuhur, Alliwal and Sobraon, medal and 3 clasps. Capt. Metcalf was present at the action fo Maharajpore, bronze star.

Lieut. J. P. Sherriff served with the 2nd Punjaub Infantry during the compaign in Hindustan in 1857-58; present at the siege, assault and capture of Delhi, including the battle of Nujufghur, accompanied the moveable column under Colonel Greathed, after the fall of Delhi, present at the battle of Boolundshuhur, was detached with a portion of the Regiment at Allyghur and subsequently commanded a mixed force in the Etawah district, where he had several engagements with the enemy, and on one occasion captured 5 guns after driving the enemy out of his position, for his conduct on this occasion he received the thanks of the Governor General, medal and clasps.

Lieut. Keen served with the 2nd Punjaub Infantry during the campaign in Hindustan in 1857-58, present at the siege, assault and capture of Delhi, accompanied the moveable column, under Colonel Greathed after the fall of Delhi; present at the battles of Boolundshuhur and Agra, the relief of the Lucknow garrison and the battles of Cawnpore and Khodagunge (near Futtyghur) the siege and capture of the City of Lucknow and the occupation of Bareilly besides many other minor affairs, medal and clasps.

Lieut. J. Watson served with the 2nd Punjaub Infantry during the campaign in Hindustan in 1857-58; accompained the moveable column under Colonel Greathed, after the fall of Delhi; present at the battles of Boolundshuhur and Agra and the relief of the Lucknow garrison, dangerously wounded, medal and clasps.

36TH REGIMENT OF NATIVE INFANTRY.

Major Faddy and Capt. Smalley, Lt. Bt. Capt. Auldjo (wounded both at Alliwal and Chillianwalla) served throughout the campaign on the Sutledge, including the action of Alliwal, medals, and with the army of the Punjaub at Ramnuggur, Sadoolapore, Chillianwalla and Goojerat, medals.

Capt, (Bt. Maj.) Garstin served during the Sutledge campaign, present at "Alliwal," (medal) and throughout the Punjaub campaign present at "Ramnuggur," "Sadoolahpore" (severely wounded) "Chillianwallah" and "Goojerat," (medal and clasp) served also as Dy. Asst. Qr. Mr. Gel. of the army at "Badleeka Serai" and throughout the siege of Delhi, with subsequent operations under Brigr. Showers against rebels and Mewatties, medal and Bt. Major.

Capt. Weston and Lieut. Godby served throughout the campaign on the Sutledge; present at the action of Alliwal, medals, and with the army of the Punjaub, at the skirmish of Ramnuggur and actions of Sadoolapore and Chillianwalla, (all wounded in the latter engagement,) medals and clasps, Capt. Weston served also with Col. Rowcroft's column, in Oude in 1858, (wounded) medal.

Capt. Stafford was present at the assault and capture of Delhi, wounded, succeeded to the command of the right wing and Head Quarters 1st European Bengal Fusiliers, to which he was attached, in the morning of the 14th Sept.; was transferred to the command of the 1st Punjaub Infantry on the 17th Sept. and remained with this Corps (in command) until the final evacuation of the City by the rebels; joined the Hurreeanah field force, under General Van Cortlandt, C. B. as Major of Brigade on 1st October, on 14th October was detached in command of the greater part of the field force to co-operate with Brigadier Showers, C. B., against Jhujjhur, was present at Narnoul on 16th November, in command of the same force, with Colonel Gerrard, when the Jodpore legion and other rebels were signally defeated in April 1858, was appointed Officiating Commandant of the 22rd Punjaub Infantry, and joined the Regiment as it entered Rohilcund; commanded it at Kukrowlee, when General Penny, C. B. was killed, and throughout the Rohilcund campaign under His Excellency the Commander-in-Chief, medal with clasp for Delhi.

Capt. Raban served during the campaign on the Sutledge, and was present at the action of Alliwal, medal.
Capt. Evatt served during the Sutledge campaign.
Lt. Bradford served throughout the campaign in the Punjaub; present at the skirmish of Ramnuggur, and actions of Sadoolapore, Chillianwalla and Goojerat, medal and two clasps.

37TH REGIMENT OF NATIVE INFANTRY.

Capt. Parrott served in Affghanistan with the force under Genl. Pollock, medal.

Capt. Bt. Col. Tytler C. B. served with the force under Genl. Pollock, (severely wounded at the mouth of the Khyber Pass :) during the campaign on the Sutledge as A.D.C. to His Excellency the C. in C.: present at the battles of Moodkee and Ferozeshuhur, and with the 9th Regt. I. C. at Sobraon, medal and 2 clasps, throughout the Punjaub campaign, including the passage of the Chenab, actions of Chillianwalla and Goojerat, and subsequent pursuit of the Seikhs and Affghans, medal, served as Asst. Quarter Master General to the force under Major General *Sir* H. Havelock in 1857, present at the actions of Futtehpore, Oung, Pandoo Nuddie. Cawnpore, Oanao, Buseerutgunge, Bhitoor, Mungulawar, and the 1st relief of Lucknow, severely wounded.

38TH REGIMENT OF NATIVE INFANTRY.

Major Tytler served during the whole of the operations in Scinde and Affghanistan 1839-40-41-42 and was present in the different engagements leading to the re-occupation of Caubul by the force under Genl. Nott, medals, also served at Maharajpore, 1843, bronze star, and was placed in charge of the Commissariat Dept. at Busse ean and Wudnee during the first Punjaub campaign.

Capts. Shelton, and Dennys served with the Candahar force throughout the operations leading to the re-occupation of Caubul, medals.

Capt. Bt. Maj. Cureton served as A. D. C. to Brigadier Genl. Cureton during the Punjaub campaign, and was present at the engagement of Ramnuggur: passage of the Chenab and battle of Goojerat: accompanied *Sir* Walter Gilbert's column in pursuit of the Seikh and Affghan army in 1849; capture of Attock and occupation of Peshawur, medal and clasp: served against the Sealkote Mutineers, under General Nicholson, and against the Gossina rebels in 1857; commanded the Mooltanee Regt. of Cavalry throughout the campaigns in Rohilcund, and Oude 1858-59, including the actions of Bhagwala, Megina, Bareilly. Shahjehanpore. and Bunae, under Brigr. General I. Jones; Shahabad, under Brigadier Herbert; Bun-ke-Jaon under Sir Thomas Seaton; and Mahadypore, Russoolpore, Mittowlee, and Biswa under Brigadier Troup, Medal and Bt. Major.

Capt. Holland served with the army of the Sutledge, Sobraon, medal.

39TH REGIMENT OF NATIVE INFANTRY.

Major Pownall and Capt. Thomas served against the Bheels 1837, and at the action of Punniar, bronze stars.

Captains Tulloh, Jackson Sherwill, Smith, Gordon and King served at Punniar, bronze stars.

Capt. MacDonald was present at the battle of Maharajpore, bronze star.

Lieut. Forster served as a Volunteer at the battle of Alliwal, medal.

40TH REGIMENT OF NATIVE INFANTRY.

Major Bt. Lt. Col. Shuckburgh served in the Bundelkund campaign of 1842-43, also served in the 2nd Burmese war in 1853, medal.

Major Shuckburgh, Captains Macdonell, Briggs, Rubie, Cahill, and Wroughton, Lieutenants Burn, Stone, Phillips, Middleton, Roberts, Waller Belli and Burlton, served against the insurgent Sonthals, in 1855, under Major Genl. Lloyd, C. B.

Capts. White, Rubie, Cahill, Brander, and Wroughton, Lieutenants Burn, Wild, Stone, and Phillips served with the Burmah Expedition: present at the operations in the vicinity and capture of Rangoon April 1852, medals. Lieut. Rubie also served in the Bundelkund campaign of 1842-43.

Capt. Briggs served with the Burmah expedition and was present at the taking of Martaban and several minor boat affairs on the Salween River, medal.

Lieut. Phillips served with Brigadier General Frank's Division previous to their March into Oude, also with the Goorkha troops, under Maharajah Jung Behadoor, 1857-58.

Lieut. Middleton served in the 2nd Burmese war of 1853, medal.

41ST REGIMENT OF NATIVE INFANTRY.

Major Bt. Lt. Col. Apthorp served at the siege and capture of Bhurtpore 1826, India medal: also during the campaign on the Sutledge: present at the battle of Sobraon, medal and clasp.

Capt. Bt. Major Kemble, Capts. Stevens and Roberts served throughout the campaign on the Sutledge and were present at the battle of Sobraon, medals and clasps. Major Kemble was wounded in the above action.

Capt. Onslow served during the war in China, including the capture of Shin Changfoo and investment of the city of Nankin, medal: throughout the Sutledge campaign: present at the battle of Sobraon, (wounded) medal and clasp.

Capt. Stevens served throughout the Campaign on the sutledge 1845-46, including the battle of Sobraon medal and clasp; Commanded the Sylhet Light Infantry Battalion, in the action fought at Binna Candy (in the Cachar district) 12th Jan. 1858, with the 34th N. I. Mutineers and in several skirmishes with the same body which ended in their defeat and total annihilation, medal.

Lieut, G. L. K. Hewett served throughout the defence of Lucknow from 30th June to 22nd Nov. 1857, (wounded 24th Sept. 1857) present and engaged as orderly officer on the Staff of Major General Sir J. Outram G. C. B. throughout the whole operations at Alumbagh and during the siege and capture of Lucknow in March 1858.

42ND REGIMENT OF NATIVE INFANTRY.

Major Bt. Lt.Col. Campbell served in Arracan 1825, Affghanistan 1839-40, and with the army of the Punjaub: present at Ramnuggur, passage of the Chenab and battles of Sadoolapore, Chillianwalla and Goojerat, medal, clasp and Brevet Major.

Capt. Bt. Major Gaussen served throughout the campaign in Affghanistan 1839-40-41-42, including the defence of Kelat-i-Ghilzie, medal; and the operations leading to the re-occupation of Caubul by the force under Genl. Nott, medal: present at the battle of Maharajpore, bronze star.

Capt Bt. Major Ross served throughout the campaign in Affghanistan 1839-40-41-42: engaged in all the operations of the Candahar force, commanded the 5th Regt. Shah Choojah's force at the action of Ghirisk, 3rd July 1841, medal: also during the war on the Sutledge, including the battles of Moodkee, Ferozeshuhur and Sobraon, medal and clasps.

Capt. Adlam served in Affghanistan with the fore under Genl. Nott, medal: present at the battle of Maharajpore, bronze star: also engaged at the action of Sobraon, medal.

Capt. Macqueen served throughout the operations of the Candahar force, including the advance upon Ghuznee and Caubul, also the taking of Istaliff, medal, and during the campaign on the Sutledge, including the battles of Moodkee, Ferozeshuhur and Sobraon, (wounded at the latter action,) medal and clasps. medal for the Suppression of the mutiny in India, clasp for the relief of Lucknow and also for the siege and capture.

Capts. Jones and Holt (slightly wounded at Moodkee) served throughout the Sutledge campaign: present at the battles of Moodkee, Ferozeshuhur and Sobraon medals and clasps.

43RD REGIMENT OF NATIVE INFANTRY.

Major Macpherson served throughout the campaign in Affghanistan, 1839-40-41-42, including the operations in the vicinity of Candahar advance on Caubul and taking of Istaliff, medal, and at the battle of Maharajpore, bronze star.

Capt. Holroyd served in Affghanistan 1839-40-41-42, throughout the whole of the operations of the Candahar force and the taking of Istaliff, medal; battle of Maharajpore, bronze star and the campaign on the Sutledge, including the action of Sobraon, medal, slightly wounded in Affghanistan.

Capt. Bt. Major Elliot served throughout the campaign in Affghanistan 1839-40-41-42, including the operations of the Candahar force under Genl. Nott, medal.

Capt. Trotter served throughout the Affghan campaign 1839-40-41-42, medal, including the re-occupation of Khelat: defence of Khelat-i-Ghilzie, medal, and taking of Istaliff: present at the battle of Maharajpore, bronze star.

Capt. Pogson served in Spain as a Cornet with the Anglo-Spanish force 1837, in Affghanistan 1840, and with the army of the Sutledge.

Capt. Bt. Maj. Robarts served in Affghanistan 1840-41-42, medal: and with the army of the Punjaub 1848-49: at the siege and surrender of Mooltan, and the action of Guzerat, medal.

Capt. Lees was present at the battle of Sobraon, medal.

Capt. Dawson served at Maharajpore, bronze star: and during the Sutledge campaign: present at the battle of Sobraon, medal.

Lieuts. Bt. Capts. Jerdan and Russell served at the action of Sobraon, medals.

Lieut. Bruce served for 3 years as an executive officer 1853-54-55, in the western Jumna Canals, and on special duty superintending the Bunds Ganjam districts after serving a six months probation, under the superintendent W. J. Canals.

Lieut. Powell, served in the Punjaub 1848-49, (with 71st N. I.,) with Brigadier Wheeler's Force in the Jullundur, medal.

44TH REGIMENT OF NATIVE INFANTRY.

Captains Clarkson. Carnegie, Moncrieff, and Rawlins served throughout the campaign on the Sutledge, including the battle of Ferozeshuhur, medals : and subsequent operations against Kote Kangrah.

Capt. James served with the force under Major Edwardes, C.B.: employed at the siege and operations in the vicinity of Mooltan, medal.

Capt. Rawlins served with the Burmese expedition (severely wounded) in the attack on the enemy's Stockades, 19th March 1853, medal.

45TH REGIMENT OF NATIVE INFANTRY.

Major Oakes and Capt. Osborn served with the army of the Punjaub, at the battles of Cillianwallah and Goojerat, medals.

Capt. Bt. Major Crossman served throughout the campaign on the Sutledge, including the actions of Moodkee Ferozeshuhur, Alliwal and Sobraon, medal and 3 clasps.

Capts. Donaldson, Bloomfield, and Tozer served throughout the Sutledge campaign, including the battles of Moodkee, Ferozeshuhur and Sobraon, medals and clasps : also with the army of the Punjaub: present at the actions of Chillianwalla and Goojerat, medals.

Captain Osborn was present throughout the Punjaub campaign, including the battles of Chillianwalla and Goojerat; medal and clasps, served as orderly Officer to Col. Gerrard at the action of Narnoul, also present at the minor affairs of Gungehree, Putteealee and Mynpooree, served with the 1st Bengal Fusiliers at the capture of Lucknow.

Lieut. Hoggan was severely wounded at an attack on a village called Mohunpore in the Bareilly district.

Lieut. Edwards was present throughout the siege and assault of Delhi, including the action of Nuzuffnuggur.

Lieut. Wavell was present throughout the siege and assault of Delhi including the action of Nuzuffnuggur, also at the action of Narnoul and the minor affairs of Gungehree, Putteealee and Mynpoory, served hroughout the operations against Lucknow and capture of that Town.

46TH REGIMENT OF NATIVE INFANTRY.

Major Drake, and Capts. Wright, Mercer, and Le Gallais, Lieutenants Speke and Ogilvie served with the army of the Punjaub: present at the affair at Ramnuggur and actions of Sadoolapore, Chillianwalla and Goojerat, medals.

Capt. Bt. Major Browne served with the army of the Punjaub, present at the affair of Ramnuggur, battles of Sadoolapore, Chillianwallah and Goojerat, medal and 2 clasp, engaged in various minor affairs on Trans Indus Frontier, Bozdar Hills March 1857, Narinjee (Eusofzaie) July and August 1857, siege and capture of Lucknow March 1858, medal clasp and Bt. Major, present at the actions of Koorsee Royah, Allehgunge and Barielly, commanded a force of Cavalry and Infantry in an attack on the enemy's position at Sarpoorah near Peeleebeet on the 30th August 1858, and capture of their 4 guns and camp, dangerously wounded in two places.

Capts. Caulfeild and Oakes (also engaged at Sadoolapore,) Lieut. Conolly served during the campaign in the Punjaub: present at the action of Goojerat, medal.

Lieut. Bt. Capt. Speke was engaged by Government in an expedition to explore Eastern Africa during the years 1854-55, was there taken prisoner and received 11 spear wounds, served with the Turkish Contingent during 1855-56.

Lieut. Bt. Capt. C. L. Brown served with the force under Genl. Whish throughout the siege and operations in the vicinity of Mooltan, and battle of Goojerat, medal and clasp.

47TH REGIMENT OF NATIVE INFANTRY.

Major Daniell served against the insurgents near Cuttack 1833 and at Punniar in the Gwalior campaign, bronze star.

Captain Renny served throughout the campaign on the Sutledge, including the actions of Moodkee, Ferozeshuhur, Buddiwal, Alliwal and Sobraon, twice severely wounded in the latter action medal and 3 clasps; commanded the 3rd Seikh Infantry in the expedition against the Bozdar tribe of Beloochees in March 1857.

Capts. McAndrew, Lucas and Walcot (wounded) served throughout the campaign on the Sutledge, including the actions of Moodkee, Ferozeshuhur, Budiwal, Alliwal and Sobraon, medals and 3 clasps each.

Capt. Campbell served at the taking of the Fort of Komonah in the Augami Naga Hills on the 10 December 1850.

Capt. Pughe was present at the actions of Budiwal and Alliwal, medal.

Capt. Campbell served during the Sutledge campaign, present at the actions of Moodkee and Ferozeshuhur, (severely wounded) medal and clasp.

Lieut. Bt. Capt. Leeds was present at the actions of Budiwal, Alliwal and Sobraon, medal and clasp.

48TH REGIMENT OF NATIVE INFANTRY.

Major Hasell commanded the 48th N. I. in the Wuzeerah Valley when six forts were taken; commanded the regiment from Thudjah to Kurnaul and six times through the Kyber Pass.

Capt. Bt. Major Bird served during the campaign in Affghanistan, including the storm and capture of Ghuznee, medal: and the operations in the Khyber Pass and Wuzeerah Valley, was also present at the battle of Alliwal, (wounded,) medal.

Captains Green, Hume, and Marhall served throughout the campaign on the Sutledge: present at the actions of Moodkee, Ferozeshuhur and Alliwal, medals and clasps. Lieut. Marshall was wounded at Alliwal. Capt. Hockin recived a medal for his services in the Punjaub.

Capt. Green served with the 2nd Punjaub Infantry at the battles of Cawnpore and Khodagunge (near Futtyghur) and the siege and capture of the City of Lucknow in 1857, medal and clasps.

Captain Hockin served throughout the campaign at the sutleg; present at the actions of Moodkee, Ferozeshuhur and Alliwal (medal and 2 clasps; Punjaub campaign (medal); engaged in the suppression of the mutiny of 1857 (medal); present at the siege of Delhi, 1857 (clasp).

Capt. Henderson served throughout the campaign on the Sutledge, including the actions of Moodkee and Alliwal, medal and clasp.

Capt. (Bt. Maj.) Hughes served during the Sutledge campaign: present at the actions of Moodkee, Ferozeshuhur and Sobraon, medal and 2 clasps, and with the force under Brigr. Wheeler employed in the Punjaub 1848-49, engaged in the attack on the Dullah heights, medal, and against the Predatory Tribes on the N.W. Frontier, 1852.

Lieut. Ouseley served with the army of the Punjaub: present at the affair of Ramnuggur and actions of Sadoolapore, Chillianwalla and Goojerat, medal.

49TH REGIMENT OF NATIVE INFANTRY.

Capt. Bt. Major Hood, and Captains Piercy, Larkins, Richardson, and Irwin, Lts. Dandridge, Allgood, and Sherer served at the siege and capture of Mooltan with the force under Genl. Whish, medal and clasp. Capts. Richardson and Irwin dangerously wounded. Capt. Larkins also served as Captain of Division in H. M.'s Land Transport corps in the Crimea up to the fall of Sevastopol, medal and Sevastopo, clasps. Major Hood served also at the siege of Mooltan and action of Soroojkund, medal and clasp; present with Brigadier Shower's column at the capture of Jujjur Fort; also present at the action of Shumshabad and the siege and capture of Lucknow, dangerously wounded.

Capt. Gordon commanded the 2nd Company of Pioneers at the siege and capture of Mooltan and the 2nd and 6th Companies of Pioneers at the battle of Goojerat, medal and 2 clasps.

Capt. Pollock served in political employ during the siege and capture of Mooltan with the Irregular force under Major Edwardes, medal and clasp.

Lt. Williamson served as Major of Brigade with the Field Force employed in the Meeranzie valley in 1855, under Brigadier Chamberlain, present with the Troops engaged at Dursummund with the Hill Tribes.

50TH REGIMENT OF NATIVE INFANTRY.

Capt. Bt. Major Gordon served with the army of the Punjaub 1848-49: present at the action of Goojerat, medal.

Capt. Bt. Major Nicoll, Capts. McMullin, Read, and Fooks served at the battle of Punniar, bronze stars: siege and capture of Mooltan and battle of Goojerat, medals. Capt. McMullin was also present at the action of Soorujkhoond, the siege and capture of Mooltan and battle of Goojerat, medal and clasps; Capt. Barlow also served against the frontier Tribes in the Campaigns of 1851 and 1852.

Capt. Plowden served against the insurgents in Bundelcund in 1842, under Genl. Young, also in the Punjaub campaign, present at the siege and surrender of the Fortress of Mooltan, repulse of the enemy's night attack on the British Camp under Genl. Whish at "Muttee Thal" and action of Soorujkhoond 7th Nov. 1848, medal and clasp. served with the Goorkah army under H. H. Maharajah Jung Bahadoor, and held Military charge of a Division of the Force, engaged and defeated the rebel forces at Peepraitch and Shahgunge in the Gooruckpore District; the enemy at the latter numbering 12,000 strong, at the "Kandoo Nuddee in Oude, in which action, the Rebels lost 600 killed, re-capture of Goruckpore and the operations attending the siege and capture of Lucknow, in which his division took seven guns; succeeded to the charge of the Goorkah army after the fall of Lucknow and conducted it through Oude to Segowlie occupying Fyzabad en route which was evacuated by the rebels on the approach of the Goorkah army.

Capt. Bacon was present at the action of Punniar, bronze star; and throughout the Punjaub campaign, including the battles of Sadoolapore, Chillianwalla and Goojerat, medal.

Lieuts. Bayley, and Munro served in the Punjaub, medals.

Lieut. Bolton served against the Sonthals, in 1855-56; present with Brigr. General Frank's Division, at the engagements of Chandah and Humeerpore, on the 19th and Sultanpore 23 Feb. 1858, also present at the siege and fall of Lucknow.

Lieut. Mathias served during the whole of the Santal Campaign in 1855-56; was 2nd in command of the Rewah and Nagode Rajah's troops at the opening of the Deccan road 1857-58, during which operations the forts of Kunchunpore, Joorah, Myhere city and fort, Jokye, Kunnwarrah, Bejeeragooghur, and 42 pieces of ordnance were taken (slightly wounded), was 2nd in command of the Rewah contingent at the storming of the enemy's position on the Punwarrah heights,taking all the enemys' guns, killing their leaders and entirely dispersing their force.

Lieut. Lawford served throughout the Oude campaign with Hodsons' horse.

Lieut. Cracroft served throughout the Sonthal campaign in 1855 56, slightly wounded; was Adjutant of the Rewah force and present at the attack and capture of the heights of Punwarree 29th December 1858.

51ST REGIMENT OF NATIVE INFANTRY.

Capt. Bt. Lt. Col. Cheape and Lieut. Hamilton served at the siege and capture of Mooltan, and action of Goojerat, medals and clasps.

Capt. Bt. Major Lamb served at the battle of Maharajpore, bronze star: siege and capture of Mooltan; and action of Goojerat, medal and clasp.

Lt. Col. Abbott served during the campaign on the Sutledge: present at the battles of Moodkee and Ferozeshuhur, (dangerously wounded) medal and clasp.

Capts. Davies, Wallace, Smith, Darnell, (wounded at Goojerat) and Blair and Ward twice (slightly wounded), served at the action of Punniar, bronze stars: at the siege and surrender of Mooltan and battle of Goojerat, medals and clasps.

Capts. Tyrwhitt and Irvine served at the action of Punniar, bronze stars; and at the siege and surrender of Mooltan, (the former twice wounded) medals.

52ND REGIMENT OF NATIVE INFANTRY.

Major Morrieson and Lieut. Oakes served at the second siege operations and surrender of Mooltan (including the attack on the Suburbs 27th December 1848,) battle of Goojerat, medal and clasps.

Capt. Moxon served at the 1st and 2nd siege operations and surrender of Mooltan, (including the repulse of the enemy's night attack on the British Camp at Mathe Ghol, 17th Aug. 1848, attack on the Suburbs of Mooltan, 27th December 1848,) battle of Goojerat, medal and clasps.

Capt. Matheson served at the 1st and 2d siege operations and surrender of Mooltan, (including the action of Soorujkhoond, 7th Nov. 1848,) battle of Goojerat, and subsequent pursuit of the Seikhs and Affghans medal and clasps.

Captain Lowther served at the 1st and 2d siege operations and surrender of Mooltan, (including the action of Soorujkhoond, 7th Nov. 1848, attack on the Suburbs of Mooltan, 27th Dec. 1848,) battle of Goojerat, (wounded) medal and clasps.

Capt. Martin served at the 1st and 2d siege operations and surrender of Mooltan, (including the repulse of the enemy's night attack on the British Camp at Mathe Ghol 17th Aug. 1848,) battle of Goojerat, medal and clasps.

Capt. Waddington served during the 1st siege operations before Mooltan, (including the repulse on the enemy's night attack on the British Camp at Mathe Ghol 17th Aug. 1848,) medal and clasp.

Lieut. Bracken served during the 1st and 2nd siege operations and surrender of Mooltan, battle of Goojerat, medal and clasps.

Capt. Campbell, and Lieut. Jackson served at the 1st and 2nd siege operati ons, and surrender of Mooltan, (including the repulse of the enemy's night attack on the British Camp at Mathe Ghol 17th August 1848, action of Soorujkhoond 7th November 1848, attack on the Suburbs of Mooltan, 27th December 1848, and battle of Goojerat: medal and clasps.

Lieut. Barton served during the Punjaub campaign of 1848-49, medal.

53RD REGIMENT OF NATIVE INFANTRY.

Major Ramsay, served in the Punjaub, medal.

Capt. Bt. Major Edgell served in Affghanistan with the force under Genl. Pollock: present at the forcing of the Khyber Pass, engagement in the Mazeenah valley and the previous operations of the Brigade commanded by Brigadier Wild, medals: and in the Punjaub, medals.

Capt. Alexander served in the Punjaub, medal; an with the Ramghur Irregular Cavalry in Burmah, medal

Capt. *Baron* VonMeyern served with Brigadier Wild's Brigade, and was severely wounded in the Khyber Pass, medal: present at the battle of Punniar, bronze star.

54TH REGIMENT OF NATIVE INFANTRY.

Maj. Paterson served in Affghanistan with the force under Genl. Pollock, medal: and at the battle of Ferozeshuhur, medal.

Captain Carter served in Affghanistan 1839-40-41-42. present at the storm and capture of Ghuznee, medal: and the operations of the force under Genl. Nott, leading to the re-occupation of Caubul, medal.

Capt. Haughton served in Affghanistan 1839-40-41-42, severely wounded, left arm amputated at Chareekar, medal.

Capt. Anderson served during the campaign on the Sutledge: present at the battle of Ferozeshuhur, medal.

Capt. Osborn was severely wounded in the mutiny at Delhi on the 11th May 1857, was present with Colonel Seaton's column in the engagements at Gungeree 14th and Putteealee 17 Dec. 1857 and subsequent advance into Mynpoory.

Lieut. Nicholson, served with the army of the Punjaub, at the actions of Sadoolapore, Chillianwaliah and Goojerat, medal and clasp.

Lieut. E. D. H. Vibart served with the 1st European Bengal Fusiliers at the siege of Delhi from the 13th August 1857, including the battle of Nujjufghur 25th August 1857, and storm and capture of Delhi; present also at the action ef Narnoul 16th Nov. 1857, and subsequently accompanied the column under Sir Thomas Seaton, K. C. B; present at the affairs of Gungeerie, Puttialee and Mynpoorie; served also with the 2nd P. I. throughout the operations against Lucknow from 2nd to 16th March 1858, and other moveable columns under Sir Hope Grant and General Walpole; present at the capture of Bareilly 5th May 1858, (medal and two clasps.)

55TH REGIMENT OF NATIVE INFANTRY.

Major Luard, Capts. Richards, Baring, Allen, Haig, Hoste, and Babbage, Lieuts. Ferris, and Nembhard served during the campaign on the Sutledge. Lieutenant Nembhard also served during the war in Burmah 1852-53, medal. Capt. Richards, and Lt. Haig were also present at the battle of Sobraon, medals.

Captain Hoste served in the Sutledge campaign 1845 46, served in the trenches before Sebastopol as Captain of a division of Land Transport, medal and clasp; against the rebels in the Eusofzye Country 1857 and led the upper column of attack against the rebel village of Narinjee for which he received the thanks of the Governor General in Council, also throughout the Oude campaign 1858 59. and present at the actions of Basee Simree Nawubgunge Sultanpore and all the minor engagements leading to the re-occupation of that country and during the latter part of the campaign, acted as assistant Qr. Mr. Genl. to Brig. Horsford C. B. medal.

56TH REGIMENT OF NATIVE INFANTRY.

Major Gott and Capt. Jervis served at the action of Maharajpore, bronze stars: and with the army of the Punjaub: present at the battles of Sadoolapore and Chillianwalla, (in which latter engagement they were both wounded, the latter severely) medals and clasps.

Capt. Cafe served at the action of Maharajpore, bronze star, and throughout the Punjaub campaign, including the battles of Sadoolapore, Chillianwalla and Goojerat, and subsequent pursuit of the Seikhs and Affghans with the force under Genl. Gilbert, medal and clasp.

Capt. Jones served at the action of Maharajpore, (bronze star) and with the army of the Punjaub, battles of Sadoolapore and Chillianwalla, in which latter engagements he was twice wounded, and had a horse killed under him, subsequent pursuit of the Seikhs and Affghans with the force under Major General Gilbert, medal and clasp; served on the staff of Major General Sir Sydney Cotton, K. C. B., in the expedition against the Hill tribes of Punjtar and Sitana April 1858, commanded the First Seikh irregular cavalry throughout the operations in Oude 1858-59, under Lord Clyde, " horse killed under him in action at Nurpalgunge Biswarra, November 1858.

Capt. Bamfield served with the army of the Punjaub, present at the battles of Chillianwalla and Goojerat, and subsequent pursuit of the Seikhs and Affghans, medal and clasp.

Captain Lambert served with the force under Major General Gilbert, medal: served throughout the Burmese expedition of 1852-53 medal; served during the rebellion of 1857-58, siege of Delhi and Rohilkund, medal, clasp and Bt. Major.

Captain Beatson served during the sutledge campaign medal; present at the capture of Kote Kangra, 1846; did duty with the 1st En. Bengal Fusiliers before Delhi in September 1857, present at the storm and capture of that city on the 16th September 1857.

Lieut. Smith served throughout the campaign in the Punjaub, including the passage of the Chenab and the actions of Chillanwallah and Goojerat, medal.

57TH REGIMENT OF NATIVE INFANTRY.

Capt. [Bt. Lt. Col.] Simpson served in the Cole country, 1835.

Capt. Sneyd served as Deputy Assistant Quarter Master General at the battle of Maharajpore, bronze star.

Lieut. MacGregor served at the action of Narnoul 16 November 1857, and also at the minor affairs of Gungehree, Putteealee and Mynpoory, present throughout the operations against Lucknow and capture of that city.

58TH REGIMENT OF NATIVE INFANTRY.

Major Meyer, Captains Duffin, Davies, D'Oyly, and Elwyn were present at the battle of Punniar, bronze stars.

Capt. Moffat served with the army of Gwalior at the battle of Punniar, bronze star, and with the force under Sir Charles Napier against the Hill Tribes in Scinde 1845.

Lieut. Richardson served in the Punjaub in 1849 (with the 18th N. I.) medal.

59TH REGIMENT OF NATIVE INFANTRY.

Major Stokes, and Capt. [Bt. Lt. Col.] Dunsford, C.B., Capts. Blackwood, Mayne, Dwyer, Gibney, and Presgrave, and Lieut. Phillips served during the campaign on the Sutledge: present at the battle of Sobraon, medals.

Capt. (Bt. Major Lumsden) served with the force under Genl. Pollock: present at the forcing of the Khyber Pass, and all the subsequent operations leading to the re-occupation of Caubul, medal: at the battle of Sobraon, (severely wounded) medal: and with the army of the Punjaub, during the siege of Mooltan, and action of Goojerat, medal and clasp.

Lieut. Angelo served as a Volunteer during the Punjaub campaign in 1848-49, as extra A. D. C. to Major Genl. Thackwell: present at the action of Sadoolapore and battle of Chillianwalla, medal and clasp served as orderly officer to Brigdr. General Nicholson at the action of Nimbooghaut 12th July 1858 (Horse Shot under him) and subsequently as Commissariat Officer to his column before Delhi, present at the action of Nujufgur 24th July 1857, present at the storm and capture of Delhi 14th September 1857. medal and clasp. accompanied Brigdr. Shower's column as Commissariat Officer in the Mewat Country and Jhujjur and Rewari Districts, served with Colonel G. V. Maxwell's column before Calpee May 1858, with Towana Horse, present at the affair at Oorain with Col. Riddell's column, May 1858.

60TH REGIMENT OF NATIVE INFANTRY.

Major (Bt. Lt. Col.) Drought C. B. was present at the siege of Bhurtpore, India medal: also served in the campaign of 1842 in Affghanistan, medal.

Capt. (Bt. Maj.) Verner, served throughout the operations in Affghanistan, with the force under Genl Pollock, medal; Commanded the Cavalry Bundelkund Legion against the Insurgents in Bundelkund and at the taking of Chirgong in 1841, Commanded the same Regiment against the Hill Tribes in Scinde under Sir Charles Napier in 1844-45.

Capt. (Bt. Lt. Col.) Whish served in the campaign in Affghanistan with the force under Genl. Pollock, medal: as Asst. Adjt. Genl. to the Mooltan Field Force and to the 1st Infy. Divn., Army of the Punjaub. and at the action of Goojerat, medal, clasp and Bt. Major.

Capt. (Bt. Major) Hay, Capts. Stansbury and Green served throughout the operations in Affghanistan with the force under Genl. Pollock, medals.

61ST REGIMENT OF NATIVE INFANTRY.

Capt. Bt. Maj. Ryves served in Affghanistan with the army, of the Indus: present at the storm and capture of Ghuznee, medal.

Capt. (Bt. Colonel) Becher C. B., served in Affghanistan 1839: present at the storm and capture of Ghuznee, medal: throughout the campaign on the Sutledge, including the actions of Moodkee, Ferozeshuhur and Sobraon, medal, 2 clasps and Bt. Major: with the army of the Punjaub 1848-49: present at the siege and surrender of Mooltan, and action of Goojerat, medal, clasp and Bt. Lt. Col.

62ND REGIMENT OF NATIVE INFANTRY.

Capts. Denniss, and Hughes served with the army of Gwalior, and have received bronze stars for the battle of Maharajpore.

Capt. Hughes served with the Shannon's naval Brigade under Capt. Sir William Peel, V. C. K. C. B. as Interpreter, at the siege and taking of Lucknow, medal and clasp.

63RD REGIMENT OF NATIVE INFANTRY.

Major Troup, Capts. Pester, Phillips, Sinclair and Barber (wounded) served throughout the campaign on the Sutledge, including the battle of Sobraon, medal and clasps.

Lieut. Ryall served throughout the Santal Insurrection in 1855-56; served as adjutant of the 2nd Hyderabad cavalry with the Kamptee moveable column. present at the forcing of the Rhonie pass. on the 10th January 1858 present at the battles of Rhobrie and Bandah (wounded, horse also wounded) and in all the minor engagements fought by the Central India Force under Major General Whitlock up to June 1858; commanded the 3rd Seikh Irregular cavalry during the Shahabad campaign under Brigadier Douglas C. B, from August 1858, commanded the southern division of cavalry at the battle and capture of Jugdispore in October 1858.

Lieut. Palliser was wounded in a skirmish with the Sheoraniee Tribe, 14 March 1853.

64TH REGIMENT OF NATIVE INFANTRY.

Major Bt. Lt. Col. Prior served with the force under Genl. Pollock at the storming of the Khyber Pass and subsequent operations in Affghanistan 1842, also against the Hill Tribes in Scinde 1845.

Capt. Bt. Major Burt, Captains Young, Nicholas Nicholson, and Nott served with the force under Genl. Pollock at the forcing of the Khyber Pass, and subsequent operations in Affghanistan, medals. Capt. Nicholas was also employed with the force under Sir Charles Napier against the Hill Tribes in Scinde 1845.

Capt. Bt. Col. Mulcaster served with the force under Genl. Pollock: present at the forcing of the Khyber Pass, (severely wounded) medal: during the campaign on the Sutledge, battles of Moodkee, Ferozeshuhur and Sobraon, medal and 2 clasps: and with the army of the Punjaub, throughout the siege and operations (including the action of Soorujkhoond) in the vicinity of Mooltan, medal and clasp.

Capt. Young served with Brigadier Wild's Brigade, was present at the forcing of the Khyber Pass and through the subsequent campaign with Sir G. Pollock's force, medal.

Capt. Bt. Maj. Rattray served in Affghanistan with the force commanded by Sir George Pollock, (severely wounded) medal: and against the Hill Tribes in Scinde under Sir Charles Napier.

Capt. Poulton served against the Hill Tribes in Scinde under *Sir* Charles Napier in 1845.

65TH REGIMENT OF NATIVE INFANTRY.

Capt Bt. Major Hinde joined His Highness Omer Pasha's army in Bulgaria in March 1854, acted as Assistant Adjutant Genl. to the force under the command of Genl. Cannon (Behram Pasha) which was despatched from Thumla to harass the Russian army before Salistria; present at the successful passage of the Danube and battle of Guirgevo, on the 7th July 1854; accompanied the Turkish army to Eupatoria in Dec. 1854, and afterwards in command of two Battalions of it, at the siege before Sebastopol, joined the Turkish army in Mingrelia, and served on the Staff of the division under His Excellency Osman Pasha, and was present at the passage of, and the battle of the Ingur on the 6th Nov. 1855, received the English Crimean medal and clasp, the Turkish gold medal for the Danubian campaign; the Turkish medal for Salistria, the Turkish medal for the Crimea; and the Order of the Medjidie; has the rank of Brevet Major and that of Honorary Lieut. Col. conferred upon him by Her Majesty; commanded the combined forces at the opening of the Deccan road in 1857-1858—during which operations the Forts of Kunchunpore—Joorah—Myhere City and Myhere Fort—Jokye—Kunwarah and Bijeera Googhur were taken, also 42 pieces of ordnance, commanded the central column of attack on the Punwarree heights 29th October 1858—capturing four guns and killing the rebel leaders

Captain Weston was in political charge and vested with special powers at the capture of the Durriabad Fort, Oude, in March and April 1850; formed one of the old Garrison Lucknow Residency from 30th June to 22nd November 1857, present throughout the whole of the subsequent operations before Lucknow with he force under *Sir* J. Outram, G. C. B. and at the siege and capture of Lucknow in March 1858.

66TH OR GOORKHA LIGHT INFANTRY REGIMENT.

Capt. Sherwill served as Deputy Asst. Quarter Master Genl. to the field force, under Major Genl. Lloyd, C. B against the insurgent Sonthals, in 1855.

Capts. Ross, Hockley and Law, Lieuts Tytler, Ruxton and Macintyre served with the force under *Sir* Colin Campbell against the Hill Tribes in 1851-52 and in the Boori Pass 1853.

Capt. Phillpotts served in the Punjaub with the force under Brigdr. Genl. Wheeler 1848-49, medal.

Captain Law was present at Cawnpore, 26-27-28, November, and at the attack made by the Rebels on the Fort, November and December, 1857; ex-commissariat Officer, Rifle Brigade, at the defeat of the Gowalior Rebels on December 7th, at Cawnpore, and subsequently of Highland Brigade throughout the campaign, present with them at Bithoor, at the action of Khadagunge, on the advance to Futtebgurh, throughout the operations at and capture of Lucknow March 1858, at the attack on Fort Rooea, and action at Allygunge, in Oudh, and at the action at and capture of Bareilly May 1858, medal and clasp: was executive commissariat officer Brigadier Troup's column in the campaign in Oudh 1858-59; present at the action of Pusgaon and Russoolpore, and at the capture of the Fort of Mittowlee.

Lieutenants Clay, Miles, Graves and Havelock served against the Hill Tribes under *Sir* Colin Campbell, 1851-52.

Lieut. Pearson served at Cawnpore 27th, 28th Nov. and at the attack made by the rebels on the fort November and December 1857, also at the defeat of the Gwalior rebels on the 6th December 1857: was present throughout the operations at and capture of Lucknow March 1858, at the attack on fort Royeah and action at Allygunge, in Oudh, and at the action at and capture of Bareilly May 1858.

67TH REGIMENT OF NATIVE INFANTRY.

Major Raikes, Capt. Spilsbury, Lts. Bushby and Judge served in Burmah, medals. Major Raikes was engaged at the battle of Punniar, bronze star. Capts. Hicks, D'Oyly and Girdlestone, and Lieut. Thompson were present at the operation in the vicinity of Donabew under Sir J. Cheape, medals. Capt. Hicks and Lieut. Thompson were present at the capture of Pegu in June 1852.

Capts. Maisey and Harris were present with the 40th B. N. I. at the capture of Rangoon, in Apl. 1852, medals.

Capt. Maisey and Lt. Smith (medal.) were present with the force under Major Minchin and again with the force under Sir J. Cheape at the operations in the vicinity of Donabew. Capt. Maisey was wounded on out post duty in Aug. 1853.

68TH REGIMENT OF NATIVE INFANTRY.

Major Roberton, and Capts. Gibbs served during the Sutledge campaign, including the battle of Sobraon, (in which action Major Roberton was wounded, in three places,) medal; also served during the war in Burmah 1852.53, medals.

Capt. (Bt. Major) Barclay served during the Sutledge campaign, including the Battle of Sobraon medal; also served during the war in Burmah 1852-53, medal, served with the Sarun filed force in charge of a Regiment of Nepaulese Troops and present in the following actions, viz. At Belwah 2nd March 1858, Amorah 5th March, 17th April and 25th April 1858 and Nuggur 29th April 1858; medal and Bt. Major, Commanded a Detachment of Madras Rifles at the affair at Kheerie in the Shahabad District on 7th October 1858.

Capt. Gordon, Lieuts. Francis. Montagu, Christian, and Stanton served during the war in Burmah 1852-53, medals. Capt. Paterson and Warde served during the war in Burmah 1852-53, also served during the Sutledge campaign, including the battle of Sobraon, medals. Lieut, Montagu served with the Regiment of Ferozepore at Allahabad under Major Genl. Neil during the months of June and July 1857, medal.

69TH REGIMENT OF NATIVE INFANTRY.

Major Sissmore, Capts. Simpson, (present at Sadoolapore) Tulloch, Black, and Willes, Lieuts. Hayley, Millett, and Thorp served with the army of the Punjaub, medals.

Capt. Nisbett was engaged at the battle of Chillianwalla, and severely wounded.

Capt Wedderburn was engaged at the battles of Chillianwalla and Goojerat, medal and 2 clasps; also in Scinde in the campaign against the Hill tribes under Sir Charles Napier in 1845.

Capt. Cracroft served during the campaign in the Sutledge, present at the battle of Sobraon, medal, and with the force under General Whish throughout the operations in the vicinity and siege and surrender of Mooltan, and the action of Goojerat, medal and clasp.

Capts. Simpson, Black, and Willis served under Sir Charles Napier in Scinde against the Hill tribes in 1845.

Lieut. Eckford was present at the siege and operations before Delhi, was severely wounded on the 9th July 1857, whilst doing duty with the Sirmoor Battalion, rejoined in August and was appointed Officiating Adjutant, and continued to act in that capacity till the capture of Delhi; was appointed to act as Deputy Asst. Quarter Master General to the Meerut Division and accompanied General Penny's column into Rohilcund was severely wounded in action at Kukerowlee on the 30th April 1858, receiving two sabre cuts in driving back Ghazees from the Guns.

70TH REGIMENT OF NATIVE INFANTRY.

Major Bt. Col Harris served as A. D. C. to Lieut. Genl. Sir John Littler at the battle of Maharajpore. bronze star and Bt. Major.

Capt. Bt. Major Hennessy served as a volunteer with H. M.'s 59th foot at the siege and capture of Bhurtpore 1825-26. India medal; also with the army of Gwalior, at the battle of Maharajpore, bronze star.

Capt. Impey served with the army of Gwalior at the battle of Maharajpore, bronze star.

Captains Greene, Robertson and Byers served with the army of Gwalior, bronze star; and at the actions of Chillianwalla and Goojerat, and were present at the affair of Ramnuggur and passage of the Chenab, and in the subsequent pursuit of the Sheiks and Affghans by the force under Genl. Gilbert, medals and clasps.

Capt. Bt. Major Fytche commanded a detachment employed against the Maleng Hill Tribes on the Arracan frontier in 1841-42; served during the campaign in the Punjaub, including the battles of Chillianwalla and Gooojerat (wounded) and in the subsequent pursuit of the Seikhs and Affghans by the force under Genl. Gilbert, medal and 2 clasps. Raised and commanded an Irregular Force with which, in conjunction with a party of Seamen and Marines, under the command of Commander Rennie, N. I., he defeated the Burmese chiefs Nga-thein and Moungthabon on the 22nd and 23rd Jan. 1853. and the Burmese Governor of the Province of Bassein on the 29th of the same month. Also co-operated with the Force under Brigadier General Sir John Cheape, K. C. B., during the month of March 1853, against the Force under Mayat-toon in the vicinity of Donabew (wounded,) medal and Bt. Major.

Capt. Coxe served with the army of Gwalior, bronze star.

Lieut. (Bt. Capt.) Whiting served with the army of the Punjaub at the battles of Chillianwalla and Goojerat. (severely wounded,) medal and clasps.

Capts Hopkinson, Garstin, and Wiggins served with the army of the Punjaub at the battles of Cillianwalla and Goojerat, all these officers (excepting Captain Hopkinson) were present at the affair of Ramnuggur and passage of the Chenab and in the subsequent pursuit of the Seikhs and Affghans by the force under Genl. Gilbert, in which latter Capt. Hopkinson was also present, medal and clasps.

Capt. Murry served with the army of Gwalior, bronze star: and with the army of the Punjaub; present at the battle of Chillianwalla and Goojerat, (wounded) and at the affair of Ramnuggur and passage of the Chenab, and in the subsequent pursuit of the Seikhs and Affghans by the force under Genl. Gilbert, medal and clasp, Capt. Murry also served in the Kohat expedition under Sir Charles Napier.

71ST REGIMENT OF NATIVE INFANTRY.

Capts. Bt. Majors Barwell Dinning, and Murray, and Lieutenants Langmore, and Anderson served with the force under Brigadier Wheeler, in the Punjaub 1848-49 medals.

Capts. Strangways and Briggs were present at the attack and defeat of the insurgents under Ram Sing at Noorpore in Sept. 1848: served also in the Punjaub 1848-49, medals.

Capt. Briggs also served with the Arracan Local Battalion in the Aeng Pass during the Burmese war 1852, medal.

Capt. Ross and Lieut. Perkins were present at the attack on the heights of Noorpore in Sept. 1848. and served with the force under Brigadier Wheeler, medals; Lieut. Perkins was also attached to the force which, with Sir C. J. Napier, proceeded through the Kohat Pass in February 1850.

Lieut. Foote served with the Goorkha Force under the Military charge of Brigadier General Macgregor, C. B. from December 1857 to June 1858, present at the capture and re-occupation of Goruckpore, the affairs of Pepraitch, Shahpore and Kandhoo Nullah, in which latter 4,000 rebels under the Nazim Banee Madho were totally defeated with a loss of their only gun and 500 killed by the advance Division of the Goorkha Army, also present at the siege and capture of Lucknow, medal and clasp.

72ND REGIMENT OF NATIVE INFANTRY.

Major Hobday served throughout the campaign on the Sutledge; present at the actions of Moodkee, Ferozeshuhur and Sobraon, medal and 2 clasps; present at the affair of Ramnuggur and served throughout the campaign in the Punjaub, medal.

Capts. Holmes, Curtis, Andrews, and Armstrong. Lieuts. Williams, and Goldsworthy served with the army of the Punjaub 1848-49; present at the siege and surrender of Mooltan, and the action of Goojerat, medals and clasps.

Capt. Gordon served in the Jullundur Doab against the insurgeonts under Ram Singh 1848-49.

Lieut. MacDougall served at the siege and surrunder of Mooltan, (wounded) medal.

Lieut. H. H. Lyster served on the staff of Major General Hugh Rose, G. C. B,, commanding the Central India Field Force, as Interpreter and A. D. C. throughout the whole of the Central India campaign from December 1857 to July 1858, including the following actions and engagements, siege and capture of the Town and Fort of Ruthghur' repulse of the rebels in an attack on the camp during the siege, action of Barodia (wounded) charger wounded; taking of Barodia, forcing the pass of Muddinpore, siege and storm of the Town, and capture of the fort of Jhansi, battle of the Betwa, action of Koonch and capture of the Town, (Charger wounded in three places) attack on the Camp of the 2nd Brigade at the village of Muttra, attack on the camp of the 1st Brigade at Goolowlee, taking of the Town and Fort of Calpi, action at and capture of the Morar Cantonments, storming of the Lushker and Fort of Gwalior.

73RD REGIMENT OF NATIVE INFANTRY,

Capt. Bt. Majors Erskine, and Lawrence. and Capt. Cookson served during the Sutledge campaign, present at the battle of Sobraon, medals. Capt. Mainwaring served in the Punjaub, medal.

Capt. Bt. Maj. Richardson and Capt. Tickell, Garstin, and Rogers served throughout the Sutledge campaign, present at the actions of Moodkee, Ferozeshuhur and Sobraon, meda ls and clasps; also served in the Punjaub, medals.

Lieuts. Fortescue, Dandridge, Clarke and Jervois served in the Punjaub, medals.

74TH REGIMENT OF NATIVE INFANTRY.

Capt. Wallace served against the insurgents in the Jullundur Doab, 1848-49, medal.

Captain Mylne served in Bengal. and N. W. P. during the suppression of the mutiny of 1857, 58, 59, was present at the action of Pandoo Nuddee and the other affairs previous to the defence of Cawnpore under Major Genl. Windham C. B., to whom he acted as extra A. D. C., on the 27th November 1857, (horse killed under him by a round shot.) was present at the battle of Cawnpore under Lord Clyde on 6th December 1857, was in commissariat charge of the force under Brigadier General Walpole at the taking of Etawah and Mynpoorie, also on the Ramgunga; served on the staff of Brigadier Sir Thomas Seaton K. C. B., at the action oj kunkur on 7th April 1858, medal.

Lieut. Gully served with the army of the Punjaub at the actions of Sadoolapore, Chillianwallah and Goojerat, medal and clasp, also subsequent pursuit of the Seikhs and Affghans to Peshawur under Genl. Gilpert (wounded at Goojerat.)

Ens. Dodd served with H. M. 23rd Fusiliers during the suppresion of the Sepoy mutiny of 1857 and was present at the taking of Futtyghur—with Lord Clyde's Army at the siege and capture of Lucknow and subsequently at the subjugation of Oude.

WAR SERVICES OF UNATTACHED OFFICERS.

Col. Forster, C. B., [Comdt. of the Shekhawattee Battn.] served during the Mahrattah and Pindare campaigns, 1817-18, with the force under Genl. Sir John Malcolm in the Dhar and Jubbooa Provinces: agains various parties of insurgents in the district of Shekhawattee 1837-38-39: at Seekur, Goodhee and Khetree, (severely wounded in the assault of the fort of Kaluk, 10th Dec. 1840:) commanded the Shekhawattee Brigade at the battle of Alliwal, (horse shot under him,) medal and C. B. Capt. Forster served in the different engagements with the insurgents in the Shekhawattee district 1837-38-39-40: including the siege and capture of the fort of Kaluk and action of Khetree: during the campaign on the Sutledge: commanded the Battalion at the battle of Alliwal, medal.

Lt. Col. Brasyer, C.B., served in Affghanistan, with the force under Genl. Pollock, 1842: present at the forcing of the Khyber Pass: actions at Mamoo Kheil, Jugdulluck, Tazeen and Huft Kotul, and assault and capture of Istaliff, medal: throughout the campaign on the Sutledge, including the actions of Moodkee, Ferozeshuhur and Sobraon, medal, 2 clasps and Ensign's commission; promoted to Captain in consideration of the important services rendered by him at Allahabad, in disarming and making Prisoners of about a Company of the 6th Regt. N. I. who were on Guard over the Main Gate and State Prisoners in the Fort, on the night of the 6th June 1857, and with but 400 men of his Regiment (Regt. of Ferozepore) present in conjunction with the few Europeans there, held that Fortress secure until the arrival of more Europeans. In the engagements with the Rebels at Allahabad between the City and Cantonments on the 12th (Charger wounded), Khydgunj, 13th; in the Town 16th and re-occupation of Town and Cantonments 17th June 1857, with Major Renaud's moveable column from 30th June till 12th July advancing towards Cawnpore, with the Force under Genl. Sir. H. Havelock at the actions of Futtehpore on the 12th, Oung and Pandoo Nuddee 15th and battle and re-occupation of Cawnpore 16th and 17th July, Bhittoor the 18th and actions of Oonao and Busseerrutgunj 5th, Boorbeean-ke-Chokee 12th (Charger wounded), and Bhittoor 16th August, Bt. Major; landed his Regiment (R. F.) on the Oude side of the River Ganges on the 17th September, two days there, in advance of the Army to protect the making of a Bridge and road for the passage of the Troops, skirmishes of 17th, 18th and 19th, actions of Munglewar 21st, Alumbaugh 23rd and first Relief of Lucknow 25th September, (led charger killed at his side, and Horse under him received five Shots, left for dead but recovered,) medal, clasps and C. B. with the entrenched, Camp under Genl. Sir J. Outram at Alumbaugh from the 25th November 1857, to the 10th March 1858 present at the affairs of Gailee 22nd December 1857, attacks of 12th and 16th January 1858, night attack of 17th February, attack of 18th, affair of 25th, also night attack of the 25th February 1858, joined the Camp of His Excellency Sir Colin Campbell Commander-in-Chief, before Lucknow on the 11th, joined the Troops in advance at the Begumkatee on the 12th, operations of the 13th, and on the 14th March under Genl. T. H. Franks, led his Regiment (R. F.) which on that day stormed and carried the Emam Barra and the Kaissur Bagh, and driving the enemy before it, by turning their own guns on them, established itself in the main square, and planted the British Standard on the top of the principal Palace therein; at the taking of the Iron Bridge, &c., under Genl. Sir J. Outram on the 16th March (severely wounded,) and at the subsequent operations about Lucknow, medal and clasp and Lt. Colonel, with Genl. J. H. Grant's moveable column at Fyzabad, &c. &c.

Ensign Bradley served in Scinde and Beloochistan under *Sir* C. J. Napier, in the Punjaub Campaign under Lord Gough, was present at the battles of Ramnuggur, passage of the Chenab, Chillianwallah and Goojerat, Wounded, medal and clasps; served with an expedition under Col. Cotton, in the Irrawaddy district, Pegu, present at the siege of Delhi, wounded, and Ensign's Commission.

Ensign Hardy served with the 1st En. B. Fls. in Burmah 1852-53. present at the relief of the garrison of Pegu 14th December 1852, and throughout the operations in the vicinity, accompanied the Martaban column under the command of General Steel (medal) present at the battle of Badlee-ke-Seraie 8th June 1857, in the subsequent actions under the walls of Delhi, present at the storm and capture of Delhi on the 14th September 1857, (wounded 15th September,) present in all the engagements with the mutineers, under the command of Brigadiers Gerrard and Sir Thomas Seaton, en route to Futeghurh; present at the storm and capture of Lucknow and with the column under command of Major General Sir J. H. Grant K. C. B.

WAR SERVICES OF THE OFFICERS OF THE MEDICAL DEPARTMENT.

Suptg. Surg. J. Row served at the siege and taking of Hattrass in 1817, and with the right division of the Grand Army under the Marquis of Hastings in 1817-18, in the Bhuttee campaign in 1818, and at Bhurtpore in 1825-26, India medal.

Suptg. Surg. J. Forsyth served as Senr. Surg. in Shah Soojah's force in Affghanistan during its occupation by the British Troops: was at the capture of Ghuznee under Sir John Keane: accompanied the expedition up the Koonar Valley: and was present at the attack of the fort of Pushoot under Col. Orchard: was with the expedition up the Valley against the Sangoo Khail under Brigadier Shelton: accompanied General Sale's Brigade from the Khoord Caubul Pass to Jellalabad, and was present at the affair of Tazeen, Jugdulluck and Mamoo Khail: defence of Jellalabad: action of the 7th April 1842: re-occupation of Caubul under General Pollock, 3 medals, Ghuznee, Jellalabad and Caubul, 3rd class Dooranee order.

Supdg. Surg. J. Greig served against the Bheels in 1827, and was present at the battle of Punniar, bronze star.

Supdg. Surg. G. G. Brown, M. D., served in Bundelkund 1842, and also in the Gwalior, Sutledge and Punjaub campaigns, bronze star and 2 medals.

H. M. Tweddell served with the Saugor and Nerbudda Field Force in 1842-43; in the Gwalior campaign, bronze star, in the Sutledge campaign, medal.

J. Barber served at the siege of Bhurtpore in 1825-26, against the Coles in 1832-33, in Bundelkund in 1842, an in the Sutledge campaign 1846, medal.

SURGEONS.

C. McKinnon, M. D., served in Affghanistan in 1839-40-41 and 42: present at the capture of Ghuznee, at the operations in and beyond Bameean in 1839, at those on the Kohistan under *Sir* Robert Sale 1840: at the defence of Kelat-i-Ghilzie in 1841-42, with the Candahar Division under *Sir* Wm. Nott in its advance on Caubul, and present at the action of Gowau and second capture of Ghuznee; with the Army of the Punjaub in 1848-49, and present at Ramnuggur and at the battles of Chillianwalla and Goojerat, 4 medals, Ghuznee, Kelat-i-Ghilzie, Candahar, Caubul and Punjaub.

H. A. Bruce, M. D., served against the Coles 1832-33, in Affghanistan 1839-40-41, present at the storm and capture of Ghuznee, crossed the Hindu Koosh with Dennie's Brigade, and was present at the battle of Bameean, and also during the campaign on the Sutledge, including the actions of Alliwal and Sobraon, 2 medals and clasp for Ghuznee, Alliwal and Sobraon.

Supdg. Surg. J. Murray, M. D., served in the Sutledge campaign, and was Field Surgeon at Alliwal, medal.

J. Anderson, M. D., served against the Coles in 1837-38, and throughout the campaign in the Punjaub 1848-49, was present at Ramnuggur, Sadoolapore, Chillianwalla and Goojerat, medal and clasp.

G. Paton, A. M., M. D., served in Scinde and Affghanistan with the Army of the Indus, present at the storm and capture of Ghuznee, medal; at the operations in the Khyber Pass, and was with the Field Hospital in the campaign of the Sutledge.

W. Brydon served in Affghanistan 1841: Zoormut Valley, Caubul and retreat from Caubul: defence of Jellalabd: with Brigr. Monteath on the Nazeem Valley, and with Genl. Pollock in the advance on Caubul 1842, Rulleea Keiree, with the Bhopal Contingent, medals, Jellalabad and Caubul, and with the Burmah Expedition, present at the operations in the vicinity and capture of Rangoon, April 1852, medal.

J. Wood served throughout the Punjaub campaign: present at the actions of Sadoolapore, Chillianwalla and Goojerat, medals.

S. H. Batson served in the Sutledge campaign: present at the action of Alliwal, medal; volunteered to carry expresses to the General commanding at Meerut, on the day of the Delhi Massacre, 11th May 1857, field Surgeon to the Army before Delhi during the *whole* sieges subsequently appointed Surgeon to the Depot Hospitals, Selimghur, Delhi.

A. Gibbon served on the Staff of *Sir* C. Napier in Scinde, medals for Meanee and Dubba.

J. C. Brown C.B., seved in the campaign in Affghanistan, from May 1840 to end of 1842: was with *Sir* R. Sale's force during the defence of Jellalabad: present at general actions with Akbar Khan on 7th April and 13th September 1842: present at the battles of Alliwal and Sobraon during the campaign on the Sutledge 1846, 3 medals, Jellalabad, Caubul, Alliwal and Sobraon.

J. Balfour served in the Burmah campaign as Field Surgeon from 15 Sept. 1852 to the end of the war, medal.

F. Anderson, M. D., served in the Sutledge campaign: was present at the battles of Moodkee, Ferozeshuhur and Sobraon, medal and two clasps.

G. Rae served with the Horse Artillery, and with Shah Shoojah's force in Affghanistan, from the first occupation of the country by the Army of the Indus 1838, until the return of the last Division *viâ* Scinde in 1843: present in actions at Quetta, Kelat-i-Ghilzie, in Zemindawar, on the Urgundâh, near Candahar, and in the Kojuck, at Lahore in 1846-47, medal "Candahar 1842."

R. C. Guise served throughout the Sutledge campaign and was present at Moodkee, Ferozeshuhur and Sobraon medal and 2 clasps; also served in the Punjaub campaign of 1848-49, medal.

G. S. Cardew, M. D., served in the Gwalior campaign, bronze star.

J. A. Dunbar, M.D., served in the Gwalior and Sutledge campaigns, and was present at the battle of Sobraon, medal.

R. W. Faithful served in Caubul 1842.

G. C. Wallich, M. D., served as Assistant Superintending Surgeon Sutledge campaign, (medal) and through the Punjaub campaign with 2nd Irregular Cavalry in Brigadier Wheeler's force, medal.

C. M. Henderson, M. D., served during the campaign on the Sutledge, present at the action of Sobraon, medal.

H. Irwin, F. R. C. S. I., was attached to Brigadier Wild's Brigade, and served with the force under General Pollock, during the campaign in Affghanistan 1842; present at the forcing of the Khyber Pass, medal.

D. McRae served with *Sir* Geo. Pollock's force in Affghanistan.

H. B. Hinton served during the Gwalior campaign, and with the Army of the Sutledge; present at the actions of Buddiwal, Alliwal and Sobraon, medal and clasp.

E. Hare served at Caubul in 1840; at Joolgah and Purwundarrah under General Sale in the same year; was in the garrison of Jellalabad under *Sir* R. Sale, medal, and the march to Caubul under *Sir* G. Pollock, medal; served in Burmah campaign in 1852-54, in charge of 1st En. B. Fusiliers, recapture of Pegu, medal; served as Surgeon of the 2nd En. B. Fusiliers throughout the siege operations before Delhi, also at the action of Badleeka Serai, 8th June 1858 and the final assault and capture of the City of Delhi, 14th September 1857.

C. G. Andrews served with the army in Burmah in 1852-53; was present with the combined force under Major Minchin and Capt. Loch, R. N., against the Rebel Chief Mya Toon in February 1853, and in the operations against the same Chief from 7th to 24th March 1853, medal.

G. Harper served with Brigadier Wild's Brigade, was present at the forcing of the Khyber Pass, and through the subsequent campaign with *Sir* George Pollock's force, medal, served with the Army throughout the Punjaub campaign, medal.

G. S. Mann served in China 1840-41, medal.

T. Cantor, M. D., served with H. M. 26th Foot, Cameronians, during the war in China in 1840-41, medal, in the Depôt Hospital army of the Sutledge, in the Field Hospital Army of the Punjaub present at Ramnuggur, Chillianwallah and Goojerat, medal and 2 clasps.

T. C. Hutchinson was present at the capture of Chusan 1840, and of Amoy, Chinhae and second capture of Chusan and occupation of Ningfoo 1841-42, served throughout the two campaigns in China in 1840-41-42-43, medal.

W Shurlock served with the 26th Cameronians in China during 1840-41: present at the taking of Chusan, medals.

E. Campbell served during the Affghan campaign. Left at Caubul in charge of wounded Europeans, on the retreat of the Army, was a prisoner there for 9 months, present at the storming of Istaliff—also at the battles of Maharajpore, Moodkee, Ferozeshuhur, Alliwal and Sobraon.

J. Macpherson, M. D. served in the Depôt Hospital. Army of the Sutledge, 1846.

A. W. Crozier F. R. C. S. served with H. M. 55th Regiment in China in 1841-42-43, was at the taking of Amoy, recapture of Chusan and occupation of Ningfoo, (Medal) served in the Gwalior campaign and was present at the battle of Punniar in charge of the 50th N. I. (Bronze star) served in the Sutledge campaign with 16th Lancers and was present at the battles of Buddiwal and Alliwal, for his services at the last battle, he received the special thanks of Lt. General Sir H. Smith Commanding. Officiated as Supr. Surgeon in the action on the 5th July 1857 near Agra, against the Neemuch and Nusseerabad mutineers, had a horse shot under him and was thanked in the despatch for services performed on the occasion; was in Medical charge of the 3rd E. Regiment in the action of the 10th Octr. Agra against the rebels from Gwalior. Was in medical charge of the 3rd in the action with rebels at Oriya; served the whole cf the hot weather campaign of 1858 against the mutineers, in the affairs of Etawah and Mynpooree districts Was in charge of the 3rd or moveable column under command, of Col Riddell which marched towards Gwalior to co-operate with Central field Force, thanked by Col. Riddel in his despatch for services rendered on the occasion. (3 Medals and one bronze Star.)

SURGEONS—*Continued.*

T. Thomson, M. D., served with the 27th Native Infantry at Ghuznee, where he was made prisoner; and in the Sutledge and Punjaub campaigns.

A. Beale served in Bundelkund in 1842, and in the Sutledge campaign, present at the battle of Ferozeshuhur, medal.

A. H. Cheek served with the Bundelkund Legion at the siege of Chirgong and in Bundelkund in 1841-42.

T. S. Lacy served throughout the Punjaub campaign, including the passage of the Chenab, battles of Chillianwalla and Goojerat, and subsequent pursuit of the Seikh army by the force under General Gilbert, medal.

J. Jowett served in China 1841-42, medal.

A. Grant served throughout the expedition to China 1841-42-43-44, present at the capture of Amoy, Chusan and Chapoo, the storming of Woosung and occupation of Shanghai and assault and capture of Chian Keang Foo and investment of Nankin, medal, attached to the Depôt Hospital army of the Sutledge 1846.

J. Campbell served in the Affghan campaign of 1842 under *Sir* George Pollock, and in Scinde in 1845-46, medal for Affghanistan.

R. Whittall served with the 26th N.I. with Genl. Pollock's force in Affghanistan in 1842, at the forcing of the Khyber Pass; at the battles of Mamoo Kheil, Jugdulluck and Tazeen, and with *Sir* J. McCaskill's division in Kohistan, and also at the capture of Istaliff; also with the Army of the Sutledge at Sobraon. 2 medals.

H. W. Rumley served with the 1st Brig. H. A. throughout the Sutledge campaign: present at the battles of Moodkee, (horse shot) Ferozeshuhur and Sobraon; with the 2nd Brig. H. A. during the Punjaub campaign; present at Ramnuggur, Sadoolapore, Chillianwalla and Goojerat.

J. Hilliard served in Bundelkund in 1842, and in the Sonthal insurrection in 1856, as Field Surgeon, Ranee gunge depôt Hospital.

A. White, M. D., served with the army under Genl. Pollock: present at the forcing of the Khyber Pass, and subsequent operations in Affghanistan, medal; also throughout the Sutledge campaign, including the action of Sobraon, medal and clasp

E. Goodeve, M. B., served in the Sutledge and Punjaub campaigns; present at Ramnuggur, Chillianwalla and Goojerat, 2 medals and 2 clasps.

W. C. B. Eatwell, M. D., served in China from 1842 to 1845.

C. L. Cox, A. B., served throughout the China expedition with the army under Lord Gough, medal, and with the force under Brigadier Genl. Wheeler in the Jullundur Dooab 1848-49, medal.

D. J. O'Callaghan served in the field hospital of the Army of the Sutlej; served the campaign of 1857, as Surgeon, in chief medical charge of the foot artillery of the army of Delhi, siege storm and capture of the City, medal and clasp.

R. H. Oakley served with the Army of the Punjaub, medal; present at the passage of the Chenab, Chillianwala and Goojerat, medal and clasps.

C. Harland served with the army of the Sutledge; emplod in the Field Hospital at Sobraon; served against the insurgent Sonthals in 1856, with the force, commanded by Major General Lloyd, C. B.

J. R. Withecombe, M. D., served in Scinde, 1843; with the Field Hospital throughout the Punjaub campaign; present at the actions of Ramnuggur, Chillianwalla and Goojerat, medal and 2 clasps.

S. A. Homan served against the Hill Tribes in Scinde 1845, and during the Punjaub campaign, including the siege and operations in the vicinity of Mooltan and battle of Goojerat, medal and clasps.

J. Harrison, M. D., served in the campaign of the Sutledge in 1845-46, and present at the battle of Ferozeshuhur, medal, with the Army of the Punjaub, including the actions of Sadoolapore, Chillianwalla and Goojerat, medal and clasp.

W. Crozier served at Moodkee and Ferozeshuhur, medal and clasp.

F. M. Clifford served in the campaigns against the Hill Tribes of Scinde under Sir C. J. Napier in 1845.

J. F. Beatson, M. D. and A. B., served in the Sutledge campaign; present at the defence of Ferozepore, and at Ferozeshuhur, medal, and with the Artillery attached to Brigr. Wheeler's force in the Punjaub campaign, medal.

J. W. Fletcher, F. R. C. S., served in the Sutledge campaign.

C. F. Warneford, M. D., served with the depôt Hospital Army of the Sutledge, throughout the Punjaub war, present at the actions of Ramnuggur and Goojerat medal and clasp.

H. B. Buckle served in the Punjaub campaign, including the passage of the Chenab and battlesof Chillianwalla and Goojerat, medal and clasps.

G. R. Playfair, M. D., served throughout the war in China, as Surgeon of the H. C. War Steamers Madagascar and Phlegethon, present at all the engagements in the Canton River at both the attacks on Chusan, taking of Amoy, assault of the heights of Chinghae, Storm of Sigoun heights, Chapoo Woosing, assault and capture of Chinkeangfoo and at Nankin, medal.

W. F. Mactier, M. D., served in the Sutledge and Punjaub campaigns.

F. Douglas, M. D., served in the Sutledge campaign: present at Budiwal, Alliwal and Sobraon, medal and clasp; also as Storekeeper to the Army of the Punjaub: present at Ramnuggur, Chillianwalla and Goojerat, medal.

F. Turnbull, M. D., served with the Sappers and Pioneers, atthe siege and surrender of Mooltan and battle of Goojerat, medal.

J. N. Tresidder served in the Sutledge campaign, and the Field Hospital, Army of the Punjaub; present at the battles of Chillianwalla and Goojerat, medal and 2 clasps.

C. M. Smith, served throughout the 1st and 2nd siege of Mooltan 1848-49: present at the action of Soorjkoond and the battle of Goojerat medal and 2 clasps.

J. P. Walker, M. D., served in the Punjaub campaign, medal.

J. T. C. Ross, F. R. C. S., served with the force under Brigadier Wheeler, in the Punjaub campaign 1848-49, medal, joined the 1st Punjaub Cavalry at Kohat after *Sir* Charles Napier's expedition through the Pass and was in Medical charge of the Regiment in the 1st Meeranzie expedition under Captain Coke in 1851; in Medical charge of the 1st Punjaub Cavalry and Infantry during the operations in the Raneezie Valley under *Sir* Colin Campbell K. C. B. in 1852; was engaged in the affairs of the Kohat-kohtul under Major Coke in 1853.

ASSISTANT SURGEONS.

G. N. Cheek was present at the siege and taking of Hattrass in 1817, and with the centre of the Grand Army during the campaign of 1817-18, has also received the Peninsular Medal for St. Sebastian and Orthes.

ASSISTANT SURGEONS.—(*Continued.*)

D. Scott served throughout the Punjaub campaign 1848-49, including the skirmish at Ramnuggur and the actions of Sadoolapore, Chillianwalla and Goojerat, and subsequent pursuit of the Seikhs and Affghans, medal and clasp; also with Brigadier Bradshaw's force in the Eusofzye country in December 1849 and with that under *Sir* C. Napier in the Kohat Pass.

T. Maxwell, M. D., served during the Punjaub campaign, and present at the affair of Ramnuggur, and the actions of Sadoolapoore, Chillianwalla and Goojerat, medal and clasps; served in 1852-53 against the Wuzeerees on Bunnoo frontier; in 1856 in the expedition under Brigr. Chamberlain, against the Belooch Tribes on Derajat Frontier; in 1857 in Iusufsaie against the revolted Tribes in that district and in two assaults and capture of fortified village and positions of Naringee. in 1858 at Siege and capture of Lucknow medal and clasp, action at Courci assault at Fort of Rooya, action at Allygunge, capture of Bareilly, action at Mohunpore, and action at Phillibheet, wounded slightly.

D. MacDonald, M. D. served with the force under Sir Hugh Wheeler in the Punjaub 1848-49, medal. With the 2nd Irregular Cavalry in the Peshawur Valley, 1851-52 and at the operations in the Raneezaie Valley with the force under Sir Colin Campbell, K.C.B., 1852.

H. M. Cannon, M. B., attached to the Army of the Punjaub: present at the actions of Ramnuggur, Chillianwalla and Goojerat, medal.

C. K. Webb served with the 2nd Punjaub Infantry at the re-occupation of Bareilly in 1857-58.

A. L. S. Campbell served throughout the 1st and 2d siege and operations before Mooltan 1848-49 and was present at the battle of Goojerat, and also at the operations against the Bussy Khel Afreedees under Lt. Col. Craigie C. B., March 1855, medal and clasps.

G. H. Ray, M. D., served during the Punjaub campaign, and was present at Ramnuggur, at the passage of the Chenab, and action of Chillianwalla, medal and clasp.

G. C. Leathes was present at the siege of Mooltan, medal and clasp.

J. Williams served in the Punjaub campaign.

T. Atchison served during the Punjaub campaign: present at the siege of Mooltan, action of Soorujkhoond and the battle of Goojerat, medal and 2 clasps.

H. Stewart was present at the siege of Mooltan, medal and clasp.

H. A. Ebden, M. D., served throughout the Punjaub war as Assistant in the Field Hospital, present at Ram nuggur, Chillianwalla, Goojerat, and accompanied *Sir* W. Gilbert's Force to Peshawur, medal.

T. Farquhar, M. D., served in the Punjaub campaign.

G. R. Pemberton, M. D. and J. C. Bow, M. D., served during the operations in the Punjaub 1848-49, present a the actions of Sadoolapore, Chillianwalla and Goojerat, medals.

W. White served with the Army of the Punjaub, present at Goojerat medal, also served with the expedition to Burmah, present at the operations in the vicinity and capture of Rangoon April 1852, medal.

A. St. A. Wilson, M. D., served with the Army of the Punjaub, present at the battle of Chillianwalla, meda and clasp: served with the expedition to Burmah, medal.

F. F. Allen, served throughout the whole of the siege operations before Delhi after the fall of the place accompanied Brigadier Showers column into the Mewattee country.

E. McKellar, A. Christison, M.D., J.P. Bowling, and G.M. Govan, M. D., served with the expedition to Burmah, present at the operations in the vicinity and capture of Rangoon, Apl. 1852 medals.

J. Fayrer, M. D., F. R. C. S. was present throughout the operations in 1848 in Palermo, between the Neapolitan and Sicilian Troops, subsequently witnessed the attack upon the city of Rome by the French forces, under General Oudinot; served in the late Burmese war on board the Hon. Company's Steamer Phlegethon in medical charge of a detachment of the 18th Royal Irish under the command of Captain Woodright at the destruction of the stockades in the Rangoon river, was present at the operations in the vicinity and capture of Rangoon and in the field hospital and as medical store-keeper of the Bengal Division, Army of Burmah, until after the proclamation of annexation was a member, of the Lucknow Garrison as Residency Surgeon, from the commencement of the disturbances until the final relief and evacuation of the Residency in November 1857, medal.

W. H. Adley present at the fight at Pung Pao between the garrison of Fort Shubkudr under Sir Colin Campbell, K. C. B., and the combined Momund Tribes, April 1852. Operations in the Raneezaie Valley under Sir Colin Campbell K. C. B., May 1852. With the force employed in the Boori Pass under Brigadier Boileau Nov. 1853. Affairs at Michnee under Brigadier Cotton, Aug. Sep. 1854. Operations against the Bussy Khel Afreedees under Lieut. Col. Craigie, C. B., March 1855.

J. B. Scriven served with the 1st E. B. Fusiliers in the Burmah campaign of 1852-53, accompanied the Martaban Column under Genl. Steel to Tonghoo, medal.

C. Stewart M. D., served with the 1st En. B. Fusiliers at the relief of Pegu and the subsequent operations in the Field under General Godwin; attached to advanced Guard of General Steels' column from Martaban to Shwegyeen, medal; in Medical charge of Major Gottreux's force at the assault and re-capture of Beeling and of Major Selon's detachment in the expedition to Womgyee; served under Major Nuthall in the operations against the Rebel Chief Goungyee.

E. McKellar served with H. M. 80th Regiment throughout the Burmese war of 1852-53, present at the capture of Martaban; at the operations before Rangoon on 12th, 13th and 14th April; in medical charge of Major Cotton's force at the capture of Prome in June 1852; at the taking of Prome, and the subsequent operations in its vicinity, medal, with 3rd European Regiment in the actions near Agra of 5th July and 10th October 1857, and in medical charge of Major Montgomerie's force in the engagement with the Rebels near Allyghur on 24th August; with Col. Seaton's column in the actions of Gungeeree and Puttialee.

A. C. C. DeRenzy served with the expedition to Burmah, present at the taking of Martaban, and operations in the vicinity and capture of Rangoon, April 1852, medal.

J. C. Corbyn served with the Umritsur moveable column, accompanied the Cashmere force under col. R. Lawrence to Delhi, and was present at the siege and capture of that place; served with the troops at Juggur and Rohtuck; had medical charge of the third Seikh Cavalry at Lucknow; present at the final capture of that City. The 3rd Seikh Cavalry formed part of the forces under Sir Edward Lugard K. C. B. with whom the Regiment was at the relief of Azimghur and afterwards accompanied Brigdr. Douglas C. B. in the rapid and celebrated pursuit after the rebel Koer Singh;—was present in every action fought by his Regiment; served with the Azimghur field force,, from 29th March to 4th June 1858, when the rebels were finally expelled the Jugdtspore Juugles; also present with the 3rd Seikh Cavalry all through the quelling of the disturbances of the Shahabad and Behar districts.

W. B. Beatson, M. D., served with Field Hospital of Burmese expedition during 1853, Medal.

C. T. Paske served in Burmah with the Field Hospital 1853, Medal; present during the engagement at Azimghur against the Pulwars, July 1857. In medical charge of the Goorkha Field Force under Lieut. Col. Wroughton, present at the actions of Guggah, Koodwah and Chandah, medal.

W. F. B. Dalzell, M. D. served with H. M. 9th Lancers from the 12th October 1857 to the 8th February 1858, at the relief of the Garrison of Lucknow by Sir Colin Campbell in November 1857, at the relief of Cawnpore by Sir Colin Campbell in December 1857 and subsequent operations against the mutineers with the Brigade under Major General Sir J. H. Grant at Serai Ghaut, December 1857, and at Shumshabad near Futtehghur

ASSISTANT SURGEONS.—(*Continued.*)

with the force under Brigr. Hope H. M. 93rd Highlanders in January 1858, and with the 1st European Bengal Fusiliers from the 8th February to the 24th March 1858, at the siege and capture of Lucknow by Sir Colin Campbell, in March 1858; was present at the action of Sassia near Agra under Brigadier Polwhele on the 5th July 1857, also with the column under Colonel G. V. Maxwell, H. M. 88th Foot at the siege and capture of Calpee, 23rd May 1858.

S. B. Partridge F. R. C. S. E. served in the Burmese campaign of 1852-53; with the force under Sir John Cheape, K. C. B. at Donabew, March 1853, medal; was a member of the old garrison throughout the defence of the Residency of Lucknow from the 30th of June to the 22nd November 1857; served as field Assistant Surgeon with the Head-Quarters of the Army during the subsequent campaign; was present at the defeat of the Gwalior rebels at Cawnpore. December 7th. 1857; at the passage of the Kali Naddi; at the re-occupation of Futtyghur, and at the final siege and capture of Lucknow in March 1858.

R. C. Knight served as an Acting Assistant Surgeon with the Scinde Field Force, during the Affghan campaign, present at the engagement near Kohun against the troops of Nasseer Khan of Khelat. 1st Dec. 1840.

T. Ringer served with the column under Brigadier. Franks, C. B. in Oude 1858; present at the siege and capture of Lucknow by Sir Colin Campbell in March 1858, at the battle and taking of Bareilly, May 1858. served with Soraon field force, under Brigadier Berkeley, C. B. present at the capture of the Forts Deghain, Turoul aud Bhyspore in 1858.

W. F. Clark served with the 2nd Punjaub Infantry at the assault on, and capture of the Bozdar strong hold on the Derajat Frontier in March 1857: also during the campaign in Hindustan in 1857-58; Present at the siege, assault, and capture of Delhi, including the battle of Nujufghur. accompanied the moveable column under Colonel Greathed after the fall of Delhi; present at the battles of Bolundshuhur and Agra, the relief of the Lucknow Garrison, the battles of Cawnpore, and Khodagunge (near Futtyghur) and the siege and capture ef the City of Lucknow, besides many other minor affairs, medal and clasps.

G. N. Cheek (Junior) served with H. M. 86th Regt. C. T. F. F. during the oper ations before and taking of Calpee and Gwalior.

A. K. Reed served in the Baltic during the campaign of 1854.

J. L. Stewart served before Delhi throughout the siege, assault and capture of that place. was also present with the expedition in the Eusofzaie Country under Major Genl. Sir S J. Cotton, K. C. B. in 1858.

J. H. Thornton served with a detachment of H. M. 5th Fusiliers at the relief of Arrah (2nd August) and at the capture. Jugdespore (11th August 1857); was present with a force under the command of Brigadier Wilson at the action of Soorajpore (18th October); proceeded with Major Barnston's force to Alumbaugh and served with the Garrison of that post from 25th October to 27th November 1857; was then attached to H. M. 90th L. I. and was present with that Regiment at several engagements with the enemy near Alumbaugh and at the assault and capture of Lucknow in March 1858; served with the 1st European Bengal Fusiliers at various operations against the enemy in the vicinity of Durriabad.

F. J. Pettingal served throughout the Punjaub Campaign of 1848-49, present at the battle of Chillianwallah, medal and clasps.

J. C. Dickinson was attached to the Pearl's Naval Brigade with Brigadier Rowcroft's column, was present at he action of Seharunpore 26 Dec. 1857, at the action of Phoolpore (Oude) the battle of Amorah, also Thelga and capture of the Fort of Nugger.

C. E. Raddock served in Medical charge of Capt. Hardy's Battery of Royal Artillery (5th Co. 11th B.) at the action of Bunteera 1857, with Sir Hope Grant's column; and at the relief of the residency (Lucknow) during the several operations under his Excellency the Commander-in-Chief, 1857. In medical charge of Capt. Middleton's Battery, Royal Artillery (6th Co. 13th B.) at the battle of Cawnpore, 1857, with the Commander-in-Chief's Foree at Serajghaut and Bithour with Sir Hope Grant's column; during the March of the Battery to Jounpore to join Genl. Frank's column and at the actions of Chanda and Umrapoora and the battle of Sultanpore, 1858, March to Lucknow and at the siege and capture of Lucknow 1858, with Genls. Outram and Lugard's divisions with the Oude field force under Sir Hope Grant from April to August 1858, at Baree and the occupation of Fyzabad, at the last named war in Medical charge of C. Co. Madras Sappers and Miners.

J. Sheil, M. B., was present in General Havelock's garrison at Alumbaugh, at the relief of Lucknow by Sir Colin Campbell; with Sir J. Outram's force of occupation at Alumbaugh; at the capture of Lucknow; relief of Azimghur. pursuitof Koer Sing and subsequent operations in Jugdespore Jungle.

G. S. Sutherland, M. D., served with the Turkish Contingent in Turkey and the Crimea from April 1855, till the conclusion of the Russian war, order of the Medjidee; with the field hospital of the army of Oude under Sir Colin Campbell, G. C. B., in 1858; present at the siege and capture of Lucknow, medal and clasp.

F. Dickson was present with H. M. "Shannon" Naval Brigade, during the siege and capture of Lucknow.

WAR SERVICES OF VETERINARY SURGEONS.

Veterinary Surgeon R. B. Parry served with the 3rd Light Cavalry during the Cole campaign.

Vety. Surgeon J. Harris served throughout the Punjaub campaign, medal and clasp.

Vety. Surgeon H. C. Hulse served with *Sir* G. Pollock's force in the Caubul campaign, medal: with the 10th Light Cavalry during the Gwalior campaign: present at the battle of Maharajpore, star: with the 1st Brigade Horse Artillery at Chillianwalla and Goojerat, medal.

Vety. Surgeon W. McDermott served with army of the Indus in 1838-39-40, under Genl. Sale, in the Kohistan, of Caubul, Sutledge campaign 1845-46, "Ferozeshuhur," medal; army of the Punjaub, "Ramnuggur," "Sadoolapore," "Chillianwalla," "Goojerat," and with the Force in pursuit of Seikhs and Affghans.

Vety. Surgeon J. Siddall served with the 2nd Brigade Horse Artillery during the Punjaub Campaigns and was present at the passage of the Chenab and battle of Chillianwalla and Goojerat, medal and clasp.

Vety. Surgeon W. Johnson present at the operations, siege, and capture of Mooltan.

Vety. Surgeon A. Turnbull served with the Army of the Punjaub, at "Ramnuggur," "Sadoolapore," "Chillianwalla," and "Goojerat," medal and clasps.

C. Corker served with Governor General's Body-guard throughout the campaign against the Sonthals 1855, served with the column under Brigadier Franks, C. B. in Oude 1858; present at the siege and capture of Lucknow by Sir Colin Campbell in March 1858; at the battle and taking of Barielly May 1858; served with Soraon field force under Brigadier Berkeley, C. B. present at the capture of Forts Deghain, Turoul, Bhyspore, in 1858.

War Services of the Officers of the Invalid Establishment.

Lt. Col. Angelo was present at the fall of Kalinger in Bundelkund under Genl. Martindell in 1812: Rewah campaign under Sir John Adams in 1813: Alwar campaign under Sir Thomas Brown in 1814: Pindaree campaign under Lord Hastings in 1817-18-19: the capture of Lamba, Rajpootana, in 1824: the siege and capture of Bhurtpore in 1826, medal: Cole campaign, served in Affghanistan in 1838-39, commanded the Cavalry of Sir Robert Sale's expedition from Candahar to the Helmund: present at the capture of Ghuznee, medal: and commanded the 3rd Lt. Cavalry during the campaign on the Sutledge, including the battles of Alliwal and Sobraon medal, clasp and Bt. Lt. Col. Lt. Col. Blake served during the Nepaul war, medal.,

Lt. Col. Thornton served in Bundelkund 1810-11, Kalinger 1812, Nepaul war 1814-15, present at the taking of Nahun and Kalinger, Pindaree campaign 1817-18, and in Assam 1826, India medal.

Lieut. Col. Blair, C. B., served at the siege and capture of Bhurtpore, medal, in Affghanistan 1842, medal and C. B., and at the action of Maharajpore, bronze star.

Lieut. Col. Smith served with the 6th Regt. Light Cavalry, during the whole time it was engaged in the Pindaree war 1816-17; present in the actions of Seetabuldee and Lukkurchurrah 1817; at the storm and capture of Chundeh in May 1818, and at the siege and capture of Bhurtpore, medal.

Major Rutledge was present at the storming of the fortified Hill of Adgurree; also at the siege and capture of the Fort of Adjeghur in Bundelkund in 1809; throughout the Nepaul war, and present at the assault of Malown in 1814-15; also in the whole of the Mahratta war, including the capture of Nagpore in 1816-17, India medal and clasps.

Major Swetenham was present at the siege and capture of Bhurtpore, medal.

Major Stevens was present at the siege of Bhurtpore, India medal; served also with the force under Major General *Sir* G. Pollock during the Affghan campaign 1842.

Major Boulton served against the insurgents at Dek Kanal near Cuttack in 1833; also with the China expedition in 1840-41, medal.

Major Grant served throughout the Punjaub Campaign 1848-49, medal.

Major Blanshard served at the siege of Bhurtpore, India medal, and throughout the campaign on the Sutledge: present at the battle of Sobraon, medal and clasp.

Lt. Col. Loftie served in the Caubul campaign of 1842 as Major of Brigade of the 3rd Infantry Brigade, Genl. Pollock's force, in the action at the mouth of the Khyber Pass, 19th Jan. 1842, (severely wounded:) present at the forcing of the Pass on the 5th April, medal: throughout the Sutledge campaign, as Major of Brigade 10th Infantry Brigade, including the action of Alliwal, medal and Bt. Major: with the army of the Punjaub, at the passage of the Chenab and battle of Chillianwalla, (twice severely wounded) medal.

Major Haslewood served with the army of the Indus 1838-39, and was present at the storm and capture of Guznee, where he was severely wounded whilst leading a sub-division of the advance, medal.

Capt. Nash served at the siege and capture of Bhurtpore, medal.

Captain Fanshawe served in Affghanistan 1839-40; present at the storm and capture of Ghuznie, medal; throughout the campaign on the Sutledge, including the actions of Ferozepore (wounded) and Sobraon, medal and clasp; in Burmah in 1852-53; present at the relief of Pegu in Dec. 1852, accompanied the Martaban Column to Tonghoo, medal.

Captain Jorden was present at siege and capture of Bhurtpore, 1825-26, India medal.

Captain Smith served throughout the Scinde campaign in 1843, and was present at the battles of Meanee and Hydrabad, (wounded, and medal,) and at the occupation of Lahore in 1846.

Bt. Major Master served with the force under *Sir* G. Pollock, G. C. B., in Affghanistan in 1842; during the campaign on the Sutledge, including the battle of Sobraon 1846, medal, with the force under General Whish at the siege and surrender of Mooltan, and battle of Goojerat, medal, clasp and Bt. Major.

Captain Magnay served with the army of the Indus from 1838 to 1841. In the advance at the storm and capture of Ghuznee, 23rd July 1839, (wounded) medal. Engagements in the Wuzeerah Valley, was also in the Sutledge campaign including the actions of Ferozeshuhur and Sobraon, where he was severely wounded, medal and clasp.

Capt. Hervey was employed with the 2nd Volunteer Battalion during the China expedition, medal, also with the force under Brigadier Wheeler in the Punjaub 1848-49.

Captain Thompson served against the Hill Tribes in Scinde under *Sir* C. Napier, with the army of the Punjaub 1848-49, present at the passage of the Chenab, actions of Chillianwalla and Goojeerat and subsequent pursuit of the Seikhs and Affghans by the force under General Gilbert, medal and clasp.

Capt. Innes served throughout the campaign on the Sutledge; present at the actions of Ferozeshuhur and Sobraon, was wounded in the latter engagement, medal and clasp.

Capt. Aubert served during the campaign on the Sutledge, present at Sobraon, (slightly wounded) medal.

Capt. Strover served during the campaign in the Punjaub and was present at the actions of Sadoolapore, Chillianwallah and Goojerat, medal.

Capt. Coombs served during the Sutledge campaign, present at the battle of Sobraon, medal.

Lieut. Pogson served with the 47th N. I. at the battle of Moodkee, wounded, medal.

Lieut. Arbuthnott served in the Sutledge campaign with the 5th Light Cavy.; present at the actions of Moodkee, (charger shot,) Ferozeshuhur, Aliwall and Sobraon, medal and three clasps.

Lieut. Kennedy served with the army of the Punjaub, including the siege and surrender Mooltan and battle of Goojerat, medal and clasp.

Lieut Moore served with the Army of the Indus, present at the assault and capture of Ghuznee, medal, during the campaign on the Sutledge including the actions of Ferozeshuhur (wounded) and Sobraon (severely wounded, lost the use of right arm,) medal, clasp and Ensign's Commission.

Lieut. Goodridge served with the army of the Punjaub 1848-49, including actions of Ramnuggur, Chillianwallah and Goojerat and subsequent pursuit of the Seikhs and Affghans, medal and 2 clasps.

War Services of the Subordinate Officers of the Army, Commissariat Dept.

Lieutenant W. May served at the siege and capture of Hattrass, 1816, and during the Pindaree campaign 1817-18, and the Burmese war of 1825-26: Burmah, 1853, medal.

Lieut. J. Burnell served in the Burmah war 1825-26 and 1852-54; was present in all the engagements by the force under Genl. Havelock from Futtehpore to taking of Cawnpore as well as the bombardment of Cawnpore in Nov. 1857.

Depy. Commy. Alleyan Evanson Madras served in Affghanistan with the army of the Indus 1839-40, present at the storm and capture of Ghuznie, medal, and during the campaign in the Sutledge, including the actions of Ferozeshuhur and Sobraon, medal and clasp.

Depy. Commy. R. Kelly served at the siege and capture of Bhurtpore in 1825-26 medal, with the Burmah expedition present at the capture of Rangoon and Prome in 1852, medal.

Depy. Commy. A. B. Fox served with the Joudpore Field Force 1839, with the Bundlekund Field Force 1842-43, present at the battle of Maharajpore 1843, bronze star, with the army of the Sutledge 1845-46, present at Moodkee, Ferozeshunur and Sobraon, medal and 2 clasps, during the campaign in the Punjaub, present at the actions of Ramnuggur, Sadolapore, Chillianwallah and Goojerat and accompanied the Field Force under *Sir* W. Gilbert, G. C. B. on its advance to Peshawur, medal and 2 clasps.

Asst. Commy. J. Atkin served in Affghanistan with the force under General Pollock; present at the forcing of the Khyber Pass 5th April 1842 medal; present at the action of Ferozeshuhur; Grape shot and Musket wounds; 2 Ribs broken, medal.

Assist. Commy. James Gillmon served in Caubul compaign 1842, medal; served in the Sutledge campaign 1845-46; present at the actions of Moodkee Ferozeshuhur and Sabraon, medal and two clasps; received a medal for the Punjaub compaign 1848-49.

Depy. Asst. Commy. D. Ryan was present at the battle of Maharajpore. bronze star.

Depy. Asst. Commy. M. Cooper served in the campaign against the Hill Tribes in Scinde under *Sir* C. Napier 1845, also with the army of the Punjaub 1848-49: present at the battle of Ramnuggur, passage of the Chenab, actions of Chillianwallah (wounded) and Goojerat, and subsequent pursuits of the Seikhs and Affghans and occupation of Peshawur by General Gilbert, medal and clsasps; served with Sir J. Cotton's field force in the Eusofzaie Country in 1858, held Commissariat charge of the force, was most favorably mentioned in Sir J. Cotton's despatches on the occasion.

Conductor C. Stokes was present at the siege and capture of Bhurtpore in 25-26, medal.

Conductor J. Woodruffe served throughout the Gwalior campaign battle of Punniar in 1843, Bonzestar with the army of the Indus in Scinde in 1846-47, under Sir C. Napier G. C. B., throughout the Punjaub, campaign of 1848-49, action of Ramnuggur, Passage of the Chenab, Actions of Chillianwallah, (severely wounded by sabre cuts, in left shoulder, and bridle arm) and Goojerat, medal and two clasps. At the siege and capture of Delhi, actions of Bulundsuhuar, Ailyghur, Agra, Akkerabad, Meerun, Seraie, Kunnoge, Relief of Lucknow, retaking of Cawnpore, &c., in 1857, capture and fall of Lucknow in March 1858, and several others under Sir J. H. Grant K. C. B.

War Services of the Subordinate Officers of the Ordnance Department.

Capt. T. Spencer served at the siege and capture of Hattrass 1817; throughout the Pindaree campaign under Lord Hastings 1817-18; with the expedition to China under *Sir* Hugh Gough 1842-43: medal, throughout the siege and capture of Mooltan under General Whish and the battle of Goojerat 1848-49, medal and clasp.

Lieut. Michell served at the siege and capture of Bhurtpore 1825-26, medal.

Lieutenant Fox served during the Nepal war 1814-15, including the storm and capture of the fortress of Hurryarpore; present at the siege and capture of Hattrass, 1817, and at the taking of Jhansi 1838.

Lieutenant Parry served during the Burmese war in 1825-26, with the army of the Indus in Affghanistan in 1839-40, present at the assault and capture of Ghuznee, medal; also in an attack near Ali Musjid in Nov. 1839.

Deputy Asst. Commissary Leonard served at the siege and capture of Bhurtpore 1825-26, (India medal,) at the taking of Jhansi in 1838, and in Bundlekund 1841-42.

Deputy Asst. Commy. J, Stotesbury served at the siege and capture of Delhi 1857, medal and clasp.

Conductor E. Postance served in Ava in 1824-25-26 in H. M. 38th Foot, was wounded at the storm of Kockaignee and present in eleven engagements during the campaign, medal, served throughout the Affghan campaign from 1838 to 1842, in the 1st European Regiment; was present at the storm and capture of Ghuznee, (medal) also at the storm of Pushoot and at all the operations in the Pushoot valley.

Conductor Halpin was present at the siege and capture of Rangoon, Kemendine and battle of Rangoon 1824; Donabew, Prome, Meeaday and Malone 1825; Pagamew, Yandaboo and Ava 1826. Received a medal with clasps for Ava.

Conductor Heffernan served in the Gwalior campaign of 1843, battle of Maharajpore. Sutledge campaign of 1845-46, battle of Allsiwal, Punjaub campaign of 1848-49, Passage of the Chenab. battles of Chillianwallah (wounded) and Goojerat, and pursuit of Seikhs and Affghans to Peshawur, Oudh campaign of 1857-58, affairs near Kunenge and Marigunges, Relief of Lucknow, battle of Cawnpore, affair near Futtyghur, siege and capture of Lucknow, affairs near Junpore and Azimghur Bronze star, medal and two clasps.

Conductor Hill served as midshipman in the Navy of H. M. F. Donna Maria 2nd during the war of succession in portugal, was present at the battle of Vigo Bay under Admiral Sartorius on the 25th July 1832, on board the Frigate Donna Maria 2nd. also at the battle of Cape St. Vincent on the 5th July 1833 under Admiral Sir Charles Napier at the capture of the Migusel te Fleet was 2nd in command at the cutting out of the Liberalle Schooner from under the Batteries and across the bar of Oporto in April 1833; Served during the Civil War in Spain in 1835-36, in the 1st Regt or Reinhe Isabellas Lancers under Col. Kinlock (severely wounded at Hernani) served in the expedition against the Hill Tribes under Genl. Sir Charles Napier in Beloochistan in 1845; served during the Punjaub Campaign present at the battles of Ramnuggur, Sadoolapore, Chillianwallah and Goojerat (wounded in the last battle) and subsequent pursuit of the Sheiks under Genl. Sir W. R. Gilbert.

Conductor J. McDermott served in the campaign against the Hill tribes in Scinde, under Sir, C. Napier in 1845; present during the whole of the operations of the capture and siege of the City and Fortress of Mooltan battle of Goojerat, received a medal and two clasps.

Sub. Conductor Hewson served in the Sutledge campaign in 1846, was present at the battle of Sobraon, medal, also with the expedition against Kangra in May 1846, under Brigadier Wheeler, C. B.; and served in the Punjaub campaign in 1848-49 medal.

Sub. Conductor Desmond served in the Burmah war 1852-53.

WAR SERVICES OF THE SUBORDINATE MEDICAL DEPARTMENT, APOTHECARIES, ETC.

(4) Served in the Burmese war, and with the expedition to China 1840-41, medal; also at Maharajpore, bronze star, and with the Sutledge campaign, medal and 2 clasps for Moodkee, Ferozeshuhur and Sobraon; was throughout the Punjaub campaign at Ramnuggur, Chillianwalla and Goojerat, medal and clasp.
(6) Served in the expedition to China, (wounded.)
(8) Served at Caubul 1842.
(9) Served in the war in Scinde under *Sir* Charles Napier—Mooltan 1848-49.
(10) Served with the Army of the Indus in Affghanistan 1838-39; at Maharajpore, and with the Sutledge and Punjaub campaigns, 3 medals.
(11) Served in the Sutledge campaign 1845-46.
(12) Served in China 1845-46, at Maharajpore, and Punjaub war 1848-49.
(13) Served in the Sutledge campaign 1845-46—Punjaub campaign 1848-49.
(14) Served in Caubul 1842, and Sutledge campaign 1845-46.
(15) Served in Caubul 1842—Mooltan 1848-49.
(16) Served in China and Sutledge campaign 1845-46.
(17) Served with the army of the Sutledge in 1845-46: present at Ferozeshuhur 21st and 22nd Dec. 1845, and at Sobraon 10th Feb. 1846, (medal and clasp) served also with the army of the Punjaub, medal; accompanied the combined Seik force of Artillery, Cavalry and Infantry in the Eusofzaie under the personal command of Colonel G. Lawrence as the medical officer in charge and present in the engagement capture and destruction of the Insurgent villages of Pullee and Babozaie near Swate while in medical charge of the Peshawur Political Agency fell into the hands of Sirdar Chutter Sing.;
(18) Served at Maharajpore, bronze star; in the reduction of Kote Kangra 1846, with the Field Hospital in the Punjaub, at the passage of the Chenab, and at the battles of Chillianwalla and Goojerat, medals and clasps.
(19) Served in Mooltan 1848-49.
(20) Served in China 1840, and Mooltan 1848-49.
(21) Served in the Punjaub campaign 1848-49.
(22) Served in the Punjaub war, made prisoner by the Seikhs.
(24) Served throughout the campaign in Affghanistan from 1839 to 1842, was present at the storm and capture of Ghuznee, (medal) assault of Tootundurrah, Joolghur, night attack at Baboo Koosh Ghur, destruction of Kawurrah, assault of Purwandurrah, Khoord Cabool heights, Tazeen, forcing the Jugdulluck Pass, reduction of Mamo Khail, defence of Jellalabad, (medal) general action and defeat of Akbar Khan 7th April 1842, before Jellalabad, re-capture of Cabool, (medal) also with the army of the Sutledge, at Moodkee and Ferozeshuhur, (medal and clasp.)
(25) Served throughout the Nepaul war in 1814-15 and 16, was present with the Bengal expedition at the Island of Ceylon in 1818.
(26) Served in the Gwalior Campaign, present at Puniar, bronze star, in the Sutledge Campaign, present at the battles of Ferozeshuhur and Sobraon, (medal and clasp) served throughout the Punjaub war, present at Ramnuggur Chillianwallah and Goozerat and accompanied *Sir* R. W. Gilbert's Force to Peshawur, medal and Clasps.
(27) Served in the Gwalior Campaign, was in Medical charge of a Detachment of H. M. Troops on board the Ship Buckinghamshire, when that vessel was totally destroyed by fire off Culpee on the night of the 3rd March 1851; on which occasion his name was brought prominently to the notice of Government by the Medical Board for his Courage and Resolution in saving the lives of several of the sick at the imminent risk of his own.
(28) Served with H. M. 53rd Foot in the Sutledge campaign, present at the battle of Sobraon, medal.

WAR SERVICES OF WARRANT OFFICERS ATTACHED TO DIFFERENT DEPARTMENTS.

Conductor G. Leach served with the Army of the Indus in Affghanistan in 1839, at the storm and Capture of Ghuznee, Medal.

CASUALTIES.

Amongst the Officers of Her Majesty's Forces in Bengal, notified during the quarter ending 30th June 1859.

RANK AND NAMES.	*Corps or Dept.*	*Date.*	REMARKS.
DEATHS.			
Becher, C. G. Bt. Lt. Col., ..	5th En. L. C., ..	3rd Apl. 59	India.
Bennett, F. H. B. Lieutenant, ..	43rd L I., ...	18th May 58	Europe.
Boezalt, J. R. Steward, ..	Sub.-Medl. Estabt,	12th July 58	India.
Bridge. R. Bt. Major, ..	72nd N. I., ..	24th Aug. 58	India.
Collins, J. Steward, ..	Sub.-Medl. Estabt.,	3rd Aug 58	India.
Copeland, J. E. Lieutenant, ..	2nd En. L. C., ..	June 58	India.
Clough, E. Ensign, ..	57th N. I., ..	11th May 57	India.
Doyle, C. Steward, ..	Sub.-Medl. Estabt.,	23rd Aug. 58	India.
Duncan, A. General, ..	5th En. Regt., ..	15th May 59	Europe.
Fitzpatrick, T. Conductor, ...	D. P. Works, ..	.. ..	India.
Goodwyn, H. Lieutenant, ...	Engineers, ..	.. ..	India.
Grant, R. I. Lieutenant, ..	22nd N. I., ..	1st Apl. 59	India.
Green, J. Apothecary, ..	Sub. Medl. Estabt.,	30th June 58	India.
Hailes H. W. Captain, ..	44th N. I., ..	18th June 59	India.
Hefferan, T. Apothecary, ..	Sub Medl. Estabt.,	25th Sep. 58	India.
Henderson, C. Vety. Surgeon, ..	Vety. Dept., ..	.. ..	India.
Hill, M. G. Asst. Surgeon, ..	Medl. Estabt., ...	.. ..	India.
James, H. Lieutenant, ..	44th N. I., ...	23rd Dec. 58	India.
Kemp, E. T. Lieutenant, ..	61st N. I., ..	17th Jan. 59	India.
Kemp, J. G. M. D. Asst. Surgeon,	Medl. Estabt., ..	.. ..	Europe.
Leathes, G. C. Asst. Surgeon, ..	Medl. Estabt., ..	.. ..	Europe.
Lyous, G. H. Apothecary, ..	Sub. Medl. Estabt.,	26th Sep. 58	India.
Lee, T. M. Asst. Surgeon, ..	Medl. Estabt., ..	.. ..	India.
MacInnes, J. General, ..	1st En. B. F., ..	13th Mar. 59	Europe.
Marshall, A. Asst. Surgeon, ..	Medl. Estabt., ..	.. ..	Europe.
Miller, F. S. Captain, ..	68th N. I., ..	19th Eeb. 59	India.
Osburne, J. A. Asst. Apothecary,	Sub. Medl. Estabt.,	17th Aug. 58	India.
Paton, A. Surgeon, ..	Medl. Estabt., ..	22d Dec. 58	India.
Pringle, W. H. W. Lieutenant, ..	22nd N.I., ...	15th Aug. 58	Europe.
Roberts, H. T. C. B. Lieut. Genl.,	2nd En. L. C., ..	3rd Feb. 59	Europe.
Spens, A. Major, General, ..	14th N. I., ..	26th Apl. 59	Europe.
Sullivan, M. Steward, ..	Sub. Medl. Estabt.,	4th May 58	India,
Tait, T. F. C. B. Bt. Col., ..	28th N. I., ..	17th Mar. 59	Europe.
Turnbull, A. Lieutenant, ..	6th En. Regt., ..	15th Mar. 59	India.
Vernal, R. Conductor, ..	D. P. Works, ..	.. ..	India.

CASUALTIES —(*Continued.*)

Rank and Names	*Corps or Dept.*	*Date*	Remarks.
Retirements.			
Antisell, C. Conductor, ..	Pension, Estabt.,..	28th Jan. 59	Europe,
Butter, D. M. D. Supdg. Surgeon,	Medl. Estabt., ..	23rd April, 59	India.
Campbell, J. H. Lieut. Col.	Artillery, ..	26th Sep. 58	Europe.
Channer, G. G. Lieut. Col. ..	Artillery, ..	10th Oct. 58	Europe.
Christie, R. Surgeon, ...	Medl. Estabt, ..	29th Oct. 58	Europe.
Davidson, A. M. D. Supdg. Surgn.,	Medl. Estabt., ..	25th April 59	India.
Douglas C. M. D. Surgeon, ...	Medl. Estabt., ..	4th June, 59	India.
Ellis, R. A. F. W. Lieutenant, ..	18th N. I., ...	9th June, 58	Europe.
Fitzgerald, G. F. C. Lieut. Col...	Artillery, ..	20th Nov. 58	Europe.
Ford, C. W. Captain, ..	42nd L. I., ..	10th Sep. 58	Europe.
Hawes, A. B. Captain, ..	38th N. I., ..	22nd Oct. 58	Europe.
Jackson, A. Conductor, ..	Ordnance Dept., ..	19th April 59	India.
Larkins, W. H. Major, ...	2nd N. I., (Grs.) ..	15th Feb. 59	India.
Leckie, T. M. D. Surgeon, ..	Medl. Estabt., ..	23rd Feb. 59	India.
Mackinnon, C. Supdg. Surgeon,...	Medl. Estabt., ...	31st Mar. 59	India.
Macdonald. J. Major, ...	66th N. I., ..	1st April 59	Europe.
Macgregor, G. H. C. B. Lt., Col.	Artillery, ...	22nd Dec. 58	India.
Mallock, Z. M. Lieut. Col., ..	Artillery, ...	1st Feb. 59	India.
Morison, A. C Surgeon, ..	Medl. Estabt., ...	20th Feb. 59	India.
Nuthall, T. J. Lieut. Col., ..	71st N. I., ..	21st Jan. 59	Europe.
Ottley, G. O.' B. Major, ..	5th En. Regt., ..	31st Mar. 59	Europe.
Pitt, W. Surgeon, ..	Medl. Estabt., ..	.. ..	Europe.
Robertson R. Capt. ...	70th N. I., ..	10th Jan. 59	Europe.
Rickards, W. H. Major, ..	14th N. I., ...	13th April 59	India.
Seaton, T. *Sir*, K. C. B., Bt. Col.,	1st En., B. F., ...	3rd June 57	India.
Staig, J. A. Surgeon, ..	Medl. Estabt, ...	20th April 59	India.
Stannus, R. T. Captain, ...	16th N. I. (Grs.) ..	23rd July 58	Europe.
Turner, S. D. Captain, ..	21st N. I, ..	6th Sep. 58	Europe.
Weller, J. A. Lieut. Col. ..	Engineers, ..	31st Dec. 58	Europe.
Thomas, H. M, A., Chaplain, ...	Ecclesiastical. Establishment, ..	7th May 59	Europe.
Resignations.			
Higginbottom, J. Asst. Apothecary,	Sub. Medl. Estabt.	21st Apl. 59	India.
Hume, C. W. Lieutenant, ..	70th N. I. ..	.. ..	India.
Kidd, H. A. Asst. Apothecary, ..	.. ..	19th Mar. 59	India.
Kidd, L. A. Apothecary, ..	.. ..	31st May 59	India.
Messiter, A. H. Lieutenant, ..	72nd N. I., ..	5th Mar. 59	Europe.
Prichard, I. T. Lieutenant, ..	15th N. I., ..	27th May 59	India.
Reilly E. Apothecary, ..	Sub. Medl. Estabt.,	19th May 59	India.
Wharton, T. C. Lieutenant, ..	30th N. I., ..	.. ..	India.
Wriford, C. R. Bt. Major, ..	1st En. B. F., ..	20th Feb., 59	India.
Yate, G. E. Asst. Chaplain, ..	Ecclesiastical Establishment, ..	7th June 59	Europe.
Pensioned.			
Green, W. Sub. Conductor, ..	Army Comt. Dept.,	7th Jan. 59	India.
Roche, J. Conductor, ..	Ordnance, Dept.,..	24th June 59	India.
Dismissed.			
Gaffney, W. Asst. Apothecary, ..	Sub. Medl. Estabt.,	29th Nov. 58	India.
Grose. S. Asst. Apothecary, ..	Sub. Medl. Estabt.,	15th Dec. 58	India.
Jones, S. Asst. Apothecary, ..	Sub. Medl. Estabt.,	24th Nov. 58	India.

REGULATIONS

OF THE

BENGAL MILITARY FUND,

ESTABLISHED 1st NOVEMBER, 1824.

Corrected to 1st January 1858.

SECTION I.

Admission of Subscribers.

Art. I. The following description of persons, and they alone, are eligible to be subscribers to the Bengal Military Fund :—

1st. Officers or Cadets in the Military Service of the Honorable Company under the presidency of Fort William.

2nd. Chaplains of the Bengal Establishment.

3rd. Officers of the Bengal Medical Establishment, and Veterinary Surgeons.

4th. Officers of the Bengal Establishment on the retired list.

Note.—Officers entering the Service with unattached commissions as Ensigns are also eligible to become Members on furnishing a health certificate and paying contributions at rates to be determined by the Actuary.

Date quoted was inserted in 1843.

Art. II. Individuals of the descriptions enumerated in the 1st article, who entered the service previous to the 30th August 1826, and who hitherto have not become subscribers, shall only be admissible on the following conditions :—

1st. That the application for admission be accompanied by the certificate of two Surgeons, that the person desiring to subscribe is then, to the best of their knowledge, in good health. This certificate being confirmed by the declaration to the same effect, from the person so applying to be admitted. Applications from married officers being also accompanied by a certificate of their marriage, and intimation of the correct age of the parties.

Last part of Clause added in 1843.

2nd. That donation and arrears of subscription, according to the rank at the time of admission, be paid with compound interest on those sums accumulated half-yearly at the rate of 8 per cent. per annum. The arrears to commence from the date of the institution of the fund, or from the entrance of the person into the service, if subsequent to the institution of the same, and prior to 30th August 1826. If the arrears are paid by instalments (which are not to exceed twelve monthly payments from the date of admission) interest at 8 per cent. per annum to be charged on all intermediate balances.

Art. III. A subscriber withdrawing from the fund, forfeits, *ipso facto*, all claims to its benefits, as also the amount of his donation and subscription, and all other sums which he may have paid up to the period of his secession. Should he afterwards be desirous of again becoming a subscriber, he will be admissible on the same terms as a new subscriber, as described in the 2nd article. Note.—This article is applicable to voluntary subscribers only.

Last Clause added in 1857.

Art. IV. Subscribers who may retire from the service on the prescribed pension of their ranks, or in ill-health before entitled thereto, or who may return, permanently, or upon furlough, to Europe, shall not forfeit their title to the benefits of the fund, provided they continue the regular payments of the monthly subscription of their ranks agreeably to the rates laid down for each rank in Table No. II. Married members who have subscribed in higher grades either according to rank or from length of service may after their retirement from the service, revert to any lower married grade of subscription which they may prefer on payment of the difference between the present value of the contingent pensions of their wives and the value of their contributions in the lower grade added to the donation paid in the higher one, where the former may be in excess of the latter, and on the understanding that should they afterwards desire to enter higher grades, it will be necessary for them to furnish a health Certificate and to pay a second time the donation and difference of subscription through each grade as on the occasion of their first enrolment therein.

Altered as at present in Nov. 1833.

Art. V. Subscribers not in ill-health retiring from the service before they are entitled to the full pension of their rank, shall not forfeit all claims on the institution, provided they continue to pay the Indian rates of subscription of their respective ranks.

Altered as at present in July 1834.

Art. VI. Officers are permitted to subscribe according to army rank, on furnishing the prescribed certificate of health, subscription and donation, as in every other case, being calculated from date of such rank. Under this rule, Medical Officers and Veterinary Surgeons may subscribe as Captains after 15 years' service.

SECTION II.

Donations and Subscriptions to be paid to the Bengal Military Fund.

Last Clause added in 1851.

ART VII. All subscribers to pay a donation or premium on entering the Fund, agreeably to the rates specified in the accompanying Table No. I., and shall also allot for the support of the Fund, as long as they shall continue subscribers, the monthly sums specified in Table No II., agreeably to their rank, whether in India or Europe. The subscriptions of Cadets to be calculated at the rank of Ensign. Though the donation is deemed to be due on the enrolment of a subscriber in any particular rank, all cadets as well as married Assistant Surgeons and Assistant Chaplains may liquidate the amounts for which they are liable on admission into the service by 24 Instalments, interest being charged as on all cases of deferred payment at the rate of 8 per cent per annum on the intermediate balances.

Though the donation is deemed to be due on the enrolment of a Subscriber in any particular grade, all Cadets and married Assistant Surgeons and Assistant Chaplains may liquidate the donations for which they are liable on admission into the Service by 24 monthly instalments; interest being charged as in all cases of deferred payment at the rate of 8 per. cent. per annum on the intermediate balances.

TABLE I.

Amount of the Premium or Donation payable by the different Ranks.

	Married.						Un-Married.									
	On joining the Institution.			*On Promotion.*			*On joining the Institution.*			*On Promotion.*			*On Marriage.*			
	Rs.	A.	P.	Rs.	A.	P.	Rs.	A.	P.	Rs.	A.	P.	Rs.	A.	P.	
Colonels and Members of the Medical Board,...	4350	0	0	723	12	0	787	8	0	157	8	0	3912	8	0	Scale fixed 1853.
Lieutenant Colonels and Superintending Surgeons,......	2501	0	0	642	8	0	630	0	0	157	8	0	2151	4	0	
Majors, Chaplains and Senior Surgeons, ...	1452	0	0	517	8	0	472	8	0	135	0	0	1190	0	0	
Captains, Surgeons and Assistant Chaplains,.....	695	0	0	455	0	0	337	8	0	135	0	0	507	8	0	
Lieutenants, Asst. Surgeons and Veterinary Surgeons, ...	450	0	0	150	0	0	202	8	0	67	8	0	225	0	0	
Cornets, 2nd Lieutenants and Ensigns,......	300	0	0	0	0	0	135	0	0	0	0	0	150	0	0	

TABLE II.

Amount of Monthly Subscriptions of the different Ranks.

	If in India.						If in Europe.						
	Married.			*Un-married.*			*Married.*			*Un-married.*			
	Rs.	As.	P.	Rs.	As.	P.	£	S.	D.	£	S.	D.	
Colonels and Members of the Medical Board,...	62	8	0	28	2	0	3	15	0	1	13	9	Scale fixed in 1853.
Lieutenant-Colonels and Superintending Surgs....	45	0	0	20	4	0	2	10	0	1	2	6	
Majors, Chaplains and Senior Surgeons, ...	35	0	0	15	12	0	2	0	0	0	18	0	
Captains, Surgeons and Assistant Chaplains, ...	20	0	0	9	0	0	1	6	3	0	11	10	
Lieutenants, Asst. Surgeons and Veterinary Surgeons, ...	12	8	0	5	10	0	0	16	3	0	7	4	
Cornets, 2nd Lieutenants and Ensigns, ...	10	0	0	4	8	0	0	13	2	0	5	11	

This Article came into effect from 1st January 1837.

ART. VIII. Officers may enter grades of subscription above their regimental or army rank under the following stipulations.

Altered as at present from 1st January 1856.

1st. All Members who have served 27 years may subscribe as Colonels; all who have served 22 as Lieutenant-Colonels; all who have served 17 as Majors; all who have served 10 as Captains; and all junior officers as Lieutenants.

2nd. Medical and Veterinary officers may subscribe as Colonels after 27 years' service; as Lieutenant-Colonels after 22 years; as Majors after 17 years; and as Captains after 10 years.

3rd. Assistant Chaplains may Subscribe after 7 years as Majors; after 12 years, as Lieut. Colonels; and after 17 years as Colonels.

4th. Admission to subscribe in the next higher rank, to which his service may render an officer eligible, shall depend on the payment of the increased donation within the period prescribed by Regulation XI. and the production of a health certificate. Further, the claim must be made to the Managers in India within 3 months, if the claimant be in India, or if at home, within 12 months, from the completion of the qualifying service.

5th. If the privilege to subscribe in the next higher rank be not embraced within the above periods, the application, whenever subsequently made, must be accompanied by a health certificate, and compound interest at 8 per cent. per annum shall be charged upon the additional donation and arrears of subscription accumulated half-yearly (as by Article II. of the existing Rules) from the date of these Rules taking effect, or from the completion of the qualifying service.

Passed in 1840.

6th. Retired officers are entitled to enter the higher classes of subscription under the above conditions, on the expiration of the several periods which, had they remained in the service, would have given them the same privilege. This Rule is applicable to subscribers under Article V.

N. B.—The period of service under this article is calculated by certificates of admission to be furnished from the Adjutant General's office. Officers embracing the privilege granted by this Rule must comply with all its provisions, calculated through each grade of service.

ART. IX. Subscribers may redeem by a single payment the periodical subscription eligible under Article VII., the equivalent sum being determined on this principle.

Altered as at present in March 1842.

1. Members in Europe to redeem at Europe rates: in India at Indian rates: calculated by two tables of different values of an annuity, one adapted for Europe (as the Northampton tables,) the other for India (as the Indian tables,) receiving back, or paying the difference of premium according to residence in one or other country. Parties visiting Europe on Furlough, or for a temporary residence not exceeding 3 years, not to receive the difference, nor parties re-visiting India to pay it, if the temporary residence does not exceed 1 year. The value to be taken from tables of which the following is a specimen:—

On promotion the subscriber will be liable to pay the donation and to pay or redeem difference of subscription.

Altered as at present in March 1842.

2. Members who may redeem their periodical subscriptions by a single payment are precluded the benefit of passage-money and equipment allowance.

Added in 1846.

3. All subscribers who may, from this date, 1st July 1846, redeem their periodical subscriptions by a single payment, shall be liable for the difference between existing rates of subscription and any future higher rates that it may be found necessary to adopt.

NORTHAMPTON TABLES.				INDIA COMMITTEE TABLES.			
Age.	Value of an Annuity in England.			Age.	Value of an Annuity in India.		
25	9	16	5	25	8	5	6
30	9	11	8	30	8	1	11
40	8	18	10	40	7	11	0

Last part of Art. added in 1843.

ART. X. Subscribers on promotion shall pay the donation of their increased rank as married or unmarried, agreeably to the rates specified in Table No. I., whether in India or Europe. If in Europe the exchange to be calculated at 2*s.* 6*d.* per Company's Rupee.

Altered as at present in Jan. 1845.

ART. XI. The donation may be paid at once, or by monthly instalments not exceeding twelve, at the option of the subscriber; in failure of which all claims shall be forfeited upon the Fund, either for himself or widow, unless the amount be paid with interest at 8 per cent. per annum from the day of admission. Subscribers paying donation by instalments pay interest at 8 per cent. per annum upon all unpaid balances until the whole is liquidated.

ART. XII. Monthly subscriptions shall be made within 4 months after they become due, in default of which 8 per cent. per annum will be charged on all arrears after that period.

Altered as at present in Jan. 1849.

It will be the duty of the Secretary to forward a statement of his account to every subscriber on his payments to the Fund, whether subscription or donation, becoming one year in arrears.

In all cases when the above notice has been given, and payment not made, interest on the arrears will be charged for the full period.

In the event of payment, as above, being refused, the name will be struck off, if the party entered the service before subscription was compulsory.

Should this account not be furnished, subscribers will not be held liable for the payment of interest beyond the first year.

Added in Dec. 1852.

The Secretary will also call on subscribers, who may fall into arrears for three months, for the amount of such arrears, and if unsuccessful in recovering them, lay the case before the Directors for their orders.

Embodied in the Rules consequent on the General Order of Dec. 1850, requiring officers who marry to subscribe in that class.

ART. XIII. All members marrying, whose cases do not come within the exceptions mentioned in the succeeding clauses of this article, are required to subscribe in the married grade according to their regimental rank, giving the earliest intimation of their marriage if in India, to the Secretary and Paymasters, or if in Europe, to the Agent there. Donations are considered to be due on the occurrence of marriages and the commencement of increased risk to the Fund and when payment is deferred, parties are liable to interest at 8 per cent. per annum. Widowers may revert to the unmarried grade after the expiry of the month in which they became such, on their apprizing the Secretary of their wish to be retransferred to the list of unmarried subscribers.

Altered in effect as at present in June 1845.

Members marrying who entered the service before subscription was compulsory, and whose cases are not otherwise specially provided for in the remaining clauses of this article, if desirous that their widows should possess claims to the eventual benefits of the Fund, are required to inform the Secretary and Paymaster (if in India and the Agent if in Europe) of their marriage, and unless the payment of the additional donation be made within six months after such marriage, the subscribers will be required to pay the amount with interest at 8 per cent. per annum, calculated from date of marriage, and to furnish a health certificate as required by Art. 2, Clause 1st, and no claim for pension on the part of the widow of an officer not subscribing as a married member at the time of his decease, shall be admissible.

Last part of Clause added in 1835.

Arrears, which may be due to the Fund by a married subscriber at the time of his death, will, if not discharged by the Paymaster of the corps to which the deceased was attached, or by the President of the Committee of Adjustment, or by his Executors or Agents, be deducted from the pension of the widow, and the whole donation and arrears to be paid, although the subscriber should become a widower before completing the full payment. In all cases when the difference of age of the husband exceeds that of the wife 15 years, the donation to be increased 10 per cent.: when 20 years 15 per cent.: when 25 years 20 per cent.: when 30 years 25 per cent.: when 35 years 30 per cent.: when 40 years 35 per cent.; and thereafter in a similar proportion in every grade of promotion.

First part of Clause passed in February 1845, and last part in December 1845.

All Members re-marrying, to pay the prescribed married donation of their rank as on their first marriage. A subscriber withdrawing his name from the married list during the life-time of his wife and afterwards wishing to be again placed in the same position for her benefit, shall pay a second time the marriage donation, and furnish a health certificate of the form laid down in the Regulation.

N. B.—A Member marrying is required to furnish his marriage certificate and to state his own and wife's age.

Clause passed December 1847.

An unmarried subscriber to the Fund marrying a person who has borne him children, or with whom he may have been cohabiting, shall not be transferred to the married list. unless he furnishes a health certificate of the form laid down in the Regulations, and pays up the prescribed marriage donation and subscription, with interest, calculated half-yearly at 8 per cent. per annum, for five years, commencing in the rank he then held, and paying the difference through each successive rank he may have attained by Regimental promotion.

For the purpose of ensuring accurate information on the required points from applicants, power is vested in the Directors, in all cases seeming to them to call for its exercise, to forward certain sealed queries, to be filled up, on honor, by the parties applying.

Last part of Art. added in 1834.

ART. XIV. Subscribers who may be prevented from drawing pay from a temporary cause over which they had no control, such as captivity, or furlough extended on Medical Certificate, shall, during such period, be exempted from the payment of monthly subscription, without forfeiture of the rights of the subscription; but on the removal of such incapacity and upon the receipt of pay, the arrears are to be made good within six months, with interest at 8 per cent. per annum for any time beyond that period. But if the incapacity to pay proceed from any other cause, dependent upon the choice or conduct of the individual, such as furlough extended on private affairs, or any penal suspension from rank and pay, not only shall the arrears so accumulatad be paid up within the above term, but compound interest charged at 8 per cent. per annum on the amount.

SECTION III.

Benefits derivable from the Bengal Military Fund.

ART. XV. The benefits derivable from the Military Fund are two-fold :—

1st. Such as are granted by the Regulations to subscribers while living.

2nd. Such as are granted to widows of deceased subscribers.

ART. XVI. The benefit granted to subscribers while alive, are considered personal, and subject to the decision of the Directors for the time being, who will be guided in their decision on each claim by the Regulations of the Fund, except when they have reason to entertain doubts with respect to any such claim; it will in such cases be their duty to call for further information from the claimant; and if this information should not be satisfactory to the Directors, they are authorized to withhold the payment of the claim.

Altered as at present from Jan. 1856.

ART. XVII. A subscriber, not being of the rank and standing of a regimental Major or in receipt at the period of going on furlough, or within six months of that time of emoluments equal to the regimental pay and allowances of a Major of Infantry on half batta, who may proceed to Europe on sick certificate, and who may not be allowed passage money from Government, shall be authorized to apply to the Military Fund if unmarried for the sum of Rupees 800 or, if married, for that of Rupees 400, towards the expense of his passage, provided his application be accompanied by a sincere and solemn declaration that he does not possess a sum of Rupees 5,000, or property of any description to that amount; and shall also be entitled on his return to India to receive towards the outward passage, if unmarried, the sum of £80, or, if married, the sum of £40, on production of a declaration that he neither possesses nor has at any time possessed £500 sterling or property of any description to that amount (exclusive of pay) during the period he has been in receipt of English pay on furlough, and likewise proving to the satisfaction of the Agent of the Fund in England, that his services are not required to proceed with or in charge of recruits to India.

All applications from subscribers for passage-money from the Fund, whether proceeding to or returning from Europe, must be accompanied by a guarantee (Form VI.) on the part of the Agents of the ship or other respectable party, that they will be responsible for a moiety of the passage-money allowed by the Fund, being returned, in cases of death previous to the Pilot quitting the vessel on which the claimant's passage may have been taken.

Added in Sept. 1846.

Art. XVIII. A subscriber not coming, as regards rank or emoluments, within the exception mentioned in the preceding Article, proceeding to England on sick certificate, shall be authorized to apply if unmarried, for the further sum of Rupees 300, or if married, for that of Rupees 150, for his equipment, his application being accompanied by a solemn and sincere declaration of his not being possessed of the sum of Rupees 2,000 or property of any description to that amount, but no allowances will in any case be made for equipment to a subscriber returning to India.

Altered as at present from Jan. 1856.

N. B.—The benefits held out in the two preceding articles should be applied for, when claimable; and no claim will be admitted, which is not preferred within 12 months from date of furlough.

Art. XIX. Subaltern officers proceeding to England on sick certificate, who shall make a solemn and sincere declaration that they do not possess from any source (exclusive of pay proper and pension for wounds) a sum of money that will enable them to expend £50 per annum, shall, if unmarried, be allowed that sum, or if married, be allowed a moiety of that sum annually during the period of receiving English pay on furlough. The declaration to be renewed annually.

Altered as at present from Jan. 1856.

N. B. The possession of Company's Rupees 1,500 or £150, precludes all claim to the above allowance. Officers proceeding to Europe on Sick Furl'o under the new Regulations can only be admitted to Income allowance on the equalization of the Pay they draw with the English Pay of their rank, which is the Pay contemplated in Art XIX, by crediting them with £50 per an. in excess of the said English Pay.

Art. XX. It having, however, been deemed necessary to set limits to the claims for gratuitous passage-money, equipment allowance, and income to subscribers proceeding to England on sick certificate, no subscriber who has received the benefits he is entitled to at any one time, shall receive a second indulgence until the expiration of eight years, reckoning from the renewal of Indian subscription and every unmarried subscriber who may draw such benefits subsequent to the 1st January 1856, shall, in the event of his marrying, be required to refund a moiety of their amount to place him on a footing with married subscribers who are restricted to half the rates paid him.

Altered as at present from Jan. 1856.

A subscriber who shall have received these benefits, before he has served 8 years in India, will not be entitled to a second indulgence until he shall have been (exclusive of first furlough) 16 years in the service.

Added in Dec. 1845.

Art. XXI. Subscribers proceeding to England from any place not under the presidency of Bengal, shall be entitled to the personal benefits which have been above enumerated, provided they shall have complied with the local regulations, and shall make immediate communication of the circumstances to the Directors of the Fund.

Art. XXII. The second class of benefits, namely, those granted to widows of deceased subscribers, are absolute, not dependent on the decision of the Directors, but controlled solely by the Regulations of the institution.

Art. XXV. The widows of deceased subscribers shall be entitled to receive the annuities specified in the annexed table:—

TABLE

Shewing the amount of Pension to Widows (during their Widowhood) of each Rank.

	In India.			In England.			
	Rs.	A.	P.	£.	S.	D.	
Widow of a Col. or of Members of the Medical Board,	214	9	0	281	12	3	Altered as at present from 1st January 1856.
,, Lieut.-Col. or of Superintending Surgeon,	171	10	5	225	5	9	
,, Majors, Chaplains or Senior Surgeons, ...	128	11	9	168	19	3	
,, Captains, Surgeons or Assistant Chaplains,	85	13	3	112	12	11	
,, Lieuts. Asst.-Surgs. or Veterinary Surgs.,	64	1	3	84	1	11	
,, Ensigns, 2nd Lieutenants or Cornets, ...	50	15	1	66	17	3	

Provided that nothing contained herein, or in any other part of these Rules of the institution shall be considered to entitle to the benefits of it, any widow who may have been legally divorced or separated from her husband for adultery, or who at the period of her husband's demise may have quitted his protection, and be living in a state of notorious adultery, though not divorced or separated from him by law, or who subsequently to her husband's decease may be living in a notorious state of incontinence.

Art. XXIV. If a widow pensioner on the Fund shall re-marry, she shall receive a third of the rate of pension granted to widows entering at the time on the same grade (provided her husband, if eligible to be a member, subscribe in the married grade); but in the event of her again becoming a widow, she shall be re-admitted to all the benefits she may have enjoyed from the Fund during her first widowhood, in like manner as if she had not re-married; but subject of course to all the limitations and conditions prescribed by the Regulations in the first instance. If the second husband shall also have been a subscriber to the Fund, the widow will receive however only one annuity, taking that which may be the greatest, that is to say, according to the rank of the first or second husband, whichever may be the higher.

Altered as at present from 1st Jan. 1856.

N. B.—The grant of part pension on remarriage is an experimental measure and subject to repeal in respect to all remarriages taking place after a date to be named, when its repeal may be determined on by subscribers.

Altered as at present from Jan. 1856.

ART. XXV. Every widow benefitting by the Military Fund previous to the 1st January 1856, and not provided by Government with a passage to Europe, shall, on the first occasion of her proceeding thither after admission to pension in India, entitled to an allowance of Rupees 1,000; but in the case of widows thereafter admitted in India, the allowance shall be Rupees 500, and their claim for the other moiety shall be dependent on the payment on their behalf of a special contribution or subscription for the additional sum, as for a survivorship assurance; the amount of such contribution in each case to be ascertained from tables of which the annexed is a specimen. All applications from widows for passage-money from the Fund must be accompanied by a guarantee (Form No. V.) on the part of the Agents of the ship or other respectable party, that they will be responsible for a moiety of the passage-money allowed by the Fund, being returned in case of death previous to the Pilot quitting the vessel in which the claimant's passage may have been taken. No claim for passage-money is admissible after lapse of one year from the date of embarking for Europe.

Table showing the amount for which a sum of Rupees 500 being a moiety of Passage-Money, may be ensured to a widow becoming such in India.

Age of Husband.	Difference of Age. Wife being Younger.		
	0	10	20
23	102·65		
28	104·55	109·00	
33	104·90	110 90	104·20
38	104·05	111·15	116 75
43	103·45	112·85	118·70
48	103·75	114·10	122·45
53	109·45	122·65	132·80
58	125·90	143·00	135·15

ART. XXVI. Should the Fund, however, at any period fall short of the demands upon it, so that the annual income will not defray the amount of the annuities and other claims, then it shall be in the power of the Directors, after submission to the army, to make a proportionate deduction from the annuity of each annuitant, excepting always the present annuitants of the Bengal Widow's Fund, and from the payments to other claimants above the rank of Subaltern, until the state of the Fund shall afford the means of complete payment; when, if a surplus income exists, the arrears shall be made good from the amount of surplus, but not otherwise.

SECTION IV.

General Regulations.

Altered as at present from Jan. 1856.

ART. XXVII. The Bengal Military Fund is to be administered by a President and Directors, the Directors to be partly ex-Officio, and partly elected by the subscribers at large. the number of those so elected to be one more than that of the ex-Officio Directors, and to be chosen from among such subscribers residing at Barrackpore, Dum-Dum and the Presidency, as may be available and willing to serve as Directors. The President to be elected by the Directors from among their own body.

There shall be also two Provisional Directors, who are to be elected by the subscribers, and are to succeed to vacancies as they may occur in the number of Constituted Directors under the foregoing clause, and on such occasions a fresh election of Provisional Directors to be made.

Altered as at present in Dec. 1852.

ART. XXVIII. A general meeting of the subscribers at the Presidency shall be held annually, at which the accounts of the Fund and proceedings of the Directors for the past year shall be submitted, for inspection and approval by the subscribers present, who were not of the direction. The accounts to be published for general information two months previous to the Annual Meeting, the precise day and place of holding which are to be notified by public advertisement simultaneously with the publication of the accounts.

ART. XXIX. All subscribers, who may have contributed to the Fund by paying donations and subscriptions in their respective ranks, during six continuous months before any meeting, are entitled to attend to examine the accounts and proceedings.

ART. XXX. On occasion of any particular and important business which may necessarily require the opinion of the society at large, special meetings will be called of the subscribers at the Presidency (others voting by proxy). Or if any alleged mismanagement, or other emergent cause should occur to any twelve subscribers to require the notice of the society at large, a special meeting shall be summoned by the President on the written requisition of such twelve subscribers.

ART. XXXI. The Directors shall have a Secretary, chosen by themselves, who also shall be Accountant, with an establishment, upon such allowances as shall be deemed adequate to the respective duties.

ART. XXXII. The Secretary will be expected to have an office at his own residence for the accommodation of the meetings of the Directors, for the preservation of the records, and for the purpose of affording access to the officers of the army at large to the books of the institution.

Altered as at present in December 1852.

ART. XXXIII. The Directors of the Fund will hold regular monthly meetings, which are to be open for the Reporters of the Public Press; but no meeting of the Directors consisting of a smaller number than five, shall be competent to the transaction of business; and it will rest with any Director, or with the Secretary, to represent the occurrence of such necessity to the President, who will convene a special meeting within ten days from the date of his receiving the application; but no special meeting shall be called with the view of re-considering resolutions which may have been already adopted by a former meeting of Directors, unless at the requisition of a number of Directors greater than that which attended such meeting.

ART. XXXIV. The Secretary will invariably lay before the Directors, either at the regular or special meetings, all letters that may have been received by him since the last meeting. Minutes of the proceedings of all meetings will be recorded and authenticated by the signatures of the Directors present. The Secretary will also submit to the Directors who attended, drafts of all the letters which in those meetings he may have been desired to write. Letters demanding an immediate answer, when such may be of an ordinary nature, may be replied to by the Secretary, without waiting for a meeting of the Directors: but every letter proposed to be dispatched by the Secretary, must previously receive the special sanction of one Director, signified by his initial to the drafts, which will be sent to him for consideration.

ART. XXXV. The Secretary will keep the set of books in use in the Military Widows' Fund under instructions which he may receive from time to time from the Directors of the Fund.

ART. XXXVI. The books and correspondence of the Fund shall be at all times open to the inspection of subscribers.

ART. XXXVII. When any new Regulation shall appear to the Directors or to any thirty subscribers, to be advisable, such Regulation shall be circulated to corps for consideration, and the affirmative or negative of the majority of individual votes to be ascertained at the expiration of 4 months, shall decide its adoption or rejection.

Altered as at present in December 1852.

Before being circulated for votes all propositions shall be printed and a copy sent a month previously for publication to each newspaper throughout the Bengal Presidency and for circulation to each division and station staff officer; in private cases at *the expense of the appellant.* The proceedings of the Directors' meetings to be published and circulated in like manner.

ART. XXXVIII. If any subscriber or claimant on the Fund shall be desirous to appeal from the decision of the Directors to that of the subscribers at large, upon any subject which may not be specifically defined by the Regulations, such appeal, provided it be approved by three Directors shall be referred by the Directors, and decided upon in the manner prescribed in the preceding article, and the decision on such appeal, or that of the Directors, in cases not appealable, shall be final in all cases whatever, any further agitation of the question, by a process of law or otherwise, being deemed in itself to be an absolute forfeiture of all claim on the Fund.

ART. XXXIX. When a reference shall be made to the subscribers at large respecting either proposed regulation, or an appeal, the result of such reference shall be communicated to corps for the information of subscribers.

ART. XL. Generally all payments due from the Fund are made quarterly in England, and monthly in India; but in cases when pensioners or claimants on the Fund are about to embark for Europe, all arrears must be paid up to the end of the preceding month.

ART. XLI. Any arrear which may be due to the Fund by a subscriber or by an annuitant who may have received an over-payment, shall in all cases be deducted from the first payment to be made from the Fund to the person owing such arrear.

ART. XLII. All income derived from the Bengal Military Fund is declared to be unalienable, and the fact of attempting the alienation of such income in any manner, or under any pretence, shall be deemed in itself a forfeiture of all future benefits from the Fund.

ART. XLIII. If a subscriber who may be dismissed from the service by a court martial or otherwise, shall afterwards be restored to the service, he shall be re-admissible to the Fund on payment of the arrear that may have accumulated, with compound interest thereon, in the same manner as if he had suffered only temporary suspension. See Art. XVI.

ART. XLIV. All property belonging to the Military Fund at any period shall be invariably vested in the Honorable Company's Securities. The necessity for retaining any balance is now dispensed with, and the Secretary's office has no cash transactions. All payments in Calcutta are, in future, to be made at the Bank of Bengal, as sanctioned by the Hon'ble the Court of Directors, in 1852. All contributions from subscribers generally must be made through the Pay Department or Public Treasuries. Private drafts are prohibited.

ART. XLV. The business of the Fund in Europe is conducted through the Home Agent of the Fund, who will from time to time receive the necessary instructions for his guidance, and to whom such applications will be preferred as cannot, with equal convenience, be submitted to the Directors of the Fund in India.

ART. XLVI. As soon as new Rules are made out, one copy shall be sent to all officers commanding stations and posts for official record and the Rules shall be corrected and published annually in the Army List printed at the *Orphan Press*, the dates when each was passed or altered, being noted in the margin.

Added in Dec. 1852.

N. B.—In general it may be mentioned that where no particular dates are referred to, the Rules have not been altered since the Establishment of the Fund.

NOTICE.

As subscribers falling into arrears often request exemption from the penalties prescribed by the Regulations, on the plea of ignorance of the Rules, or of no demand having been made by the Secretary, the Directors notify that they do not admit either of these reasons as sufficient to entitle a subscriber to the exemption called for, and that every penalty incurred by non-payment of Donations and Subscriptions must invariably and strictly be enforced, as prescribed by the Rules of the Institution. The Secretary will continue to give notice when arrears are due, in all cases when they come to his knowledge, but every subscriber should protect his own interests, and see that his Subscriptions and Donations are regularly deducted by his paymaster, and immediately rectify any errors or omissions of that functionary.

APPENDIX No. I.

Form of Certificates of Health to accompany the applications of an Officer to become a Subscriber.

SECTION 1ST, ARTICLE 2ND.

We, the undersigned medical Officers of Her Majesty's or the Hon'ble East India Company's service, (as the case may be), do hereby solemnly and sincerely declare that we have carefully and personally examined into the state of A. B.'s health and that we pronounce him free from any bodily complaint of a dangerous tendency, and believe him to be a good life.

(Station and date.) *C. D. } E. F. } *Rank, corps and service.*

I, A. B., hereby solemnly and sincerely declare, that the contents of the above certificate are in all respects true to the best of my knowledge and belief; that I have disclosed to Messrs. C. D. and E. F. every thing relating to my health and constitution, and that I do believe myself to be a perfectly good life.

A. B. *(Rank, corps and date.)*

Signed and declared in my presence, this day of 18 at Station or Camp.

G. H. *(Rank.)*
Commanding at Camp or Station.

No. II.

Form of Declaration to accompany the application of an Officer for Passage-Money—Homeward.

SECTION 3RD, ARTICLE 19TH.

I, J. K., Captain Regt. N. I., do hereby solemnly and sincerely declare that I do not possess the sum of rupees 5,000 or convertible property† of any description which can raise my means above that limitation, and being on sick certificate to Europe, agreeably to my furlough as published in G. O. of the I claim from the Military Fund the sum of rupees under Article XIX. of the Regulations.

(Station and date.) J. K. *Regt. N. I.*

N. B.—" 800" to be filled in if the claimant be unmarried or " 400" if he be married, and if on Staff Employ it is necessary that he should state whether his Emoluments within six months of going on Furlough did or did not exceed the Regimental Pay and allowances of a Major on half Batta Rs. 640-14 6 per mensem; moreover unmarried subscribers are liable to refund a moiety of whatever benefits they may draw subsequent to 1st January 1856 in the event of their marrying.

Form of Declaration to accompany the application of an Officer for Passage-Money—Outward.

I, J. K., Captain Regt. N. I., do hereby solemnly and sincerely declare that I do not possess nor have at any time possessed £500 sterling (exclusive of pay) during the period I have been in receipt of English pay on furlough.

I therefore claim from the Military Fund the sum of £ under Article XVII. of the Regulations.

(Station and date.) J. K. *Regt. N. I.*

N. B. Only claimable when not allowed Passage-money by Government £80 to be filled in if the claiman be unmarried or £40 if he be married.

No. III.

Form of Declaration to accompany an application for Equipment Allowance.

SECTION 3RD, ARTICLE 20TH.

I, J. K., Captain Regt. N. I., do hereby solemnly and sincerely declare that I do not possess the sum of rupees 2,000 in money or convertible property of any description, which can raise my means above that limitation, and being on sick certificate to Europe, agreeably to my furlough as published in G. O. of the

I therefore claim from the Military Fund the sum of rupees under Article XVIII. of the Regulations.

(Station and date.) J. K. *Regt. N. I.*

N. B.—" 300" to be filled in if the claimant be unmarried and " 150" if he be married.

---

* In cases where it is not practicable to obtain the counter-signature of a second medical officer within reasonable distance, the same should be noticed at the bottom of the certificate by the medical officer subscribing it.

† By convertible property is meant horses, houses, plate, and such articles as are usually sold by persons proceeding on furlough. Wearing apparel and other requisites for comfort and convenience not deemed convertible.

No. IV.

Form of Declaration to accompany the application of an Officer for Income Allowance.

SECTION 3RD, ARTICLE 21ST.

I, J. K., Regt. N. I., do hereby solemnly and sincerely declare that I do not possess from any source (exclusive of pay proper and pension for wounds) convertible property of any description to the amount of Company's Rs. 1,500 or a sum of money that will enable me to expend £ per annum during my furlough of three years, and that I claim that sum yearly from the Military Fund, under the Regulations of that institution (Article XIX.) for my support, being on sick certificate to Europe, to my furlough as published in G. O. of the

J. K. *Regt. N. I.*

N. B. The possession of Co.'s Rs. 1,500 or £150 precludes all claim to income allowance, £50 to be filled in if the claimant be unmarried and £25 if he be married, and if on Staff Employ it is necessary that he should state whether his Emoluments within six months of going on Furlough did or did not exceed the Regimental Pay and allowances of a Major on half Batta, Rs. 640 14 6 per mensem; moreover unmarried Subscribers are liable to refund a moiety of whatever benefits they may draw subsequent to 1st January 1856 in the event of their marrying. Officers going on Sick Furlough under the New Regulations can only claim Income allowance when the excess Pay they draw above the English Pay of their rank is absorbed by crediting them with £50 per annum in addition to the ordinary English Pay alluded to and their applications should be sent through the Home Agent of the Fund for the consideration of the Directors.

No. V.

Form of Guarantee for Passage-Money.

On the part of (we or I as the case may be) agree to act up to the spirit of the Bengal Military Fund Regulations relative to a re-fund of a moiety of rupees , Passage-money allowed by the Fund to proceeding as a passenger on board the Ship

(Date)

(Signature)

No. VI.

Form of Declaration to be made by the Widow.

I widow of the late on the Bengal Establishment, do hereby solemnly and sincerely declare that I now live in the Parish of in the county of and that I have not contracted marriage with any person since the decease of the said

(Signed) *Widow of the late*

Form of Certificate.

This is to certify that Mrs. widow of the late on the Bengal Establishment, is living in the Parish of in the county of and that to be best of my knowledge and belief she has not contracted marriage with any person since the decease of the said

(Signed)

[To be signed either by the Minister of the Parish, one Church Warden, or by one Justice of the Peace, or by any retired or other Civil or Military Officer of the Hon'ble Company's Service, as may be most suitable to the convenience of the widow.

The above papers are required quarterly, and must be dated on or after every 1st January, 1st April, 1st July, and 1st October of each year.]

Table showing the amount of Pension to Widows (during their Widowhood) according to rank as obtaining before 1856.

	IN INDIA.			IN ENGLAND.		
	Rs.	A.	P.	£.	S.	D.
Widw of a Colonel or Board,	238	6	5	312	18	0
,, ,, Lieutenant-Colonel or Superintending Surgeon,	190	11	6	250	6	4
,, ,, Major, Chaplain or Senior Surgeon,	143	0	7	187	14	8
,, ,, Captain, Surgeon or Assistant Chaplain,	95	5	9	125	3	2
,, ,, Lieutenant, Assistant Surgeon or Veterinary Surgeon,	71	3	1	93	8	9
,, ,, Ensign, 2nd Lieutenant	56	9	8	74	5	10

LORD CLIVE'S FUND.

Pension from Lord Clive's fund is not given to any officer who is entitled to half or full pay, or to other retiring pension, or who is possessed of or entitled to real or personal property to the extent of £2,000 if a Chaplain, £1,000 if a Lieutenant, Assistant Surgeon or Veterinary Surgeon, and £750 if an Ensign.

The following are admissable when rendered incapable of further service in India, viz:—

1. Subalterns, Assistant Surgeons, Veterinary Surgeons, of less than 3 years service in India; and compelled to quit the service by wounds received in action, or ill health contracted on duty, likewise those of between 3 and 6 years service in India who are otherwise disabled.

2. Chaplains of less than 7 years service in India will receive as follows:—

	Per annum. £.	s.	d.		Per diem. s.	d.
Lieutenants, Assistant Surgeons, and Veterinary Surgeons, ...	45	12	6	or	2	6
Ensigns, 2nd Lieutenants and Cornets, ...	36	10	0	,,	2	0
Chaplains of less than 7 years service, ...	63	17	6	,,	3	6

The widows of Commissioned and Warrant officers must furnish an affidavit, in duplicate, setting forth that their husbands did not die possessed in their own name or through others, of property to the following amount viz:—

	£
If Colonel, ...	4000
,, Lieutenant Colonel,	3000
,, Major, ...	2500
,, Captain, Surgeon or Veterinary Surgeon above 20 years service,	2000
,, Lieutenant, Assistant Surgeon, or Veterinary Surgeon, under 20 years service,	1000
,, Ensign 2nd Lieutenant or Cornet,	750
,, Chaplain under 7 years service,	1000
,, ,, above 7 ,, ,,	2000
,, ,, ,, 15 ,, ,,	2500
Commissary of Ordnance,	2000
Deputy Commissary, Senior Apothecary,	1000
,, all other inferior Warrant Officers,	750

The pensions of widows who are entitled to that advantage are as follows:—

		Daily rate. £	s.	d.		per Mensem. Rs.	As.	P.
Of a Colonel and Member of the Medical Board, ...		,,	6	3	or	93	2	10
,, Lieut Colonel and Superintending Surgeon, ...		,,	5	0	,,	74	8	8
,, Major, ...		,,	3	9	,,	55	14	6
,, Captain, Surgeon or Veterinary Surgeon above 20 years service, ...		,,	2	6	,,	37	4	4
,, Lieutenant, Assistant Surgeon or Veterinary Surgeon under 20 years service, ...		,,	1	3	,,	18	10	2
,, Ensigns 2nd Lieutenants and Cornets, ..		,,	1	0	,,	14	14	6
Chaplains. Appointed before 1st Sep. 1836,	If above 18 years service including three years furlough, ...	,,	5	0	,,	74	8	8
Chaplains. Appointed after 1st Sep. 1836,	If above 15 years actual service in India, ...	,,	3	9	,,	55	14	6
	If above 7 years actual service in India, ...	,,	2	6	,,	37	4	4
	If under 7 years actual service in India, ...	£	31	18	9 a year.			
,, Commissary, ...		,,	2	6	,,	37	4	4
,, Deputy Commissary, ...		,,	1	3	,,	18	10	2
,, Assistant and Deputy Assistant Commissary, ...		,,	0	0	,,	15	2	1
,, Senior Apothecary, ...		,,	1	3	,,	18	10	2
,, Conductor, Riding Master, Apothecary, ...		,,	1	0	,,	14	14	6
,, Sub-Conductor, Steward, ...		,,	0	7½	,,	9	5	1
,, Assistant Apothecary, Assistant Steward, ...		,,	0	0	,,	6	4	0

These rates for the widows of officers have effect from the 1st June 1855.

Every Widow, applying for a Pension, must furnish two attested copies of the certificate of her marriage; and if it occurred a few days before her husband's death, the clearest proof will be required that the Marriage was not contracted for the express purpose of placing her on the pension list.

MILITARY ORPHAN FUND.

Rates of Monthly Subscription from the 1st January 1856. *G. G. O. Fort William 29th March* 1856.

	Rs.	As.	P.
Colonels, Archdeacons, and Members of Medical Board,..	25	0	0
Lieutetant-Colonels, ...	20	0	0
Majors, Chaplains, and Superintending Surgeons,..	15	0	0
Captains, Surgeons, and Assistant Chaplains,..	10	0	0
Lieutenants, Assistant Surgeons, and Veterinary Surgeons, ...	6	4	0
Ensigns, Second Lieutenants, Cornets, and Deputy Commissaries, ...	5	0	0

Rates of Monthly Contribution to be paid from the 1st January 1856.

	Rs.	As.	P
For each Male Child until he attains the age of 19, ...	1	0	0
For each Female Child until Marriage or Death, ...	3	0	0

BENEFITS.

To be received by Orphans from the Fund under the New Rules, which came into operation on the 1st of January 1856.

1*st.*—Every Male Child whether legitimate or illegitimate, who may become an Orphan subsequent to the 1st of January 1856, (and whose father has paid the encreased Subscription and Family Contribution) shall be entitled, if under the age of 19 at the time of his father's death, to receive

In England.

If under 6 years of age, £30 per Annum.
If above 6 years of age, £40 per Annum.

In India.

If under 5 years of age, Rs. 20 per month. If above 5 years of age, Rs. 35 per month, until he becomes 19 years of age, or is in a position to gain his own livelihood previous to that time, when he will be struck off the List of Wards and

Will be entitled to receive as an Apprentice Fee or Final Grant as follows:—

In India, Rs. 500,

at the discretion of the General Management, unless previously provided with a maintenance to their satisfaction.

2*nd.*—Every Female unmarried Child whether legitimate or illegitimate, who may become an Orphan subsequent to the 1st January 1856 (and whose father has paid the encreased Subscription and Family Contribution) is entitled to admission to the Fund from the date of her father's death without any reference to her own age at the time of that event, and to receive until her marriage or death as follows:—

In England.

If under 6 years of age, £30 per Annum.

If above 6 years and under 18 years of age, £45 per Annum. And on her becoming 18 years of age, she will receive £35 per Annum.

In India.

If under 5 years of age, Rs. 20 per month.
If above 5 years of age, Rs. 35 per month.
She will receive this latter sum per month until marriage or death.

Every Female Orphan will also receive as a Portion on her Marriage, if sanctioned by the General Management, and at their discretion the sum of £150 if in England, and Rs. 1,500 if in India.

It is only in extreme cases that the Marriage Portion will be withheld from female Orphans.

All legitimate Orphans of Subscribers will be sent to England for education, if from their age the General Management consider it proper and necessary, and they will receive Passage money as follows:—

If one Orphan be going alone,........................	Rupees 600
If two are going, ...	„ 500 each
If more than two, ...	„ 450 „

The illegitimate Orphans of Subscribers will not be sent to England for their education, but the Females will be domiciled in Kidderpore House, and the Males will be placed at some suitable School.

In addition to the above extended benefits, it is to be distinctly understood that the Military Orphan Society cannot in any manner interfere with any Property which may belong to or be left to any Ward who may have become an Orphan subsequent to the 1st of January 1856, and whose father had paid the encreased Subscription and Family Contribution as ordered by the Hon'ble Court of Directors, the Government and the Votes of the Subscribers in 1847 and 1855. In short all Orphans who have become such since 1st January 1856, are entitled to the Full extended Benefits of the Fund, whether rich or poor, their claims being entirely irrespective of their property.

Note.—The above is a Statement of the Extended Benefits as sanctioned by the Hon'ble Court of Directors and the Government. A regular Code of the New Rules is in preparation, and when perfected will be submitted to the Subscribers and Government for confirmation.

Addition to the Old Rules passed by the Board of General Management at the Monthly Meeting on the 26th February, 1857.

That all money bequeathed to a Ward of the Society being *bonâ fide* savings from the income of the widowed mother, or the sum effected by her means on the Insurance of her life be not claimed by the Society, but be allowed to be paid over as bequeathed without prejudice to Allowance Apprentice Fees, Final Grant or Marriage Portion.

NEW FURLOUGH REGULATIONS.

General Orders by the Most Noble the Governor General of India in Council.

Fort William, 17th November 1854.

No. 1150 *of* 1854.—The Hon'ble the Court of Directors having transmitted to the Government of India further explanatory instructions regarding the Furlough Regulations published in Government General Order, No. 110, of the 1st of February 1854, the Most Noble the Governor General in Council is pleased to cancel that General Order, and to promulgate in a connected form the Rules which have been laid down by the Hon'ble Court for regulating Furloughs and leaves of Absence.

With the view of adapting the Regulations to the present increased facilities of communication, and to correct, as far as possible, any tendency in them to deter Officers from resorting to the places which may be most conducive to the restoration of their health, when a change of climate is required for that purpose, the following Rules are established, and are to have effect from the 1st February 1854:—

1. All Regimental Officers in the Service on the 1st February 1854, who prefer retaining what may be considered the advantages of the old Regulations, may do so, provided they signify their wish to that effect when they next apply for Furlough or leave of absence, without any limitation whether such leave be in India or elsewhere; and Officers, who once make their election, will not be entitled to any other choice, but will be afterwards subject to the new or old Regulations according to their decisions.

2. Staff Officers, as such, have not the above option allowed them, but they may retain the advantages of the old Regulations by giving up their appointments, which, in such cases, will be considered vacated from the date of embarkation.

3. To those Officers who adopt them, the new Regulations will apply retrospectively in respect of Furlough and leave of absence beyond sea, and in computing their time of service for retirement, so that their Furloughs or leaves of absence, whether under the old or the new Rules, and whether on private affairs or sick certificate within or beyond India, will count for service to the authorized extent only, in computing the time for retirement on full pay.

4. Officers who have availed themselves of the option of the old Rules, are allowed to re-consider the question under the modifications now sanctioned.

5. Officers who have not taken leave subsequent to the publication of the new Rules on the 1st February 1854, and who consequently may not have been called upon to declare whether they would abide by the old or the new Regulations, will, on retirement from the Service, be entitled to take full advantage of the privileges given by the new Regulations.

Furloughs on Private Affairs.

6. Every Officer will be allowed a Furlough to Europe or elsewhere, beyond sea for a period of two years at the expiration of ten years' service, and for a second period of two years after twenty years' service in India.

7. The second Furlough of two years will only be granted after ten years' service in India from the date of the return to duty after the first Furlough of two years. These furloughs are not to be cumulative, under any circumstances, but are limited to two years'

Officers who have taken leave of absence on sick certificate to Europe or elsewhere beyond sea, will be ineligible to a Furlough on private affairs until they have served six years from their last return to duty. This Rule does not apply to short leaves to sea.

8. All grants of Furlough on private affairs are subject to the exigencies of the Public Service, and to the Regulations framed for the preservation of the efficiency of each Regiment by limiting the number of absentees.

9. Officers holding Staff or other detached appointments may be allowed Furlough for a period of six months without losing their appointments; but, during that period, they will not be entitled to any portion of their Staff Salary, which will be drawn in full by the Officers officiating for them.

10. All Officers, whether Staff or Regimental, while on Furlough on private affairs will be entitled to "Furlough pay" only.

Leave of Absence on Sick Certificate.

11. Leave of Absence on sick certificate will be granted for a term not exceeding eighteen months, whether it be to any place in Europe or elsewhere out of India.

12. Extensions of such leave may be granted, as at present, on production of Medical certificates, for further periods not exceeding eighteen months in the whole.

13. An Officer holding a Staff or other detached appointment will be allowed to be absent on sick certificate in England or elsewhere, beyond sea, for a period of fifteen months, without losing his appointment; and during the first six months only of such absence, he will be entitled to draw half the Staff Salary of his appointment, the Officer officiating for him drawing the remaining half salary during the first six months, and the whole salary during the remainder of the time.

14. An Officer's claim to half Staff Salary for six months, as sanctioned in the preceding Rule, will not be effected by his subsequently retiring from the Service in Europe or elsewhere.

15. No portion of Command Allowance, Medical Staff Salary or other similar allowance, which under the old Rules was inadmissible to Officers absent from their Corps or Stations at the Cape or elsewhere, will be allowed to absent Officers under these Regulations.

16. All Officers, whether Staff or Regimental, while on leave of absence on sick certificate, will be entitled for a period of six months to the same rate of Indian Pay and Allowances, as was allowed under the old Regulations to Officers proceeding to the Cape on Medical certificate, and for the remaining period of their leave they will receive Furlough pay only.

17. If the leave on sick certificate be extended, Furlough pay will be continued; but under no circumstances for a longer period than three years altogether from the commencement of the absence.

Staff Officers.

18. The term Staff Officer applies to all Officers holding Staff or detached appointments, Military, (General or Regimental,) Political or Civil; also to General Officers commanding Divisions, Members of the Medical Board, Superintending Surgeons, and others who, under the old Rules, were entitled to draw half Staff allowance when absent at the Cape.

19. Staff Officers, absent on leave beyond the periods stated in Rules 9 and 13 respectively, cannot retain their appointments and allowances except on special grounds, to be sanctioned by the Government of the Presidency. Any such special grant of leave is to be reported at once to the Hon'ble the Court of Directors, with the reasons for it, and to be subject to their approbation.

20. The privilege of retaining Staff appointments during leave of absence on sick certificate, or on Furlough on private affairs, will not be available a second time, if the fresh leave is on sick certificate, until an Officer has been three years, or if on private affairs, until he has been six years in the discharge of the duties of his appointment, from the date of last return to it.

21. This Rule, however, does not apply to leaves of absence, whether on sick certificate or on private affairs in India, or for brief periods to Ceylon, the Mauritius, or other places out of India.

22. Officers commanding Troops of Horse Artillery and Light Field Batteries, and Officers generally in employment, will be allowed leave out of India under the same Rules with respect to allowances and tenure of Command, or Office as regulated the grant of leave to the Cape to such Officers under the old Regulations, except as to the duration of those advantages, the time for their continuance being subject to the provisions of the new Regulations.

Date of Furlough and Advances of Pay.

23. The period of Furlough on private affairs, or leave of absence on sick certificate, is to be calculated from the date of the departure from India of the ship in which the Officer proceeds.

24. Advances of Pay and Allowances, Staff and Regimental, to Officers proceeding on leave of absence on sick certificate, who may be entitled to them, will be made in India for three months from date of embarkation. Payments in continuation will be made in England at the rates of exchange fixed annually for re-payment of advances made on account of Her Majesty's Government. Furlough pay will continue to be issued in advance for six months when required by Officers obtaining Furlough on private affairs.

25. The existing Regulations regarding Passage Money to Officers are not affected by these Rules.

26. The certificates issued to Officers who are granted Furloughs on private affairs, or leave of absence on sick certificate, are to specify the time each Officer has been absent on leave within Indian limits, as well as the time of his previous absence in Europe ; but will not include the periods allowed for proceeding to the Presidency or port of embarkation, and to enable Officers to rejoin their Regiments or Stations, after their return to India, nor the leave of one month's absence in six months as unauthorized by the Regulations. The last pay certificate of all Officers proceeding to England on sick certificate is to specify the rate of Regimental pay and allowances and Staff salary to which they would have been entitled under the old Regulations if proceeding to sea on Medical Certificate. This information is necessary in order that no difficulties may arise in the Pay Department of the India House in adjusting the several payments which may be due.

Officers of H. M.'s Service.

27. Officers of Her Majesty's Service in India, whether employed Regimentally or in Staff or detached situations, are entitled to the advantages above laid down in respect to allowances and tenure of office when on Furlough or leave of absence.

28. In the case of Officers of Her Majesty's Service on Furlough or Sick Certificate in England or elsewhere, who may retire or exchange into Regiments not on the Indian establishment, the grant to these Officers of Indian allowance will cease from the date of their retirement or exchange, if it take place before the expiration of six months from the date of quitting India.

Periods of absence allowed to be counted as Service for Retiring Pensions.

29. In order that all Officers quitting India on Furlough, or Sick Certificate, may be placed on an exact equality as regards loss of time, the period allowed by Regulation for proceeding to the Presidency or to the nearest port of embarkation, as well as the time to enable Officers to rejoin their corps or station after their return to India, will be considered as time counting for service for the Retiring Pension.

30. No Furlough or leave of absence, as announced in General Orders, exceeding two years in twenty years' aggregate service, three years in twenty-five years' service, and four years in thirty years' service, shall be allowed to count as service for the Retiring Pension ; and no difference will be made in this respect between leave of absence taken in Europe or elsewhere, in or out of India, or whether the leave be on sick certificate or on private affairs.

31. In the term "Leave of Absence as announced in General Orders" is to be included all leave of absence except the period allowed in Rule 29, and the ordinary indulgence of one month's leave in six months, as authorized by the existing Regulations, and which are in all cases, whether of Regimental or Staff Officers, to be allowed to count as service for the pension. All leave to a greater extent, granted by Political and other authorities, which may not hitherto have been published in General Orders, must be so announced hereafter.

32. Officers to be entitled to retire on the full pay of their Regimental Rank (under the Regulation of 1796,) must have served twenty-two years in India, out of which leaves of absence for two years in the aggregate, and not more, will be allowed to count as service for the Retiring Pension.

33. Officers to be entitled to retire on the full pay of Captains and Majors (under the Regulations of 1835-7,) must have served twenty and twenty-four years respectively, out of which time leaves of absence for two years in the aggregate, and not more, will be allowed to count as service.

34. Officers to be entitled to retire as Lieutenant-Colonels must have served twenty-eight years, out of which leaves of absence for three years in the aggregate, and not more, will be allowed to count as service.

35. Officers to be entitled to retire as Colonels, must have served thirty-two years, out of which leaves of absence for four years in the aggregate, and not more, will be allowed to count as service.

36. The scale, for Medical Officers and Veterinary Surgeons, of privileged Furlough and leave of absence as counting for the Retiring Pension, will be as follows :—

Years.	Months.	
1	8	in 17 and under 20 years' service.
2	0	in 20 „ „ 25 „ „
3	0	in 25 „ „ 30 „ „
4	0	in 30 and upwards.

37. It is to be distinctly understood, that under no circumstances whatever will an Officer be permitted to retire on full pay, until he has completed the *full time of service* above specified, whether he be in England at the close of his service or elsewhere.

38. The privileged time of absence may, with the permission of the local Government, be taken at any time subject to these Regulations. If therefore, at the end of twenty years' service, of which eighteen had been passed on actual duty in India, an Officer should be on Furlough, or Sick Certificate in Europe, or elsewhere, he will be entitled to retire on the full pay of a Captain without returning to India, and so in the other terms of service for the higher pensions. In like manner a Medical Officer on Furlough, or Sick Certificate in Europe, or elsewhere, at the end of seventeen years service, fifteen years and four months of which had been passed on actual duty in India will be entitled to retire on the lowest rate-pension, without returning to India, and so in the other terms of service for the higher pension.

39. These Rules do not in any way affect the existing Regulations regarding the grant of leave in India, or for short periods to sea, whether on private affairs or on sick certificate, except as to the periods of such absence being taken into calculation in the time allowed to count as service for retirement on full pay.

G. O. C. C. 23rd February 1854.

His Excellency the Commander-in-Chief desires to call the attention of all Officers concerned to the necessity for their intimating, when applying for Furlough or leave of absence, whether or not they desire to retain what may be considered the advantages of the old Regulations as in the absence of any such intimation it will be presumed that they prefer to adopt the new Rules ; and transmitting Officers will be careful not to forward to Head Quarters applications deficient in this respect.

G. O. C. C. 18th October 1854.

G. G. O. No. 110 of 1st Feb. 1854.
G. O. C. C. 23rd Feb. 1854.

With reference to the General Orders marginally noted, the Commander-in-Chief finds it necessary to point out that when Officers shall have once declared whether they desire to abide by the old leave Rules, or to adopt the new ones, it is quite unnecessary to repeat the declaration in any subsequent applications they may prefer for leave of absence ; but in order to afford a record on the subject in the Adjutant General's department, His Excellency is pleased to direct that in the statement of previous leave, annexed to the form of application prescribed in General Order 10th July 1849, it shall be notified under what Rules, new or old the first leave obtained subsequent to the promulgation of Government General Order 1st February 1854 was granted.

G. O. C. C. 8th April 1848.

Officers proceeding to the Presidency, on leave of absence, with a view to submitting applications, on their arrival there, for Furlough to Europe, or to retire from the service are reminded of the necessity that such applications must receive the sanction of the Right Honorable the Commander-in-Chief, previous to their being laid before Government. It is therefore advisable for Officers intending to embark soon after reaching Calcutta, to forward their applications to Army Head Quarters, in sufficient time to admit of His Excellency's authority being conveyed to the Assistant Adjutant General at the Presidency, to submit them for the orders of Government. These instructions are equally applicable to Officers holding Civil situations, with reference to the 2nd Paragraph of Government General Orders of the 12th of December 1818.

It is only in urgent cases, and on Medical Certificate, as announced in General Orders of the 10th January 1833, that the Assistant Adjutant General at the Presideency is authorized to submit applications of the above nature to Government, without first obtaining the sanction of the Commander-in-Chief.

1. The rules under which the period of services required to entitle Officers to the Retiring Regulations is calculated are as follows :—

2. Officers appointed direct, count service from the date of arrival within the limits of the Bengal Presidency—unless specially authorized by the Court of Directors to embark in a ship bound for another Presidency.

3. Officers appointed from Addiscombe subsequently to the 22nd November 1837 to the Cavalry, Artillery, or Infantry, count service as above, with the addition of the period passed at Addiscombe after attaining the age of sixteen.

4. Officers of Engineers count service from the date of arrival of the first Artillery Cadet of the same examination, with the addition of the Addiscombe period as above.

5. Officers appointed in India, if within the limits of the Bengal Presidency, count service from the date of the Government Order notifying their appointment—otherwise from the date of arrival within the limits.

6. Medical Officers and Veterinary Surgeons count service from the date of arrival within the limits of the Bengal Presidency.

7. Officers who may be compelled to quit the service by wounds received in action or by ill-health contracted on duty, after three years' service in India, will be permitted to retire on the half-pay of their rank, on the production of the usual certificates that their health will not permit them to serve in India. This indulgence, however, can be granted only in England, by the Court of Directors.

G. O. G. G Fort William, 19th April 1844, No. 122 of 1844

The following paras. of a Military Letter No. 3 from the Honorable the Court of Directors to the Governor General of India in Council, dated 28th Eebruary 1844, establishing an increased rate of Retiring Pension for Medical Officers, are published for general information :

Para. 1. Referring to our Military Letter of the 4th May 1842, No. 6, announcing the introduction of a New Scale of Pensions for our Medical Officers, we have now to apprize you, that we have resolved to establish an intermediate period between the Services of 20 and 28 years (three years' Furlough included,) on completing which, our Medical Officers shall be permitted to retire on an increased Pension, and that, accordingly, from the date of this Despatch, Medical Officers who have served 24 years, (three years Furlough included,) will be entitled to retire on a Pension of £250 a year.

2. The periods of Service and rates of Pension will in consequence hereafter, be as follows, viz :—

After	20 years' Service,	3 years furlough included,	£191	a year.
„	24	„	£250	„
„	28	„	£300	„
„	32	„	£365	„
„	35	„	£500	„
„	38	„	£700	„

3. With the above exception, no alteration can be admitted in the Scales of Retiring Allowances which have been established for the various branches of our Service.

18. A Veterinary Surgeon is allowed to retire after seventeen years' service in India upon seven shillings a day—or provided his health shall not permit him to continue to serve in India, then after ten years upon five shillings and six pence, and after six years upon three shillings a day.

19. Officers who have completed the prescribed period of service, are allowed to retire either in England or in India.

20. Officers retiring in England are allowed the benefit of the rank they may hold at the expiration of twelve months from their arrival in Europe.

21. Officers retiring from the service in England will be considered to have retired from the date of their application, or from the expiration of two years and a half from the date of the commencement of their furloughs whichever may first happen.

22. Applications from Officers to retire from the service in India, are to be addressed to the Right Honorable the Governor-General in Council under the signature of the parties, and transmitted through the ordered channel of correspondence. Each application is to be accompanied by a Certificate of Service from the Adjutant General.

23. The rates of full Pension and Half Pay allowed to all Officers, whether of Cavalry, Artillery, Engineers, or Infantry, are as under :

	Full Pay.						Half Pay.					
	Per Diem.			Per Annum.			Per Diem.			Per Annum.		
	£	s.	d.	£	s.	d.	£.	s.	d.	£	s.	d.
Colonels,	1	5	0	456	5	0	0	12	6	228	2	6
Lieutenant-Colonels,	1	0	0	365	5	0	0	11	0	200	17	9
Majors,	0	16	0	292	4	0	0	9	6	173	9	10½
Captains and Surgeons,	0	10	6	191	15	1½	0	7	0	127	16	9
Lieutenants, Assistant Surgeons,	0	6	6	118	14	1½	0	4	0	73	1	0
Ensigns, 2nd Lieutenants, Cornets,	0	5	3	95	17	3¾	0	3	0	54	15	9

The following rates of retiring pensions are fixed for Warrant Officers of the Ordnance Department :—

Commissary,	£182	10	0
Deputy Commissary,	„ 91	5	0
Assistant Commissary, Deputy Assistant Commissary,	„ 74	2	0
Conductor,* Riding Master,	„ 60	0	0
Sub-Conductor, Assistant Riding Master,	„ 45	12	6

To entitle Warrant Officers to such retiring pensions they must have served—

27	years in India, including,	12 in the department.
25		14
22		17

G. O. P. C., Fort William, 3rd September, 1855.

No. 904 *of* 1855.—The following paragraph of a Military letter from the Honorable the Court of Directors to the Government of India, No. 84, dated 27th June 1855, is published for general information :—

Letter dated 5th April 1855. No. 82.—Submit the question whether as officers are, on their first application for leave of absence on Furlough, to declare whether they will abide by the old or accept the new Furlough Rules, Staff officers who apply for leave to the Hills or elsewhere in India, are to vacate their offices like those who take leave to the Cape or elsewhere beyond sea. Government observe, that if this were so, the Rule would have the effect of debarring such officers from all leave, however, short, in excess of the privileged leave of one month in six.

7th. Staff Officers applying for leave in India are not required, by the new Furlough Rules, to vacate their Staff appointments. We therefore approve and confirm the view you have taken of this question.

NOTIFICATION.

HEAD QUARTERS, NYNEE TAL.

General Department, the 6th October, 1855.

No. 2040 *A.*—With reference to instructions from the Government of India, it is notified for the information of parties applying for Furlough or permission to retire from the service, that such applications cannot be granted until the prescribed certificates of no demand from the officers of Audit and Account, or Security for the Adjustment of any demand against the applicants in the Public Books, are furnished.

G. O. P. C., Fort William, 26th October, 1855.

No. 1079 *of* 1855.—With reference to the Notification in the Home Department No. 884, under date the 13th July last, the Honorable the President in Council is pleased to direct that the Pilos' certificates and reports of Departure required to be furnished by Military Officers proceeding on leave by Sea, or beyond the limits of the Bengal Presidency, under the orders noted in the margin, shall be transmitted by Post only to the Secretary to Government, Military Department, Calcutta.

G. G. O., dated 21st January 1817.
„ „ 27th September 1820.
„ „ 17th January 1851.

The Reports ordered to be furnished to the other authorities named in the above quoted General Orders, are no longer required.

GENERAL ORDERS BY THE MOST NOBLE THE GOVERNOR GENERAL OF INDIA IN COUNCIL.

Fort William, 4th February, 1856.

No. 195 *of* 1856.—The following Notification from the Financial Department is published in General Orders :—

No. 4, *dated 22nd January,* 1856.—The following copies of letters to the Secretaries to the Governments of the North Western Provinces and Bengal, are published for general information:—

* A conductor of Stores is allowed to retire on £60 per annum after 25 years actua service in India.

No. 4584.

TO THE SECRETARY TO THE GOVERNMENT OF THE NORTH WESTERN PROVINCES.

FINANCIAL DEPARTMENT.

SIR,—I am directed to acknowledge the receipt of your letter, No. 2092 A., dated 13th ultimo, and its enclosures containing certain suggestions from the Accountant in the North Western Provinces, relative to the practice of demanding Security from Civil Servants proceeding to Europe.

2nd. In reply, I am desirous to state, for the information of the Honorable the Lieutenant Governor, that the Honorable the President in Council is pleased to resolve :—

1st. That Security from Civil Servants on leave under Medical certificate, or on private affairs, retaining their appointments shall not be taken, and

2nd. That Security shall be taken in cases of Furlough, or of resignation of the service as heretofore.

3rd. The Honorable Court will be advised by this Government not to accept a resignation from any Civil Servant whilst on sick leave, or on leave on private affairs, without ascertaining that there are no demands against him.

FORT WILLIAM,
The 14th of November, 1855.

No. 224.

To W. GREY, ESQ.,
Secretary to the Government of Bengal.

FINANCIAL DEPARTMENT.

SIR,—I am directed to acknowledge the receipt of your letter, No. 1529, of the 24th ultimo, and to state in reply, for the information of the Honorable the Lieutenant Governor, that the Most Noble the Governor General in Council in pleased to resolve, that the Rule laid down in my letter of the 14th November last, dispensing with the taking of Security from Civil Servants on leave under Medical certificate, or on private affairs, retaining their appointments, shall be applicable also to Military Officers holding Civil appointments.

I have, &c.
(Signed) C. H. LUSHINGTON
Secy. to the Govt. of India.

COUNCIL CHAMBER,
18th January, 1856.

G. G. O., Fort William, 18*th March*, 1856.

No. 462 *of* 1856.—The Right Honorable the Governor General of India in Council directs that the following paragraph of a Military letter from the Honorable the Court of Directors to the Government of India No. 8, dated 23rd January, 1856, be published in General Orders.

Letter No. 213, dated 29th September, 1855.—Government forward correspondence relative to certain questions connected with the new Furlough Regulations, and request to be informed as to claims of an officer to the residue of his Furlough on private affairs, when he has hasn already absent on leave to England on private affairs for six months.

Para. 8. We have to state in reply to your enquiry, that an Officer proceeding on leave to England for six months, retaining his appointment or otherwise, is not to be considered as having taken his authorized Furlough after ten or twenty years, as the case may be, but may, with your permission be allowed at any time to take the remainder of the two years' authorized Furlough on private affairs.

G. G. O., Fort William, the 10*th April* 1856.

The grant of leave of absence to Staff Officers on Medical certificate, with half Staff allowances for six months, and with the privilege of returning to their offices if their absence from India be not prolonged beyond fifteen months, is bestowed by the Honorable Court in order to enable such officers to regain their health, and in the expectation that they will be thereby qualified to render additional service to the Government. But if leave of absence be taken merely to run out a prescribed period of service, and without any intention of returning to duty, the principle on which the rule is founded is infringed, and the indulgence of the Honorable Court is abused ; wherefore the Right Honorable the Governor General in Council hereby notifies for general information, that if there be an avowed intention on the part of an officer not to return to duty, or if the Government have valid grounds for concluding that the officer has no intention to return to duty, the indulgence of leave on sick certificate, retaining office will not be granted in future.

G. O. C. C., 2nd June, 1856.

His Excellency the Commander-in-Chief is pleased to announce for general information, that Government has fixed three (3) months as the maximum period, which is to be understood by the terms "short leaves," and "leaves for brief periods," used in Rules 7 and 21 of the new Furlough Regulations.

G. G. O., Fort William, 16th June, 1856.

No. 859 *of* 1856.—The Right Honorable the Governor General of India in Council is pleased to notify that the Honorable the Court of Directors, in their letter No. 56, of the 25th April 1856, have communicated the following decisions regarding the new Furlough Rules, published in Government General Order No. 1150, dated the 17th November, 1854.

Referring to Rules 6, 7, officers who take their first Furlough after twenty years service in India, may take their second Furlough after an additional service of five years from the date of their last return to duty.

Referring to Rule 9. Absence for six months under this rule does not preclude an officer from taking his Furlough to Europe after ten years' service.

(Copy) No. 3073 of 1856.

FROM C. H. LUSHINGTON, ESQ.,
Secretary to the Government of India.

TO C. B. THORNAILL, ESQ.,
Officiating Secretary to the Government of the N. W. P.

Dated the 4th July, 1856.

FINANCIAL DEPARTMENT.

SIR,—I am directed to acknowledge the receipt of your letter No. 648 A., dated the 9th ultimo, submitting for consideration certain enquiries from the Chief Engineer, N. W. Provinces, relative to the new Furlough Rules and Military Regulations.

The Chief Engineer's first enquiry is, whether a Staff Officer on return from Sick Furlough can be allowed half Staff Salary from the date on which he may report his arrival, and on this point "I am directed to inform you that it was decided by the Government of India on the 11th April last, that Staff Officers returning from leave beyond Sea under the new Furlough Regulations, are entitled to half Staff allowance from the date of their return to India ; and that the Officers acting for them who may be at the time in receipt of the full Staff allowances, must, from the date of the return to India of the incumbents, revert to the half Staff allowance of the appointments."

In respect to the 2nd point, "whether a Staff Officer obtaining 30 days privilege leave of absence to the Presidency can, without rejoining his appointment, obtain Furlough beyond Sea on Medical certificate or on private affairs as well as private leave, in full of 6 months." I am desired to state that it has been decided in the Military Department that if an officer obtain leave to proceed to the Presidency preparatory to embarking for Europe on Furlough, or on leave for six months on private affairs, under Section IX. of the new Military Leave Rules, no portion of such preparatory leave can be treated at privilege leave.

I have, &c.,
(Signed) C. H. LUSHINGTON,
Secy. to the Govt. of India.

FORT WILLIAM,
The 4th July, 1856.

No. 366 *of* 1855.—The following Military letter, No. 25, from the Hon'ble the Court of Directors to the Government of India, dated 7th February 1855, is published for general information :—

Military Department, No. 25 *of* 1855.

OUR GOVERNOR GENERAL OF INDIA IN COUNCIL.

1. Consequent upon the changes which have been made in the system of promotion in Her Mejesty's Army by the Royal Warrant, dated on the 6th October 1854, and by the Order, dated Horse Guards, the 23rd November 1854, the following changes, in the system of promotion in the Armies of the East India Company, have been approved and authorized by Her Majsety's Government. General periodical Brevets are abolished. A fixed establishment of General Officers of all Arms of the Service arranged in one list for the three Presidencies is authorized.

The Establishment to consist of :—

25 Generals.
50 Lieutenant-Generals.
145 Major-Generals.

Vacancies in the grades of General Officers respectively, are to be filled by the promotion of the Senior Officers standing next in succession in the Gradation List of General Officers and Colonels at the three Presidencies.

Major Generals hereafter promoted for distinguished service, will, after the number of General Officers, on the fixed Establishment has been completed, be placed in the Permanent General Officeres List, in the proportion of one Major-General for two vacancies; the second vacancy being filled by seniority from the Colonel's List.

Officers of Artillery, Engineers, Cavalry, and Infantry, after serving three years from the date they attain the rank of Lieutenant-Colonel, whether with their Regiment, or on the Staff, or on detached Military employment, in situations which, by the Regulations in force at the time, can be held by Lieutenant-Colonels, will be promoted to the rank of Colonel.

Field Officers, commissioned as such, before the 20th June 1854, will be allowed to rise by Brevet as under the Regulations then in force; but no Officer promoted to the rank of Field Officer, on or after that date is to rise from the rank of Lieutenant-Colonel to that of Colonel, otherwise than by three years' service in the former rank, as abovedescribed, or as a reward for distinguished service, or by appointment to be Queen's Aide-de-Camp.

The Governor General of India may, if in his opinion the good of the Service requires it, appoint any Colonel selected for Field Service or a Divisional Command, to the temporary rank of Major General without regard to seniority; and may, in like manner in the same circumstances, appoint a Major-General selected for a Command to the rank of Lieutenant General.

In cases where Colonels shall be so appointed without regard to seniority, to commands as Major Generals, their temporary rank, if they should have conducted themselves to the satisfaction of the Government of the Presidency to which they belong, may, after having held such Command for five years in peace, or after any shorter period in war upon the recommendation, of the Commander-in-Chief, under whom they have served, transmitted with his own approbation by the Governor General of India, and further recommanded by the Commander-in-Chief of Her Majesty's Forces, be made permanent at the pleasure of the Queen, if Her Majesty shall so determine. In like manner the temporary rank of Lieutenant-General, as conferred by the Governor General of India, may be confirmed and made permanent at Her Majesty's pleasure.

In addition to the Colonels promoted by seniority to be Major-Generals, Colonels will be eligible for promotion by Her Majesty to the rank of Major-General, and Lieutenant-Generals to the rank of General, for distinguished service in the field. In the case of Officers promoted to the rank of General Officers as a reward for distinguished service in war, the recommendation, in which the service of the Officer shall be detailed, shall be published in the General Orders of the Army and in the *Gazette*, with a view to ensure the responsibility attaching to an appointment thus made out of the regular course of Army Promotion.

Every vacancy on the fixed Establishment of General Officers is to be filled by the promotion when there is no supernumerary of the Senior Colonel qualified to succeed to the rank of Major-General and to be placed on the fixed establishment under the regulations now in force; and vacancies in the ranks of General and Lieutenant-General, will be filled in the same manner. If there be more than one supernumerary who has been promoted for distinguished service, the promotion of the Senior Colonel to take place on every second vacancy only, until the supernumeraries be reduced by the appointment, alternately, of a supernumerary and the promotion of a Colonel.

Promotion shall be made in the ranks of Field Officers below the rank of Colonel, from time to time, or as vacancies occur in the Major-General's fixed Establishment.

Any Captan, Major, or Lieutenant-Colonel, may be rewarded by promotion to Brevet rank for distiniguished service in the Field, on the recommendation, as at present, of the General Commanding-in-Chief.

The names of Officers above the rank of Captain who have already retired, or may hereafter retire from the Service on full pay, are to be retained in the Army List in italics; and Officers now on the retired Full Pay List, or hereafter retiring upon full pay are to receive a step of Brevet rank, but such Officers cannot be further promoted.

2. One of the provisions of the Royal Warrant is, that "the Commands of General Officers and other situations on the Staff, both at home, and abroad, shall not be held for more than five years unless by re-appointment." This rule already obtains in the Service as regards General Officers on the Staff; and we have now resolved that it shall be extended, as in Her Majesty's Service, to all other situations on the Staff and on detached employment.

3. Immediate effect will be given to portions of the above arrangement by the promotion by Her Majesty of Officers to complete the establishment of G eeral Officers for the three Presidencies, and of the Officers now retired on full pay who are to receive a step of Brevet rank.

4. Your Government will forthwith promote to be Colonels the Lieutenant-Colonels entitled to that advantage.

5. In making these promotions, time of absence beyond sea, on furlough, or sick certificate on leave granted, will not be allowed to reckon as a part of the three years' service, except absence on account of wounds received in action, or from ill-health contracted by service with an Army in the Field, which must be duly certified by the report of a Medical Board, when each case will be separately examined. In all other cases the time of absence of the Officer before he has completed the required three years' service as Lieutenant-

Colonel will be deducted, so that the Officer shall have actually served that time before he be promoted to the rank of Colonel.

6. Having considered the position of the Lieutenant-Colonels now in the Service who have held that rank for three years and upwards, it has been resolved that the above rule shall not be applied in its full strictness to them; but that the circumstances of each case, and the length and causes of absence shall be taken into consideration, and the proper deductions, if any, from their time of service be made accordingly.

7. We leave it to the Governor General of India in Council to specify in General Orders the Officers on the Staff or other detached Military employment, in which service a Lieutenant-Colonel shall, from the date of the promulgation in General Orders of the present arrangements be held equivalent to actual Regimental Command as Lieutenant-Colonel in qualifying Officers to be promoted to Colonels.

8. The Commissions of Colonels to all Lieutenant-Colonels qualified according to the arrangement now communicated, by three years' service as Lieutenant-Colonels, on the 28th November 1854, are to bear that date, being the date assigned to the first promotions made in Her Majesty's Service under the Royal Warrant.

We are, &c.,
(Signed) J. OLIPHANT,
And Eleven other Directors.

London, 7th February, 1855.

Fort William, 4th April, 1855.

No. 410 *of* 1855.—The following Military letter, No. 34, from the Honorable the Court Directors, to the Government of India, dated 21st February 1855, is published for general information:—

Military Department, No. 34 *of* 1855.

OUR GOVERNOR GENERAL OF INDIA IN COUNCIL.

Para 1.—Referring to our letter of the 7th Instant, No. 25,* we have now to apprize you that promotions consequent on vacancies in the fixed Establishment of Major-Generals are to be made in the following manner, *viz.* :—

* Published in G. G. O., *No.* 366, dated 23rd March 1855.

The Senior Colonel in the Armies of the three Presidencies is to be appointed to the vacancy of Major-General.

The Senior Lieutenant-Colonel of those Armies to succeed to be a Brevet-Colonel.

The Senior Major and Captain of those Armies are to succeed as Brevet Lieutenant-Colonel and Major respectively.

Seniority is in all these cases to be determined by Army Rank.

2. The promotion to the rank of Major-General will be made under Her Majesty's Commands, and will be announced in the *London Gazette*, and the promotion of the Lieutenant-Colonel, Major, and Captain, will, as usual, be made by the local Governments.

3. When the last Field Officers commissioned as such before the 20th June 1854, and remaining in the Army shall have been promoted to the rank of Colonel, such part of the above arrangement as relates to the promotion of Lieutenant-Colonels, to Colonels, will cease to have effect under the Clause of the new Regulation as copied in the margin.

"Field Officers, commissioned as such before the 20th of June 1854, will be allowed to rise by Brevet as under the Regulations then in force, but no Officer promoted to the rank of Field Officer, on or after that date, is to rise from the rank of Lieutenant-Colonel to that of Colonel, otherwise than by the three years' service in the former rank as above described, or as a reward for distinguished service, or by appointment to be Queen's Aide-de-Camp."

We are, &c.,
(Signed) J. OLIPHANT,
And Thirteen other Directors.

LONDON, 21*st February,* 1855.

No. 814 *of* 1855.—With reference to General Order, No. 655, of the 16th June last, the Hon'ble the President in Council is pleased to direct that the following Military letter from the Hon'ble the Court of Directors to the Government of India, No. 80, dated 20th June 1855, be published in General Orders :—

Military Department, No. 80 *of* 1855.

OUR GOVERNOR GENNRAL OF INDIA IN COUNCIL.

Referring to our letter of the 7th February 1855, No. 25, we have to apprise you that Her Majesty has been graciously pleased to approve of the rank of Colonel being given to Officers who obtain the rank of Brevet Lieutenant-Colonel for services in the Field, after the period of six years' actual service with that rank; and that the same advantage is to be extended to the Officers of the East India Company's Army.

We are, &c.,
(Signed) E. MACNAGHTEN,
And Ten other Directors.

LONDON, 20*th June,* 1855

No. 1275 *of* 1855.—With reference to Government General Orders noted in the margin, the Most Noble the Governor General of India in Council is pleased to direct that the following military letter from the Honorable the Court of Directors to the Government of India, No. 140, of the 24th October 1855, be published in General Orders :—

No. 366 dated 23rd March 1855.
„ 814 dated 10th Augt. 1855.

Military Department, No. 140 *of* 1855.

OUR GOVERNOR GENERAL OF INDIA IN COUNCIL.

With reference to our letters dated the 7th February and 20th June last, Nos. 25 and 80, we have to apprize you that, under the Regulation introduced into Her, Majesty's Service, of which a copy is given in the margin, the time of service during any period exceeding one month passed in command of regiments by Senior Majors, who are also Brevet Lieutenant-Colonels, may count towards the three years required to qualify a Lieutenant-Colonel to be promoted to the rank of Colonel, under the Regulations sent with the letters above referred to.

Brevet.

" Officers holding the rank of Regimental Majors, but being Lieutenant-Colonels by Brevet, shall receive the pay and allowances of Regimental Lieutenant-Colonels during any period exceeding one month, whilst they may be in command of their Regiments by the absence of the Lieutenant-Colonel ; which period of command the senior Major and Brevet Lieutenant-Colonel may count towards the three years required to qualify a Lieutenant-Colonel to be promoted to the rank of Colonel in accordance with the Royal Warrant of the 6th October 1854."

London, 24th October 1855.

G. O. C. C., 13*th March* 1856.

The Commander-in-Chief is pleased to notify, for the information of all concerned, that the Government have decided that all Officers returning from furlough to Europe, and intending to adopt the Overland route, who may be ordered to do duty with recruits proceeding to India by the Cape of Good Hope, will be allowed to reckon service for pension under the new furlough Regulations, from the date of arrival at their respective Presidencies of the Overland Mail Steamers, on which they would have otherwise proceeded.

No. 904 *of* 1855.—The following paragraph of a Military letter, from the Hon'ble the Court of Directors to the Government of India, No. 84, dated 27th June 1855, is published for general information :—

7. " Staff Officers applying for leave in India are not required, by the new Furlough Rules, to vacate their Staff appointments. We therefore approve and confirm the view you have taken of this question."

Letter dated 5th April 1855, *No.* 82.

Submit the question whether, as Officers are, on their first application for leave of absence on Furrough, to declare whether they will abide by the old or accept the new Furlough Rules, Staff Officers who apply for leave to the Hills or elsewhere in India, are to vacate their Offices like those who take leave to the Cape or elsewhere beyond sea. Government observe, that if this were so, the Rule would have the effect of debarring such Officers from all leave, however short, in excess of the privileged leave of one month in six.

F. D. ATKINSON,

Offg. Secy. to the Govt. of India, in the Military Department.

GENERAL ORDERS BY THE MOST NOBLE THE GOVERNOR GENERAL OF INDIA.

Ootacamund, 21st September, 1855.

The most Noble the Governor General of India is pleased to notify for general information, that the Hon'ble the Court of Directors have, in reply to a reference made to them by his Lordship, transmitted in their Military letter No. 100, dated the 8th of August 1855, the following instructions, relative to the new system of promotion which was brought into operation by the Hon'ble Court's letter No. 25, dated the 7th of February 1855, published in General Orders by the Government of India, No. 336, of the 23rd of March 1855 :—

Promotion of Lieutenant-Colonels.

1. The service of three years as Lieutenant Colonels by which Officers of Artillery, Engineers, Cavalry, and Infantry, whether with their Regiments, or on the Staff, or on detached Military employment, in situations which by the Regulations in force at the time can be held by Lieutenant-Colonels, become entitled to be promoted to the rank of Colonel, is required to be service in the Regimental rank of Lieutenant-Colonel.

The Leaves of Absence in India granted to Regimental Lieutenant-Colonels are not to be deducted from the three years qualifying them for promotion to be Colonels.

The following are the Offices on the Staff or other detached Military employment in which service as Lieutenant-Colonel shall be held equivalent to actual Regimental Commands as Lieutenant-Colonel, in qualifying Officers to be promoted to Colonel, *viz.* :

Adjutant General of the Army.

Quarter-Master General of the Army.

Commandant of Subsidiary or Field Forces, Districts or Garrisons, including Chief Commands of Irregular Forces.

Chief Commands in the Armies of Native Allied Powers.

Town and Fort Major.
Deputy Adjutant General of the Army.
Deputy Quarter-Master General of the Army.
Commandant of Sappers and Miners.
Secretary to Government Military Department.
Deputy Secretary to Government Military Department.
Secretary to Government Public Works Department.
Military Secretary to the Chief Commissioner, in the Punjaub.
Judge Advocate General of the Army.
Commissary General.

Such offices filled by Lieutenant-Colonels of Artillery and Engineers as belong to those particular Arms of the Service.

II. The vacation of all offices shall take place after they have been held for five years.

Tenure of Office.

It will be in the discretion of the respective Governments of the three Presidencies to re-appoint for a second or even a third tour of five years, when the Government may consider that the re-appointment is required for the good of the Service,

This rule is inapplicable to General Officers and Brigadiers, whose tour of command is limited by existing Regulations to one tour of five years.

Present occupants of Staff Appointments will not be effected by this rule, until the expiration of five years from the 23rd of March 1855, when the rule limiting the tenure of Staff employment was published in General Orders; unless, in consequence of promotion, they are required to vacate the appointments sooner, under the Regulations of the Service as already in force.

Brigadiers and Staff Officers filling appointments, which under existing Regulations cannot be held with the rank of Major General, shall, as a general rule, vacate their Commands and Appointments on promotion to that rank.

Officers holding such Commands and Appointments, who have already been promoted to complete the permanant establishment of General Officers, are to vacate their Commands and Appointments under the Regulations heretofore in force. But in consideration of the effect of the late promotions on them, they will be permitted to continue in their respective situations for a period of six months from the 14th of September 1855, the date of the receipt of the Honorable Court's Despatch; provided that, in the case of Brigadiers, their tour of Command shall not by this indulgence be extended beyond the limit of five years.

The several Governments shall have the power of retaining, on special grounds, to be separately reported to the Hon'ble Court, Major Generals for the following Offices in the three Presidencies, *viz*:

Secretary to Government in the Military Department.
Adjutant General of the Army.
Quarter-Master General of the Army.
Military Auditor General.
Judge Advocate General, ... *G. G O., No.* 321, *dated* 26 *February* 1856.
Chief Engineer of Public Works, ...
Inspector General of Ordnance, ...
Commissary General, ... } *G. G. O., No.* 648, *dated* 25 *April* 1856.

III. The adjustment of rank among the Lieutenant-Colonels of the three Presidencies

Rank of Officers in the different Presidencies.

heretofore made under the instructions of the Hon'ble Court's letter No. 9, dated the 27th of July 1836, published in General Orders by the Government of India No. 226, of the 4th November 1836, will henceforward be discontinued. The general list of Lieutenant-Colonels of the three Presidencies as now existing, will remaim unaltered; and by it the Government of India will be guided in making promotions to the rank of Colonel as directed in the Honorable Court's Despatch No. 34, dated 21st of February 1855, promulgated in General Orders No. 410, of the 4th of April 1855. But henceforward promotions of Lieutenant-Colonels to be Colonels, whether to supply casualties in ordinary course, or under the provisions of the new system of promotion, will be made in the three Presidencies without reference to the relative rank of the Lieutenant-Colonels in the Armies of Fort St. George and Bombay, with that of the Lieutenant-Colonels of the Bengal Army.

R. J. H. BIRCH, *Colonel*,
Secy. to the Govt. of India, Mily. Dept.,
with the Governor General.

No. 1164 *of* 1856.—The Right Hon'ble the Governor General of India in Council is pleased to direct that the following Military letter from the Hon'ble the Court of Directors to the Government of India, No. 117, dated 23rd July 1856, be published in General Orders:—

Military Department.
No. 117 *of* 1856.

OUR GOVERNOR GENERAL OF INDIA IN COUNCIL.

Para. 1. Referring to the several communications received from your Government relating to the promotion to the rank of Colonel of Lieutenant-Colonels who had obtained, leave of absence from India prior to the 23rd March 1855, we have now to announce to you that the sanction of the Queen has been given to the following Regulation, as concurred in by the Secretary of State-for-War and by the Field Marshal Commanding-in-Chief; *viz.* :—

"That all Regimental Lieutenant-Colonels who quitted India on Furlough prior to the 23rd March 1855, but who had previously commanded Regiments as Majors or Lieutenant-Colonels, or performed other equivalent Military duty in the situations prescribed in the Royal Warrant of 6th October 1854, for not less than two years, shall be promoted to the rank of Colonel when they shall have held the rank of Lieutenant-Colonel for 3 years."

"Lieutenant-Colonels by special Brevet for distinguished conduct in the Field who quitted India on Furlough prior to 23rd March 1855, but who had previously done duty in that rank for not less than two years, to be in like manner promoted to the rank of Colonel when they shall have held the Brevet rank of Lieutenant Colonel for 6 years."

"The time passed on leave of absence in India, and which had been granted prior to 23rd March 1855, to be also allowed to reckon as service."

"In cases of leaves of absence commencing after the 23rd March 1855, no longer period than one month in each year, or a total of 3 months in 3 years or 6 months in 6 years, shall be allowed to reckon, whether the leave shall have been spent in India or out of the Country, except in cases of wounds or illness contracted by service in the Field duly certified by a Medical Board, when each case will be separately considered with reference to the time to be allowed."

"The above Regulation to be applicable to Lieutenant-Colonels of Her Majesty's Troops serving in India, as well as to those of the East India Company's Service."

2. You will take immediate measures for carrying this Regulation into effect, so far as relates to the Service of the East India Company.

3. We now forward for your information and guidance copy of a letter and its enclosure, received this day from Major General Sir C. Yorke, K. C. B., on the subject of the claim of the Indian Army to Line Promotion under the arrangement contained in the Royal Warrant of 6th October 1854, in succession to Colonels promoted to complete the Establishment of General Officers of that Army on the 28th November 1854.

We are, &c.,

(Signed) W. H. Sykes.

And Nine other Directors.

London,
23rd July 1856.

Horse Guards,
22nd July 1856.

W. Leach, Esquire.

Sir,

With reference to the correspondence which has taken place on the subject of the claim of the Indian Army to Line Promotion, under the arrangement contained in the Royal Warrant of the 6th October 1854, in succession to Colonels promoted to complete the Establishment of General Officers of that Army on the 28th of November 1854, and particularly to the List of Lieutenant-Colonels of the East India Company's Army, who would have been promoted to the rank of Colonel from the 28th of November 1854, had the promotion been made under that arrangement, and which List was forwarded with your letter of the 28th ultimo, I am directed by His Royal Highness the General Commanding-in-Chief to acquaint you, that his Predecessor, Field Marshal Viscount Hardinge, having observed by that List, that in point of fact there remain only three Lieutenant-Colonels to be promoted, of whom one (Lieutenant-Colonel Day) has retired from the Service, in order to carry out the arrangement, and twenty-three remaining in the Service, whose appointments will be ante-dated, His Lordship communicated with Lord Panmure on the subject, expressing his opinion that on this understanding the application might be acceded to.

In this view Lord Panmure has concurred, and I am therefore to acquaint you that there will be no objection to these promotions and those in the other ranks consequent thereon being made accordingly.

In order to prevent any misunderstanding, I enclose a List of the Colonels remaining in the Service, whose Commissions would be ante-dated under this arrangement, extracted from the List forwarded with your letter of the 28th ultimo, and of the 3 Lieutenant-Colonels to be promoted; and I am to acquaint you that His Royal Highness considers that this question will then be closed.

I have, &c.,

(Signed) C. Yorke.

FURLOUGH PAY.

Officers on Furlough receive pay at the following rates per diem. General Officer in the Army, not being Colonels of Regiments, receive the following rates of pay while in Europe on Furlough :—

	£	s.	d.
General,	1	18	0
Lieutenant General,	1	12	6
Major General,	1	5	0

	Cavalry.			Infantry.			Artillery and Engineers.		
	£	s.	d.	£	s.	d.	£	s.	d.
Colonels,	1	5	0	1	3	0	1	3	0
Physician General, Surgeon General, and Inspector General of Hospitals,	0	0	0	1	3	0	0	0	0
Lieutenant-Colonels,	1	3	0	1	0	0	1	0	0
Superintending Surgeons,	0	0	0	1	0	0	0	0	0
Majors,	0	19	0	0	16	0	0	16	11
Captains,	0	14	7	0	10	6	0	11	1
Lieutenants,	0	9	0	0	6	6	0	6	10
2nd Lieutenants, Cornets, Ensigns,	0	8	0	0	5	3	0	5	7

On a review of the whole of the circumstances connected with these appointments, we have resolved to grant to Veterinary Surgeons the same Pay and Allowances when in India, and the same Furlough Pay in Europe—

As Cornets of Cavalry during their first 10 years' service.
As Lieutenants of Cavalry after .... 10 years' service and
As Captains of Cavalry after .... 20 years' service.

The Furlough Pay of Warrant Officers is as follows :—

		£.	s.	d.
Commissary,	per annum	182	10	0
Deputy Commissary of Ordnance,	„	91	5	0
Assistant ditto, Deputy Assistant ditto,	„	80	0	0
Conductor, Riding Master,	„	75	0	0
Sub-Conductor, Assistant Riding Master,	„	45	12	6
Apothecaries,	„	75	0	0
Stewards,	„	45	12	6

HOME REMITTANCES.

European Commissioned and Warrant Officers are permitted to make Family Remittances to Europe to the following extent, for the benefit only of their Parents, Wives Children, Brothers and Sisters :—

Major General,	£400	per annum.
Brigadier General,	„ 400	„
Colonel,	„ 300	„
Lieutenant-Colonel,	„ 200	„
Major and Chaplain,	„ 150	„
Captain, Surgeon and Assistant Chaplain,	„ 100	„
Lieutenant and Assistant Surgeon,	„ 70	„
Cornet aud Ensign,	„ 50	„
Deputy Commissaries,	„ 50	„
Assistant and Deputy Assistant Ditto,	„ 40	„
Conductor and Riding Master,	„ 30	„
Sub-Conductor,	„ 20	„

The rate of Exchange is fixed annually. Officers on the Pension Establishment are not entitled to the indulgence.

The above remittances are effected quarterly, reckoning the year from 1st May to 30th April, and cannot be remitted in advance ; for instance, no party can remit during the first quarter more than ¼ of the amount exhibited above. During the 2nd quarter more than ½ the amount, provided he may not have already remitted for the first quarter. During the 3rd quarter more than ¾ of the amount, provided also that he may have not remitted for the two previous quarters, and during the 4th quarter, more than the established amount under the above proviso, and no arrears of remittances can be allowed beyond the official year.

Table of Indian Pay and Allowances.

MONTHLY.		Pay and Indian Allowance.			Regimental House Rent.			Horse Allowance.			Tentage.			Extra Batta.			Total.		
		Rs.	A.	P.	Rs.	A.	P.	Rs.	A.	P.	Rs.	A.	P.	Rs.	A.	P.	Rs.	A.	P.
COLONEL.																			
Horse Art. and Cavy.	In Garrison,	1158	7	0	0	0	0	120	0	0	200	0	0	0	0	0	1478	7	0
	In the Field,	1158	7	0	0	0	0	120	0	0	200	0	0	0	0	0	1478	7	0
Foot Arty., Engrs., European & Native Infantry.	In Garrison,	1065	5	0	0	0	0	30	0		200	0	0	0	0	0	1295	5	0
	In the Field,	1065	5	0	0	0	0	30	0	0	200	0	0	0	0	0	1295	5	0
LIEUT.-COLONEL.																			
Horse Arty. and Cavy.	In Garrison,	582	10	0	100	0	0	120	0	0	150	0	0	0	0	0	952	10	0
	In the Field,	582	10	0	0	0	0	120	0	0	150	0	0	304	6	0	1157	0	0
Foot Arty., Engrs., European & Native Infantry.	In Garrison,	547	14	0	100	0	0	30	0	0	150	0	0	0	0	0	827	14	0
	In the Field,	547	14	0	0	0	0	30	0	0	150	0	0	304	6	0	1032	4	0
MAJOR.																			
Horse Arty. and Cavy.	In Garrison,	461	1	10	80	0	0	120	0	0	120	0	0	0	0	0	781	1	10
	In the Field,	461	1	10	0	0	0	120	0	0	120	0	0	228	4	6	929	6	4
Foot Arty., Engrs., European & Native Infantry.	In Garrison,	410	14	6	80	0	0	30	0	0	120	0	0	0	0	0	640	14	6
	In the Field,	410	14	6	0	0	0	30	0	0	120	0	0	228	4	6	789	3	0
CAPTAIN.																			
Horse Arty. and Cavy.	In Garrison,	306	11	4	50	0	0	90	0	0	75	0	0	0	0	0	521	11	4
	In the Field,	306	11	4	0	0	0	90	0	0	75	0	0	91	5	0	563	0	4
Foot Artillery & Engineers.	In Garrison,	267	5	0	50	0	0	0	0	0	75	0	0	0	0	0	392	5	0
	In the Field,	267	5	0	0	0	0	0	0	0	75	0	0	91	5	0	438	10	0
European and Native Infantry.	In Garrison,	249	1	0	50	0	0	0	0	0	75	0	0	0	0	0	374	1	0
	In the Field,	249	1	0	0	0	0	0	0	0	75	0	0	91	5	0	415	6	6
LIEUTENANT.																			
Horse Arty. and Cavy.	In Garrison,	194	6	0	30	0	0	60	0	0	50	0	0	0	0	0	334	6	0
	In the Field,	194	6	0	0	0	0	60	0	0	50	0	0	60	14	0	365	4	0
Foot Artillery & Engineers.	In Garrison,	154	14	0	30	0	0	0	0	0	50	0	0	0	0	0	234	14	0
	In the Field,	154	14	0	0	0	0	0	0	0	50	0	0	60	14	0	265	12	0
European and Native Infantry.	In Garrison,	145	12	0	30	0	0	0	0	0	50	0	0	0	0	0	225	12	0
	In the Field,	145	12	0	0	0	0	0	0	0	50	0	0	60	14	0	256	10	0
CORNET, 2D LT. OR ENS.																			
Horse Arty. and Cavy.	In Garrison,	154	15	10	25	0	0	60	0	0	50	0	0	0	0	0	289	15	10
	In the Field,	154	15	10	0	0	0	60	0	0	50	0	0	45	10	6	310	10	4
Foot Artillery & Engineers.	In Garrison,	117	10	6	25	0	0	0	0	0	50	0	0	0	0	0	192	10	6
	In the Field,	117	10	6	0	0	0	0	0	0	50	0	0	45	10	6	213	5	0
European and Native Infantry.	In Garrison,	107	1	11	25	0	0	0	0	0	50	0	0	0	0	0	182	1	11
	In the Field,	107	1	11	0	0	0	0	0	0	50	0	0	45	10	6	202	12	5
Surgeons as Captains.																			
Asst. Surgeons as Lieuts.																			

INDEX

TO

HER MAJESTY'S INDIAN FORCES.

APPOINTMENTS SINCE GOING TO PRESS.

Mr C S Belli to be Magistrate and Collector of Patna.

Mr C H Campbell to be Magistrate and Collector of Mymensing.

Mr W H Brodhurst to be Magistrate and Collector of Tirhoot, but to continue to Officiate until further orders as Civil and Sessions Judge of Purneah.

Mr C F Carnac to be Magistrate and Collector of Dacca, but to continue to Officiate until further orders, as Magistrate, Collector and Salt Agent of Cuttack.

Mr W T Tucker to be Magistrate and Collector of Backergunge.

Mr A Pigou to be Magistrate and Collector of Sarun, but to continue to Officiate until further orders as Civil and Sessions Judge of Moorshedabad.

Mr H L Dampier to Officiate until further orders as Magistrate and Collector of Tirhoot.

Mr H A R Alexander to Officiate until further orders as Magistrate and Collector of Dacca.

Mr H C Richardson to Officiate until further orders as Magistrate and Collector of Sarun.

Mr H C Richardson to be Joint Magistrate and Deputy Collector of Patna, but to continue to Officiate until further orders as Magistrate and Collector of Sarun.

Mr A J Jackson to be Joint Magistrate and Deputy Collector of Mymensing, but to continue to Officiate until further orders as Joint Magistrate and Deputy Collector of Bograh.

Mr H Balfour to be Joint Magistrate and Deputy Collector of Tirhoot.

Mr C Limond to be Joint Magistrate and Deputy Collector of Dacca, but to continue to Officiate until further orders as Collector of Tipperah.

Mr H A R Alexander to be Joint Magistrate and Deputy Collector of Backergunge, but to continue to Officiate until further orders as Magistrate and Collector of Dacca.

Mr A J Elliot to be Joint Magistrate and Deputy Collector of Sarun, but to continue to Officiate until further orders as Collector of Midnapore.

Mr A V Palmer to Officiate until further orders as Joint Magistrate and Deputy Collector of Patna

Mr J D Ward to Officiate until further orders as Joint Magistrate and Deputy Collector of Mymensing.

Mr C F Harvey to Officiate until further orders as Joint Magistrate and Deputy Collector of Dacca.

Mr A J R Bainbridge to Officiate until further orders as Joint Magistrate and Deputy Collector of Backergunge.

Mr R J Wigram to Officiate until further orders as Joint Magistrate and Deputy Collector of Sarun.

Mr E E Woodcock to be Collector of Nuddea.

Mr L R Tottenham to Officiate temporarily as Collector of Nuddea, or until the arrival of Mr Woodcock.

Mr S H C Tayler to Officiate as Magistrate of Purneah.

Mr T Walton to Officiate temporarily as Magistrate of Purneah, or until the arrival of Mr Tayler.

Mr C J Mackenzie to be Joint Magistrate and Deputy Collector of the 2nd Grade.

Mr R J Wigram to be Register of Deeds and Marriage Registrar of Sarun.

Mr H H Robinson to be Register of Deeds of Chumparun..

Leave of Absence—Mr G B Pasley, Joint Magistrate and Deputy Collector of Agra, for three months, under Section XII of the Absentee Rules, from the date on which he may avail himself of the leave.

Mr C J H Richardes to Officiate as Joint Magistrate and Deputy Collector of Agra, during the absence of Mr Pasley, or till further orders.

1.—*In the Meerut Division.*

Mr F Williams, Commissioner, Meerut Division.

Mr G D Turnbull, Judge of Meerut.

2.—*In the Agra Division.*

Mr A Ross, Officiating Commissioner, Agra Division.

Mr R B Thornhill, Officiating Judge of Agra.

3.—*In the Rohilcund Division.*

Mr J H Batten, Officiating Commissioner, Rohilcund Division.

Mr A Shakespear, Officiating Judge of Moradabad.

4.—*In the Allahabad Division.*

Including the Humeerpore District, and for the Benares Division, including the Gorruckpore District.

Mr F B Gubbins, Commissioner, Benares Division.

Mr S J Becher, Officiating Judge of Benares.

LIST

OF

CIVIL SERVANTS

IN THE

PRESIDENCY OF FORT WILLIAM.

Corrected up to the 19th July 1859.

ABBREVIATIONS.

g. p. stand for	.. .. ..	General proficiency and diligence.
p.	,, ...	Proficiency.
h. p.	,, ...	High proficiency.
P.	,, ...	Persian.
O.	,, ...	Oordoo.
H.	,, ...	Hindee.
S.	,, ...	Sanscrit.
B.	,, ...	Bengallee.
A.	,, ...	Arabic.

HOME GOVERNMENT.

SECRETARY OF STATE.

The Right Hon'ble Sir Charles Wood, President, M. P.

COUNCIL.

Sir F. Currie, *Bart.*, Vice-President.

Charles Mills, Esq.

Sir James Weir Hogg, *Bart.*

Elliot Macnaghten, Esq.

Ross Donnelly Mangles, Esq.

Wm. Joseph Eastwick, Esq.

Hy. Thoby Prinsep, Esq.

J. P. Willoughby, Esq.

Lieut.-Col. *Sir* H. C. Rawlinson, K. C. B.

Major Genl. *Sir* R. J. H. Vivian, K. C. B.

Sir H. C. Montgomery, *Bart.*

Sir John L. M. Lawrence, *Bart.* G. C. B.

Colonel *Sir* P. T. Cautley, K. C. B.

William Urquhart Arbuthnot, Esq.

Colonel Henry M. Durand, C. B.

UNDER SECRETARIES OF STATE.

T. Baring, Esq. M. P.

Sir Geo. Russell Clerk, K. C. B.

James Cosmo Melvill, Esq. (Assistant.)

SUPREME COUNCIL OF INDIA.

The Right Hon'ble CHARLES JOHN VISCOUNT CANNING, Viceroy and Governor General of India, Governor and Commander-in-Chief of the Fort and Garrison of the Presidency of Fort William in Bengal, and of the Town of Calcutta.

Took his seat, 29th Feb. 1856.

Major Genl. The *Hon'ble Sir* JAMES OUTRAM, BART, G. C. B., 1st Ordinary Member.

Took his seat, 16th April 1858.

The *Hon'ble* HENRY RICKETTS.—(On leave,) ... ... 2nd Ordinary Member.

Took his seat, 1st May 1858.

The *Hon'ble* HENRY BYING HARINGTON, ... Temporary 3rd Ordinary Member.

Took his seat, 17th June 1859.

The *Hon'ble* BARNES PEACOCK, ... 4th Ordinary Member.

Took his seat, 2nd June 1852.

LEGISLATIVE COUNCIL OF INDIA.

... Vice-President.

THE MEMBERS OF THE COUNCIL OF INDIA.

HENRY FORBES, ESQ., ... Madras Civil Service.

Took his seat, 1st May 1858.

PHILLIP WILLIAM LEGEYT, ESQ., ... Bombay Civil Service.

Took his seat, 14th April 1855.

A. SCONCE, ESQ., ... Bengal Civil Service.

Took his seat, 9th May 1859.

The *Hon'ble Sir* C. R. M. JACKSON, *Kt.*, ... Judge of the Supreme Court.

Took his seat, 29th January 1859.

SECRETARIES TO THE GOVERNMENT OF INDIA.

FINANCIAL DEPARTMENT.

C. H. Lushington, Esq., ... *Secretary.*
R. B. Chapman, Esq., ... *Under-Secretary.*

HOME DEPARTMENT.

W. Grey, Esq., ... *Secretary.*
R. B. Chapman, Esq., ... *Under-Secretary.*

FOREIGN DEPARTMENT.

C. Beadon, Esq., ... *Secretary.*
R. Simson, Esq., ... *Under-Secretary.*

DEPARTMENT OF PUBLIC WORKS.

Lieut. Col. Henry Yule, Engrs., ... *Secretary.*
Capt. Alexander Fraser, Engrs., ... *Under Secretary.*
Captain C. H. Dickens, Artillery, .. *Offg. ditto.*

CONSULTING ENGINEERS TO THE GOVERNMENT OF INDIA RAILWAY DEPARTMENT.

Major R. Strachey, Engrs., ... *Consulting Engineer.—(On leave.)*
Captain C. J. Hodgson, Engrs.,.. .. .. *Deputy ditto, (Offg. ditto.)*

BENGAL.

The Hon'ble J. P. Grant, ... *Lieut. Governor of Bengal.*
A. R. Young, Esq., ... *Secretary to Government of Bengal.*
A. R. Thompson, Esq., ... *Junior Secy. to Government.*
Lord H. U. Browne, ... *Under Secretary.*
Capt. J. R. Pughe, ... *Acting Private Secy. and Aide-de-Camp.*
Lieut. E. H. D. Macpherson, 93rd Highlanders, *Aide-de-Camp.*

No. in Bengal.	*No. in Genl. List.*	*Names.*	*Commencement of Service.*	*Date of Arrival.*	*Appointments, &c.*
1	1	William Dampier, ..	20 *Nov.* 17	8 *May* 18	Member of the Board of Revenue L. P., 19 May 1855.
2	2	William Popham Palmer,	3 *June* 19	23 *Oct.* 19	Civil Auditor, 10 Feb. 1848.
3	3	The *Hon.* Henry Ricketts,	19 *July* 20	23 *May* 21	Member of the Council of India, 1 May 1858.—Leave for 6 months on Med. Cer. 26 May 1859.
4	4	James Hardwicke Patton,	12 *Dec.* 21	23 *June* 22	Judge of the Sudder Dewanny and Nizamut Adawlut, with powers of a special commr. under Regn. III. of 1828, 12 December 1854.
5	5	Francis Gouldsbury, ..	9 *May* 22	26 *Dec.* 22	Commissioner of Revenue and circuit, Rajshahye division, 25 Jan. 1854.
6	6	John Inglis Harvey, (1) ..	12 *Feb.* 23	20 *Sep.* 23	Sub-treasurer of Fort William, 6 March 1851. Government director of the Bank of Bengal and a member of the Mint Committee, 14 Feb. 1851.—Ex-officio Secretary Government Saving's Bank, 25 January 1857.

(1) Received a medal for p. in O.

No. in Bengal	No. in Genl. List.	Names.	Commencement of Service.	Date of Arrival.	Appointments, &c.
7	7	James Grant, ...	2 *Feb.* 25	9 *Jan.* 26	Civ. and sess. judge of Dinagepore, 19 Sept. 1839; vested with powers of a special Comr. under Reg. III. of 1828, 28 April 1851.
8	8	Henry Stainforth, ..	23 *June* 24	27 *Oct.* 24	Member of the Board of Reve., L. P. 7 Feb. 1857.
9	10	Henry Thomas Raikes, ..	13 *Dec.* 26	14 *Aug.* 27	Judge of the Sudder Dewanny and Nizamut Adawlut, with the powers of a special commissioner under Regn. III. of 1828, 15 Nov. 1853.
10	11	George Wynyard Battye,	25 *Apl.* 27	27 *Oct.* 27	Salt agent of Hidgellee, 1 May 1855.
11	12	Teignmouth Sandys, ..	25 *Apl.* 27	29 *Oct.* 27	Civil and session judge of Bhaugulpore, 17 Dec. 1856.
12	13	The *Hon'ble* John Peter Grant, ..	18 *July* 27	31 *July* 28	Lieutenant-Governor of Bengal 1 May 1859.
13	16	Charles Tierney Davidson,	21 *June* 27	3 *Feb.* 28	Commissioner of revenue and circuit, Dacca divn., 25 January 1854.
14	23	Geo. Augustus Chicheley Plowden,(1) ..	15 *Oct.* 28	4 *May* 29	Commissioner and agent to the Govr. General in the province of Nagpore, 1 Feb. 1856.
15	26	Archibald Sconce,(2) ..	26 *Dec.* 28	2 *May* 29	Member of the Legislative Council of India 9th May 1859.
16	27	Pierce Gilbert Edward Taylor, ..	6 *May* 29	21 *Oct.* 29	Civil and session judge of Bancoorah with powers of a special Comr. under Reg. III. of 1828, 10 Feb. 1852.
17	28	Henry Cranstoun Metcalfe,	6 *Apl.* 29	6 *Oct.* 29	Civil and session judge of Tipperah, 20 May 1852.
18	30	Rt. Nesham Farquharson,	4 *June* 29	21 *Oct.* 29	Opium agent of Behar, 23 July 1857.
19	31	Henry Craigie Halkett, ..	1 *July* 29	21 *Dec.* 29	Civil and sess. judge of Hooghly, 28 Jan. 1859.
20	32	Charles Steer, ..	18 *Nov.* 29	1 *May* 30	Commissioner of revenue and circuit Chittagong division, 1 May 1856.
21	33	Henry Charles Hamilton,	30 *Dec.* 29	13 *May* 30	Opium agent of Benares, 2 July 1855; at Ghazeepore.

(1) Received a medal for p. in P., ditto in B.
(2) Received a medal for p. in P., ditto in H. and certificate of h. p. in P.

No. in Bengal.	No. in Genl. List.	Names.	Commencement of Service.	Date of Arrival.	Appointments, &c.
22	35	John Samuel Torrens, ..	13 *Jan.* 30	11 *Sep.* 30	Judge of the Sudder Dewanny and Nizamut Adawlut, with powers of a special commr. under Regn. III. of 1828, 4 April 1857.—On leave S. C. 15 months, from 21 May 1858.
23	37	The *Hon'ble* Humphrey Bohun Devereux, ..	7 *July* 30	16 *Mar.* 31	Judicial commr. in the territories of the Rajah of Mysore, inspector of jails and supdt. of police and educational operations in Mysore, 7 Feb. 56. And Judicial commr. of Coorg, 25 July 1856.
24	39	James Gordon Campbell,(1)	6 *Mar.* 30	27 *Jan.* 31	Contr. of salt chokies, 20 April 1854.—On leave S. C. for 15 months, from 10 March 1859.
25	41	William Joseph Allen, ..	18 *Oct.* 30	11 *July* 31	Member of the Board of Revenue, L. P. 1 May 1858.
26	44	Henry Atherton,(2) ..	12 *Jan.* 31	14 *Sep.* 31	Civil and session judge of Sarun, 24 March 1858.
27	46	Richard Hugh Snell, ..	12 *Jan.* 31	21 *May* 31	Out of employ from 7 June 1858.
28	47	Geo. Gordon Mackintosh,	12 *Jan.* 31	28 *Aug.* 31	On leave S. C. for 15 months, 7 June 1857; extension for 6 months, 16 June 1858. Ditto 3 months, 12 Jan. 1859.
29	49	Francis Baring Kemp, ..	12 *Jan.* 31	11 *Nov.* 31	Civil and session judge of Backergunge, 10 April 1855.
30	51	George Udny Yule, ..	6 *July* 31	16 *May* 32	Commissioner of revenue and circuit in the Bhaugulpore division, and commr. in the Sonthal Pergunnahs, 20 May 1856.
31	52	Robert Hampton, ..	6 *July* 31	19 *Mar.* 32	Salt agent and supt. of salt chokies at Tumlook, 2 July 1855.
32	53	Octavius Warre Malet, ..	12 *Jan.* 31	4 *Dec.* 31	Civil and session judge of Beerbhoom, with the powers of a special commr. under Regn. III. of 1828, 10 April 1856.
33	54	James Henry Young, ..	6 *July* 31	3 *Dec.* 31	Commr. of Revenue and circuit Burdwan, divn., 6 June 1859.
34	55	Charles Hugh Lushington,	6 *July* 31	24 *Sep.* 32	Secretary to the Government of India Financial Department, and a Govt. Director and President Bank of Bengal, 20 Dec. 1854.
35	56	Charles Binny Trevor, ..	9 *Nov.* 31	12 *June* 32	Judge of the Sudder Dawanny and Nizamut Adawlut from 10 March 1859.

(1) Mr. J. G. Campbell served as Cornet in the 6th Regt. L. C. at the siege of Bhurtpore, for which he is entitled to a medal.

(2) Received a medal for p. in B.

No. in Bengal.	No. in Genl. List.	Names.	Commencement of Service.	Date of Arrival.	Appointments, &c.
36	57	Edward Alex. Samuells,..	18 *Jan.* 32	19 *June* 32	Judge of the Sudder Dewanny and Nizamut Adawlut, 14 May 1859.
37	58	George Percival Leycester,	18 *Jan.* 32	19 *June* 32	Civil and sess. judge of Midnapore, 19 Jan. 1857.
38	61	George Dashwood Wilkins,	9 *May* 32	6 *Mar.* 33	Collr. of Customs of Calcutta, 19 Jan. 1857.—On leave to Europe S. C. for 15 months, from 11 August 1857; extension for 6 months, 25 August 1858.
39	62	The *Hon'ble* Edmd. Drummond,(1)	9 *May* 32	6 *Mar.* 33	Accountant General to the Govt. of India, Govt. Director of the Bank of Bengal, and member of the Mint Committee, 1 Jan. 1856.
40	63	Fras. Anstruther Elphinstone-Dalrymple, ..	9 *May* 32	6 *Mar.* 33	Collr. of Dinagepore, 10 April 1855.
41	64	Ewd. Elborough Woodcock,	3 *Dec.* 28	2 *May* 29	Collector of Patna, 1 May 1856.
42	65	James Jackson Ward, (2)..	28 *Dec.* 32	21 *June* 33	Civil and session judge of Cuttack, 25 April 1856.
43	66	Arthur Grote, ..	14 *Jan.* 33	14 *June* 33	Commr. of revenue and circuit Nuddea division, 7 Feb. 1857. Offg. member Board of Revenue, 9 June 1859.
44	68	Edward deLautour, ..	3 *July* 33	31 *Dec.* 33	Civil and session judge of the 24-Pergunnahs, 4 April 1857.
45	69	Charles Chapman, ..	21 *June* 33	19 *Oct.* 33	Salt agent at Chittagong, 28 July 1853.
46	70	Alex. Geo. Macdonald, ..	16 *Jan.* 33	22 *July* 34	Collr. of Rungpore, 23 Nov. 1854.
47	71	George Loch, ..	15 *Jan.* 34	25 *Sep.* 34	Civil and session judge of Purneah, 10 April 1855. Offg. judge of the Sudder Dewanny and Nizamut Adawlut, 17 Dec. 1856.
48	73	Edmund Ford Radcliffe,..	15 *Jan.* 34	17 *June* 34	Additional civil and sess. judge of Chittagong, 15 Jan. 1858. Offg. judge of ditto 14 May 1859.
49	74	George Louis Martin, ..	15 *Jan.* 34	8 *July* 34	Civil and session judge of Tirhoot, with power of a jndge in Chumparun 24 March 1858.
50	75	Merrick Atr. Gethin Shawe,	25 *June* 34	19 *Apl.* 35	Civil and session judge of Sylhet, 7 July 1857.
51	76	Henry Vincent Bayley, ..	13 *May* 35	25 *Sep.* 35	Civil and ses. judge of Rungpore continuing to Officiate as judge of the Sudder Dewanny and Nizamut Adawlut 6 June 1859.

(1) Received a medal for p. in B.

(2) Received a medal for p. in B.

No. in Bengal.	No. in Genl. List.	Names.	Commencement of Service.	Date of Arrival.	Appointments, &c.
52	77	Richard Pryce Harrison,..	28 *Jan.* 35	19 *Sep.* 35	Accountant to the Government of Bengal, from 7 June 1859.
53	78	Arthur Littledale, ..	28 *Jan.* 35	26 *Oct.* 35	Civil and session judge of Nuddea, 1 May 1858.
54	79	Fredk. Astell Lushington,	13 *May* 35	26 *Sep.* 35	Collector of Rajshahye, 14 March 1859.
55	80	Thomas Coutts Trotter, ..	8 *Jan.* 36	6 *Aug.* 36	Civil and session judge of Behar, 14 April 1857.
56	86	David Cunliffe, ..	4 *June* 35	13 *Dec.* 35	Collr. of Behar, 14 March 1859.
57	84	Cecil Beadon, ..	15 *June* 36	31 *Dec.* 36	Secretary to the Government of India, Foreign Dept., 5 April. 1859.
58	85	Archibald Roberts Young,	21 *June* 36	31 *Dec.* 36	Secretary to the Govt. of Bengal, 25 Jan. 1857.
59	86	Geo. Fergusson Cockburn,	15 *June* 36	17 *Jan.* 37	Commr. of revenue and circuit Cuttack divn. and supdt. of Tributary Mehals, 5 Aug. 1857.
60	87	Henry Mountford Reid,..	15 *June* 36	20 *Jan.* 37	Civil and session judge of Burdwan. 9 June 59. Officiating Commissioner of Nuddea, 7 June 1859.
61	88	Hew Dalrymple Hamilton Fergusson, ..	15 *June* 36	10 *Feb.* 37	Commissioner of the Patna division. 14 May 1859.
62	96	Richard Cairnes Raikes,..	11 *Jan.* 37	15 *Sep.* 37	Collr. of Moorshedabad, 7 May 59. —On leave S. C. to Europe, for 15 months, 23 July 1857. Extension for 6 months, 8 Dec. 1858.
63	99	Edward Taylor Trevor, ..	28 *June* 37	17 *Dec.* 37	Secretary to the Board of reve. L. P. 7 Feb. 1857.
64	100	Francis Lestock Beaufort,	1 *June* 37	29 *Nov.* 37	Supdt. and remembrancer of legal affairs and Government Advocate, 14 March 1859.
65	106	Wm. Henry Brodhurst, ..	7 *Aug.* 39	19 *Jan.* 40	Collector of Tirhoot continuing to Officiate as civil and session judge of Purneah, 26 April 1859.
66	109	Edgar Fredk. Lautour, ..	30 *July* 39	18 *Jan.* 40	Additional civil and session judge of Behar and Patna, 23 July 1857.
67	111	George Charles Fletcher,..	7 *Aug.* 39	8 *Feb.* 40	Civil and session judge of Chittagong, with the powers of a special commr. under Regn. III. of 1828, 6 Nov. 1856.—Leave for 15 months on S. C., 14 June 1859.
68	113	William Boyd Buckle, ..	15 *Jan.* 40	4 *Oct.* 40	Collr. of Hooghly, 12 December 1854.

No. in Bengal.	No. in Genl. List.	Names.	Commencement of Service.	Date of Arrival.	Appointments, &c.
69	114	Richard Nowell Shore, ..	15 *Jan.* 40	4 *Oct.* 40	Magte. collr. and salt agent of Cuttack and assistant to supdt. of Tributary Mehals, 16 Jan. 1856.—Leave for 6 months, 26 April 1859.
70	115	Richard Henry Russell, ..	15 *Jan.* 40	11 *Sep.* 40	Europe on S. C. from 25 Dec. 1857.
71	118	Robert Abercrombie, ..	15 *Jan.* 40	10 *Sep.* 40	Civil and session judge of Dacca, to 15 Jan. 1858.
72	121	John Ed. Sutherland Lillie,	17 *July* 40	23 *Nov.* 40	Additional civil and session judge of 24-Pergunnahs and Hooghly, 15 Jan. 1858.—On leave S. C. for 15 months, 20 July 1858.
73	124	William Grey, ..	31 *July* 40	27 *Dec.* 40	Secretary to the Govt. of India in the Home Department 5 April 1859.
74	127	Ed. Harbord Lushington,	16 *Jan.* 41	22 *June* 41	Junr. secy. to the Board of Reve. L. P. 25 Jan. 1857.
75	128	Robert James Scott, ..	20 *Jan.* 41	21 *Sep.* 41	Civil and session judge of Patna, 23 July 1857.
76	129	George Gordon Balfour, ..	20 *Jan.* 41	21 *Sep.* 41	Furlough for 3 years Europe 8 February 1857.
77	131	Samuel Wauchope, ..	28 *July* 41	9 *Feb.* 42	Commr. of police for the town of Calcutta 5 Aug. 1857. Municipal commr. for the town of Calcutta, 1 Jan. 1857.
78	135	Vernon Hugh Schalch,(1)	1 *Feb.* 42	12 *Oct.* 42	Magt., collr. and salt agent of Balasore, 4 Jan. 1859.
79	138	Archibald Adam Swinton,	1 *Feb.* 42	8 *Oct.* 42	Collr. of Shahabad, 14 March 1859.
80	139	Edward Jenkins,(2) ..	13 *Jan.* 42	11 *May* 42	Additional judge of Tirhoot and Sarun, 16 December 1857.—Leave for 12 months on S. C., 19 April 1859.
81	144	Walter Scott Seton-Karr,(3) ..	27 *July* 42	12 *Dec.* 42	Civil and session judge of Jessore, 14 March 1859.
82	147	Elphinstone Jackson, ..	21 *July* 42	12 *Dec.* 42	Civil and sess. judge of Shahabad continuing to officiate as additional judge of the 24-Pergunnahs and Hooghly, 26 April 1859.
83	149	Jn. Warrender Dalrymple,	27 *July* 42	25 *Dec.* 42	Civil and session judge of Mymensing, 6 June 1859.

(1) Received a medal for g. p., ditto for p. in H., a certificate of h. p. in B. and ditto in H.
(2) Received a degree of honor in B. and a certificate of h. p. in P.
(3) Received a medal for g. p., a certificate of h. p. in S., ditto in B. and a degree of honor in B.

No. in Bengal.	No. in Genl. List.	Names.	Commencement of Service.	Date of Arrival.	Appointments, &c.
84	151	Edward Stanhope Pearson,	18 *July* 42	25 *Dec.* 42	On furlough for 3 years Europe, 24 Nov. 1858.
85	152	Edwin Sandys,(1) ..	27 *July* 42	16 *Dec.* 42	Collector of Tipperah, 23 July 1857. Offg. Addl. Judge of Chittagong, 14 May 1859.
86	153	Arthur Pigou, ..	27 *July* 42	25 *Dec.* 42	Collr. of Sarun, continuing to Officiate as civil and session judge of Moorshedabad, 24 Feb. 1858.
87	154	Fulwar Craven Fowle, ..	27 *July* 42	25 *Dec.* 42	Furlough for three years Europe.
88	155	James Combe, ..	27 *July* 42	20 *Jan.* 43	Joint magt. and depy. collr. of the 2nd grade, Shahabad, 25 April 1856.
89	156	William Morris Beaufort,	27 *July* 42	25 *Mar.* 43	Magt. of Dinagepore, continuing to Officiate as collector of Moorshedabad, 1 May 1858.
90	159	Thomas Binny Mactier, ..	30 *Dec.* 42	16 *June* 43	Collr. of Midnapore continuing to Officiate as magt., collr. and salt agent of Pooree, 17 May 1859.
91	162	Louis Steuart Jackson, ..	30 *Dec.* 42	23 *July* 43	Civil and session judge of Rajshahye, 7 May 1859.
92	163	Charles Francis Montresor,	13 *Dec.* 42	24 *Mar.* 43	Magt. of the 24 Pergunnahs and supdt. of the Allipore jail, 14 May 1859.
93	166	Alonzo Money, ..	30 *Dec.* 42	9 *Aug.* 43	Magt., collr. and Salt Agent Pooree continuing to officiate as controller of Salt Chowkies, 26 Apl. 1859.
94	169	William Gordon Young,(2)	12 *July* 43	25 *Jan.* 44	Director of Public Instruction, L. P., 26 Jan. 1855.—Leave for 6 months, from 25 Apl. 1859.
95	170	Horatio Nelson, ..	26 *July* 43	3 *Feb.* 44	Collr. of 24 Pergunnahs, continuing to officiate as additional judge of Tirhoot and Sarun, 14 March 1859.
96	172	James Randall Muspratt,	19 *July* 43	26 *Nov.* 43	Magt. and collr. of Bhaugulpore, 4 Nov. 1858.
97	173	Francis Tucker, ..	26 *July* 43	17 *Oct.* 43	Collr. of Jessore, 20 June 1859.
98	174	Charles Thos. Buckland,(3)	23 *Jan.* 44	21 *Apl.* 44	Judge of Moorshedabad, 8 July 1859.—Leave for 6 months, on P. A. from 23 Mar. 1859.
99	178	Charles Parry Hobhouse,	28 *Feb.* 44	23 *July* 44	Collr. of Burdwan, 28 Jan. 1859. Offg. C. S. Judge of Burdwan, 9 June 1859.
100	182	Robert John Richardson,	31 *July* 44	22 *Nov.* 44	Collr. of Chittagong continuing to officiate as judge of Shahabad, 7 May 1859. Commr. under Sec. 7, Act 14 of 1857.
101	183	Charles Forbes Carnac, ..	31 *July* 44	21 *Jan.* 45	Collector of Dacca continuing to officiate as magt. collr. and Salt Agent Cuttack, 29 April 1859.
102	184	Robert Alexander, (Junr.)	31 *July* 44	4 *May* 45	Collr. of Purneah, 26 Apl. 1859.

(1) Received a medal for p. in B.
(2) Received a certificate of h. p. in B.
(3) Received a medal for p. in B., a certificate of h. p. in B. and a degree of honor in B.

No. in Bengal.	No. in Genl. List.	Names.	Commencement of Service.	Date of Arrival.	Appointments, &c.
103	185	Campbell Limond, ..	31 *July* 44	23 *Dec.* 44	Magt. of Tirhoot continuing to officiate as collr. of Tipperah, 22 June 1859.
104	186	Fredk. Augt. Barnard Glover,(1) ..	22 *Jan.* 45	1 *July* 45	Collector of Sylhet, 10 April 1856. Offg. civil and session judge of Rungpore, 5 Dec. 1856.
105	187	Charles Scott Belli, ..	9 *Jan.* 45	4 *May* 45	Collector of Nuddea, 7 May 1859.
106	188	Chs. Hallyburton Campbell,	5 *Feb.* 45	1 *July* 45	Collr. of Mymensing, 17 May 1859.
107	289	Richard Oliver Heywood,	5 *Feb.* 45	1 *July* 45	Magistrate and collector of Monghyr, 6 June 1859.
108	190	Octavius Toogood, ..	18 *Dec.* 44	27 *May* 45	On furlough England, 25 Mar. 1859.
109	192	Fras. Berkeley Drummond,	29 *Jan.* 45	9 *Apl.* 45	On furlough, Europe, 7 March 1859.
110	193	William James Longmore,	5 *Feb.* 45	29 *June* 45	Joint magt. and depy. collr. of Pubna continuing to officiate as collr. of Sylhet, 26 April 1859.
111	194	Wm. Thornhill Tucker,(2)	6 *Aug.* 45	7 *Nov.* 45	Collector of Backergunge, 9th June 1859.
112	195	William Ainslie,(3) ..	5 *Aug.* 45	7 *Nov.* 45	Railway Commissioner, 4 Nov. 1858. Calcutta.
113	198	Francis Jeffry Cockburn,	6 *Aug.* 45	6 *Jan.* 46	Deputy collector of Government Customs at Calcutta, 1 May 1856. Offg. collr. of customs Calcutta, 30 May 1859.
114	200	Alexander Eliot Russell,	6 *Aug.* 45	16 *Jan.* 46	Joint magt. and depy. collr. of Maldah, 14 March 1859.
115	203	John Crawford Dodgson,	6 *Aug.* 45	7 *Nov.* 45	On furlough, 11 August 1858.
116	204	Alexander Hope, ..	6 *Aug.* 45	8 *Dec.* 45	Magt. collr. of Beerbhoom continuing to officiate as collr. of Shahabad, 7 May 1859.
117	205	Henry Campbell Raikes,	6 *Aug.* 45	8 *Dec.* 45	Joint magt. and depy. collector of Chumparun, 10 September 1855. —On leave S. C. to Europe for 1 year, from 25 April 1858. Extension for 6 months.
118	209	George Augustus Pepper,	14 *Jan.* 46	23 *Sep.* 46	On leave S. C., for 15 months, 10 March 1857. Extension for 6 months, 28 April 1858. Ditto 6 months, 8 Dec. 1858. Ditto 6 months, 28 June 1859.

(1) Received a medal for g. p. and ditto for p. in P. (2) Received a certificate of h. p. in B.
(3) Received a medal for g. p. and a ditto for p. in B.

No. in Bengal.	No. in Genl. List.	Names.	Commencement of Service.	Date of Arrival.	Appointments, &c.
119	215	Alexander Abercrombie,..	16 *July* 46	4 *Oct.* 46	Joint magt. and deputy collr. of Bograh Continuing to officiate as collr. of Chittagong, 17 May 1859.
120	216	Hodgson Pratt, ..	29 *July* 46	25 *Dec.* 46	On furlough 5 June 1858.
121	221	George Bright, ..	6 *Jan.* 47	3 *Oct.* 47	Magt. of Shahabad continuing to officiate as collr. and salt agent of the 24-Pergunnahs and collr. of Calcutta, 9 April 1859.
122	222	Alexr. Wood Russell,(1)..	6 *Jan.* 47	5 *June* 47	Register of the Sudder Dewanny and Nizamut Adawlut, 19 Jan. 1857.
123	223	Edmund Craster Craster,	6 *Jan.* 47	6 *July* 47	On Furlough from 25 Feb. 1859.
124	230	Augustus John Elliot, ..	6 *Jan.* 47	3 *Oct.* 47	Magt. of Sarun continuing to officiate as collector of Midnapore, 25 May 1859.
125	231	Henry Rose, ...	6 *Jan.* 47	6 *July* 47	On furlough for 3 years, 22 July 1857.
126	233	James Shiels Spankie, ..	6 *Jan.* 47	15 *July* 47	Joint magistrate and deputy collector of Bancoorah, 19 May 1855.
127	240	James Watson, ..	21 *July* 47	8 *Jan.* 48	Furlough for 3 years from 25 April 1859.
128	243	Francis Bruce Simson, ..	21 *July* 47	6 *Mar.* 48	On Furlough from 11 Oct. 1858.
129	244	HenrySomersetMackenzie,	7 *July* 47	7 *Dec.* 47	Resident Councillor at Singapore, 1 Dec. 1856.
130	246	Sulivan Francis Davis, ..	21 *July* 47	8 *Jan.* 48	Magt. of Tipperah 20 June 1859. On leave S. C. for 15 months, 16 Jan. 1858. Extention for 6 months, 12 Jan. 1859.
131	248	Harington Balfour, ..	26 *Jan.* 48	9 *Apl* 48	Joint magistrate and deputy collector 2nd grade of Bancoorah, 1 October 1857. Offg. magt. of Purneah, 9 Jan. 1857.
132	250	Hy. Cockburn Richardson,	26 *Jan.* 48	3 *May* 48	Magistrate of Patna, 14 July 1857. Offg. magt. and collr. of Sarun, 29 March 1859.
133	251	Thomas Pascal Larkins,..	26 *Jan.* 48	22 *Aug.* 48	Magt. of Chittagong, 10 February 1858.
134	253	Henry Abbott Rt. Alexander,(2) ..	19 *July* 48	9 *Nov.* 48	Magt. of Backergunge, 6 July 1855. Offg. collector of Dacca, 29 April 1859.

(1) Received a certificate of h. p. in B. and ditto in O.

(2) Received a medal for g. p.

No. in Bengal.	No. in Genl. List.	Names.	Commencement of Service.	Date of Arrival.	Appointments, &c.
135	256	Charles Edward Lance, ..	19 *July* 48	22 *Nov.* 48	Joint magt. and deputy collector of Noacolly, 20 April 1859.
136	259	Henry Lucius Dampier,(1)	24 *Jan.* 49	18 *Sep.* 49	Jt. Magistrate and depy. collr. of Furreedpore, continuing to officiate as magt. and collector of Tirhoot, 4 Nov. 1858.
137	260	Ernest George Birch, ..	24 *Jan.* 49	13 *Oct.* 49	Magt. of Monghyr, 2 Mar. 1859.
138	263	Edward Francis Harrison,	24 *Jan* 49	6 *May* 49	1st Assistant Accountant Genl. to the Govt. of India, from 8 July, 19 Sept. 1857.
139	264	Thomas Edw. Ravenshaw,	24 *Jan.* 49	13 *June* 49	Commissioner for the suppression of dacoity, with powers of a magt. in Hooghly, Howrah, Baraset, Nuddea, Jessore, Burdwan, Midnapore, 24-Pergunnahs, Moorshedabad, Pubnah and Furreedpore, 27 April 1858.
140	265	Wm. Henry Henderson,..	11 *Jan.* 49	26 *June* 49	Magistrate of Sylhet, 10 Feb. 1858. —Lv. S. C. for 1 year, 10 Mar. 1858. Extension for 6 months, 8 Dec. 1858.
141	266	George Gordon Morris,(2)	15 *Aug.* 49	7 *Dec.* 49	Superintendent of reve. surveys 4th or western division with powers of a collr. in Jessore, Furreedpore, Pubnah, Backergunge 24-Pergunnahs aud Sunderbunds, 7 May 1859.
142	271	Wm. Fraser McDonell, ..	15 *Aug.* 49	10 *Jan.* 50	Settlement officer in Shahabad 21 May 1859.
143	274	Alexander James Jackson,	15 *Aug.* 49	7 *Dec.* 49	Magt. of Mymensing continuing to officiate as joint magt. &c. of Bograh, 31 May 1859.
144	275	Edmond Weldon Molony,	15 *Aug.* 49	10 *Jan.* 50	Magistrate of Jessore, 11 August 1856. Offg. joint magistrate and deputy collr. of Pubna, 26 April 1859.
145	276	Robt. Barclay Chapman,(3)	2 *Jan.* 50	6 *Mar.* 50	Under secretary to the Govt. of India, Home and Financial depts. 15 Jan. 1858.—Leave for 3 months on S. C. 8 July 59.
146	278	Henry Muspratt, ..	2 *Jan.* 50	5 *Apl.* 50	Magistrate of Moorshedabad, 9 April 1859.
147	279	Fracs. Richard Cockerell,(4)	2 *Jan.* 50	5 *Apl* 50	Magt. of Nuddea, 25 June 1857.
148	282	Henry Baring Lawford, ..	2 *Jan.* 50	15 *Oct.* 50	Magt. of Burdwan, 16 March 1857.

(1) Received a medal for g. p. and ditto for p. in O.

(2) Received a medal for g. p., a certificate of h. p. in H., ditto in O., a degree of honor in O. ditto in P. and a certificate of h. p. in B.

(3) Received a medal for g. p., ditto for p. in P., a certificate of h. p. in P., ditto in O., ditto in H. ditto in S., a degree of honor in O., ditto in P., ditto in H. and ditto in B.,

(4) Received a certificate of h. p. in B., ditto in O. and ditto in P.

No. in Bengal.	No. in Genl. List.	Names.	Commencement of Service.	Date of Arrival.	Appointments, &c.
149	283	John Mangles Lowis,(1) ..	2 *Jan.* 50	30 *Sep.* 50	Magistrate of Midnapore, and ex-officio asst. to supdt. of the Tributary Mehals, 13 April 1858.
150	284	Wm. Cavendish Spencer,	2 *Jan.* 50	5 *Mar.* 51	Supdt. of surveys, 3rd or Eastern divn., with powers of a collr. under Regs. VII. of 1822 and IX. of 1825, in Dacca, Furreedpore, Backergunge, Bullooah, Mymensing, Sylhet, Tipperah, Bograh, Pubnah, Rungpore, and Rajshahye, 13 Oct. 1858.
151	289	Charles Jenkins, ..	14 *Aug.* 50	27 *Dec.* 50	Died May 1859.
152	290	Jas. Alex. Crawford, ..	14 *Aug.* 50	6 *Dec.* 50	Supdt. of stamps and stationery, 22 June 1858. Commr. to enquire into claims for compensation for losses in Lower Bengal, 6 July 1858.
153	292	Augts. Rivers Thompson(2)	14 *Aug.* 50	23 *Dec.* 50	Jr. Secretary to the Govt. of Bengal, 8 July 1859.
154	297	Wm. LeFleming Robinson,	15 *Jan.* 51	3 *May* 51	Deputy commissioner of the Sonthal Pergunnahs, 12 Oct. 1858.
155	299	Jervoise John Grey, ..	2 *Jan.* 50	8 *Oct.* 51	Magt. of Howrah, 31 March 1857.
156	300	Herwald Crawford Wake,.	15 *Jan.* 51	8 *Oct.* 51	Magistrate of Behar, 7 September 1858.—Leave for 15 months to Europe on S.C. from 11 April 1858. In extension 6 months, 28 June 59.
157	301	*Lord* Henry Ulick Browne,	15 *Jan.* 51	1 *Sep.* 51	Under Secretary to the Govt. of Bengal, 8 July 1859.
158	303	James Henry Mangles,(3)	10 *Sep.* 51	2 *Jan.* 52	On leave S. C. for 15 months, 10 October 1856. Extension for 6 months, 4 Nov. 1857; ditto for 6 months, 28 April 1858.
159	304	Thomas Blomefield Lane,(4)	10 *Sep.* 51	31 *Jan.* 52	On leave S. C. for 15 months, 4 April 1855; 6 months in extension, 13 May 1856; ditto, 24 March 1857; ditto 18 Nov. 1857; ditto for 6 months from 17 May 1858. Ditto 6 months from 17 Nov. 1858; ditto, 6 months 28 June 1859.
160	310	Thos. Bruce Lane,(5) ..	13 *Jan.* 52	24 *Sep.* 52	Magt. of Rajshaye, 31 May 1859.
161	313	Joseph David Ouseley, ..	11 *Jan.* 52	28 *Apl.* 52	Assistant magt. and collr. of Burdwan, 12 Dec. 1857.
162	317	The *Hon'ble* Ashley Eden,	14 *Jan.* 52	29 *May* 52	Joint magt. and deputy collector of Baraset, 13 April 1858.

(1) Received a medal for g. p.　　(2) Received a certificate of h. p. in B. and ditto in O.

(3) Received a certificate of h. p. in B. ditto in O.

(4) Received a certificate of h. p. in B. ditto in O.

(5) Received a certificate of h. p. in B., ditto in O. and ditto in H.

No. in Bengal.	No. in Genl. List.	Names.	Commencement of Service.	Date of Arrival.	Appointments, &c.
163	318	Wm. Waterfield,(1) ..	11 *Aug.* 52	19 *Nov.* 52	1st Assistant Accountant General Madras 3 June 1859.
164	319	John Henry Ravenshaw,..	11 *Aug.* 52	7 *Jan.* 53	Joint magt. and deputy collector, 2nd grade, 14 May 1859. Offg. Jt. magt. and deputy collr. of Furredpore, 2 Mar. 1859.
165	324	Henry Bruce Simson, ..	11 *Aug.* 52	18 *Mar.* 53	Assistant magt. and collr. of Bhaugulpore with special powers, 10 Nov. 1858. Offg. magt. of Behar, 27 June 1859.
166	326	Edward Drummond, ..	11 *Aug.* 52	6 *Jan.* 53	Magt. of Rungpore, 20 June 1859.
167	327	Wm. James Herschel,(2) ..	5 *Jan.* 53	2 *Mar.* 53	Joint magt. &c. 2nd grade, 27 June 1859. Offg. magistrate of Shahabad, 24 Feb. 1859.
168	328	Edward Grey,(3) ..	5 *Jan.* 53	18 *Nov.* 53	Supt. 1st or N. Div. of survey with powers of a collr. in Purneah, Bhaugulpore, Dinagepore, Rungpore, Maldah, Monghyr, Beerbhoom, Moorshedabad, Jessore, Furreedpore, Mymensing, Rajshahye, Pubnah and Bograh, 27 June 1859.
169	329	Ross Lowis Mangles, ..	5 *Jan.* 53	14 *July* 53	Leave S. C. for 15 months, to Europe from 23 Sep. 1858.
170	330	Archdale Villiers Palmer,	5 *Jan.* 53	6 *Nov.* 53	Joint magistrate and deputy collector, of Tirhoot, 19 Oct. 1857. Offg. magt. of Patna, 2 March 1859.
171	331	Atholl James Hay, ..	5 *Jan.* 53	12 *Aug.* 53	On leave S.C. for 15 months 24 April 1857. Extension for 6 months, 23 March 1858. Ditto 6 months, 8 Dec. 1858,
172	333	Robert Jas. Wigram, ..	5 *Jan.* 53	14 *July* 53	Joint magt. and deputy collr. 24-Pergunnahs, 22nd Oct. 1858. Offg. magt. of Sarun, 25 May 1859.
173	334	Horace Abel Cockerell, ..	5 *Jan.* 53	31 *Oct.* 53	Supt. of survey 2nd or S. division with powers of a collr. in Dinagepore, Purneah, Maldah, Rajshahye, Bograh and Rungpore, 8 July 1859.
174	335	Skipwith Hy. Churchill Tayler, ..	31 *Dec.* 52	2 *Mar.* 53	Joint magt. and depy. collector Hooghly, 20 April 1859.
175	345	Henry Albert Mangles, ..	30 *Dec.* 53	3 *Dec.* 54	2nd Assist. Accountant Genl. to Govt. of India, 4 Oct. 1856.—Leave for 3 months
176	349	Charles Bruce Skinner, ..	15 *Dec.* 53	30 *Jan.* 54	Joint magt. and deputy collector, 2nd grade, Jessore, 25 May 1859. Offg. magt. of Jessore 24 Feb. 1859.

(1) Received a medal for g. p., ditto for p. in O., ditto in B., ditto in H. and ditto in P. a certificate of h. p. in P., ditto in H., ditto in O., ditto in S. and ditto in B. a degree of honor in B. ditto in S., ditto in H. and a medal in A.

(2) Received a certificate of h. p. in B., ditto in H. and a degree of honor in B.

(3) Received a certificate of h. p. in H.

No. in Bengal.	*No. in Genl. List.*	*Names.*	*Commencement of Service.*	*Date of Arrival.*	*Appointments, &c.*
177	350	Arthur Magniac, ..	30 *Dec.* 53	1 *Aug.* 54	Assist. Magt. and collr. of Rajshahye 20 Nov. 1855. With powers of a Jt. magt. and deputy collr. 18 May 1858. Offg. magt. of Tipperah 26 Apl. 1859.
178	353	Anthony John Richards Bainbridge,	26 *July* 54	3 *Dec.* 54	Jt. magt., &c., 2nd Grade, 8 July 1859. Offg. magt. of Backergunge 29 Apl. 1859.
179	358	James Davidson Gordon,	26 *July* 54	10 *Nov.* 54	Joint magt. and depy. collr. 2nd Grade 31 May 1859. Offg. magt. of Dinagepore 28 March 1858.
180	360	Henry Houlton Robinson,	26 *July* 54	28 *Aug.* 54	Joint magt. and depy. collr., 2nd Grade Bhaugulpore 31 May 1859. Offg. joint magt. &c. Chumparun 25 May 1859.
181	361	Charles George Wynch,..	26 *July* 54	31 *Jan* 55	Assistant magt. and collector of Rajshahye, 13 April 1858. Vested with special powers, 19 Nov. 58—On leave S. C. for 15 months, 13 Dec. 1858.
182	362	James Duff Ward, ..	26 *July* 54	13 *Nov.* 54	Assist. magistrate and collr. of Mymensing with powers of a joint magt. &c. 19 Nov. 1859. Offg. magt. of Ditto 28 May 1859.
183	367	Colin James Mackenzie,	10 *Jan.* 55	13 *June* 55	Assist. magt. and collector of Shahabad with powers of a joint-magt. and deputy collr. 20 Oct. 1858. Offg. Magt. of Sylhet 8 July 1859.
184	373	Charles Fletcher Harvey,	15 *Dec.* 55	31 *Jan.* 55	Assist. Joint magt. &c- of Pubnah 21 July 1856. with powers of joint-magt. and deputy collr. in Mymensing, Pubnah and Bograh, 19 Nov. 1858. Offg. magt. of Dacca 28 May 1859.
185	374	John Frederick Browne,..	1 *Aug.* 55	22 *Jan.* 56	Assist. supdt. of Surveys, 1st or Northern division, 9 Oct. 1858.
186	375	John Petty Hamilton Ward,	1 *Aug.* 55	22 *Jan.* 56	Assist. magt. and collr. of Nuddea with powers of a Joint magt. 15 July 1858. Offg. collr. of Burdwan 9 June 1859.
187	376	Geo. Nelson Barlow, ..	1 *Aug.* 55	6 *Nov.* 55	Assist. to the magt. and coll. of Sarun, 22 Oct. 1856. With powers, of a Joint magt. &c. 14 Apl. In charge of the Sub-Div. of Sewan 2 May 1859.

No. in Bengal.	No. in Genl. List.	Names.	Commencement of Service.	Date of Arrival.	Appointments, &c.
188	378	Henry Thoby Prinsep, ..	1 *Aug.* 55	7 *Dec.* 55	Assist. magt. and collr. of Hooghly with powers of a joint magt. and deputy collr. 19 May 1859. In charge of the Sub-division of Serampore, 14 May 1859.
189	379	Rowland Vyner Cockerell,	1 *Aug.* 55	22 *Jan.* 56	Asst. magt. and collr. of Burdwan 18 Nov. 1856. Vested with powers, of a jt. magt. and depy. collr. in Burdwan and Bancoorah 15 July 1858. Offg. magt. of Hooghly 8 July 1859.
190	382	John Peter Grant, ..	1 *Aug.* 55	6 *Nov.* 55	Assist. to the magt. and collr. of 24-Pergunnah, 17 May 1859.
191	383	Wm. Vansittart Graham Tayler, ..	1 *Aug.* 55	6 *Nov.* 55	Assist. magistrate and collr. of Monghyr, 9 April 57. Vested with special powers, 9 Nov. 1858.
192	386	Stewart Colvin Bayley, ..	27 *Dec.* 55	4 *Mar.* 56	Assist. magt. and collr. of the 24-Pergunnahs. in charge of the Sub-division of Barripore, vested with special powers, 9 Nov. 1858.
193	387	Loftus Richd. Tottenham,	23 *Jan.* 56	14 *July* 56	In charge of the sub-div. of Nettore with powers of a jt. magt. and depy. collr. in Rajshahye 26 Apl. 1859.
194	391	Henry Wallis Alexander,	13 *Dec.* 55	1 *Feb.* 56	Assist. magt. and collr. of Bancoorah in charge of the sub-division of *Raneegunge*, with powers of a jt. magte. and depy. coll. 16 Feb. 1859.
195	396	Villiers Thos. Taylor, ..	5 *Jan.* 56	19 *Mar.* 56	Assist. magt. and coll. of Midnapore, 1 Dec. 1857. In charge of the sub-div. of Nugwan with special powers 18 May 1859.
196	399	Daniel Jas. McNeile, ..	6 *Aug.* 56	31 *Jan.* 57	Assist. magistrate and collector of Midnapore, 24 Dec. 1857. Vested with special powers 19 May 1859.
197	404	Edmond Elliot Lowis, ...	6 *Aug.* 56	1 *Feb.* 57	Assist. magistrate and collector of Midnapore, 11 August 1858.
198	406	Ed. Dowdeswell Lockwood	6 *Aug.* 56	30 *Oct.* 56	Asst. magt. and collr. of Patna, 29 Oct. 1858.
199	407	Geo. Lucian Taylor Harris,	6 *Aug.* 56	22 *Oct.* 56	Asst. to the Jt. magt. and deputy collr. of Pubnah, 16 Nov, 1858.
200	409	Fred. Mytton Halliday, ..	6 *Aug.* 56	30 *Oct.* 56	In charge of the sub-div. of Magoorah with special powers in Jessore, 6 May 1859.
201	410	Wm. Goldsmith Lester Lane, ..	6 *Aug.* 56	1 *Feb.* 57	Asst. magistrate. and coll. of Burdwan, 7 Oct. 1858.

No. in Bengal.	No. in Genl. List.	Names.	Commencement of Service.	Date of Arrival.	Appointments, &c.
202	411	Wm. Macpherson, ..	6 *Aug.* 56	30 *Nov.* 56	In charge of Bood Bood, with special powers in Burdwan and Bancoorah, 12 July 1859.
203	413	Wells Butler, ..	4 *July* 56	29 *Aug.* 56	Died 20 June 1859.
204	414	William Cornell, B. A., ..	11 *July* 56	20 *Nov.* 56	Assist. Magt. and collr. of Dacca, 17 March 1858. Vested with special powers 19 May 1859. In charge of the sub-div. of Munseegunge 6 June 1859.
205	415	Herbert John Reynolds,	18 *July* 56	24 *Sep.* 56	Assist. supdt. of surveys 3rd or Eastern division, with powers of collector under Regs. VII. of 1822 and IX. of 1825 in Dacca, Furreedpore, Backergunge, Bullooah, Mymensing, Sylhet, Tipperah, Bograh, Pubnah, Rungpore and Rajshahye, 9 Oct. 1858.
206	416	Robert Hugh Munro Warrand,	10 *July* 56	24 *Sep.* 56	Asst. supdt. of Reve. survey 4th or Western division, with full powers of a collr. in Jessore, Pubnah, Furreedpore, Backergunge, 24-Pergunnahs and the Soonderbuns, 5th Jan. 1859.
207	422	Henry Bell, ..	15 *July* 56	29 *Aug.* 56	In charge of the sub-div. of Seragegunge 28 May 1859. With powers of a Jt. Magt. &c. in Mymensing, Pubna, and Bograh, 19 May 1859.
208	426	Wilfred Lucas Heeley, BA.	19 *July* 56	30 *Nov.* 56	Assist. magistrate collector and salt agent Cuttack, 8 Dec. 1857. And also Asst. salt agent 19 Nov. 1858.
209	428	Alex. Thos. Maclean, ..	14 *Jan.* 57	3 *Mar.* 57	Assist. magistrate and collector of Nuddea, 12 Dec. 1857. In charge of the sub-div. of Damoorhoodah with special powers in Nuddea 25 June 1859.
210	429	Frederick George Millett,	14 *Jan.* 57	15 *Oct.* 57	Asst. magistrate and collector of Bhaugulpore, 18 Sep. 1858. Vested with special powers 19 May 1859.
211	434	Wm. Sutherland Wells, ..	14 *Jan.* 57	12 *Feb.* 57	Asst. magt. and collr. of Hoogly with special powers 15 Mar. 1859. In charge of Govindpore 13 Apl.59.
212	440	Thomas Walton, ..	1 *Oct.* 55	16 *Dec.* 56	Assist. magt. and collr. of Purneah 14 Oct. 1858. With special powers 19 Nov. 1858.

No. in Bengal.	No. in Genl. List.	Names.	Commencement of Service.	Date of Arrival.	Appointments, &c.
213	442	James Wyburd Furrell, .	1 *Sep.* 56	3 *Jan.* 57	Assist. magt. and collr. of Moorshedabad, 10 April 1858. With special powers, 19 Nov. 1858. In charge of the sub-div. of Aurungabad 24 Feb. 1859.
214	444	John Burney Worgan, ..	4 *Sep.* 56	16 *Dec.* 56	Assist. magt. and collr. of Sarun, 10 June 1858. In charge of the sub-division of Sussaram, with special powers, 8 July 1859.
215	447	Anthony Burn Falcon, ..	3 *Sep.* 56	16 *Dec.* 56	Assist. joint magt. and depy. collr. of Noacolly 8 Dec. 1857. Vested with special powors 19 May 1859.
216	448	Alex. Smith, ..	1 *Oct.* 56	16 *Dec.* 56	In charge of the sub-division of Shergotty, with special powers in Behar, 27 June 1859.
217	451	Fras. James Alexander. ..	5 *Aug.* 57	11 *Nov.* 57	Asst. magt. and collr. of Moorshedabad, 29 March 1859.
218	453	Chas. Theo. Metcalfe, ..	5 *Aug.* 57	30 *Oct.* 57	Asst. magt. and collr. of Rajshahye, 17 Dec. 1858.
219	454	Hy. Fitzmaurice John Kean	5 *Aug.* 57	30 *Oct.* 57	Asst. magt. and collr. of Dinagepore, 27 June 1859.
220	456	Jas. Sutherland Drummond	5 *Aug.* 57	11 *Nov.* 57	Assist. Magt. and collr. of 24-Pergunnahs with special powers, 17 May 1859.
221	461	Alex. Champion Mangles,	30 *Dec.* 57	8 *Apl.* 58	Asst. magt. and collr. of Bhagulpore 7 June 1859.
222	462	Henry Laurence Olephant,	30 *Dec.* 57	8 *Apl.* 58	Asst. magt. and collr. of Nuddea, 7 June 1859.
223	465	Trevor John Chicheley Grant, ..	30 *Dec.* 58	27 *Jan.* 58	Asst. magt. and collr. of Tirhoot 9 Dec. 1858.
224	467	Wilson Hastings D'Oyly,	30 *Dec.* 58	28 *May* 58	Asst. magt. and collr. of Tirhoot 10 March 1859.
225	469	Charles Bazell Garrett, ..	26 *Jan.* 58	2 *Mar.* 58	Asst. magt. and coll. of Midnapore 4 Feb. 59.
226	471	Fleetwood Hugo Pellew,	26 *Jan.* 58	8 *Apl.* 58	Asst. magt. and collr. of Cuttack, 13 Oct. 1858
227	478	Percy Adolphus Humphery	26 *Jan.* 58	8 *Apl.* 58	Asst. magt. and collr. of Sylhet 2 May 1859.
228	483	Henry Beveridge, ..	16 *Aug.* 57	20 *Jan.* 58	Asst. magt. and collr. of Mymensing, 17 Dec. 1858.
229	485	James Munro, ..	16 *Sep.* 57	27 *Jan.* 58	Asst. to the jt. magt. and depy. collr. of Furreedpore, 14 Sep. 1858.
230	487	William Wavell, ..	16 *Sep.* 57	27 *Jan.* 58	Asst. magt. collr and salt agent of Pooree, 10 Nov. 1858.
231	493	Henry Cobbe Sutherland,	16 *Sep.* 57	27 *Jan.* 58	Asst. magt. and collr. of Tipperah, 13 Nov. 1858.

PUNJAB

AND

THE NORTH-WESTERN PROVINCES.

The Hon'ble Sir R. Montgomery, K. C. B.,	*Lieut.-Governor of the Punjaub and its dependencies.*
R. H. Davis, Esq., ...	*Secretary to Government of the Punjab.*

The Hon'ble G. F Edmonstone, ...	*Lieut-Governor of the North-West Provinces.*
Lieut. Col. G. W. Williams, 29th N. I.,	*Military Secy. to the Lieut. Governor.*
G. E. W. Couper, Esq., ...	*Secretary.*
C. J. Daniell, Esq., ...	*Under Secretary. (On leave.)*
F. B. Outram, Esq., ...	*Junior Assistant Ditto. Offg. Ditto.*
J. D. Sandford, Esq., ...	*Officiating Ditto.*

No. in N. W. P.	*No in Genl. List.*	*Names.*	*Commencement of Service.*	*Date of Arrival.*	*Appointments, &c.*
1	9	Ewd. Anderson Reade,(1)	18 *Jan.* 26	22 *June* 26	Sr. Member Sudder Board of Revenue, N. W. P., 6 February 1854. Agra.
2	14	James Lean, ...	18 *July* 27	29 *Jan.* 28	Civ. and sess. judge of Mirzapore, 1 May 1854.
3	15	George Frederick Harvey,	14 *June* 27	29 *Jan.* 28	Commissioner and Agent to the Govt. N. W. Provinces, at Agra. 1 May 1856.—Leave for 15 months on S. C. to Europe from 5th June 1859.

(1) Received a medal for p. in P.

No. in N. W. P.	No. in Genl. List.	Names.	Commencement of Service.	Date of Arrival.	Appointments, &c.
4	17	Trevor John Chicheley Plowden,([1])	17 *Oct.* 27	29 *Apl.* 28	Civ. and sess. judge of Ghazeepore, 10 March 1851.
5	18	Henry Byng Harington,([2])	6 *May* 28	27 *Sep.* 28	Member of the Legislative Council of India, for the N. W. P. 28 Nov. 1857. Temporary Member of Council of India 17 June 1859.
6	19	*The Hon.* Robt. Montgomery, ...	6 *June* 28	13 *Nov.* 28	Lieut. Governor of the Punjab and its dependencies, from 1st May 1859.
7	20	Donald Friell McLeod,([3])	20 *June* 28	10 *Dec.* 28	Financial comr. in the Punjab, 16 April 1854. Leave for 15 Months on S. C. 6th May 1859.
8	21	Henry Unwin,([4]).. ..	25 *June* 28	20 *Oct.* 28	Judge of the Sudder Dewanny and Nizamut Adawlut, 1 May 1856. —On leave S. C. for 15 months, 13 November 1857. In extension 6 months, 22 June 1859.
9	22	William Pulteney Masson,	6 *Aug.* 28	10 *Apl.* 29	Civil and sess. judge of Allahabad, 10 March 1856.
10	24	Wigram Elliot Money, ..	3 *Dec.* 28	2 *May* 29	Commr. of customs N. W. P. 4 April 1854.
11	25	Robert Brooke Morgan,..	6 *Aug.* 28	4 *May* 29	Judge of the Sudder Dewanny and Nizamut Adawlut, 1 May 1857.

([1]) Received a medal for p. in P. and ditto in B.
([2]) Received a medal for p. in H., ditto in P.
([3]) Received a medal for p. in B.
([4]) Received a medal for p. in B.

No. in N. W. P.	No. in Genl. List.	Names.	Commencement of Service.	Date of Arrival.	Appointments, &c.
12	29	John Hallet Batten, ..	5 *June* 29	22 *Nov.* 29	Civil and sess. judge of Cawnpore, 1 May 1858. Offg. commr. of the Rohilcund div. 9 Apl. 1859.
13	34	Edward Thornton, ...	13 *Jan.* 30	28 *May* 30	Judicial commr. in the Punjab, 16 April 1858.
14	36	Martin Richard Gubbins, ..	7 *July* 30	8 *Mar.* 31	Civil and session judge of Moradabad, 17 Jan. 1859. Offg. judge of the Sudder Dewanny & Nizamut Adawlut, N. W. Provinces.
15	38	Fleetwood Williams, ..	7 *July* 30	14 *Jan.* 31	Commissioner and agent to the Government N. W. P. at Meerut, 30 June 1857.
16	40	Rowland Money, ..	7 *July* 30	10 *May* 31	Civil and session judge of Saharunpore, continuing to officiate as judge of Sudder Dewanny and Nizamut Adawlut, N. W. P. 6 Sep. 1858.
17	42	John Adair Craigie, ..	10 *Nov.* 30	11 *July* 31	Civil and session judge of Saugor, 1 May 1857.
18	43	Henry Carre Tucker,(1) ..	12 *Jan.* 31	14 *Sep.* 31	On furlough for 3 years, 10 March 1858.
19	45	John Shore Dumergue, ..	12 *Jan.* 31	20 *Oct.* 31	Civil and sess. judge of Allyghur, 8 April 1857. Vested with powers of a commr. of Rev. and Police in do., 23 Jan. 1858.
20	48	Charles Raikes, ..	12 *Jan.* 31	14 *Sep.* 31	Judge of the Sudder Dewanny and Nizamut Adawlut, 1 May 1857. Leave for 15 months on S. C. Europe 24 Mar. 1858.
21	50	*The Hon'ble* Geo. Fredk. Edmonstone,(2) ..	6 *July* 31	28 *Dec* 31	Lieut.-Governor of the North-West Provinces, 20th Jan. 1859.

(1) Received a medal for p. in H.
(2) Received a medal for p. in P. & ditto in B.

No. in N. W. P.	No. in Genl. List.	Names.	Commencement of Service.	Date of Arrival.	Appointments, &c.
22	59	Sulivan James Becher, ..	18 *Jan.* 32	17 *Oct.* 32	Civil and session judge of Azimghur, continuing to officiate as judge of Benares, 19 Oct. 1858.
23	60	Robert Alexander, Sr.,(1)	23 *Mar.* 32	24 *July* 32	Commr. and agent to the Govt. N. W. P., Rohilkund division, 24 Feb. 1855.—On leave S. C. for 15 months Europe, 6 May 1859.
24	67	Charles Chester, ..	2 *Jan.* 33	22 *May* 33	Commissioner of the Allahabad division, 22 Jan. 1856. On leave for 6 months Europe 31 Jan. 1858. extension for 6 months 13 July 1858; Ditto 6 months, 8 Dec. 1858.
25	72	Henry Godfrey Astell, ..	15 *Jan.* 34	10 *Sep.* 34	Civil and sess. judge of Jaunpore, 22 Nov. 1857.
26	80	Charles Theodore LeBas,	8 *Jan.* 36	6 *Oct.* 36	On leave S. C. to Europe for 15 months from 24 Mar. 1858.
27	82	Fred. Bebb Gubbins, ..	27 *Jan.* 36	12 *Aug.* 36	Commr. in the Benares division. Agent to the Governor General, 16 March 1858.
28	89	William Edwards, ..	11 *Jan.* 37	10 *Oct.* 37	Civil and session judge of Benares, 1 Feb. 1858.—On leave S. C. to Europe for 1year, 11 April 1858.
29	90	Alexander Ross,(3) ..	11 *Jan.* 37	7 *Oct.* 37	Civil and sess. judge of Furruckabad, 17 April 1858. Offg. chief commr. Agra div. 5 May 1859.
30	91	Arthur Austin Roberts, ..	26 *May* 37	6 *Oct.* 37	Commr. and superintendent of the Jhelum division, 16 April 1858. Offg. Financial commr. Punjab 31 May 1859.
31	92	Edward Michael Wylly, ..	11 *Jan.* 37	19 *June* 37	Civil and sess. judge of Agra, 1 May 1857.—On leave S. C. to Europe for 15 months, 5 June 1858.
32	93	George Edmonstone, ..	11 *Jan.* 37	6 *Oct.* 37	Civil and sess. judge of Futtehpore, 16 March 1858.
33	94	Henry Vansittart,(4) ..	11 *Jan.* 37	15 *Sep.* 37	Civil and session judge of Bareilly, 3 September 1858.
34	95	William Wynyard, ..	11 *Jan.* 37	8 *July* 37	Civil and session judge of Shajehanpore, 19 Oct. 1858.
35	97	William Muir, ..	28 *June* 37	16 *Dec.* 37	Jr. member of the Sudder Board of Revenue, N.W.P. 13 June 1858.

(1) Received a medal for p. in P. and a certificate of h. p. in ditto.
(2) Received a medal for p. in P.
(3) Received a medal for p. in P.
(4) Received a medal for p. in P.

No. in N. W. P.	No. in Genl. List.	Names.	Commencement of Service.	Date of Arrival.	Appointments, &c.
36	98	George Carnac Barnes, ..	28 *June* 37	27 *Nov.* 37	Commr. and supt. in the Punjab (Cis-Sutlej States,) (at Umballah,) 4 Feb. 1853.
37	101	Arthur Herbert Cocks, ..	8 *June* 37	27 *Nov.* 37	Civil and session judge of Mynpooree, 13 Jan. 1858. Offg. comr. of the Jubbulpore division, 13 Nov. 1858.
38	102	Cudbert Bensley Thornhill, ..	4 *Jan.* 38	15 *Sep.* 38	Inspector General of prisons, N. W. P., 6 April 1852. Offg. Commr. of the Allahabad division, 24 Feb. 1858.
39	103	William Galloway, ..	22 *June* 58	7 *Feb.* 39	Leave S.C. to Europe for 15 months, from 15 March 1858.
40	104	Geo. Dundas Turnbull,(1)	9 *Jan.* 39	29 *July* 39	Civil and sess. judge of Meerut, 3 Sep. 1857.
41	105	William Roberts,(2) ..	9 *Jan.* 39	21 *Sep.* 39	Civil and sess. judge of Goruckpore, 1 May 1856.—On leave, S. C. for 15 months 11 April 1857. Extension for 6 months, 23 March 1858. Ditto 6 months, 8 Dec. 1858.
42	107	Henry Philip Archibald Buchanan Riddell, ..	7 *Aug.* 39	8 *June* 40	Director General of Post Offices in India, 11 February 1854.—On leave S. C. for 15 months, 10 March 1858.
43	108	George Montague Balmbrough Berford, ..	31 *July* 39	2 *Jan.* 40	On leave P.A. to Europe 18 Mar. 58.
44	110	Andrew Ross, ..	7 *Aug.* 39	19 *Jan.* 40	Magt. and collector of Ghazeepore, 11 Feb. 1856. Offg. civil and sess. judge of Azimghur, 8 Dec. 1858.
45	112	Charles John Wingfield,..	7 *Aug.* 39	29 *Mar.* 40	Chief commr. of Oude from 1 May 1859.
46	116	John Adam Loch, ..	15 *Jan.* 40	10 *Sep.* 40	(Unattached) Offg. civil auditor, N. W. P., 14 Jan. 1858, Allahabad.
47	117	Alexander Shakespear, ..	15 *Jan.* 40	27 *Nov.* 40	Magt. and collr. of Bijnour, 11 Feb. 1856. Offg. judge of Moradabad, 3 Sep. 1358.
48	119	William Smoult Paterson,	15 *Jan.* 40	24 *Dec.* 40	Offg. magt. and collr. of Jaunpore, 25 Feb. 1859.
49	120	Mark Bensley Thornhill,..	23 *Sep.* 40	29 *Dec.* 40	Magt. and collector of Muttra, 24 Feb. 1855. Offg. judge of Agra 3 Sep. 1858.
50	122	Wm. Jno. Rivett Carnac,	28 *Sep.* 40	30 *Jan.* 41	Europe on S. C., 28 Apl. 1856.

(1) Received a medal for p. in P.
(2) Received a certificate of h. p. in H.

No. in N. W. P.	No. in Genl. List.	Names.	Commencement of Service.	Date of Arrival.	Appointments, &c.
51	123	Francis Boyle Pearson, ..	31 *July* 40	27 *Dec.* 40	Magistrate and collr. of Goruckpore, 3 September 1858. Offg. civil and session judge, Cawnpore 9 Apl. 1858.
52	125	Major Henry Court, ..	31 *July* 40	30 *Jan.* 41	Magistrate and collr. of Allahabad, 21 Feb. 1855. On leave S. C. to Europe for 15 months, 25 April 1858.
53	126	Jno. Forbes David Inglis,	23 *Sep.* 40	30 *Jan.* 41	Magt. and collr. of Bareilly, 15 March 1858.
54	130	Edward Clive Bayley, ..	28 *July* 41	9 *Feb.* 42	Magt. and collr. of Azimghur, 22 Jan. 1858. Officiating civil and session judge of Furruckabad 5 May 1859.
55	132	Francis Macan Lind, ..	28 *July* 41	28 *Dec.* 41	Magt. and collector of Benares, 27 March 1858.—On leave S. C. to Europe for 15 months, 11 Sep. 1858.
56	133	Edward James Boldero, ..	8 *July* 41	21 *Oct.* 41	Magistrate and collr. of Mynpooree, 3 Sep. 1858. Offg. civil and sess. judge of ditto, 8 Dec. 1858.
57	134	John Strachey, ..	1 *Feb.* 42	12 *Dec.* 42	Offg. Magte. and collr. of Moradabad, 14 Jan. 1859.
58	136	St. George Tucker, ..	1 *Feb.* 42	8 *Oct.* 42	Commissioner in Oude, 10 April 1858.
59	137	Wm. Jennings Bramly,	1 *Feb.* 42	13 *Oct.* 42	Magt. and collr. of Allyghur, 1 April 1858. Offg. judge of Banda 6 April 1859.
60	140	The *Hon'ble* Rt. Andrew John Drummond, ..	1 *Feb.* 42	8 *Oct.* 42	Civil and session judge of Banda 24 Mar. 1858. On leave S. C. for 15 months, 25 Nov. 1857; Europe from 1 Oct. 1857.
61	141	William Ford, ..	19 *Jan.* 42	7 *July* 42	Deputy commr. of the 1st class, Goorgaon, 10 April 1858.
62	142	Gilbert Pocklington Money, ..	1 *Feb.* 42	6 *July* 42	Furlough Europe from 5 June 1859.
65	143	Robert Needham Cust,(1)	27 *July* 42	24 *Mar.* 43	Commr. of the Umritsur division, 19 Jan. 1859.
64	145	George Campbell, ..	27 *July* 42	25 *Dec.* 42	Judicial Commr. of Oude, 26 May 1858.

(1) Received a medal for p. in O., ditto in B., a certificate of h. p. in B., ditto in S., ditto in P and degree of honor in P.

No. in N. W. P.	No. in Genl. List.	Names.	Commencement of Service.	Date of Arrival.	Appointments, &c.
65	146	Josh. Edward Lyall Brandreth,(1) ..	27 *July* 42	25 *Dec.* 42	Commr. of the Hissar division, 12 Mar. 1858. Offg. commr. Delhie div. 31 May 1859.—Leave for 15 Months on S. C.
66	148	Alan Swinton, ..	27 *July* 42	16 *Feb.* 43	Magt. and collr. of Budaon, continuing to officiate as judge of Goruckpore 29 April 1858. Also Offg. judicial commr. 25 Mar. 1859.
67	150	Philip Henry Egerton, ..	27 *July* 42	22 *Feb.* 43	Deputy commr. of the 1st class, Delhi, 10 April 1858.
68	157	Henry Prinsep Fane, ..	27 *July* 42	12 *Dec.* 42	Magistrate and collr. of Moradabad, 4 Oct. 1858. Offg. magt. and collr. of Agra 23 Apl. 1859.
69	158	Randolph Marriott, ..	30 *Dec.* 42	27 *Sep.* 43	Offg. magte. and collr. of Azimghur, 7 Aug. 1858.
70	160	Chas. Burslem Saunders,..	30 *Dec.* 42	18 *Aug.* 43	Commr. of the Delhi division, 10 April 1858. Offg. commr. Jhelum div. 31 May 1859.
71	161	Charles Horne, ..	30 *Dec.* 42	16 *June* 43	Magt. and collr. of Jaunpore, 2 Oct. 1858.—On leave to Europe for 15 months, 25 Feb. 1859.
72	164	Brand Sapte, ..	12 *Apl.* 43	26 *Sep.* 43	Magt. and collr. of Meerut, 12 Mar. 1859.
73	165	Edward Hamilton Anson,	21 *Jan.* 43	24 *Mar.* 43	On leave S. C. for 15 months, 17 Feb. 1856.
74	167	John Power, ..	30 *Dec.* 42	24 *Mar.* 43	Magt. and collr. of Futtehpore, 3 Sep. 1858.—Leave for 15 months on S. C. to Europe 6 May 1859.
75	168	Lewin Bentham Bowring,[2]	26 *July* 43	25 *Jan.* 44	Private Secretary to the Govr. Genl. 1 April 1858.
76	171	Robert Henry Wallace Dunlop,(3) ..	26 *July* 43	25 *Jan.* 44	On Furlough 25 Feb. 1859.

(1) Received a medal for g. p. and a certificate of h. p. in H.

(2) Received a medal for p. in B., ditto in H., a certificate of h. p. in B., ditto in H. and a degree of honor in B.

(3) Received a certificate of h. p. in O.

No. in N. W. P.	No. in Genl. List.	Names.	Commencement of Service.	Date of Arrival.	Appointments, &c.
77	175	Robert Henry Davies, ..	7 *Feb.* 44	18 *Apl.* 44	Secretary to the Lieut. Govr, of the Punjab, at Lahore 9 Jan, 1859,
78	176	Robert Spankie, ..	12 *Feb.* 44	13 *July* 44	Magt. and collr. of Saharunpore, 24 March 1856. Offg. judge of Saharunpore, 3 Sep. 1858.
79	177	Hugh David Sandeman,..	28 *Feb.* 44	22 *Sep.* 44	Sub-Treasurer Madras 3 June 1859.
80	179	George Edwin Lance, ..	28 *Feb.* 44	22 *Sep.* 44	(Unattached.) Offg. magte. and collr. of Mynpooree, 8 Dec. 1858.
81	180	William Robert Best, ..	31 *July* 44	23 *Dec.* 44	On furlough from 5 May 1855.
82	181	Charles Robert Lindsay,..	31 *July* 44	18 *Feb.* 45	Jt. magt. and deputy collr. of the 1st grade, Futtehghur, 5 March 1858. Offg. magt. and collr. of Furruckabad, 30 April 1858.
83	191	Hy. Roberts Madocks, ..	5 *Feb.* 45	27 *Sep.* 45	On Furlough, 25 March 1859.
84	196	John Rycroft Best,(1) ..	6 *Aug.* 45	16 *Jan.* 46	(Unattached.) Offg. magt. and collr. of Muttra, 22 Dec. 1857.
85	197	Christopher Beckett Denison, ..	6 *Aug.* 45	7 *Nov.* 45	Magt. and coll. of Mirzapore, 10 April 1858.
86	199	Hy. Barkley Henderson,	6 *Aug.* 45	8 *Dec.* 45	On Furlough.
87	201	Henry Lushington, ..	10 *July* 45	14 *Nov.* 45	On Furlough 10 Mar. 1858.
88	202	*Lord* Wm. Montague Hay,	9 *July* 45	8 *Dec.* 45	Depy. commr. 1st class at Simla and supt. of Hill states, 18 Jan. 1856.
89	206	David Simson,(2) ..	14 *Jan.* 46	5 *Apl.* 46	Commr. in Oude 17 June 1859.
90	207	Henry Stewart Reid,(3) ..	14 *Jan.* 46	4 *May* 46	Director of Public Instruction, N. W. P., 20 Feb. 1855.
91	208	Philip Sandys Melvill,(4)	14 *Jan.* 46	4 *Oct.* 46	Deputy commissioner of the 1st class in the Punjab, 24 Feb. 1858, at Umballah. Offg. Commr. of the Hissar div. 31 May 1359.
92	210	Francis Otway Mayne, ..	14 *Jan.* 46	18 *June* 46	Magt. and collr. of Banda, 29 April 1858.

(1) Received a certificate of h. p. in O.
(2) Received a medal for g. p. and a certificate of h. p. in H.
(3) Received a medal for p. in P., ditto for p. in H., ditto in O., a certificate of h. p. in H. and ditto in O.
(4) Received a medal for p. in B.

No. in N. W. P.	No. in Genl. List.	Names.	Commencement of Service.	Date of Arrival.	Appointments, &c.
93	211	Alfred Lisle March-Phillipps ..	14 *Jan.* 46	23 *Sep.* 46	Magte. and collector of Agra, 10 July 1857.—On leave to England for 6 months with 6 weeks preparatory leave, 1 Apl. 1859.
94	212	George Elienezer Wilson Couper, ..	14 *Jan.* 46	23 *Sep.* 46	Secretary to the government N. W. P. 1 May 1859.
95	213	Fendall Thompson, ..	14 *Jan.* 46	5 *Apl.* 46	On Furlough, 6 May 1859.
96	214	Richard Temple,(1) ..	29 *July* 46	8 *Jan.* 47	Commr. of the Lahore div. 19 Jan. 1859.
97	217	William Blunt, ..	18 *July* 46	4 *Oct.* 46	Joint magt. and depy. collr. of the 1st grade, at Cawnpore, 1 April 1858.
98	218	Richard Palmer Jenkins, ..	29 *July* 46	8 *Jan.* 47	On Furlough, 25 Mar. 1859.
99	219	John Walter Sherer, ..	29 *July* 46	15 *Dec.* 46	Magt. and collr. of Cawnpore, 28 Sep. 1857.
100	220	Henry Monckton,(2) ..	6 *Jan.* 47	11 *Mar.* 47	On Furlough 8 March 1859.
101	224	Robert Simson,(3) ..	6 *Jan.* 47	6 *May* 47	Under Secretary to the Govt. of India, Foreign Dept., 24 April 1858.
102	225	Wm. Ashburner Forbes,(4)	5 *Jan.* 47	11 *Mar.* 47	On Furlough.
103	226	James Hunter Prinsep, ..	6 *Jan.* 47	6 *May* 47	(Unattached.) Offg. magt. and collr. of Allyghur 9 Apl. 1859.
104	227	Gore Ouseley, ..	6 *Jan.* 47	6 *Apl.* 47	Depy. commr. 1st class in the Punjab (at Shahpore,) 15 May 1858.
105	228	Fredk. Henry Cooper, ..	6 *Jan.* 47	3 *Oct.* 47	Deputy commissioner 1st class in the Punjab (at Umritsur,) 15 May 1858.
106	229	Henry Goo. Keene, ..	6 *Jan.* 47	3 *Oct.* 47	Supdt. of Dehra Dhoon, 1 May 1856.
107	232	William McChlery, ..	6 *Jan.* 47	6 *May* 47	On leave S. C. for 15 months, 13 March 1857. Extension for 6 months, 23 March 1858. Ditto 6 months, 12 Jan. 1859.
108	234	Geo. Henry Mildmay Ricketts, ..	23 *Dec.* 46	11 *Mar.* 47	On Furlough 25 March 1859.

(1) Received a medal for p. in B., a certificate of h. p. in H., a ditto in O. and a ditto in P.
(2) Received a medal for g. p., a ditto in P., a certificate of h. p. in P., a ditto in O., a ditto in H. and a degree of honor in P.
(3) Received a certificate of h. p. in H.
(4) Received a medal for g.

No. in N. W. P.	No. in Genl. List.	Names.	Commencement of Service.	Date of Arrival.	Appointments, &c.
109	235	William George Probyn,..	6 *Jan.* 47	6 *Apl.* 47	Magt. and collector of Furruckabad 3 Sep. 1858.—On leave S. C. to Europe for 15 months, 20 June 1858.
110	236	John Henry Morris,(1) ..	21 *July* 47	8 *Jan.* 48	Settlement officer at Mooltan, 1 Nov. 1856.—Lv. for 15 months on S. C.
111	237	Ewd. Augs. Prinsep,(2) ..	21 *July* 47	4 *Nov.* 47	Deputy commr. 1st class in the Punjab, 15 May 1858. At Sealkote. On leave to England for 6 months 3 Mar. 1859.
112	238	John Scarlett Campbell, ..	21 *July* 47	2 *Jan.* 48	Deputy commr. of the 1st class, in charge of the Jhujjur in the Hissar division, 29 March 1858. Offg. magt. and collr. Allahabad 15 Apl. 1859.
113	239	James Naesmyth, ..	21 *July* 47	4 *Nov.* 47	Depy. commr. 1st class in the Punjab, (at Goordaspore,) 11 Nov. 1858.
114	241	Roderick Mck. Edwards,	21 *July* 47	5 *Feb.* 48	Magt. and collr. of Moozuffernuggur, 9 March 1858.—Leave for 3 months 29 June 1859.
115	242	John Henry Bax, ..	19 *July* 47	8 *Jan.* 48	Jt. magt. and depy. collr. of 1st grade Ghazeepore, 3 Feb. 1857. Offg. magt. and collr. of ditto, 8 Dec. 1858.
116	245	Charles Jas. Haley Richardes, ...	21 *July* 47	8 *Jan.* 48	Offg. magt. and depy. coll. of the 1st grade Futteghur 11 Mar. 1859.
117	247	Thos. Douglas Forsyth,(3)	15 *Jan.* 48	6 *Mar.* 48	Secretary to the chief commr. of Oude, 2 April 1858.—Leave for 3 months from 16 July 1859.
118	249	James Vans Agnew, ..	26 *Jan.* 48	4 *June* 48	Joint magt. and deputy collr. of the 1st grade, Saharunpore, 9 March 1858. Offg. magt. and collr. of ditto, 24 Dec. 1858.
119	252	Richard Charles Oldfield,	19 *July* 48	9 *Nov.* 48	On furlough for 3 year 10 Apl. 1859.
120	254	Simon Nicolson Martin,..	19 *July* 48	9 *Nov.* 48	On Furlough 25 Mar. 1859.
121	255	*Sir* Theophilus John Metcalfe, *Bt* ..	12 *July* 48	4 *Sep.* 48	Leave for 15 months on S. C. to Europe 8 May 1858.
122	257	James William Power, ..	19 *July* 48	7 *Mar.* 49	Joint magt. and deputy collr. of the 1st grade, Banda, 27 August 1858. Offg. magt. and collr. of Futtehpore 5 Apl. 1859.

(1) Received a medal for g. p., certificate of h. p. in H., a ditto in O. and a ditto in P.
(2) Received a certificate of h. p. in H., a ditto in S. and a degree of honor in S.
(3) Received a medal for g. p., a ditto for p. in P., a certificate of h. p. in O. and a ditto in P.

No. in N. W. P.	No. in Genl. List.	Names.	Commencement of Service.	Date of Arrival.	Appointments, &c.
123	258	William Balmain, ..	4 *Jan.* 49	7 *Mar.* 49	Accountant Punjab, 3rd June 1859.
124	261	Allan Octavian Hume, ..	16 *Jan.* 49	7 *Mar.* 49	Magt. and collr. of Etawah, 9 March 1858.
125	262	Chas. Paget Carmichael,(1)	21 *Dec.* 48	7 *Mar.* 49	(Unattached.) Offg. magt. and collr. of Budaon, 3 May 1858.
126	267	Henry Walmsley Hammond,(2) ..	1 *Aug.* 49	7 *Dec.* 49	Offg. magt. and collr. at Shajehanpore, 16 April 1859.
127	267	George Palmer, ..	15 *Aug.* 49	4 *Feb.* 50	Joint magt. and depy. collr. 1st grade, at Bijnour, 26 Apl. 1858. Offg. magt. & collr. of Bijnour 3 Sept. 58.
128	269	Fergusson Floyer Hogg,(3)	15 *Aug.* 49	7 *Dec.* 49	Joint magt. and deputy collr. 1st grade of Meerut, 9 Apl. 1859.
129	270	Frederick Merttins Bird,(4)	15 *Aug.* 49	7 *Dec.* 49	Jt. magistrate and deputy collector of the 1st grade Goruckpore, 16 Dec. 1857. Offg. magt. and collr. of Goruckpore, 24 March 1858.
130	272	Henry Dundas Robertson,	15 *Aug.* 49	4 *Feb.* 50	Joint magistrate and deputy collector of the 1st grade Furruckabad, 23 Nov. 1857.—Leave for 15 months on S. C. 25 Apl. 1859
131	273	Robt. Eyles Egerton,(5) ..	15 *Aug.* 49	10 *Jan.* 50	Deputy commr. 1st class Punjab Lahore 6 Apl. 1859.
132	277	Charles Grant, *Junior*, ..	1 *Jan.* 50	6 *Mar.* 50	Joint magistrate and deputy collector 1st grade Moozuffernuggur, 29 April 1858. Offg. magt. and collr. of ditto 20 July 1859.
133	286	Maynard Brodhurst, ..	2 *Jan.* 50	15 *Oct.* 50	Extra joint magistrate and deputy collector of the 1st grade at Seharunpore, 17 Jan. 1859.
134	281	Bazett Wetenhall Colvin, ..	2 *Jan.* 50	29 *June* 50	Senior assist. commr. of Kumaon, 10 March 1857.
135	285	Francis Charles Forbes, ..	2 *Jan.* 50	5 *Apl.* 50	Leave on S. C. to Europe, 22 July 1857.
136	286	Archibald Reid Swiney Pollock, ..	2 *Jan.* 50	5 *Apl.* 50	Joint magt. and depy. collr. of the 1st grade at Benares, 5 Feb. 1859. Offg. magt. and coll. of Benares, 17 Feb. 1859.

(1) Received a medal for g. p. and a ditto for p. in P.
(2) Received a medal for g. p. and a ditto for p. in H.
(3) Received a medal for g. p.
(4) Received a medal for g. p.
(5) Received a certificate of h. p. in H.

No. in N. W. P.	No. in Genl. List.	Names.	Commencement of Service.	Date of Arrival.	Appointments, &c.
137	287	Charles Currie,(1) ..	14 *Aug.* 50	6 *Dec.* 50	Joint magt. and depy. collr. of the 1st grade, Boolundshuhur, 25 March 1858. Offg. magt. and collr. of ditto 20 April 1858.
138	288	Geo. Hamilton Freeling,..	5 *July* 50	31 *Oct.* 50	Magt. and collr. Humeerpore, 31 May 1858.
139	291	Francis Spencer Wigram,	16 *July* 50	31 *Oct.* 50	Joint magt. and depy. collr. of Etah, 16 Aug. 1858.
140	293	Arthur Levien, ..	14 *Aug.* 50	31 *Oct.* 50	Assist. commr. 1st class in the Punjab, Jhung 1 May 1857. Offg. Depy Commr. 20 April 1859.
141	294	Stephen Lushington,(2) ..	15 *Jan.* 51	3 *May* 51	Assistant magistrate and collector of Goruckpore, with powers of a jt. magt. and deputy collector 29 Oct. 1858.
142	295	Hy. Wodehouse Dashwood, (3) ..	15 *Jan.* 51	3 *May* 51	Register of the Sudder Dewanny and Nizamut Adawlut, N. W. P., 10 Nov. 1855.
143	296	William Henry Lowe,(4)..	20 *Dec.* 50	5 *Mar.* 51	Secy. to the Sudder Board of Revenue, N. W. P. 10 Aug. 1858.
144	298	Robert Manderson, ..	20 *Dec.* 50	5 *Mar.* 51	Joint magt. and deputy collr. 2nd grade, at Jaunpore, 22 Nov. 1858.
145	302	Arthur Brandreth, ..	10 *Sep.* 51	2 *Jan.* 52	Settlement officer Punjab, (Jhelum) 10 July 1855.
146	305	Wm. Ralph Benson, ..	13 *Aug.* 51	5 *Dec.* 51	Jt. magt. and deputy collr. of the 1st grade, at Allahabad, 12 June 1858.
147	306	Reginald Flayer Saunders,	10 *Sep.* 51	5 *Dec.* 51	Assist. commr. 2nd class in the Punjab, (at Kangra,) 2 Jan. 1857. Offg. depy. commr. at Kangra, 24 Mar. 59.
148	307	Jas. Wm. Macnabb, ..	10 *Sep.* 51	2 *Jan.* 52	Assist. commr. 1st class in the Punjab, 1 May 1856. On leave S. C. to Europe for 15 months, 25 Nov. 1858.
149	308	William Copeland Capper,	10 *Sep.* 51	2 *Jan.* 52	Depy. commr. 2nd class in Oude 18 March 1859. On leave S. C. to England for 15 months, 18 May 1858.
150	309	Geo. Boles Pasley,(5) ..	4 *July* 51	5 *Dec.* 51	Joint magt. and deputy collr. 2nd grade, Agra 21 Feb. 1859, In charge of the office of the Asst. Supdt. Thuggee from 5 April 1859.

(1) Received a medal for p. in P., a certificate of h. p in O. and ditto in P.
(2) Received a medal for g. p.
(3) Received a medal for g. p., a certificate of h. p. in P., ditto in O. and ditto in H.
(4) Received a medal for g. p., a certificate of h. p. in P., a ditto in O. and ditto in H.
(5) Received a certificate of h. p., in H.

No. in N. W. P.	No. in Genl. List.	Names.	Commencement of Service.	Date of Arrival.	Appointments &c.,
151	311	William Johnston, ..	19 *Dec.* 51	1 *Apl.* 52	Joint magt. and depy. collr. of the 2nd grade, Allahabad. 13 April 1858.—On leave S. C. to Europe for 15 months, 6 July 1858.
152	312	Geo. Henry Lawrence, ..	14 *Jan.* 52	1 *Apl.* 52	Deputy commr. of 2nd class in Oude, 20 Dec. 1858.—On leave S. C. to Europe for 15 months, 10 Apl. 59.
153	314	Henry Robt. Clarke, ..	14 *Jan.* 52	9 *Sep.* 52	Extra joint magt. and deputy collector of the 2nd grade at Bareilly, 17 Jan. 1859.
154	315	Henry Minchin Chase, ..	14 *Jan.* 53	1 *Apl.* 52	Joint magt. and deputy collr. 2nd grade of Mynpooree, 7 Jan. 1858.
155	316	William Christopher Sherwood, ..	14 *Jan.* 52	1 *Apl.* 52	On leave, S. C. for 15 months, 6 March 1855; 33 months in extension; permitted to remain in Europe for 6 months from 9 march 1859.
156	319	Charles Ed. Chapman,[1]..	11 *Aug.* 52	5 *Dec.* 52	Extra joint magistrate and deputy collr. of the 2nd grade at Bijnour, 17 Jan. 1859.
157	320	Wm. Chicheley Plowden,..	6 *Aug.* 52	29 *Sep.* 52	Assistant commr. 1st class Delhi Rohtuck, 21 June 1858.
158	322	Francis Macnaghten, ..	11 *Aug.* 52	5 *Dec.* 52	Assist. commr. 1st class in the Punjab 25 April 1856, at Umballah.
159	323	Geo. Hy. Maxwell Batten,	11 *Aug.* 52	29 *Sep.* 52	Junior assistant commr. at Kumaon, 20 Feb. 1856. Vested with powers of a joint magt. and depy. collr. 19 Jan. 1857, at Nainee Tal.
160	325	Swinton Saml. Melville,..	11 *Aug.* 52	28 *Oct.* 52	Joint magistrate and deputy collector of Saharunpore, 5 September 1857. On leave S. C. to Europe for 15 months, 9 April 1858.
161	332	George Elliot Watson, ..	15 *Dec.* 52	3 *Feb.* 53	Assistant magt. and collr. in the Allahabad division, 17 Feb. 1859. Vested with powers of a jt. magte. and deputy collr. 16 March 1859.
162	336	Henry Davis Willock, ..	15 *Dec.* 52	3 *Feb.* 53	Jt. magt. and depy. collr. of the 2nd grade, at Shajehanpore 10 Nov. 58.—Leave for 6 months. Europe 5 June 59.
163	337	Wm. Jas. Money, ..	15 *Dec.* 52	3 *Feb.* 53	Assist. magt. and collr. of Etah, 29 Oct. 58 Vested with powers of a jt. magt. and depy. collr. 2 Dec. 58. On leave S. C. for 6 months 24 Mar. 59.
164	338	Wm. Sterling Halsey, ..	5 *Jan.* 53	13 *Mar.* 53	Assist. magt. and collr. of Gorruckpore, 9 June 1855. Vested with powers of a joint magt. and deputy collector 29 May 1856.—On leave S. C. Europe 9 April 1858.
165	339	Stuart Saunders Hogg, ..	15 *Dec.* 52	3 *Feb.* 53	Depy. commr. 3rd class in Oude, 10 March 1859.—Leave for 3 months from 1 Augt. 1859.
166	340	Bradford Hardinge, ..	27 *July* 53	1 *Dec.* 53	Assist. commr. 1st class in the Punjab (at Rawul-Pindee,) 10 January 1859. Offg. deputy Commissioner Goojrat 15 April 1859.
167	341	Richard Henry Clifford, ..	27 *July* 53	1 *Dec.* 53	Joint magt. and depy. collr. 2nd grade Muttra, 11 Nov. 1857.
168	342	Geo. Welstead Colledge, [1]	15 *Oct.* 53	27 *July* 53	Jt. magt. and deputy collr., of the 2nd grade, Boolundshuhur, 10 Dec. 57.

[1] Received a medal for g. p., ditto in O., a certificate of h. p. in O., ditto in P. ditto in B. ditto in H. ditto in S. and a degree of honor in B.

No. in N. W. P.	No. in Genl. List.	Names.	Commencement of Service.	Date of Arrival.	Appointments, &c.
169	343	Andrew Chad Barnard, ..	27 *July* 53	5 *Jan.* 54	Assistant magt. and collr. with powers of a jt. magt and deputy collr. in Saharunpore, 29 Oct. 1858.—Leave for 6 months, from 1 May 59.
170	344	Donald Campbell Macnabb	27 *July* 53	22 *Mar.* 54	Assist. commr. 1st class, in the Punjab (at Shahpore,) 11 Nov. 1858.
171	347	Lesley Charles Probyn, ..	15 *Dec.* 53	30 *Jan.* 54	Jt. magt. and depy. collr. of the 2nd, grade, Ghazeepore, 30 April 1858.
172	348	Charles Pearson Elliott, ..	15 *Dec.* 53	30 *Jan.* 54	Assist. commr. 1st class in the Punjab 24 Feb. 58. Posted to the Paneeput dist. & to officiate as Depy. Commr. of ditto 8 Jan. 1859.
173	351	Henry Binny Webster, ..	30 *Dec.* 53	16 *June* 54	Assist. magt. and collr. of Benares, 11 Sep. 1857. On leave S. C. to Europe for 15 months 6 May 1858.
174	352	Cairnes Anthony Daniell,	30 *Dec.* 53	2 *Nov.* 54	Asst. magt. and collr. in the Meerut division, 9 Feb. 1859.
175	354	Richard Gwatkin Melvill,..	26 *July* 54	2 *Nov.* 54	Assist. commr. 2nd class Delhi (Hissur) 1 May 57 vested with special powers 3rd June 1859.
176	355	James Simson, ..	26 *July* 54	14 *Oct.* 54	Jt. magt. & depy. collr. 2nd grade, Mirzapore, 5 June 1857; Depy. Supt. of the Domains of the Rajah of Benares 10 Mar. 58.
177	356	Wilmot Lane, ..	26 *July* 54	11 *Jan.* 55	Joint magt. and deputy collr. of the 2nd grade, Allyghur, 5 May 1858.
178	357	Edward Waterfield, ..	26 *July* 45	3 *Dec,* 54	Assist magt. and collr. of Budaon with special powers 29 Oct. 1858.
179	359	Basil Francis Hall, ..	26 *July* 54	14 *Nov.* 54	Jt. magt. & depy. collr. of the 2nd grade, at Moradabad, 14 Aug. 1858.
180	363	Thomas Edwd. Fairfax,..	26 *July* 54	14 *Oct.* 54	Assistant magt. & collr. of Budaon, 29 January 1857.—On leave S. C. for 1 year, 19 Nov. 1857. Extension for 6 months, 12 Jan. 1859.
181	364	Jas. Casmajor Robertson,	26 *July* 54	31 *Jan.* 55	Asst. supdt. of Dehra Dhoon, with powers of a jt. magt. 18 Dec. 59.
182	365	EdmundBensley Thornhill,	28 *June* 54	16 *Aug.* 54	Assist. magt. and collr. with powers of a jt. magt. and deputy collr. in the Rohilkund division, at Moradabad, 17 May 1858.—On leave S.C. to England for 10 months, 26 Sep. 58.
183	366	George Boileau Willock,..	28 *June*54	16 *Aug.* 54	Assist. in the Allahabad divn. (Futtehpore) 2 July 1856.—Lv. for 3 months on S. C. 6 June 1859.
184	368	Henry Anthony Harrison,	10 *Jan.* 55	3 *Apl.* 55	Assist. magt. and collr. of Benares, at Azimghur with powers of a joint magt. &c., 17 January 1859.
185	369	William Robertson, ..	10 *Jan.* 55	21 *Mar.* 55	Asst. commr. of the 3rd class in the Punjab, at Delhi, 20 Apl. 1858. —On leave S. C. to Europe for 15 months, 20 Dec. 1858.
186	370	Jas. Colquhoun Colvin, ..	10 *Jan.* 55	3 *Apl.* 55	Asst. magt. and collr. of Moradabad with powers of a jt. magt. & depy. collr. 28 Feb. 59.
187	371	Henry Grosvenor Paynter,	10 *Jan.* 55	22 *Mar.* 55	Assist. commr. of the 3rd class in the Punjab at Loodiana, 8 April 58. Vested with special powers 3 June 1859.
188	362	Colin Lindsay, ..	10 *Jan.* 55	3 *Apl.* 55	Assist. commr. of the 3rd class in the Punjab and Delhi division, 8 April 1858. Goorgoan.
189	377	Alfred Comyns Lyall, ..	1 *Aug.* 53	2 *Jan.* 56	Assist. magt. and collr. with powers of a joint magt. and deputy collr. in the Rohilkund division, at Shajehanpore, 17 May 1858.

([1]) Received a medal for g. p.

No. in N. W. P.	No. in Genl. List.	Names.	Commencement of Service.	Date of Arrival.	Appointments &c.
190	380	Clarmont John Daniell, ..	1 *Aug.* 55	7 *Dec.* 55	Under-Secy. to the govt. N. W. P. 11 Mar. 1858.—Leave on S. C. to Europe from 10 Apl. 1859.
191	381	Elliot Colvin, ..	1 *Aug.* 55	6 *Nov.* 55	Assistant commr. Kumaon, 25th Nov. 1858.
192	384	Arthur Boulderson, ..	11 *July* 55	6 *Nov.* 55	Assist. commr. 3rdclass in Oude, 13 April 1857.—On leave S. C. for 15 months, 20 Jan. 1858. Extension for 6 months.
193	385	Francis Boyd Outram, ..	1 *Jan.* 56	25 *Feb.* 56	Junior asst. secy. to the govt. N. W. P. 25 Feb. 1858. Offg. under-secretary from 10 April 1859.
194	388	Elliot Macnaghten, ..	13 *Dec.* 56	1 *Feb.* 56	Assist. magt. and collr. of Mirzapore, with powers of a joint magt. and deputy collector, 10 Nov. 1858. On leave to England for 6 months, from 25 April 1859.
195	389	Ed. George Jenkinson, ..	24 *Dec.* 55	25 *Feb.* 56	Assist. Magt. and collr. with powers of a joint magt. and deputy collr. at Benares 17 May 1858.
196	390	Wm. Malcolm Low, ..	14 *Dec.* 55	1 *Feb.* 56	Assist. magt. and collr. with powers of a jt. magt. and deputy collr. in the Rohilkund division, at Barielly, 24 April 1858.
197	392	Wm. Maxwell Alexander,	23 *Jan.* 56	30 *Oct.* 56	Assist. magt. and collr. of Mynpooree, 7 Jan. 58. Vested with special powers, 27 May 1858.
198	393	*Hon.* Fred. Henry North,	29 *Dec.* 55	27 *April* 56	Assist. in the Benares division, 4 May 1857.—On leave S. C. for 15 months, 25 Feb. 1858.
199	394	Charles Wm. Moore, ..	3 *Jan.* 56	27 *Apl.* 56	Assist. magt. and collr. of Mirzapore, 22 Jan. 1857.—On leave S. C. for 15 months, 25 Feb. 1858. In extension 6 months 22 June 1859.
200	395	Herbert Hankey, ..	23 *Jan.* 56	14 *June* 56	Assist. commr. of the 3rd class in the Punjab and Delhi division, 8 April 1858. (Paneeput.)
201	397	David Halkett Craigie Inglis, ..	23 *Jan.* 56	22 *Oct.* 56	Asst. in the Benares division, at Budaon, 10 Aug. 1858.
202	398	Wm. Charles Turner, ..	12 *Dec.* 55	1 *Feb.* 56	Assist. magt. and collr. of Jaunpore, 9 Nov. 57.—On leave S. C. to Europe 11 April 1858.
203	400	Joseph Sladen, ..	6 *Aug.* 56	16 *Nov.* 56	Asst. magt. and collr. with special powers, at Moradabad, 4 Aug. 1858.
204	401	Percy Wigram, ..	6 *Aug.* 56	30 *Oct.* 56	Assist. magt. and collr. of Humeerpore, 5 July 1858. Vested with powers of a joint magt. and depy. collr. 20 Aug. 1858.
205	402	Melvill Wm. Sandys, ..	2 *July* 56	22 *Oct.* 56	Assist. in the Allahabad division, Azimghur with special powers, 29 Oct. 1858.
206	403	John Jas. Foote Lumsden,	6 *Aug.* 56	16 *Nov.* 56	Assist. magt. and collr. in the Benares divn. (Goruckpore) 3 Nov. 1857.
207	405	Alxr. John Lawrence, ..	6 *Aug*, 56	10 *Nov.* 56	Assist. in the Meerut division, Moozuffernuggur. 30 March 1858.
208	408	Horatio Senfenberg John Ross, ..	6 *Aug.* 46	16 *Nov.* 56	Assist. magt. and collr. in the Benares divn. Mirzapore 10 Mar. 58.
209	412	Hercules Grey Ross, ..	6 *Aug.* 56	16 *Nov.* 56	Assist. commr. 3rd class Oude 28 June 1858.
210	417	Chas. Umpherston Aitchison,(1) ..	26 *June* 56	24 *Sep.* 56	Assist. commr. 3rd class, in the Punjab, 8 April 1857. Personal Asst. to the judicial commissioner 25 Aug. 1858.

(1) Received a medal for g. p.

No. in N. W. P.	No. in Genl. List.	Names.	Commencement of Service.	Date of Arrival.	Appointments &c.
211	468	Robert Moss King, ..	10 *July* 56	22 *Oct.* 56	Assist. commr. of the 2nd class in Oude, 17 June 1859.
212	419	John Graham Cordery, ..	23 *July* 56	22 *Oct.* 56	Asst. commr. of the 3rd. class in the Punjab, 17 July 1858. Goojerat vested with special powers, 3rd June 1859.
213	420	Thos. Henry Thornton, ..	21 *July* 56	15 *Sep.* 56	Assist. commr. 3rd class, in the Punjab, 8 April 1857, at Goojerat.
214	421	Herbert Wilson, ..	23 *July* 56	22 *Oct.* 56	Asst. magt. and collr. of Goruckpore, with special powers, 4 September 1858.
215	422	Henry Edward Perkins,(1)	23 *July* 56	21 *Sep.* 56	Assist. commr. 2nd class, in Oude, 10 April 1858. Placed at the disposal of the Govt of the Punjab 12 July 59.
216	424	John Douglas Sandford, ..	3 *July* 56	22 *Oct.* 56	Assist. magistrate and collector of Futtehpore, 17 Nov. 1858. Vested with powers of a jt. magt. and depy. collr. 28 Feb. 1859. Offg. Jt. Secy. to the Govt. N. W. P. from 10 Apl. 59.
217	425	Wm. Britain Jones,(2) ..	8 *July* 56	15 *Sep.* 56	Assist. commr. 3rd class, in the Punjab, 8 April 1857, at Lahore, vested with full powers 3 June 1859.
218	427	Alex. McLaurin Monteath,	14 *Jan.* 57	12 *Feb.* 57	Asst. in the Allahabad division, 20 April 1858.
219	430	Robert George Currie, ..	14 *Jan.* 57	1 *Feb.* 57	Asst. magt. and collr. of Meerut, with special powers, 27 Aug. 1858.
220	431	Fredk. Barnes Peacock, ..	14 *Jan.* 57	1 *Feb.* 57	Asst. in the Benares division, 23 June 1858.
221	432	Fredk. Russell Hogg, ..	14 *Jan.* 57	12 *Feb.* 57	Asst. magt. and collr. of Seharunpore, 6 Jan. 1858. Vested with special powers, 14 Dec. 1858.
222	433	*Lord* Fredk. Hay, ..	14 *Jan.* 57	1 *Apl.* 57	Asst, Commr. 3rd class Punjab, Umballa 13 Aug. 58.—Leave for 6 months on S. C. 25 June 1859.
223	435	Edward Fairlie, ..	14 *Jan.* 57	29 *Apl.* 57	Asst. commr. of the 3rd class, in the Punjab, Goozaria, 3 May 1859.
224	436	Swinton Henry Boult, ..	1 *Oct.* 56	30 *Nov* 56	Assist. magt. and collr. of Etawah, with powers of a jt. magt. &c., 21 Feb. 1859.
225	437	William Young, ..	1 *Oct.* 56	16 *Dec.* 56	Assist. magt. and collr. in the Benares division, at Jaunpore, 24 March 1858. Vested with special powers, 8 Sep. 1858.
226	438	Jas. Wallace Quinton, ..	18 *Sep.* 56	16 *Nov.* 56	Assist. magt. and collr. of Ghazeepore, 28 Oct. 1857. Vested with powers of a jt. magt. and depy. collr. and posted to Bulliah, in Eastern Ghazeepore, 28 Feb. 1859.

(1) Received a medal for h. p. in H. prize in P., a certificate of h. p. in O. and ditto in P.
(2) Received a medal for h. p. in H.

No. in N. W. P.	Nos. in Genl. List.	Names.	Commencement of Service.	Date of Arrival.	Appointmentes, &c.
227	439	Charles Robertson, ..	1 *Oct.* 56	16 *Dec.* 56	Assist. magt. and collr. of Futtehghur, 26 Feb. 1858. with powers of a jt. magt. &c., 14 Jan. 1859.
228	441	Wilton Oldham, ..	11 *Sep.* 56	16 *Nov.* 56	Assist. magt. and collr. of Mirzapore, 28 Oct. 1857. Vested with special powers, 3 May 1858.
229	443	Edwd. Stanley Robertson,	1 *Oct.* 56	16 *Dec.* 56	Assist. magt. and collr. of Cawnpore, 5 Apl. 1858.
230	445	Charles Alfred Elliott, ..	1 *Oct.* 56	30 *Nov.* 56	Assist. commr. of the 2nd class in Oude 10 March 1859.
231	446	Richard Wall, ..	23 *Sep.* 56	16 *Dec.* 56	Assist. in the Agra div. (Muttra). 22 April 1858.
232	449	Robert Taylor, ..	12 *Sep.* 56	16 *Nov.* 56	Assist. magt. and collr. of Benares, Jaunpore 28 Oct. 1857, with powers of a jt. magt. &c., 20 Dec. 1858.
233	450	Auckland Colvin, ..	5 *Aug.* 57	27 *Jan.* 58	Asist. in the Rohilkund division, Bijnour 3 Dec. 1858.
234	451	*Sir* Alxander Huchinson Lawrance, *Bart.* ..	5 *Aug.* 57	12 *Feb.* 58	Asst. commr. of the 3rd class in the Punjab, 4 March 1859, at Kangra.
235	455	Henry James Sparks, ..	5 *Aug.* 57	29 *Dec.* 57	Asst. commr. 3rd class Oude 31 May 1859.
236	457	Charles Edward Bernard,	30 *Dec.* 57	12 *Feb.* 58	Asst. commr. of the 3rd class in the Punjab, Jullunder 2 Sep. 1858. vested with special powers, 3 June 59.
237	458	Geo. Robert Elsmie, ..	30 *Dec.* 57	12 *Feb.* 58	Assit. commr. 3rd class in the Punjab, 18 Oct. 1858. At Mithunkote Derah Ghagee Khan district.
238	459	Geo. Lukes Lang, ..	30 *Dec.* 57	2 *Mar.* 58	Supernumery Asst. comr. 3rd class in Oude, 4 Nov. 1858.
239	460	John Burnett Craigie, ..	30 *Dec.* 57	2 *Mar.* 58	Assist. commr. 3rd class in the Punjab, Goojranwalla 10 Dec. 1858.
240	463	Jas. Broadwood Lyall, ..	30 *Dec.* 57	8 *Apl.* 58	Assist. commr. 3rd class in the Punjab, Googaira, 15 March 1858.
241	468	Charles Temple, ..	26 *Jan.* 58	8 *Apl.* 58	Assist. in the Benares division, 20 Dec. 1858, at Jaunpore
242	470	James Beames, ..	26 *Jan.* 58	16 *Mar.* 58	Asst. commr. 3rd class Punjab 15 Jan. 1859.
243	472	Charles Grant, ..	26 *Jan.* 58	8 *Apl.* 58	Asst. magt. and collr. of Agra 14 Jan. 1859.
244	473	Frank Eden Elliot, ..	26 *Jan.* 58	16 *Mar.* 58	Assist. in the Meerut division, Boolundshuhur, 23 Nov. 1858.
245	474	Richard Thomas Burney..	26 *Jan.* 58	12 *Feb.* 58	
246	484	Charles Wm. Carpenter,..	16 *Sep.* 57	29 *Dec.* 57	Assist. in the Allahabad division, Futthepore, 23 Nov. 1858.
247	486	David Graham Barkley, M. A. ..	16 *Sep.* 57	29 *Dec.* 57	Assist. commr. 3rd class Punjab, 3 May 1859.
248	588	Wm. Duthoit, ..	16 *Sept.* 57	17 *Dec.* 57	Asst. in the Meerut division, 17 September 1858, Allyghur.
249	489	Arthur Pearse Howell, ..	16 *Sep.* 57	27 *Jan.* 58	Asst. commr. 3rd class Punjab, 31 May 1859.
250	490	Thos. Burrows Tracey, ..	16 *Sep.* 57	29 *Dec.* 57	Assist. in the Allahabad division, Cawnpore, 23 Nov. 1858.
251	491	Chas. Hukes Tod Crosthwaite, ..	16 *Sep.* 57	9 *Nov.* 57	Asst. in the Allahabad division, Banda, 23 Nov. 1858.
252	492	John Watt Symth, ..	16 *Sep.* 57	29 *Dec.* 57	Assist. commr. 3rd class Punjab, 3 May 1859.
253	494	Seaburne May Moens, B.A.	16 *Sep.* 57	17 *Dec.* 57	Asst. in the Rohilcund division, Bareilly 17 September 1858.

UNPOSTED CIVILIANS STUDYING THE LANGUAGE.

Nos. in Genl. List.	Names.	Commencement of Service.	Date of Arrival.	Remarks.
477	L. S. Saunders,	30 *Dec.* 57	26 *Sep.* 58	Studying at Delhi.
479	J. A. Graham, ..	30 *Dec.* 57	8 *Apl.* 58	
488	G. S. Park, ..	26 *Jan.* 58	23 *June* 58	
489	R. H. Middlemas, ..	26 *Jan.* 58	28 *May* 58	
490	W. Kaye, ..	26 *Jvn.* 58	8 *Apl.* 58	
492	J. H. R. Carnac, ..	26 *Jan.* 58	12 *Nov.* 58	Studying at Dacca.
493	W. Kemble, ..	26 *Jan.* 58	8 *Apl.* 58	Ditto.
494	J. D. Maclean, ..	26 *Jan.* 58	28 *May* 58	
495	N. S. Alexander, ..	26 *Jan.* 58	10 *July* 58	
508	Henry Ler. Poe Wynne, ..	8 *Nov.* 58	10 *Jan.* 59	
509	Hugh Morris, ..	8 *Dec.* 58	1 *Jan.* 59	
510	Alexander Brown, ..	8 *Dec.* 58	1 *Jan.* 59	
511	John Geoghegan, ..	8 *Dec.* 58	29 *Jan.* 59	
512	Theodore Fras. Wm. Smith,	8 *Dec.* 58	12 *Feb.* 59	
513	Dennis Fitzpatrick, ..	8 *Dec.* 58	29 *Jau.* 59	
514	Charles Wm. Paxton Watts,	8 *Dec.* 59	10 *Jan.* 59	
515	Childers George Sperling, ..	8 *Dec.* 58	12 *Feb.* 58	
516	David Mason Gardner, ..	8 *Dec.* 58	12 *Feb.* 58	
517	Charles John Powlett, ..	8 *Dec.* 58	12 *Feb.* 58	
518	Jas. Fras. Katherinus Hewitt,	8 *Dec.* 58	12 *Feb.* 58	
519	Edward Henry Whinfield ..	8 *Dec.* 58	25 *Feb.* 58	
520	Wm. Christopher Eades, ..	8 *Dec.* 58	25 *Feb.* 58	
521	John Ward, ..	8 *Dec.* 58	14 *Mar.* 59	
522	Jas. Samuell Armstrong, ..	8 *Dec.* 58	14 *Mar.* 59	
523	Alex. Mair McGregor, B. A.	8 *Dec.* 58	14 *Mar.* 56	
524	Frederick Jones, ..	8 *Dec.* 58	14 *Mar.* 58	
525	William Tyrrell, ..	24 *Mar.* 59	12 *May.* 59	

CASUALTIES.

E. Jenkins, Died, .. Mymensing, 23rd May 59.
W. Butler, Ditto, .. Shergotty, 20th June 59.
C. T. LeBas, Ditto, .. 7th Decr 58.

Sir R. N. C. Hamilton, retired 1st May 1859.
E. Currie, Ditto.
F. J. Halliday, Ditto.
B. J. Colvin, Ditto.
J. C. Wilson, Ditto.
D. I. Money, Ditto.
C. Grant, Ditto.

W. T. Taylor, retired 1st May 1859,
Sir J. L. M. Lawrence, Bt. G. C. B., Ditto.
W. Bell, Ditto.
W. Tayler, Ditto
J. Guthrie, 9th May 1859.
Coutts Trotter, 30th May 1859.
W. H. Elliott, 5th June 1859.

CIVIL SERVATS RETIRED, BUT NOT YET OBTAINED ANNUITIES.

E· H. C. Monckton. —H. S. Revenshaw.

MEMBERS ON FURLOUGH OR ON LEAVE TO EUROPE.

W. C. Sherwood, ...	6 March 1855	F. C. Forbes, ...	22 July 1857	F. B. Drummond, ..	7 March 185
T. Blomefield Lane,..	4 April ,,	H. Rose, ...	22 July ,,	S. N. Martin, ...	25 March 1859
W. R. Best, ...	5 May ,,	W. Galloway, ...	15 March 1858	G. H. M. Ricketts, ..	25 March ,,
E. H. Anson, ...	17 Feb. 1856	H. Lushington, ...	10 March ,,	R. P. Jenkins, ...	25 March ,,
W. J. R. Carnac, ...	28 April ,,	H. C. Tucker, ...	10 March ,,	O. Toogood, ...	25 March ,,
J. H. Mangles, ...	9 Oct ,,	H. Pratt, ...	5 June ,,	H. Monckton, ...	8 March ,,
R. H. Russell, ...	25 Dec. ,,	J. C. Dodgson, ...	11 Aug. ,,	H. R. Madocks, ...	25 March ,,
G. G. Balfour, ...	8 Feb. 1857	F. B. Simson, ...	11 Oct. ,,	W. A. Forbes, ...	
A. J. Hay, ...	25 April ,,	E. S. Pearson, ...	24 Nov. ,,	J. Watson, ...	25 April ,,
G. G. Mackintosh, ...	7 June ,,	G. M. B. Berford, ...	18 March ,,	F. Thompson, ...	6 May ,,
G. A. Pepper, ...	10 March ,,	R. H. Dunlop, ...	25 Feb. 1859	F. C. Fowle, ...	5 June ,,
W. McChlery, ...	13 March ,,	R. C. Oldfield, ...	10 April ,,	H. B. Henderson, ...	
W. Roberts, ...	11 April ,,	E. C. Craster, ...	25 Feb. ,,	G. P. Money, ...	5 June ,,

---

OUT OF EMPLOY.

R. H. Snell.

MEMBERS ON LEAVE UNDER MEDICAL CERTIFICATE HOLDING THEIR APPOINTMENTS.

R. C Raikes, ...	23 July 1857	M. H. Court, ...	25 April 1858	W. Robertson, ...	20 Dec. 1858
G. D. Wilkins, ...	11 Aug. ,,	H. C. Raikes, ...	April ,,	J. W. Macnabb, ...	25 Nov. ,,
T. E. Fairfax, ...	19 Nov. ,,	W. S. Halsey, ...	9 April ,,	C. Horne, ...	25 Feb. 1859
Honorable R. A. J. Drummond, ...	1 Oct. ,,	A. Boulderson, ...	20 Jan. ,,	G. H. Lawrence, ...	10 April ,,
W. C. Turner, ...	11 April 1858	W. C. Capper, ...	18 May ,,	R. Alexander, ...	6 May ,,
H. Unwin, ...	2 Jan. ,,	W. G. Probyn, ...	20 June ,,	J. Power, ...	6 May ,,
S. F. Davis, ...	16 Jan. ,,	J. E. S. Lillie, ...	20 July ,,	C. J. Daniell, ...	10 April ,,
C. Chester, ...	31 Jan. ,,	W. Johnston, ...	6 July ,,	H. D. Robertson, ...	25 April ,,
C. Raikes, ...	24 March ,,	J. S. Torrens, ...	17 May ,,	J. G. Campbell, ...	10 March ,,
H. B. Webster, ...	6 May ,,	E. M. Wylly, ...	5 June ,,	E. Jenkins, ...	10 April ,,
Hon'ble F. H. North,	25 May ,,	Sir T. J. Metcalfe, ...	8 May ,,	H. A. Mangles, ...	
C. W. Moore, ...	25 May ,,	S. S Melville, ...	9 April ,	G. F. Harvey, ...	5 June ,,
H. P. A. B. Riddell,..	10 March ,,	F. B. Thornhill, ...	26 Sept. ,,	D. F. McLeod, ...	
W. H. Henderson, ...	10 March ,,	R. L. Mangles, ...	23 Sept. ,,	G. C. Fletcher, ...	
H. C. Wake, ...	11 April ,,	F. M. Lind, ...	11 Sept. ,,	J. H. Morris, ...	
W. Edwards, ...	11 April ,,	W. T. Taylor, ...	26 Sept. ,,	J. E. L. Brandeth, ...	
		C. G. Wynch, ...	26 Nov. ,,		

MEMBERS ON LEAVE FOR SIX MONTHS.

W. J. Money, 31st March.
C. T. Buckland, 23rd March.
E. A. Prinsep, 3rd March.
E. Macnaghten, 25th April.
A. L. M. Phillipps, 1st April.

W. G. Young.
A. C. Barnard, 1st May 59.
H. D. Willock, 5th June 59.
Lord F. Hay,

DISTRIBUTION

OF THE

CIVIL SERVICE.

GOVERNMENT OF INDIA.

Secretaries.

	Salary.
C. Beadon, Secy. For. Dept., ..	4,166
C. H. Lushington, Secy. Financial Dept.	4,166
W. Grey, Secy. Home Dept., ..	4,166
L. B. Bowring, Private Secretary, ..	2,000
R. B. Chapman, Under-Secy. Home Dept.	1,250
R. Simson, Under-Secy. Foreign Dept.,	1,250

Accountants.

Hon'ble E. Drummond, Acct. Gen. India,	3,500
G. L. Pandergast, Acct. Genl. Madras,	3,000
S. D. Birch, ditto, Bombay,	3,000
R. P. Harrison, Accountant Bengal, ..	3,000
F. Lushington, ditto, N. W P.	2,500
W. Balmain, ditto, Punjab, ..	1,500
E. F. Harrison, 1st Asst. Acct. Gen. India,	1,500
W. R. Lodwick, ditto, Bombay,	1,200
W. Waterfield, ditto, Madras,	1,200
H. A. Mangles, 2nd Asst. Acct. Gen. India,	1,000

Sub-Treasurers.

J. I. Harvey, Bengal, ..	3,000
G. Grant, Bombay, ..	2,500
H. D. Sandeman, Madras, ..	2,000

Civil Auditors.

W. P. Palmer, Bengal, ..	3,000
A. L. Lushington, Madras, ..	2,000
A. K. Corfield, Bomday, (on leave.) ..	2,000
J. M. Erskine, N. W. P. Offg. ditto,	1,500-400
J. A. Loch, Offg, N. W. P.,	1,000-300

Commissioners, &c.

H. P. A. B. Riddell, Director General of Post Offices, (on leave,) ..	£1,000
S. Wauchope, Commr. of Police, ..	2,500

Mysore and Coorg.

Hon'ble H. B. Devereux, Judicial Commissioner, ..	3,200

Singapore.

	Salary.
H. S. Mackenzie, Resident Councillor,	1,500

Oude.

C. J. Wingfield, Chief Commr. ..	5,000
G. Campbell, Judicial Commr. ..	3,500
St. George Tucker, Commr. ..	2,750
D. Simson, Commr. ..	2,750
T. D. Forsyth, Secretary, ..	2,000
W. C. Capper, Dep. Commr. 2nd class, (on leave,) ..	£500
G. H. Lawrence, Deputy Commr. 2nd class, (on leave,) ..	£500
S. S. Hogg, Depy. Commr. 3rd class, ..	700
C. A. Elliot, Asst. Commr. 2nd class, ..	600
A. Boulderson, ditto 3rd ditto, (on leave,)	£500
E. G. Ross, Asst. Commr. 3rd class, ..	400
R. M. King, Asst Commr. 2nd class, ..	400
G. L. Lang, Asst. Commr. 3rd class, ..	400
H. J. Sparks, Asstt. Commr. 3rd class,	400
A. P. Howell, Asstt. Commr. 3rd class,	400

GOVERNMENT OF BENGAL.

A. R. Young, Secy. Govt. of Bengal, ..	3,000
A. R. Thompson, Junior Secretary, ...	1,250
Lord H. U. Browne, Under Secretary,	1,250
F. L. Beaufort, Supt. Remembrancer of Legal Affairs, ..	2,500
W. G. Young, Director of Public Instruction (on Leave,) ..	2,500
T. E. Ravenshaw, Commr. for Suppression of Dacoity, ..	1,500
J. A. Crawford, Supt. of Stamps and Stationery, ..	1,500
W. Ainslie, Railway Commr.	1,916-250

Sudder Dewanny and Nizamut Adawlut.

J. H. Patton, Judge, ..	4,166
H. T. Raikes, ditto, ..	4,435
J. S. Torrens, ditto, (on leave,) ..	£1,000
C B. Trevor, ditto, ..	4,166

f

	Salary.
E. A. Samuells, ditto, ..	4,166
G. Loch, Offg. ditto, (see Purneah,) ..	616
H. V. Bayley, Offg. ditto, (see Hooghly,)	616
A. W. Russell, Registrar, ..	1,700

Sudder Revenue Board.

W. Dampier, Member, ..	4,166
H. Stainforth, Member, ..	4,166
W. J. Allen, Member, ..	4,166
A. Grote, Offg. ditto, (see Nuddea,) ..	616
E. T. Trevor, Secretary, ..	2,500
E. H. Lushington Jr. ditto, ..	2,333

Calcutta Custom House.

G. D. Wilkins, Collector, (on leave,)	£1,000
F. J. Cockburn, Deputy Collector, Offg. ditto, ..	1,700

Superintendents of Survey.

G. G. Morris, Supt. of Survey 4th or W. Div. ..	1,500
W. C. Spencer, Supt. of Survey, 3rd or E. Div. ..	1,000
E. Grey, Supt. 1st or N. Div., ...	1,000
H. A. Cockerell, Supt. 2nd or S. Div.	1,000
J. F. Browne, Asstt. 1st or N. Div. ..	400
H. J. Reynolds, Asstt. 3rd or E. Div.	400
R. H. M. Warrand, Asstt. 4th or W. Div.	400

24-Pergunnahs.

J. E. S. Lillie, Addl. Judge, (on leave,)	£1,000
E. Jackson, Offg. ditto, (see Shahabad,)	250
E. De Lautour, Judge, ..	2,500
J. G. Campbell, Controller of Salt Chowkies, (on leave,) ..	£1,000
A. Money, Offg. ditto, (see Pooree,) ..	166
C. F. Montresor, Magistrate, ..	2,500
H. Nelson, Collr. (on dep. Tirhoot,) ..	1,916
G. Bright, Offg. ditto, (see Shahabad,)	383
R. J. Wigram, Jt. Magt. (on dep. Sarun,)	700
J. S. Drummond, Assistant, ..	400
J. P. Grant, Assistant, ..	400
S. C. Bayley, Assistant (in charge of Burriapore,) ..	400

Backergunge.

F. B. Kemp, Judge, ..	2,500
W. T. Tucker, Collector, ..	1,916
H. A. R. Alexander, Magistrate, (on dep. Dacca,) ..	900
A. J. R. Bainbridge, Jt. Magt. &c., ..	700-200
H. Bell, Assistant, ..	400

Bancoorah, (West Burdwan.)

P. G. E. Taylor, Judge, ..	2,500
J. S. Spankie, Jt. Magistrate, &c. ..	1,000
H. Balfour, Jt. Magt. &c., (on dep. Purneah,) ..	700
H. W. Alexander, Assistant, (in charge of Raneegunge,) ..	500

Burdwan, (East.)

	Salary.
J. H. Young, Commissioner,	2,916-250
H. M. Reid, Judge, (on dep. Nuddea)..	2,500
C. P. Hobhouse, Collr. Offg. ditto,	1,916-250
J. H. P. Ward, Offg. ditto, (see Nuddea,)	383
H. B. Lawford, Magistrate, ..	900
R. V. Cockerell, Assistant, (on dep. Burdwan,) ..	500
J. D. Ouseley, Assistant, ..	400
W. G. L. Lane, Assistant, ..	400
A. T. Mclean, Asst. in charge of Damoorhoodah, ...	400
W. Macpherson, Asst. in charge of Bood Bood, ...	400

Baraset.

Hon'ble A. Eden, Jt. Magistrate, &c. ..	1,000

Beerbhoom.

O. W. Malet, Judge, ..	2,500
A. Hope, Magt. and Collector (on dep. Shahabad,) ...	1,500

Behar.

R. N. Farquharson, Opium Agent, ...	3,500
T. C. Trotter, Judge, ..	2,500
D. Cunliffe, Collector, ..	1,916
H. C. Wake, Magistrate, (on leave,) ..	£500
H. B. Simson, Offg. ditto (see Bhaugulpore,)	700
A. Smith, Assistant in charge of Shirgotty,	400

Bhaugulpore.

G. U. Yule, Commissioner.	2,916-250
T. Sandys, Judge, ..	2,500
J. R. Muspratt, Magt. and Collr. ..	1,500
H. H. Robinson, Jt. Magt. &c., (on dep. Chumparun) ...	700
H. B. Simson, Assst. (on dep. Behar,)	400
F. G. Millett, Assistant, ..	400
A. C. Mangles, Assistant, ..	400

Bograh.

A. Abercrombie Jt. Magistrate, &c. (on dep. Chittagong,) ..	1,500
A. J. Jackson, Offg. ditto, (see Mymensing) ..	300

Balasore, (Cuttack N. D.)

V H. Schalch, Magt. Collr. and Salt Agent, ...	2,333

Chittagong.

C. Steer, Commissioner, ..	2,916-250
C. Chapman, Salt Agent, ..	2,500
G. C. Fletcher, Judge (on leave), ..	£1,000
E. F. Radcliffe, Addl. Judge, Offg. ditto	2,500

Salary.

E. Sandys Offg. Ditto (see Tipperah,) 450
J. Richardson, Collr. (on dep. Shahabad,) 1,916
A. Abercrombie, Offg. ditto, (see Bograh,) 383
T. P. Larkins, Magistrate, .. 900

Cuttack.

G. F. Cockburn, Commissioner, .. 2,916-250
J. J. Ward, Judge, .. 2,500
R. N. Shore, Magt. Collr. and Salt Agent, (on leave,) .. 2,333
C. F. Carnac, Offg. ditto (see Dacca,) .. 416
W. L. Heeley, Assistant, .. 400
F. H. Pellew, Assistant, .. 400

Chumparun.

H. C. Raikes, Jt. Magt. &c., (on leave,) £500
H. H. Robinson, Offg. ditto, (see Bhaugulpore,) .. 200

Dacca.

C. T. Davidson, Commissioner, 2,916-250
R. Abercrombie, Judge, .. 2,500
C. F. Carnac, Collr. (on dep. Cuttack,) 1,916
H. A. R. Alexander, Offg. ditto, (see Backergunge,) .. 383
C. F. Harvey, Offg. Magt. (see Pubna,) 200
W. Cornell, Assistant, (in charge of Munseegunge,) .. 400
H. Bell, Assistant, .. 400

Dinagepore.

J. Grant, Judge, ... 2,500
F. A. E. Dalrymple, Collector, ... 916
W. M. Beaufort, Magistrate, (on dep. Moorshedabad,) 900
J. D. Gordon, Offg. ditto, Jt. Magt. &c., 700-200

Furreedpore.

H. L. Dampier, Joint Magistrate, &c. (on dep. Tirhoot,) .. 1,000
J. H. Ravenshaw, Joint. Magistrate, &c. Offg. ditto, 700-200
J. Munro, Assistant, .. 400

Howrah.

J. J. Grey, Magistrate, .. 900

Hooghly.

H. C. Halkett, Judge, .. 2,500
W. B. Buckle, Collector, .. 1,916
R. V. Cockerell, Offg. Magistrate, (see Burdwan,) .. 900
S. H. C. Tayler, Jt. Magt. &c. .. 700
H. T. Prinsep, Asst. in charge of Serampore, .. 500
W. S. Wells, Assistant, in charge of Govindpore, .. 400

Hidgellee.

Salary.

G. W. Battye, Salt Agent, .. 2,500

Jessore.

W. S. Seton-Karr, Judge, ... 2,500
F. C. Fowle, Collector, (on leave), ...
F. Tucker, Offg. ditto, (see Sylhet,)
E. W. Molony, Magistrate, (on dep. Pubna), ... 900
C. B. Skinner, Joint Magistrate, &c. Offg. ditto, 700-200
F. M. Halliday, Asstt. (in charge of Magoorah,) .. 400

Maldah.

A. E. Russell, Joint Magistrate, &c. ... 1,500
E. Drummond, Assistant (on dep. Rungpore,) ... 500

Midnapore.

G. P. Leycester, Judge, 2,500-116
T. B. Mactier, Collector, (on dep. Pooree,) 1,916
A. J. Elliot, Offg. ditto, (See Sarun,) ... 383
J. M. Lowis, Magistrate, .. 900
V. T. Taylor (in charge of Nugwan) ... 400
D. J. McNeil, Assistant, ... 400
E. E. Lowis, Assistant, .. 400
C. B. Garrett, Assistant, .. 400

Monghyr.

R. O. Heywood, Collector .. 1,500
E. G. Birch, Magistrate, ... 900
W. V. G. Tayler, Assistant, .. 400

Moorshedabad.

C. T. Buckland, Judge, (on leave,) ... 2,500
A. Pigou, Offg. ditto. (see Sarun,) .. 450
R. C. Raikes, Collector, (on leave,) ... £1,000
W. M. Beaufort, Offg. ditto, (see Dinagepore,) .. 383
H. Muspratt, Magistrate, ... 900
J. W. Furrell, Assistant, (in charge of Aurungabad,) .. 400
H. F. J. Kean, Assistant, .. 400
F. J. Alexander, Assistant, ... 400

Mymensing.

J. W. Dalrymple, Judge, .. 2,500
C. H. Campbell, Collector, .. 1,916
A. J. Jackson, Magt. (on dep. Bograh,) 900
J. D. Ward, Assistant, Offg. ditto, . 500-200
H. Beveridge, Assistant, .. 400

Nagpore.

G. A. C. Plowden, Commissioner, .. 4,166

Noacolly (Bullooah.)

	Salary.
C. E. Lance, Joint Magistrate, &c., ..	1,500
A. B. Falcon, Assistant, ..	400

Nuddea.

A. Grote, Commr. (on dep. Revenue Board,) ..	2,916
H. M. Reid, Offg. ditto, (see Burdwan,)	416-250
A. Littledale, Judge, ..	2,500
C. S. Belli, Collector, ..	1,916
F. R. Cockerell, Magistrate, ..	900
J. P. H. Ward, Asst. (on dep. Burdwan,)	500
A. T. Maclean, Assistant, ..	400
H. L. Oliphant, Assistant, ..	400

Patna.

H. D. H. Fergusson, Commissioner,	2,916-250
R. J. Scott, Judge, ..	2,500
E. F. Lautour, Additional ditto, ..	2,166
E. E. Woodcock, Collector, ..	1,916
H. C. Richardson, Magt.,(on dep.Sarun,)	900
A. V. Palmer, Offg. Magt. (see Tirhoot,)	200
E. D. Lockwood, Assistant,	400

Pooree, (Cuttack S. D.) Khoordah.

T. B. Mactier, Magt. Collr. and Salt Agent, ..	2,333
W. Wavell, Assistant, ..	400

Pubna.

W. J. Longmore, Joint Magt., &c. (on dep. Sylhet,)	1,500
E. W. Molony, Offg. ditto, (see Jessore.)	300
C. F. Harvey, Assistant, (on dep Dacca.)	500
G. L. T. Harris, Assistant, ...	400

Purneah.

Geo. Loch, Judge, (on dep. Sudder Adawlut,) ...	2,500
W. H. Brodhurst, Offg. ditto, (see Tirhoot,) ...	450
R. Alexander, Collector, ...	1,916
G. A. Pepper, Magistrate, (on leave,) ...	£500
H. Balfour, Offg. ditto, (see Bancoorah,)	200
T. Walton, Assistant, ...	400

Rajshahye.

F. Gouldsbury, Commissioner,	2,916-250
L. S. Jackson, Judge, ..	2,500
F. A. Lushington, Collector, ...	1,916
T. Bruce Lane, Magistrate, ...	900
W. J. Longmore, Jt. Magt. &c. (on dep. Sylhet.) ...	700
A. Magniac, Assistant, (on dep. Tipperah,) ..	500
C. G. Wynch, Assistant, on leave,	£400
L. R. Tottenham, Assistant in charge of Nettore, ..	500
C. T. Metcalfe, Assistant, ..	400

Rungpore.

	Salary.
H. V. Bayley, Judge, (on dep. 24-Pergunnahs,) ..	2,500
F. A. B. Glover, Offg. ditto, (see Sylhet,)	450
A. G. Macdonald, Collector, ..	1,916
E. Drummond, Magistrate, ..	900

Santhal Pergunnah.

W. L. F. Robinson, Depy. Commissioner,	1,200

Sarun.

H. Atherton, Judge, ..	2,500
A. Pigou, Collector, (on dep. Moorshedabad,) ...	1,916
H. C. Richardson, Offg. Collr. (see Patna,)	383
A. J. Elliot Magistrate, (on dep. Midnapore,)	900
R. J. Wigram Offg. ditto (see 24-Pergunnahs,) ..	200
G. N. Barlow, Assistant, (in charge of Sewan,) ..	500
J. B. Worgan, Assistant, ..	400

Shahabad.

E. Jackson, Judge, (on dep. 24-Pergunnahs,) ..	2,500
R. J. Richardson, Offg. ditto, (see Chitta gong,) ..	416
A. A. Swinton, Collector, (on leave,) ...	1,916
A. Hope, Offg. (see Beerbhoom,) ..	383
G. Bright, Magt., (on dep. 24-Pergunnahs,) ..	900
W. J. Herschel, Jt. Magt. &c., Offg. ditto, ..	700-200
W. F. McDonell, settlement Officer, ..	
J. Combe, Jt Magt. &c. ..	700
C. J. Mackenzie, Assistant (on dep. Sylhet, ..	500

Sylhet.

M. A. G. Shawe, Judge, ..	2,500
F. A. B. Glover, Collector, (on dep. Rungpore,) ..	1,916
W. J. Longmore, Offg. ditto, (see Pubnah, ..	383
W. H. Henderson, Magistrate, (on leave)	£500
C. J. Mackenzie, Offg. ditto, (see Shahabad,) ..	200
P. A. Humphrey Assistant, ..	400

Tipperah.

H. C. Metcalfe, Judge, ..	2,500
E. Sandys, Collector, (on dep. Chittagong,)	1,916
C. Limond, Offg. ditto, (see Tirhoot,)..	383
F. Tucker, Magistrate, (on dep. Jessore,)	900
A. Magniac, Offg. ditto (see Rajshahye,)	200
H. C. Sutherland, Assistant, ..	400

Tirhoot.

G. L. Martin, Judge, ..	2,500

Salary.

E. Jenkins, Additional Judge, (on leave,) .. £1,000
H. Nelson, Offg. ditto, (see 24-Pergunnahs,) .. 450
W. H. Brodhurst, Collr. (on dep. Purneah,) .. 1,916
H. L. Dampier, Offg. Magt. and Collr. (see Furreedpore,) ... 400
C. Limond, Magt. (on dep. Tipperah,) 900
A. V. Palmer, Jt. Magt. &c., (on dep. Patna,) .. 700
T J. C. Grant, Assistant, .. 400

Tumlook.

R. Hampton, Salt Agent, .. 2,500

GOVT. OF THE N. W. P.

Secretaries and Accountant.

G. E. W. Couper Secretary, ... 2,500
C. J. Daniell, Under-Secy., (on leave,)... £500
F. B. Outram, Jr. Asst. Secretary, Offg. ditto, 700
J. D. Sandford, Offg. ditto (see Futtehpore,) ... 200

Commissioners, &c.

W. E. Money, Commr. of Customs, 2,916-250
C. B. Thornhill, Inspector of Prisons, also on dep. Allahabad, .. 2,500-250
H.S. Reid, Director of Public Instruction, 2,500

Sudder Dewanny and Nizamut Adawlut.

H. Unwin, Judge, (on leave,) ... £1 000
C. Raikes, Judge, (on leave,) .. £1,000
R. B. Morgan, Judge, ... 3,750
M. R. Gubbins, Offg. ditto, (see Moradabad,) ... 575
R. Money, Offg. ditto, (see Seharunpore,) 575
H. W. Dashwood, Register, ... 1,200

Sudder Revenue Board, (Agra.)

E. A. Reade, Member, ... 4,000
W. Muir, Member, ... 3,700
W. H. Lowe, Secretary, ... 2,000

Agra.

G. F. Harvey, Commr. and Agent, (on leave,) ... £1,000
A. Ross, Offg. ditto (see Furruckabad,) 416-250
E. M. Wylly, Judge, (on leave,) .. £1,000
M. B. Thornhill, Offg. ditto, (see Muttra,) 250
A. L. M. Phillipps, Magt. and Collr. (on leave,) .. £1,000
H. P. Fane Offg. ditto, (see Moradabad,) .. 435

Salary.

G. B. Pasley, Jt. Magt. ... 700
C. Grant, Assistant, .. 400

Allahabad.

C. Chester, Commissioner, (on leave,) £1,000
C. B. Thornhill, Offg. ditto, (see Agra,) .. 416-250
W. P. Masson, Judge, .. 2,500
M. H. Court, Magt. and Collr. (on leave,) ... £1,000
J. S. Campbell, Offg. ditto, (see Punjab,) 425
W. R. Benson, Jt. Magt. &c. ... 1,000
W. Johnston, Jt. Magt. &c. (on leave,)... £500
G. E Watson, Assistant, ... 500
A. M. Monteath, Assistant, ... 400

Allyghur.

J. S. Dumergue, Judge, ... 2,500
W. J. Bramly, Magt. and Collr. (on dep. Banda,) ... 2,250
J. H. Prinsep, Offg. do., (unattached,) .. 1,000-425
W. Lane, Jt. Magt. &c. .. 700
W. Duthoit, Assistant .. 400

Azimghur.

S. J. Becher, Judge, (on dep. Benares,) 2,500
And. Ross, Offg. ditto, (see Ghazeepore,) 250
E. C. Bayley, Magt. and Collr. (on dep. Furruckabad,) .. 2,250
R. Marriott, Offg. ditto, 325-1,125
H. A. Harrison, Assistant, .. 500
M. W. Sandys, Assistant, .. 400
D. G. Barkley, Assistant, 400

Bareilly (Rohilcund.)

R. Alexander, Commr. and Agent Lieut.-Govr. (on leave,) .. £1,000
J. H. Batten, Offg. ditto, (see Cawnpore,) .. 416-250
H. Vansittart, Judge, .. 2,500
J. F. D. Inglis, Magt. and Collector, ... 2,250
H. R. Clarke, Extra Jt. Magt. &c. .. 700
W. M. Low, Assistant, .. 500
S. M. Moens, Assistant, .. 400

Benares.

F. B. Gubbins, Commr. and Agent Govr.-General, .. 2,916-250
H. C. Hamilton, Opium Agent, .. 3,000
W. Edwards, Judge, (on leave,) .. £1,000
S. J. Becher, Offg. ditto, (see Azimghur,) ..
F. M. Lind, Magt. and Collr. (on Lv.,) .. £1,000
A. R. S. Pollock, Jt. Magt. &c. Offg., ditto, .. 1,000-425
E. G. Jenkinson, Assistant, .. 500
F. H. North, Assistant, (on leave,) .. £400
F. B. Peacock, Assistant, .. 400
H. B. Webster Assistant, (on leave,) .. £500

Boolundshuhur.

	Salary.
———Magt. and Collr.	..
C. Currie, Jt. Magt. &c. Offg. ditto,	1,000-450
G. W. Colledge, Jt. Magt. &c.	.. 700
F. E. Elliot, Assistant,	.. 400

Banda, (Bundlecund S. D.)

Hon'ble R. A. J. Drummond, Judge, (on leave,)	.. £1,000
W. J. Bramly, Offg. ditto, (see Allighur,)	250
F. O. Mayne, Magistrate and Collr.	.. 2,250
J. W. Power, Jt. Magt., &c. (on dep. Futtehpore,)	.. 1,000
C. H. T. Crosthwaite, Assistant,	.. 400

Bijnour, (Moradabad N. D.)

A. Shakespear, Magt. and Collr. (on dep. Moradabad,)	.. 2,250
G. Palmer, Jt. Magt. &c. Offg. ditto,	1,000-425
C. E. Chapman, Extra Jt. Magt. &c.,	.. 700
A. Colvin, Assistant,	.. 400

Budaon, (Suheswan.)

A. Swinton, Magt. and Collr. (on dep. Goruckpore,)	.. 2,250
C. P. Carmichael, Officiating ditto, (unattached,)	.. 1,000-425
E. Waterfield, Assistant,	.. 400
T. E. Fairfax, Assistant, (on leave,)	.. £400
D. H. C. Inglis, Assistant,	.. 400

Cawnpore.

J. H. Batten, Judge, (on dep. Bareilly,)	2,500
F. B. Pearson, Offg, ditto, (see Goruckpore,)	.. 250
J. W. Sherer, Magt. and Collr.	.. 2,250
W. Blunt Jt. Magt.	.. 1,000
E. S. Robertson, Assistant,	.. 400
G. B. Willock, Assistant, (on leave,)	.. £400
T. B. Tracey, Assistant,	.. 400

Dehra Dhoon.

H. G, Keene Superintendent,	.. 1,000
J. C. Robertson, Assistant.	.. 500

Etawah.

A. O. Hume, Magt. and Collr.	.. 2,250
S. H. Boult, Assistant,	.. 500

Furruckabad or Futtehgur.

A. Ross, Judge, (on dep. Agra,)	.. 2,500
E. C. Bayley Offg. ditto, (see Azimghur)	250
W. G. Probyn, Magt. and Collr. (on Lv.)	£1,000
C. R. Lindsay, Jt. Magistrate &c. Offg. ditto,	.. 1,000-425
F S. Wigram, Jt. Magt. &c. (Etah,)	.. 1,000
C. J. H. Richardes, Jt. Magt. &c.,	.. 1,000

	Salary.
H. D. Robertson, Jt. Magt. &c. (on Lv.)	£500
W. J. Money, Assistant, Etah, (on Lv.,)	500

Futtehpore.

G. Edmonstone, Judge,	.. 2,500
J. Power, Magt. and Collr. (on leave,)	£1,000
J. W. Power, Offg. ditto. (see Banda,)	425
J. D. Sandford Assistant, (on dep. Agra,)	500
C. W. Carpenter, Assistant,	.. 400

Ghazeepore.

T. J. C. Plowden, Judge,	.. 2,500
And. Ross, Magt. and Collr. (on dep. Azimghur,)	.. 2,250
J. H. Bax, Jt. Magt. &c. Offg. ditto,	1,000-425
L. C. Probyn, Jt. Magt. (at Bulleah,)	.. 700
J. W. Quinton, Assistant, (at Bulleah,)	500

Goruckpore.

A. Swinton, Offg. Judge, also Offg. Commr. (see Budaon,)	.. 250
F. B. Pearson, Magt. and Collr. (on dep. Cawnpore,)	.. 2,250
F. M. Bird, Jt. Magt. &c. Offg ditto,	1,000-425
W. S Halsey, Assistant (on leave,)	.. 500
S. Lushington, Assistant,	.. 500
J. J. F. Lumsden, Assistant,	.. 500
H. Wilson, Assistant,	.. 400

Humeerpore, Bundlecund, (N. D.) or Calpee.

G H. Freeling, Magt. and Collr.	.. 2,250
P. Wigram, Assistant,	.. 500

Jaunpore.

H. G. Astell, Judge,	.. 2,500
C. Horne, Magt. and Collr. (on leave,)	£1,000
W. S. Patterson, Offg. ditto,	.. 325-1,125
R. Manderson, Jt. Magt. &c.,	.. 700
R. Taylor, Assistant,	.. 500
W. Young, Assistant,	.. 400
W. C. Turner, Assistant,	.. 400
C. Temple, Assistant,	.. 400

Kumaon.

B. W. Colvin, Sr. Asst Commr..	.. 700
G. H. M. Batten, Jr. Asst. Commr.	.. 500
E. Colvin, Assistant,	.. 400

Meerut.

F. Williams, Commr.,	.. 2,916-250
G. D. Turnbull, Judge,	.. 2,500
B. Sapte, Magt. and Collr.	.. 2,250
F. F. Hogg, Jt. Mag. &c.	.. 1,000
C. A. Daniell, Assistant,	.. 400
R. G. Currie, Assistant,	.. 400

Mirzapore.

	Salary.
J. Lean, Judge, ..	2,500
C. B. Denison, Magt. and Collr. ..	2,250
J. Simson, dep. Supt. Raja's Domains,	700
E. Macnaghten, Assistant, (on leave,) ..	£500
W. Oldham, Assistant, ..	400
C. W. Moore, Assistant (on leave,) ..	£400
H. S. J. Ross, Assistant, ..	400

Moradabad.

M. R. Gubbins Judge, (on dep. Agra,)	2,500
A. Shakespear, Offg. Judge (see Bijnore,)	250
H. P. Fane, Magt. and Collr. (on dep. Agra,) ..	2,250
J. Strachey, Offg. ditto,	325-1,125
B. F. Hall, Jt. Magt. &c. ..	700
E. B. Thornhill, Assistant (on leave,) ..	£500
J. C. Colvin, Assistant, ..	500
J. Sladen, Assistant, ..	400

Moozuffernugur.

R.M. Edwards, Magt. and Collr.(on Lv.)	2,250
C. Grant, Jt. Magt. &c. Offg. ditto, ..	1,000
A. J. Lawrence Assistant, ...	400

Muttra.

M. B. Thornhill, Magt. and Collr. (on dep. Agra,) ..	2,250
J. R. Best, Offg. ditto, (unattached,)	1,000-425
R. H. Clifford, Jt. Magt. &c., ..	700
R. Wall, Assistant, ..	400

Mynpooree.

A. H. Cocks, Judge, (on dep. Jubbulpore,) ..	2,500
E. J. Boldero, Magt. and Collr. Offg. ditto, ..	2,250-250
G. E. Lance, Offg. ditto, (Unattached), ..	1,000-425
H. M. Chase, Jt. Magt. &c., ..	700
W M. Alexander Assistant, ..	400

Saugore (Jubulpore.)

A. H. Cocks, Offg. Commr. (see Mynpooree,) ..	416-250
J. A. Craigie, Judge, ..	2,500

Seharunpore.

R. Money, Judge, (on dep. S. D. N. D.)	2,500
R. Spankie, Magt. and Collr. Offg. ditto,	2,250-250
J. Vans Agnew, Jt. Magt. &c , Offg. ditto,	1,000-425
F. C. Forbes, Jt. Magt. &c. (on leave..	£500
M. Brodhurst, Extra Jt. Magt. &c. ..	1,000
S. S. Melville, Jt. Magt. &c. (on leave,)	500
A. C. Barnard, Assistant, (on leave,) ..	500
F. R. Hogg, Assistant, ..	400

Shajehanpore.

	Salary.
W. Wynyard, Judge, ..	2,500
H. W. Hammond, Offg. Magistrate and Collr., ..	2,250
H. D. Willock, Joint Magistrate, ..	700
A. C. Lyall, Assistant, ..	500

PUNJAB.

D. F. MacLeod, Financial Commissioner, (on leave,) ..	£1,000
A. A. Roberts Offg. ditto (see Jhelum,)	
E. Thornton, Judicial, ..	3,500
R. H. Davis Secretary, ..	2,500
H. E. Perkins, Assist. Commr. 2nd class,	600
A. U. Aitchison, Asst. Judicial Commr,	700
D. G. Barkley, Asst. Commr. 3rd class,	400
J. W. Smyth, ditto, ..	400
H. R. Maddock, ..	

Delhi Division.

C. B. Saunders, Commissioner, Delhi (see Jhelum,) ..	2,750
J. E. L. Brandreth, Offg. ditto, (see Hissar,)	
P. H. Egerton, depy. Commissioner 1st class, Delhi, ..	2,250
W. Ford, ditto Goorgaon, ..	2,250
H. B. Henderson, ditto Goorgaon, ..	
C. P. Elliott, Assistant Commissioner, 1 class, Paneeput, Offg. depy. ditto,	700-246
J. B. Beamis, Assistant Commissioner 3rd class Goorgaon, ...	400
H. Hankey, Assistant Commissioner 3rd class Paneeput, ..	400
C. Lindsay, Assistant Commissioner 3rd class Goorgaon, ...	400
W. Robertson, Assistant Commissioner 3rd class, ...	400

Hissar Division.

J.E. L. Brandreth, Commissioner Hissar, (on dep. Delhi,) ..	2,750
P. S. Melville, Offg. ditto, at Umballa (see Delhi,) ..	
J. S. Campbell, depy. Commissioner Jhujur, (on dep. Allahabad.) ..	
W. C. Plowden, Assistant Commissioner 1st class, Rohtuck, Offg. Depy. Commissioner,	700-246
R. G. Melvill, Assistant Commissioner 2nd class, Hissar, ..	500
H. G. Paynter, Assistant Commissioner 3rd class, Rohtuck, ..	400

Cis Sutlej Division.

G. C. Barnes, Commissioner and Supt., Umballa, ..	2,750

	Salary.
Lord W. M. Hay, Depy. Commr. Simla,	1,500
P. S. Melville, Depy. Commissioner Umballa, (see Hissar,) ..	1,500
F. Macnaghten, Asst. Commissioner 1st class Umballa, ...	700
Lord F. Hay, Asst. ditto, 3rd class, Umballa, ...	400

Trans Sutlej Division.

D. Simson, Depy. Commissioner Hoshyarpore, ..	1,500
R. F. Saunders, ditto 2nd class Kanghur, ...	700
Sir A. H. Lawrence, Asst. Commissioner 3rd class, Kanghur, ..	400
C. E. Bernard, Asst. Commissioner 3rd class, Jullunder, ...	400
J. B. Lyall, Assistant Commissioner 3rd class, Hoshyarpore, ...	400

Lahore Division.

R. Temple, Commissioner Lahore, ...	2,750
R. E. Egerton, Depy. ditto, ..	1,200
W. B. Jones, ditto Lahore, ..	400
J. A. Craigie, ditto Goojranwalla, ..	400

Umritsur Division.

R. N. Cust, Commissioner and Supt. Umritsur, ..	2,750
F. H. Cooper, Depy. Commr. Umritsur,	1,500
J. Naesmyth, ditto Goordaspore, ..	1,500
E. A. Prinsep, ditto Sealkote (on leave,)	1,500
J. G. Cordery, Asst. Commr. 3rd class, Umritsur, ..	400

Jhelum Division.

	Salary.
A. A. Roberts, Commissioner and Supt. Jhelum, (Offg. Finl. ditto.,) ..	2,750
C. B. Saunders, Offg. ditto. (see Delhi ..	
G. Ouseley, Depy. Commissioner Shahapore, ...	1,500
A. Brandreth, Settlement Officer, Jhelum,	1,000
J. W. Macnabb, Assistant Commissioner 1st class Jhelum, (on leave,) ..	£500
D. C. Macnabb, Assistant Commissioner 1st class Shahapore, ..	700
B. Hardinge, Assistant Commissioner Rawul Pindee, Offg. depy. Commissioner Goojerat,	700-246
W. B. Jones, Assistant Commissioner 3rd class Jhelum, ..	400
T. H. Thornton, Assistant Commissioner 3rd class Goojerat, ..	400
G. R. Elsmie, Assistant Commissioner 3rd class Jhelum, ..	400

Mooltan Division.

J. H. Morris, Settlement Officer Mooltan.	1,500
A. Levien, Asst. Commr. 1st class Jhung Offg. Depy. Commr., ...	700
C. Fairlie, Assistant Commr. 3rd class.	246-400

Lea Division.

H. B. Henderson, Depy. Commissioner Khangur, ..	1,500
G. R. Elsmie, Assistant Commissioner 3rd class, ...	400

GENERAL LIST

OF

COVENANTED CIVIL SERVANTS ATTACHED TO THE PRESIDENCY

OF

FORT WILLIAM.

Ranked according to the Civil Auditors Gradation List down to Mr. S. M. Moens.

Class I.

Season.		
1817	1	W Dampier.
1818	2	W P Palmer.
1819	3	H Ricketts.
1820	4	J H Patton.
1821	5	F Gouldsbury.
1822	6	J I Harvey.

Class II.

Season.		
1823	7	J Grant.
1823	8	H Stainforth.
1825	9	E A Reade.
	10	H T Raikes.
	11	G W Battye.
	12	T Sandys
	13	The *Hon'ble* J P Grant.
1826	14	J Lean.
	15	G F Harvey.
	16	C T Davidson.
	17	T J C Plowden.

Class II.—(*Continued.*)

Season.		
	18	The *Hon'ble* H B Harington.
	19	*Sir* R Montgomery, K. C. B.
	20	D F MacLeod.
	21	H Unwin.
1827	22	W P Masson.
	23	G A C Plowden.
	24	W E Money.
	25	R B Morgan.
	26	A Sconce.
	27	P G E Taylor.
	28	H C Metcalfe.
1828	29	J H Batten.
	30	R N Farquharson.
	31	H C Halkett.
	32	C Steer.
	33	H C Hamilton.
	34	E Thornton.
	35	J S Torrens.
	36	M R Gubbins.
	37	The *Hon'ble* H B Devereux.
1829	38	F Williams.
	39	J G Campbell.
	40	R Money.
	41	W J Allen.
	42	J A Craigie.
	43	H C Tucker.
	44	H Atherton.
	45	J S Dumergue.
	46	R H Snell.
	47	G G Mackintosh.
	48	C Raikes.
	49	F B Kemp.
1830	50	The *Hon'ble* G F Edmonstone.
	51	G U Yule.
	52	R Hampton.
	53	O W Malet.
	54	J H Young.
	55	C H Lushington.
	56	C B Trevor.
1831	57	E A Samuells.

Class II.—(*Continued.*)

Season		
	58	G P Leycester.
	59	S J Becher.
1831	60	R Alexander, (Senr.)
	61	G D Wilkins.
	62	The *Hon.* E Drummond.
	63	F A Elphinstone-Dalrymple.
1827	64	E E Woodcock.
	65	J J Ward.
	66	A Grote.
1832	67	C Chester.
	68	E deLautour.
	69	C Chapman.
	70	A G Macdonald.
	71	G Loch.
1833	72	H G Astell.
	73	E F Radcliffe.
	74	G L Martin.
	75	M A G Shawe.
	76	H V Bayley.
	77	R P Harrison.
1834	78	A Littledale.
	79	F A Lushington.
	80	C T LeBas.
	81	T C Trotter.
1835	82	F B Gubbins.
	83	D Cunliffe.
	84	C Beadon.
	85	A R Young.
1836	86	G F Cockburn.
	87	H M Reid.
	88	H D H Fergusson.
	89	W Edwards.
	90	A Ross.
	91	A A Roberts.
	92	E M Wylly.
1837	63	G Edmonstone.
	94	H Vansittart.
	95	W Wynyard.
	96	R C Raikes.
	97	W Muir.

Class II.—(Continued.)

Season.	No.	Name
1837	98	G C Barnes.
	99	E T Trevor.
	100	F L Beaufort.
	101	A H Cocks.
1838	102	C B Thornhill.
	103	W Galloway.

Class III.

Season.	No.	Name
1839	104	G D Turnbull.
	105	W Roberts.
	106	W H Brodhurst.
	107	H P A B Riddell.
	108	G M B Berford.
	109	E F deLautour.
	110	A Ross.
	111	G C Fletcher.
	112	C J Wingfield.
1840	113	W B Buckle.
	114	R N Shore.
	115	R H Russell.
	116	J A Loch.
	117	A Shakespear.
	118	R Abercrombie.
	119	W S Paterson.
	120	M B Thornhill.
	121	J E S Lillie.
	122	W J R Carnac.
	123	F B Pearson.
	124	W Grey.
	125	M H Court.
	126	J F D Inglis.
1841	127	E H Lushington.
	128	R J Scott.
	129	G G Balfour.
	130	E C Bayley.
	131	S Wauchope.
	132	F M Lind.
	133	E J Boldero.
1842	134	J Strachey.
	135	V H Schalch.
	136	St.G Tucker.
	137	W J Bramly.
	138	A A Swinton.
	139	E Jenkins.
	140	The *Hon.* R A J Drummond.
	141	W Ford.
	142	G P Money.
	143	R N Cust.
	144	W S Seton-Karr.
	145	G Campbell.
	146	J E L Brandreth.
	147	E Jackson.
	148	A Swinton.
	149	J W Dalrymple.
	150	P H Egerton.

Class III.—(Continued.)

Season.	No.	Name
1842	151	E S Pearson.
	152	E Sandys.
	153	A Pigou.
	154	F C Fowle.
	155	J Combe.
	156	W M Beaufort.
	157	H P Fane
1843	158	R Marriott.
	159	T B Mactier.
	160	C B Saunders.
	161	C Horne.
	162	L S Jackson.
	163	C F Montresor.
	164	B Sapte.
	165	E H Anson.
	166	A Money.
	167	J Power.
	168	L B Bowring.
	169	W G Young.
	170	H Nelson.
	171	R H W Dunlop.
	172	J R Muspratt.
	173	F Tucker.
1844	174	C T Buckland.
	175	R H Davies.
	176	R Spankie.
	177	H D Sandeman.
	178	C P Hobhouse.
	179	G E Lance.
	180	W R Best.
	181	C R Lindsay.
	182	R J Richardson.
	183	C F Carnac.
	184	R Alexander, (Junr.)
	185	C Limond.
1845	186	F A B Glover.
	187	C S Belli.
	188	C H Campbell.
	189	R O Heywood.
	190	O Toogood.
	191	H R Madocks.
	192	F B Drummond.
	193	W J Longmore.
	194	W T Tucker.
	195	W Ainslie.
	196	J R Best.
	197	C B Denison.
	198	F J Cockburn.
	199	H B Henderson.
	200	A E Russell.
	201	H Lushington, (Junr.)
	202	*Lord* W M Hay.
	203	J C Dodgson.
	204	A Hope.
	205	H C Raikes.
	206	D Simson.
1846	207	H S Reid.
	208	P S Melvill.
	209	G A Pepper.
	210	F O Mayne.
	211	A L March-Phillipps.
	212	G E W Couper.
	213	F Thompson.
	214	R Temple.
	215	A Abercrombie.
	216	H Pratt.
	217	W Blunt, (Junr.)
	218	R P Jenkins.
	219	J W Sherer.

Class IV.

Season.	No.	Name
1847	220	H Monckton.
	221	G Bright.
	222	A W Russell.
	223	E C Craster.
	224	R Simson.
	225	W A Forbes.

Class IV.—(Continued.)

Season.	No.	Name
1847	226	J H Prinsep.
	227	G Ouseley.
	228	F H Cooper.
	229	H G Keene.
	230	A J Elliot.
	231	H Rose.
	232	W MacChlery.
	233	J S Spankie.
	234	G H M Ricketts.
	235	W G Probyn.
	236	J H Morris.
	237	E A Prinsep.
	238	J S Campbell.
	239	J Nasmyth.
	240	J Watson.
	241	R M Edwards.
	242	J H Bax.
	243	F B Simson.
	244	H S Mackenzie.
	245	C J H Richardes.
	246	S F Davis.
1848	247	T D Forsyth.
	248	H Balfour.
	249	J Vans Agnew.
	250	H C Richardson.
	251	T P Larkins.
	252	R C Oldfield.
	253	H A R Alexander.
	254	S N Martin.
	255	*Sir* T J Metcalfe.
	256	C E Lance.
	257	J W Power.
1849	258	W Balmain.
	259	H L Dampier.
	260	E G Birch.
	261	A O Hume.
	262	C P Carmichael.
	263	E F Harrison.
	264	T E Ravenshaw.
	265	W H Henderson.
	266	G G Morris.
	267	H W Hammond.
	268	G Palmer.
	269	F F Hogg.
	270	F M Bird.
	271	W F McDonell.
	272	H D Robertson.
	273	R E Egerton.
	274	A J Jackson.
	275	E W Molony.
1850	276	R B Chapman.
	277	C Grant Jr.
	278	H Muspratt.
	279	F R Cockerell.
	280	M Brodhurst.
	281	B W Colvin.
	282	H B Lawford.
	283	J M Lowis.
	284	W C Spencer.
	285	F C Forbes.
	286	A R S Pollock.
	287	C Currie.
	288	G H Freeling.
	289	C Jenkins.
	290	J A Crawford.
	291	F S Wigram.
	292	A R Thompson.
	293	A Levien.

Class V.

Season.	No.	Name
1851	294	S Lushington.
	295	H W Dashwood.
	296	W H Lowe.
	297	W LeF Robinson.
	298	R Manderson.
	299	J J Grey.

CLASS V.—*(Continued.)*

Season.

1851
300 H C Wake.
301 *Lord* H U Browne.
302 A Brandreth.
303 J H Mangles.
304 T B Lane.
305 W R Benson.
306 R F Saunders.
307 J W Macnabb.
308 W C Capper.
309 G B Pasley.

1852
310 T Bruce Lane.
311 W Johnston.
312 G H Lawrence.
313 J D Ouseley.
314 H R Clarke.
315 H M Chase.
316 WC Sherwood.
317 The *Hon'ble* A Eden.
318 Wm Waterfield.
319 C E Chapman.
320 W C Plowden.
321 J H Ravenshaw.
322 F Macnaghten.
323 G H M Batten.
324 H B Simson.
325 S S Melville.
326 E Drummond.

1853
327 Wm Jas Herschel.
328 Ed Grey.
329 R L Mangles.
330 A V Palmer.
331 A J Hay.
332 G E Watson.
333 R J Wigram.
334 H A Cockerell.
335 S H C Tayler.
336 H D Willock.
337 W J Money.
338 W S Halsey.
339 S S Hogg.
340 B Hardinge.
341 R H Clifford.
342 G W Colledge.
343 A C Barnard.
344 D C Macnabb.

CLASS VI.

1854
345 H A Mangles.
346 C Trotter.
347 L C Probyn.
348 C P Elliott.
349 C B Skinner.
350 A Magniac.
351 H B Webster.
352 C A Daniell.
353 A J R Bainbridge.
354 R G Melvill.
355 J Simson.
356 W Lane.
357 E Waterfield.
358 J D Gordon
359 B F Hall.
360 H H Robinson.
361 C G Wynch.
362 J D Ward.
363 T E Fairfax.
364 J C Robertson.
365 E B Thornhill.
366 G B Willock.

CLASS VI.—*(Continued.)*

Season.

1855
367 C J Mackenzie.
368 H A Harrison.
369 W Robertson.
370 J C Colvin.
371 H G Paynter.
372 C F Lindsay.
373 C F Harvey.
374 J F Browne.
375 J P H Ward.
376 G N Barlow.
377 A C Lyall.
378 H T Prinsep.
379 R V Cockerell.
380 C J Daniell.
381 E Colvin.
382 J P Grant.
383 W V G Tayler.
384 A Boulderson.

1856
385 F B Outram.
386 S C Bayley.
387 L R Tottenham.
388 E Macnaghten.
389 E G Jenkinson.
390 W M Low.
391 H W Alexander.
392 W M Alexander.
393 The *Hon'ble* F H North.
394 C W Moore.
395 H Hankey.
396 V T Taylor.
397 D H C Inglis.
398 W C Turner
399 D J McNeill.
400 J Sladen.
401 P Wigram.
402 M W Sandys.
403 J J F Lumsden.
404 E E Lowis.
405 A J Lawrence.
406 E D Lockwood.
407 G L T Harris.
408 H S J Ross.
409 F M Halliday.
410 W G L Lane.
411 W Macpherson.
412 H G Ross.
413 W Butler.
414 Wm Cornell, B A.
415 H J Reynolds.
416 R H M Warrand.
417 C U Aitchison.
418 R M King.
419 J G Cordery.
420 T H Thornton.
421 H Wilson.
422 H Bell.
423 H E Perkins.
424 J D Sandford.
425 W H Jones.
426 W L Heeley.
427 A M Monteath.
428 A T Maclean.
429 F G Millett.
430 R G Currie.
431 F B Peacock.
432 F R Hogg.
433 *Lord* F Hay.
434 W S Wells.
435 E Fairlie.
436 S H Boult.
437 W Young.
438 J W Quinton.
439 C Robertson.
440 T Walton.
441 W Oldham.

CLASS VI.—*(Continued.)*

Season.

1856
442 J W Furrell.
443 E S Robertson.
444 J B Worgan.
445 C A Elliot.
446 R Wall.
447 A B Falcon.
448 A Smith.
449 R Taylor.
450 A Colvin.

1857
451 F J Alexander.
452 *Sir* A H Lawrence, *Bart.*
453 C T Metcalfe.
454 H F J Kean.
455 H J Sparks.
456 J S Drummond.

1858
457 C E Bernard.
458 G R Elsmie.
459 G L Lang.
460 J B Craigie.
461 A C Mangles.
462 H L Oliphant.
463 J B Lyall.
464 L S Saunders.
465 T J C Grant.
466 J A Graham.
467 W H D'Oyly.
468 C Temple.
469 C B Garrett.
470 J Beames.
471 F H Pellew.
472 C Grant.
473 F E Elliot.
474 R T Burney.
475 G S Park.
476 R H Middlemas.
477 W Kaye.
478 P A Humphrey.
479 J H R Carnac.
480 W Kemble.
481 J D Maclean.
482 N S Alexander.
483 H Beveridge.
484 C W Carpenter.
485 Jas Munro.
486 D G Barkley, M A.
487 Wm Wavel.
488 W Duthoit.
489 A P Howell.
490 T B Tracey.
491 C H T Crosthwaite.
492 J W Smyth.
493 H C Sutherland.
494 S M Moens, B A.

1859
495 H LePoer Wynne.
496 H Morris.
497 Alex. Brown.
498 J Geoghegan.
499 T F W Smith.
500 D Fitzpatrick.
501 C W P Watts.
502 C G Sperling.
503 D M Gardner.
504 C J Powlett,
505 J F K Hewitt.
506 E H Whinfield.
507 Wm C Eades.
508 John Ward.
509 J S Armstrong.
510 J M McGregor, B A.
511 F Jones.
512 W Tyrrell.
513 T F Bignold,

INDEX

TO

THE CIVIL LIST.

Students in College.

* Students in College.

* Students in College.

* Students in College.

P. M. CRANENBURGH, BENGAL MILITARY ORPHAN PRESS.